ANNUAL REVIEW OF PHYSIOLOGY

ANNUAL REVIEW OF PHYSIOLOGY

ERNST KNOBIL, *Editor*
University of Pittsburgh School of Medicine

RALPH R. SONNENSCHEIN, *Associate Editor*
University of California, Los Angeles

I. S. EDELMAN, *Associate Editor*
University of California School of Medicine, San Francisco

VOLUME 38

1976

ANNUAL REVIEWS INC.   4139 EL CAMINO WAY   PALO ALTO, CALIFORNIA 94306

ANNUAL REVIEWS INC.
Palo Alto, California, USA

International Standard Book Number: 0-8243-0338-5
Library of Congress Catalog Card Number: 39-15404

REPRINTS

The conspicuous number aligned in the margin with the title of each article in this volume is a key for use in ordering reprints. Available reprints are priced at the uniform rate of $1 each, postpaid. The minimum acceptable reprint order is 10 reprints and/or $10.00, prepaid. A quantity discount is available.

PRINTED AND BOUND IN THE UNITED STATES OF AMERICA

PREFACE

This volume of the *Annual Review of Physiology* is the last organized under the stimulating and perspicacious leadership of Julius H. Comroe. His direct contributions to this series, now in its 38th year, will be greatly missed by our readers and by those of us who have had the privilege and pleasure of working with him on the Editorial Committee.

The ever expanding, shifting, and dissolving boundaries of physiology have rendered the selection of the topics to be reviewed in any given year increasingly difficult and, at times, somewhat arbitrary. In general, as the field grew in complexity and diversity, the subject matter covered by individual chapters became more circumscribed. What has been gained in depth has been lost in breadth, a dimension that remains one of consequence in our editorial policy.

The current volume introduces an attempt to address this dilemma. This year's review of renal physiology, organized and edited by Dr. Gerhard Giebisch, is comprised of four sections, each written by a different author who deals with his subject in depth and in detail. We hope that the whole of this endeavor is greater than the sum of its parts and that, it favorably received, this prototype, or a variant thereof, may become a standard editorial instrument.

We do know that the *Annual Review of Physiology* is used by a heterogeneous international readership for a wide variety of purposes, but how well we meet these purposes is a matter of growing concern. We require our readers' critical responses to our efforts if we are to be effective. Unfortunately, sales figures tell us very little and may even lead us astray.

But, in the final analysis, the quality and utility of a volume such as this are dependent on the thoughtful labors of its contributing authors. We are deeply grateful to them for their efforts. We also acknowledge with thanks and admiration the indispensable contributions of our new Assistant Editor, Susan Futterman, whose unerring grammatical eye and orthographic wisdom have made the task of editing this volume a pleasant one.

THE EDITORS AND THE EDITORIAL COMMITTEE

CONTENTS

Annual Reviews are published in the following sciences: Anthropology, Astronomy and Astrophysics, Biochemistry, Biophysics and Bioengineering, Earth and Planetary Sciences, Ecology and Systematics, Energy, Entomology, Fluid Mechanics, Genetics, Materials Science, Medicine, Microbiology, Nuclear Science, Pharmacology and Toxicology, Physical Chemistry, Physiology, Phytopathology, Plant Physiology, Psychology, and Sociology. In addition, two special volumes have been published by Annual Reviews Inc.: *History of Entomology* (1973) and *The Excitement and Fascination of Science* (1965).

Robert F. Pitts

WHY A PHYSIOLOGIST? ❖1141

Robert F. Pitts

Renal Medicine and Physiology, College of Medicine, University of Florida, Gainesville, Florida 32610

First year medical students frequently ask me why I decided to enter the medical profession. The way one answers such a question is often of importance, the more so if the student is finding himself overwhelmed by the mass of seemingly irrelevant information that he is required to assimilate. It is doubly important if he is beginning to doubt that medicine is really his "bag." All too frequently, he has been propagandized into embarking on a medical career by the popular view of the glamour of the profession or by pressures exerted by a doting family. Perhaps medicine is not his bag.

An equally difficult question to answer is why I decided to become a physiologist, not a teacher of one of the clinical disciplines or a practicioner of one of the clinical specialties. This question, although of importance to me, is less significant for the student in his first year of medicine. The answers to both questions are related.

The profession an individual elects should be determined by his educational background and capabilities, both of which are requisite for success. It should be one that will provide him with the most complete and lasting happiness and sense of fulfillment. Medicine demands the first two and provides the last two for the proper person, but admittedly not for all. It would be most unfortunate were medicine the only profession. My response to these two questions and to others as well are presented in the paragraphs that follow.

My educational background was somewhat more extensive than that of most medical students. It qualified me as a physiologist and, up to a point, as a clinical teacher. My parents promised me two years of collegiate education; it was all they could afford. If I wished to graduate from college, I would be on my own for the last two years. I could live at home in Indianapolis while a student at Butler College, a not inconsiderable financial assistance.

For three years, my collegiate goal was a major in chemistry, to be followed by graduate work in this discipline. Between my junior and senior years, I was offered a summer scholarship to take the invertebrate course at the Marine Biological Laboratory at Woods Hole, Mass. I was obliged to return to a teaching assistantship in zoology the succeeding fall. This experience converted me from an embryonic

1

chemist to a novice in biology. During my senior year, I finished a major in zoology as well as in chemistry. Fortunately, I received a half-tuition scholarship during my junior year and a full scholarship during my senior year. Coupled with two part-time jobs, I saved money for graduate work in biology at the Johns Hopkins University. At Hopkins, I had accepted a graduate teaching fellowship, which I held for two years. The third year of graduate work was supported by an Adam T. Bruce Fellowship.

I graduated from Butler College in late spring of 1929. That year and subsequent ones bore a certain resemblance to those we are experiencing now. Graduate work taught me a number of lessons, not the least of which was that a depression is an excellent time to further one's education. Most of my college classmates were attempting to sell life insurance on commission during the time I was in graduate and medical schools. Graduate school fostered an interest in research, and graduate courses I took at the Hopkins Medical School stimulated my desire to expand my intellectual horizons.

Toward the close of my graduate studies, I wrote a personal letter to every chairman of a department of physiology in every medical school in the United States (more than 70 in all), asking if he could provide me with a position teaching physiology that would also permit me to go to medical school. I received two acknowledgments of my letters; one from John Fulton at Yale, commending me on my idea but regretting that he had no position available; the other, from Homer Smith at New York University Medical School, saying that he had a position available, but that I could not go to medical school. Needless to say what my decision was; this was 1932, the bottom of the Depression. I have always had a warm spot in my heart for Homer for providing my first post in physiology and eventually the opportunity to go to medical school, and also for John who answered my letter and encouraged me to persevere.

How the opportunity developed for me to go to medical school is too long to recount here. However, I am indebted to James Shannon and to the late Dean John Wyckoff for pressuring Homer on my behalf. It must not have been too distasteful to him, for as a medical student I published as much research as any departmental member, other than Smith himself and Shannon, made the highest grades ever achieved at New York University College of Medicine, was elected to Alpha Omega Alpha in my third year, taught physiology, and won the Cellano Medal in pathology and the senior first prizes in both medicine and surgery. Homer underwent a complete change of heart. He subsequently provided opportunities for several to follow in my footsteps.

An abbreviated version of the above biographical sketch prefaced my answers to the inquisitive student. I never at any time seriously considered the practice of medicine, nor even the combination of clinical teaching and research. My entire career had been directed toward that of a physiologist.

"Did I have House-staff training when I graduated from medical school?" was another query. The answer is no. I had no intention of pursuing a clinical career; I felt that additional research training in a different field would be more valuable to me as a physiologist than clinical experience. I applied for, and obtained, a two year postdoctoral Fellowship from the Rockefeller Foundation. At that time, a Rockefeller Fellowship was a more prestigious appointment than any other. Furthermore, it permitted training in a new and different field. In addition, it required that I return to NYU. I therefore had a position to which to return. Frankly, in those days, I was a bit of an intellectual snob; perhaps I still am. Nevertheless my fellowship years in neurophysiology with Stephen Walter Ranson, Horace Magoun, Detlev Bronk, and Martin Larrabee were rewarding ones.

There is a touch of serendipity in many staff appointments in the sense that the appointee must be in the right place, at the right time, and know the right people. This was certainly true of my association with the department of physiology at Cornell, which extended from 1942 to 1946 and continued from 1950 until my retirement in 1974. Walter Ranson had recommended me to Joseph Hinsey, then dean and chairman of anatomy at Cornell, who passed the word on to Eugene DuBois, chairman of physiology. Eugene wanted a person to run departmental affairs while he was on active duty as a captain in the Navy; with, of course, the counsel and veto power of Dayton Edwards, who divided his time between teaching physiology and the duties of assistant dean. This administrative internship taught me a valuable lesson: procrastinate judiciously with the hope that the problem will solve itself, which it frequently does. If it does not, then talk it over with one whom one respects, in this instance Dayton Edwards, get his counsel, and then act promptly and positively.

Another question frequently asked by students is, "Why did I give up neurophysiological research and return to renal research?" In 1942 the United States was deeply involved in World War II. All electronic equipment and components were unobtainable. One could still buy glassware and a colorimeter. When I moved from New York University to Cornell, I could move none of my electronic equipment. I could either sit out the war in research idleness or return to the study of my old love, the kidney. Obviously, I did the latter.

By 1946, when I moved to Syracuse University as chairman of the department of physiology, I was irrevocably a renal physiologist, had I not actually been one all along. Returning to Cornell in 1950 to succeed Eugene DuBois, I continued an association that lasted nearly another quarter century. At no time have I ever doubted the wisdom of my career decisions. However, as I look back, most of them have been more serendipitous than planned choices.

"Would I advise the medical student to become a physiologist?" No, I would not, nor would I advise him to enter into any other biomedical specialty. The ideal career for any person is one within his capabilities and one that will provide him with the most complete satisfaction. Because educational backgrounds and psychological and emotional makeups of individuals differ, one cannot advise, only consider the alternatives. So far I have described the educational background of one who became a physiologist. In the succeeding paragraphs, I consider some aspects of his psychological and emotional makeup and those factors that have given him happiness in his career.

There are obvious drawbacks to any career, including that of teaching and research in physiology. To the lay public, physiology is an unknown term. I remember one day overhearing my young daughter explaining carefully to her classmates that her father was not a real doctor, just a dog doctor. The attitude of the lay adult that "he who can, does; he who can't, teaches" is somewhat timeworn, shopworn, and not especially amusing to me. Subsequently, I advised my daughter to say that I was engaged in medical research, a profession for which the layman has a high and somewhat overinflated opinion. Most irritating is the statement that "doctors have shown," equating "doctors" with practicioners of medicine. If such statements seriously disturb c ˙e, my advice would be to go into the clinical practice of medicine, not into teaching and investigation, and certainly not into physiology.

Somewhat more difficult for the physiologist to accept is the "put-down" one receives from some of one's clinical colleagues. This takes the form of a general derogation of all basic sciences, the view that these sciences should be taught on the undergraduate campus, and the concept that the clinical disciplines are preeminent and sufficient unto themselves. I maintain that some close contact of basic scientists with those in clinical disciplines is necessary to keep some of the latter honest. One advantage of having both degrees is that one can thumb one's nose at the special conceits of both groups.

The economic hierarchy existing in most medical schools is disturbing to some basic scientists. It does not especially bother me for reasons I develop below. It is an example of the operation of the economics of the marketplace. If you have a service to sell, as does the surgeon, the radiologist, and even the pathologist, who tries his best to keep a foot in both the basic science and clinical camps, you can command more money. One of the advantages of the basic scientist is that he has nothing to sell except his discipline to medical students and his research to his peers, nor does he utilize his time trying to sell it to the public. I have always maintained that a medical school is an integral part of a university and thus should concern itself primarily with advancing knowledge in medicine and imparting that knowledge to students of medicine. It should not be concerned with provision of health care to the general public beyond that required for adequate teaching of undergraduate medical students and housestaff. Adherence to this maxim would solve many of the usual town-gown problems, make life less hectic for teachers of the clinical disciplines, and free more of their time for research and other scholarly activities. I well realize that this is not a popular view among government planners, hospital administrators, legislators, and even the clinical staff. However, I would not trade my freedom from patient care responsibilities for the economic advantages of the clinical staff member. I have never considered my salary too low, only that the salaries of some of my clinical associates were too high.

"When should I become involved in research?" is another question of students. The answer is, as soon as possible, certainly before the ultimate career choice must be made. Some individuals simply do not enjoy research. Others could not be happy without it. The choice of a career should be based on recognition of this fact.

"After I finish my medical training, should I continue my studies toward a PhD degree?" Here I would break my rule and unequivocally say no. The prestige added by a second degree is insignificant in comparison with the time and energy involved. If one has developed an interest in research during medical school, it would be much wiser to spend several years in postdoctoral research training. A fair part of PhD training is concerned with "taking the jumps," not with real educational experiences. If one chooses the proper postdoctoral advisor and works closely under his immediate supervision on a problem of direct interest to him, one learns most rapidly and readily. One of the mistakes of a beginning postdoctoral fellow is to come to a laboratory with a ready-made problem in mind, outside the interest and competence of his mentor. He forgets that his major goal should be to learn, not to produce independent personal research. Accordingly, he wastes time and does not fully avail himself of the advantages that can be provided by the laboratory he has chosen.

The reverse question of the PhD student—"should I take a medical degree after I finish my PhD training?"—is a more complicated one. If, despite his training, he finds that his interests are not in basic science teaching and research, and if his contacts with medicine have been sufficient for him to predict that clinical practice will satisfy his psychological and emotional needs, then by all means he should take a medical degree. Different but equally valid reasons motivated my medical training. I wanted the intellectual experience of a medical education. Furthermore, I felt that I would be a better teacher of physiology to medical students if I had a medical background. An unanticipated dividend was that my medical education influenced the course of my subsequent research on the kidney, more specifically on the renal regulation of acid-base balance, which occupied me for more than 20 years.

Let us turn to a closer consideration of those emotional and psychological factors that ultimately should direct one into either a basic science or a clinical career. The common stereotype of the basic scientist is that of one devoted to pure science, steely-eyed, critical, and completely lacking in compassion. The stereotype of the clinician is that of a warm, compassionate individual, widely knowledgeable, and exuding confidence from every pore. Within limits, both concepts have their elements of truth; neither is completely correct.

To be a successful physiologist, one should enjoy teaching, both lecturing and conference teaching. This is not to say that the clinical teacher should be any less devoted to these aspects of academic life. However, clinical teachers, as I have observed them, are more apt to talk "off the cuff" and, in general, devote less time to the preparation of a scholarly presentation, in many instances excusable on the basis of responsibilities of patient care. The clinician should be devoted to patient care, the physiologist should not; rather, his consuming interest should be research. This does not imply that he should be any less compassionate than the clinician, only that compassion is not his stock in trade, except in his social life and in his dealings with medical students.

The clinician must have a sure and confident bedside manner, capable of inspiring trust in his patients. Carried to an extreme this leads to his belief that he really is omniscient; he develops a "God complex," which to me is anathema. A related fault in a physiologist is dogmatism or excessive positivism.

I have always felt that I personally did not want to take a patient's life in my hands and accept responsibility for the outcome of any course of therapy I might prescribe. This is an important and necessary task of the clinician. I would not be happy doing this as a daily routine. I can well understand the many satisfactions that can be derived from this kind of activity and from the adulation of the grateful patient. It is not my "bag." I recognize the fact, therefore, that I would make a poor clinician. Whether other basic scientists feel the same is unknown to me. Do these facts make me less compassionate?

My satisfactions as a physiologist come from preparing and presenting a good lecture, planning and executing a penetrating experiment, writing and publishing an informative and understandable scientific paper. It has been said that my style of lecturing and writing is lucid and terse. I have found that a good rule to follow in either lecturing or writing is to "tell them what you'll tell them, tell them, and then tell them what you've told them." Another good rule to follow is "use only words with a precise and generally accepted meaning." Don't use laboratory jargon. A young mother, who was somewhat sociosexually emancipated, resolved to raise her infant daughter by inculcating a modern attitude toward sex, free of artificiality, false modesty, or inhibitions. One day shortly after her fourth birthday, the little girl asked, "Mummy, do you and daddy have sex relations?" "Ah," thought her mother, "Her first question; I must answer it carefully and in such a manner that I keep her mind free and open." "Yes, my dear," she answered. "Daddy and I have lovely sex relations." After a few moments of hesitation, the little girl continued her query, "Then why haven't they ever visited us?"

Retirement is a necessity for the good of any educational institution although it is not an unmixed blessing for the individual retiring. Having spent the greater part of my adult life in scholarly academic pursuits, it is logical that I spend the remainder of my declining years in similar activities. I could have remained at Cornell but it did not seem fair to my successor as chairman, Dr. Windhager. It is difficult enough for a new chairman to come to grips with his responsibilities without having his predecessor breathing down his neck. Fortunately, I was offered several opportunities to continue to do what I truly enjoy most, namely research. This has been achieved in pleasant surroundings with congenial associates in renal medicine and in physiology at the University of Florida School of Medicine in Gainesville.

RENAL PHYSIOLOGY ❖1142

FOREWORD

Gerhard Giebisch
Department of Physiology, Yale University School of Medicine, New Haven,
Connecticut 06510

Progress in the field of renal physiology during the last few years has been rapid, and research in this area continues to expand into several highly specialized areas. Hence it has become increasingly difficult to provide a complete and comprehensive appraisal of the current status of renal physiology even at time intervals as short as one or two years. This year's renal chapter of the Annual Review of Physiology departs from the usual format by highlighting four topics written by individual authors. It is hoped that this approach allows for a more complete and in-depth coverage of areas which have been of particular recent interest.

The first subsection focuses on the mechanism of glomerular filtration. Estimates of the driving forces of glomerular filtrate formation in the past, particularly those in the mammalian kidney, have been largely indirect. Direct measurements of glomerular capillary and capsular pressures have now become possible by techno-logical advances in hydrostatic pressure measurements and by the availability of a mutant strain of rats with superficial glomeruli. Not only is it now possible to examine directly the hemodynamic factors regulating the rate of glomerular filtrate formation but also to arrive at quantitative estimates of the permeability of the glomerular membrane. Extension of this work to other species and to pathological states of renal function promises to lead to further fundamental advances of our understanding of renal hemodynamics.

The second subsection reviews advances in tubular electrophysiology. Measure-ments of transepithelial and cellular transmembrane potential differences and elec-trical conductances have allowed for a precise definition 1. of the ionic permeability properties of tubular and cellular structures, 2. of the active and passive nature of individual ionic transport modes, and 3. of the direct electrogenic nature of ionic transport processes. In addition, electrophysiological measurements on single am-phibian and mammalian tubules have firmly established the presence of a function-ally important intercellular shunt path between the peritubular and luminal fluid. Observations on the intraepithelial current distribution have also allowed for a

7

definition of the properties of cell-to-cell coupling within the renal tubular epithelium.

The third section of this chapter deals with new insights into the mode of salt transport in the loop of Henle. One of the significant recent advances in renal physiology has been the successful perfusion of isolated segments of the mammalian nephron in vitro. Extension of this technique to the thick ascending limb of Henle's loop, a nephron site that cannot be investigated by micropuncture from the surface, has allowed, for the first time, a precise definition of the transport properties of this nephron segment. What has emerged from electrophysiological and tracer flux measurements is the clear indication that active, electrogenic chloride transport is a major function of this tubular segment. Importantly, the most powerful diuretics presently known have a major site of action on chloride transport along the thick ascending loop of Henle.

The final section of this year's renal chapter deals with advances in the field of tubular biochemistry. Emphasis has been placed upon an incisive review of the energy requirements of active sodium transport and the substrate specificity of renal tubular ion transport. In addition, the problem of renal tubular ammonia production is reviewed, with special attention focused on the continuingly intriguing problem of the cellular mechanism underlying the adaptive increase of ammonia production in chronic metabolic acidosis.

DETERMINANTS OF GLOMERULAR FILTRATION RATE

Barry M. Brenner

Kidney Research Laboratory, Veterans Administration Hospital, San Francisco,
California 94121, the Departments of Medicine and Physiology,
and the Cardiovascular Research Institute of the University of California,
San Francisco, California 94143

William M. Deen

Kidney Research Laboratory, Veterans Administration Hospital, San Francisco,
California 94121 and the Departments of Medicine and Physiology,
University of California, San Francisco, California 94143

Channing R. Robertson

Department of Chemical Engineering, Stanford University,
Stanford, California 94305

Introduction

In mammals, about one fifth to one third of the large volume of blood plasma
entering the renal glomerulus normally passes through the walls of its capillaries.
By use of micropuncture techniques, the composition of this fluid has been found
to conform to that of a nearly ideal ultrafiltrate, closely resembling plasma water
with respect to low molecular weight solute concentrations (14). For solutes with
molecular weights greater than approximately 5000, however, transport becomes
restricted; the extent of restriction is almost complete for molecules the size of serum
albumin or larger (22).

The rate of ultrafiltrate formation is governed by the same driving force governing
fluid movement across other capillary membranes, that is, the imbalance between
transcapillary hydraulic and colloid osmotic pressures. At any point along a
glomerular capillary, this relationship may be expressed as

$$J_v = k\,(\Delta P - \Delta\pi)$$
$$= k[(P_{GC} - P_T) - (\pi_{GC} - \pi_T)], \qquad\qquad 1.$$

where J_v is the local rate of ultrafiltration, k is the effective hydraulic permeability
of the capillary wall, and ΔP and $\Delta\pi$ are the transcapillary hydraulic and colloid
osmotic pressure differences, respectively. P_{GC} and π_{GC} are the hydraulic and
colloid osmotic pressures in the glomerular capillary, and P_T and π_T are the
corresponding pressures in Bowman's space. As the protein concentration in
glomerular ultrafiltrate is extremely small (13), π_T may be regarded as negligible.
Although it has been possible for some time to provide reasonably accurate estimates in mammals of several of the terms shown in equation 1, namely, π at afferent

and efferent ends of the glomerular capillary, and P_T, a meaningful description of the overall dynamics of glomerular ultrafiltration has been lacking until recently because of the inability to obtain direct measurements of P_{GC}. This is so because glomeruli are not generally present as surface structures accessible to micropuncture in the mammal. This restriction has been overcome in the past few years, however, a result primarily of the discovery of a mutant strain of Wistar rats possessing glomeruli on the surface of the renal cortex, thereby making possible the direct measurement of P_{GC} in this mammalian species. Using the servonull pressure-measuring technique of Wiederhielm et al (26), Brenner, Troy & Daugharty (3) found P_{GC} in these rats to average approximately 45 mm Hg, or some 40% of the mean aortic pressure. Essentially the same findings have since been obtained in other laboratories (1, 2). Moreover, in the squirrel monkey, a small primate that also possesses surface glomeruli, P_{GC} has again been found to average some 45 mm Hg (20).

Normal Glomerular Dynamics

From these measurements of P_{GC}, together with the other measured pressures, it is possible to evaluate the net driving force for ultrafiltration at the afferent and efferent ends of the glomerular capillary network. As shown for the rat in Table 1, the value of P_{GC} of 45 mm Hg is taken to be the same at the afferent and efferent ends of the network, since the axial pressure drop along the network due to flow has been found to be quite small (4).[1] Proximal tubule pressure, P_T, is normally about 10 mm Hg. Measurements of afferent and efferent arteriolar plasma protein concentrations indicate that the colloid osmotic pressure, π_{GC}, increases from about 20 mm Hg at the afferent end to 35 mm Hg at the efferent end of the glomerular

Table 1 Glomerular capillary hydraulic and oncotic pressures (in mm Hg)[a]

Glomerular Capillary Site	P_{GC}	P_T	π_{GC}	P_{UF}
Afferent end	45	10	20	15
Efferent end	45	10	35	0

[a] Abbreviations: P_{GC} and P_T, local glomerular capillary and Bowman's space (or early proximal) hydraulic pressures, respectively; π_{GC}, local glomerular capillary plasma colloid osmotic pressure; P_{UF}, local net ultrafiltration pressure.

[1] Some axial pressure drop must exist in order for blood to flow through the capillary. That this pressure drop is small is given by the finding that the sum of the pressures opposing filtration at the efferent end of the glomerular capillary (as inferred from the sum of efferent arteriolar oncotic pressure, π_E, plus proximal tubule hydraulic pressure, P_T) reaches a value which, on average, balances P_{GC}. Since P_{GC} is measured at statistically random sites along the glomerular capillary, the finding that $\pi_E + P_T = P_{GC}$ indicates that P_{GC} changes little along capillary segments at this level of the renal vascular circuit. The sensitivity of the methods used to determine π_E, P_T, and P_{GC} makes it likely that this pressure drop is no greater than 2–3 mm Hg. Thus, the measured value of P_{GC} is essentially the same as the value of P_{GC} averaged over the length of the glomerular capillary, denoted as $\bar{P}_{GC}$.

capillary because of the largely protein-free nature of the ultrafiltrate (2–4, 6, 21, 23). P_{UF}, the local net ultrafiltration pressure (as given in Table 1) thus declines from a maximum value of about 15 mm Hg at the afferent end essentially to zero by the efferent end. In other words, it has been shown that by the efferent end of the capillary network $\Delta\pi$ rises to a value that, on the average, exactly equals ΔP (2– 4, 6, 21, 23). This equality of ΔP and $\Delta\pi$ is referred to as *filtration pressure equilibrium.*

These relationships are summarized graphically in Figure 1, in which the abscissa represents the normalized distance along an idealized glomerular capillary; 0 is the afferent end and 1 the efferent end. As already indicated, ΔP, the difference between P_{GC} of 45 and P_T of 10, or 35 mm Hg, is essentially constant along the length of the capillary. $\Delta\pi$, equal to π_{GC}, as π_T is negligible, increases from 20 to 35 mm Hg along the capillary. Accordingly, the decline in P_{UF} from a maximum value of 15 mm Hg essentially to zero is the consequence, not of an appreciable decline in ΔP, but rather of a progressive increase in $\Delta\pi$. Because the measurements of π can only be performed on samples of systemic blood (taken as representative of blood at the afferent end of the glomerular capillary) and blood from efferent arterioles, the exact profile of the change in π with distance along the capillary cannot be determined directly. The $\Delta\pi$ profile in Figure 1 is one of an infinite number of profiles consistent with the measurements of π_A and π_E in hydropenia: hence the point along the capillary at which $P_{UF} = 0$ cannot be determined from these measurements alone.

The rate of glomerular ultrafiltration may be expressed as

$$\text{SNGFR} = K_f \cdot \overline{P}_{UF} = k \cdot S[\overline{\Delta P} - \overline{\Delta\pi}], \qquad\qquad 2.$$

where SNGFR, the single nephron glomerular filtration rate, is the product of the ultrafiltration coefficient, K_f, and the net driving pressure averaged over the length of the capillary, $\overline{P}_{UF}$. $\overline{P}_{UF}$ is the difference between the mean transcapillary hydraulic and oncotic pressure differences, $\overline{\Delta P}$ and $\overline{\Delta\pi}$, respectively, equal to the shaded

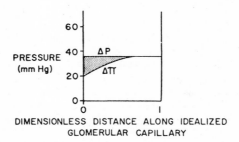

Figure 1 Hydraulic and colloid osmotic pressure profiles among an idealized glomerular capillary in the rat. $\Delta P = P_{GC} - P_T$ and $\Delta\pi = \pi_{GC} - \pi_T$, where P_{GC} and P_T are the hydraulic pressures in the glomerular capillary and Bowman's space, respectively, and π_{GC} and π_T are the corresponding colloid osmotic pressures.

area between the ΔP and $\Delta \pi$ curves in Figure 1. K_f is the product of the effective hydraulic permeability of the capillary wall (k) and the surface area available for filtration (S). As mentioned above, under conditions of filtration pressure equilibrium it is impossible to estimate $\overline{P}_{UF}$ due to the uncertainty in determining the exact $\Delta \pi$ profile. Since the local rate of ultrafiltration is proportional to the local value of $\Delta P - \Delta \pi$, $\Delta \pi$ will tend to increase most rapidly near the afferent end of the capillary, so that any $\Delta \pi$ profile at equilibrium must, as shown in Figure 1, be highly nonlinear (8). A multiplicity of $\Delta \pi$ curves, including the one shown in Figure 1, satisfy the requirement that the net driving pressure, $\Delta P - \Delta \pi$, decline from a maximum value at the afferent end of the capillary to zero by the efferent end. Because $\overline{P}_{UF}$ is equal to the area between the ΔP and $\Delta \pi$ curves, $\overline{P}_{UF}$, and therefore K_f, cannot be determined uniquely from the available measurements at equilibrium.

Mathematical Model of Glomerular Filtration

Uncertainty in the determination of $\Delta \pi$ profiles has provided the incentive for the development of a mathematical model of glomerular ultrafiltration (8). In this model, conservation of mass and the Starling hypothesis (equation 1) are used to derive a differential equation giving the rate of change of protein concentration with distance along the glomerular capillary. This formulation makes possible the calculation of $\Delta \pi$ profiles along the capillary, which, together with measured values of $\overline{\Delta P}$, π_A, π_E, and SNGFR, permit determination of $\overline{P}_{UF}$, and hence K_f, under a variety of conditions discussed below. This approach has the additional advantage of enabling one to examine the effects of selective perturbations in π_A, $\overline{\Delta P}$, K_f, and glomerular plasma flow rate (Q_A) on SNGFR.

In this model, the glomerular capillary network is simplified to be a single tube of equivalent total surface area (S), with local plasma flow rate (Q) and protein concentration (C) functions only of the length coordinate $(\hat{x})$. The latter is normalized so that $0 \leq \hat{x} \leq 1$. Conservation of volume and protein requires that the following differential equations be satisfied:

$$dQ/d\hat{x} = -J_v S, \quad Q = Q_A \text{ at } \hat{x} = 0 \tag{3.}$$

and

$$d(QC)/d\hat{x} = 0, \quad QC = Q_A C_A \text{ at } \hat{x} = 0, \tag{4.}$$

where Q_A is the initial glomerular plasma flow rate and C_A is the afferent arteriolar or systemic protein concentration.

Equations 1, 3, and 4 may be combined to yield a single differential equation giving the rate of change of C (and hence $\Delta \pi$)[2] with distance along the glomerular capillary:

[2]$\Delta \pi$ increases in a nonlinear fashion with increases in C:

$$\Delta \pi = a_1 C + a_2 C^2.$$

For protein concentrations in the range $4 \leq C \leq 10$ g/100 ml, and normal albumin to globulin concentration ratio of unity, $a_1 = 1.63$ mm Hg/(g/100 ml) and $a_2 = 0.294$ mm Hg/(g/100 ml)^2.

$$d\hat{C}/d\hat{x} = F\hat{C}^2[(\Delta P - \Delta\pi)/\overline{\Delta P}], \quad \hat{C}(0) = 1, \qquad\qquad 5.$$

where $\hat{C} = C/C_A$ and $F = K_f\overline{\Delta P}/Q_A$. Since ΔP normally declines by no more than ∿1–2 mm Hg with distance along the capillary (4), ΔP differs from $\overline{\Delta P}$ by no more than ∿6%. A more detailed discussion of this and other features of the model, together with the method of solution of equation 5, is given elsewhere (8). For measured or assumed values of F, solution of equation 5 yields protein concentration and oncotic pressure profiles along a glomerular capillary, information that cannot yet be obtained from direct measurement.

The value of K_f is an important determinant of $\Delta\pi$ profiles, as the parameter F is proportional to K_f. The difficulty in calculating K_f from experimental data is illustrated once again by Figure 2, which shows $\Delta\pi$ profiles corresponding to several values of the dimensionless parameter F. In this figure, consider $\overline{\Delta P}$ to be constant so that changes in F are proportional to changes in the ratio K_f/Q_A. Note that filtration pressure equilibrium, the previously discussed equality of ΔP and π_E achieved in the normally hydrated rat and monkey (2–4, 6, 21, 23), is obtained in this illustration for values of F greater than ∿3. It is clear that for a given value of $\overline{\Delta P}$ at equilibrium, $\Delta\pi$ rises to the same value at the efferent end of the capillary, irrespective of the value of K_f. In other words, so long as K_f is sufficiently large to yield equilibrium, further increases in K_f will only shift the point at which equilibrium is achieved further toward the afferent end of the capillary. Thus, from measurements of $\Delta\pi$ at the afferent and efferent ends of the glomerular capillary, it is not possible to distinguish among the many $\Delta\pi$ profiles consistent with equilibrium; only a minimum value of K_f can be estimated. On the other hand, Figure 2 also suggests that if K_f and $\overline{\Delta P}$ remain relatively constant, large values of Q_A, corresponding to lower values of F, should prevent achievement of filtration pressure equilibrium. Of importance in this case, only one $\Delta\pi$ profile can connect measured values of π at afferent and efferent ends of the capillary. The value of F corresponding to this unique $\Delta\pi$ profile, together with measured values of $\overline{\Delta P}$ and Q_A, yields the value of K_f.

This approach has been used by Deen et al to estimate the value of K_f in the normal rat (12). Intravenous infusion of a volume of isoncotic rat plasma equal to

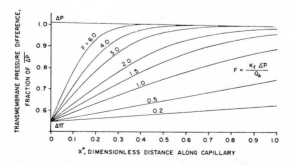

Figure 2 Transmembrane colloid osmotic pressure profiles as a function of the dimensionless parameter, *F*. Reprinted from *Fed. Proc.* 33:14–20, 1974.

~5% of body weight was found to increase Q_A to some 200 nl/min, approximately three times the normal hydropenic value of 75 nl/min, and sufficiently high to give disequilibrium. The value of K_f was found to average about 4.8 nl/(min·mm Hg). Of interest, K_f was found to remain essentially unchanged within a twofold range of changes in Q_A, strongly suggesting that K_f is independent of Q_A (12). In addition, it was confirmed that this value of K_f is sufficiently large to permit attainment of equilibrium at the lower values of Q_A characteristic of hydropenia in the normal rat (12).

Taking this value of K_f together with measured values for SNGFR, it follows that the mean ultrafiltration pressure, $\overline{P}_{UF}$, attains a value of approximately 4–6 mm Hg in the normal hydropenic rat (2–4, 6, 21, 23) and increases to roughly 10 mm Hg under conditions of marked plasma volume expansion, thereby accounting for the large rise in SNGFR observed experimentally (4, 7, 11, 12, 21).

Effective Hydraulic Permeability of the Glomerular Capillary Wall

Since $K_f = kS$ (equation 2), the effective hydraulic permeability[3] (k) of the glomerular capillary can be estimated from K_f and the surface area available for ultrafiltration (S). Taking $K_f = 4.8$ nl/(min·mm Hg) and $S = 0.0019$ cm^2 for the rat glomerulus (15), $k = 2.5$ μl/(min·mm Hg·cm^2). This permeability is approximately 1–2 orders of magnitude greater than that reported for capillaries in other tissues in a variety of species, including frog mesentery (5, 16, 17), rat skeletal muscle (24), rat peritubular capillaries (9), and rabbit omentum (18, 27). Thus the relatively high permeability of the glomerular capillaries enables glomerular ultrafiltration to proceed at a rapid rate despite a mean driving pressure of normally only about 5 mm Hg.

The Effects of Selective Alterations in the Determinants of Glomerular Filtration Rate

As discussed above, the model of glomerular filtration provides the opportunity to examine the effects on glomerular filtration rate of selected perturbations in the four determinants of ultrafiltration, namely, Q_A, K_f, $\overline{\Delta P}$, and π_A. In the present context, SNGFR is best expressed as

$$SNGFR = SNFF \cdot Q_A, \qquad \qquad 6.$$

[3]Concentration polarization, the accumulation of retained solute next to an ultrafiltering membrane, elevates osmotic pressure above that which would exist in the absence of polarization. For ultrafiltration in a cylindrical tube, use of the radially averaged solute concentration results in an underestimate of osmotic pressure, yielding an effective hydraulic permeability (k) less than the actual membrane hydraulic permeability (k_m). The extent to which k and k_m might differ in an ultrafiltering capillary has been examined theoretically by solution of the momentum and species transport equations for idealized capillaries with and without erythrocytes (10). For diameters, flow velocities, protein concentrations and diffusivities, and ultrafiltration pressures representative of the rat glomerular capillary network, results indicate that the effects of polarization are substantial without erythrocytes ($k/k_m = 0.7$) and persist, but to a lesser extent, with erythrocytes ($k/k_m = 0.9$); the reduction in polarization in the latter case is due to enhanced plasma mixing.

where SNFF is the single-nephron filtration fraction. Because only a negligible amount of protein appears in glomerular filtrate, conservation of protein requires that

$$Q_A C_A = (Q_A - \text{SNGFR})C_E, \qquad\qquad 7.$$

where C_E is the efferent protein concentration and the other terms are as defined above. When equation 7 is rearranged and compared with equation 6, SNFF is related to C_A and C_E:

$$\text{SNFF} = 1 - (C_A/C_E). \qquad\qquad 8.$$

It is clear from Figure 2 that, for given values of C_A (hence π_A), K_f, and $\overline{\Delta P}$, C_E (hence π_E) will be unaffected by changes in Q_A so long as equilibrium is maintained. Under these conditions, SNFF will remain constant. Further increases in Q_A, which cause disequilibrium, lead to progressively lower values of C_E. Thus, for given values of K_f, $\overline{\Delta P}$, and C_A at disequilibrium, it is evident from equation 8 that SNFF must decrease with increasing Q_A. The theoretical interrelationships among SNFF, SNGFR, and Q_A are shown in Figure 3, calculated for values of K_f, C_A, and $\overline{\Delta P}$ representative of the normal hydropenic rat. It follows from Equation 6 that as long as SNFF remains constant, SNGFR will vary in a linear manner with Q_A, as shown for values of Q_A up to $\sim$100 nl/min. This linear relationship at equilibrium, indicating that SNGFR is highly plasma-flow dependent, has been observed experimentally (4, 6, 21, 23). For higher values of Q_A, where disequilibrium occurs and SNFF decreases, SNGFR increases less than in proportion to increases in Q_A (7, 12, 21), hence the departure from the dashed line in Figure 3, the latter denoting a constant filtration fraction of 0.33. Even at disequilibrium SNGFR will be highly plasma-flow dependent, but to a lesser extent than when equilibrium obtains. In the absence of experimental measurements of $\overline{\Delta P}$ and K_f in larger mammals, including man, it is not yet possible to quantify the interrelationships among SNFF, SNGFR, and Q_A in the same detail as that shown for the rat in Figure 3. Nevertheless, it has been shown in both man and dog that SNFF tends to vary inversely with changes in renal plasma flow (25).

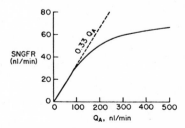

Figure 3 The effects on SNGFR of selective perturbations in Q_A, assuming values for K_f, ΔP, and π_A typical of the normal hydropenic rat, that is, $K_f = 4.8$ nl/ (min·mm Hg), $\Delta P = 35$ mm Hg, and $\pi_A = 19$ mm Hg ($C_A = 5.7$ g/100 ml). The dashed line is given by SNGFR = 0.33Q_A.

To understand the theoretical relationship between SNGFR and K_f, it is important to recognize that low values of K_f lead to disequilibrium, and hence to low values of SNFF. For a given value of Q_A, SNGFR will vary in direct proportion to SNFF (equation 6); thus the dependence of SNGFR on K_f will follow the pattern shown in Figure 4, where values of Q_A, C_A, and $\overline{\Delta P}$ are again chosen to be representative of the normal hydropenic rat. It can be seen in Figure 4 that once K_f achieves a value large enough to yield filtration pressure equilibrium, ~4 nl/(min·mm Hg), further increases in K_f will fail to affect the value of SNGFR. In the normal rat, where K_f averages ~4.8 nl/(min·mm Hg), a reduction in K_f of at least 50% would be required to effect a 20% reduction in SNGFR. Accordingly, it is unlikely that K_f will be an important determinant of SNGFR except in pathological states in which capillary hydraulic permeability and/or surface area are reduced markedly. This has indeed been shown to be the case in a recent study of experimental glomerulonephritis in the rat (19).

The changes in SNGFR expected from changes in $\overline{\Delta P}$ alone are shown in Figure 5. Ultrafiltration of fluid across the walls of the glomerular capillary network occurs when $\overline{\Delta P}$ exceeds $\overline{\Delta \pi}$ (equation 2). Since π_A in the rat is approximately 19 mm Hg (3, 4, 6), filtrate is formed only when $\overline{\Delta P}$ exceeds this value. As $\overline{\Delta P}$ is elevated, SNFF and SNGFR increase in parallel. Of interest is the prediction in Figure 5 that the rate of increase in SNGFR diminishes for larger values of $\overline{\Delta P}$. These nonlinear

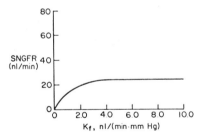

Figure 4   The effects on SNGFR of selective alterations in K_f. Q_A is now taken as 75 nl/min and ΔP and π_A are as defined in the legend to Figure 3.

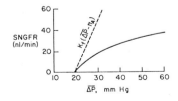

Figure 5   The effects on SNGFR of selective changes in ΔP. All other determinants assumed constant at values given in the legends to Figures 3 and 4. The dashed line is given by SNGFR $= K_f(\Delta P - \pi_A)$.

relationships result from the fact that as $\overline{\Delta P}$ is increased, the resulting increase in the rate of ultrafiltration leads to a concurrent, but lesser increase in $\overline{\Delta \pi}$. Were this increase in $\overline{\Delta \pi}$ not to occur, SNGFR would increase in a linear fashion with increases in $\overline{\Delta P}$, as in the dashed line in Figure 5. As evident from equation 2, the slope of this line is K_f.

Only in the mutant Wistar rat has it been possible to examine the extent to which $\overline{\Delta P}$ varies in response to experimental maneuvers designed to produce large changes in SNGFR (2, 4, 6, 7, 12, 21, 23). In these studies, $\overline{\Delta P}$ rarely changes by more than ~5 mm Hg, indicating that $\overline{\Delta P}$ is effectively autoregulated. Given this relative constancy of $\overline{\Delta P}$ under a variety of experimental conditions, and the relative insensitivity of SNGFR to changes in $\overline{\Delta P}$ (Figure 5), it seems clear that changes in this determinant of ultrafiltration will usually play a less important role in determining SNGFR than will changes in Q_A. This conclusion has been shown to hold under a number of experimental conditions in the rat (2, 4, 6, 7, 12, 21, 23).

It is important to recognize that $\overline{\Delta P}$ and π_A set the upper limit on the value of SNFF. To appreciate this, equation 8 may be rewritten thus:

$$
\begin{aligned}
\text{SNFF} &\approx 1 - (\pi_A/\pi_E) \\
&\approx 1 - (\pi_A/\overline{\Delta P}).
\end{aligned}
\qquad 9.
$$

Equation 9 is not exactly equivalent to equation 8 because of the nonlinear relationship between π and C. At filtration pressure equilibrium, π_E equals $\overline{\Delta P}$. Hence for a given value of π_A at equilibrium, $\overline{\Delta P}$ determines the value of SNFF by determining the value of π_E.

As shown in Figure 6, the effect of changes in π_A alone on SNGFR is in many ways similar to that of changing $\overline{\Delta P}$ alone; decreases in π_A are nearly equivalent to selective increases in $\overline{\Delta P}$. Again, because Q_A is assumed to be constant, SNFF and SNGFR change in parallel. The theoretical relationship in Figure 6 is in keeping with recent observations in the rat by Blantz (2), who found that, to a large extent, the increase in SNGFR induced by mannitol infusion is due to the decrease in π_A brought about by hemodilution. Also shown in Figure 6 are the values of C_A that correspond to values of π_A. As π_A approaches $\overline{\Delta P}$ (found to be 35 mm Hg for the rat), SNGFR approaches zero.

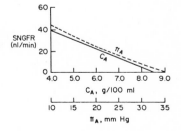

Figure 6   The effects on SNGFR of selective perturbations in C_A (hence π_A), the other determinants assumed constant at values given in the legends to Figures 3 and 4.

ACKNOWLEDGMENTS

This study was supported in part by grants from the Veterans Administration and National Institutes of Health (HE14945 and AM 13888).

Dr. Brenner is a Medical Investigator of the Veterans Administration.

Literature Cited

1. Arendshorst, W. J., Gottschalk, C. W. 1974. Apparent filtration pressure disequilibrium and filtration coefficient in the rat kidney. *Kidney Int.* 6:18A (Abstr.)
2. Blantz, R. C. 1974. Effect of mannitol on glomerular ultrafiltration in the hydropenic rat. *J. Clin. Invest.* 54: 1135–43
3. Brenner, B. M., Troy, J. L., Daugharty, T. M. 1971. The dynamics of glomerular ultrafiltration in the rat. *J. Clin. Invest.* 50:1776–80
4. Brenner, B. M., Troy, J. L., Daugharty, T. M., Deen, W. M., Robertson, C. R. 1972. Dynamics of glomerular ultrafiltration in the rat. II. Plasma-flow dependence of GFR. *Am. J. Physiol.* 223:1184–90
5. Brown, E., Landis, E. M. 1947. Effect of local cooling on fluid movements, effective osmotic pressure and capillary permeability in the frog's mesentery. *Am. J. Physiol.* 149:302–15
6. Daugharty, T. M., Ueki, I. F., Mercer, P. F., Brenner, B. M. 1974. Dynamics of glomerular ultrafiltration in the rat. V. Response to ischemic injury. *J. Clin. Invest.* 53:105–16
7. Deen, W. M., Maddox, D. A., Robertson, C. R., Brenner, B. M. 1974. Dynamics of glomerular ultrafiltration in the rat. VII. Response to reduced renal mass. *Am. J. Physiol.* 227:556–62
8. Deen, W. M., Robertson, C. R., Brenner, B. M. 1972. A model of glomerular ultrafiltration in the rat. *Am. J. Physiol.* 223:1178–83
9. Deen, W. M., Robertson, C. R., Brenner, B. M. 1973. A model of peritubular capillary control of isotonic fluid reabsorption by the renal proximal tubule. *Biophys. J.* 13:340–58
10. Deen, W. M., Robertson, C. R., Brenner, B. M. 1974. Concentration polarization in an ultrafiltering capillary. *Biophys. J.* 14:412–31
11. Deen, W. M., Robertson, C. R., Brenner, B. M. 1974. Glomerular ultrafiltration. *Fed. Proc.* 33:14–20
12. Deen, W. M., Troy, J. L., Robertson, C. R., Brenner, B. M. 1973. Dynamics of glomerular ultrafiltration in the rat. IV. Determination of the ultrafiltration coefficient. *J. Clin. Invest.* 52:1500–1508
13. Gaizutis, M., Pesce, A. J., Lewy, J. E. 1972. Determination of nanogram amounts of albumin by radioimmunoassay. *Microchem. J.* 17:327–37
14. Harris, C. A., Baer, P. G., Chirito, E., Dirks, J. H. 1974. Composition of mammalian glomerular filtrate. *Am. J. Physiol.* 227:972–76
15. Kirkman, H., Stowell, R. E. 1942. Renal filtration surface in the albino rat. *Anat. Record* 82:373–91
16. Landis, E. M. 1927. Micro-injection studies of capillary permeability. II. Relationship between capillary pressure and the rate at which fluid passes through the walls of single capillaries. *Am. J. Physiol.* 82:217–38
17. Landis, E. M. 1928. Micro-injection studies of capillary permeability. III. The effect of lack of oxygen on the permeability of the capillary wall to fluid and to the plasma proteins. *Am. J. Physiol.* 83:528–42
18. Lee, J. S., Smaje, L. H., Zweifach, B. W. 1971. Fluid movement in occluded single capillaries of rabbit omentum. *Circ. Res.* 28:358–70
19. Maddox, D. A., Bennett, C. M., Deen, W. M., Glassock, R. J., Knudson, D., Daugharty, T. M., Brenner, B. M. 1975. Determinants of glomerular filtration in experimental glomerulonephritis in the rat. *J. Clin. Invest.* 55:305–18
20. Maddox, D. A., Deen, W. M., Brenner, B. M. 1974. Dynamics of glomerular ultrafiltration. VI. Studies in the primate. *Kidney Int.* 5:271–78
21. Myers, B. D., Deen, W. M., Robertson, C. R., Brenner, B. M. 1975. Dynamics of glomerular ultrafiltration in the rat. VIII. Effects of hematocrit. *Circ. Res.* 36:425–35
22. Renkin, E. M., Gilmore, J. P. 1973. Glomerular filtration. In *Renal Physiology*, ed. J. Orloff, R. W. Berliner. Washington DC: Am. Physiol. Soc.
23. Robertson, C. R., Deen, W. M., Troy, J. L., Brenner, B. M. 1972. Dynamics of

glomerular ultrafiltration in the rat. III. Hemodynamics and autoregulation. *Am. J. Physiol.* 223:1191–1200

24. Smaje, L., Zweifach, B. W., Intaglietta, M. 1970. Micropressure and capillary filtration coefficients in single vessels of the cremaster muscle in the rat. *Microvasc. Res.* 2:96–110

25. Smith, H. W. 1951. *The Kidney. Structure and Function in Health and Disease.* New York: Oxford Univ. Press

26. Wiederhielm, C. A., Woodbury, J. W., Kirk, S., Rushmer, R. F. 1964. Pulsatile pressures in the microcirculation of frog's mesentery. *Am. J. Physiol.* 207:173–76

27. Zweifach, B. W., Intaglietta, M. 1968. Mechanics of fluid movement across single capillaries in the rabbit. *Microvasc. Res.* 1:83–101

RECENT ADVANCES IN ELECTROPHYSIOLOGY OF THE NEPHRON

Emile L. Boulpaep

Department of Physiology, Yale University School of Medicine, New Haven, Connecticut 06510

Introduction

Since the extensive review by Windhager & Giebisch in 1965 (129), several symposia and monographs have been concerned with electrophysiological approaches and techniques in renal studies (30, 40, 41, 43). The last review of kidney physiology covering transport of water and strong electrolytes was published in 1971 (78). Accordingly, this chapter surveys recent advances of the past five years. The electrical parameters to be described for renal tubular epithelia deal with overall transepithelial phenomena or with measurements of membrane properties of single tubule cells. Generally, information is obtained from measurements of either potential differences or conductances.

Transepithelial Potential Differences and Conductances

Stable potential differences have been recorded across most tubular segments of the nephron either from in vivo kidneys, perfused kidneys, isolated perfused tubules, or tissue slices. Problems in the investigation of nephron segments located at the surface of the intact kidney by means of Ling-Gerard microelectrodes have been discussed (10, 29). Marked improvements have been made in accessibility, stability, and reliability of the electrical recordings, in addition to proper localization of the microelectrode and control of tip potential artifacts (10, 29). Perfused kidney preparations (14, 39) or tissue slices (101) may circumvent any instability due to respiratory or pulsatile displacement of the tubules. Pitfalls resulting from poor localization or artifactual junction potentials with nonflowing microelectrodes may be avoided for transepithelial measurements by using fairly large sharpened micropipettes (2–11 μm OD) inserted across the tubular wall (5, 6, 33, 49, 68, 79, 109). However, a truly flowing junction should be established between the fluid filling the micropipette and the surrounding biological solution of different composition. Alternatively, the recording micropipette can be filled with a solution identical in composition to the biological compartment it is impaling, voiding the need for an appropriate tip correction when the pipette is positioned in a surface or reference bath of different ion content (29, 30). Errors caused by reversible contamination of the electrode tip with foreign material (49) may be obviated in this manner. Spring has inserted axial platinized tungsten electrodes in the center of in vivo amphibian proximal tubules for passing current (91). Electrical insulation around the metal wire was obtained by means of an oil block occluding the tubular lumen, which rules out measurements under tubular free flow. In addition, the variable electrode potential at the metal-liquid interface precludes the determination of transepithelial potential differences by means of platinum electrodes. Hybrid Ag-AgCl filament electrodes (15 μm OD) were used by U. Hegel and E. L. Boulpaep for the determination of transepithelial potential differences in *Necturus* proximal tubule in vivo (unpublished). The introduction of techniques for perfusing isolated renal tubules (15) has opened the way to long-term, stable transepithelial potential recordings in combination with simultaneous water and solute flux measurements. Following early determinations of transepithelial potential across isolated perfused rabbit tubules plagued by significant leaks at the perfusion pipettes (19), improved electrical sealing by means of Sylgard 184 has established the validity of such in vitro techniques for transepithelial electrical determinations (20, 54).

A survey of the transepithelial potential differences along the nephron (Table 1) clearly dispels the earlier conclusion (112) that all segments of the tubular lumen are normally electrically negative to the peritubular interstitium or bath.

Table 1 Representative values of transepithelial potential difference and resistance for different segments of the nephron

Species	Preparation	Potential difference[a] (mV)	Refs.	Specific transverse resistance[a] (ohm cm^2)	Refs.
Proximal convoluted tubule					
Necturus	in vivo	−15	(9)	70, early	(11)
Necturus	perfused	−6 to −12	(44)	430, late	(44)
rat	in vivo, early	−1.5	(31)	11.6	(87)
rat	in vivo, intermediate & late	+1.8	(31)	5.6	(87)
rabbit	isolated perfused	−4 to −6	(20,63)	7.0	(69)
dog	autoperfused in vivo	−2	(14)	5.6	(14)
Proximal straight tubule					
rabbit	isolated perfused, superficial	−1.3 to −2	(69,86)	8.2	(69)
rabbit	isolated perfused, juxtamedulla	−1.8	(59)	—	—
Thin descending limb of Henle					
hamster	in vivo	−3	(110)	—	—
rabbit	isolated perfused	0	(61)	—	—
Thick ascending limb of Henle					
hamster	in vivo	−9 to −11	(74,110)	—	—
rabbit	isolated perfused	0	(58)	—	—
Thick descending limb of Henle					
rabbit	isolated perfused, cortical	+3.5 to +6.4	(16)	21.5 to 24.6	(16)
rabbit	isolated perfused, medullary	+6.7	(81)	—	—
Intermediate segment of amphibians					
Necturus	in vivo	+6	(109)	—	—
Distal convoluted tubule					
frog, salamander	isolated perfused, early	+12	(95)	—	—
frog, salamander	isolated perfused, late	−33	(95)	—	—
rat	in vivo, early	−9 to −12	(71,113)	—	—
rat, mutant Wistar	in vivo, early	+3.7	(5)	—	—
rat	in vivo, late and random	−37 to −60	(112)	377	(71)
dog	in vivo, random	−43	(14)	600	(14)
rabbit	isolated perfused	−40	(46)	—	—
Amphiuma	in vivo	−45	(98)	—	—
Necturus	in vivo	−35	(77)	—	—
Cortical collecting tubule					
rabbit	isolated perfused	−35	(96)	867	(54)
Medullary collecting duct					
hamster	in vivo	−34	(79)	1000 to 2000	(80)

[a] Representative mean value taken from the references in parentheses.

Transepithelial conductance can be determined in several ways (10, 112). Current application by means of a point source is unlikely to achieve a uniform potential across the epithelium (10, 112). Spring and Paganelli developed an axial metal electrode for amphibian tubules that permits uniform current application and a direct measurement of tubular resistance from confined tubular segments (91, 94). Voltage clamping by this method can estimate short-circuit current (91–94). Hegel & Boulpaep used similar electrodes for electrical impedance studies (48). For determination of transepithelial resistance, infinite cable analysis was used extensively in in vivo preparations (10, 11, 14, 26, 37, 44, 49, 71, 80, 87, 88, 112). Finite cable analysis is the method of choice for isolated tubule preparations (19, 51, 54, 69) and could be applied to long tubular segments in vivo confined by means of oil blocks (80). Finally, cable analysis for an infinite but branching cable was required for analyzing the medullary collecting duct tree (80). Table 1 lists a summary of specific resistance values (ohm cm^2) for several segments of the nephron.

PROXIMAL CONVOLUTED TUBULE   In recent years, substantial controversy has surrounded the exact value of the proximal tubular transepithelial potential difference. Sizable potential differences of −20 mV (lumen negative) had been reported both for amphibian and mammalian kidney (112). Subsequently, with improved techniques, values of −10 to −15 mV were recorded from in vivo *Necturus* proximal tubules (7–9, 11, 13, 47, 67, 92, 94, 97) and somewhat lower values during bilateral microperfusion with identical solutions (13) or whole kidney perfusion (44). However, free flow transepithelial potential differences not different from zero were reported by Frömter & Hegel in rat proximal tubules (33) and about −2 mV by Boulpaep & Seely in dog proximal tubule (14). In the rat in vivo, de Mello & Malnic found −2 to −4 mV (26) and Khuri et al (64) −0.7 mV. In the presence of identical salt solutions without organic solutes on both sides of the epithelium, Maude detected no potential difference in rat cortical slices (76) and Frömter, Muller & Wick described a signal of −1 mV, which they found resistant to cyanide poisoning and attributed to a tip potential artifact (37). All these studies used Ling-Gerard microelectrodes and despite improved techniques for stability, localization of the microelectrode, and detection of leaky impalements, small reversible changes in tip potential during puncture cannot be ruled out. Microelectrodes filled with a solution identical to the expected tubular fluid in late or intermediate proximal segments gave in random impalements, a value of +1.8 mV in free flow and zero during bilateral perfusion with salt solutions (29, 37).

In contrast, isolated rabbit proximal tubules bathed in serum and adequately perfused with serum ultrafiltrate or an artificial ultrafiltrate exhibited consistently mean potential differences between −3.8 and −5.8 mV (20, 22, 62, 63, 69). The findings by Kokko & Rector indicating that the potential difference in isolated rabbit proximal tubule is a saturable function of perfusion rate provided a clue (63). Potential difference was maximal during perfusion at rates between 130 and 10 nl min^{-1} and was sharply reduced when perfusion rate was between 10 and 1 nl min^{-1}, reaching a minimum value of −1 to −2 mV. Changes in tubular geometry and hydrostatic pressure per se were ruled out as possible mechanisms, and the authors suggested that the depletion of critical substrates for transport at low flow rates might cause a drop in potential. Using an artificial ultrafiltrate solution, Kokko demonstrated by means of selective removal that the presence of glucose, amino acids, and bicarbonate contributes to the generation of a sizable negative potential (62). Moreover, the absence of glucose and alanine in the lumen together with a decrease of bicarbonate concentration substituted by chloride led to a reversal of potential difference to +3.2 mV and is clearly due to the imposed transepithelial chloride concentration difference (62). Cardinal et al (22) investigated the effect of simultaneous removal of bicarbonate from the bath and the luminal fluid and found an unaltered negative transepithelial potential. However, these authors confirmed the existence of a +1.1 mV potential difference when the bicarbonate concentration was reduced to 5 meq in the lumen only and a chloride concentration difference (higher in lumen than in bath) existed across the tubular wall (22). Because glucose, amino acid, bicarbonate, and chloride concentrations change along the length of the proximal tubule in vivo, associated modification in electrical potential is predictable in the intact nephron.

The results from rabbit isolated tubules stimulated a reassessment of transepithelial proximal potential difference in intact kidneys. Chirito & Seely noted in the earliest accessible proximal convolution of the rat kidney in vivo negative potential differences up to –4.5 mV, which rapidly changed polarity along the length and reached up to +4.5 mV in later convolutions (23). Frömter and associates (30, 31, 34) and Barratt et al (6) used a mutant strain of rats with surface glomerula and described in free flow conditions negative potential differences in the first tubular loop averaging –1.5 and –0.8 mV, respectively, with maximum values of –2.4 mV. Punctures of intermediate late or random proximal tubules yielded mean values of +1.8 (30, 31, 86) +1.5 mV (6). Frömter & Gessner (32) also studied the potential difference and perfused the lumen and capillaries with identical Ringer-bicarbonate solutions without organic solutes. Early loops averaged +1.0 mV and late loops +0.2 mV. These investigators concluded that the early segment either absorbs HCO_3^- or secretes H^+ actively. Early lumen negative potentials may be derived from active sodium transport in excess of active bicarbonate absorption and are enhanced by the presence of glucose and amino acids (31, 32). Late lumen-positive potentials are considered the result of chloride diffusion potentials together with a contribution from active H^+ secretion or HCO_3 absorption (31, 32). Evidence from isolated rabbit tubule and measurements on in vivo rat kidney using saline-filled Ling-Gerard microelectrodes (30, 31, 34) or large KCl-filled micropipettes (6) thus appear to be in qualitative agreement.

Some uncertainties and discrepancies remain. The predicted profile along the length of the proximal tubules depends critically on small changes in concentration of the tubular fluid. With respect to chloride, for example, species differences may exist. Boulpaep and G. B. de Mello (unpublished) recently analyzed tubular fluid chloride concentration and potential difference in the in vivo rabbit kidney. Although similar changes from negative to positive potential differences along the length of the proximal tubule were observed in the rabbit, the sign reversal does not occur as early as implied by the rat studies. Accordingly, earlier observations of small negative potentials in random impalements of the autoperfused dog kidney (14) cannot be dismissed as simply tip potential artifacts (30), unless information is available regarding segmental localization and actual chloride, bicarbonate, and organic solute concentration at the recording site for that species. Readings of random impalements were not different in one study (6), whether KCl-filled micro-electrodes of 1 μm, KCl micropipettes of 3–5 μm, or Ringer-filled electrodes were used, whereas another report (31) mentioned, in Ringer-bilaterally perfused tubules, −1.6 mV from KCl-filled microelectrodes, but +0.2 mV from Ringer-filled micro-electrodes. In contrast to the observations by Frömter & Gessner (32), removal of glucose and amino acids from a bilateral bicarbonate containing perfusion does not generate a positive potential difference in the isolated rabbit tubule (62). Finally, it is not clear why isolated tubules perfused with ultrafiltrate show a potential differ-ence twice in magnitude that reported for early proximal segments of the rat kidney (32).

The origin of the transepithelial potential difference remains doubtful except for those segments in which ion concentration differences exist, e.g. late proximal positive potentials, which are, in part, the result of a chloride permeability of the epithelium exceeding the bicarbonate permeability (9, 14, 37). With respect to transepithelial potential differences occurring in *Necturus* proximal tubule in the absence of concentration gradients, several alternatives have been discussed within the framework of an equivalent electrical circuit (13). In principle, the potential difference could be caused by a diffusion potential generated by intraepithelial local concentration differences along the paracellular shunt, however, large concentration differences would be required. Alternatively, the transepithelial potential difference may result from an intraepithelial current loop, maintained by means of active transport. Frömter & Gessner (32) defined as *active potential* any potential differ-ence that remains after abolition of all overall osmotic and concentration difference and in the absence of external current flow. This phenomenologic description, however, does not allow one to determine whether a potential difference is the direct consequence of 1. ion pump currents (rheogenic transport) supported by metabolism or of 2. ion concentration differences also ultimately driven by metabolism and giving rise to diffusion potentials. Elimination of the negative potential difference by ouabain or cooling in the isolated rabbit proximal tubule (20, 22, 63, 69), by cyanide in rat tubules in vivo (32), or reduction of the potential difference in *Necturus* by iodoacetate and ouabain (7) does not allow one to infer mechanisms regarding the electrogenesis of the transepithelial potential difference. Amphotericin B markedly enhances both transepithelial potential difference and net sodium reabsorption by the proximal tubule of *Necturus* (97), presumably mediated by an increase in luminal uptake of Na. A link between sugar or amino acids and the tubular potential difference has been observed (6, 30, 32, 35, 62, 75). It was suggested that sugar-coupled influx of sodium across the luminal membrane depolarizes primarily the luminal cell membrane and thereby enhances the transepithelial potential difference (35, 75).

Of special interest is the difference in the amplitude of the negative potential elicited by microperfusion with glucose or amino acids in various tubular segments. Early loops invariably showed a larger response for each solute than did late loops

(32, 89). In addition, a larger positive potential was observed in early segments during bilateral perfusion with Ringer-bicarbonate solutions, perhaps indicating more intense H^+ secretion (32). Seely (87) reported that resistance per unit length and specific resistance fell with tubular length of rat proximal tubule; the highest value was demonstrated in early loops and a plateau was obtained in the mid and late loops. These findings may be related to some intrinsic heterogeneity of the transport characteristics or permeability properties with length.

Frömter, Rumrich & Ullrich calculated the contribution of electrochemical driving forces for sodium, chloride, and bicarbonate absorption by simultaneous determination in split drops of electrochemical potential differences and net ion flux (38). The authors could account for all chloride movement in passive terms in agreement with earlier estimates for the dog proximal tubule (14). Only one third of sodium transport is suggested to be transported by electrical transference, whereas bicarbonate absorption appears entirely active. However, in sharp contrast, Cardinal et al (22) explored fluid absorption by the rabbit tubule in the condition where the potential difference is positive and the perfusate lacks glucose, amino acid, and bicarbonate. Neither the positive potential difference nor the chloride concentration difference was essential for the maintenance of a normal fluid absorption rate. This latter study would indicate that small physiological changes in electrochemical potential difference for chloride and bicarbonate which may occur along the proximal tubule do not play a critical role in the control of fluid reabsorption.

The ionic permeability properties of the proximal tubule epithelium have been examined in *Necturus,* dog, and rat kidney by means of single- and double-sided single-ion substitutions or salt dilutions (8, 9, 13, 14, 26, 37, 76). Boulpaep & Seely, for the dog proximal tubule (14), and Frömter, Muller & Wick (37), for the rat, presented strong support for the view that the resulting ionic selectivity pattern resides not in the individual cell membrane, but in paracellular channels. In mammals, the relative permeability ratios indicate a greater permeability to cations than to anions when compared to free solution (14, 37) and a ranking of ion permeabilities within the cation or anion series similar to, but more progressive than in free solution (14, 37). Transference numbers for Na exceed those of Cl in the mammalian kidney (14, 37); transepithelial chloride conductance dominates sodium conductance in the amphibian kidney (1, 3, 8, 9, 13). Sizable streaming potentials could be induced across rat and dog proximal tubule (14, 36) but were negligible across the amphibian proximal epithelium (13). The basis of these differences is not yet resolved.

Hegel, Frömter & Wick, for rat proximal tubule (49), and Boulpaep & Seely, for dog proximal tubule (14), calculated a specific resistance of the tubular epithelium of 5–6 ohm cm^2, which is very low compared to other epithelia or single cell membranes. Seely reported marked differences in tublar resistance with length (87). *Necturus* proximal tubule exhibits a somewhat higher specific resistance of 70 ohm cm^2 in vivo when measured by means of cable analysis (11) and 43 ohm cm^2 from axial electrode measurements (94). In late proximal segments of perfused *Necturus* kidney, Grandchamp & Boulpaep observed a larger specific resistance of 430 ohm cm^2 (44). Lutz, Cardinal & Burg measured electrical resistance in isolated perfused rabbit tubule by means of two techniques averaging 964 ohm cm or a specific resistance of 7 ohm cm^2 (69). The low values of transepithelial resistance support the conclusion that transepithelial ion movements occur principally via paracellular pathways. Electrical resistance of the proximal tubule is increased by ouabain (69), hypotonic fluids (93, 111), hyperosmotic perfusion of the lumen of dog proximal tubule (14), and increased capillary colloid osmotic pressure (44, 88). Transepithelial electrical resistance is decreased by volume expansion (11, 88), decreased capillary colloid osmotic pressure (44, 88), hypertonic solutions (93, 111), and hyperosmotic perfusion of the capillaries (14). According to Burg et al (21), the presence of furosemide in the lumen of proximal convoluted tubule of the rabbit has no effect on either potential difference or resistance. Spring & Paganelli reported short circuit currents of 36 μA cm^{-2} in reasonable agreement with net Na$^+$ transport rate under short-circuit conditions (94). Current-voltage relationships are linear over a wide range (9, 94). Voltage transients described by Spring during or after voltage or current clamps were associated with changes in resistance (92). On the basis of a model, he concluded that marked changes in concentration within the paracellular compartment are responsible for the transients.

PROXIMAL STRAIGHT TUBULE   The pars recta of the proximal tubule is not accessible to micropuncture in vivo. Transepithelial potential difference in isolated superficial proximal straight tubules ranges from −1.3 to −2.1 mV (59, 69, 86) lumen negative when perfused with *symmetrical* solutions containing organic solutes, but does not depend on the presence of glucose or amino acids (86). Schafer et al (86) abolished the potential difference during cooling or ouabain treatment and found a sign reversal of potential after replacement of bicarbonate by chloride in the perfusion solution. When the perfusion of normal bicarbonate-Ringer was stopped, potential difference rose to +0.9 or +1.6 mV in agreement with values noted during omission of bicarbonate (59, 86). These authors (86) also calculated a transference number ratio for T_{Na}/T_{Cl} of 0.3 from salt dilution potentials, a value close to estimates for *Necturus* convoluted proximal tubule (3, 103) but deviating from results in mammalian proximal convoluted tubules (14, 37).

Juxtamedullary proximal straight tubules in the presence or absence of organic solutes are characterized by potential differences analogous to those of superficial straight proximal segments (59). However, Kawamura et al (59) distinguished an ion selectivity for juxtamedullary nephrons T_{Na}/T_{Cl} of 1.7 against 0.5 for superficial nephrons. An opposite polarity of streaming potentials for the two nephrone population under identical osmotic gradients confirms the discrepancy in permselectivity (60). Lutz et al (69) pointed out a higher resistance for straight than for convoluted tubules.

THIN DESCENDING LIMB OF HENLE   Ideally, potential differences should be determined between tubular lumen and medullary interstitium. Windhager (110) found −3 mV across descending limbs of golden hamsters against an isotonic saline reference electrode in the peritoneal cavity. Marsh & Solomon (74), used a similar approach and preparation, and reported comparable absolute potential values but emphasized the absence of any potential difference when referred to the vasa recta both in antidiuresis and osmotic diuresis. Kokko confirmed zero potential values across isolated perfused segments of rabbit descending limb of Henle (61, 82).

THIN ASCENDING LIMB OF HENLE   Windhager (110) and Marsh & Solomon (74) on hamster kidney found thin ascending limbs –9 to –11 mV negative. Windhager (110) ascribed the potential to active transport, whereas Marsh & Solomon (74) did not find active transport, and proposed streaming potentials as the source of the potential difference. Imai & Kokko (58), using isolated thin ascending limbs of rabbit kidney, also did not detect active transport and noted no transepithelial potential difference when identical solutions bathed both sides of the epithelium. Considering the possible liquid junction artifacts in the medulla (110, 112), the discrepancy between in vivo and perfused limbs remains unexplained. Imai & Kokko (57) further investigated the ion selectivity of thin ascending limbs by means of salt dilution and single-ion substitution potentials. Chloride transference numbers exceeded sodium values by a factor of 3 to 4.

THICK ASCENDING LIMB OF HENLE   The thick ascending limb appears to be the major source of energy for the formation of concentrated urine and can be functionally defined as the diluting segment. Burg & Green (16), in perfused cortical portions of thick ascending limb, and Rocha & Kokko (81), in medullary thick ascending limbs, noted the existence of a lumen positive potential difference of about +6 mV. Both groups concluded that the electrical potential is probably caused by active Cl transport. Pertinent evidence is discussed by Burg in this volume. Chloride removal from all perfusion solutions abolished the potential difference (16, 81). Sodium removal from lumen and bath increased the positive potential difference in cortical segments (16), while a similar bilateral solium replacement decreased the potential difference in medullary segments (81). Cooling and ouabain treatment reversibly decreased the potential difference (81). From NaCl salt gradient experiments, both laboratories concluded that Na permeability exceeds chloride permeability (16, 81). Moreover, decreased flow rate enhanced the potential difference significantly (16, 81). From the available evidence, the problem of whether rheogenic chloride transport generates the full extent of transepithelial potential appears unsettled.

Thick ascending limbs rank among the leaky epithelia with a specific transepithelial resistance of 22–25 ohm cm^2. The most effective diuretics exert their action at the level of the thick ascending limb. While 10^{-5} M furosemide in the lumen decreased the transepithelial potential difference, higher concentration in the bath remained without immediate or with a very small effect (21). Mersalyl (17), ethacrynic acid, and ethacrynic-cysteine (18) were shown by Burg & Green to reversibly inhibit the potential difference only when added from the lumen. Furosemide, mersalyl, and ethacrynic acid all failed to alter relative Na and Cl permeability but decreased the total transepithelial conductance (17, 18, 21). Amiloride did not modify the potential difference (96).

In *Necturus* kidney, Wilbrandt (109) found positive potential differences of about +6 mV by introducing a micropipette into the intermediate segment starting from the most distal end of the proximal tubule. Because the intermediate segment is short, it can be argued that Wilbrandt measured the potential difference across early distal tubule. Of particular importance is the observation by Stoner (95) of an early distal diluting segment in amphibian distal tubule that exhibits a positive potential and transports chloride actively.

DISTAL CONVOLUTED TUBLE   The distal convolution consists of two regions defined both morphologically and electrophysiologically. In the earliest accessible loops, the distal tubule is characterized by a small potential difference –9 to –12 mV in the rat kidney in vivo (71, 113) and by a +12 mV potential difference in perfused segments of early frog or salamander distal tubules (95). By means of large micropipettes, Barratt et al (5) measured a potential difference of +3.7 mV in the first loop of the distal tubule of mutant Wistar rats with surface glomerula. Late or random punctures of distal tubules in vivo offer larger potential differences ranging from –37 to –60 mV in rat (27, 33, 42, 55, 66, 68, 70–73, 90, 100, 107, 108, 112, 113), –43 mV in the dog (14), –45 mV in *Amphiuma* (98), and –35 mV in *Necturus* (77, 112). Isolated perfused late distal tubules of frog or salamander have a –33 mV potential difference (95), whereas isolated rabbit distal tubules show –40 mV negativity (46). Wright (113) concluded both from changes in transepithelial potential and from approximate estimates of resistance during changes in luminal concentration of sodium and potassium, that overall conductance and partial Na and K conductances do not change with distal tubular length. Electrophysiological studies by Malnic & Giebisch (71) and Wright (113) support the view that overall K conductance exceeds Na conductance, while the latter markedly exceeds Cl conductance. Transepithelial potential and resistance are independent of changes in pH (71). Sullivan (98) and Wiederholt & Giebisch (106) investigated the dependence of transepithelial potential difference on changes in Na and K concentrations in *Amphiuma* distal tubules. Transepithelial potential difference is influenced by the diet (43, 46, 64, 72, 114, 115), metabolic acidosis (64, 73), metabolic alkalosis (64, 73), adrenalectomy (107, 108), aldosterone (108), cycloheximide (107), actinomycin (107), ouabain (46), acetazolamide (73), and amiloride (27, 46). It is unaltered by furosemide (70) and acute K infusion (72, 115). Relative K conductance is enhanced by K loading and decreased by K depletion (114), depressed by adrenal insufficiency (107), but normalized by aldosterone administration (107). Aldosterone increases relative Na conductance of the distal tubule in both normal and adrenalectomized rats (108).

In several studies (14, 24, 25, 71, 113), transepithelial resistance has been inferred from input or effective resistance. The validity of such measurements is restricted (10) and these estimates are useful only for assessing relative changes in resistance. In this manner, wall resistance was monitored during luminal ion substitutions (71, 113), bicarbonate infusion (71), acute KCl infusion (71), respiratory acidosis (71), osmotic gradients (25), and chlorothiazide (24). Using cable analysis in rat distal tubule, Malnic & Giebisch (71) obtained a length constant of 477 μm and a specific wall resistance of 377 ohm cm^2.

CORTICAL COLLECTING TUBULE   Information on the electrical parameters of cortical collecting ducts is confined to studies on isolated perfused segments of the rabbit kidney (15, 45), as segments beyond the confluence of two distal convoluted tubules only rarely appear at the kidney surface. Transepithelial potential difference in perfused rabbit cortical collecting duct is quite variable, ranging from +4 to –67 mV (19, 28, 45, 46, 54, 96), with averages close to –25 mV lumen negative. The preparations were mounted mostly at room temperature, but perfusion at 37°C improves the average potential values to −35 mV (96). Frindt & Burg (28) pointed out that a high K, low Na diet is associated with potential values around −40 mV, whereas a low K, high Na diet produces small or positive potential differences. These findings were corroborated by Gross et al (46), who noted that DOCA pretreatment added to a regular diet also enhances the negative potential difference. Potential differences tended to be higher at slower perfusion rates or lower luminal perfusion pressures (19, 28, 45) and with increments of bath pressure (28).

Grantham et al (45) detected no difference in electrical potential between both ends of the tubule despite marked modifications of Na and K luminal concentrations. Na and K gradients always exceeded those predicted by a passive distribution according to the potential gradient, and the deviation was more marked for longer contact times (45). Collecting tubules perfused with low luminal Na concentrations develop high potential differences, but as the Na concentration dropped or the contact time increased, the negative potential difference declined or even switched polarity. Moreover, as K concentrations in the bath were elevated above normal, the transepithelial potential diminished or became positive. Omitting K from the bath was followed by a prompt depolarization (45).

Transepithelial resistance is extremely variable with specific resistance values between 100 and 2700 ohm cm^2 (19, 50, 51, 54, 96). Helman (50) pointed out that such variability depends in part on differences of ionic conductance (g), where g Cl$>$$g$K in low resistance segments and gK$>$$g$Cl in high resistance tubules. From ion substitution studies, Helman (50, 53) concluded that the paracellular shunt is primarily Cl-permeable in low resistance tubules and K-permeable in high resistance convolutions. Strong evidence was also presented by Helman (51) that the dominating resistance is located near the apical border of the epithelium. Electrical resistance per unit length was not modified by changes in luminal diameter (54).

Ouabain caused the potential difference to fall or turn positive (19, 45) as K secretion and Na absorption were inhibited. Vasopressin was reported to transiently increase and subsequently depress the potential difference (19, 28, 46, 54) without a change in electrical resistance (54). The transient increase coincides with a period of enhanced lumen to bath Na flux (28). Amiloride in the lumen induced a +2.3 mV positive potential difference as both K and Na transport stopped and resistance rose (96). The positive potential found after ouabain or amiloride treatment, or after removal of sodium, is probably generated by acidification and is sensitive to acetazolamide (96). Furosemide had no effect on the potential difference (21).

MEDULLARY COLLECTING DUCT   The papilla of the golden hamster has been the favored preparation for the study of medullary collecting tubules. By means of Ling-Gerard microelectrodes, transepithelial differences of −14 to −17 mV were measured against a reference electrode of saline in the peritoneal cavity (68, 74, 84, 110), with lower values near the tip of the papilla than in the medulla (84). However, Laurence & Marsh (68) found such potential differences invariant with length and the diuretic state. By means of wider micropipettes of about 2 μm filled with KCl, Laurence & Marsh (68) found −4.4 mV for transmural impalement in antidiuresis and −1.5 mV during axial insertion 500 μm upstream in ducts of Bellini. The potential difference rose with mannitol or sodium sulfate diuresis. Those authors argued that the measurements obtained with Ling-Gerard electrodes were unreliable. However, several sources of uncertainty remain, such as the variability of the composition of the collecting duct fluid, liquid junction potentials at the electrode tip or between interstitium and reference electrodes, and current leaks through the orifice of the Bellini duct or at the impalement site (10, 68). Laurence & Marsh (68) concluded that the potential could not be explained from the known concentration gradients for Na, K, or Cl using a Goldman equation.

Rau & Frömter (79) circumvented many of these problems by the use of large pipettes filled with modified Ringer solution against a saline reference and, in addition, prevented leaks through the open end by injecting Sylgard 185 or castor oil. These investigators noted, following transmural impalement in free flow, a potential difference of about –25 mV, which was oscillatory in nature in synchrony with changes in papillary tissue pressure. During stop flow by occlusion of the open tip of the duct, the potential rose to –34 mV. Stable values of –55 mV were observed during bilateral perfusion of the duct and the adjacent vasa recta with NaCl. The latter value is unaffected when Na is substituted by K, but depolarized when Na is substituted by choline to reach positive values. Replacement of Cl by sulfate hyperpolarized the epithelium. Rau & Frömter (80) also determined the electrical transepithelial resistance using three different approaches on the basis of finite unbranched or branched cable analysis with values ranging between 1000 and 2000 ohm cm².

Potential Differences and Conductances of Single Boundaries

All renal tubules are single cell layer epithelia. At least two boundaries separate compartments at different electrochemical potential: the peritubular cell membrane, which probably includes basal and lateral portions of the cell borders, and the luminal cell membrane at the apical end of the cell. Kidney epithelia as seen from Table 1 may be very leaky and offer a bypass for ion permeation via the paracellular pathway (9, 103), which may behave as a separate single or multiple boundary. The conductance properties of individual renal cell membranes have recently been reviewed extensively (43).

PROXIMAL TUBULE The peritubular cell membrane potential of the proximal tubule is about –70 mV, cytoplasm negative to blood in *Necturus* (8, 9, 11, 12, 39, 43, 44, 65, 67, 92, 94, 112), newt (75), rat (37, 64, 85, 104), and guinea pig kidney (101, 102). In his studies on perfused *Necturus* kidney, Boulpaep (8, 9, 12) confirmed that the peritubular cell membrane closely resembles a K and Cl battery with only limited Na permeability. In addition to steady-state voltage measurements, short-term and long-term potential transients were determined subsequent to rapid changes in ionic concentration gradients. Transference numbers and relative permeability coefficients were quantified together with estimates of absolute permeability coefficients. In addition, these investigations obtained information on relative ionic conductances from measurements of peritubular membrane resistance. Taking into consideration the existence of a low resistance paracellular shunt, the author has presented an electrical equivalent model in terms of peritubular emf, peritubular ionic conductances, and possible rheogenic pumps that account for the overall behavior of that cell barrier (8, 12). Similar approaches for determination of ionic conductance and relative ion permeability were used by Frömter and associates (37, 104), using the rat proximal tubule and superfusion techniques. These investigations have recently been extended by Sato by means of semifloating electrodes and peritubular capillary perfusion (85). Peritubular cell membrane potentials were also determined by Whittembury (101, 102) in kidney slices in an attempt to correlate electrical driving forces across the cell membrane with sodium extrusion. Hyperpolarizations of the peritubular membrane recorded during warming of cells rich in Na and poor in K were in excess of the electrochemical potential difference for K, and taken as support for the view that Na extrusion is at least partly rheogenic. Tadokoro & Boulpaep (99) injected Na or other cations into single proximal tubule cells electrophoretically to explore the mechanism of sodium extrusion from the cell. Although rheogenic pumping could be unmasked, a coupled Na-K pump appeared to dominate in most conditions. Asterita & Windhager (4) have recently used the time course of K depolarization of the peritubular cell membrane as a measure of the thickness of the interstitial space. An interesting observation is the glucose dependence of the cell membrane potential observed by Maruyama & Hoshi in the newt (75) and by Frömter & Lüer (35) in the rat.

The luminal membrane potential is about +50 mV (lumen positive to cell cytoplasm) in *Necturus* (8, 9, 13, 39, 43, 112) and newt kidney (56). Properties of the luminal cell membrane were further investigated (8, 9, 13) in *Necturus* proximal tubule. Boulpaep reassessed the contribution of K ions to the luminal membrane potential as well as extended the observation to other ions (13). Changes in potential difference were recorded during single-sided ion substitutions. From the obvious electrical interaction between luminal and peritubular membrane, strong evidence emerged in favor of a low resistance paracellular shunt. Within the framework of an equivalent electrical circuit for the entire epithelium, the relative role of cell membrane emf and intraepithelial current flow was emphasized in the generation of the cell membrane potential (13).

Subsequent to the work of Windhager, Boulpaep & Giebisch (111), using a double core cable analysis, various approaches by Hoshi & Sakai (56) and Anagnostopoulos & Velu (2) have confirmed the view that the combined resistance of peritubular and luminal cell membrane exceeds by two orders of magnitude the overall transepithelial resistance. Evidence for a paracellular pathway of low resistance has been extensively summarized in a number of papers (9, 13, 37, 103).

Treating the paracellular pathway as another intraepithelial diffusion barrier, little is known directly about its selectivity. On the basis of indirect evidence, overall properties of the epithelium are ascribed to the paracellular shunt (9, 13, 37, 103). Recently, Asterita & Boulpaep (3) have taken a more direct approach to estimate the permselectivity of the shunt. They corroborated that changes in overall transepithelial potential induced by ion substitutions can be used as an accurate estimate of the paracellular ion selectivity.

The ionic conductance of the paracellular path has been found to play a determinant role in the regulation of net Na reabsorption. Changes in net Na absorption can result from modification in active Na outflux or from alterations in the passive backflow of Na from blood to lumen. Boulpaep (11) and Grandchamp & Boulpaep

(44) demonstrated in *Necturus* kidney that the paracellular conductance is modified by such factors as volume expansion and alterations of colloid osmotic pressure, while cell membrane conductance is unchanged. Seely (88) reached a comparable conclusion for the rat kidney. The paracellular conductance appears as a powerful regulator of net transport. Sackin & Boulpaep (83) have incorporated properties and driving forces of the various intraepithelial barriers in two associated epithelial transport models and tested the control exerted by paracellular permeability on overall reabsorption.

DISTAL TUBULE   Peritubular membrane potential differences range from −61 to −90 mv (cytoplasm negative to blood) in *Amphiuma* (98, 106), *Necturus* (77), and rat kidney (66, 71, 105, 112, 113). Peritubular membrane potential is lower in early than late segments (113), is affected by K in the diet (114), lower after adrenalectomy (105) and metabolic acidosis (71), but changed by metabolic alkalosis (71). Luminal membrane potential difference is +30 mV (lumen positive to cytoplasm) in *Amphiuma* (98, 106). Sullivan (98) found that both the peritubular and luminal membrane depolarize after elevation of the K concentration, but that peritubular K permeability most likely exceeds luminal K permeability. Replacement of Na by choline depolorized the peritubular membrane, whereas a similar luminal substitution hyperpolarized the luminal cell membrane. Wiederholt & Giebisch (106) calculated a transport number $T_K = 0.6$ for the luminal membrane from luminal concentration changes in K. Whereas the peritubular membrane potential was insensitive to one-sided luminal changes in K, peritubular potential difference rose and fell as luminal Na concentration was elevated or diminished. Wiederholt & Giebisch suggested that rheogenic pumps may be involved in the generation of the peritubular potential difference.

CORTICAL COLLECTING TUBULE   Peritubular membrane potential was recorded from isolated rabbit cortical tubules by Helman (52). High K diet and deoxycorticosterone elevate the potential difference, whereas ouabain reduces it. As in the proximal tubule (13), luminal membrane resistance exceeds peritubular membrane resistance (52). Moreover, Helman presented evidence for low resistance shunts between the cells of cortical collecting ducts (52).

Literature Cited

1. Anagnostopoulos, T. 1973. Biionic potentials in the proximal tubule of Necturus kidney. *J. Physiol.* 233:375–94
2. Anagnostopoulos, T., Velu, E. 1974. Electrical resistance of cell membranes in Necturus kidney. *Pflügers Arch.* 346:327–39
3. Asterita, M. F., Boulpaep, E. L. 1975. Ion selectivity of the paracellular pathway in Necturus proximal tubule. *Biophys. J.* 15:228a
4. Asterita, M. F., Windhager, E. E. 1975. Estimate of relative thickness of peritubular interstitial space in Necturus kidney. *Am. J. Physiol.* 228:1393–1402
5. Barratt, L. J., Rector, F. C., Kokko, J. P., Tisher, C. C., Seldin, D. W. 1973. Transepithelial potential difference profile of the distal tubule of the rat kidney. *6th Ann. Meet. Am. Soc. Nephrol. Wash. D.C.,* p. 7 (Abstr.)
6. Barratt, L. J., Rector, F. C., Kokko, J. P., Seldin, D. W. 1974. Factors governing the transepithelial potential difference across the proximal tubule of the rat kidney. *J. Clin. Invest.* 53:454–64

7. Bentzel, C. J. 1974. Expanding drop analysis of Na and H_2O flux across Necturus proximal tubule. *Am. J. Physiol.* 226:118–26
8. Boulpaep, E. L. 1967. Ion permeability of the peritubular and luminal membrane of the renal tubular cell. In *Transport und Funktion Intracellulärer Elektrolyte.* ed. F. Krück, 98–107
9. Boulpaep, E. L. 1971. Electrophysiological properties of the proximal tubule: importance of cellular and intercellular transport pathways. In *Electrophysiology of Epithelial Cells.* Symp. Med. Hoechst., ed. G. Giebisch, 91–118. Stuttgart: Schattauer
10. Boulpaep, E. L. 1972. Electrophysiological techniques in kidney micropuncture. *Yale J. Biol. Med.* 45:397–413
11. Boulpaep, E. L. 1972. Permeability changes of the proximal tubule of Necturus during saline loading. *Am. J. Physiol.* 222:517–31
12. Boulpaep, E. L. 1975. Electrophysiology of the proximal tubule of Necturus kidney. I. The peritubular cell membrane. *J. Gen. Physiol.* Submitted
13. Boulpaep, E. L. 1975. Electrophysiology of the proximal tubule of Necturus kidney. II. The luminal cell membrane and the paracellular pathway. *J. Gen. Physiol.* Submitted
14. Boulpaep, E. L., Seely, J. F. 1971. Electrophysiology of proximal and distal tubules in the autoperfused dog kidney. *Am. J. Physiol.* 221:1084–96
15. Burg, M. B., Grantham, J., Abramow, M., Orloff, J. 1966. Preparation and study of fragments of single rabbit nephrons. *Am. J. Physiol.* 210:1293–98
16. Burg, M. B., Green, N. 1973. Function of the thick ascending limb of Henle's loop. *Am. J. Physiol.* 224:659–68
17. Burg, M., Green, N. 1973. Effect of mersalyl on the thick ascending limb of Henle's loop. *Kidney Int.* 4:245–51
18. Burg, M., Green, N. 1973. Effect of ethacrynic acid on the thick ascending limb of Henle's loop. *Kidney Int.* 4:301–8
19. Burg, M. B., Isaacson, L., Grantham, J., Orloff, J. 1968. Electrical properties of the isolated perfused rabbit renal tubules. *Am. J. Physiol.* 215:788–94
20. Burg, M. B., Orloff, J. 1970. Electrical potential difference across proximal convoluted tubules. *Am. J. Physiol.* 219:1714–16
21. Burg, M., Stoner, L., Cardinal, L., Green, N. 1973. Furosemide effect on isolated perfused tubules. *Am. J. Physiol.* 225:119–24
22. Cardinal, J., Lutz, M. D., Burg, M. B., Orloff, J. 1975. Lack of relationship of potential difference to fluid absorption in the proximal renal tubule. *Kidney Int.* 7:94–102
23. Chirito, E., Seely, J. F. 1973. Evidence for a change in the potential difference along the length of the rat proximal tubule in vivo. *Clin. Res.* 21:680
24. Constanzo, L. S., Windhager, E. E. 1975. Effect of chlorothiazide on distal tubular function: electrophysiological study. *Fed. Proc.* 34:393
25. de Bermudez, L., Windhager, E. E. 1974. Osmotically induced changes in electrical resistance across distal tubules of rat kidney in vivo. *Fed. Proc.* 33:387
26. de Mello, G. B., Malnic, G. 1971. Electrophysiological study of proximal tubules of rat kidney. *Proc. Int. Union Physiol. Sci.* 9:152
27. Duarte, C. G., Chomety, F., Giebisch, G. 1971. Effect of amiloride, ouabain, and furosemide on distal tubular function in the rat. *Am. J. Physiol.* 221:632–39
28. Frindt, G., Burg, M. B. 1972. Effect of vasopressin on sodium transport in renal cortical collecting ducts. *Kidney Int.* 1:224–31
29. Frömter, E. 1972. Progress in microelectrode techniques for kidney tubules. *Yale J. Biol. Med.* 45:414–25
30. Frömter, E. 1974. Electrophysiology and isotonic fluid absorption of proximal tubules of mammalian kidney. *MTP Int. Rev. Sci. Physiol. Ser. One* 6:1–38
31. Frömter, E., Gessner, K. 1974. Free flow potential profile along rat kidney proximal tubule. *Pfluegers Arch.* 351:69–83
32. Frömter, E., Gessner, K. 1974. Active transport potentials, membrane diffusion potentials and streaming potentials across rat kidney proximal tubule. *Pfluegers Arch.* 351:85–98
33. Frömter, E., Hegel, U. 1966. Transtubuläre Potentialdifferenzen an proximalen und distalen Tubuli der Rattenniere. *Pfluegers Arch.* 291:107–20
34. Frömter, E., Lüer, K. 1973. Free flow potential profile along rat proximal tubule. *Pfluegers Arch.* 339:R47
35. Frömter, E., Lüer, K. 1973. Electrical studies on sugar transport kinetics of rat proximal tubule. *Pfluegers Arch.* 343:R47

36. Frömter, E., Müller, C. W., Knauf, H. 1968. Fixe negative Wandladungen im proximalen Konvolut der Rattenniere und ihre Beeinflussung durch Calciumionen. *6th Symp. Ges. Nephrol. Vienna,* 61–64

37. Frömter, E., Müller, C. W., Wick, T. 1971. Permeability properties of the proximal tubular epithelium of the rat kidney studied with electrophysiological methods. See Ref. 9, 119–48

38. Frömter, E., Rumrich, G., Ullrich, K. J. 1973. Phenomenologic description of Na^+, Cl^- and HCO_3^- absorption from proximal tubules of the rat kidney. *Pfluegers Arch.* 343:189–220

39. Giebisch, G. 1961. Measurements of electrical potential differences on single nephrons of the perfused Necturus kidney. *J. Gen. Physiol.* 44:659–78

40. Giebisch, G., ed. 1971. See Ref. 9, Session 2:89–186

41. Giebisch, G., ed. 1972. Renal micropuncture techniques: A Symposium. Section VII. Microelectrode techniques. *Yale J. Biol. Med.* 45:395–435

42. Giebisch, G., Malnic, G., Klose, R. M., Windhager, E. E. 1966. Effect of ionic substitutions on distal potential differences in rat kidney. *Am. J. Physiol.* 211:560–68

43. Giebisch, G., Windhager, E. E. 1973. Electrolyte transport across renal tubular membranes. *Handb. Physiol. Sect. 8: Renal Physiol.,* 315–76

44. Grandchamp, A., Boulpaep, E. L. 1974. Pressure control of sodium reabsorption and intercellular backflux across proximal kidney tubule. *J. Clin. Invest.* 54:69–82

45. Grantham, J. J., Burg, M., Orloff, J. 1970. The nature of transtubular Na and K transport in isolated rabbit renal collecting tubules. *J. Clin. Invest.* 49:1815–26

46. Gross, J. B., Imai, M., Kokko, J. P. 1974. Functional comparison of the distal convoluted tubule and the cortical collecting tubule. *7th Ann. Meet. Am. Soc. Nephrol. Wash. DC,* p. 34

47. Hayslett, J. P. 1973. Effect of changes in hydrostatic pressure in peritubular capillaries on the permeability of proximal tubule. *J. Clin. Invest.* 52:1314–19

48. Hegel, U., Boulpaep, E. L. 1975. Studies of electrical impedance of kidney proximal tubular epithelium in Necturus. *6th Int. Congr. Nephrol. Firenze* (Abstr. 45)

49. Hegel, U., Frömter, E., Wick, T. 1967. Der elektrische Wandwiderstand des proximalen Konvolutes des Rattenniere. *Pfluegers Arch.* 294:274–90

50. Helman, S. I. 1971. Effect of ionic substitutions on transepithelial p.d. and electrical resistance of the renal cortical collecting tubule. *5th Ann. Meet. Am. Soc. Nephrol. Wash. DC,* p. 51 (Abstr)

51. Helman, S. I. 1972. Determination of electrical resistance of the isolated cortical collecting tubule and its possible anatomical location. *Yale J. Biol. Med.* 45:339–45

52. Helman, S. I. 1973. Microelectrode studies of isolated cortical collecting tubules. *6th Ann. Meet. Am. Soc. Nephrol. Wash. DC,* p. 49 (Abstr.)

53. Helman, S. I. 1975. Studies of the transepithelial potential difference and its origin in isolated perfused cortical collecting tubules. *Fed. Proc.* 34:392

54. Helman, S. I., Grantham, J. J., Burg, M. B. 1971. Effect of vasopressin on electrical resistance of renal cortical collecting tubules. *Am. J. Physiol.* 220:1825–32

55. Hierholzer, K., Wiederholt, M., Holzgreve, H., Giebisch, G., Klose, R. M., Windhager, E. E. 1965. Micropuncture study of renal transtubular concentration gradients of sodium and potassium in adrenalectomized rats. *Pfluegers Arch.* 285:193–210

56. Hoshi, T., Sakai, F. 1967. A comparison of the electrical resistance of the surface cell membrane and cellular wall in the proximal tubule of the newt kidney. *Jpn. J. Physiol.* 17:627–37

57. Imai, M., Kokko, J. P. 1973. Relative permeability of the thin ascending limb of Henle to various ions. *6th Ann. Meet. Amer. Soc. Nephrol. Wash. DC,* p. 52

58. Imai, M., Kokko, J. P. 1974. Sodium chloride urea and water transport in the thin ascending limb of Henle. Generation of osmotic gradients by passive diffusion of solutes. *J. Clin. Invest.* 53:393–402

59. Kawamura, S., Imai, M., Kokko, J. P. 1974. Evidence for electrogenic transport processes in the two different types of proximal straight tubules. *J. Clin. Invest.* 53:39a

60. Kawamura, S., Seldin, D. W., Kokko, J. P. 1974. Functional differences between superficial and juxtamedullary straight segments of proximal tubules. *7th Ann. Meet. Am. Soc. Nephrol. Wash. DC,* p. 44

61. Kokko, J. P. 1970. Sodium chloride and water transport in the descending limb of Henle. *J. Clin. Invest.* 49:1838–46

62. Kokko, J. P. 1973. Proximal tubule potential difference. Dependence on glucose, HCO₃ and amino acids. *J. Clin. Invest.* 52:1362–67

63. Kokko, J. P., Rector, F. C. 1971. Flow dependence of transtubular potential difference in isolated perfused segments of rabbit proximal convoluted tubule. *J. Clin. Invest.* 50:2745–50

64. Khuri, R. N., Agulian, S. K., Bogharian, K. 1974. Electrochemical potentials of potassium in proximal renal tubule of rat. *Pfluegers Arch.* 346:319–26

65. Khuri, R. N., Agulian, S. K., Bogharian, K., Nassar, R., Wise, W. 1974. Intracellular bicarbonate in single cells of Necturus kidney proximal tubule. *Pfluegers Arch.* 349:295–99

66. Khuri, R. N., Agulian, S. K., Kalloghlian, A. 1972. Intracellular potassium in cells of the distal tubule. *Pfluegers Arch.* 335:297–308

67. Khuri, R. N., Hajjar, J. J., Agulian, S., Bogharian, K., Kalloghlian, A., Bizri, H. 1972. Intracellular potassium in cells of the proximal tubule of Necturus maculosus. *Pfluegers Arch.* 338:73–80

68. Laurence, R., Marsh, D. J. 1971. Effect of diuretic states on hamster collecting duct electrical potential differences. *Am. J. Physiol.* 220:1610–16

69. Lutz, M. D., Cardinal, J., Burg, M. B. 1973. Electrical resistance of renal proximal tubule perfused in vitro. *Am. J. Physiol.* 225:729–34

70. Malnic, G., Enokibara, H., Mello-Aires, M., Vieira, F. L. 1969. Die Wirkung von Furosemid und NaCl-Belastung auf die Chloridausscheidung im Einzelnephron der Rattenniere. *Pfluegers Arch.* 309:21–37

71. Malnic, G., Giebisch, G. 1972. Some electrical properties of distal tubular epithelium in the rat. *Am. J. Physiol.* 223:797–808

72. Malnic, G., Klose, R. M., Giebisch, G. 1966. Micropuncture study of distal tubular potassium and sodium transport in rat nephron. *Am. J. Physiol.* 211:529–47

73. Malnic, G., Mello-Aires, M., Vieira, F. L. 1970. Chloride excretion in nephrons of rat kidney during alterations of acid base equilibrium. *Am. J. Physiol.* 218:20–26

74. Marsh, D. J., Solomon, S. 1965. Analysis of electrolyte movement in thin Henle's loop of hamster papilla. *Am. J. Physiol.* 208:1119–28

75. Maruyama, T., Hoshi, T. 1972. The effect of d-glucose on the proximal electrical potential profile across the proximal tubule of newt kidney. *Biochim. Biophys. Acta* 282:214–25

76. Maude, D. L. 1970. Mechanism of salt transport and some permeability properties of rat proximal tubule. *Am. J. Physiol.* 218:1590–95

77. Maude, D. L., Shehadeh, I., Solomon, A. K. 1966. Sodium and water transport in single perfused distal tubules of Necturus kidney. *Am. J. Physiol.* 221:1043–49

78. Orloff, J., Burg, M. 1971. Kidney. *Ann. Rev. Physiol.* 33:83–130

79. Rau, W. S., Frömter, E. 1974. Electrical properties of the medullary collecting ducts of the golden hamster kidney. I. The transepithelial potential difference. *Pfluegers Arch.* 351:99–111

80. Rau, W. S., Frömter, E. 1974. Electrical properties of the medullary collecting ducts of the golden hamster kidney. II. The transepithelial resistance. *Pfluegers Arch.* 351:113–31

81. Rocha, A. S., Kokko, J. P. 1973. Sodium chloride and water transport in the medullary thick ascending limb of Henle. Evidence for active chloride transport. *J. Clin. Invest.* 53:612–23

82. Rocha, A. S., Kokko, J. P. 1973. Membrane characteristics regulating potassium transport out of the isolated perfused descending limb of Henle. *Kidney Int.* 4:326–30

83. Sackin, H., Boulpaep. E. L. 1975. Models for coupling of salt and water transport: Proximal tubular reabsorption in Necturus kidney. *J. Gen. Physiol.* 66: In press

84. Sakai, F., Tadokoro, M. 1966. Transtubular potential differences of the renal collecting duct of golden hamster. *Jpn. J. Pharmacol.* 16:491–92

85. Sato, K. 1974. The application of semifloating electrodes to the study of cell p.d.s of the rat kidney proximal tubule. *Pfluegers Arch.* 347:R32

86. Schafer, J. A., Troutman, S. L., Andreoli, T. E. 1974. Volume reabsorption, transepithelial potential differences, and ionic permeability properties in mammalian superficial proximal straight tubules. *J. Gen. Physiol.* 64:582–607

87. Seely, J. F. 1973. Variation in electrical resistance along length of rat proximal convoluted tubule. *Am. J. Physiol.* 225:48–57

88. Seely, J. F. 1973. Effects of peritubular oncotic pressure on rat proximal tubule electrical resistance. *Kidney Int.* 4: 28–35

89. Seely, J. F., Chirito, E. 1973. Role of glucose and HCO_3 in the rat proximal tubule potential difference. *6th Ann. Meet. Am. Soc. Nephrol. Wash. DC,* p. 93

90. Solomon, S. 1957. Transtubular potential differences of rat kidney. *J. Cell. Comp. Physiol.* 49:351–65

91. Spring, K. R. 1972. Insertion of an axial electrode into renal proximal tubule. *Yale J. Biol. Med.* 45:426–31

92. Spring, K. R. 1973. Current-induced voltage transients in Necturus proximal tubule. *J. Membr. Biol.* 13:299–322

93. Spring, K. R., Giebisch, G. 1974. Efficiency of Na^+ transport in Necturus proximal tubule. *7th Ann. Meet. Am. Soc. Nephrol. Wash. DC,* p. 87

94. Spring, K. R., Paganelli, C. V. 1972. Sodium flux in Necturus proximal tubule under voltage clamp. *J. Gen. Physiol.* 60:181–201

95. Stoner, L. C. 1975. New segment of the amphibian distal nephron which actively transports chloride. *Fed. Proc.* 34:981

96. Stoner, L. C., Burg, M. B., Orloff, J. 1974. Ion transport in cortical collecting ducts; effect of amiloride. *Am. J. Physiol.* 227:453–59

97. Stroup, R. F., Weinman, E., Hayslett, J. P., Kashgarian, M. 1974. Effect of luminal permeability on net transport across the amphibian proximal tubule. *Am. J. Physiol.* 226:1110–16

98. Sullivan, J. 1968. Electrical potential differences across distal renal tubules of Amphiuma. *Am. J. Physiol.* 214:1096–1103

99. Tadokoro, M., Boulpaep, E. L. 1972. Electrophoretic method of ion injection in single kidney cells. *Yale J. Biol. Med.* 45:432–35

100. Vieira, F. L., Malnic, G. 1968. Hydrogen ion secretion by rat renal cortical tubules as studied by an antimony microelectrode. *Am. J. Physiol.* 214: 710–18

101. Whittembury, G. 1965. Sodium extrusion and potassium uptake in guinea pig kidney cortex slices. *J. Gen. Physiol.* 48:699–717

102. Whittembury, G. 1971. Relationship between sodium extrusion and electrical potential in kidney cells. See Ref. 9, 153–86

103. Whittembury, G., Rawlins, F. A., Boulpaep E. L. 1973. Paracellular pathway in kidney tubules: electrophysiological and morphological evidence. In *Transport Mechanisms in Epithelia.* ed. H. H. Ussing, N. A. Thorn, 577–95. Copenhagen: Munksgaard

104. Wick, T., Frömter, E. 1967. Das Zellpotential des proximalen Rattenniere in Abhängigkeit von der peritubulären Ionenkonzentration. *Pfluegers Arch.* 294:R17

105. Wiederholt, M., Agulian, S. K., Khuri, R. N. 1974. Intracellular potassium in the distal tubule of the adrenalectomized and aldosterone treated rat. *Pfluegers Arch.* 347:117–23

106. Wiederholt, M., Giebisch, G. 1974. Some electrophysiological properties of the distal tubule of the Amphiuma kidney. *Fed. Proc.* 33:387

107. Wiederholt, M., Schoormans, W., Fisher, F., Behn, C. 1973. Mechanism of action of aldosterone on potassium transfer in the rat kidney. *Pfluegers Arch.* 345:159–78

108. Wiederholt, M., Schoormans, W., Hansen, L., Behn, C. 1974. Sodium conductance changes by aldosterone in the rat kidney. *Pfluegers Arch.* 348:155–65

109. Wilbrandt, W. 1938. Electrical potential differences across the wall of kidney tubules of Necturus. *J. Cell. Comp. Physiol.* 11:425–31

110. Windhager, E. E. 1964. Electrophysiological study of renal papilla of golden hamsters. *Am. J. Physiol.* 206:694–700

111. Windhager, E. E., Boulpaep, E. L., Giebisch, G. 1966. Electrophysiological studies on single nephrons. *Proc. Int. Congr. Nephrol., 3rd, Washington DC* 1:35–47

112. Windhager, E. E., Giebisch, G. 1965. Electrophysiology of the nephron. *Physiol. Rev.* 45:214–44

113. Wright, F. S. 1971. Increasing magnitude of electrical potential along the renal distal tubule. *Am. J. Physiol.* 220:624–38

114. Wright, F. S. 1971. Alterations in electrical potential and ionic conductance of renal distal tubule cells in potassium adaptation. *Proc. Int. Union Physiol. Sci.* 9:609

115. Wright, F. S., Strieder, N., Fowler, N. B., Giebisch, G. 1971. Potassium secretion by distal tubule after potassium adaptation. *Am. J. Physiol.* 221:437–48

RENAL TUBULAR CHLORIDE TRANSPORT AND THE MODE OF ACTION OF SOME DIURETICS

M. Burg and L. Stoner

National Heart and Lung Institute, Bethesda, Maryland 20014

Introduction

A major function of renal tubules is to reabsorb the large amounts of sodium chloride present in the glomerular filtrate. Until recently, all of the reabsorption of sodium chloride was believed to depend on active sodium transport, and although it was recognized that the process differed in detail between various nephron segments such as proximal tubules and distal tubules, the primacy of sodium transport was not seriously questioned. Some investigators suggested that there might also be some active chloride transport in proximal (25, 32) and distal (15, 30) tubules, but this was considered to be in addition to the active sodium transport and subsidiary to it. With certain notable exceptions (1, 38), investigators also believed that diuretic drugs caused natriuresis by inhibiting the active sodium transport in renal tubules. In order to elucidate the action of the drugs, their effects were tested on various nonrenal tissues such as frog skin and toad bladder, which actively transport sodium and are more easily manipulated experimentally than are kidney tubules. It was found that the nonrenal tissues were not very sensitive to the diuretic drugs and, although the drugs caused changes, it was difficult to relate the results to the kidney. Current studies continue to support the traditional belief that active sodium transport is the basic process in proximal tubules, distal convoluted tubules, and the collecting ducts (21). The findings in the thick ascending limb of Henle's loop or, as we prefer to call it, the *diluting segment*[1] are in striking disagreement, however, with the traditional concept. In this segment, it is now apparent that active chloride transport, rather than sodium transport, is the primary event, and that the major effect of several important diuretics is to inhibit this active chloride transport, rather than sodium transport.

In what follows, we first summarize the experimental evidence for active chloride transport in the diluting segment and then discuss how the diuretic drugs affect it.

---

[1]The nephron segments were first identified by anatomists and named according to their appearance in particular species or after their discoverer. This has led to cumbersome nomenclature (e.g. "thin ascending limb of Henle's loop") or literally incorrect (e.g. "proximal straight tubule," which, in juxtamedullary nephrons, is hardly straight at all). At this point attempts to change the nomenclature are more likely to confuse the situation than to help. One possible exception is the "thick ascending limb of Henle's loop," named for its location in mammalian kidneys. The functionally identical segment is present in amphibia, which of course do not have a loop of Henle. We prefer to call this segment by the same name in both orders, and have chosen *diluting segment,* which is concise and descriptive. The name is appropriate, as the bulk of urinary dilution occurs in this segment in both orders and the diluting function is invariant despite the diuretic state of the animal. We do not mean to imply that it is the only segment in which the urine is diluted. The urine is diluted in various other distal nephron segments (in the absence of the antidiuretic hormone), but dilution in these other segments is much less important quantitatively than in the diluting segment.

The Diluting Segment

In mammals, the diluting segment does not approach the surface of the kidney and therefore has been studied directly only by dissection and perfusion in vitro. Its function was initially deduced from micropuncture studies. Fluid sampled from the beginning of the distal convoluted tubule was found to be dilute and to contain a relatively low concentration of sodium (30–60 mEq liter^{-1}) in various species (2, 3, 18, 19, 21). The dilution was attributed to reabsorption of salt in the diluting segment that immediately precedes the distal tubule. It was recognized that for urinary dilution to occur, the diluting segment must not only reabsorb salt but be virtually impermeable to water. Significantly, dilution of the tubule fluid was found to occur in the diluting segment even when the final urine was concentrated. Therefore, homeostatic adjustment of the urine osmolality was known to occur in other more distal nephron segments.

Direct studies by in vitro perfusion have recently provided more detailed information about the transport processes involved in the diluting segments of rabbits (8, 37) and various amphibia (39). These studies confirmed that the permeabiliby to water (calculated from changes in the reabsorption of water caused by osmotic gradients) is very low, compared to other nephrone segments. For example, the permeability to water was 5.0×10^{-9} cm^2 sec^{-1} atm^{-1} in diluting segments of rabbit and frog (Table 1), compared to $177–395 \times 10^{-9}$ cm^2 sec^{-1} atm^{-1} in rabbit proximal convoluted tubules (26). Because of the low permeability to water, there is essentially no reabsorption of water from the diluting segments, even when the tubule fluid becomes very dilute. Net reabsorption of sodium chloride was found in diluting segments of both rabbit and amphibia (Table 1). In the absence of water absorption, this resulted in dilution of the urine. When rabbit diluting segments were perfused at rates slow enough to allow a steady state of concentration to be reached, the mean sodium concentration in the tubule fluid was 65 mEq liter^{-1} (8), with 150 mEq liter^{-1} in the bath. This is comparable to the concentration of sodium found in the early distal convoluted tubule of the other mammalian species. Thus the in vitro studies confirmed the previous inferences that sodium chloride is absorbed preferentially to water in the diluting segment.

Transepithelial voltage was found to be oriented positive in the lumen (Table 1), contrary to the expectation if sodium transport were the active process. Chloride

Table 1 Transport characteristics of the renal diluting segment

Species	Rabbit	Frog
Permeability to water ($\times 10^9$ cm^2 sec^{-1} atm^{-1})	5	5
Transepithelial voltage (mV)	+ 6	+14
Sodium absorption (pM cm^{-1} sec^{-1})	10	14
Chloride absorption (pM cm^{-1} sec^{-1})	9	10

was absorbed against an electrochemical gradient, evidence of active chloride transport (8, 37). Sodium transport followed the electrochemical gradient, consistent with passive transport. The diluting segment is highly permeable to sodium, as shown by measurements of both sodium radioisotope flux (8, 37) and partial conductance of sodium (8). Therefore, even the small voltage that was present was sufficient, theoretically, to drive sodium out of the tubule lumen at the rapid rate observed. It was concluded that much, and possibly all, of the sodium reabsorption is passive (8, 37). The positive voltage was also found at the beginning of the distal convoluted tubule of a number of amphibia including the frog (39).

Chloride was required for the positive voltage in both rabbits and amphibia as shown in Table 2. The voltage was measured across rabbit or frog diluting segments with identical solution as perfusate and bath. When the principal salt in the solutions was sodium chloride, the voltage was oriented positive in the lumen. When all of the chloride was replaced by sulfate or nitrate, however, the voltage fell to zero. Sodium absorption, not shown in the table, measured in some of the same experiments, also fell to zero. Thus chloride is necessary for both the voltage and the associated passive movement of sodium. In contrast, sodium is not necessary for the voltage. It remained positive when all of the sodium was removed and replaced by choline. In the experiments with rabbit tubules (Table 2), cortical portions of the diluting segments were studied (8). Similar results were obtained using the medullary portion of the thick ascending limb (37). The results of ion replacement were opposite in nephron segments that actively transport sodium. For example, in the rabbit proximal convoluted tubule, perfused in vitro, replacement of all the sodium in the bathing solutions with choline resulted in a marked decrease in the voltage (normally negative in the lumen) and impairment of fluid absorption, whereas replacement of chloride with nitrate did not affect the voltage or the fluid absorption (M. Burg and N. Green, manuscript in preparation). The results of the ion substitutions in the diluting segment reinforced the view that chloride transport is primary and active, whereas sodium transport is secondary and passive in that part of the nephron.

The voltage in the diluting segment probably increases with distance along that segment as the concentration of salt in the lumen decreases. When diluting segments were perfused in vitro with hypotonic solutions, the voltage was higher than with isotonic solutions. The voltage was approximately 25 mV with 60 mM sodium chloride in the perfusate, compared to 6 mV with 150 mM (8). The additional voltage is a diffusion potential indicative that permeability to sodium exceeds that

Table 2 Effect of ion replacement on voltage across renal diluting segments

Principal salt	Voltage (mV)	
	Rabbit	Frog
NaCl	+ 7	+14
Choline Cl	+14	+ 9
Na_2SO_4 or $NaNO_3$	+ 0.3	+ 0.2

to chloride (8). This conclusion was confirmed by measurement of radioisotope flux (8). The higher voltage at the end of the diluting segment is the driving force for the relatively large sodium concentration gradients that develop there. The positive voltage also provides a driving force for the passive reabsorption of other cations as well as sodium. There is extensive reabsorption of calcium (27), magnesium (6, 27), and potassium (27) in the loop of Henle, which possibly occurs in the diluting segment by the same mechanism.

The rate of reabsorption of salt in the diluting segment should in theory vary directly with the load of salt entering it, because the rate of transport is dependent on the concentration of salt in the lumen. Normally, the concentration of salt in the tubule fluid reaches a low steady state value before the end of the diluting segment, so that there is relatively little reabsorption of salt in the terminal portions. An increased load of salt entering the diluting segment should change the profile of salt concentration along the segment, elevating salt concentration over a portion of the tubule and thereby enhancing reabsorption. This mechanism is a likely explanation for the load dependence of salt reabsorption in the loop of Henle, which has been observed by micropuncture (21).

MECHANISM OF ACTION OF DIURETIC DRUGS   As discussed earlier, the action of diuretic drugs was generally ascribed to inhibition of active sodium reabsorption from the renal tubules. Not all of the evidence favored this view, however. It had been noted that the additional urine excreted following administration of the mercurial diuretics contained a relative excess of chloride. Virtually no bicarbonate was excreted, and the amount of chloride excreted was so great as to exceed at times the amount of sodium (5). Based on this observation, Schwartz & Wallace (38) and Axelrod & Pitts (1) proposed that the mercurials acted primarily to inhibit chloride reabsorption and that the inhibition of sodium reabsorption was a secondary or passive consequence. Their theory was not generally accepted at the time. There was no other evidence for active chloride transport in the kidney and, in addition, their findings could be rationalized on the basis of active sodium transport (36). Direct study of the effect of mercurials on the diluting segment, however, now substantiates their theory.

The mercurial diuretics were initially studied by clearance techniques and it was by no means simple to identify their site of action in the nephron. It was concluded that their principal site of action was in the ascending limb of Henle's loop (22), but the results were not clear-cut, and their interpretation was the subject of contention. The conclusion was correct, however, as later confirmed by micropuncture studies. The mercurial diuretic chlormerodrin did not affect salt and water reabsorption in the proximal tubule of dogs, but did cause sodium concentration and osmolality to increase in the early distal tubule, presumed to be a result of inhibition of reabsorption of salt from the diluting segment (16, 20).

More recently, the effects of mercurial diuretics were studied directly in isolated perfused diluting segments from rabbit kidneys (9). The mercurial diuretic mersalyl, added to the perfusate, caused both the voltage and the net chloride transport to decrease (Table 3), evidence that the drug inhibited active chloride transport in that segment. The effect was reversed when the drug was removed (9).

Table 3 Effect of diuretic drugs in the perfusate on voltage and sodium chloride absorption of rabbit renal diluting segments

	Percent of Control	
Drug concentration	Voltage	NaCl absorption
Furosemide (10^{-5}M)	15	20
Mersalyl (3×10^{-5}M)	54	62
Ethacrynic acid (0.3 to 2×10^{-3}M)	34	—
Ethacrynic-cysteine (10^{-5}M)	15	25

Because the mercurials contain a toxic heavy metal, they have many biological actions and inhibit numerous cellular functions. Therefore, additional studies were required to determine whether the effect observed in vitro was related to the diuretic effect in vivo. Evidence for this was provided by a study of the antagonistic effect of the nondiuretic mercurial p-chloromercuribenzoate (PCMB). Although both PCMB and the mercurial diuretics inhibit electrolyte transport in kidney slices (29, 35) and tubule suspensions, and inhibit the renal Na- and K-activated adenosine triphosphatase (28), PCMB antagonizes the action of mercurial diuretics in the intact kidney. In dogs, administration of PCMB interrupted the diuresis caused by a mercurial diuretic and, after PCMB was given, the mercurial diuretic was no longer effective (33, 34). The identical result was found in the isolated diluting segments. When PCMB replaced mersalyl in the perfusate (or was added in the presence of mersalyl), the voltage immediately returned to the control value (9) and the transport of chloride was restored. PCMB restored the voltage much more rapidly than did the removal of mersalyl itself (9). The observation that PCMB and mersalyl are antagonists in the isolated tubules in vitro just as they are in vivo suggests that the effects of the diuretic in vitro are related to its specific diuretic action.

In order to act as a diuretic, the mercurial must be present in the tubule lumen. A low concentration of mersalyl (3×10^{-5}M) inhibited active chloride absorption from isolated rabbit diluting segments when present in the perfusate but had no effect in the bath (9). Higher concentrations in the bath were inhibitory, but the effect was slower and did not reverse when the drug was removed (9). The action of high concentrations of mersalyl in the bath was prevented when the bath contained serum rather than a simple salt solution (9). The mercurials presumably are bound to plasma proteins (or thiols) while in the circulation; this reduces their toxicity. The drugs probably reach the tubule fluid (where they are active) following secretion by the proximal tubules, although the evidence concerning the latter point is conflicting (22, 40).

Mersalyl had no measurable effect on permeability to sodium and chloride of the isolated diluting segments (9). It presumably inhibits the active chloride transport more or less directly, although the molecular mechanism is unknown.

Ethacrynic acid is one of a class of aryloxyacetic acid derivatives synthesized in order to produce more effective diuretic agents than the organic mercurials, which were the most potent diuretics then known (4, 13). Ethacrynic acid proved to be an extremely potent diuretic, even more effective than the organomercurials (22).

The renal site of action of ethacrynic acid was identified by the clearance technique to be the diluting segment (22). The results of in vitro perfusion studies of rabbit diluting segments are confirmatory (7, 10). When the drug was added to the perfusate, the transepithelial voltage decreased (Table 3). Therefore, ethacrynic acid acts by inhibiting active chloride transport in this segment, in a manner analogous to the effect of the mercurial diuretics. The drug had little effect on the permeability to sodium or chloride (10).

The active form of the drug is not ethacrynic acid itself. When ethacrynic acid is ingested, it becomes chemically modified. The major urinary excretion product is its cysteine adduct (4). Ethacrynic-cysteine in the lumen of the diluting segment inhibited active chloride transport at a hundredfold lower concentration than etacrynic acid itself (Table 3) (10).

Ethacrynic acid is very active in biological systems and has multiple effects on isolated tissues [reviewed in (10)], but most of these probably are not related to its diuretic action. The drug affects sodium transport in toad bladders, red blood cells, muscle cells, oocytes, intestinal cells, and renal cells. However, it is inhibition of active transport of chloride, not of sodium, that is responsible for its diuretic effect. Ethacrynic acid inhibits respiration and glycolysis in both intact cells and tissue homogenates from nonrenal and renal tissue. However, the concentration of the drug required to inhibit glycolysis is higher than that present in vivo during diuresis (14). Ethacrynic acid also inhibits sodium- and potassium-activated adenosine triphosphatase. The enzyme is not inhibited, however, in kidneys removed during diuresis caused by ethacrynic acid (24). Most of the in vitro effects of ethacrynic acid were elicited only by a high concentration of the drug. Approximately $10^{-3}M$ was used in most in vitro studies; $10^{-4}M$ generally had little effect. Further, the addition of cysteine or dithiothreitol blocked the effect of ethacrynic acid. When ethacrynic acid itself was perfused into isolated renal diluting segments, a similarly high concentration was required for inhibition (Table 3). In contrast to the effects in other tissues, however, premixing the ethacrynic acid with cysteine (forming the adduct) greatly increased its inhibitory effect in the renal tubule. Therefore, the effect on chloride transport in the diluting segment differs qualitatively from the numerous effects in other tissues. The effects of ethacrynic acid or ethacrynic-cysteine on the diluting segment in vitro depended on whether the drug was present in the perfusate or bath. Whereas a low concentration ($3 \times 10^{-6}M$) of ethacrynic-cysteine in the perfusate inhibited chloride transport, a higher concentration ($10^{-5}M$) in the bath had no effect. Evidently, the ethacrynic-cysteine must be present in the tubule lumen to exert its diuretic effect (10). Because ethacrynic acid is bound to plasma proteins, its glomerular filtration is limited. Most of the drug that reaches the tubule fluid probably is secreted via the organic acid transport system in the proximal tubules (4). A high concentration ($10^{-3}M$) of ethacrynic acid in the bath caused the voltage across isolated diluting segments to decrease, but the effect was irreversible and was presumed to be a toxic action (10). The same concentration of ethacrynic acid in the bath had no effect when the bath contained serum rather than a simple salt solution (7, 10). The effect of ethacrynic acid in the bath was, as noted above, considered to be a toxic reaction. In vivo toxicity presumably is prevented by binding of the drug to proteins or complexing with thiols in the serum. Perhaps these characteristics explain how a compound as reactive as ethacrynic acid can greatly reduce salt reabsorption in the renal diluting segment with so little toxicity in the kidney and other tissues.

Furosemide is a potent diuretic with a rapid onset of action that quickly subsides when the drug is removed. It was concluded on the basis of clearance studies that the drug inhibited sodium chloride reabsorption in the diluting segment (22). Micropuncture studies were confirmatory. Fluid sampled from the early distal convoluted tubule of rats treated with small doses of furosemide contained a higher concentration of sodium chloride than samples from untreated animals (2, 3, 18, 19, 22).

When diluting segments from rabbits were studied in vitro, a low concentration of furosemide in the perfusate (10^{-5}–10^{-6}M) inhibited the active chloride transport responsible for sodium chloride reabsorption in this segment (11). The drug caused both the rate of chloride absorption and the voltage to decrease (Table 3). In contrast, 10^{-4}M of furosemide placed in the bath had little effect (11). Like the mercurials and ethacrynic acid, the drug evidently must act at the lumen surface.

Because furosemide also is bound to plasma proteins, glomerular filtration is not thought to be the route by which it reaches the tubule fluid. More likely it is secreted into the tubule fluid in the proximal tubules (17) by the organic acid transport system. Probenecid, which is a competitive inhibitor of transport by this system, blocked the diuretic effect of small doses of furosemide (23), presumably by preventing access of the drug to the tubule fluid.

Furosemide also caused sodium chloride permeability and electrical conductance of diluting segments to decrease (11). This effect was small, however (the electrical conductance decreased only 12%), and the decrease in sodium chloride reabsorption was attributed to inhibition of active chloride transport rather than to the change in permeability.

The way in which furosemide inhibits chloride transport is not understood. Recently furosemide was reported to inhibit active chloride transport across the frog cornea (12), which may be more conveniently studied experimentally. It is possible that further study of that system will elucidate the drug's molecular action.

Summary

The renal diluting segment (thick ascending limb of Henle's loop) reabsorbs sodium chloride in excess of water and is responsible for dilution of the urine as well as reabsorption of a large fraction of the salt present in the glomerular ultrafiltrate. There is active reabsorption of chloride, which causes the voltage to be positive in the tubule lumen. Most, if not all, of the sodium transport is passive, driven by the voltage. Three major diuretics (mersalyl, furosemide, and ethacrynic acid) act in the lumen of the diluting segment to inhibit active chloride transport, not sodium transport as previously believed. This specific action on chloride transport may explain how these drugs are able to inhibit salt transport in the kidney while having so little effect on the transport processes elsewhere in the body.

Literature Cited

1. Axelrod, D. R., Pitts, R. F. 1952. The relationship of plasma pH and anion pattern to mercurial diuresis. *J. Clin. Invest.* 31:171–78
2. Bennett, C., Brenner, B., Berliner, R. 1968. Micropuncture study of nephron function in the Rhesus monkey. *J. Clin. Invest.* 47:203–16
3. Bennett, C., Clapp, J., Berliner, R. 1967. Micropuncture study of the proximal and distal tubule in the dog. *Am. J. Physiol.* 213:1254–62
4. Beyer, K. H., Baer, J. E., Michaelson, J. R., Russo, H. F. 1965. Renotropic characteristics of ethacrynic acid: a phenoxyacetic saluretic-diuretic agent. *J. Pharmacol. Exp. Ther.* 147:1–22
5. Blumgart, H. L. 1936. Action of diuretic drugs. II. Effect of diuretic drugs on the acid-base equilibrium of the blood in patients with cardiac edema. In *Medical Papers Dedicated to Henry Ashbury Christian,* 191–203. Baltimore, Md: Waverly
6. Brunette, M. G., Vigneault, N., Carriere, S. 1974. Micropuncture study of magnesium transport along the nephron in the rat. *Am. J. Physiol.* 227:891–96
7. Burg, M. 1974. The mechanism of action of diuretics in renal tubules. In *Recent Advances in Renal Physiology and Pharmacology,* ed. L. Wesson, G. Fanelli, p. 104. Baltimore, Md: Univ. Park Press
8. Burg, M., Green, N. 1973. Function of the thick ascending limb of Henle's loop. *Am. J. Physiol.* 224:659–68
9. Burg, M., Green, N. 1973. Effect of mersalyl on the thick ascending limb of Henle's loop. *Kidney Int.* 4:245–51
10. Burg, M., Green, N. 1973. Effect of ethacrynic acid on the thick ascending limb of Henle's loop. *Kidney Int.* 4:301–8
11. Burg, M., Stoner, L., Cardinal, J., Green, N. 1973. Furosemide effect on isolated perfused tubules. *Am. J. Physiol.* 225:119–24
12. Candia, O. 1973. Short-circuit current related to active transport of chloride in frog cornea: effects of furosemide and ethacrynic acid. *Biochim. Biophys. Acta* 298:1011–14
13. Cannon, P. J., Heinemann, H. O., Stason, W. B., Laragh, J. H. 1965. Ethacrynic acid. Effectiveness and mode of diuretic action in man. *Circulation* 31:507

14. Case, D., Gunther, S., Cannon, P. 1973. Ethacrynate induced depression of respiration in transport systems and kidney mitochondria. *Am. J. Physiol.* 224:769–80
15. Clapp, J. R., Rector, F. C. Jr., Seldin, D. W. 1962. Effect of unreabsorbed anions on proximal and distal tubular potentials in rats. *Am. J. Physiol.* 202:781–86
16. Clapp, J. R., Robinson, R. R. 1968. Distal sites of action of diuretic drugs in the dog nephron. *Am. J. Physiol.* 215:228–35
17. Deetjen, P. 1966. Micropuncture studies on site and mode of diuretic action of furosemide. *Ann. NY Acad. Sci.* 139:408–15
18. Dirks, J. H., Seely, J. F. 1970. Effect of saline infusions and furosemide on the dog distal nephron. *Am. J. Physiol.* 219:114–21
19. Edwards, B., Baer, P., Sutton, R., Dirks, J. 1973. Micropuncture study of diuretic effects on sodium and calcium reabsorption in the dog nephron. *J. Clin. Invest.* 52:2418–27
20. Evanson, R. L., Lockhart, E. A., Dirks, J. H. 1972. Effect of mercurial diuretics on the tubular sodium and potassium transport in dogs. *Am. J. Physiol.* 222:282–89
21. Giebisch, G., Windhager, E. E. 1973. Electrolyte transport across renal tubular membranes. *Handb. Physiol., Sect. 8: Renal Physiology,* 315–76
22. Goldberg, M. 1973. The renal physiology of diuretics. *Handb. Physiol., Sect. 8: Renal Physiology,* 1003–31
23. Hook, J. B., Williamson, H. E. 1972. Influence of probenecid and alterations in acid-base balance in the saluretic activity of furosemide. *J. Pharm. Exp. Ther.* 149:404–8
24. Inagaki, C., Martinez-Maldonado, M. Schwartz, A. 1973. Some *in vivo* and *in vitro* effects of ethacrynic acid on renal Na^+, K^+-ATPase. *Arch. Biochem. Biophys.* 158:421–34
25. Kashgarian, M., Warren, Y., Levitin, H. 1965. Micropuncture study of proximal renal tubular chloride transport during hypercapnea in the rat. *Am. J. Physiol.* 209:655–58
26. Kokko, J., Burg, M. B., Orloff, J. 1971. Characteristics of NaCl and water transport in the renal proximal tubule. *J. Clin. Invest.* 50:69–76

27. LeGrimellec, C., Roinel, N., Morel, F., Philippe, P., Malorey, P. 1974. Simultaneous Mg, Ca, P, K, and Cl analysis in rat tubular fluid. III. During acute Ca plasma loading. *Pfluegers Arch.* 346:171–88

28. Nechay, B. R., Palmer, R. F., Chinary, D. A., Posey, V. A. 1967. The problem of Na$^+$ + K$^+$ adenosine triphosphatase as the receptor for diuretic action of mercurials and ethacrynic acid. *J. Pharm. Exp. Ther.* 157:599–617

29. Macknight, A. D. C. 1968. Water and electrolyte contents of rat renal cortical slices incubated in medium containing p-chloromercuribenzoic acid or p-chloromercuribenzoic acid and ouabain. *Biochim. Biophys. Acta* 163:500–5

30. Malnic, G., Giebisch, G. 1972. Some electrical properties of distal tubule epithelium in the rat. *Am. J. Physiol.* 223:797–808

31. Malnic, G., Klose, R. M., Giebisch, G. 1964. Micropuncture study of renal potassium excretion in the rat. *Am. J. Physiol.* 206:674–86

32. Malnic, G., Mello Aires, M. 1970. Microperfusion study of anion transfer in proximal tubules of rat kidney. *Am. J. Physiol.* 218:27–32

33. Miller, T. B., Farah, A. E. 1962. On the mechanism of the inhibition of mercurial diuresis by p-chloromercuribenzoate. *J. Pharm. Exp. Ther.* 136:10–19

34. Miller, T. B., Farah, A. E. 1962. Inhibition of mercurial diuresis by nondiuretic mercurials. *J. Pharm. Exp. Ther.* 135:102–11

35. Mudge, G. H. 1951. Electrolyte and water metabolism of rabbit kidney slices. *Am. J. Physiol.* 167:206–23

36. Orloff, J., Berliner, R. W. 1961. Renal pharmacology. *Ann. Rev. Pharmacol.* 1:287–314

37. Rocha, A. S., Kokko, J. P. 1973. Sodium chloride and water transport in the medullary thick ascending limb of Henle: Evidence for active chloride transport. *J. Clin. Invest.* 52:612–23

38. Schwartz, W. B., Wallace, W. M. 1951. Electrolyte equilibrium during mercurial diuresis. *J. Clin. Invest.* 30:1089–1104

39. Stoner, L. 1975. "New" segment of the amphibian distal nephron which actively transports chloride. *Fed. Proc.* 31:981 (Abstr.)

40. Weiner, I., Farah, A. 1968. Pharmacology of mercurial diuretics. In *Salt and Water Balance. Proc. Int. Pharmacol. Meet.* 8:15–36. Oxford & New York: Pergamon

RECENT ADVANCES IN RENAL TUBULAR BIOCHEMISTRY[1]

Jeffrey S. Stoff and Franklin H. Epstein
Department of Medicine and Thorndike Laboratory, Harvard Medical School
and Beth Israel Hospital, Boston, Massachusetts 02214

Robert Narins and Arnold S. Relman
Department of Medicine, University of Pennsylvania School of Medicine,
Philadelphia, Pennsylvania 19174

Introduction

Various aspects of the relationship between renal metabolism and renal function have been considered in several comprehensive reviews (28, 104, 116). This review focuses on selected facets of the general problem, including the relationship of sodium reabsorption to tubular metabolism, the utilization of various substrates by the kidney, the localization of ATPases within tubular cells, and the production and metabolism of ammonia. Citations are limited in most cases to the most recent reference.

Sodium Reabsorption by Renal Tubules and Its Relation to Renal Metabolism

Early assessments of renal function considered the work of the kidney in terms of its excretory function and osmotic work load (13, 123). Later workers initially sought a relationship between oxygen uptake and solute excretion (12, 169) but failed to demonstrate a convincing connection. It was not recognized that the chief metabolic work of the kidney was expended on the reabsorption of an isotonic glomerular ultrafiltrate of plasma. One of the earliest observations linking sodium transport to oxidative metabolism was that of cyanide-induced natriuresis (156). Subsequent studies of frog skin (166) and toad urinary bladder (100) demonstrated that the net rate of oxygen uptake (Q_{O_2}) was directly related to net sodium (Na^+) transport (T_{Na^+}), and a stoichiometric relation was calculated of 4–5 equivalents of Na^+ transported per equivalent of oxygen utilized, or 16–20 eq per mole. These studies suggested that a similar relationship between sodium transport and metabolism might be established in the mammalian kidney. Using standard clearance techniques and measuring renal arteriovenous oxygen differences, several investigators established the constancy of the ratio between sodium reabsorption and oxygen consumption over large variations in the filtered load of sodium. They observed a stoichiometric relationship of approximately 20–30 eq Na^+ reabsorbed per mole of oxygen consumed in the dog (99, 161), 30 eq Na^+ in the rabbit (162), and 15 eq Na^+

[1]Supported in part by US PHS. grants #AM 18087, #HL 11414, and Massachusetts Kidney Foundation.

in the rat (177). The latter figure, however, was computed without subtracting basal oxygen consumption (see below). During hypertonic mannitol diuresis alone (87), or in the presence of distal tubule blockade with ethacrynic acid or furosemide (83, 105), the oxygen cost of sodium reabsorption rose as the ratio $\dot{T}_{Na}/\dot{Q}_{O_2}$ fell to 16 eq Na^+. In the isolated rat kidney, on the other hand, the anticipated constant relationship between net sodium reabsorption and oxygen consumption over a wide range of perfusion pressures and flows has not been regularly encountered (P. Vinay, B. Ross, H. A. Krebs; unpublished observations).

Because net sodium reabsorption is a resultant of active and passive processes that occur in different segments of the renal tubule by differing mechanisms (22, 48) it is not surprising that the $\dot{T}_{Na^+}/\dot{Q}_{O_2}$ ratio in the intact kidney might vary under different circumstances. Micropuncture studies clearly demonstrate that alterations in sodium transport in the proximal tubule result from inhibition of oxidative metabolism, whereas distal tubules are more resistant to the effects of metabolic inhibitors, except those that interfere with glycolysis (60, 174–177). Studies of isolated perfused rabbit proximal convoluted tubules suggest dependence upon glucose as well as upon gluconeogenic amino acids to maintain ion transport (88); subsequent studies, although confirming this relationship, indicate that transport of fluid in the proximal convolution may also occur independently of the presence of these metabolites (24). Such experiments illustrate both the relationship of metabolism to transport and its complexity.

Changes in net sodium reabsorption need not reflect faithfully the active component of sodium transport and, even if they did, the metabolic processes through which sodium reabsorption is energized are not necessarily derived from oxidative metabolism (60, 176). Indeed, a number of studies utilizing metabolic inhibitors of glycolysis have demonstrated increased sodium excretion (157, 176) and depressed urinary concentrating ability (110). Consequently, any alterations in sodium transport by those tubular cells which rely on nonoxidative metabolism will lead to a change in $\dot{T}_{Na}/\dot{Q}_{O_2}$ ratio.

A major problem in all studies attempting to correlate sodium transport with oxygen consumption is the difficulty of identifying that moiety of metabolism associated with nontransport processes. If the basal oxygen consumption is subtracted from the O_2 consumed while the kidney is transporting the $\dot{T}_{Na^+}/\dot{Q}_{O_2}$ ratio will be higher and the kidney will appear more efficient than if this is not done. Basal oxygen consumption is, however, difficult to determine for the intact perfused kidney. It is not clear that it can reliably be estimated from the study of kidney slices. The Q_{O_2} of slices of rat kidney, in which the tubular lumen is thought to be collapsed, averages 200 μM O_2(g wet wt)$^{-1}$hr^{-1} compared with the perfused rat kidney, which averages 300–400 μM O_2(g wet wt)$^{-1}$hr^{-1}. Basal respiration varies considerably with the metabolic substrate supplied and is higher both in slices (172) and in the perfused kidney (P. Vinay, B. Ross, H. A. Krebs; unpublished observations) when gluconeogenesis is stimulated by supplying precursors of glucose such as pyruvate or lactate. Another approach might be to measure the oxygen consumption of the intact or isolated perfused kidney during complete obstruction of the ureter. This maneuver, however, does not entirely eliminate glomerular filtration and some sodium and water continue to be transported out of the tubule (108). Finally, the slope of the line (or curve) relating $\dot{T}_{Na^+}$ to $\dot{Q}_{O_2}$ can be determined over a wide range of filtration rates obtained by altering perfusion pressure and flow. This is likely to be more accurate than reliance on one or two points on that curve, but the underlying assumption that basal metabolism (as well as passive backflow and reabsorption) remains constant all along the curve at different pressures and flows may not be correct. Thus, for example, the observation that the $\dot{T}_{Na^+}/\dot{Q}_{O_2}$ ratio falls when the dog kidney is exposed to furosemide (83) might result from a stimulation of nontransport respiration counterbalancing a roughly equal decrease in transport respiration caused by a concomitant decrease in active sodium reabsorption. It is noteworthy in this connection that gluconeogenesis, an active process requiring energy, is increased by furosemide (46) while glycolysis is inhibited (18, 84). The same fall in $\dot{T}_{Na^+}/\dot{Q}_{O_2}$ ratio could, of course, also be caused by an increase in passive back diffusion of sodium into the tubules without any change in transport-related energy consumption, as postulated to occur during mannitol diuresis (87) or during diuretic-induced distal tubule blockade (83, 105).

Some controversy remains as to whether high-energy bonds generated by the metabolism of foodstuffs may be transferred directly to energize transport without the intermediation of ATP. That energy for transport might be derived directly from oxidative processes was deduced from studies with dinitrophenol, in which no alteration of net tubular sodium reabsorption in dogs was produced despite uncoupling of oxidative phosphorylation (173). These clearance studies do not exclude an inhibitory effect of uncoupling agents on ATP-dependent proximal sodium reabsorption in a way that might be masked by a compensatory increase in transport in the distal tubule. It is, however, difficult to visualize how chemical energy generated in the mitochondria might be transferred to the plasma membrane where ion transport presumably takes place, if not via a high-energy compound such as ATP, and ATP is presumably necessary for any transport reactions linked to an ATPase. The essential role of high-energy compounds such as ATP has been strongly emphasized by micropuncture experiments in which metabolic inhibitors and uncoupling agents of oxidative phosphorylation were applied in concentrations high enough to reduce ATP generation (60). This procedure interrupted isotonic reabsorption by the proximal tubule. Transport was then restored by incorporating phosphoenolpyruvate (PEP) into the cell, thus permitting the phosphorylation of ADP to ATP in the cytosol. Transport could not be restored, however, if the metabolic inhibitor (e.g. oligomycin) also blocked Na-K-ATPase.

It appears that if the intracellular concentration of ATP is decreased to sufficiently low levels by a variety of metabolic inhibitors, transport will be interrupted (173). The precise intracellular level of ATP necessary for the maintenance of normal rates of sodium transport is not known. The problem is complicated by the fact that the ATP distribution within the cell may not be uniform, but rather compartmentalized, although evidence at present suggests a uniform distribution of ATP concentration in cortex, medulla, and papilla (122). This issue is central to many practical questions involving renal function. For example, if minor fluctuations in the cellular level of ATP greatly influenced transport, this would probably be a major locus of diuretic action as well as a likely point of feedback control over reabsorptive processes. It has actually been suggested that aldosterone might influence sodium transport by a primary action on energy-producing enzymes of the tricarboxylic acid cycle (62, 82). Other evidence, however, indicates that the normal ambient level of ATP within the kidney (about 2 mM ATP per g wet wt) is well above the critical concentration required for the reactions affecting sodium transport; small fluctuations in the tissue level of ATP would therefore not greatly affect the rate of transport. The K_m of Na-K-ATPase derived from kidney tissue is 0.5–1.0 mM (77). Infusions of fructose, which regularly reduce ATP levels in the kidney tissue of rats by 30–50% (21), produce little or no diuresis in rats (P. Silva and F. H. Epstein; unpublished observations) or humans (117). Only in human patients with aldolase deficiency (hereditary fructose intolerance), in whom adenine nucleotide depletion in the proximal tubules by fructose is presumably greatly exaggerated, does evidence of impaired proximal tubular transport (in the form of the acquired Fanconi syndrome) accompany fructose administration (117).

Na-K-ATPase has been implicated in the process linking metabolic energy to sodium transport (78, 155, 179). Evidence indicating its important role in sodium reabsorption by the kidney relates to: 1. its strategic localization at the basolateral membrane (146, 147, 180), especially in the outer medulla and in the thick ascending limb of Henle (3, 163); 2. the adaptive change in enzymatic activity when transport of sodium or potassium is altered (44, 77, 151); and 3. the stoichiometric parallelism between enzyme inhibition by cardioactive glycosides and concomitant changes in sodium reabsorption (121, 163). In addition, ouabain binding to a highly purified enzyme preparation derived from kidney cells was activated by sodium (K_a 16, 0.63 mm) and antagonized by potassium (K_1 11, 0.008 mm) (72). Related studies with reconstituted phospholipid vesicle preparations containing purified Na-K-ATPase from *Squalus acanthias* demonstrate a stoichiometric relationship between active Na^+ uptake and ATP hydrolysis and specific polarity with respect to ouabain inhibition of ion transport (69). Similarly reconstituted inside-out vesicles derived from dog renal medulla maintained electric neutrality by actively cotranslocating chloride (Cl^-) in a stoichiometric ratio with Na^+ (1:1) in the absence of K^+ transport (51a). It remains unclear whether the absence of a stoichiometric relationship between Na^+ and K^+ in this latter study relates to the methods of enzyme purification and vesicle formation or rather to the source of the enzyme in the renal medulla where active chloride transport has been reported (22).

Despite the evidence derived from these diverse studies, the degree of dependence of sodium reabsorption on Na-K-ATPase activity remains unsettled. Recent studies offer evidence for more than a single mechanism for sodium transport. Studies of the perfused isolated rat kidney demonstrated that, despite concentrations of ouabain sufficient to inhibit Na-K-ATPase in vitro completely, sodium reabsorption continues at approximately 50% of the control level (142). This residual ion transport was supported by either oxidative metabolism or glycolysis and was not inhibited by furosemide. Approximately half of the tubular reabsoption of sodium remaining after ouabain inhibition was blocked by the further addition of acetazolamide or by the removal of bicarbonate from the perfusing medium (156). Micropuncture studies of proximal tubules in rat kidney slices offer additional evidence for net transport of sodium independent of Na-K-ATPase activity and of the presence of potassium but requiring active bicarbonate transport (112). Other studies in intact rat kidneys utilizing microperfusion and micropuncture techniques demonstrated that, despite high concentrations of ouabain (10^{-3} M) perfusing proximal convoluted tubules via postglomerular capillaries, the reabsorptive transport of sodium in the proximal tubule continued at approximately 50% of control (61). It would therefore appear that, at least in the rat kidney, transport dependent on Na-K-ATPase activity accounts for perhaps half of all sodium reabsorption, transport related to bicarbonate reabsorption for about one quarter, and practically all of the remainder is dependent in some way on active metabolism, as this remaining portion of sodium reabsorption is inhibited in the cold or by the interruption of oxidation and glycolysis. The situation may be different in different species, as well as in different functional segments of the nephron. Ouabain appears to inhibit little if any sodium reabsorption in the spiny dogfish (64), but produces 80–90% inhibition of fluid reabsorption in isolated tubules of the rabbit kidney (23, 89).

Utilization of Substrates by the Kidney

Some intrinsic problems in relating metabolic data to renal function should be mentioned. 1. The kidney is heterogeneous, from the standpoints of both structure and function. While the physiologist has recognized and partially solved this problem, utilizing the methods of micropuncture and microperfusion of isolated nephron segments, analogous techniques have only recently been applied to metabolic investigation. Consequently, data derived from intact functioning kidneys and isolated perfused kidneys, as well as from slices and suspensions of separated tubules, do not provide precise localization for the correlation of function and metabolism. 2. Because the chief work of the kidney is the reabsorption of glomerular filtrate, metabolic data generated from kidney slices (where the tubular lumen is collapsed) and homogenates or subcellular fractions (where cell polarity is lost) may not reflect relationships present in the perfused organ. 3. The kidney, like the liver, conducts a vast array of complex metabolic activities. While many of these are linked to reabsorptive and secretory transport, a significant amount of metabolic work is unrelated to transport, including work necessary for gluconeogenesis, synthesis and degradation of proteins and polypeptide hormones, detoxification of drugs, and maintenance of cell structure. No attempt to correlate tubular metabolism to transport events can be conclusive without correction for this underlying basal metabolism. 4. Because the kidney possesses an inordinately large blood flow equal to approximately 25% of the cardiac output, absolute arteriovenous differences are usually extremely narrow and correspondingly difficult to estimate. Accurate measurement of arteriovenous differences as well as the rate and distribution of blood flow are essential if uptake or production of metabolites are estimated by the Fick technique. The possibility of simultaneous synthetic as well as degradative processes must always be taken into account. Lastly, because the kidney not only excretes a given substance, but also varies the net extraction of water from the filtrate, renal arteriovenous concentration differences are subject to error unless appropriate corrections are applied (181).

Metabolism of Fatty Acids

Early studies of kidney cortex slices established a respiratory quotient of approximately 0.75, which suggested that fat was the principal fuel of respiration. This finding was supported by subsequent studies using ^{14}C-labeled substrates in kidney cortical slices of rabbit (103) and rat (172), as well as in clearance experiments in dog (51) and man (126). However, this conclusion was based on the specious assumption that substrate uptake results in complete oxidation yielding energy for transport. In the dog kidney, less than 10% of palmitate uptake was completely oxidized to carbon dioxide (11). A significant fraction of fatty acids extracted by the kidney is accounted for by their incorporation into neutral lipids rather than by oxidative metabolism (11, 129). More recent studies of the localization of fatty acid uptake and metabolism in rat kidney slices demonstrate high rates of oxidation in the cortex and outer medulla (71), with a high degree of [^{3}H]palmitate uptake in the proximal tubule, as indicated by autoradiography (57). None of the above studies, however, indicates whether fatty acid oxidation is utilized to support tubular transport. Although several observations suggest a correlation between fatty acid uptake and net sodium transport (10), others have failed to establish this relationship (40). In intact anesthetized dogs, the oxidation of palmitate, oleate, and stearate (the principal fatty acids circulating in blood) accounts for only 15–20% of renal oxygen consumption (129). Nevertheless, intrarenal arterial infusion of 4-pentenoic acid, a putative inhibitor of long chain fatty acid oxidation, produces in dogs a marked natriuresis accompanied by a significant phosphaturia and glucosuria with a minimal kaliuresis and aminoaciduria (70). Similar experiments were performed in the isolated perfused rat kidney (164) utilizing α-bromopalmitate, a competitive inhibitor of acyl-CoA synthetase and acylcarnitine transferase. It was concluded that fatty acids both maintained endogenous substrate support for sodium reabsorption and stimulated an increased level of sodium reabsorption when added as an exogenous substrate. In comparison with exogenously added glucose, however, fatty acids were less effective in the support of net sodium reabsorption and excretion of potassium (141). The utilization of free fatty acids by the kidney may support mainly the major energy utilization processes other than the reabsorption of sodium and secretion of potassium ions.

Free fatty acids produce a significant stimulation of gluconeogenesis from lactate (172), as well as inhibition of glucose oxidation in cortical slices (167). An effect of fatty acids on the control of gluconeogenesis is also suggested by studies in which α-bromopalmitate, an inhibitor of fatty acid oxidation, produced a fivefold increment in glucose oxidation (113). A mechanism for this effect is suggested by the finding that free fatty acids inhibit the activity of pyruvate dehydrogenase, a key enzyme in controlling the entry of pyruvic acid into the tricarboxylic acid cycle (59). Fatty acids (oleate) prevented the activation of this enzyme, in contrast to the stimulatory effect of glucose and dihydroxyacetone, whereas gluconeogenic precursors, including lactate, glutamine, glycerol, and malate, had no significant effect. Earlier studies on cortical slices of rat kidney demonstrated that exogenous free fatty acids and starvation (endogenous fatty acids and ketone bodies) stimulated gluconeogenesis from glycerol or dihydroxyacetone. This effect is presumably me-

diated through the generation of citrate and its inhibitory effect on phosphofructokinase (165). Related studies reporting long chain fatty acid stimulation of pyruvate
carboxylase activity within hepatic mitochondria (158) suggest an alternative site
for control of gluconeogenesis, and it should be remembered that complex metabolic
processes are rarely controlled by single effects (95, 96). Rather than exclusively
subserving the function of electrolyte transport, an important role of the renal
utilization of fatty acids is probably the regulation of gluconeogenesis and the
maintenance of the integrity of cell membranes.

Metabolism of Lactate

The net uptake of lactate by the kidney has been well documented in cortical slices
of the rabbit (32) and rat (97, 103, 172) as well as in the intact functioning dog
kidney (20, 38, 101). Lactate uptake varied directly with its arterial concentration
(20, 38). Considerable controversy remains concerning both the metabolic disposition and the role of lactate in supporting energy-dependent functions of the kidney.
It is apparent from slice studies that lactate may be oxidized to carbon dioxide and
water, or converted to glucose or to amino acids such as alanine or glutamine (97,
103, 172). In a recent study of the intact dog kidney during maintenance of physiologic lactate concentration, essentially all the lactate utilization was accounted for
by either oxidative metabolism (70–80%) or gluconeogenesis, although no correction for extrarenal metabolic conversion during recirculation was reported (101).
Several factors may be important in regulation of the metabolic fate of lactate. It
has been shown that acetoacetate (97) and oleate (172) direct the flow of lactate
toward gluconeogenesis. The precise control mechanism has not been established,
but either increased activation of pyruvate carboxylase – pyruvate carboxykinase or
decreased activity of pyruvate dehydrogenase or of phosphofructokinase may be
important (see above). In the intact dog kidney, both lactate uptake and gluconeogenesis from lactate varied directly with arterial lactate concentration (38). Furthermore, during chronic metabolic alkalosis in dogs, lactate extraction and oxidative
metabolism increased, while gluconeogenesis from lactate was suppressed (10–20%
total lactate utilized) (101). In this way, the energy available to the kidney remained
constant, despite a shift in the pattern of renal substrate utilization. Thus during
alterations of acid-base balance, the substrate contributions of glucose (20–26%),
citrate (10–14%), and free fatty acids (16–22%) to metabolic oxidation remain
essentially constant while there is preferential utilization of either lactate or glutamine. During acidosis, glutamine (40%) contributes approximately twice as much
as lactate (22.4%); alkalosis results in a reversal of this pattern (101, 129, 133, 134).

Previous attempts to relate the role of lactate metabolism to renal oxygen
utilization and sodium reabsorption ($\dot{T}_{Na^+}$) have resulted in both positive (40) and
negative (20) correlations. In part, these divergent results may be explained by a
failure of the earlier studies to discriminate among several interrelated factors, e.g.
uptake, release, synthesis, and degradation, the resultant of which is measured as
net uptake. In addition, uncontrolled metabolic factors resulting in alterations in
other substrate levels, e.g. free fatty acids, may have competing effects with lactate
uptake and/or utilization. At present, no clear pattern of lactate utilization coupled

Lowry (33) have found that the distal tubule of normal rats has five times more PDG than the proximal tubule, but only the enzyme in the proximal tubule increases its activity in acidosis. PIG is localized primarily in the straight portion of the proximal tubule and is unaffected by chronic acidosis. Similar results have been reported by Goodman (55), who found that PDG in rat cortex, but not PDG in medulla, increased with chronic acidosis. PIG is entirely extramitochondrial, primarily associated with microsomes (34, 75, 92); PDG, on the other hand, is clearly a mitochondrial enzyme (34, 75), but there is some uncertainty whether it is tightly bound to the inner mitochondrial membrane. This question requires further study because it is of critical importance in understanding the transport of glutamine across the mitochondrial membrane. If glutaminase were tightly bound to the membrane, one would expect a close coupling between transport and deamidation of glutamine; as a consequence, there would be little or no free glutamine within the matrix space. But if the enzyme were free within the matrix then transport and deamidation would be independent processes, and one would expect measurable glutamine in the matrix.

Inasmuch as the transport of glutamine through the mitochondrial membrane and the conversion of glutamine to glutamate within the mitochondrion are believed to be the first steps in ammoniagenesis, there is much current interest in these processes. It was demonstrated earlier that isolated rat and pig mitochondria need a source of energy to achieve maximal glutaminase I activity (93). More recent work by Crompton & Chappell (31) revealed that, in the absence of energy, intramitochondrial glutamine falls and glutamate concentration rises; the provision of energy promptly reverses this effect and increases ammonia production. These data suggest that there may be an energy-dependent transport system in the mitochondrial membrane, which links glutamine efflux to glutamine uptake.

Adam & Simpson (1) have studied glutamine transport in rat kidney mitochondria. Using 1 mM [^{14}C]glutamine in the medium, they observed rapid uptake of radioactivity into the matrix, ammonia production, and accumulation of [^{14}C]glutamate. Unlike Crompton & Chappell (9), these workers found no detectable intramitochondrial [^{14}C]glutamine under any circumstances, even when inhibitors of deamination were used. Mitochondria from chronically acidotic rats transported more glutamine than controls, but not more glutamate or α-ketoglutarate (α-KG). Three hours after a single acid load, before any increase in the level of extracted glutaminase activity, they could detect an increase in matrix uptake of radioactivity from [^{14}C]glutamine and an increase in ammonia production. Adam & Simpson concluded that transport of glutamine across the inner mitochondrial membrane occurs by a specific carrier, which may or may not be glutaminase itself, but which is the rate-controlling factor in glutamine metabolism. They suggested that increased deamidation of glutamine in chronic acidosis is due to an adaptation in this carrier. This latter suggestion had been made earlier by Pitts (132).

A recent preliminary report by Goldstein (53) confirms the existence of an energy-dependent transport system for glutamine in rat renal mitochondria, which appears to adapt in chronic acidosis. A nonmetabolized analog of glutamine, 6-diazo-5-oxo-L-norleucine (DON), was used to differentiate between adaptation of the transport system and adaptation of glutaminase. Mitochondria from acidotic rats were found to accumulate increased [^{14}C]DON, thereby suggesting that the adaptation was in the transport system rather than the enzyme. No data on intramitochondrial glutamine or glutamate concentrations were reported.

In the experiments of Adam & Simpson (1), an increased glutamate content was found in acidotic mitochondria. As renal tissue levels of glutamate are known to be reduced in acidosis, and as glutamate is an end-product inhibitor of glutaminase I, these findings would seem to contradict present views of the control of glutaminase by tissue glutamate levels (137). Adam & Simpson suggested that a decrease in cytosolic concentration of glutamate could mask an increase in concentration in the matrix space. Yet, if glutaminase activity is indeed controlled through feedback inhibition by its product, it is difficult to see how it could also be enhanced by increased delivery of its substrate unless there were a concomitant stimulation of product removal. Furthermore, because the deamination and further metabolism of glutamate occur mainly in the mitochondrion, it seems unlikely that the cytosolic concentration of glutamate in chronic acidosis would be reduced unless the intramitochondrial concentration also were low. The rise in matrix glutamate concentration in chronic acidosis reported by Adam & Simpson might be an artifact of their in vitro preparation. They added rotenone and arsenite to inhibit the mitochondrial metabolism of glutamate, and they omitted phosphate from the medium, which would inhibit the efflux of malate. Under these conditions, it would be difficult to determine precisely which of the intramitochondrial reactions in Figure 1 might be rate limiting in the response to acidosis. This issue obviously is troublesome and further data will be required for its resolution.

Glutaminase II   Glutaminase II is the term applied to the reaction sequence that involves the transamination of glutamine with an α-keto acid to form α-ketoglutaramate and the corresponding α-amino acid, followed by the hydrolysis of the amide group to form α-KG and ammonia (Figure 1). The cytosol of renal cells is known to contain the necessary enzymes (glutamine transaminase and ω-amidase), but the pathway has been assumed to play a minor role in ammoniagenesis because of relatively low in vitro reaction rates in preparations from rat (52), dog (135), and human (43) kidneys. However, all of these studies employed pyruvic acid as the α-keto acid substrate for the glutamine transaminase reaction, whereas Cooper & Meister (29) recently found that phenylpyruvate is far more specific for the form of the transaminase found in rat kidney cytosol. In current studies, published so far only in abstract (90), Kopyt & Narins used phenylpyruvate to assay the activity of the glutaminase II pathway in the cytosol of rat kidney. They found it to be relatively low and to be only slightly increased by acute or chronic acidosis. It was of interest, however, that they found the renal tissue concentration of phenylpyruvate to be well above the K_m of the glutamine transaminase for this substrate (29). They also report evidence that transamination between phenylalanine and α-KG may result in the cyclic regeneration of phenylpyruvate as well as the formation of glutamate (Figure 1).

Other pathways   Recently two other mechanisms of ammonia production have been suggested: a purine nucleotide cycle (16) and a so-called glutamyl transferase reaction (178). None of these reactions has yet been proven to be a significant source of ammonia in the kidney and their ultimate importance remains to be determined. These reactions have been omitted from Figure 1.

GLUCONEOGENESIS AND AMMONIA PRODUCTION   The relationship between ammoniagenesis and the formation of glucose from the carbon skeleton of glutamine has been a controversial issue ever since Goodman, Fuisz & Cahill (56) first suggested that the control of ammonia production in acidosis might be effected through increased conversion of α-KG to glucose. They proposed that the reduced renal tissue levels of glutamate in chronically acidotic rats might be due to increased gluconeogenesis, with a consequent reduction in feedback inhibition of the glutaminase I reaction. The literature on this subject up to 1971 has been reviewed elsewhere (54) and is not discussed again here. In the past few years, considerable progress has been made in resolving the controversy, and so it may be useful to summarize our present understanding very briefly.

One argument against the gluconeogenesis theory is that net production of glucose cannot be clearly demonstrated in the intact kidney. Two recent reports on the net glucose metabolism of the kidney in the intact dog (143) and in the rat (27) provide new evidence that there is no detectable and consistent addition of glucose to renal venous blood in these species, either under normal conditions or in chronic acidosis when ammonia production is increased. It is well to remember, however, that renal blood flow is so rapid that expected renal venous-arterial differences in glucose concentration would be close to the analytical limit, even in the unlikely event that all extracted glutamine was coverted to glucose. Furthermore, any net synthesis of glucose by the cortex of the intact kidney might be concealed by net consumption of glucose in the medulla, a tissue that in vitro is, unlike the cortex, unable to convert glutamine or glutamate to glucose. For this latter reason, we do not regard the question of the net renal production of glucose in vivo as crucial to the hypothesis that ammonia production is controlled by gluconeogenesis.

Recent studies dealing with the in vitro metabolism of glutamine by rat or dog cortical tissue describe many ways in which gluconeogenesis and ammonia production can be dissociated, such as with the use of metabolic inhibitors (2, 136) or by the manipulation of the concentration of calcium (140) or phosphate (25) in the medium. The addition of pyruvate, lactate, or propionate to rat cortex slices incubated with glutamine enhanced glucose synthesis but reduced ammonia production (73, 144). Most interesting of all is the fact, reported by many workers (25, 55, 138–140), that a reduction in the pH of the medium either reduces ammoniagenesis or fails to affect it, while simultaneously increasing gluconeogenesis. It is apparent that there is no tight linkage between ammonia production and glucose synthesis, nor is there a single mechanism that controls both processes under all circumstances.

Experiments with U-^{14}C-labeled glutamine have provided a more detailed picture of the metabolism of the carbon skeleton of glutamine. Dog kidney slices appear to convert 3–6 times as much glutamine carbon to CO_2 as to glucose (130, 153). Kamm & Strope (76) compared the metabolism of glutamine in kidney cortex slices taken from normal, alkalotic, and acidotic rats. They found that glutamine carbon was converted mainly to CO_2 and glutamate, in roughly equal proportions. Acidosis increased glutamine uptake and the conversion to both products. Glucose constituted about 10% of the glutamine carbon taken up in alkalosis and rose to 20% with acidosis; the increase in labeling of glucose accounted for most of the increased uptake of glutamine. Pitts et al (134) infused tracer amounts of U-^{14}C-labeled glutamine into intact dogs and found that, in alkalosis, approximately 10% of the glutamine extracted by the kidneys was converted to glucose, the remainder appearing mostly as CO_2. In acidotic dogs, glutamine extraction and conversion to CO_2 increased threefold, although total production of CO_2 was unchanged. Conversion to glucose increased by more than fivefold, but glucose carbons still represented only 20% of the utilized glutamine. The authors concluded that gluconeogenesis could not be rate limiting for ammonia production.

That a relatively small fraction of the renal glutamine uptake goes to the synthesis of glucose was also suggested by the work of Hems (66), who studied the metabolism of the isolated rat kidney perfused with 5 mM glutamine and found that kidneys from normal rats converted only about 15% of the extracted glutamine to glucose. Kidneys from chronically acidotic animals extracted more glutamine and converted about 50% to glucose.

Pitts noted that adaptive increase in ammonia production plays a vital role in enabling an animal to survive acidosis, whereas renal gluconeogenesis at best plays only a minor role in the maintenance of blood glucose, and he asked, "Why in evolutionary development would an animal tie a vital life-preserving function to one that is insignificant in the economy of the body?" (132). This seems to put too narrow an interpretation on the gluconeogenesis hypothesis. Although this hypothesis might be strictly construed as requiring a constant, if not a one-to-one, relationship between ammoniagenesis and net glucose formation (which obviously does not exist), a more general formulation would relate the control of ammonia formation to the rate at which α-KG is metabolized to either glucose or CO_2 and H_2O. Glutamine is a neutral substance, but when it forms a α-KG and two molecules of NH_3, it releases two protons (Figure 1). Subsequent conversion of the α-KG to glucose or to CO_2 and H_2O is essential if the acid released during the production of α-KG from glutamine is to be removed. The overall reactions for these two processes are

$$\alpha\text{-KG}^{(2-)} + 2H^+ \longrightarrow 5\ CO_2 + 5\ H_2O$$
and
$$2\ \alpha\text{-KG}^{(2-)} + 4H^+ \longrightarrow 4\ CO_2 + \text{glucose.}$$

In each case, the metabolism of the dicarboxylate anion, α-KG, consumes two protons, thereby balancing the two protons released by the PDG and glutamic dehydrogenase (GDH) reactions (Figure 1). Without this metabolic removal of protons, the excretion of ammonium ions in the urine would result in no net gain of bicarbonate to the body, and the essential acid-base function of ammonia production would be lost.

The only way that the carbon skeleton of α-KG can be converted to CO_2 or glucose is to get out of the mitochondrion and be converted to phosphoenolpyruvate

(PEP), as shown in Figure 1. If there were no flux of substrate out of the mitochondrion, there could be no net consumption of α-KG, since each turn of the tricarboxylic acid cycle requires the additon of two carbons as acetate and results in the consumption of only two carbons. Thus a constant efflux of substrate from the mitochondrion is a necessary condition for the removal of the carbon skeleton of glutamine. In the rat, phosphoenolpyruvate carboxykinase (PEPCK) is largely cytosolic, so one of the tricarboxylic acid cycle acids derived from α-KG must traverse the mitochondrial membrane. Present evidence suggests the transported acid to be malate, although oxaloacetic acid (OAA) may also serve that function (49, 63). Once malate is converted to PEP, the flow of substrate can go either to glucose or back into the mitochondrion by conversion to pyruvate.

It should be obvious, however, that net synthesis of glucose is not a requirement for ammonia production, but transport of malate (and possibly also OAA) across the mitochondrial membrane, with subsequent conversion to PEP through the PEPCK reaction, is essential for the removal of α-KG. In that sense, the rate of metabolic flux through the PEPCK reaction must be closely linked to the rate at which ammonia is being formed from glutamine within the mitochondrion. It would be surprising if there were not control mechanisms that assured the close functional association of these two processes.

Control

Although many theories have been proposed, there still is no entirely satisfactory explanation for the control of ammonia production in acidosis (12, 131, 132). In view of what has been said about the relation between the rate of ammonia formation and the rate of formation of PEP, it should be apparent that ammonia could be regulated by mechanisms that control any of the series of reactions beginning with glutamine transport and ending with the formation of PEP (Figure 1). The most likely control points would be irreversible reactions such as glutaminase, α-KG and succinate dehydrogenases, and PEPCK. Other likely points would be the transport steps at the mitochondrial membrane.

As already noted, there is recent evidence (1, 53) that glutamine uptake by mitochondria is stimulated by chronic acidosis. Glutaminase is induced by sustained acidosis, but this induction is clearly not required for adaptation to acidosis (52, 131, 132). It is a curious fact that, in the rat at least, the initial kinetic effect of low pH is to inhibit the glutaminase reaction (120, 139). Sustained acidosis overrides this effect within 12 hr by inducing enough new enzyme to increase the flux through the reaction (63, 67).

There is also some evidence that low pH in vitro stimulates succinic dehydrogenase (98). Recently it has been suggested that low pH in vitro enhances the transport of malate and that chronic acidosis induces similar effects (91, 120). Renal, but not hepatic, PEPCK has been shown to be induced by sustained acidosis after a lag of about 4–6 hr (4, 5, 107). The inductive process has been said to be due to a reduction the turnover of the protein and to be resistant to actinomycin D (106). These latter ings have been recently challenged by Iynedjian, Ballard & Hanson (74), who d that chronic acidosis in rats stimulates synthesis of renal PEPCK.

Much remains to be learned, but there is already much evidence that control of ammonia production in acidosis is multifactorial, involving a variety of mechanisms at multiple sites. That should not be be surprising, since nature rarely entrusts the regulation of important processes to a single mechanism.

Literature Cited

1. Adam, W., Simpson, D. P. 1974. Glutamine transport in rat kidney mitochondria in metabolic acidosis. *J. Clin. Invest.* 54:165–74
2. Adler, S., Preuss, H. G. 1972. Interrelationships between citrate metabolism, ammoniagenesis, and gluconeogenesis in renal cortex in vitro. *J. Lab. Clin. Med.* 79:505–15
3. Alexander, J. C., Lee, J. B. 1970. Effect of osmolality on Na$^+$-K$^+$-ATPase in outer renal medulla. *Am. J. Physiol.* 219:1742–45
4. Alleyne, G. A. O. 1970. Renal metabolic response to acid-base change. II. The early effects of metabolic acidosis on renal metabolism in the rat. *J. Clin. Invest.* 49:943–51
5. Alleyne, G. A. O., Scullard, G. H. 1969. Renal metabolic response to acid-base change. I. Enzymatic control of ammoniagenesis in the rat. *J. Clin. Invest.* 48:364–70
6. Anderson, J., Stowring, L. 1973. Glycolytic and gluconeogenic enzyme activities in renal cortex of diabetic rats. *Am. J. Physiol.* 224:930–36
7. Balagura-Baruch, S., Burich, R. L., King, V. F. 1973. Effects of alkalosis on renal citrate metabolism in dogs infused with citrate. *Am. J. Physiol.* 225:385–88
8. Balagura-Baruch, S., Burich, R. L., King, V. F. 1973. Pyruvate handling by the intact functioning kidney of the dog. *Am. J. Physiol.* 225:389–92
9. Bank, N., Aynedjian, H. 1973. A micropuncture study of potassium excretion by the remnant kidney. *J. Clin. Invest.* 52:1480–90
10. Barac-Nieto, M., Cohen, J. J. 1968. Non-esterified fatty acid uptake by dog kidney. Effects of probenecid and chlorothiazide. *Am. J. Physiol.* 215:98–107
11. Barac-Nieto, M., Cohen, J. J. 1971. The metabolic fates of palmitate in the dog kidney in vivo: Evidence for incomplete oxidation. *Nephron* 8:488–91
12. Barcroft, J., Brodie, T. G. 1904. The gaseous metabolism of the kidney. *J. Physiol. London* 32:18–27
13. Borsook, H., Winegarden, H. M. 1931. The work of the kidney in the production of urine. *Proc. Nat. Acad. Sci. USA* 17:3–12, 13–28
14. Baumann, K., Huong, K. C. 1969. Micropuncture and microperfusion study of L-glucose secretion in rat kidney. *Pfluegers Arch.* 305:155–66
15. Bernanke, D., Epstein, F. H. 1965. Metabolism of the renal medulla. *Am. J. Physiol.* 208:541–45
15b. Besarab, A., Silva, P., Ross, B., Epstein, F. H. 1975. Bicarbonate and sodium reabsorption by the isolated perfused kidney. *Am. J. Physiol.* 228:1525–30
16. Bogusky, R. T., Lowenstein, L. M., Lowenstein, J. M. 1974. The purine nucleotide cycle: A new pathway for renal ammonia production. *Proc. Am. Soc. Nephrol.* Nov. 25–26, Washington DC, p. 11
17. Bowman, R. H. 1970. Gluconeogenesis in the isolated perfused rat kidney. *J. Biol. Chem.* 245:1604–12
18. Bowman, R. H., Dolgin, J., Coulson, R. 1973. Furosemide, ethacrynic acid, and iodoacetate on function and metabolism in perfused rat kidney. *Am. J. Physiol.* 224:416–24
19. Bowman, R. H., Dolgin, J., Coulson, R. 1973. Interaction between furosemide and ouabain on Na and K excretion in perfused rat kidney. *Am. J. Physiol.* 224:1200–5
20. Brand, P. H., Cohen, J. J., Bignall, M. C. 1974. Independence of lactate oxidation from net Na$^+$ reabsorption in dog kidney in vivo. *Am. J. Physiol.* 227:1255–62
21. Burch, H. B., Max, P. Jr., Chyu, K., Lowry, O. H. 1969. Metabolic intermediates in liver of rats given large amounts of fructose or dihydroxyacetone. *Biochem. Biophys. Res. Commun.* 34:619–26
22. Burg, M. B. Green, N. 1973. Effect of mersalyl on the thick ascending limb of Henle's loop. *Kidney Int.* 4:245–51
23. Burg, M. B., Orloff, J. 1968. Control of fluid absorption in the renal proximal tubule. *J. Clin. Invest.* 47:2016–24
24. Cardinal, J., Lutz, M. D., Burg, M. B., Orloff, J. 1975. Lack of relationship of potential difference to fluid absorption

in the proximal renal tubule. *Kidney Int.* 7:94–102

25. Cartier, P., Belanger, P., Lemieux, G. 1975. Characteristics of in vitro ammonia and glucose production by dog kidney cortex. *Am. J. Physiol.* 228: 934–43

26. Chabardès, D., Imbert, M., Clique, A., Montégut, M., Morel, F. 1975. PTH sensitive adenyl cyclase activity in different segments of the rabbit nephron. *Pfluegers Arch.* 354:229–39

27. Churchill, P. C., Belloni, F. L., Churchill, M. C. 1973. Net renal glucose release in the rat. *Am. J. Physiol.* 225:528–31

28. Cohen, J. J., Barac-Nieto, M. 1973. Renal metabolism of substrates in relation to renal function. *Handb. Physiol. Sect. 8, Renal Physiol.*, Chap. 27, 909–1001

29. Cooper, A. J. L., Meister, A. 1974. Isolation and properties of a new glutamine transaminase from rat kidney. *J. Biol. Chem.* 249:2554–61

30. Costello, J., Scott, J. M., Wilson, P., Bourke, E. 1973. Glucose utilization and production by the dog kidney in vivo in metabolic acidosis and alkalosis. *J. Clin. Invest.* 52:608–11

31. Crompton, M., Chappell, J. B. 1973. Transport of glutamine and glutamate in kidney mitochondria in relation to glutamine deamidation. *Biochem. J.* 132:35–46

32. Cross, R. J., Taggart, J. V. 1950. Renal tubular transport: Accumulation of aminohippurate by rabbit kidney slices. *Am. J. Physiol.* 161:181–90

33. Curthoys, N. P., Lowry, O. H. 1973. The distribution of glutaminase isoenzymes in the various structures of the nephron in normal, acidotic and alkalotic rat kidney. *J. Biol. Chem.* 248:162–68

34. Curthoys, N. P., Weiss, R. F. 1974. Regulation of renal ammoniagenesis. *J. Biol. Chem.* 249:3261–66

35. Dahl, J. L., Hokin, L. H. 1974. The sodium-potassium adenosinetriphosphatase. *Ann. Rev. Biochem.* 43:327–56

36. Davis, R. P., Rand, G. F. 1963. Potassium depletion: A disorder of the Pasteur effect. *J. Clin. Invest.* 42:928a

37. DeLorenzo, R. J., Greengard, P. 1973. Activation by adenosine 3':5'-monophosphate of a membrane-bound phosphoprotein phosphatase from toad bladder. *Proc. Nat. Acad. Sci. USA* 70:1831–35

38. Dies, F., Herrera, J., Matos, M., Avelar, E., Ramos, G. 1970. Substrate uptake by dog kidney in vivo. *Am. J. Physiol.* 218:405–10

39. Dies, F., Lotspeich, W. D. 1967. Hexose monophosphate shunt in the kidney during acid-base and electrolyte imbalance. *Am. J. Physiol.* 212:61–71

40. Dies, F., Ramos, G., Avelar, E., Matos, M. 1969. Relationship between renal substrate uptake and tubular sodium reabsorption in the dog. *Am. J. Physiol.* 218:411–16

41. Dousa, T. P., Barnes, L. D. 1974. Effects of colchicine and vinblastine on the cellular action of vasopressin in mammalian kidney. *J. Clin. Invest.* 54:252–62

42. Ferguson, D. R., Twite, B. R. 1974. Effects of vasopressin on toad bladder membrane proteins: Relationship to transport of sodium and water. *J. Endocrinol.* 61:501–7

43. Fine, A., Scott, J. Bourke, E. 1972. Studies on the glutamine aminotransferase-ω-amidase pathway in human kidney in vitro. *J. Lab. Clin. Med.* 80: 591–97

44. Franke, H., Mályusz, M., Weiss, Ch. 1975. Acute changes of the Na-K-ATPase activity in plasmamembranes of isolated cell-free perfused rat kidney. *Pfluegers Arch.* 353:97–106

45. Frohnert, P., Höhmann, B., Zwiebel, R., Baumann, K. 1970. Free flow micropuncture studies of glucose transport in the rat nephron. *Pfluegers Arch.* 315:66–85

46. Fülgraff, G., Nünemann, H., Sudhoff, D. 1972. Effects of the diuretics furosemide, ethacrynic acid and chlorothiazide on gluconeogenesis from various substrates in rat kidney cortex slices. *Arch. Pharmakol.* 273:86–98

47. Garza-Quintero, R., Cohen, J. J., Brand, P. H., Kook, Y. J. 1975. Steady-state glucose oxidation by dog kidney in vivo: relation to Na+ reabsorption. *Am. J. Physiol.* 228:549–55

48. Giebisch, G., Windhager, E. E. 1973. Electrolyte transport across renal tubular membranes. *Handb. Physiol. Sect. 8, Renal Physiol.*, Chap. 11, 315–76

49. Gimpel, J. A., Dehaan, E. J., Tager, J. M. 1973. Permeability of isolated mitochondria to oxaloacetate. *Biochim. Biophys. Acta* 292:582–91

50. Glynn, I. M., Karlish, S. J. D. 1975. The sodium pump. *Ann. Rev. Physiol.* 37:13–55

51. Gold, M., Spitzer, J. J. 1964. Metabolism of free fatty acids by myocardium and kidney. *Am. J. Physiol.* 206:153–58

51b. Goldin, S. M., Tong, S. W. 1974. Reconstitution of active transport catalyzed by the purified sodium and potassium ion-stimulated adenosine triphosphatase from canine renal medulla. *J. Biol. Chem.* 249:5907–15

52. Goldstein, L. 1967. Pathways of glutamine deamination and their control in the rat kidney. *Am. J. Physiol.* 213:983–89

53. Goldstein, L. 1975. Regulation of renal glutamine deamination. In *Symposium on Renal Metabolism. Med. Clin. N. Am.* 59:667–80

54. Goodman, A. D. 1972. Relationship of gluconeogenesis to ammonia production in the kidney. *Isr. J. Med. Sci.* 8:285–94

55. Goodman, A. D. 1973. Effect of acid-base changes and dehydration on renal medullary production of ammonia. *J. Lab. Clin. Med.* 81:905–18

56. Goodman, A. D., Fuisz, R. E., Cahill, G. F. 1966. Renal gluconeogenesis in acidosis, alkalosis and potassium deficiency: Its possible role in regulation of renal ammonia production. *J. Clin. Invest.* 45:612–19

57. Graf, J., Hohenegger, M. 1972. Autoradiographic pattern of ^{3}H-palmitate distribution in the mouse kidney. In *Biochemical Aspects of Kidney Function,* ed. M. Hohenegger, 18–86. Munich: Goldmann

58. Guder, W. G., Schmidt, U. 1974. The localization of gluconeogenesis in rat nephron. Determination of phosphoenolpyruvate carboxykinase in microdissected tubules. *Z. Physiol. Chem.* 355:273–78

59. Guder, W. G., Wieland, O. H., Stukowski, B. 1974. Metabolism of isolated kidney tubules. Regulation of pyruvate dehydrogenase by metabolic substrates. *Eur. J. Biochem.* 42:529–38

60. Györy, A. Z., Kinne, R. 1971. Energy sources for transepithelial sodium transport in rat renal proximal tubules. *Pfluegers Arch.* 327:234–60

61. Györy, A. Z., Brendel, U., Kinne, R. 1972. Effect of cardiac glycosides and sodium ethacrynate on transepithelial sodium transport in *in vivo* micropuncture experiments and on isolated plasma membrane Na-K-ATPase *in vitro* of the rat. *Pfluegers Arch.* 335:287–96

62. Handler, J. S., Preston, A. S., Orloff, J. 1969. The effect of aldosterone on glycolysis in the urinary bladder of the toad. *J. Biol. Chem.* 244:3194–99

63. Haslam, J. M., Krebs, H. A. 1968. The permeability of mitochondria to oxaloacetate and malate. *Biochem. J.* 107:659–67

64. Hayslett, J. P. et al 1973. Role of Na-K-ATPase in the renal reabsorption of sodium in the elasmobranch *Squalus acanthias. Comp. Biochem. Physiol. A* 44:417–22

65. Heidrich, H. G., Kinne, R., Kinne-Saffran, E., Hannig, K. 1972. The polarity of the proximal tubule cell in rat kidney. Different surface charges for the brush border microvilli and plasma membranes from the basal infoldings. *J. Cell Biol.* 54:232–45

66. Hems, D. A. 1972. Metabolism of glutamine and glutamic acid by isolated perfused kidneys of normal and acidotic rats. *Biochem. J.* 130:671–80

67. Hems, D. A., Brosnan, J. T. 1971. Effects of metabolic acidosis and starvation on the content of intermediary metabolites in rat kidney. *Biochem. J.* 123:391–97

68. Hems, D. A., Gaja, G. 1972. Carbohydrate metabolism in the isolated perfused rat kidney. *Biochem. J.* 128:421–26

69. Hilden, S., Rhee, H. M., Hokin, L. E. 1974. Sodium transport by phospholipid vesicles containing purified Na + K ion-activated adenosine triphosphatase. *J. Biol. Chem.* 249:7432–40

70. Hohenegger, M., Brechtelsbauer, H., Finsterer, U., Prueksunand, P. 1974. Effects of inhibitors of fatty acid oxidation on renal function *Pfluegers Arch.* 351:231–40

71. Hohenegger, M., Wittmann, G., Dahlheim, H. 1973. Oxidation of fatty acids by different zones of the rat kidney. *Pfluegers Arch.* 341:105–12

72. Inagaki, C., Lindenmayer, G. E., Schwartz, A. 1974. Effects of sodium and potassium on binding of ouabain to transport adenosine triphosphatase. *J. Biol. Chem.* 249:5135–40

73. Irias, J. J., Greenberg, R. E. 1972. Relationship of renal gluconeogenesis to control of ammonia formation. *Am. J. Physiol.* 223:750–55

74. Iynedjian, P. B., Ballard, J., Hanson, R. W. 1975. Induction of renal phosphoenolpyruvate carboxykinase (GTP) synthesis in acidosis. *Fed. Proc.* 34:408

75. Kalra, J., Brosnan, J. T. 1974. The subcellular localization of glutaminase isoenzymes in rat kidney cortex. *J. Biol. Chem.* 249:3255–60

76. Kamm, D. E., Strope, G. L. 1972. The effects of acidosis and alkalosis on the metabolism of glutamine and glutamate in renal cortex slices. *J. Clin. Invest.* 51:1251–63

77. Katz, A. I., Epstein, F. H. 1967. Role of sodium-potassium activated adenosine triphosphatase in reabsorption of sodium by kidney. *J. Clin. Invest.* 46:1999–2011

78. Katz, A. I., Epstein, F. H. 1968. Physiologic role of sodium-potassium-activated adenosine triphosphatase in the transport of cations across biological membranes. *N. Engl. J. Med.* 278:253–61

79. Katz, A. I., Epstein, F. H. 1971. Effect of anions on adenosine triphosphatase of kidney tissue. *Enzyme* 12:499–507

80. Kinne-Saffran, E., Kinne, R. 1974. Localization of a calcium-stimulated ATPase in the basal-lateral plasma membranes of the proximal tubule of rat kidney cortex. *J. Membr. Biol.* 17:263–74

81. Kinne-Saffran, E., Kinne, R. 1974. Presence of bicarbonate stimulated ATPase in the brush border microvillus membranes of the proximal tubule. *Proc. Soc. Exp. Biol. Med.* 146:751–53

82. Kirsten, E., Kirsten, R., Leaf, A., Sharp, G. W. G. 1968. Increased activity of enzymes of the tricarboxylic acid cycle in response to aldosterone in the toad bladder. *Pfluegers Arch.* 300:213–25

83. Kjekshus, J., Aukland, K., Kiil, F. 1969. Oxygen cost of sodium reabsorption in proximal and distal parts of the nephron. *Scand. J. Clin. Lab. Invest.* 23:307–16

84. Klahr, S., Yates, J., Bourgoignie, J. 1971. Inhibition of glycolysis by ethacrynic acid and furosemide. *Am. J. Physiol.* 221:1038–43

85. Kleinzeller, A. 1970. The specificity of the active sugar transport in kidney cortex cells. *Biochim. Biophys. Acta* 211:264–76

86. Kleinzeller, A., Ausiello, D. A., Almendares, J. A., Davis, A. H. 1970. The effect of pH on sugar transport and ion distribution in kidney cortex cells. *Biochim. Biophys. Acta* 211:293–307

87. Knox, F. G., Fleming, J. S., Rennie, D. W. 1966. Effects of osmotic diuresis on sodium reabsorption and oxygen consumption of kidney. *Am. J. Physiol.* 210:751–59

88. Kokko, J. P. 1973. Proximal tubule potential difference. Dependence on glucose, HCO_3^- and amino acids. *J. Clin. Invest.* 52:1362–67

89. Kokko, J. P., Rector, F. C. 1971. Flow dependence of transtubular potential difference in isolated perfused segments of rabbit proximal convoluted tubule. *J. Clin. Invest.* 50:2754–50

90. Kopyt, N., Narins, R. G. 1975. Stimulation by acidosis of a new renal ammoniagenic pathway. *Clin. Res.* 23:367A

91. Kopyt, N., Narins, R. G., Whereat, A., Relman, A. S. 1974. Regulation of mitochondrial transport of malate by pH, a possible control of ammoniagenesis. *Clin. Res.* 22:535A

92. Kovacevic, Z. 1974. Distribution of glutaminase isoenzymes in kidney cells. *Biochim. Biophys. Acta* 334:199–207

93. Kovacevic, Z., McGivan, J. D., Chappell, J. B. 1970. Conditions for activity of glutaminase in kidney mitochondria. *Biochem. J.* 118:265–74

94. Kranhold, J. F., Loh, D., Morris, R. C. Jr. 1969. Renal fructose metabolizing enzymes: Significance in hereditary fructose intolerance. *Science* 165:402–3

95. Krebs, H. A. 1963. Renal gluconeogenesis. *Adv. Enzyme Regul.* 1:385–400

96. Krebs, H. A. 1970. Rate control of the tricarboxylic acid cycle. *Advan. Enzyme Regul.* 8:335–53

97. Krebs, H. A., Hems, R., Weidemann, M. J., Speake, R. N. 1966. The fate of isotopic carbon in kidney cortex synthesizing glucose from lactate. *Biochem. J.* 101:242–49

98. Kurokawa, K., Rasmussen, H. 1973. Ionic control of gluconeogenesis. I. The interrelated effect of calcium and hydrogen ions. *Biochim. Biophys. Acta* 313:17–31

99. Lassen, N. A., Munck, O., Thaysen, J. H. 1961. Oxygen consumption and sodium reabsorption in the kidney. *Acta Physiol. Scand.* 51:371–84

100. Leaf, A., Anderson, J., Page, L. B. 1958. Active sodium transport by the isolated toad bladder. *J. Gen. Physiol.* 41:657–68

101. Leal-Pinto, E., Park, H. C., King, F., MacLeod, M., Pitts, R. F. 1973. Metabolism of lactate by the intact functioning kidney of the dog. *Am. J. Physiol.* 224:1463–67

102. Lee, J. B., Peter, H. M. 1969. Effect of oxygen tension on glucose metabolism in rabbit kidney cortex and medulla. *Am. J. Physiol.* 217:1464–71

103. Lee, J. B., Vance, V. K., Cahill, G. F. Jr. 1962. Metabolism of C^{14} labelled sub-

strates by rabbit kidney cortex and medulla. *Am. J. Physiol.* 203:27–36

104. Lewy, P. R., Quintanilla, A., Levin, N. W., Kessler, R. H. 1973. Renal energy metabolism and sodium reabsorption. *Ann. Rev. Med.* 24:365–84

105. Lie, M., Johannesen, J., Kiil, F. 1973. Glomerulotubular balance and renal metabolic rate. *Am. J. Physiol.* 225:1186–86

106. Longshaw, I. D., Alleyne, G. A. O., Pogson, C. I. 1972. The effect of steroids and ammonium chloride acidosis on phosphoenolpyruvate carboxykinase in rat kidney cortex. II. The kinetics of enzyme induction. *J. Clin. Invest.* 51:2284–91

107. Longshaw, I. D., Pogson, C. I. 1972. The effect of steroids and ammonium chloride acidosis on phosphoenolpyruvate carboxykinase in rat kidney cortex. I. Differentiation of the inductive processes and characterization of enzyme activities. *J. Clin. Invest.* 51:2277–83

108. Lorentz, W. B., Lassiter, W. E., Gottschalk, C. W. 1972. Renal tubular permeability during increased intrarenal pressure. *J. Clin. Invest.* 51:484–92

109. Lowry, O. H., Passonneau, J. V. 1972. *A Flexible System of Enzymatic Analysis.* New York: Academic 221–60

110. Martinez-Maldonado, M., Eknoyan, G., Suki, W. N. 1970. Importance of aerotic and anaerobic metabolism in renal concentration and dilution. *Am. J. Physiol.* 218:1076–81

111. Mattenheimer, H. 1967. Enzymology of kidney tissue. In *Enzymes in Urine and Kidney.* ed. W. C. Dubach, Chap. 5, 119–45. Berne: Huber

112. Maude, D. L. 1969. Effects of K and ouabain on fluid transport and cell Na in proximal tubule in vitro. *Am. J. Physiol.* 216:1199–1206

113. Maxild, J. 1971. Role of fatty acid metabolism on renal transport of *p*-aminohippurate in vitro. *Biochim. Biophys. Acta* 233:434–45

114. McCann, W. P. 1962. Renal glucose production and uptake in separate sites, and its significance. *Am. J. Physiol.* 203:572–76

115. McCann, W. P., Gulati, O. D., Stanton, H. C. 1961. Renal glucose metabolism during diuresis induced by infusions of hypotonic saline, *Bull. Johns Hopkins Hosp.* 103:77–93

116. Morel, F., deRouffignac, C. 1973. Kidney. *Ann. Rev. Physiol.* 35:17–54

117. Morris, R. C. Jr. 1968. An experimental renal acidification defect in patients with hereditary fructose intolerance. I. Its resemblance to renal tubular acidosis. *J. Clin. Invest.* 47:1389–98

118. Mudge, G. H., Taggart, J. V. 1950. Effect of 2,4-dinitrophenol on renal transport mechanisms in the dog. *Am. J. Physiol.* 161:173–80

119. Nagata, N., Rasmussen, H. 1970. Parathyroid hormone, 3'5'-AMP, Ca^{++} and renal gluconeogenesis. *Proc. Nat. Acad. Sci. USA* 65:368–74

120. Narins, R. G., Relman, A. S. 1974. Acute effects of acidosis on ammoniagenic pathways in the kidneys of the intact rat. *Am. J. Physiol.* 227:946–49

121. Nechay, B. R., Nelson, J. A. 1970. Renal ouabain-sensitive adenosine triphosphatase activity and Na^+ reabsorption. *J. Pharmacol. Exp. Ther.* 175:717–26

122. Needleman, P., Passonneau, J. V., Lowry, O. H. 1968. Distribution of glucose and related metabolites in rat kidney. *Am. J. Physiol.* 215:655–59

123. Newburgh, J. D. 1943. The changes which alter renal osmotic work. *J. Clin. Invest.* 22:439–46

124. Newsholme, E. A., Gevers, W. 1967. Control of glycolysis and gluconeogenesis in liver and kidney cortex. *Vitam. Horm.* 25:1–87

125. Nicholson, T. F. 1949. Renal function as affected by experimental unilateral kidney lesions. II. The effect of cyanide. *Biochem. J.* 45:112–15

126. Nieth, H., Scholmeyer, P. 1966. Substrate utilization of the human kidney. *Nature* 209:1244–45

127. Nishiitsutsuji-Uwo, J. M. Ross, B. D., Krebs, H. A. 1967. Metabolic activities of the isolated perfused rat kidney. *Biochem. J.* 103:852–62

128. Orloff, J., Burg, M. 1971. Kidney. *Ann. Rev. Physiol.* 33:83–130

129. Park, H. C., Leal-Pinto, E., MacLeod, M. B., Pitts, R. F. 1974. CO_2 production from plasma free fatty acids by the intact functioning kidney of the dog. *Am. J. Physiol.* 227:1192–98

130. Pilkington, L. A., O'Donovan, D. J. 1971. Metabolism of glutamine in cortex slices from dog kidney during acid-base alterations. *Am. J. Physiol.* 220:1634–39

131. Pitts, R. F. 1972. Control of renal production of ammonia. *Kidney Int.* 1:297–305

132. Pitts, R. F. 1973. Production and excretion of ammonia in relation to acid-base regulation. *Handb. Physiol. Sect. 8, Renal Physiol.,* Chap. 15, 455–96

133. Pitts, R. F., MacLeod, M. B. 1975. Metabolism of blood glucose by the intact functioning kidney of dog. *Kidney Int.* 7:130–36

134. Pitts, R. F., Pilkington, L. A., MacLeod, M. B., Leal-Pinto, E. 1972. Metabolism of glutamine by the intact functioning kidney of the dog. *J. Clin. Invest.* 51:557–65

135. Pollack, V. E., Mattenheimer, H., DeBruin, H., Weinman, K. J. 1965. Experimental metabolic acidosis: the enzymatic basis of ammonia production by the dog kidney. *J. Clin. Invest.* 44:169–81

136. Preuss, H. G., Baird, K., Goldin, H. 1974. Oxygen consumption and ammoniagenesis in isolated dog renal tubules. *J. Lab. Clin. Med.* 83:937–46

137. Preuss, H. G., Vivatsi-Manos, O., Vertuno, L. L. 1973. Effects of glutamine deamination on glutamine deamidation in rat kidney slices. *J. Clin. Invest.* 52:755–64

138. Preuss, H. G., Vavatsi-Manos, O., Vertuno, L., Baird, K. 1974. The effects of pH change on renal ammoniagenesis in vitro. *Proc. Soc. Exp. Biol. Med.* 146:803–8

139. Relman, A. S., Narins, R. G. 1974. The control of ammonia production in the rat. In *Symposium on Renal Metabolism. Med. Clin. N. Am.* 59:583–93

140. Roobol, A., Alleyne, G. A. O. 1974. Control of renal cortex ammoniagenesis and its relationship to renal cortex gluconeogenesis. *Biochim. Biophys. Acta* 362:83–91

141. Ross, B. D., Epstein, F. H., Leaf, A. 1973. Sodium reabsorption in the perfused rat kidney. *Am. J. Physiol.* 225:1165–71

142. Ross, B., Leaf, A., Silva, P. Epstein, F. H. 1974. Na-K-ATPase in sodium transport by the perfused rat kidney. *Am. J. Physiol.* 226:624–29

143. Roxe, D. 1972. Renal gluconeogenesis after NH_4Cl, $NaHCO_3$, hypoglycemia, or pregnancy. *Am. J. Physiol.* 222:55–60

144. Roxe, D. M., Schreiner, G. E., Preuss, H. G. 1973. Regulation of renal gluconeogenesis and ammoniagenesis by physiologic fuels. *Am. J. Physiol.* 225:908–11

145. Sacktor, B., Berger, S. J. 1969. Formation of trehalose from glucose in the renal cortex. *Biochem. Biophys. Res. Commun.* 35:796–800

146. Schmidt, U., Dubach, U. C. 1969. Activity of (Na-K)-stimulated adenosine triphosphatase in the rat nephron. *Pfluegers Arch.* 306:219–26

147. Schmidt, U., Dubach, U. C. 1971. Na-K-stimulated adenosine triphosphatase: Intracellular localization within the proximal tubules of the rat nephron. *Pfluegers Arch.* 330:265–70

148. Schmidt, U., Schmid, H., Funk, B., Dubach, U. C. 1974. The function of Na-K-ATPase in single portions of the rat nephron. *Ann. NY Acad. Sci.* 242:489–500

149. Schurek, H. J., Brecht, J. P., Lohfert, H., Hierholzer, K. 1975. The basic requirements for the function of the isolated cell free perfused rat kidney. *Pfluegers Arch.* 354:349–65

150. Schwartz, I. L., Shlatz, L. J., Kinne-Saffran, E., Kinne, R. 1974. Target cell polarity and membrane phosphorylation in relation to mechanism of action of antidiuretic hormone. *Proc. Nat. Acad. Sci. USA* 74:2595–99

151. Silva, P., Hayslett, J. P., Epstein, F. H. 1973. The role of Na-K-activated adenosine triphosphatase in potassium adaptation: stimulation of enzymatic activity by potassium loading. *J. Clin. Invest.* 52:2665–71

152. Silverman, M., Aganon, M. A., Chinard, F. P. 1970. D-Glucose interactions with renal tubule cell surfaces. *Am. J. Physiol.* 218:735–42

153. Simpson, D. P. 1972. Pathways of glutamine and organic acid metabolism in renal cortex in chronic metabolic acidosis. *J. Clin. Invest.* 51:1969–78

154. Simpson, D. P., Sherrard, D. J. 1969. Regulation of glutamine metabolism in vitro by bicarbonate ion and pH. *J. Clin. Invest.* 48:1088–96

155. Skou, J. C. 1965. Enzymatic basis for active transport of Na^+ and K^+ across cell membrane. *Physiol. Rev.* 45:596–617

156. Starling, E. H., Verney, E. B. 1925. The secretion of urine as studied in the isolated kidney. *Proc. R. Soc. London Ser. B* 97:321–63

157. Strickler, J. C., Kessler, R. H. 1963. Effect of certain inhibitors on renal excretion of salt and water. *Am. J. Physiol.* 205:117–22

158. Stucki, J. W., Brawand, F., Walter, P. 1972. Regulation of pyruvate metabolism in rat-liver mitochondria by adenine nucleotides and fatty acids. *Eur. J. Biochem.* 27:181–91

159. Taggart, J. V. 1958. Mechanisms of renal tubular transport. *Am. J. Med.* 24:774–84

160. Taylor, A., Mamelak, M., Reaven, E., Maffly, R. 1973. Vasopressin: possible role of microtubules and microfilaments in its action. *Science* 181:347–49

161. Thurau, K. 1961. Renal Na-reabsorption and O_2-uptake in dogs during hypoxia and hydrochlorothiazide infusion. *Proc. Soc. Exp. Biol. Med.* 106:714–17

162. Torelli, G., Milla, E., Faelli, A., Constantini, S. 1966. Energy requirement for sodium reabsorption in the in vivo rabbit kidney. *Am. J. Physiol.* 211:576–80

163. Torretti, J., Hendler, E., Weinstein, E., Longnecker, R. E., Epstein, F. H. 1972. Functional significance of Na-K-ATPase in the kidney. Effects of ouabain inhibition. *Am. J. Physiol.* 222:1398–1405

164. Trimble, M. E., Bowman, R. H. 1973. Renal Na^+ and K^+ transport: Effects of glucose, palmitate and α-bromopalmitate. *Am. J. Physiol.* 225:1057–62

165. Underwood, A. H., Newsholme, E. A. 1967. Control of glycolysis and gluconeogenesis in rat kidney cortex slices. *Biochem. J.* 104:300–5

166. Ussing, H. H., Zerahn, K. 1951. Active transport of sodium as the source of electric current in short-circuited isolated frog skin. *Acta Physiol. Scand.* 23:110–27

167. Vancura, P., Malt, R.A., 1973. Aerobic and anaerobic energy metabolism in compensatory renal hypertrophy. *Am. J. Physiol.* 225:281–86

168. Van Handel, E. 1969. Do trehalose and trehalasc function in renal glucose transport? *Science* 163:1075–76

169. Van Slyke, D. D., Rhoads, C. P., Hiller, A., Alving, A. S. 1934. Relationship between urea excretion, renal blood flow, renal oxygen consumption and diuresis. *Am. J. Physiol.* 109:336–74

170. Waldman, R. H., Burch, H. B. 1963. Rapid method for the study of enzyme distribution in rat kidney. *Am. J. Physiol.* 204:749–52

171. Walton, K. G., DeLorenzo, R. J., Curran, P. F., Greengard, P. 1975. Regulation of protein phosphorylation and sodium transport in toad bladder. *J. Gen. Physiol.* 65:153–77

172. Weidemann, M. J., Krebs, H. A. 1969. The fuel of respiration of rat kidney cortex. *Biochem. J.* 112:149–66

173. Weiner, I. M., Roth, L., Skulan, T. W. 1971. Effect of dinitrophenol and cyanide on T_{PAH} and sodium reabsorption. *Am. J. Physiol.* 221:86–91

174. Weinstein, S. W. 1970. Proximal tubule energy metabolism, sodium transport, and permeability in the rat. *Am. J. Physiol.* 219:978–81

175. Weinstein, S. W. 1972. Micropuncture studies on renal tubular effects of 2,4,-dinitrophenol in the rat. *Am. J. Physiol.* 223:583–87

176. Weinstein, S. W., Klose, R. M. 1969. Micropuncture studies on energy metabolism and sodium transport in the mammalian nephron. *Am. J. Physiol.* 217:498–503

177. Weinstein, S. W., Szyjewicz, J. 1974. Individual nephron function and renal oxygen consumption in the rat. *Am. J. Physiol.* 227:171–77

178. Welbourne, T. C. 1974. Ammonia production and pathways of glutamine metabolism in the isolated perfused rat kidney. *Am. J. Physiol.* 226:544–48

179. Wheeler, K. P., Whittam, R. 1964. Structural and enzymatic aspects of hydrolysis of adenosine triphosphate by membranes of kidney cortex and erythrocytes. *Biochem. J.* 93:349–63

180. Windhager, E. E., Giebisch, G. 1965. Electrophysiology of the nephron. *Physiol. Rev.* 45:214–44

181. Wolf, A. V. 1941. Total renal blood flow at any urine flow rate or extraction fraction. *Am. J. Physiol.* 133:496–97

182. Wright, F. S., Strieder, N., Fowler, N. B., Giebisch, G. 1971. Potassium secretion by distal tubule after potassium adaptation. *Am. J. Physiol.* 221:437–48

PULMONARY GAS EXCHANGE[1]   ❖1143

Robert E. Forster and Edward D. Crandall

Departments of Physiology and Medicine, School of Medicine, University of Pennsylvania, Philadelphia, Pennsylvania 19174

INTRODUCTION

This review includes certain articles on respiratory gas exchange in alveoli published from 1971 through 1974 of particular interest to and considered important by the authors. For convenience the articles are discussed in five groups: methodological aspects of pulmonary diffusing capacity of the lung (D_L); physiological variables affecting D_L; nonuniformity, including stratification; alveolar-arterial partial pressure gradients; and CO_2, O_2, and CO exchanges and reactions within the blood. Clinical aspects of respiratory gas exchange are not included, nor is gas exchange in tissues. This review essentially picks up where that of Piiper & Scheid (58) in this series left off.

In the course of reviewing the literature, it appeared remarkable that so many studies on D_L continue to be done, long after the scientific novelty has worn off. Can it be that this measurement is useful?

In accordance with past policy of this series and in view of the restrictions on length, we have markedly limited the scope of the review. We have attempted to include all pertinent important papers for the period covered, but if we have missed any, our apologies to those authors now.

METHODOLOGICAL ASPECTS OF PULMONARY DIFFUSING CAPACITY

Morphometric Techniques

A significant advance has been made in the study of diffusional gas exchange in the lung by the development of techniques for the calculation of alveolar and capillary surface area and capillary blood volume (Vc) from morphometric measurements on histological lung sections. The methods have been worked out for the lung largely by Weibel and colleagues (81–84) and consist basically of: (*a*) calculating the total capillary surface area from a statistical measurement of the number of intercepts of capillary walls with a standard test line superimposed on the microscopic section

[1]This study was supported in part by US Public Health Service Grant R01 HL 4108.

69

of the septa and (b) calculating total surface area of the alveoli from a similar statistic on the intersections of the septal surface with a test line. The diffusing capacity (DL) can be calculated as the sum of the reciprocals of the conductances of the components of the diffusion path from alveolar gas to hemoglobin molecule (alveolar surface lining; pulmonary membrane tissue, including epithelium, basement membrane, and endothelium; plasma; and red cell). Each conductance equals area times specific permeability/thickness. By morphometrics the surface area and the effective average thickness can be obtained from histological sections. The specific permeabilities (or reaction velocity constant for red cells) of the several layers can be obtained with sufficient precision from the literature.

The agreement between the morphometric estimates of lung parameters and those obtained by direct measurement is striking. For example, Vc in a tall man ranged between 120 and 160 ml, comparable to values obtained from DL,CO measurements in the literature. These results give confidence in the use of the morphometric techniques to investigate the effect of physiological variables on DL.

Membrane diffusing capacity (DM) and D_{L,O_2} were found to be approximately linear functions of body weight in the dog (68). An extension of these studies to a series of animals of varying size from the shrew to the dog showed that a similar relationship held among animals of different species (82). The effects of varying inflation pressures and of regional differences were also investigated (25, 84) in the dog lung.

Vreim & Staub (77), working with anesthetized, open-thorax cats, determined indirect Vc from breath-holding measurements of DL,CO at 2 levels of alveolar P_{O_2} in the manner of Roughton & Forster (65). They compared these values with direct Vc obtained by microscopic measurements of total alveolar surface area, average wall thickness, and red cell volume/alveolar wall volume in quick-frozen lung sections. Indirect Vc averaged 3.7 ml and average direct Vc was 4.5 ml; the difference was significant. Total alveolar wall volume averaged 8.2 ml; thus the capillary blood represents about half the volume of the alveolar septa. Thirty minutes of breathing either 100% O_2 or 10% O_2 had no significant effect on Vc. The authors concluded that the difference in the results using the two methods was explicable on methodologic grounds and that either method would provide a reliable estimate of Vc. It is useful to have the theory of the indirect method validated by direct experimentation.

These same authors investigated the effect of changes in pulmonary capillary blood flow on DL as observed by microscopic measurements in anesthetized cats (78). Tying off the pulmonary artery to the left lower lobe, corresponding to West's Zone I conditions, decreased its Vc by half. Tying the pulmonary vein from the left lower lobe, corresponding to West's Zone III conditions, increased its Vc by 50%.

Gas Exchange Methods for Measuring D_{L,O_2}

STEADY-STATE METHODS FOR D_{L,O_2} The gradients between alveolar and arterial $P_{O_2} [\Delta P_{O_2} (A-a)]$ at high ($\sim$100 mm Hg) and low ($\sim$50 mm Hg) alveolar P_{O_2} can be subdivided by the Lilienthal-Riley method into venous admixture (shunt + $V_A/\dot{Q}$ unevenness) and diffusion (alveolar to end-capillary P_{O_2}) components; this requires the assumption that the venous admixture component is markedly reduced at the low alveolar Po_2. Riley & Permut (61), under stimulation from West, reevaluated this classic assumption by computing the venous admixture component of a two-compartment lung model and found that if ventilation were even, but blood flow varied, the venous admixture component was the same or even larger at low alveolar Po_2 as compared to high alveolar Po_2. Thus it appears that the Lilienthal-Riley analysis may overestimate the alveolar to end-capillary Po_2 difference and therefore the average ΔPo_2 (A–a) at low alveolar Po_2, resulting in an underestimation of D_{L,O_2}. If blood flow were even and ventilation varied, the venous admixture component of ΔPo_2 (A–a) decreased at low alveolar Po_2, just as Lilienthal & Riley had expected. These authors appreciated the effect of the shape of the Hb-O_2 equilibrium curve on venous admixture, but their use of a three-compartment model gave them, apparently by mathematical coincidence, an erroneous impression of the general case. All those who indulge in numerical computations should note this danger.

Cohen et al (12) approached the determination of the critical end-capillary gradient by reducing to zero the true shunt and uneven V_A/Q contributions to the Po_2 (A–a) gradient, so that the residual measured ΔPo_2 (A–a) equals the end-capillary gradient. According to theory, when $F_{I,O_2} = 1$ (that is, when inspired $F_{N_2} = 0$), the respiratory exchange ratio of every alveolus becomes the same, and nonuniformity of V_A/Q no longer produces a contribution to the (A–a) gradient. If alveolar Po_2 is reduced to the linear part of the Hb-O_2 equilibrium curve as well, the true shunt contribution to ΔPo_2 (A–a) also disappears. These requirements were met in normal male subjects at rest by having them breathe 100% O_2 at a reduced ambient pressure so that arterial Po_2 was 59 mm Hg; under these circumstances the measured (A–a) gradient averaged 0 mm Hg. When the subjects breathed 14% O_2 at sea level pressure, arterial Po_2 was again about 59 mm Hg, but in this case the ΔPo_2 (A–a) was 9 mm Hg. The authors concluded that the normal alveolar to end-capillary Po_2 difference due to diffusion at this low alveolar Po_2 was negligible. This is in disagreement with the rebreathing estimates of D_{L,O_2} (10) and the results of Weiskopf & Severinghaus (85). The latter found that after two days at an altitude of 4380 m and a P_{A,O_2} of 52 mm Hg that the entire experimentally measured ΔPo_2 (A–a) could be explained by the diffusion end-gradient in the capillary. However, the end-gradient by the rebreathing method is only several mm Hg at this alveolar Po_2 and Cohen et al (12) are under a severe handicap to achieve this order of accuracy in comparing an arterial Po_2 with an alveolar Po_2.

Rosenhamer et al (62) have reported a bloodless and approximate method for the estimation of D_{L,O_2} in the exercising subject. During heavy exercise and few seconds of hypoxia, an ear oximeter is used to provide an arterial HbO_2 saturation, which is then converted to a Po_2 using the hemoglobin-O_2 equilibrium curve. This Po_2 is compared with a simultaneous end-expiratory alveolar Po_2. By means of a series of reasonable assumptions it was possible to calculate an average D_{L,O_2} during exercise + hypoxia of 77 ml min^{-1} (mm Hg)$^{-1}$, not an unreasonable value. The method ignores the possible contributions of changes in V_A/Q to the (A–a) gradient and would appear to be of limited applicability in precise measurements of D_{L,O_2}.

REBREATHING METHOD FOR D_{L,O_2} Micheli & Haab (51), Piiper and colleagues (57), and Cerretelli et al (10) have reported an ingenious and relatively simple rebreathing technique for estimating D_{L,O_2} in man and animals. P_{O_2} is continuously measured at the mouth while the subject rebreathes from a bag system, first a mixture containing N_2O and then a low P_{O_2} gas. Reduced to its simplest terms the method consists of calculating end-capillary P_{O_2}, the critical datum in any method for D_{L,O_2}, by adding the pulmonary arteriovenous P_{O_2} difference to mixed venous P_{O_2}. Arteriovenous P_{O_2} difference is obtained from instantaneous O_2 uptake divided by pulmonary blood flow ($\dot{Q}c$) and by the effective solubility of O_2 in blood, αO_2. This last approximates the slope of the O_2-Hb equilibrium curve between mixed venous and alveolar P_{O_2}, and was represented by a single value (a reasonable assumption when alveolar P_{O_2} is low and close to mixed venous P_{O_2}). Mixed venous P_{O_2} is obtained by extrapolating a plot of instantaneous O_2 uptake against alveolar P_{O_2} to zero. Pulmonary blood flow is calculated from the uptake of N_2O from the rebreathing volume. Because effective O_2 solubility in blood is constant along the capillary, the Bohr integration becomes a simple exponential process and end-capillary P_{O_2} equals

$$\text{(alveolar } P_{O_2} - \text{mixed venous } P_{O_2}) \exp(-D_{L,O_2}/\dot{Q}\alpha O_2) + \text{alveolar } P_{O_2} \qquad 1.$$

Alveolar, end-capillary, and mixed venous P_{O_2}, $\dot{Q}$, and αO_2 are known, so D_{L,O_2} can be calculated.

It is difficult to measure D_{L,O_2} experimentally because the alveolar to end-capillary P_{O_2} difference is so small. The rebreathing D_{L,O_2} has a major advantage in this regard. Mixed venous and end-capillary P_{O_2} are calculated as increments from alveolar P_{O_2}, causing several potential errors to cancel out and eliminating those related to the differences between mixed arterial P_{O_2} and end-capillary P_{O_2}.

The most recent values of D_{L,O_2} rebreathing for seated man at rest averaged 31 ml min^{-1} (mm Hg)$^{-1}$, to be compared with 25 ml min^{-1} (mm Hg)$^{-1}$ using the single breath $^{18}O_2$ method. The $^{18}O_2$ technique is based on the same principle of calculating the end-capillary P_{O_2} in reference to alveolar P_{O_2} with the added advantage, and complication, that mixed venous blood has a minimal [$^{18}O_2$] amplifying the alveolar to end-capillary $P^{18}O_2$ difference.

The major practical disadvantage of the rebreathing D_{L,O_2} is that the measurements have to be performed during brief, but severe, arterial hypoxia, and require a well-trained subject.

Adaro et al (1) extended the application of the rebreathing D_{L,O_2} technique to isolated lung lobes in anesthetized dogs. Scheid et al (66) from the same laboratory then compared rebreathing estimates of D_{L,O_2} with steady-state measurements. In 10 anesthetized dogs (average weight 22.5 kg), D_{L,O_2} calculated by the rebreathing method (which required artificial ventilation) was 19 ml min^{-1} (mm Hg)$^{-1}$ as compared with 26 ml min^{-1} (mm Hg)$^{-1}$ for the steady-state technique in which the anesthetized animals breathed spontaneously. The difference in the results between the two methods led Scheid et al to explore the effect of inhomogeneities in a two-compartment model. The theoretical predictions were that nonuniformity would produce an estimate of D_{L,O_2} less than the true value for both methods, except for steady-state D_{L,O_2} in which alveolar P_{O_2} was computed from arterial P_{CO_2} ("ideal").

A major error in the rebreathing technique is the assumption that the gas in the rebreathing bag is of the same composition as alveolar gas; this also implies homogeneity in the lung alveolar gas itself. Scheid et al (66) derived a factor involving rebreathing ventilation and lung gas volume that corrects, at least in part, for this limitation. Even so D_{L,O_2} rebreathing was reduced by the several types of nonuniformity tested to a greater extent than was steady-state D_{L,O_2}.

A partial rebreathing technique, combining breath-holding and rebreathing, has been devised by Nishida and associates (54). The subject makes a maximal inspiration from a bag-in-box and then rebreathes over about 15 sec from a smaller bag in the same box. This technique maintains the maximal lung volume and the end expiratory lung volume constant during rebreathing. The values for D_L, D_M, and V_c are similar to those in the literature.

BREATH-HOLDING METHOD FOR D_{L,O_2} Gong et al (26) measured the disappearance of CO, C_2H_2, and $^{18}O_2$ during breath-holding in six normal healthy males seated at rest with alveolar P_{O_2} averaging 42 mm Hg, the same as that of mixed venous blood. From these data, they calculated $D_{L,CO}$ and pulmonary capillary blood flow, and from the latter plus the disappearance of $^{18}O_2$ they calculated the breath-holding D_{L,O_2}. $D_{L,CO}$ averaged 54 ml min^{-1} (mm Hg)$^{-1}$ at this low alveolar P_{O_2} while D_{L,O_2} averaged only 33 ml min^{-1} (mm Hg)$^{-1}$. The value of D_{L,O_2} expected from the value of $D_{L,CO}$ according to the Roughton-Forster relationship, using estimates of D_M/V_c and θ_{CO} from the literature, was 82 ml min^{-1} (mm Hg)$^{-1}$. The authors concluded that the best explanation for the relatively low D_{L,O_2} found experimentally was uneven distribution of $D_L/\dot{Q}$, which would be expected to affect D_{L,O_2} much more than $D_{L,CO}$. There was, incidentally, no difference between the values obtained using doubly labeled O_2, $^{18}O_2$, and those reported for singly labeled O_2, $^{18}O^{16}O$.

Gas Exchange Methods for $D_{L,CO}$

The mass spectrometer with its rapid response and continuous output should be an ideal instrument for the analysis of CO in the measurement of D_L. However, the molecular weight of $^{14}N_2$ is greater than that of $^{12}C^{16}O$ by only 1 part in 10,000 a separation beyond the resolution of most instruments. In addition $^{12}C^{16}O$ is produced by the oxidation of carbides in some mass spectrometers. Wagner, Mazzone & West (79) have used an isotopic form of CO, $^{12}C^{18}O$, with a molecular weight of 30 to measure D_L with a respiratory mass spectrometer, as there is no significant concentration of an interfering isotope in normal respiratory gases. Their instrument was a 4-channel apparatus with a noise level of 0.0015% $^{12}C^{18}O$ at a 95% response time of 0.05–0.08 sec, which permitted them to follow the expired $^{12}C^{18}O$ concentration continuously at the mouth.

By following $^{12}C^{18}O$ and argon (inert tracer) concentrations continuously at the mouth during expiration after a single-breath $D_{L,CO}$ maneuver with these two gases, they are able to calculate $D_{L,CO}$ for each volume of expired alveolar gas. As reported in the past by others, $D_{L,CO}$ tended to increase as alveolar gas was sampled later in expiration. Most of this increase was eliminated if the average alveolar volume during the breath-holding period up to the instant of expired alveolar analysis were used for the calculation. There was also a marked drop in $D_{L,CO}$ at the extreme end of expiration, presumably caused by a greater proportional delivery of alveolar gas from the upper zones whose lower D_L/V_A results from closure of the small airways to the lower zone alveoli. Anatomical dead space for CO was practically the same as that for argon.

PHYSIOLOGICAL VARIABLES AFFECTING D_L

Pulmonary Blood Flow and Exercise

In considering the mechanism of the increase in D_L with exercise that is reported by all techniques, the older experiments of Kötter et al (44) and of Piiper and colleagues (56) should not be forgotten. Kötter et al (44) found that breath-holding $D_{L,CO}$ in the anesthetized resting dog increased only 15% with a dose of DNP that was found to increase oxygen consumption 7-fold and pulmonary blood flow 2.5-fold. Because the fall in alveolar P_{O_2} that must have occurred would have increased θ_{CO} and D_L in addition to any effect of the increased pulmonary blood flow, the authors reasonably concluded that an increased oxygen consumption per se does not increase the true D_L. In contrast, the finding of Piiper et al (56) that DNP markedly increased steady-state D_{L,O_2}, led Piiper (55) to examine theoretically the effect of an increase in oxygen consumption on measured D_{L,O_2} in a nonuniform lung. He came to the important and general conclusion that, while inhomogeneity of D_L/Q and V_A/Q decreases experimentally determined D_{L,O_2}/true D_{L,O_2}, an increase in O_2 consumption, necessarily accompanied by some increase in alveolar ventilation and pulmonary blood flow, increases this ratio. This raises the important question as to whether exercise increases true D_{L,O_2} (that is, the area of the capillary bed) or whether it acts by reducing the attenuating effect of lung nonuniformity.

Cross et al (13), using the technique of Gong et al (26) above, measured $D_{L,CO}$ and D_{L,O_2} at rest and and at moderate exercise (100 W) in 5 normal subjects. $D_{L,CO}$ increased only from 45 to 49 ml min^{-1} (mm Hg)$^{-1}$ with exercise, while D_{L,O_2} increased from 25 to 43 ml min^{-1} (mm Hg)$^{-1}$. The ratio of experimentally determined D_{L,O_2} to that predicted from $D_{L,CO}$ rose from 0.37 at rest to 0.6 during exercise, using assumed rather than measured values of D_M, V_C, θ_{O_2}, and θ_{CO}. Uneven D_L/Q was the primary cause of the discrepancy: with increased pulmonary blood flow the relation of distribution of blood flow to D_L within the lung improved, as is generally the case. Several possible causes of the uneven D_L/Q, such as gravitational forces, pulsatile blood flow, and structural inhomogeneities were postulated. It is not clear why the $D_{L,CO}$ increases so little on exercise.

Gurtner & Fowler (30) reported that $D_{L,CO}$ in normal subjects in the supine position, measured by either rebreathing, breath-holding, or steady-state techniques, did not increase with exercise up to 2 l min^{-1} O_2 consumption as long as alveolar volume was kept constant, but did not increase with increasing alveolar volume. This is a striking finding in view of the large number of reports that $D_{L,CO}$ increases significantly with increasing pulmonary blood flow. $D_{L,CO}$ at rest in the erect position increased with alveolar volume, but to a lesser extent, and did increase markedly with exercise. Alveolar P_{CO} fell exponentially with time during breath-holding in the supine position either at rest or during exercise and in the erect position during exercise, but not in the erect position at rest. This is interpreted to mean that D_L/V_A is uniform throughout the lung in the first three conditions, but nonuniform in the last. Gurtner & Fowler went on to study the distribution of Q/V_A in the lung using intravenous and inspired radio-Xenon and external counters on the chest. They found that Q/V_A is more uniform at low lung volumes and higher total pulmonary blood flows. These results suggest that once the capillary bed is fully distended, as by hydrostatic pressure or blood flow, $D_{L,CO}$ becomes dependent only on alveolar volume. The mechanism by which this occurs at constant capillary pressure is not clear.

Lawson (46) measured breath-holding $D_{L,CO}$ and inert gas $\dot{Q}$ in the erect position before and after maneuvers and the administration of drugs that might be expected to increase pulmonary blood flow (e.g. hypoxia, hyperventilation, infusions of epinephrine and isoproterenol, and the release of a Valsalva maneuver). Pulmonary blood flow and D_L increased equivalently during all these procedures with the possible exception of hypoxia, during which the rate of increase of $D_{L,CO}$ was relatively greater than the increase in pulmonary blood flow. Control $D_{L,CO}$ and its value after hypoxia were both measured at an alveolar P_{O_2} around 50 mm Hg, which increased the absolute value of $D_{L,CO}$ and may have altered $dD_{L,CO}/d\dot{Q}$. This report adds to the number of observations where D_L increases as a function of pulmonary blood flow.

The possibility of achieving a true maximal lung-diffusing capacity by increasing pulmonary blood flow has always tantalized investigators from Barcroft onward because of the need to assess the total capillary bed in the lung. Aside from the original work of Riley and collaborators on D_{L,O_2}, few have found diffusing capacity to reach a plateau with achievable cardiac outputs. Andrew & Baines (3) are no exception. Measuring steady-state $D_{L,CO}$ with an assumed dead space for the calculation of alveolar P_{CO}, they did not find a plateau for $D_{L,CO}$ up to an oxygen consumption of more than 4 l min^{-1} and a cardiac output of over 32 l min^{-1}.

Barlett et al (4) sought the best method for predicting the increase in steady-state end-tidal $D_{L,CO}$ with exercise and concluded that empirical expression

$$D_{L,CO}, ex = D_{L,CO}, rest \frac{(\text{thickness of pulmonary membrane})^2}{\text{surface area}} \qquad 2.$$

was the best, with a correlation coefficient of 0.81 and SE of ± 9.3 ml min^{-1} (mm Hg)$^{-1}$. The surface area was proportional to [resting functional residual capacity (FRC) + V_A/respiratory frequency]$^{2/3}$. Total volume of the pulmonary membrane is considered constant so that its thickness during exercise equals thickness at rest times surface area at rest/surface area at exercise. The values at rest were obtained from Weibel's morphometric results. The result is that $D_{L,CO,ex}$ is proportional to (resting FRC $+$ V_A/respiratory frequency)$^{-2}$. However, these authors did not consider the Roughton-Forster analysis of D_L (that it consists of both diffusion and chemical reaction) so, while their empirical relationship may be useful, its theoretical basis is unclear.

Menkes et al (49), in Dubois's laboratory, developed a water-filled human body plethysmograph with sufficient sensitivity (about 0.25 ml) to detect pulsations in the rate of uptake of CO in the lungs following an inspiration of 2% CO. These pulsations correspond to a variation in CO uptake during the cardiac cycle of from 40% to 200% of the mean value. These data suggest that pulmonary capillary blood volume varies during the cardiac cycle.

Alveolar Volume and Ventilation

Cuomo, Tisi & Moser (16) found that breath-holding $D_{L,CO}$ in anesthetized supine dogs was approximately proportional to V_A, including measurements at different lung volumes in one dog as well as variations in alveolar volume among different dogs. This means that D_L/V_A or the Krogh constant, which equals $[D_L (P_B-47)/V_A]$, was approximately constant, which is not unexpected and is of practical advantage in predicting D_L. When the right and left lungs were ventilated separately by means of a tracheal divider, but with equal gas volumes, the total lung D_L decreased, presumably because of the relative decrease in the blood flow of the smaller (left) lung brought about by its overdistension. This maldistribution of pulmonary blood flow was further exaggerated by inflating one lung and allowing the other to remain deflated; this reduced still more the sum of D_L for both lungs. This points out the importance of the uniformity of distribution of blood flow on the effective D_L of the whole lung.

The effect of spontaneous versus artifical respiration (whole body box) on steady-state D_{L,O_2} in the anesthetized dog was studied by Adaro et al (2). They used the rebreathing method as well as the classical steady-state O_2 method, in which end-capillary P_{O_2} was computed from mixed venous and arterial HbO_2 and P_{O_2} and the pulmonary shunt, this last obtained while breathing at 100% O_2. D_{L,O_2} by both methods during artificial ventilation was only one third of its value during spontaneous ventilation. The authors concluded that the smaller end expiratory volume during artificial ventilation, secondary to the positive pressure in the body box, increases the inhomogeneity in the lung as well as decreasing the true D_{L,O_2}.

Kindig & Hazlett (41) undertook a theoretical study of the relation between true $D_{L,CO}$ and the $D_{L,CO}$ steady-state method (Bates end-tidal sample) as a function of the pattern of breathing. The authors constructed a model with idealized dead space and calculated alveolar [CO] as a function of time during the steady-state respiratory cycle and mixed expired [CO] for the following breathing patterns: square wave (instantaneous inspiration) and expiration, ramp inspiration and expiration, and ramp inspiration and expiration with inspiratory and expiratory pauses. They found that if the breathing pattern is known or assumed, two characteristic numerical constants (the effective breath-holding time and $\int dt/V_A$) are needed to correct the experimental value of steady-state D_L for the fact that it is not truly a continuous ventilatory process. Previous workers have developed an analogous correction for the single-breath $D_{L,CO}$, which produces about a 20% reduction in the measured value (40), while Kindig & Hazlett suggested that an approximately 13% increase in steady-state $D_{L,CO}$ is needed. These two opposing corrections bring the values of $D_{L,CO}$ by the two techniques into line. There is some danger in these procedures, as there are arbitrary aspects of the critical numbers that could mask other mechanisms of error.

Hypoxia

D_L appears to adapt to environmental P_{O_2} (in relation to O_2 consumption) at least during growth. Young rats were exposed for approximately three weeks to a reduced inspired P_{O_2} (100 mm Hg) and their D_{L,O_2} increased significantly, as compared to controls that breathed air. Animals exposed to an increased ambient P_{O_2} (290 mm Hg) developed with a decreased D_{L,O_2} (8). Geelhaar & Weibel (24) found that the lungs of waltzing Japanese mice, which consumed 80% more O_2 than control mice, had a 55% increase in D_{L,O_2}.

Turek, Frans & Kreuzer (75) measured steady-state $D_{L,CO}$ in anesthetized rats that had been raised at about 3500 m from the time they weighed 76 g until they weighed about 200 g, a mean of 29 days, by a technique they had developed previously (74). $D_{L,CO}$ was 0.20 ml min^{-1} (mm Hg)$^{-1}$ in control animals under sea level conditions and 0.24 ml min^{-1} (mm Hg)$^{-1}$ in those adapted to high altitude, all studied at an alveolar P_{O_2} of 45–49 mm Hg. This difference (which was significant) could be explained by the effect of the increase in hematocrit on θ_{CO}, so that there was no evidence of a change in the pulmonary capillary bed per se. There was also a decrease in ΔP_{O_2} (A–a) in the adapted animals, which could be explained by the increase in blood O_2 capacity and the increased arteriovenous O_2 content. Turek and other colleagues (76) extended these studies to rats born at 3500 m altitude. Again the rats' $D_{L,CO}$ was raised, but their growth was retarded and mixed venous P_{O_2} was reduced, indicating that they were less well adapted to the hypoxia than animals born at sea level.

Removal of sea level residents to high altitude (about 3600 m) does not increase the end-tidal steady state (28) or single-breath $D_{L,CO}$ (17) provided that the following factors have been taken into account: (*a*) the increase in the blood reaction rate with CO (θ_{CO}), which occurs when P_{O_2} is reduced, as well as the increase proportional to the hematocrit; (*b*) the increase in steady-state $D_{L,CO}$ secondary to the increase in ventilation resulting from the adaption to high altitude. On the other hand, the natives of this altitude have an increased $D_{L,CO}$, 29 ml min^{-1} (mm Hg)$^{-1}$, compared to an expected 23 ml min^{-1} (mm Hg)$^{-1}$, which does not decrease when they remove to sea level. This fits in with the finding of Burri & Weibel (8) that hypoxia during the growth period in rats increases the morphometric pulmonary diffusing capacity, but that once the animals are past the developing stage, hypoxia no longer has this effect. Other workers, however (9), found that adapted lowlanders were capable of raising D_M and V_C.

Weiskopf & Severinghaus (85) measured breath-holding $D_{L,CO}$ of normal sea-level residents after acute (helicopter) removal to 4300 m. They found that, as compared to measurements made at sea level and the same alveolar P_{O_2}, approximately 50 mm Hg, $D_{L,CO}$ decreased significantly by the second day at altitude. V_C was calculated and found to decrease as well. The entire ΔP_{O_2} (A–a) difference could be explained by the end-capillary diffusion gradient. The explanation for their findings is not clear; there may have been constriction of pulmonary vessels. No experimental data are available for θ_{CO} at P_{O_2} between 0 and 150 mm Hg, and therefore the authors had to interpolate existing published data. However, any resulting error would also have occurred in the control measurements.

Miscellaneous Factors Affecting D_L

Power et al (59) determined the decrease in single-breath $D_{L,CO}$ at mean alveolar P_{O_2} of 137, 199, 313, and 531 mm Hg in an isolated perfused cat lung with constant vascular inflow and outflow pressures as a function of temperature, and found that at 5°C it decreased to about one tenth of its value at 40°C; the activation energy was 11.9 kcal. Using in vitro reaction rate data of Lawson (45), most of the decrease in $D_{L,CO}$ with temperature could be explained. However, D_M at 5°C was found to have decreased to one fifth of its value at 37°C. On the other hand, the value of V_C at 5°C was 4 times its control value at 37°C. In addition, the total blood content of these lungs increased as the temperature was lowered, paralleling the change in V_C. These results are important for gas exchange in vivo under hypothermic conditions and should be followed by further work.

Nishida et al (53) measured single breath $D_{L,CO}$ in 342 normal men and 131 normal women. D_L decreased 1.6 ml min^{-1} (mm Hg)$^{-1}$ yr^{-1} in males and 0.7 ml min^{-1} (mm Hg)$^{-1}$ yr^{-1} in females. D_L/V_A also decreased with age. Other pulmonary function tests showed the same trends with age as reported elsewhere in the literature. These changes may result from the aging process per se or from repeated infection and insult.

Increasing CSF pressure in supine anesthetized dogs from a control value of 13 mm Hg to 200 mm Hg caused a doubling of breath-holding $D_{L,CO}$, from 12.9 to 28.6 ml min^{-1} (mm Hg)$^{-1}$ and concurrent increases from 144 mm Hg to 204 mm Hg, in aortic pressure, from 16 to 24 mm Hg in pulmonary artery pressure, and from 2 to 5 mm Hg in right atrial pressure (6). These increases in pulmonary vascular pressure alone would not have been expected to lead to such a large increase in $D_{L,CO}$. Therefore it seems likely that additional factors acted on the pulmonary vasculature, such as constriction of the venous outflow.

Sundström, Zauner & Arborelius (72) determined steady-state $D_{L,CO}$ by end-tidal sample before and after the administration of intravenous soybean oil emulsion. In seven normal human volunteers, $D_{L,CO}$ decreased 15% on the average during the infusion, but returned to the control level in 45 min. At the same time ΔP_{O_2} (A–a) decreased during infusion, but did not return to control values afterwards. There were changes in the spectrophotometric properties of lipemic blood and in the P_{O_2} electrode calibration in such blood, which had to be taken into account in the analyses. Effects of intravenous fat on $D_{L,CO}$ have been reported before, but have not been entirely consistent. The decrease in $D_{L,CO}$ steady state was concluded not to be of clinical importance, and no adequate explanation for the phenomenon could be provided.

EFFECTS OF STRATIFICATION ON D_L

It is largely accepted that gas in a given alveolus proper can be considered perfectly mixed. In other words, the diffusion gradients within the alveolar gas phase are negligible compared to those in the capillary blood and across the pulmonary membranes. It is also accepted that dead space gas is of a different composition than alveolar gas; diffusion within the gas phase does limit exchange between the blood and gas at points in the airways distant from the capillaries. Therefore the importance or even the existence of stratification in alveolar gas becomes a matter of the precise definition of the boundary of the alveoli. The classical anatomical boundary is a sphere about 200 μm in diameter. Cumming et al (15), by implication, defined alveolar gas as including all the gas in lungs + airways. Because diffusion exchange between gas in the anatomical alveoli and that in airways does increase the effective alveolar ventilation, it may properly be considered part of gas exchange and several articles on this subject have been included.

Theoretical Models

Cumming (14) summarized a number of models of the alveoli and airways published by several authors and the resultant conclusions concerning diffusion and mixing in the lungs. With the advent of the electronic computer, diffusion equations in a complex geometry, completely beyond the analytical approach to which earlier investigators were limited, can be solved. However, the results of these computations are completely dependent on the model of the anatomy assumed. It is possible to obtain, for example, a flat or a sloped expired alveolar N_2 plateau, depending on the boundary conditions.

As gas moves into the lungs during inspiration, the cross-sectional area increases and the linear velocity decreases until a point may be reached at which the rate of diffusion of the alveolar gases toward the mouth equals the convective flow of inspired gas towards the alveoli, and at which movement of the inspired gas to alveoli ceases. This point is only 250 ml into the lung in one model discussed by Cumming et al (15).

Experimental Measurements

Engel and collaborators (19, 20) measured the gas concentration in the bronchial tree of a dog by passing a fine catheter through the walls of airways ranging from 0.25 to 1.6 cm in diameter and out through the lung parenchyma and chest wall to a N_2 meter. They found that within 1 sec following a respiration of O_2, some N_2 from the alveolar gas had migrated out as far as those airways with a diameter of 1.6 cm, and by 10 sec all airways had an N_2 concentration approximately half that in the alveoli.

Large oscillations in N_2 concentration of airway gas synchronous with the heartbeat and bearing a superficial resemblance to an arterial pressure pulse were seen (19, 20). These resulted from pulsations of N_2-containing alveolar gas up and down the airway produced by heart movements rather than pulsations of the pulmonary vessels, because ligating the pulmonary arterial supply did not affect them. The volume of gas and velocity of its movement could be estimated from the data available and were striking. For example, in an airway with a diameter of 0.3 cm, the mean velocity during pulsation was found to be 7.7 cm sec^{-1} and the mid-concentration point of the front moved about 1 cm to and fro. These oscillations mixed the lung gases about five times as fast as in a dead animal, in which only diffusion mixing could take place.

These authors emphasized the importance of Taylor mixing in the airways. Taylor mixing consists of radial diffusion from a parabolic concentration front that should amplify the cardiogenic oscillatory mixing. An interesting and unexpected prediction was that gas of greater molecular weight, such as SF_6, would mix more rapidly by this mechanism; the converse is true for diffusion alone.

Bondi & Van Liew (5) recorded arterial pH continuously in the anesthetized dog by drawing peripheral arterial blood through a glass capillary pH electrode with a reference electrode placed deep in the mouth. Arterial pH varied cyclically with respiration, rising with inspiration and falling with expiration, a total range of 0.001–0.05 pH units. When respiration stopped at the end of a normal inspiration, arterial pH did not plateau at the level of the preceding peaks in the pH waves, but continued to rise during breath-holding, reaching pH levels 0.001–0.013 pH greater than the preceding peaks. The authors suggested that this resulted from the mixing of alveolar gas with gas of lower P_{CO_2} in the airways and air spaces distant from the capillaries; this mixing would be a result of diffusion and heart action. Clearly this represents stratification. Johnson & Van Liew (37) extended this approach to the investigation of stratification in the lung, using the same preparation but following arterial P_{O_2} continuously with an electrode. During breath-holding with He substituted for the normal 80% N_2, the rate of drop in arterial P_{O_2} was less rapid, suggesting again that mixing of stratified gas in the alveoli and airways of the lung had made more O_2 available to the capillary blood than during breath-holding with air. When breathing was resumed with 80% He and 20% O_2, the rate of increase of arterial P_{O_2} at a constant ventilatory rate and volume was lower than when air was breathed. This indicated that during inspiration, O_2 is delivered more efficiently to alveolar capillary blood if N_2 is present than if 80% He is present. This conclusion is intuitively surprising, because the more rapid diffusion of He, for example, would decrease the dead space. Johnson & Van Liew suggested that Taylor diffusion increases the mixing of fresh gas in the airway with alveolar gas, increasing effective alveolar ventilation more in the case of the heavier gas, N_2.

NONUNIFORMITY

Although we have specifically avoided discussing pathological conditions that may affect D_L, several brief points about the general relation between uneven V_A/Q and/or D_L/Q and reduction in D_L should be made. In 1951 the syndrome of pure diffusion defect was presented, but doubts were cast on its very existence in 1961, when the pulmonary function abnormalities were all explained by unevenness. Today we seem to have reached a middle ground; many cases of fibroses are seen with both nonuniformity and diffusion defect, but a smaller group of patients appear to have primarily a reduction in D_L.

Chinet et al (11) investigated the effect of inhomogeneity of D_L, V_A, and $\dot{Q}$ on the value of D_L calculated from mixed arterial and expired alveolar gas samples in a model that assumed steady-state conditions and contained 15 compartments with a log-normal distribution of the three variables. The ratio of the experimentally determined D_L to the true D_L (the sum of D_L of each of the compartments), (a) was less for O_2 than for CO, (b) decreased as the extent of inhomogeneity increased, except for $D_{L,CO}$ calculated from "ideal" alveolar gas, and (c) decreased as D_L increased in absolute value, except again in the case of $D_{L,CO}$ calculated from "ideal" alveolar gas, which increased. Although several of the conclusions have been reported before, these results are on firmer ground because of the numerical proof that 15 compartments approaches the limit of a continuous distribution. Thews et al (73) developed a technique for the analysis of inhomogeneity in the distributions of V_A, $\dot{Q}$, and D_L in the lung, based on computations from the transients in expired alveolar argon, CO_2, and O_2 concentrations measured by mass spectrometer when the subject starts to breathe a gas mixture with increased argon and CO_2 concentrations, and reduced O_2 concentration. A computer program was used to resolve the transients into 2 compartments and calculate the values of V_A, $\dot{Q}$, and D_L for each compartment.

Michaelson et al (50) studied the variation in $D_L/\dot{Q}$ with vertical distance in the lung by utilizing the known pattern of distribution of inspired gas to different levels of the lung, as confirmed by external counting of inspired radioactive xenon. A 100 ml bolus of gas containing Ne, CO, and C_2H_2 was added to an inspiration at residual volume or FRC, the breath held for 5–20 sec, and an expired alveolar sample collected and analyzed for the concentrations of these gases and of O_2. $\dot{Q}/V_A$ could be calculated from the disappearance curve of C_2H_2, and D_L/V_A from that of CO. When the bolus was inspired from residual volume (RV), it was distributed primarily to the upper zones, and $\dot{Q}/V_A$ and D_L/V_A were greater than when the bolus was inspired from FRC, in which case it was distributed largely to the lower zones. In normal seated subjects, $\dot{Q}/V_A$ and D_L/V_A increased from apex to base, but the rate and amount of the slope were greater for $\dot{Q}/V_A$. Thus $D_L/\dot{Q}$ is greater at the apex than at the base and surprisingly this difference is the same at P_{A,O_2} of 150 mm Hg and 650 mm Hg, suggesting that D_M and V_c vary in the same proportion.

These results may be of interest in relation to two older findings. First, the disappearance curve of alveolar CO is not exponential, but curves upwards, suggesting that D_L/V_A is nonuniform through the lung. The findings of Michaelson et al are compatible with this, but cannot explain the extent of this curvature quantitatively. Second, D_L generally increases with increased alveolar volume, a result that can be at least partially explained by the fact that with a larger inspiration more of the inspired gas tends to distribute to the bases.

If alveolar P_{CO} is made high enough during a breath-holding measurement of $D_{L,CO}$, sufficient CO will diffuse into the alveolar capillary blood during its transit to form a large [HbCO] and a back-pressure of P_{CO} in the blood, reducing the value calculated for $D_{L,CO}$. In normal subjects inspiring a breath of 4% CO, if D_L is distributed uniformly throughout the lung in respect to blood flow, capillary [HbCO] will not become great enough to interfere with CO uptake and to decrease measured $D_{L,CO}$. On the other hand, if $D_L/\dot{Q}$, is nonuniform, in those alveoli with larger than average $D_L/\dot{Q}$, capillary [HbCO] will rise and CO uptake will decrease, reducing the experimental $D_{L,CO}$ for the whole lung. Hyde et al (36) took advantage of this principle to gain an estimate of uneven $D_L/\dot{Q}$ in man by comparing the single-breath $D_{L,CO}$ obtained when the inspired CO was about 0.2% ($D_{L,CO,0.2}$) with that obtained when the inspired CO concentration was 4% ($D_{L,CO,4}$).

In supine normal subjects, $D_{L,CO,4}$ averaged 29.4 ml min^{-1} (mm Hg)$^{-1}$, 14% less than $D_{L,CO,0.2}$, which averaged 33.7 ml min^{-1} (mm Hg)$^{-1}$. These discrepancies could be explained by a two-compartment lung model in which 19% of the blood flow was distributed in alveoli that possessed 50% of the total $D_{L,CO}$. The findings in sitting subjects were approximately the same, so that gravitational forces were not an important factor in producing the nonuniformity of $D_L/\dot{Q}$.

A–a GRADIENTS FOR CO_2

It has been well accepted that CO_2 diffuses across the pulmonary membrane 20 times as fast as O_2 and therefore that the arterial P_{CO_2}, at least at the end of the capillary, equals alveolar P_{CO_2}. This is a basic tenet in the application of respiratory physiology in the clinic and a first principle for medical students. However, there have been a number of reports since the original work of Jones et al in 1967 (38) that during rebreathing alveolar P_{CO_2} becomes greater than arterial P_{CO_2}. This field was reviewed by Piiper & Scheid (58) in 1971, but there have been further publications of interest since that time. Fortunately, while this more recent work indicates that CO_2 does not equilibrate with blood as rapidly as thought, as a practical matter the ancient law still holds.

One possible remaining explanation for the reports on the existence of an alveolar P_{CO_2} greater than pulmonary venous P_{CO_2} is that they are technical errors. Scheid et al (67) carried out a series of careful studies on dog lungs: perfusing an excised lung with donor blood; isolating the airways of a single lobe in situ; rapidly rebreathing a whole lung in vivo so as to reduce recirculation; and rebreathing the whole lung on O_2 in vivo and allowing P_{CO_2} to rise. They found no significant P_{CO_2} difference between the steady-state or plateau alveolar P_{CO_2} and pulmonary venous or peripheral arterial blood. The authors could offer no adequate explanation for the discrepancy between their findings and many reports in the literature, other than technical errors in estimation of alveolar P_{CO_2} and the lack of exercise per se in their studies.

Guyatt, Yu, and co-workers (31, 86) reported careful measurements of P_{O_2} and P_{CO_2} in expired alveolar gas, pulmonary arterial (or mixed venous) blood, and pulmonary venous blood from a single lung, single lobe of a lung, or both lungs of an anesthetized dog during steady-state rebreathing. These authors took great care to see that steady-state conditions existed at the time of their measurements, and analyzed the errors in the gas tension measurements. They confirmed the reports of a number of previous authors that alveolar P_{CO_2} during steady-state rebreathing was greater than that in blood leaving the lung; in only three measurements in 48 dogs was this not true. For example, in ll dogs in which a single lung or lobe was rebreathed, mean alveolar P_{CO_2} was 41.2 mm Hg, average mixed venous P_{CO_2} was

40.1 mm Hg, and pulmonary arterial P_{CO_2} was 37.3 mm Hg. In these same dogs, the average gas tensions for O_2 were 29.3 mm Hg for alveolar gas, 24 mm Hg for mixed-venous blood, and 25.1 for pulmonary venous blood. Thus there was also a gradient for P_{O_2}.

They found that increasing blood P_{CO_2}, either by infusing HCl intravenously or by rebreathing the whole lung, led to an increase in (alveolar P_{CO_2}–pulmonary venous P_{CO_2}). Inhibition of blood carbonic anhydrase also led to an increase in this gradient, whereas delaying the transit of blood from right heart to pulmonary artery led to a decrease in the alveolar-pulmonary venous gradient, as would be expected if there normally were a lack of chemical equilibrium of CO_2 in pulmonary arterial blood. On the other hand, they found that varying pulmonary blood flow had no effect on the alveolar-pulmonary venous P_{CO_2} gradient, a relationship that had been reported by others. These authors considered a number of possible explanations for this alveolar-pulmonary venous P_{CO_2} gradient including metabolism in the rebreathing lung tissue, gas exchange with the bronchial blood flow, Wien potential effect, N_2 absorption in the lungs, temperature gradients in blood, and skimming of cells free from plasma during blood transit in the lungs, as well as incomplete chemical equilibrium in the blood, but they could come to no definitive conclusion as to the cause.

Laszlo et al (47) measured the downstream ΔP_{CO_2} (end-tidal P_{CO_2}– arterial blood P_{CO_2}) in healthy humans at rest rebreathing from a bag. Whereas on the average the downstream ΔP_{CO_2} was negligible during air breathing, it increased to 3.1 mm Hg during rebreathing with continuously rising P_{CO_2}, but fell to near zero again in about 10 min if bag P_{CO_2} was held constant during further rebreathing by adjusting the CO_2 scrubber. In their experiments a positive downstream ΔP_{CO_2} was only present during transient changes in alveolar P_{CO_2}, which was not the case in other reports such as those of Guyatt et al (31). Laszlo et al suggested that the downstream ΔP_{CO_2} is the result of a continuing readjustment in blood chemistry after the blood has left the lung capillaries.

Jones and co-workers (39) reached a similar conclusion when they found that ΔP_{CO_2} was not a function of P_{CO_2} at rest, but that it increased along with P_{CO_2} and $[H^+]$ during exercise. These data were supported by later work (48) in which no ΔP_{CO_2} was found in hypercapnic patients at rest, although it is present in exercise in subjects with hypercapnia. Other workers, however (21), did find a ΔP_{CO_2} in patients with chronic airways obstruction at rest. These discrepancies are yet to be resolved.

Gurtner and associates (see 58) have hypothesized that a negative charge on the inner surface of the pulmonary capillaries would attract H^+ and increase the product $[H^+] \times [HCO_3^-]$ near to this surface; by dehydration of H_2CO_3 this would produce an increased P_{CO_2} next to the endothelium. As this is nearer to alveolar gas, an elevation in alveolar P_{CO_2} over that in the axial capillary blood and the blood leaving the lung would result. Gurtner (29) has extended the experimental support of his hypothesis by measuring the distribution of radioactively labeled weak acids and bases between mixed venous blood and alveolar fluid (isosmotic sucrose, dextran, or plasma), in one lobe of a dog lung. He found that calculated values of uncharged DMO (5,5-dimethyloxazolidine dione) and barbital were greater in the alveolar fluid than in the pulmonary venous blood, and that they increased with increasing blood $[H^+]$. The uncharged form of the weak base had a lesser concentration in the pulmonary venous blood and the difference decreased as blood $[H^+]$ rose. These experimental results are consistent with Gurtner's hypothesis. At the same time, a major technical difficulty in this type of experiment is the attainment of equilibrium between blood and gas phases, and little information is given on this point. A systematic underestimation of blood $[H^+]$ or overestimation of alveolar fluid $[H^+]$ would also explain the results.

The hypothesis of Gurtner and colleagues has stimulated numerous papers, one of the attributes of exciting research. However, we find the hypothesis for the production of an alveolar-pulmonary venous Pco_2 gradient difficult to accept for several reasons, among which the following are outstanding. Over macromolecular distances there can be no significant separation of charge, simply because the quantity of electric charge (ion) required to produce a voltage difference is so extremely small. Therefore no measurable $[H^+]$ can move without parallel movements of a counterion. If a measurable excess of H^+ moves to the wall of the capillary, there must be compensating movement of either anion or cation at the same rate. Second, the theory requires a significant Pco_2 gradient from the immediate vicinity of the endothelium to the bulk of the flowing blood, at least the axial region. A large mass of literature provides experimental evidence that, within the limits of measurement, inert gases diffuse so rapidly from alveolus through all layers of the pulmonary membrane and of the blood that the average partial pressure in the pulmonary venous blood is equal to that in the alveolar gas. It thus seems distinctly unlikely that a large Pco_2 gradient could exist over only a small portion of the total path. Effros (18) made essentially the same point by calculating the energy required to maintain such a gradient in the capillary blood in spite of the continuous "leak" of CO_2 down the gradient from the perimeter to the central bulk of the blood stream. The energy required, with reasonable values chosen for the necessary constants, was greater than the total mechanical energy in the pulmonary blood.

CO_2, O_2, AND CO EXCHANGE WITHIN BLOOD

There have been two basic approaches to the study of O_2 and CO_2 exchange in alveolar capillary blood: the first is to measure in vitro the rate of uptake of these gases by red cell suspensions and hemolysates; the other is to calculate the chemical composition of blood as a function of time from diffusion and chemical kinetic theory, using available data for the diffusing capacity of the alveolar membrane (Dм), pulmonary capillary blood volume (Vc), and the rate of gas reaction with red cells (θ).

Wagner & West (80) followed the computational approach; they investigated the simultaneous time course of O_2 and CO_2 along the alveolar capillary, treating overall gas exchange in the alveolus as two diffusion resistances in series according to the Roughton-Forster approach. Wagner & West took the interaction of H^+, CO_2, and O_2 with hemoglobin into account by using pertinent equilibrium curves. They used published data for θ_{O_2}, D_M, V_C, and $\dot{Q}$, and assumed that CO_2 exchange with blood was exponential with a half-time of 0.15 sec. They investigated the effect of varying $V_A/\dot{Q}$ while keeping mixed venous P_{O_2} and P_{CO_2} constant.

In contrast to standard physiological teaching, even with the chemical reactions in the blood assumed infinitely rapid, the time required for half-equilibration of CO_2 between alveolar gas and blood is appreciably greater than that for O_2. While it is true that D_M for CO_2 can be expected to be about 20 times that for O_2 because of its solubility in water, which makes up most of the endothelial and epithelial layers, the effective solubility of CO_2 in blood is more than 20 times that of O_2, in the higher HbO_2 saturation ranges. Therefore although CO_2 passes through the pulmonary membrane more easily than O_2, the amount of CO_2 needed to decrease the blood P_{CO_2} is greater than the amount of O_2 needed to increase the blood P_{O_2} at high P_{O_2}, so that the equilibration process is about as fast for the two gases.

Fortunately the usefulness of arterial P_{CO_2} as a measure of alveolar P_{CO_2} in abnormal lungs depends on the small arteriovenous P_{CO_2} difference and not on sophisticated considerations of equilibration processes or subtlety of $V_A/\dot{Q}$. If alveolar capillary blood P_{CO_2} fails to equilibrate with alveolar gas by 20% (that is, the equilibration process reaches 80% completion by the end of the capillary), this represents a difference of only 1 mm Hg between arterial and alveolar P_{CO_2}, which is of little consequence in most clinical situations and could not be reliably determined anyway.

Wagner & West found that decreases in D_M affected CO_2 and O_2 equilibration in capillary blood to about the same extent. The interactions between the two gases produced some unexpected effects. In an alveolus with a decreased D_M and increased $V_A/\dot{Q}$, alveolar P_{CO_2} is decreased and CO_2 leaves the blood more rapidly than O_2 enters at first, so intracellular pH rises and, owing to the Bohr effect, P_{O_2} of the blood at points along the capillary can be less than mixed venous P_{O_2} in spite of the fact that O_2 has actually moved into the blood. With a normal D_{M,O_2} of 40 ml min^{-1} (mm Hg)$^{-1}$, there is a large reserve, and at an alveolar P_{O_2} of 100 mm Hg, D_M has to fall by 75% before a significant end-capillary P_{O_2} difference appears. If D_{M,CO_2}, which is considered equal to 40 times D_{M,O_2}, decreases to one eighth of its normal value, the P_{CO_2} end gradient is 20% of (alveolar P_{CO_2}–mixed venous P_{CO_2}). These calculations are based on a constant and normal V_C and an infinite rate of ligand interaction.

Hill, Power and Longo advanced the computational art in considering alveolar and placental gas exchanges by including the kinetics of the exchanges of chloride for bicarbonate ion across the red cell membrane and the kinetics of the reaction of CO_2 with hemoglobin to form carbamate. These papers (32, 33), as well as the earlier report of Sirs (69), and that of Forster & Crandall (23), introduced an aspect of CO_2 exchanges with blood that is nearly qualitatively different and had not been mentioned authoritatively since Roughton's review of the subject in 1935 (64). This consideration is that the pH adjustments of plasma during CO_2 exchanges of blood must take place by the hydration-dehydration reactions of CO_2 in the plasma which, being uncatalyzed, are slow, on the order of tens of seconds. The difference in [H^+] between plasma and cells may be small, but may require the movement of much larger amounts of other ions and molecules to reach equilibrium. While plasma Po_2 may not equal red cell Po_2 at the end of a capillary, the relatively small amount of dissolved O_2 equilibrates with the large O_2 capacity of the intracellular hemoglobin in hundredths of a second after the blood exits. The analogous CO_2 readjustments take much longer because they involve the uncatalyzed and therefore very slow CO_2 reactions and exchanges across the red cell membrane.

Hill et al (33) found that in their model, if the Bohr effect were eliminated, O_2 exchange from the alveolus only decreased 2%, from which they concluded it was not an important phenomenon. On the other hand, the Haldane effect—the elimination of CO_2 produced by oxygenation of hemoglobin—represented 46% of the total CO_2 output.

Hlastala (34) developed a model of gas exchange for a single alveolus that included diffusion between blood moving along the capillary, lung tissue, and alveolar gas. O_2 reactions in the blood were included and relationships among Pco_2, Po_2, pH, and blood O_2 and CO_2 contents were computed for each step from equilibrium data D_{M,O_2} was taken as 56 ml min^{-1} (mm Hg)$^{-1}$ and D_{L,CO_2} taken as 435 ml min^{-1} (mm Hg)$^{-1}$. Cyclic variations in alveolar volume with respiration and pulmonary capillary blood flow with the heartbeat were incorporated. An interesting finding was that blood Pco_2 could become greater than alveolar Pco_2 along part of the pulmonary capillary during expiration or breath-holding. This seeming paradox occurs because during expiration alveolar Pco_2 rises steadily as CO_2 is continuously added by mixed venous blood entering the capillaries. If the rate of increase of alveolar Pco_2 is rapid enough in comparison to blood transit time, it may become greater than the Pco_2 of blood in the latter part of the capillaries. By analogy, capillary Po_2 can become higher than alveolar Po_2 at certain points along the capillary. This mechanism depends upon a rate of rise of alveolar Pco_2, which is significant in comparison to the transit time of capillary blood.

Hlastala went on in a second paper (35) to compute profiles of Pco_2 and Po_2 along the alveolar capillary, taking into account diffusion + chemical reactions within the blood for both CO_2 and O_2, using data in the literature for θ_{O_2} and θ_{CO_2}. He investigated the effects of the interactions of O_2 and CO_2 with hemoglobin (Bohr and Haldane effects) upon the speed of equilibration of these gases in the pulmonary capillaries by assuming that the intramolecular allosteric changes occurred as an exponential process. By applying the data of Forster & Steen (22) to his model for the Bohr shift during oxygenation, he obtained a half-time of 0.025 sec for the process. He found that the existence of a noninfinite rate of Bohr-Haldane shift slowed the equilibration of both O_2 and CO_2 along the capillary of the alveolus, and that the early rapid movement of O_2 into the capillary blood caused an initial rise in blood Pco_2, even though CO_2 was moving from blood to gas.

Several investigators have followed the direct experimental approach and measured the rate of gas exchange of red cells in vitro. Klocke (42) determined the speed of CO_2 displacement by oxygenation of hemoglobin (Haldane effect). He mixed a deoxygenated human red cell suspension of NaCl–bicarbonate at Pco_2 equal to 42 mm Hg with an analogous buffer solution equilibrated with the same Pco_2 in O_2 at 37°C in a continuous-flow Hartridge-Roughton apparatus. By using Pco_2 and

P_{O_2} electrodes he could follow simultaneously the decrease in P_{O_2} with hemoglobin oxygenation and the increase in P_{CO_2} as CO_2 was released. O_2 entered the red cell and oxygenated the hemoglobin to its equilibrium value in less than 0.1 sec, releasing protons from hemoglobin (which in turn releases CO_2 from HCO_3^-) and CO_2 from hemoglobin carbamate by allosteric interactions in the hemoprotein itself. The two mechanisms for CO_2 formation can be separated by addition of acetazolamide, which slows down the production of CO_2 from Bohr protons (several seconds half-time), but leaves the release of CO_2 from hemoglobin carbamate (half-time about 0.05 seconds) unchanged. At normal intracellular [2,3-DPG] and pH, about half the Haldane CO_2 comes from carbamate and half from bicarbonate. Increasing intracellular [2,3-DPG] leads to a decrease in carbamate because of the competition of the organophosphate with CO_2 for the terminal valine NH_2 of the hemoglobin.

In one experiment the mobilization of carbamate CO_2 by oxygenation had a half-time of 0.144 sec, while the half-time for HbO_2 formation was about 0.03 sec. The half-time for carbamate formation following a step increase in P_{CO_2} is known to be about 0.06 sec, so that if one accepts the generally held belief that the allosteric changes in the hemoglobin molecule are communicated in less than a millisecond, the experimentally determined Haldane carbamate CO_2 production is much slower than the sum of the three processes: oxygenation of the hemoglobin, allosteric change, and release of carbamate CO_2. There appears to be no explanation at the moment for this discrepancy.

The production of CO_2 from HCO_3^- in the Haldane effect is not exponential with time, but has a long slow phase from beyond 0.2 sec, presumably rate limited by HCO_3^- –Cl^- exchange. Klocke computed that this anion permeability gave a 0.16 sec half-time and decreased as pH increased, compatible with the fixed-charge hypothesis of red cell membrane anion permeability. Sirs (69) measured the time course of the CO_2 reactions with blood by following, in a split-beam spectrophotometric apparatus, the dissociation of O_2 from HbO_2 after rapid mixing of a suspension of oxygenated red cells, at a P_{CO_2} of zero, with 20 times as great a volume of an O_2-free solution, with a P_{CO_2} of 30 mm Hg. [HbO_2] fell rapidly, initially undershooting the eventual equilibrium value. This phenomenon resulted from a rapid rise in intracellular [H^+] because of the catalyzed hydration of CO_2, which augmented the dissociation of HbO_2. Later in the process, after P_{O_2} had reached a quasi-equilibrium with [HbO_2], H^+ was transferred to the extracellular fluid, increasing the intracellular pH and causing the reassociation of O_2 and hemoglobin. From the speed of this process, which was slow, Sirs could estimate semiquantitatively the speed of the CO_2 exchange processes. His conclusions are closely related to those of Forster & Crandall (23) and Hill et al (33).

The fundamental experimental problem in determining the permeability of the red cell membrane to O_2, CO or CO_2 is that its value appears to be so great that the velocity of the red cell exchanges is rate limited by diffusion + reaction inside the cell. A weak acid (or a base) has the advantages that its chemical reaction in the cell, namely proton binding, is nearly instantaneous and the products are small and diffuse out easily, reducing intracellular gradients nearly to the theoretical minimum and amplifying the effect of transmembrane gradients.

Klocke et al (43) used a continuous-flow rapid-mixing apparatus with a glass pH electrode to follow the movement of valeric acid from a low pH extracellular fluid into human red cells in suspension at 37°C, obtaining a permeability of 0.025 cm sec.$^{-1}$. Assuming that membrane permeability is proportional to lipid solubility/ molecular weight$^{\frac{1}{2}}$, the value for O_2 turns out to be 0.09 cm sec.$^{-1}$. Using accepted values, one can calculate λ (diffusion coefficient membrane/membrane thickness)/ (diffusion coefficient of interior/half-width of cell) as 0.9, which is close to the best estimates from gas reaction rates and means that the diffusion resistance of the membrane is less than or equal to the diffusion resistance of the cell in terms of dissolved O_2 alone. The specific diffusion resistance of the cell substance, taking into account ligand reactions with relatively immobile hemoglobin, is several orders of magnitude less than that of the membrane.

Stein et al (71) measured the diffusion coefficient of O_2 in packed red cell suspensions and in suspensions up to 100% hematocrit in 1% agar gel, both at 25°C. The diffusion coefficient in packed cells was the same as that previously obtained in the same laboratory on hemoglobin solution of equal concentration, indicating that the red cell membrane permeability to O_2 may be considered infinite in comparison with diffusion + reaction processes within the cell. Gros & Moll (27) carried out analogous experiments on packed cells and lysate with CO_2, again finding no difference in the overall permeability. The estimated red cell membrane permeability to CO_2 was 3 cm sec^{-1}, thirty times the minimal value of Klocke et al (43).

Elimination of the intracellular diffusion gradient, as by stirring of the cell contents, could speed up the rate of cell O_2 exchange. In their passage through capillaries and larger blood vessels, the red blood cells are subjected to shear forces and distortions in shape that should cause some convection of their content. Zander & Schmid-Schönbein (87, 88) have attempted to determine experimentally the possible influence of shear forces on cell O_2 release rates. They measured the rate at which O_2 diffused out of a 5–800 μm thick layer of red cells, through a thin teflon membrane on which the blood film rested, and into a gas chamber where Po_2 was continuously monitored. The rotating cone of a viscosimeter was placed close above the teflon film, leaving a layer of cell suspension of only 5 μm at the thinnest part. When the O_2 in the gas phase was replaced by N_2, a process that required the best part of a minute, O_2 diffused out of the cell suspension into the gas phase at a rate four times faster when the cone was rotating than when it was still. The authors interpreted this to mean that convection within the red cell had increased the O_2 exchange rate of the individual cell by this same proportion. However, the rate of O_2 release from the film was about three orders of magnitude slower than the rate of O_2 release from red cells as measured in a rapid-mixing apparatus, making it difficult to believe that this process is rate limited by the exchange rates of cells themselves. Rather it seems more reasonable to conclude that the shear increases the macroscopic stirring of the suspension. Further work is indicated.

Bryant & Navari (7) measured the diffusion coefficient (d) at 37°C for O_2 in reconstituted plasma produced by adding normal concentrations of all the usual protein constituents of plasma but one, and varying this over a wide range. They found that d dropped by 50% as the albumin concentration increased from 2 g

(100 ml)$^{-1}$ to about 4 g (100 ml)$^{-1}$ [corresponding to total protein concentrations of about 5.28 g (100 ml)$^{-1}$ to 7.28 g (100 ml)$^{-1}$]. They found similar results for α and β globulins, but concentration of lipoprotein had minimal effect. The authors implied that in vivo alterations in plasma protein concentration might change effective D_{L,O_2}. However, this seems unlikely as the diffusion resistance of plasma must make up only a small fraction of that of the pulmonary membrane, which itself is extremely low.

Mochizuki et al (52) have developed a microspectrometric split-beam rapid-reaction apparatus and used it to measure the rate of the reactions of CO and O_2 with red cells in blood and within the capillaries of chick chorioallantoic membrane. The material is placed on a microscope slide, the instrument focused on a single cell, and an iris adjusted to eliminate light that does not pass through this cell. The gas over the sample can be changed rapidly and the rate of alteration of HbCO or of HbO$_2$ can be followed. This technique may have the potential to provide estimates of θco at values of Pco that are "physiological." Reported in vitro measurements of θco have been made at Pco approximating 100 mm Hg or higher, while alveolar Pco during $D_{L,CO}$ measurements is 4 mm Hg or less. However, the rate of change of [HbCO] in individual red cells, taken from the published figures of Mochizuki et al, appears to be about one twentieth of that obtained in rapid-mixing instruments. This discrepancy suggests that the process is not rate limited by gas movements and reactions in the cell itself.

The values of θ obtained by Roughton & Forster (65) were confined to normal physiological conditions and cells from healthy individuals. These data should be extended to include the variety of abnormalities seen in patients. For example, they made a cursory inspection of the effect of pH on θco and concluded it could be neglected, a finding confirmed by Lawson (45). On the other hand, Sirs (70) found in human and sheep cell suspensions and hemoglobin solutions that Pco$_2$ affects the reaction of CO with HbO$_2$ and, in effect, that θ varies with Pco^2. Rankin et al (60) found that increasing alveolar Pco$_2$ caused an increase in $D_{L,CO}$ within 1–2 sec, suggesting that CO$_2$ had a direct physicochemical effect on the intracellular hemoglobin reactions. However, Weiskopf & Severinghaus (85) did not find any effect of a decrease in Pa,co$_2$ on $D_{L,CO}$.

Values for θ from patients with several common hematological disorders have been reported. Smaller and hypochromic red cells have a slower rate of CO uptake per cell (45). Thus in comparison to a normal subject, θ in an anemic patient is decreased both because the rate of CO uptake per cell is decreased and because the total number of cells per milliliter of blood is reduced. The rate of CO uptake by deoxygenated cells containing SS hemoglobin is about 20% less than in normal cells, although the comparable reaction velocity in solution is the same for SS and normal adult hemoglobin. Presumably it is the increased diffusion resistance to CO and O_2 within the sickle cell that slows up the reaction.

Very few measurements of θ under physiological conditions are available for animals other than man in spite of the number of studies of $D_{L,CO}$ in laboratory animals. Lawson (45) has reported values of θ for the dog, which were about 20% greater than for man, and more limited results on cat and sheep cells. In general, θ in these animals is similar to its value in humans.

Literature Cited

1. Adaro, F., Scheid, P., Teichmann, J., Piiper, J. 1973. A rebreathing method for estimating pulmonary DO_2: theory and measurements in dog lungs. *Respir. Physiol.* 18:43–63
2. Adaro, F., Teichmann, J., Lüdtke-Hanjery, A., Scheid, P., Piiper, J. 1974. Comparison of rebreathing and steady-state pulmonary DO_2 in dogs ventilated by body respirator. *Respiration* 31:71–84
3. Andrew, G. M., Baines, L. 1974. Relationship of pulmonary diffusing capacity (D_L) and cardiac output (Q_L) in exercise. *Eur. J. Appl. Physiol.* 33:127–37
4. Bartlett, H. L., Kollias, J., Hodgson, J. L., Buskirk, E. R. 1973. A possible explanation of exercise $D_{L_{CO}}$ based on estimations of SA_L and τh. *Respir. Physiol.* 19:333–43
5. Bondi, K. R., Van Liew, H. D. 1973. Fluxes of CO_2 in the lung gas studied by continuously recorded arterial pH. *J. Appl. Physiol.* 35:42–46
6. Brashear, R. E., Pamintuan, R. L. 1971. Increased pulmonary diffusing capacity and elevated cerebrospinal fluid pressure. *J. Appl. Physiol.* 30:844–46
7. Bryant, S. C., Navari, R. M. 1974. Effect of plasma proteins on oxygen diffusion in the pulmonary capillaries. *Microvasc. Res.* 7:120–30
8. Burri, P. H., Weibel, E. R. 1971. Morphometric estimation of pulmonary diffusion capacity. II. Effect of Po_2 on the growing lung. Adaption of the growing rat lung to hypoxia and hyperoxia. *Respir. Physiol.* 11:247–64
9. Cerny, F. C., Dempsey, J. A., Reddan, W. G. 1973. Pulmonary gas exchange in non-native residents of high altitude. *J. Clin. Invest.* 52:2993–99
10. Cerretelli, P., Veicsteinas, A., Teichmann, J., Magnussen, U., Piiper, J. 1974. Estimation by a rebreathing method of pulmonary O_2 diffusing capacity in man. *J. Appl. Physiol.* 37:526–32
11. Chinet, A., Micheli, J. L., Haab, P. 1971. Inhomogeneity effects on O_2 and CO pulmonary diffusing capacity estimated by steady-state method. *Respir. Physiol.* 13:1–22
12. Cohen, R., Overfield, E. M., Kylstra, J. A. 1971. Diffusion component of alveolar-arterial oxygen pressure difference in man. *J. Appl. Physiol.* 31:223–26
13. Cross, C. E., Gong, H. Jr., Kurpershoek, C. J., Gillespie, J. R., Hyde,

R. W. 1973. Alterations in distribution of blood flow to the lung's diffusion surfaces during exercise. *J. Clin. Invest.* 52:414–21
14. Cumming, G. 1974. Alveolar ventilation: recent model analysis. In *Respiratory Physiology*, Ser. 1, MTP Int. Rev. Sci., 139–66. London: Butterworths
15. Cumming, G., Horsfield, K., Preston, S. B. 1971. Diffusion equilibrium in the lungs examined by nodal analysis. *Respir. Physiol.* 12:329–45
16. Cuomo, A. J., Tisi, G. M., Moser, K. M. 1973. Relationship of $D_{L_{CO(SB)}}$ and K^{m-1} to lung volume and partition of pulmonary perfusion. *J. Appl. Physiol.* 35:129–35
17. Dempsey, J. A., Reddan, W. G., Birnbaum, M. L., Forster, H. V., Thoden, J. S., Grover, R. F., Rankin, J. 1971. Effects of acute through lifelong hypoxic exposure on exercise pulmonary gas exchange. *Respir. Physiol.* 13:62–89
18. Effros, R. M. 1972. Pulmonary capillary CO_2 gradients and the Wien effect. *J. Appl. Physiol.* 32:221–24
19. Engel, L. A., Menkes, H., Wood, L. D. H., Utz, G., Joubert, J., Macklem, P. T. 1973. Gas mixing during breath holding studied by intrapulmonary gas sampling. *J. Appl. Physiol.* 35:9–17
20. Engel, L. A., Wood, L. D. H., Utz, G., Macklem, P. T. 1973. Gas mixing during inspiration. *J. Appl. Physiol.* 35:18–24
21. Field, G. B., Jones, G., McFadden, E. R. Jr. 1971. Alveolar-arterial Pco_2 diffusion during rebreathing in chronic airways obstruction. *J. Appl. Physiol.* 31:490–96
22. Forster, R. E., Steen, J. B. 1968. Rate limiting processes in the Bohr shift in human red cells. *J. Physiol. London* 196:541–62
23. Forster, R. E., Crandall, E. D. 1975. Time course of exchanges between red cells and extracellular fluid during CO_2 uptake. *J. Appl. Physiol.* 38:710–18
24. Geelhaar, A., Weibel, E. R. 1971. Morphometric estimation of pulmonary diffusion capacity. III. The effect of increased oxygen consumption in Japanese waltzing mice. *Respir. Physiol.* 11:354–66
25. Gehr, P., Weibel, E. R. 1974. Morphometric estimation of regional differences in the dog lung. *J. Appl. Physiol.* 37:648–53

26. Gong, H. Jr., Kurpershoek, C. J., Meyer, D. H., Cross, C. E. 1972. Effects of cardiac output on $^{18}O_2$ lung diffusion in normal resting man. *Respir. Physiol.* 16:313–26

27. Gros, G., Moll, W. 1971. The diffusion of carbon dioxide in erythrocytes and hemoglobin solutions. *Pfluegers Arch.* 324:249–66

28. Guleria, J. S., Pande, J. N., Sethi, P. K., Roy, S. B. 1971. Pulmonary diffusing capacity at high altitude. *J. Appl. Physiol.* 31:536–43

29. Gurtner, G. H. 1972. Nonequilibrium steady-state differences in P_{CO_2} and in concentration of weak acids and bases between blood and tissue. *Biophys. J.* 12:597–608

30. Gurtner, G. H., Fowler, W. S. 1971. Interrelationship of factors affecting pulmonary diffusing capacity. *J. Appl. Physiol.* 30:619–24

31. Guyatt, A. R., Yu, C. J., Lutherer, B., Otis, A. B. 1973. Studies of alveolar-mixed venous CO_2 and O_2 gradients in the rebreathing dog lung. *Respir. Physiol.* 17:178–94

32. Hill, E. P., Power, G. G., Longo, L. D. 1973. A mathematical model of carbon dioxide transfer in the placenta and its interaction with O_2. *Am. J. Physiol.* 224:283–99

33. Hill, E. P., Power, G. G., Longo, L. D. 1973. Mathematical stimulation of pulmonary O_2 and CO_2 exchange. *Am. J. Physiol.* 224:904–17

34. Hlastala, M. P. 1972. A model of fluctuating alveolar gas exchange during the respiratory cycle. *Respir. Physiol.* 15:214–32

35. Hlastala, M. P. 1973. Significance of the Bohr and Haldane effects in the pulmonary capillary. *Respir. Physiol.* 17: 81–92

36. Hyde, R. W., Marin, M. G., Rynes, R. I., Karreman, G., Forster, R. E. 1971. Measurement of uneven distribution of pulmonary blood flow to CO diffusing capacity. *J. Appl. Physiol.* 31:605–12

37. Johnson, L. R., Van Liew, H. 1974. Use of arterial P_{O_2} to study convective and diffusive gas mixing in the lungs. *J. Appl. Physiol.* 36:91–97

38. Jones, N. L., Campbell, E. J. M., McHardy, G. J. R., Higgs, B. E., Clode, M. 1967. The estimation of carbon dioxide pressure of mixed venous blood during exercise. *Clin. Sci.* 32:311–27

39. Jones, N. L., Robertson, D. G., Kane, J. W., Campbell, E. J. 1972. Effect of

P_{CO_2} level on alveolar-arterial P_{CO_2} difference during rebreathing. *J. Appl. Physiol.* 32:782–87

40. Jones, R. S., Meade, F. 1961. A theoretical and experimental analysis of anomalies in the estimation of pulmonary diffusing capacity by the single breath method. *Q. J. Exp. Physiol.* 46:131–43

41. Kindig, N. B., Hazlett, D. R. 1974. The effects of breathing pattern in the estimation of pulmonary diffusing capacity. *Q. J. Exp. Physiol.* 59:311–29

42. Klocke, R. A. 1973. Mechanism and kinetics of the Haldane effect in human erythrocytes. *J. Appl. Physiol.* 35: 673–81

43. Klocke, R. A., Andersson, K., Rotman, H. H., Forster, R. E. 1972. Permeability of human erythrocytes to ammonia and weak acids. *Am. J. Physiol.* 222: 1004–13

44. Kötter, D., Huch, A., Stotz, H., Piiper, J. 1969. Single breath CO diffusing capacity in anesthetized dogs with increased oxygen consumption. *Respir. Physiol.* 6:202–8

45. Lawson, W. H. Jr. 1971. Effect of anemia, species, and temperature on CO kinetics with red blood cells. *J. Appl. Physiol.* 31:447–57

46. Lawson, W. H. Jr. 1972. Effect of drugs, hypoxia and ventilatory maneuvers on $D_{L_{CO}}$ in man. *J. Appl. Physiol.* 32: 783–94

47. Laszlo, G., Clark, T. J. H., Pope, H., Campbell, E. J. M. 1971. Differences between alveolar and arterial P_{CO_2} during rebreathing experiments in resting human subjects. *Respir. Physiol.* 12: 36–52

48. McEvoy, J. D. S., Jones, N. L., Campbell, E. J. M. 1973. Alveolar-arterial P_{CO_2} difference during rebreathing in patients with chronic hypercapnia. *J. Appl. Physiol.* 35:542–45

49. Menkes, H. A., Sera, K., Rogers, R. M., Hyde, R. W., Forster, R. E., DuBois, A. B. 1970. Pulsatile uptake of CO in human lung. *J. Clin. Invest.* 49:335–45

50. Michaelson, E. D., Sackner, M. A., Johnson, R. L. Jr. 1973. Vertical distributions of pulmonary diffusing capacity and capillary blood flow in man. *J. Clin. Invest.* 52:359–69

51. Micheli, J. L., Haab, P. 1970. Estimation de la capacité de diffusion pulmonaire pour l'oxygène chez l'homme au repos par la méthode du rebreathing hypoxique. *J. Physiol. Paris* 62, Suppl. 1:194–95

52. Mochizuki, M., Tazawa, H., Ono, T. 1973. Microphotometry for determining the reaction rate of O_2 and CO with red blood cells in the chorioallantoic capillary. In *Oxygen Transport to Tissue,* ed. D. F. Bruley, H. I. Bicher, 997–1006. New York: Plenum

53. Nishida, O., Masaki, S., Kakugawa, M., Kambe, M., Nishimoto, Y. 1973. Aging influence on pulmonary function in healthy adults. *Hiroshima J. Med. Sci.* 22:1–15

54. Nishida, O., Takano, M., Yoshimi, T., Sewake, N., Nishimoto, Y. 1973. Determination of pulmonary diffusing capacity, membrane diffusing capacity and pulmonary capillary blood volume by partial rebreathing technique. *Hiroshima J. Med. Sci.* 22:17–28

55. Piiper, J. 1969. Apparent increase of O_2 diffusing capacity with increased O_2 uptake in inhomogeneous lungs: theory. *Respir. Physiol.* 6:209–18

56. Piiper, J., Huch, A., Kötter, D., Herbst, R. 1969. Pulmonary diffusing capacity at basal and increased O_2 uptake levels in anesthetized dogs. *Respir. Physiol.* 6:219–32

57. Piiper, J., Cerretelli, P., Rennie, D. W., di Prampero, P. E. 1971. Estimation of the pulmonary diffusing capacity for O_2 by a rebreathing procedure. *Respir. Physiol.* 12:157–62

58. Piiper, J., Scheid, P. 1971. Respiration: Alveolar gas exchange. *Ann. Rev. Physiol.* 33:131–54

59. Power, G. G., Aoki, V. S., Lawson, W. H. Jr., Gregg, J. B. 1971. Diffusion characteristics of pulmonary blood-gas barrier at low temperatures. *J. Appl. Physiol.* 31:438–46

60. Rankin, J., McNeill, R. S., Forster, R. E. 1961. The effect of anemia on the alveolar-capillary exchange of carbon monoxide in man. *J. Clin. Invest.* 40:1323–30

61. Riley, R. L., Permutt, S. 1973. Venous admixture component of the $AaPo_2$ gradient. *J. Appl. Physiol.* 35:430–31

62. Rosenhamer, G. J., Frierson, W. O., McIlroy, M. B. 1971. A bloodless method for measurement of diffusing capacity of the lungs for oxygen. *J. Appl. Physiol.* 30:603–10

63. Rotman, H. H., Klocke, R. A., Anderson, K. K., D'Alecy, L., Forster, R. E. 1974. Kinetics of oxygenation and deoxygenation of erythrocytes containing hemoglobin S. *Respir. Physiol.* 21:9–17

64. Roughton, F. J. W. 1935. Recent work on carbon dioxide transport by the blood. *Physiol. Rev.* 15:241–96

65. Roughton, F. J. W., Forster, R. E. 1957. Relative importance of diffusion and chemical reaction rates in determining rate of exchange of gases in the human lung, with special reference to true diffusing capacity of pulmonary membrane and volume of blood in the lung capillaries. *J. Appl. Physiol.* 11:290–302

66. Scheid, P., Adaro, F., Teichmann, J., Piiper, J. 1973. Rebreathing and steady state pulmonary Do_2 in the dog and in inhomogeneous lung models. *Respir. Physiol.* 18:258–72

67. Scheid, P., Teichmann, J., Adaro, F., Piiper, J. 1972. Gas-blood CO_2 equilibration in dog lungs during rebreathing. *J. Appl. Physiol.* 33:582–88

68. Siegwart, B. P., Gehr, P., Gil, J., Weibel, E. R. 1971. Morphometric estimation of pulmonary diffusion capacity. IV. The normal dog lung. *Respir. Physiol.* 13:141–59

69. Sirs, J. A. 1970. The interaction of carbon dioxide with the rate of exchange of oxygen by red blood cells. In *Blood Oxygenation,* ed. D. Hershey, 116–36. London: Plenum

70. Sirs, J. A. 1974. The kinetics of the reaction of carbon monoxide with fully oxygenated hemoglobin in solution and erythrocytes. *J. Physiol. London* 236:387–401

71. Stein, T. R., Martin, J. C., Keller, K. H. 1971. Steady-state oxygen transport through red blood cell suspensions. *J. Appl. Physiol.* 31:397–402

72. Sundström, G., Zauner, C. W., Arborelius, M. 1973. Decrease in pulmonary diffusing capacity during lipid infusion in healthy men. *J. Appl. Physiol.* 34:816–20

73. Thews, G., Schmidt, W., Schnabel, K. H. 1971. Analysis of distribution inhomogeneities of ventilation, perfusion and O_2 diffusing capacity in the human lung. *Respiration* 28:197–215

74. Turek, Z., Frans, A., Kreuzer, F. 1971. Steady-state diffusing capacity for carbon monoxide in the rat. *Respir. Physiol.* 12:346–60

75. Turek, Z., Frans A., Kreuzer, F. 1972. Hypoxic pulmonary steady-state diffusing capacity for CO and alveolar-arterial O_2 pressure difference on growing rats after adaption to a simulated altitude of 3500 m. *Pfluegers Arch.* 335:1–9

76. Turek, Z., Grandtner, M., Ringnalda, B. E. M. Kreuzer, F. 1973. Hypoxic pulmonary steady state diffusing capacity for CO and cardiac output in rats born at a simulated altitude of 3500 m. *Pfluegers Arch.* 340:11–18
77. Vreim, C. E., Staub, N. C. 1973. Indirect and direct pulmonary capillary blood volume in anesthetized open-thorax cats. *J. Appl. Physiol.* 34:452–59
78. Vreim, C. E., Staub, N. C. 1974. Pulmonary vascular pressures and capillary blood volume changes in anesthetized cats. *J. Appl. Physiol.* 36:275–79
79. Wagner, P. D., Mazzone, R. W., West, J. B. 1971. Diffusing capacity and anatomic dead space for carbon monoxide ($C^{18}O$). *J. Appl. Physiol.* 31:847–52
80. Wagner, P. D., West, J. B. 1972. Effects of diffusion impairment on O_2 and CO_2 time courses in pulmonary capillaries. *J. Appl. Physiol.* 33:62–71
81. Weibel, E. R. 1970–1971. Morphometric estimation of pulmonary diffusing capacity. I. Model & Method. *Respir. Physiol.* 11:54–75
82. Weibel, E. R. 1972. Comparative analysis of mammalian lungs. *Respir. Physiol.* 14:26–43
83. Weibel, E. R. 1973. Morphological basis of alveolar-capillary gas exchange. *Physiol. Rev.* 53:419–95
84. Weibel, E. R., Untersee, P., Gil, J., Zulauf, M. 1973. Morphometric estimation of pulmonary diffusion capacity. VI: Effect of varying positive pressure inflation of air spaces. *Respir. Physiol.* 18:285–308
85. Weiskopf, R. B., Severinghaus, J. W. 1972. Diffusing capacity of the lung for CO in man during acute acclimation to 14,246 ft. *J. Appl. Physiol.* 32:285–89
86. Yu, C. J., Lutherer, B., Guyatt, A. R., Otis, A. B. 1973. Comparison of blood and alveolar gas composition during rebreathing in the dog lung. *Respir. Physiol.* 17:162–77
87. Zander, R., Schmid-Schönbein, H. 1972. Influence of intracellular convection on the oxygen release by human erythrocytes. *Pfluegers Arch.* 335:58–73
88. Zander, R., Schmid-Schönbein, H. 1973. Intracellular mechanisms of oxygen transport in flowing blood. *Respir. Physiol.* 19:279–89

PHYSIOLOGICAL ASPECTS OF GROWTH AND DEVELOPMENT OF THE PREIMPLANTATION MAMMALIAN EMBRYO

❖1144

John D. Biggers and Raymond M. Borland

Department of Physiology and Laboratory of Human Reproduction and Reproductive Biology, Harvard Medical School, Boston, Massachusetts 02115

INTRODUCTION

This review deals with the physiology of the preimplantation stages of pregnancy, with particular emphasis on the mammalian embryo between fertilization and implantation. Fertilization takes place in the ampullary region of the oviduct and implantation takes place in the uterus. The passage of the embryo from the ampulla to the uterus is called the *tubal journey;* throughout this period the embryo can easily be flushed from the female genital tract without disrupting any fixed morphological relationship between it and its mother. During this free-living period, the embryo undergoes first the cleavage divisions and then becomes regionalized into the trophoblast and inner cell mass, which enclose the blastocoele fluid to form the blastocyst. The general background for this area is provided by several recent textbooks and monographs (4, 8, 19, 68, 69, 71, 115). The time of the tubal journey varies according to species (17). Moreover, the free-living period and tubal journey are not necessarily coincident because of the phenomenon of delayed implantation which occurs in some species (55, 138).

The embryo is the hub of this system. An analysis of the physiology of the preimplantation embryo, however, is complicated; during its journey to the uterus, the embryo follows an internally programmed sequence of development while moving from one environment to another. Thus the potential for exchange between the embryo and its environment depends both on its stage of development and its location.

The developmental sequence followed by the embryo is an irreversible process. Studies on the embryos of oviparous species indicate that the developmental se-

95

quence follows a program determined partly by the transcription of the maternal genome during oogenesis and partly by the reading of the new genome after fertilization (50, 67, 120). The available evidence also suggests that qualitatively similar processes occur in mammals (19, 36). A major part of this review deals with recent biochemical work on these developmental processes in the preimplantation embryo. The literature covered is primarily that published since January 1973. However, it has had to be selective. Until recently, this area has been largely descriptive, first in morphological and then in biochemical terms (17). We have tried to present the information in functional terms, raising, for example, questions concerning the nature of the control mechanisms, the role of transport mechanisms, and the effects of metabolic pools and compartmentalization. We feel that such approaches are essential if further fundamental progress is to be made in understanding the initial stages of pregnancy.

ANABOLIC AND CATABOLIC PROCESSES

The volume of the preimplantation embryo of several species falls during the initial cleavage divisions (17, Table 1). In contrast, during the growth of the blastocyst, the volume increases (14); in some species, such as the rabbit, the increase in volume is large and rises exponentially. Table 1 also shows that a significant fall in total protein occurs during the initial cleavage divisions of the mouse in parallel with the decrease in volume. It has been argued from this data that catabolic processes predominate during the early cleavage stages.

Recent studies on the total dry weight of preimplantation mouse embryos using a quartz-fiber balance (74, Table 1) and interference microscopy (1) indicate that more complex changes occur during the initial cleavage stages. The absolute values observed differ considerably between methods. Nevertheless, both studies show that no change in dry weight occurs after the first cleavage division. It is clear that if proteins are lost during this period other substances must replace them. One con-

Table 1 The volume, dry weight, total protein, DNA, and RNA per embryo in several stages of preimplantation development of the mouse. (The stages have been approximated for the dry weight and nucleic acid data as the authors timed the stages in terms of the time of HCG injection.)

Stage	Volume (nl)[a]	Dry weight (ng)[b]	Total protein (ng)[c]	DNA (ng)[d]	RNA (ng)[d]
Unfertilized ovum					
1-cell fertilized	0.192	23	27.8	29.3	0.55
2-cell	0.158	24.2	26.1	41.1	0.40
8-cell	0.138	—	23.4	155	0.46
morula – early blastocyst	0.219	22.6	20.6–23.9	439	1.37

[a] From measurements of projections (86).
[b] From measurements with a quartz fiber balance (74).
[c] Using Lowry's method (26).
[d] Using fluorometric assays (100).

tributor is glycogen, which is rapidly accumulated between the 1- and 8-cell stages (101, 121). The contribution of other substances has yet to be determined.

A significant fall in dry weight of the ovum has been demonstrated between fertilization and the first cleavage division (1). The initial loss could be caused by the cortical reaction and the extrusion of the first polar body, which follow sperm penetration. These possibilities emphasize that loss of cytoplasm may also contribute to changes in the volume and mass of embryos during the initial cleavage divisions. A phenomenon known to classical embryologists, called *deutoplasmolysis* —meaning elimination of yolk (24)—should always be considered in accounting for the gross loss of material during the cleavage stages.

The contents of several macromolecules change during preimplantation development (Table 1). The list includes complex, heterogeneous mixtures such as total protein, and RNA; substances that may be compartmentalized, such as DNA found in both the nucleus and cytoplasm (100); and specific substances such a glycogen and enzymes, which may or may not be compartmentalized. Perhaps the amount of RNA is the simplest case to consider. The mean values of RNA measured in the unfertilized ovum, 1-, 2-, 8- 16-cell and blastocyst stages of the mouse demonstrate that no significant change in RNA per embryo occurs until after the 8-cell stage (100). Similarly, in the rabbit, the amount of RNA per embryo changes little until the 16-cell stage (90). In both species, the RNA per embryo then rapidly increases. Thus the increase in RNA occurs at about the same stage in both species. A simple interpretation of these results is that RNA synthesis is low during the early cleavage stages and that it increases rapidly at the early morula stage. The amount of several enzymes has been measured in several preimplantation stages of the mouse (17, 27, 57). Some of these enzymes increase, others decrease, some decrease and then increase, some increase and then decrease, and some do not change. The results summarized by Epstein (57) are based on the total enzyme activity assayed under optimal conditions. The results are therefore estimates of the total specific protein at each stage and do not reflect the functional activity of the enzymes. Nevertheless, the results are significant physiologically in that they demonstrate that simultaneously some proteins may accumulate whereas others may be lost. Thus major shifts in the patterns of accumulation and loss of proteins may occur during development; presumably such changes are correlated with the amounts of different RNAs.

The balance between synthesis and breakdown of macromolecules in a preimplantation embryo can be usefully analyzed by compartmental analysis (5). At present a two-compartment model may be appropriate (Figure 1). where Q_1 is the amount

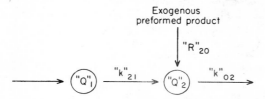

Figure 1 Two-compartment model of macromolecule metabolism in the preimplantation embryo.

of precursor, Q_2 is the amount of product, R_{20} is the rate of transport of preformed exogenous product directly into the embryo, k_{21} is the rate constant for conversion of precursor to product, and k_{02} is the rate constant for removal of the substance from the embryo.

The behavior of Q_2 is described by the differential equation

$$dQ_2/dt = R_{20} + k_{21}Q_1 - k_{02}Q_2. \qquad 1.$$

The component represented by R_{20} provides for the uptake by the embryo of a macromolecule present in the environment, for example by pinocytosis. There is ample evidence from ultrastructural studies that preimplantation embryos can assimilate materials by this route (72). To what extent this process is important under normal conditions is unknown. However, it may be relevant that the isthmic region of the mouse oviduct secretes glycogen into its lumen at a time when resident 2-cell embryos rapidly accumulate this substance (109). Also uteroglobin (blastokinin), a protein of maternal origin, accumulates in the blastocoele fluid (10) after the differentiation of tight junctions that prevent the entry of macromolecules between the outer trophoblast cells (52, 73).

The third term in equation 1, $k_{02}Q_2$, represents the rate of degradation of the particular substance. Little is known about such processes other than that they occur. The loss of several enzymes and glycogen during development in vivo of the mouse implies that degradation can become the dominant term. A particularly interesting example is the partial replacement of lactate dehydrogenase I by lactate dehydrogenase V during the cleavage stages of the mouse (7).

Most attention has been focused on the second term of equation 1, with special reference to the overall rates of RNA and protein synthesis. In the earlier work in this area (17), embryos of different stages were exposed for short times to labeled precursors, usually [³H]uridine for RNA and [³H]amino acids for protein. The labeled macromolecules were detected by autoradiography or the uptakes quantitatively measured by scintillation counting. The rate of incorporation of [³H]uridine into RNA of mouse embryos is low until the 8-cell stage, at which time there is a marked increase. A major part of the precursor is incorporated into rRNA (54). In the rabbit embryo, the correspondence is less precise because uridine incorporation into RNA is low until the transition from morula to blastocyst (90). Such studies support the view that RNA synthesis is low until a critical stage of development. The results show in addition that synthesis of proteins occurs at all stages of preimplantation development of the mouse (58). Nevertheless, the rate of protein synthesis is low until the 8-cell stage, after which it rapidly increases. The reality of this pattern of protein synthesis is also supported by the observations that fertilized ova contain very few ribosomes, whereas morulae and blastocysts are abundantly supplied with ribosomes and polyribosomes (33). Similar studies on the preimplantation stages of the rabbit suggest a slightly different pattern in the rate of protein synthesis in that it remains low until the blastocyst has formed (day 3 postcoitum) after which a rapid increase occurs (80).

Recently, it has been pointed out that a comparison between stages of the uptake of precursors into macromolecules is not simple (21, 58). An estimate of the rate of incorporation of a labeled amino acid into protein is a measure of the rate of protein synthesis only if adequate concentrations are available at the intracellular site of synthesis. Should the supply of a labeled precursor be limited by the permeability of the cell or by dilution by a large endogenous pool, the rate of protein synthesis estimated from the amount of isotope incorporation may be seriously in error. The observed differences in the incorporation of an amino acid between developmental stages could, in fact, be the result of complex differential changes in cell permeability, the size of the endogenous pool, and the rate of protein synthesis. The existence of a significant amino acid pool in preimplantation mouse embryos should be kept in mind because protein synthesis occurs in the absence of any exogenous amino acids (35), and single amino acids such as [^{3}H]leucine and [^{3}H]methionine are incorporated linearly with time in the absence of any other endogenous amino acids or amino nitrogen source (21).

Recent studies on the rate of protein synthesis in the preimplantation mouse embryo have tried to avoid these difficulties (21, 58) by determining for each stage the relation between accumulation of the labeled amino acid into the trichloroacetic acid-soluble pool and into the macromolecule. The uptake of the labeled amino acid into the acid-soluble pool continues to rise at very high concentrations of the precursor, whereas the incorporation into protein reaches a maximum at relatively low concentrations. It is thus possible to find a concentration of precursor that does not limit the inherent rate of protein synthesis. Using this method, Epstein & Smith (58) have shown in the mouse that, prior to the 8–16-cell stage, there is a low level of protein synthesis after which a marked increase occurs. Borland (21) has also demonstrated in the mouse a 2–8-fold increase in protein synthesis between the 4-cell and early blastocyst stage.

By expressing incorporation rates at each stage on a per cell basis, it becomes clear that the early cleavage stages of the mouse, between the 1- and 8–16-cell stages, do not increase protein synthesis in proportion to the increase in cell number. This finding suggests that part of the synthesis taking place during this period is determined by preexisting messengers partitioned to the cells. In contrast, between the 8–16-cell stage and the early blastocyst stage, there is a 4–6-fold increase in synthesis and a 3–4-fold increase in cell number. Thus this burst of protein synthesis may represent little more than a relatively constant rate of synthesis per cell over a period of 2–3 divisions. Nevertheless, the overall change still represents a departure from the pattern at earlier stages (58). In the rabbit, no increase in incorporation occurs until blastocyst formation, at which time the rate of incorporation per cell increases 8–10-fold (80). Despite an increase in cell number, the rate per cell remains constant during the blastocyst stage.

The developmental changes in protein synthesis in early mammalian embryos differ considerably from the pattern present in lower organisms. In sea urchin embryos, within minutes after fertilization, there is a 2.5–5-fold increase in the rate of protein synthesis (56, 129). Similarly, in the mollusc, *Illyanassa,* there is a 5-fold increase in leucine uptake and a 12.5-fold increase in incorporation into protein by two hours after fertilization (97).

Recent work indicates that specific proteins are synthesized at certain stages of development (59), although the full spectrum is unknown. The electrophoretic pattern of proteins synthesized by preimplantation mouse embryos on days 1–4 has been analyzed using electrophoresis on polyacrylamide disc gels containing sodium dodecyl sulfate (SDS). For comparisons between stages, the embryos were incubated pairwise in sufficiently high concentrations of [³H]- and [¹⁴C]-labeled amino acids to minimize the effects of endogenous pools. The two groups of embryos were then combined and the proteins isolated and electrophoresed simultaneously. Although the resolving power of polyacrylamide gel electrophoresis is limited, 20–25 labeled protein components of apparent molecular weights 25,000–115,000 were identified, five of which were dominant. The rates of synthesis of three proteins increased with development, one decreased, and the other did not change. The comparisons showed that the greatest changes occurred between the 2- and 8–16-cell stages. The finding is unexpected as this is a period when only a slight increase in the rate of protein synthesis occurs; however, it does coincide with the period when the morphology of the mitochondria undergoes major changes (122). There were fewer differences between the 8–16-cell stage and the early blastocyst stage, with an increase in a single protein being the only major event. Between the early blastocyst and late blastocyst (day 4) stages, there was again only one major change, a decrease in a protein peak at 67,500 daltons. Possibly these changes represent the synthesis of major, quantitatively important structural proteins such as microtubular protein and membrane constitutents. It is relevant that the synthesis of microtubular protein with a molecular weight of 52,000 has been demonstrated at the 16-cell stage in sea urchins (78, 108).

The quantitative patterns of protein synthesis in preimplantation rabbit embryos grown in vivo and in vitro have been measured using SDS polyacrylamide gel electrophoresis followed by autoradiography (131).

These results show that most of the quantitative changes in the pattern of protein synthesis occur during cleavage (day 0.5–3, postcoitum), that the blastocyst period (day 3–6) is characterized by a uniform and constant pattern of protein synthesis, and that the quantitative pattern of protein synthesis in embryos cultured from the 1-cell stage to the blastocyst stage is identical to the pattern in vivo. The most obvious changes in the pattern of protein synthesis occurs during the first few days of development, especially between days 0.5–1.5. Of particular interest are the protein bands at 200,000, 51,000, and 45,000 daltons that appear after day 1.5. The band at 45,000 daltons is quite dense by day 2.5 and represents several percent of the total protein synthetic activity of the embryo. Preliminary studies have indicated that these bands are probably myosin, tubulin, and actin, respectively (131). From days 3–6, during blastocyst expansion, the pattern of protein synthesis remains remarkably uniform and constant, with the exception of two bands.

Petzoldt (102) has separated the soluble proteins from early rabbit blastocysts and, in later stages, from the embryoblastic and trophoblastic parts. Twenty or more proteins were detected. At the beginning of blastocyst formation, there is an increase in protein synthesis in the embryoblastic part. The protein pattern also changes qualitatively. These changes nearly coincide with the passage of the embryo through the uterotubal junction and thus with possible changes in the environment. No changes were observed in the spectrum of detectable proteins during the rapid growth and rapid accumulation of proteins that occurs in blastocysts developing in utero.

CONTROL OF PROTEIN SYNTHESIS

The control of protein synthesis in early mammalian embryos is not understood. A priori, there are several physiological conditions that could regulate protein synthesis: (a) the synthesis and availability of mRNA, rRNA, and tRNA could be limited by low RNA polymerase activities, (b) the nature and availability of tRNAs may control both rRNA and protein synthesis, and/or (c) the supply of ribosomes may limit translation of existing mRNAs.

There are at least three species of RNA polymerase having specific subcellular localizations (111): polymerase I is present primarily within the nucleolus and is involved in the synthesis of rRNA; polymerase II is localized in the nucleoplasm and is associated with the synthesis of DNA-like RNA; and a third minor polymerase, whose transcriptive properties are still unknown, is present in the nucleoplasm. Total RNA polymerase activity as measured by total [^{3}H]UTP incorporation in vitro with an embryo homogenate is very low in unfertilized eggs and in 1-cell mouse embryos (118). This activity increases in an exponential fashion during subsequent development. From the 2-cell to the early blastocyst stage, RNA polymerase activity increases 8-fold, in contrast to a 30-fold increase in number of cells per embryo. This difference indicates that the amount of RNA polymerase per cell actually decreases with embryonic development at the same time that the rate of RNA synthesis increases faster than the number of blastomeres (99). No apparent correlation can be detected between the enzymatic activity present at a certain stage and the amount of RNA synthesized. Two points must be remembered in evaluating this data: 1. total RNA polymerase activity was measured, and a totally different pattern may exist for each of the three polymerases, and 2. true RNA synthetic rates are not known for day 2 of development (45).

An estimate of the relative activities of RNA polymerase I and II in mouse blastocysts has been obtained by measuring the RNA polymerase activity in vitro in the presence or absence of α-amanitin, an inhibitor of RNA polymerase II (137). The assays were performed at high ionic strength, which favors the detection of RNA polymerase II, and at low ionic strength. The enzymes are inhibited 6% at low ionic strength and 35% at high ionic strength, indicating that more RNA polymerase I relative to RNA polymerase II is present in blastocysts. This result, as well as the effect of α-amanitin on development in vitro (see below), provides evidence for the presence and function of both forms of polymerase in preimplantation mouse embryos.

The role of newly synthesized RNA in early mammalian development is not clear. The sensitivity of the 1-cell mouse embryo to inhibition by actinomycin D and α-amanitin has suggested that normal development depends upon immediate genomic activation following fertilization (66, 96, 128). Other studies show that α-amanitin can arrest development of mouse embryos at the 2-cell stage (137). Although 67% of the untreated embryos developed to the morula or blastocyst stages, less than 1% of the embryos exposed to 1 μg ml^{-1} of α-amanitin developed to the morula or blastocyst stage. Thus 1- and 2-cell mouse embryos probably express their own genome; moreover, the class of RNA synthesized during the first cleavage division is probably mRNA, as there are no mature nucleoli present at the 1-cell stage (76) and the earliest demonstration of rRNA synthesis has been at the 4-cell stage (81).

In the cleaving rabbit embryo, actinomycin D causes an immediate arrest of cleavage, whereas α-amanitin allows limited further development (91). A decreasing ratio of amino acid incorporation caused by continuous exposure of cleaving rabbit embryos to α-amanitin suggests that a relatively homogenous embryonic mRNA supports early protein synthesis and turns over with a half-life of approximately 24 hr. Polysome associated mRNA containing polyadenylic acid sequences are detectable from the 16-cell stage through the blastocyst stage in preimplantation rabbit embryos (113). The metabolic stability of this polysomal poly(A) containing mRNA in 6-day rabbit blastocysts has been examined under conditions which do not involve the use of inhibitors of RNA synthesis (114). Because the rRNA is stable and increases linearly with the time, mRNA decay could be analyzed by comparing the ratio of mRNA to 18S RNA labeling. Such a comparison has shown that mRNAs can be divided into two groups: those with a half-life of approximately 7 hr and those with a half-life of approximately 18 hr. Unfortunately, the 2-cell rabbit embryo does not synthesize rRNA (89) and this technique could not be applied to early cleavage stages. Because the half-life of mRNA molecules in rabbit blastocyst is long (as in growing mammalian cell lines), rapid changes in rates of protein synthesis probably depend on control mechanisms which operate at the translational level rather than at the level of transcription. The nature and synthesis of tRNAs could provide this translational control.

Limited information is available on the presence of tRNAs in mouse embryos. Different stages have been incubated in the presence of labeled uridine and the classes of RNA separated on columns of methylated albumin keiselguhr (MAK) (54, 139). Several classes of RNA are separable by the 8-cell stage. The first major component eluted from the column contains soluble RNA (sRNA). The sRNA has been further separated on Sephadex G-100 columns into 4S and 5S fractions. The sRNA from 8-cell mouse embryos was found to have a high proportion of 5-ribosyl uracil, which suggests that it contains tRNA. No further studies have been undertaken on the nature of tRNAs and their synthesis in the mouse. In the rabbit, however, Manes & Sharma (92) have used simultaneous labeling of embryonic tRNA with [^{32}P] phosphoric acid and L-[methyl-^{3}H]methionine to facilitate a comparison between the rate of synthesis of the nucleic acid polymer and the rate and extent of its subsequent methylation in the intact embryo. Transfer RNA methylation decreases approximately 6-fold between the 52nd and 84th hour of embryonic development, a period coinciding with blastocyst formation, increased protein synthesis, and increased ribosome production (80).

The hypermethylation of tRNA in the cleaving rabbit embryo resembles that demonstrated in transformed and neoplastic cells (20). The methylated bases of tRNA are known to be determinants in amino acid acceptance (117), codon response (34), and ribosomal binding (61). Thus decreased methylation in rabbit embryos may be directly and causally related to the elevated protein and ribosome synthesis that occurs with blastocyst formation.

Bernstein & Mukherjee (12) have accumulated evidence that a cytoplasmic factor is involved in the regulation of RNA synthesis in the early mouse embryo. By producing heterokaryons between the 2- and 4-cell stage mouse embryos and adult somatic cells using Sendai virus-mediated cell fusion, it was found that the cytoplasm of 2-cell blastomeres contains factor(s) that inhibit RNA synthesis in previously competent somatic cell mouse nuclei. Inhibitory factors were largely lost by the 4-cell stage. The nature of this cytoplasmic factor, however, is not known, but the possibility that it is a tRNA should be considered.

An additional point of control of protein synthesis could be the availability of ribosomes. Highly ordered lattice-like structures in the cytoplasm of mouse oocytes are probably ribosomes stored in an inactive form (32). They may be released after fertilization to be used for protein synthesis until the embryo can make its own functional ribosomes. Some protein synthesis occurs in the mouse embryo shortly after fertilization, i.e. before rRNA synthesis begins, and this suggests that maternal ribosomes are functional during these very early stages of development. Although rRNA synthesis begins at the 4–8-cell stage in the mouse and rat (125), this does not, in itself, indicate that functioning ribosomes are being produced. Little is known concerning the synthesis of ribosomal proteins during the preimplantation period or how quickly new ribosomes are formed or are capable of functioning in protein synthesis.

Tasca & Willis (126) obtained biochemical evidence for the assemblage of ribosomes from newly synthesized rRNA and ribosomal proteins (rPr) during mouse cleavage. Large numbers of synchronously developing embryos in vitro were labeled with either [^{14}C]amino acids or [5-^{3}H]uridine to label rPr and rRNA respectively. Ribosomes of labeled embryos were coextracted with mouse liver ribosomes to provide optical density markers for 40S and 60S ribosomal subunits on sucrose gradients. The 40S and 60S marker regions were heavily labeled with both [^{14}C]amino acids and [5-^{3}H]uridine within 6 hr, as early as the 8-cell stage. To ensure the removal of nascent proteins from the two subunits, 0.2 M NaCl was used in the extraction of the ribosomal subunits. The rate of rPr synthesis relative to general protein synthesis was expressed as the percentage of all incorporated labeled amino acid entering the two ribosomal subunits. In the early 8-cell stage, only 2% of the incorporated amino acids entered ribosomal proteins. In contrast to this low rate of synthesis, at the late 8-cell, morula, and blastocyst stages, 6–7% of the incorporated label entered ribosomal proteins. At these stages, the rate of rPr synthesis relative to the rate of general protein synthesis approaches that found in growing cell cultures, both mammalian and bacterial.

The [^{14}C]amino acids are associated with both subunits and separation of the rPrs by acrylamide gel electrophoresis (R. J. Tasca and D. W. Willis, personal communication) has indicated a low level of labeling throughout the gels. Presumably, rPr synthesis is coordinated with rRNA synthesis. These data correlate well with electron microscopical studies, which show an increase in the number of polyribosomes as cleavage progresses (33) and as the nucleolus progressively differentiates (76).

In the rabbit, Karp, Manes & Hahn (80) have shown that protein synthesis markedly increases at the morula stage of rabbit development (60-hr embryo). In the late morula, an increase in cytoplasmic ribosomes is observed, suggesting that ribosome availability may be rate-limiting for protein synthesis during cleavage. As shown by radioautography [3H]amino acids become highly localized within the nucleoli of late morulae that have been pulse labeled for 10 min. This localization indicates that rPr synthesis increases at the same time as rRNA synthesis increases. Concurrent synthesis of rRNA and rPr in preimplantation embryos is similar to the situation in L cells (37), where rPrs must be synthesized concurrently with rRNA in order to be used in the formation of ribosomal subunits, which are assembled in the nucleolus (116).

Work with rat skeletal muscle and bacteria suggests that protein degradation, as well as protein synthesis, is regulated by the same mechanisms that control rRNA synthesis, possibly by a lack of complete complement of aminoacyl tRNA (65). Existing evidence indicates that the production of ribosomes in bacteria is dependent on the intracellular supply of aminoacyl tRNA (53), and that when a cell lacks a full complement of charged tRNA, synthesis of rRNA ceases (65).

GENERATION OF ATP

One general measure of the overall metabolic activity of the preimplantation embryo is its adenylate content. The ATP and ADP contents of several stages of preimplantation mouse embryos have been measured (62, 104) using the firefly luciferase assay. The 1-cell embryo is characterized by a high concentration of ATP, which decreases gradually through the blastocyst stage. Most importantly, the ATP/ADP ratio is very high in early stages. In this respect, the mouse ovum resembles the ovum of the teleost fish (140) rather than that of the sea urchin or sea squirt (49) with regard to the levels of ATP present before and after fertilization. In the ovum of the sea squirt and sea urchin, a marked decrease in ATP occurs immediately after fertilization.

The effect of culturing mouse embryos on the ATP and ADP contents has been determined (105). Both 8-cell and morula stage embryos cultured for 24–48 hr in medium containing pyruvate and lactate have greater amounts of ATP than embryos cultured in either energy substrate-free medium or medium containing glucose. At the 1- and 2-cell stage, a combination of pyruvate and lactate is more effective than either energy substrate alone in maintaining the levels of ATP during a 6-hr culture period. As development progresses, the higher levels of ATP in embryos cultured in glucose than in embryos cultured in energy substrate-free medium indicate that glycolysis plays an increasingly important role in ATP synthesis.

During short-term culture of the early mouse embryo, only pyruvate and lactate, but not glucose, can maintain levels of ATP equivalent to those in embryos in vivo. Therefore, it seems probable that oviducal mouse eggs derive most of their energy from the oxidative phosphorylation of pyruvate and lactate (70). Unlike the mouse, large increases in ATP do not occur until the blastocyst stage in the rabbit (28).

Ginsberg & Hillman (62) have determined the rates of synthesis and turnover of ATP in 2-, 4-, 8-cell, late morula, and late blastocyst stage mouse embryos in vitro. Progressive decreases in total ATP and the ATP/ADP ratio from the 2-cell stage to the late blastocyst stage are accompanied by increases in the rates of ATP turnover and ATP synthesis. Significant differences in the levels of ATP synthesis between preimplantation stages suggest that an altered concentration or availability of energy coupling sites during development might account for the observed differences (63). The actual and the potential activities of the cytochrome system were studied in cleavage-stage mouse embryos by assaying for total ATP and rates of [^{32}P] ATP synthesis both before and after incubation in medium supplemented either with an energy coupling site inhibitor: amytal (site I active), antimycin (site II active), cyanide (site III active), or with the FADH-linked substrate succinate. None of the coupling site-specific inhibitors produces more than a 20% inhibition of total ATP at the 2-cell stage. At the 4–8-cell stage, the inhibiting effects of the three agents rise markedly. Assuming that the permeability of the different-stage embryos to the inhibitors is constant, this rise could be caused by a higher rate of ATP metabolism at the late 4-cell stage compared to the 2-cell stage. The level of aerobic ATP synthesis at the 2-cell stage suggests that the activity of the citric acid cycle is low. Addition of succinate to the medium bypasses the NADH-linked isocitrate dehydrogenase (IDH) (EC 1.1.1.41) and stimulates ATP synthesis, indicating that low citric acid cycle activity is due to a low level of IDH activity. Beginning at the late 4-cell stage and continuing through the 8-cell stage, the ATP/ADP ratio decreases, IDH activity increases, and succinate no longer stimulates ATP production.

A second shift in metabolism occurs between the 8-cell and late morula stage of the mouse. Although a large increase in O_2 uptake starts at the late morula stage (95), no accompanying increase in ATP synthesis occurs (62). These conditions of high O_2 uptake and low ATP synthesis suggest that late morulae mitochondria are uncoupled. The three inhibitors are less effective at this stage than at the 8-cell stage (63) and ATP synthesis probably occurs predominantly by glycolysis. Net ATP synthesis and sensitivity to the three inhibitors increase at the late blastocyst stage, indicating that the citric acid cycle is again functional. These changes in metabolism are well correlated with structural changes in the mitochondria of the preimplantation rat (93), rabbit (3), and mouse (122). In the mouse, mitochondria contain few transverse cristae and have a dense matrix up to the 4–8-cell stage, at which time they appear to undergo a transition to a more orthodox structure that is finally realized in the morula and maintained in the blastocyst.

Although it is known that the turnover of ATP increases with development, the mechanisms by which ATP is utilized are obscure. Studies from other systems indicate that at least four means of utilizing ATP can be highly significant: 1. for microtubule assembly (49); moreover tubules may be synthesized in preimplantation rabbit embryos, 2. for amino acid activation (98), 3. for phosphorylation processes such as the synthesis of NADP from NAD^+ (2), and 4. increased activity of various ATPases (112).

METABOLIC PATHWAYS AND THEIR CONTROL

The changes in the ATP content and ATP synthetic and turnover rates in the early mouse embryo suggest the occurrence of major changes in the activity of metabolic pathways. Recent work has helped to elucidate the mechanisms controlling these changes. Barbehenn et al (9) investigated the metabolite levels and enzyme activity in single mouse embryos using the techniques of amplification through enzymatic cycling (87). Hexokinase (EC 2.7.2.2) is probably not the site of control of glucose metabolism because glucose-6-phosphate levels rise rapidly after refeeding starved embryos, indicating that neither low amounts of hexokinase nor glucose entry into the embryo is a direct cause of the failure of the early embryo to survive on glucose alone. This failure is probably due to inhibition of 6-phosphofructokinase (PFK) (EC 2.7.1.11). There is little change in the absolute amount of this enzyme from the 2-cell stage to the blastocyst stage measured in vitro under optimal conditions (57). Lack of full functional activity of PFK in vivo could be due to the high concentrations of ATP, a powerful allosteric inhibitor of this enzyme. Among the deinhibitors of PKF, ADP and fructose-6-phosphate probably increase during this period, whereas P_i does not change (134). These factors, and failure of hexokinase to generate sufficiently high levels of hexose monophosphate, may be the true causes of blockage of glucose utilization.

The activity of the citric acid cycle has been partially assessed by the effects of succinate on ATP levels (63). Enzyme activity and substrate level measurements (9) indicate that restoration of pyruvate to embryos after starvation causes the citrate and 2-oxoglutarate levels to increase at all stages faster than the initial decline in citrate that follows starvation. In contrast, at the 2- and 8-cell stage, malate fell transiently during refeeding with pyruvate, indicating a slow rate of conversion of 2-oxoglutarate to malate. At the morula stage, malate does not fall and presumably the slow step is removed. Regulation of IDH may cause these shifts (63).

The complex shifts in the function of metabolic pathways in the preimplantation embryo may be related to the energy charge (15), defined by Atkinson (6) as ([ATP] + 0.5 [ADP])/([ATP] + [ADP] + [AMP]). The energy charge can range from 0 to 1. When the energy charge is near unity, the proportion of ATP is very high and certain energy generating enzymes such as IDH and PFK are inhibited. The evidence described previously indicates that both of these enzymes are inhibited in the preimplantation mammalian embryo. Unfortunately no measurements of AMP levels have been made in preimplantation embryos to test this hypothesis.

Metabolic function is also controlled by other factors such as the redox states of various oxidation-reduction couples of the cell (84). The redox states of the NAD^+ couple and the NADP couple are defined as $[NAD^+_{free}]/[NADH_{free}]$ and $[NADP^+_{free}]/[NADPH_{free}]$, respectively. These ratios determine: (a) the direction of reversible reactions, (b) the extent to which pyridine nucleotides are effective as reducing agents in reactions such as the synthesis of fatty acids and nonessential amino acids, and (c) the magnitude of the free energy changes of oxidation-reduction reactions such as those involved in the transport of electrons along the respiratory chain.

Little work has been done on the role of $NAD^+/NADH$ in early mammalian development. Streffer, Elias & van Beuningen (123) showed that NAD^+ (0.23 mM) could improve the development of 2-cell embryos in culture in the presence of pyruvate, whereas higher concentrations appeared toxic. The NAD(H) (total NAD^+ plus NADH) content was found to decrease during cleavage (85, 124).

Recently, the reduced and oxidized forms of NAD in single embryos were measured by enzymatic cycling (134). The total content of NAD(H) falls from the 1- to 2-cell stage. This fall is apparently not caused by conversion to NADP (85). There does not appear to be any overall change in the redox state of NAD-NADH during development, and 30–40% of the NAD^+ pool is present in the reduced form at each stage. These estimates, however, do not differentiate between bound and free nucleotide or between mitochondrial and cytoplasmic pools. Significant shifts between these pools could be important in controlling metabolism.

The values of the redox states are also related to the relative concentrations of adenylates. Krebs (84) has shown that the phosphorylation state defined as $[ATP]/[ADP] [P_i]$ is directly proportional to $[NAD^+_{free}]/[NADH_{free}]$ in the cytoplasm and indirectly proportional to the same ratio in the mitochondria. The study of these interrelations in preimplantation embryos may provide further insight into the control of energy generating and energy utilizing processes in early development. Fortunately techniques for approaching these problems are available (87).

ANABOLIC FUNCTIONS OF METABOLIC PATHWAYS

Glucose

The activity of the metabolic pathways also affects synthetic processes in the embryo. For example, culture experiments with chemically defined media have shown that the mouse oocyte, fertilized ovum (18), and 2-cell embryo (25) cannot develop when glucose is the sole carbon source. The 8-cell and morula stages, however, can utilize glucose for a number of synthetic processes (133). By characterizing the labeled products derived from the metabolism of [U-14C]glucose, Wales showed that 14C incorporation increases with development, and that only 50% appears in the acid-soluble fraction, with the remainder found in protein, lipids, and nucleic acids. Both the 8-cell and morula stage embryos cultured for 24 hr in [U-14C]glucose exhibit increasing isotope incorporation into RNA. Moreover, the relative incorporation of carbon from glucose into the various classes of RNA differs significantly from the pattern of incorporation of [3H]uridine (54). Thus the existence of different precursor pools for the entry of glucose or uridine into the various classes of RNA needs to be considered along with differential entry of the compounds into the same precursor pools. The results seriously question the reliance on the incorporation of a single precursor as the criterion for estimating the relative rates of synthesis of RNA species in the embryo. Subsequent experiments following the incorporation of C1 and C6 labeled glucose into RNA (133) have demonstrated no difference in the incorporation of specifically labeled sugars and have confirmed the insignificant part the hexose monophosphate shunt plays in the metabolism of the mouse embryo (27). Nevertheless nonoxidative interconversion of hexose and pentose phosphates must occur to account for labeling of the sugar moiety in the nucleic acids.

Preimplantation rabbit embryos in vitro cannot develop in the presence of glucose alone until the blastocyst stage (47). The uptake of glucose carbon by the embryo increases with development, with a substantial increase in the incorporation of carbon from glucose occurring after blastocyst formation (106). A considerable amount of the label incorporated is present in the embryos as the parent substrate, indicating that the uptake of glucose is greater than its conversion to other metabolites. Throughout development, glucose carbon is incorporated into acidic and basic acid-soluble compounds, proteins, and lipids. The blastocyst tissue incorporates carbon from glucose into lactate, citrate, and malate, as well as glutamate, alanine, and aspartate, demonstrating the operation of glycolysis and the citric acid cycle. As glucose carbon was also detected in lactate, pyruvate, and acetate in the incubation medium prior to the blastocyst stage, glycolysis must occur throughout preimplantation development in the rabbit, contrary to earlier studies indicating little or no glycolytic activity prior to blastocyst formation (60).

Pyruvate and Lactate

The ability of lactate to support development of 2-cell mouse embryos in vitro is less than that of pyruvate (25), and the incorporation of substrate carbon from lactate alone, as compared to that from pyruvate, is also lower at this stage (107). This difference occurs up to the morula stage, but after this stage the incorporation of C2 of lactate is greater than that of pyruvate.

The incorporation of both pyruvate and lactate carbon increases with the development of the preimplantation mouse embryo (107). Before the morula stage, the presence of unlabeled lactate in the medium depresses incorporation of C2 of pyruvate, whereas the opposite effect occurs when embryos are cultured in $[2\text{-}^{14}C]$lactate in the presence of unlabeled pyruvate.

The failure of 1- and 2-cell mouse embryos to develop in culture media containing lactate as the sole energy source may depend ultimately on the high ATP/ADP ratio, which probably limits the flux of reducing equivalents through the electron transfer chair. This limitation may cause a gross imbalance in the redox state of the NAD^+ and NADH couple when lactate is converted to pyruvate (107). The simultaneous production of excessive amounts of NADH by lactate dehydrogenase, and the inability of the electron transfer chain to regenerate adequate levels of NAD^+, may limit the activity of the citric acid cycle (83) to such a degree that it prevents the metabolic conversion of adequate amounts of lactate to various essential intermediary metabolites needed for both biosynthetic and energy generating purposes.

Carbon Dioxide

The distribution of radioisotope fixed from $^{14}CO_2$ has been studied in various macromolecular fractions of mouse embryos (16). At early stages, the degree of $^{14}CO_2$

fixation is small. As development progresses, an increasing amount of $^{14}CO_2$ is fixed directly into DNA and RNA (103). No label was found in RNA at the 2-cell stage. At all subsequent stages, all RNA subclasses were labeled. The purine, adenine, was most heavily labeled, but label was also found in the various other bases. Significant fixation of carbon dioxide for the de novo synthesis of RNA probably occurs via the enzymes, ATP:carbamate phosphotransferase (dephosphorylating) (EC 2.7.2.5) and phosphoribosylaminoimidazole carboxylase (EC 4.1.1.21). The similarity of the pattern of $^{14}CO_2$ incorporation into RNA to labeled uridine incorporation supports the claim that RNA synthesis increases with development.

Intermediary Metabolites

Although acetate, like citrate, will not support development of 2-cell mouse embryos (25), its pattern of uptake is considerably different from that of citrate (135). Although significant amounts of substrate carbon accumulate from acetate between the 2- and 8-cell stage, there is no change in incorporation. This observation is in contrast to the findings for citric acid cycle intermediates (82) and probably explains why these latter compounds rather than acetate can act as suitable energy sources at this stage (25). Because acetate can enter the cell (136), its inability to support development probably arises either from a limited conversion of acetate to acetyl CoA or from an insufficient endogenous pool of oxaloacetate to act as acceptor for the acetyl CoA that is formed.

Malate and oxoglutarate are also unable to support the development of 2-cell embryos (25). The accumulation of citrate, malate, and oxoglutarate in vitro is significantly greater in 8-cell embryos than in 2-cell embryos (82). The low uptake of these three citric acid cycle intermediates by 2-cell mouse embryos compared to later stages may indicate that transport mechanisms in mitochondria are deficient at this stage and become active after the 2-cell stage.

TRANSPORT PHENOMENA

Amino Acid Transport

Epstein & Smith (58) reported that the uptake of leucine and perhaps lysine in preimplantation mouse embryos is saturable, temperature sensitive, and mediated by active transport systems. No developmental changes in the transport system were described, and the kinetic characteristics of amino acid transport were not examined. Borland & Tasca (22) analyzed the transport properties of methionine and leucine in late 4-cell, late morulae, and early blastocysts. Late 4-cell embryos and early blastocysts that had developed in vitro concentrated both amino acids by processes exhibiting saturable, Michelis-Menten-type kinetics, characteristic of carrier-mediated active transport. The uptake is temperature sensitive and inhibited by certain large neutral amino acids competing for the same uptake site. Kinetic analyses indicate that the uptake of methionine is mediated by a single transport system at the 4-cell stage, and by two distinct transport systems at the early blastocyst stage. There is a 2–2.5-fold increase in V_{max} values for methionine and leucine between the 4-cell and early blastocyst stage. Most importantly, leucine, methionine, and phenylalanine transport is Na^+ independent at the 4-cell stage, methionine transport is partially Na^+ dependent at the late morula stage, and the transport of all three amino acids is Na^+ dependent at the early blastocyst stage.

Specific amino acids are required for outgrowth of the mouse trophoblast cells in vitro. The increased uptake and activation of the Na^+-dependent amino acid transport system may serve to regulate growth mechanisms by controlling the internal concentrations of nutrients (77).

The fact that the Na^+-dependent transport systems are activated at the late morula and early blastocyst stages suggests that they may be involved in normal blastocyst formation and expansion. The nature of the ion requirements and energy requirement was further investigated by determining if increased transport is energy dependent and the nature of the Na^+ requirement for transport (23). Embryos were preincubated for 1 hr in inhibitor(s) and incubated an additional hour in inhibitor(s) plus labeled methionine. Methionine transport was inhibited by oligomycin (5 μg ml^{-1}) at the late 4-cell stage, indicating an energy requirement for transport. At the early blastocyst stage, iodoacetate (1 mM) and oligomycin (5 μg ml^{-1}) effectively blocked methionine transport. Iodoacetate was ineffective as a transport inhibitor at the 4-cell stage. These data indicate that oxidative phosphorylation is necessary for transport at the 4-cell stage, but transport at the early blastocyst stage is energized by both glycolysis and oxidative phosphorylation. These results are not surprising considering the increasingly important role of glycolysis at the later stage in preimplantation mouse embryos.

The cation dependency of [^{3}H]methionine transport was studied at the late morula and early blastocyst stage (23). The effect of Na^+-depleted medium on [^{3}H]methionine uptake by early mouse blastocysts indicates a competitive type of inhibition. This result suggests that Na^+ serves to increase the affinity of methionine for the carrier. The effect of Na^+-depleted medium is specific for Na^+-dependent amino acid transport and does not appear to be a nonspecific effect on overall cell metabolism. For example, [^{3}H]methionine transport is Na^+ dependent in late morulae, whereas [^{3}H]phenylalanine transport at this stage is not affected by Na^+-depleted medium. It was not shown if amino acids accumulated at the blastocyst stage of the mouse are accumulated in the blastocoele fluid as reported for the rabbit blastocyst (79).

Ions and Blastocyst Formation

Variations in the concentrations of several ions can affect the development of the 2-cell mouse embryos (132). Potassium and calcium were the only ions found to be essential for development to the blastocyst stage. Calcium may be needed for stabilization of membranes and junctional complexes. Calcium and ferrous iron are necessary for development of the preimplantation rabbit embryo, whereas K^+ was not essential (48). The role of these ions in preimplantation development is not understood. The role of some of these ions in mammalian blastocyst formation is, however, partially defined.

The mammalian blastocyst develops in part by the internal accumulation of fluid consisting of inorganic and organic substances dissolved in water (14, 88). Almost all of the work has been done on the rabbit, a species especially suitable for pioneering studies because of the large increases in volume from about 2 nl between the third and fourth day postcoitum to about 2.5 ml on the tenth day.

A transtrophoblastic electrical potential difference (TPD), presumably indicating active transport, was demonstrated in rabbit (42) and in mouse blastocysts (44). This TPD was greatly reduced by anoxia and metabolic inhibitors and could be altered by replacement of Na^+ and Cl^- with other ions (43). Direct demonstration of active transport came when Cross (39) applied the Ussing and Zerahn short-circuit method to 6-day rabbit blastocysts. In the absence of electrochemical gradients, net sodium and chloride transport are both three times larger than the short-circuit current (SCC) and account for only 5% of the SCC. The average rate of bicarbonate transport is in good agreement with the nonsodium, nonchloride component of the SCC, suggesting that bicarbonate accumulation in the 6-day rabbit blastocoele is also due to active transport (41). H^+ is passively distributed across the blastocoele wall (40).

R. M. Borland, J. D. Biggers, and C. P. Lechene (unpublished) have used electron probe microanalysis of picoliter samples of fluid to measure the concentration of Na, Cl, K, Ca, Mg, S, and P in rabbit blastocysts at 110, 135, and 159 hr postcoitum. Using these data and the calculated rate of accumulation of blastocoelic fluid (46), the rate of accumulation of fluid and solutes during the first 3 days of blastocyst development was estimated. The rates of accumulation of both fluid and solute show striking increases during each 24-hr interval. These increases in accumulation rates of both fluid and solutes are not proportional to the increase in cell number or embryo surface area and indicate that the capacity of transport mechanisms for solute and fluid movement increases with development. These increases may be a result of the development of carrier systems or of morphological changes in the rabbit blastocyst. Electron microscopical studies of the mouse embryo at the early morula stage show focal tight junctions near the cell apices (52). As the morula develops, these become zonular and exclude lanthanum, thereby separating the inner cells from the maternal environment. In rabbit embryos, both gap and tight junctions were visualized in freeze-fracture replicas of rabbit blastocysts (52, 73). The zonula occludens forms a lanthanum impermeability barrier consistent with the high transtrophoblastic electrical resistance of 2188 ohms cm^2 found by Cross (38). Freeze fractures of 5- and 6-day rabbit blastocysts showed that the 5-day blastocysts averaged 2–3 ridges per tight junction lattice; 6-day blastocysts had lattices that averaged 5–6 ridges (73). These morphological changes could partially explain the increased fluid and solute accumulation rates during development.

The mechanisms involved in mouse blastocyst formation remain obscure. Mouse blastocysts can be mechanically collapsed with a bevelled pipette and reexpansion will occur (64). Neither actinomycin D (0.1 μg ml^{-1}) nor puromycin (50 μg ml^{-1}) inhibited reexpansion, although both agents eventually destroyed the embryos. Other studies have used the mold metabolite cytochalasin B to collapse mouse blastocysts (51). Early mouse blastocysts incubated for 2 hr in a concentration of 5 μg ml^{-1} of culture medium collapsed in 2 hr, but 95% of them recovered in 3 hr after removal of the drug. Na$^+$-depleted medium (25 mM Na$^+$), K$^+$-free medium, and ouabain (1 mM) all blocked reexpansion in the recovery medium. This blockage was reversible upon reincubation in normal medium. The mode of action of cytochalasin B on the early mouse embryo is not known; one possibility is that it may weaken the junctional complexes. If this mode of action is correct, the data support the suggestion that ouabain-sensitive sites may be localized on the blastocoelic surface of the trophoblast cells (23). A similar situation has been directly demonstrated in early *Xenopus laevis* embryos in which ouabain did not influence the development of the embryos unless it was injected into the blastocoele (119).

The elemental composition of the early mouse blastocoele fluid (84–87 hr postcoitum) in embryos in vivo has recently been measured in our laboratory by electron probe microanalysis. The mouse blastocoele contains very high concentrations of K, Mg, and Ca (33, 5, and 6 mM, respectively). Mouse serum in comparison contains only 5.3 mM K and 3.8 mM Ca. The composition of mouse blastocoele fluid is very unlike that of the rabbit blastocyst. This difference may be due to the fact that rabbit embryos undergo rapid expansion from days 4–8 postcoitum, whereas the mouse blastocyst expands very little (14). These elements in the mouse and rabbit blastocyst may be critical in creating a microenvironment for differentiation of the inner cell mass (75). A possible role of ions in differentiation has recently been discussed by McMahon (94). Unfortunately, elemental analyses of the uterine fluids of the mouse and rabbit are not available during the time the embryos are present in the uterus.

The mechanism of accumulation of fluid in the mouse and rabbit is not known. Tuft & Böving (130) have suggested from measurements of chemical potential that active water transport occurs on day 7–8 postcoitum. Active water transport is not widely accepted by physiologists, and this phenomena needs further exploration.

PREIMPLANTATION EMBRYO AND ITS ENVIRONMENT

Most of this review has focused upon the irreversible developmental aspects of the preimplantation embryo. The embryo, however, is located within the female genital tract whose local secretions contribute to its microenvironment. Because the embryo migrates down the oviduct during this period of development, theoretically the environment can change. As yet, relatively little is known about these microenvironments because of the very low rates of secretion of oviductal fluid (110). As pointed out by Biggers & Bellvé (16), the analysis of oviductal fluids collected by catheterization over extended periods may give a poor indication of the tubal environment. Recently, it has been possible to sample the fluid surrounding mouse 1-cell embryos in the ampulla and 2-cell embryos in the isthmus using micropuncture techniques, and analyze the droplets for Na, Cl, K, Ca, Mg, S, and P by electron microprobe analysis (unpublished, L. Roblero, J. D. Biggers, and C. P. Lechene). The results show that the elemental compositions of ampullary and isthmal fluid are dissimilar and that both are very different in composition from blood plasma. A very striking feature is the very high level of potassium—up to 30 mM.

Figure 2 illustrates the relationship of a preimplantation embryo to its surroundings and the factors that influence the composition of the environment. Three types
of exchange can be recognized: 1. those between the embryo and its environment,
2. those between the microenvironment and the maternal tissues in its immediate
neighborhood, and 3. those between the microenvironment and the neighboring
regions of the genital tract. As yet, we know very little about these processes.
Quantitative aspects of exchanges between the embryo and its microenvironment are
unknown although, as discussed already, the nature of these exchange mechanisms
is now under active study. For example, a start has been made in the study of the
maternal contribution to the microenvironment by studies on the active transport
of Na and Cl by the ampullary region of the oviduct (29–31) and by studies of the
longitudinal flow of fluids along the length of the oviduct (11). The application of
micropuncture techniques and the techniques of ultramicrochemistry show promise
of opening up this field of investigation.

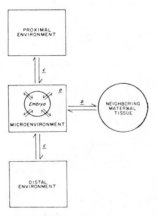

Figure 2   The relationship of a preimplantation embryo to its microenvironment and the
factors influencing the microenvironment. (*a*) Exchanges between the embryo and its microenvironment; (*b*) exchanges between the microenvironment and maternal tissue; (*c*) exchanges
between the microenvironment and adjacent regions of the female genital tract.

CONCLUSION

The evidence presented in this review demonstrates that many complex processes
occur during mammalian preimplantation development. The general pattern is
similar to that found in nonmammalian forms. However, there are two major
differences. First, the rate of development and biochemical change is much slower
in mammalian forms. Second, the mammalian embryo is not completely self-contained but undergoes important exchanges with its mother. These exchanges are of
three types: 1. those concerned with homeostatic functions that preserve the internal
environment of the embryo, e.g. pH, osmotic pressure, 2. those involving the uptake

of substances that can be metabolized, e.g. glucose and amino acids, and 3. specific signals that pass between mother and embryo whose role is to synchronize development and maternal function (13).

It is sometimes argued that the oviducal environment is not important because embryos can develop in ectopic sites and, in some species, in very artificial chemically defined media. These arguments, however, do not prove that exchanges between the embryo and microenvironment are not important or that the embryos are self-contained, but rather that the embryos concerned are very adaptable. The preimplantation stages of many species cannot be successfully cultured with present techniques and may require more specific conditions than the mouse and rabbit. As more is known about the composition of oviducal and uterine fluids, the in vitro development of these other species may soon be possible, as has been demonstrated with preimplantation sheep embryos (127).

ACKNOWLEDGMENTS

The preparation of this review has been made possible by grants from the Rockefeller Foundation RF65040, the NICHD grant HD–06916–01A1, and the NIH Centers Grant 1 P01 HD 06645–03.

Dr. Borland is a postdoctoral fellow supported by the Ford Foundation.

Literature Cited

1. Abramczuk, J., Sawicki, W. 1974. Variation in dry mass and volume of nonfertilized oocytes and blastomeres of 1-, 2- and 4-celled mouse embryos. *J. Exp. Zool.* 188:25–35
2. Aketa, K., Biachett, R., Marre, E., Monroy, A. 1964. Hexose monophosphate level as a limiting factor for respiration in unfertilized sea urchin eggs. *Biochim. Biophys. Acta* 86:211–15
3. Anderson, E., Condon, W., Sharp, D. 1970. A study of oogenesis and early embryogenesis in the rabbit, *Oryctolagus cuniculus,* with special reference to the structural changes of mitochondria. *J. Morphol.* 130:67–92
4. Arey, L. B. 1974. *Developmental Anatomy.* Philadelphia: Saunders. 695 pp.
5. Atkins, G. L. 1969. *Multicompartment Models for Biological Systems.* London: Methuen. 153 pp.
6. Atkinson, D. E. 1968. The energy charge of the adenylate pool as a regulatory parameter. Interaction with feedback modifiers. *Biochemistry* 7:4030–34
7. Auerbach, S., Brinster, R. L. 1967. Lactate dehydrogenase isozymes in the early mouse embryo. *Exp. Cell. Res.* 46:89–92
8. Austin, C. R., Short, R. V. 1972. *Reproduction in Mammals,* Vol. 2. Cambridge, England: Cambridge Univ. Press. 153 pp.
9. Barbehenn, E. K., Wales, R. G., Lowry, O. H. 1974. The explanation for the blockage of glycolysis in early mouse embryos. *Proc. Nat. Acad. Sci. USA* 71:1056–60
10. Beier, H. M. 1974. Ovarian steroids in embryonic development before nidation *Adv. Biosci.* 13:200–18
11. Bellvé, A. R., McDonald, M. F. 1970. Directional flow of Fallopian tube secretion in the ewe at onset of the breeding season. *J. Reprod. Fert.* 22:147–49
12. Bernstein, R. M., Mukherjee, B. B. 1973. Cytoplasmic control of nuclear activity in preimplantation mouse embryos. *Dev. Biol.* 34:47–66
13. Biggers, J. D. 1971. New observations on the nutrition of the mammalian oocyte and the preimplantation embryo. See Ref. 19, Chap. 18, 319–29
14. Biggers, J. D. 1972. Mammalian blastocyst and amnion formation. In *The Water Metabolism of the Fetus,* ed. A. C. Barnes, A. E. Seeds, 1–31. Springfield, Ill: Thomas. 171 pp.
15. Biggers, J. D. 1975. Bioenergetic aspects of fertilization and embryonic development in the mouse. *Proc. VIII*

World Congr. Fert. Steril. Amsterdam: Excerpta Medica. In press

16. Biggers, J. D., Bellvé, A. R. 1973. Carbon dioxide in developmental processes. In *Carbon Dioxide and Metabolic Regulation,* ed. G. Nahas, K. E. Schaefer. Berlin: Springer

17. Biggers, J. D., Stern, S. 1973. Metabolism of the preimplantation mammalian embryo. *Adv. Reprod. Physiol.* 6:1–60

18. Biggers, J. D., Whittingham, D. G., Donahue, R. P. 1967. The pattern of energy metabolism in the mouse oocyte and zygote. *Proc. Nat. Acad. Sci. USA* 58:560–67

19. Blandau, R. J. 1971. *The Biology of the Blastocyst.* Chicago: Univ. Chicago Press, 560 pp.

20. Borek, E. 1971. Transfer RNA and transfer RNA modification in differentiation and neoplasia. *Cancer Res.* 31:596–97

21. Borland, R. M. 1974. Uptake and incorporation of neutral amino acids in preimplantation mouse embryos: Activation of a Na^+-dependent amino acid transport system. PhD thesis. Univ. Delaware, Newark, Del. 190 pp.

22. Borland, R. M., Tasca, R. J. 1974. Activation of a Na^+-dependent amino acid transport system in preimplantation mouse embryos. *Develop. Biol.* 36: 169–83

23. Borland, R. M., Tasca, R. J. 1975. Na^+-dependent amino acid transport in preimplantation mouse embryos. II. Metabolic inhibitors and nature of the cation requirement. *Develop. Biol.* 46:192–201

24. Boyd, J. D., Hamilton, W. J. 1961. *Marshall's Physiology of Reproduction,* ed. A. S. Parkes, 2: Chap. 1, 40–41. Boston: Little, Brown. 880 pp.

25. Brinster, R. L. 1965. Studies on the development of mouse embryos in vitro. II. The effect of energy source. *J. Exp. Zool.* 158:59–68

26. Brinster, R. L. 1967. Protein content of the mouse embryo during the first five days of development. *J. Reprod. Fert.* 13:413–20

27. Brinster, R. L. 1967. Carbon dioxide production from glucose by the preimplantation mouse embryo. *Exp. Cell Res.* 47:271–77

28. Brooks, D. E., Lutwak-Mann, C. 1971. Content of ATP and ADP in rabbit blastocysts. *Nature London* 229:202–3

29. Brunton, W. J. 1971. Active halide transport by isolated rabbit oviduct and

stimulation by isoproterenol. *Fed. Proc.* 30:674 (Abstr.)

30. Brunton, W. J. 1971. Ion transport by isolated rhesus monkey oviduct and stimulation by human seminal plasma and prostaglandin E_1. *Biol. Reprod.* 5:105 (Abstr.)

31. Brunton, W. J., Brinster, R. L. 1971. Active chloride transport in the isolated rabbit oviduct. *Am. J. Physiol.* 221: 658–61

32. Burkholder, G. D., Comings, D. E., Okada, T. A. 1971. A storage form of ribosomes in mouse oocytes. *Exp. Cell Res.* 69:361–71

33. Calarco, P. G., Brown, E. H. 1969. An ultrastructural and cytological study of preimplantation development of the mouse. *J. Exp. Zool.* 171:253–84

34. Capra, J. D., Peterkofsky, A. 1968. Effect of in vitro methylation on the chromatographic and coding properties of methyl-deficient transfer RNA. *J. Mol. Biol.* 33:591–607

35. Cholewa, J. A., Whitten, W. K. 1970. Development of two-cell mouse embryos in the absence of a fixed-nitrogen source. *J. Reprod. Fert.* 22:553–55

36. Church, R. B., Schultz, G. A. 1974. Differential gene activity in the pre- and postimplantation mammalian embryo. *Curr. Top. Dev. Biol.* 8:179–202

37. Craig, N., Perry, R. P. 1971. Persistent cytoplasmic synthesis of ribosomal proteins during the selective inhibition of ribosomal RNA synthesis. *Nature New Biol.* 229:75–80

38. Cross, M. H. 1971. Rabbit blastocoele perfusion technique. *Nature London* 232:635–37

39. Cross, M. H. 1973. Active sodium and chloride transport across the rabbit blastocoele wall. *Biol. Reprod.* 8:566–75

40. Cross, M. H. 1974. Rabbit blastocoele pH. *J. Exp. Zool.* 186:17–23

41. Cross, M. H. 1974. Rabbit blastocoele bicarbonate: accumulation rate. *Biol. Reprod.* 11:654–62

42. Cross, M. H., Brinster, R. L. 1969. Trans membrane potential of the rabbit blastocyst trophoblast. *Exp. Cell Res.* 58:125–27

43. Cross, M. H., Brinster, R. L. 1970. Influence of ions, inhibitors and anoxia on transtrophoblast potential of rabbit blastocyst. *Exp. Cell Res.* 62:303–9

44. Cross, M. H., Cross, P. C., Brinster, R. L. 1973. Changes in membrane potential during mouse egg development. *Develop. Biol.* 33:412–17

45. Daentl, D. L., Epstein, C. J. 1971. Developmental interrelationships of uridine uptake, nucleotide formation and incorporation into RNA by early mammalian embryos. *Develop. Biol.* 24: 428–42

46. Daniel, J. C. 1964. Early growth of rabbit trophoblast. *Am. Natur.* 98:85–98

47. Daniel, J. C. 1967. The pattern of utilization of respiratory metabolic intermediates by preimplantation rabbit embryos in vitro. *Exp. Cell Res.* 47:619–23

48. Daniel, J. C., Millward, J. T. 1969. Ferrous ion requirement for cleavage of the rabbit egg. *Exp. Cell Res.* 54:135–36

49. D'Anna, T. 1969. ATP-content in unfertilized and fertilized eggs of *Ciona intestinalis*. *Experientia* 25:542–43

50. Davidson, E. H. 1968. *Gene Activity in Early Development*. New York: Academic. 375 pp.

51. DiZio, S. M., Tasca, R. J. 1974. Iondependent, ouabain-sensitive re-expansion of mouse blastocysts collapsed with cytochalasin B. *Proc. Am. Soc. Cell Biol.* (Abstr. 63:85a)

52. Ducibella, T., Albertini, D. F., Anderson, E., Biggers, J. D. 1975. The preimplantation mammalian embryo: characterization of intercellular junctions and their appearance during development. *Develop. Biol.* 45:231–50

53. Edlin, G., Broda, P. 1968. Physiology and genetics of the "Ribonucleic acid control" locus in *Escherichia coli*. *Bacteriol. Rev.* 32:206–26

54. Ellem, K. A. O., Gwatkin, R. B. L. 1968. Patterns of nucleic acid synthesis in the early mouse embryo. *Develop. Biol.* 18:311–30

55. Enders, A. 1963. *Delayed Implantation*. Chicago: Univ. Chicago Press. 318 pp.

56. Epel, D. 1967. Protein synthesis in sea urchin eggs: a "late" response to fertilization. *Proc. Nat. Acad. Sci. USA* 57:899–906

57. Epstein, C. J. 1975. Gene expression and macromolecular synthesis during preimplantation embryonic development. *Biol. Reprod.* 12:82–105

58. Epstein, C. J., Smith, S. A. 1973. Amino acid uptake and protein synthesis in preimplantation mouse embryos. *Develop. Biol.* 33:171–85

59. Epstein, C. J., Smith, S. A. 1974. Electrophoretic analysis of proteins synthesized by preimplantation mouse embryos. *Develop. Biol.* 40:233–44

60. Fridhandler, L. 1961. Pathways of glucose metabolism in fertilized rabbit ova

at various preimplantation stages. *Exp. Cell Res.* 22:303–15

61. Gefter, M. L., Russell, R. L. 1969. Role of modifications in tyrosine transfer RNA: a modified base affecting ribosome binding. *J. Mol. Biol.* 39:145–57

62. Ginsberg, L., Hillman, N. 1973. ATP metabolism in cleavage-staged mouse embryos. *J. Embryol. Exp. Morphol.* 30:267–82

63. Ginsberg, L., Hillman, N. 1975. Shifts in ATP synthesis during preimplantation of mouse embryos. *J. Reprod. Fert.* 43:83–90

64. Glass, R. H., Lin, T. P., Florence, J. 1973. Mouse blastocyst re-expansion following puncture and treatment with inhibitors. *J. Reprod. Fert.* 35:533–37

65. Goldberg, A. L., Howell, E. M., Li, J. B., Martel, S. B., Proutz, W. F. 1974. Physiological significance of protein degradation in animal and bacterial cells. *Fed. Proc.* 33:1112–20

66. Golbus, M. S., Calarco, P. G., Epstein, C. J. 1973. The effects of inhibitors of RNA synthesis (α-amanitin and actinomycin D) on preimplantation mouse embryogenesis. *J. Exp. Zool.* 186: 207–16

67. Gurdon, J. B. 1974. *The Control of Gene Expression in Animal Development*. Cambridge, Mass: Harvard Univ. Press. 160 pp.

68. Hafez, E. S. E., Blandau, R. J. 1969. *The Mammalian Oviduct*. Chicago: Univ. Chicago Press. 546 pp.

69. Hafez, E. S. E., Evans, T. N. 1973. *Human Reproduction*. New York: Harper & Row. 778 pp.

70. Hafez, E. S. E., Sugawara, S. 1969. Biochemistry of oviductal eggs in mammals. See Ref. 68, 373–85

71. Hamilton, W. J., Mossman, H. W. 1972. *Human Embryology*. Baltimore: Williams & Wilkins. 646 pp.

72. Hastings, R. A., Enders, A. C. 1974. Uptake of exogenous protein by the preimplantation rabbit. *Anat. Rec.* 179:311–31

73. Hastings, R. A., Enders, A. C. 1975. Junctional complexes in the preimplantation rabbit embryo. *Anat. Rec.* 181: 17–34

74. Hensleigh, H. C., Weitlauf, H. M. 1974. Effect of delayed implantation on dry weight and lipid content of mouse blastocysts. *Biol. Reprod.* 10:315–21

75. Herbert, M. C., Graham, C. F. 1974. Cell determination and biochemical differentiation of the early mammalian embryo. *Curr. Top. Dev. Biol.* 8:151–78

76. Hillman, N., Tasca, R. J. 1969. Ultra-structural and autoradiographic studies of mouse cleavage stages. *Am. J. Anat.* 126:151–74

77. Holley, R. W. 1972. A unifying hypothesis concerning the nature of malignant growth. *Proc. Nat. Acad. Sci. USA* 69:2840–41

78. Hynes, R. O., Raff, R. A., Gross, P. R. 1972. Properties of the three cell types in sixteen-cell sea urchin embryos: aggregation and microtubule protein synthesis. *Develop. Biol.* 27:150–64

79. Jaszczak, S., Hafez, E. S. E., Moghissi, K. S., Kurrie, D. A. 1972. Concentration gradients of amino acids between uterine and blastocoelic fluid in the rabbit. *Fert. Steril.* 23:405–9

80. Karp, G. C., Manes, C., Hahn, W. E. 1974. Ribosome production and protein synthesis in the preimplantation rabbit embryo. *Differentiation* 2:65–75

81. Knowland, J., Graham, C. 1972. RNA synthesis at the two-cell stage of mouse development. *J. Embryol. Exp. Morphol.* 27:167–76

82. Kramen, M. A., Biggers, J. D. 1971. Uptake of tricarboxylic acid cycle intermediates by preimplantation mouse embryos in vitro. *Proc. Nat. Acad. Sci. USA* 68:2656–59

83. Krebs, H. A. 1970. Rate control of the tricarboxylic acid cycle. *Adv. Enzyme Regul.* 8:335–53

84. Krebs, H. A. 1973. Pyridine nucleotides and rate control. *Rate Control of Biological Processes Symp. Soc. Exp. Biol.* ed. D. D. Davies 27:299–318. Cambridge, Engl.: Cambridge Univ. Press. 583 pp.

85. Kuwahara, M., Chaykin, S. 1973. Biosynthesis of pyridine nucleotides in early embryos of the mouse (*Mus musculus*). *J. Biol. Chem.* 248:5095–99

86. Lewis, W., Wright, E. 1935. On the early development of the mouse egg. *Contrib. Embryol. Carnegie Inst.* 25:113–44

87. Lowry, O. H., Passonneau, J. V. 1972. *A Flexible System of Enzymatic Analysis.* New York: Academic. 291 pp.

88. Lutwak-Mann, C. 1971. The rabbit blastocyst and its environment: physiological and biochemical aspects. See Ref. 19. 243–60

89. Manes, C. 1971. Nucleic acid synthesis in preimplantation rabbit embryos. II. Delayed synthesis of ribosomal RNA. *J. Exp. Zool.* 176:87–97

90. Manes, C. 1969. Nucleic acid synthesis in preimplantation rabbit embryos. I. Quantitative aspects, relationship to early morphogenesis and protein synthesis. *J. Exp. Zool.* 172:303–10

91. Manes, C. 1973. The participation of the embryonic genome during early cleavage in the rabbit. *Develop. Biol.* 32:453–59

92. Manes, C., Sharma, O. K. 1973. Hypermethylation of tRNA in cleaving rabbit embryos. *Nature London* 244:283–84

93. Mazanec, K. 1965. Submikroskopsche Veranderungen wahrend der Furchung eines Saugetiereies. *Arch. Biol.* 76:49–85

94. McMahon, D. 1974. Chemical messengers in development: a hypothesis. *Science* 185:1012–21

95. Mills, R. M., Brinster, R. L. 1967. Oxygen consumption of preimplantation mouse embryos. *Exp. Cell Res.* 47:337–44

96. Mintz, B. 1964. Synthetic processes and early development in the mammalian egg. *J. Exp. Zool.* 157:85–100

97. Mirkes, P. E. 1970. Protein synthesis before and after fertilization in the eggs of *Ilyanassa obsoleta*. *Exp. Cell Res.* 60:115–18.

98. Molinaro, M. 1963. *Rend. Accad. Naz. Lincei* 34. 8:563

99. Monesi, V., Salfi, V. 1967. Macromolecular synthesis during early development in the mouse embryo. *Exp. Cell Res.* 46:632–35

100. Olds, P. J., Stern, S., Biggers, J. D. 1973. Chemical estimates of the RNA and DNA contents of early mouse embryos. *J. Exp. Zool.* 186:39–47

101. Ozias, C. B., Stern, S. 1973. Glycogen levels of preimplantation mouse embryos developing in vitro. *Biol. Reprod.* 8:467–73

102. Petzoldt, U. 1974. Micro-disc electrophoresis of soluble proteins in rabbit blastocysts. *J. Embryol. Exp. Morphol.* 31:479–87

103. Pike, I. L., Murdoch, R. N., Wales, R. G. 1974. The in vitro incorporation of carbon dioxide in the RNA of the mouse embryo prior to implantation. *Proc. Aust. Biochem. Soc.* 7:97

104. Quinn, P., Wales, R. G. 1971. Adenosine triphosphate content of preimplantation mouse embryos. *J. Reprod. Fert.* 25:133–35

105. Quinn, P., Wales, R. G. 1973. The effect of culture in vitro on the levels of adenosine triphosphate in preimplantation mouse embryos. *J. Reprod. Fert.* 32:231–41

106. Quinn, P., Wales, R. G. 1973. The in vitro metabolism of [U-14C]glucose by

the preimplantation rabbit embryo. *Aust. J. Biol. Sci.* 26:653-89

107. Quinn, P., Wales, R. G. 1973. Uptake and metabolism of pyruvate and lactate during preimplantation development of the mouse embryo in vitro. *J. Reprod. Fert.* 35:273-87

108. Raff, R. A., Kaumeyer, J. F. 1973. Soluble microtubule proteins of the sea urchin embryo: partial characterization of the pool in early development. *Develop. Biol.* 32:309-20

109. Reinius, S. 1969. *Morphology of Oviduct, Gametes and Zygotes as a Basis of Oviductal Function in the Mouse.* Uppsala: RK-tryck

110. Restall, B. J., Wales, R. G. 1968. The fallopian tube of the sheep. V. Secretion from the ampulla and isthmus. *Aust. J. Biol. Sci.* 21:491-98

111. Roeder, R. G., Rutter, W. J. 1970. Specific nucleolar and nucleoplasmic RNA polymerases. *Proc. Nat. Acad. Sci. USA* 65:675-82

112. Scholnick, P., Long, D., Racker, E. 1973. Regulatory mechanisms in carbohydrate metabolism. X. Stimulation of aerobic glycolysis by energy-linked ion transport and inhibition by dextran sulfate. *J. Biol. Chem.* 248:5175-82

113. Schultz, G. A. 1973. Characterization of polyribosomes containing newly synthesized messenger RNA in preimplantation rabbit embryos. *Exp. Cell Res.* 82:168-75

114. Schultz, G. A. 1974. The stability of messenger RNA containing polyadenylic acid sequences in rabbit blastocysts. *Exp. Cell Res.* 86:190-93

115. Segal, S. J., Crozier, R., Corfman, P. A., Condliffe, P. G. 1973. *The Regulation of Mammalian Reproduction.* Springfield, Ill: Thomas. 586 pp.

116. Shepherd, J., Maden, B. E. H. 1972. Ribosome assembly in HeLa cells. *Nature London* 236:211-14

117. Shugart, L., Novelli, G. D., Stulberg, M. P. 1968. Isolation and properties of undermethylated phenylalanine transfer ribonucleic acids from a relaxed mutant of *Escherichia coli. Biochim. Biophys. Acta* 157:83-90

118. Siracusa, G. 1973. RNA polymerase during early development in mouse embryo. *Exp. Cell Res.* 78:460-62

119. Slack, C., Warner, A. E. 1973. Intracellular and intercellular potentials in the early amphibian embryo. *J. Physiol.* 232:313-30

120. Stearns, L. W. 1974. *Sea Urchin Development.* Stroudsburg, Pa: Dowden, Hutchinson, Ross. 339 pp.

121. Stern, S., Biggers, J. D. 1968. Enzymatic estimation of glycogen in the cleaving mouse embryo. *J. Exp. Zool.* 168:61-66

122. Stern, S., Biggers, J. D., Anderson, E. 1971. Mitochondria and early development of the mouse. *J. Exp. Zool.* 176:179-92

123. Streffer, C., Elias, S., van Beuningen, D. 1974. Influence of NAD$^+$ on development of mouse blastocysts in vitro. *Nature London* 250:434-35

124. Streffer. C., van Beuningen, D. 1974. The content of pyridine dinucleotides in the mouse embryo before implantation. *Develop. Biol.* 38:401-3

125. Suzuki, S., Iizuka, R., Inoue, M., Hamada, Y., Kami, K. 1971. Nucleic acid synthesis in the developing rat embryos in the pre-implantation stages. *Biol. Reprod.* 5:89 (Abstr.)

126. Tasca, R. J., Willis, D. W. 1971. Ribosome biogenesis in late cleavage stage mouse embryos. *Proc. Am. Soc. Cell Biol.* 51:300 (Abstr. 592)

127. Tervit, H. R., Whittingham, D. G., Rowson, L. E. A. 1972. Successful culture in vitro of sheep and cattle ova. *J. Reprod. Fert.* 30:493-97

128. Thomson, J. L., Biggers, J. D. 1966. Effect of inhibitors of protein synthesis on the development of preimplantation mouse embryos. *Exp. Cell Res.* 41:411-27

129. Timourian, H., Watchmaker, G. 1970. Protein synthesis in sea urchin eggs. II. Changes in amino acid uptake and incorporation at fertilization. *Develop. Biol.* 23:478-91

130. Tuft, P. H., Böving, B. G. 1970. The forces involved in water uptake by the rabbit blastocyst. *J. Exp. Zool.* 174:165-72

131. Van Blerkom, J., Manes, C. 1974. Development of preimplantation rabbit embryos. II. A comparison of qualitative aspects of protein synthesis. *Develop. Biol.* 40:40-51

132. Wales, R. G. 1970. Effects of ions on the development of the preimplantation mouse embryo in vitro. *Aust. J. Biol. Sci.* 23:421-29

133. Wales, R. G. 1973. Biochemistry of the developing embryo. *J. Reprod. Fert. Suppl.* 18:117-25

134. Wales, R. G. 1975. Maturation of the mammalian embryo: biochemical aspects. *Biol. Reprod.* 12:66-81

135. Wales, R. G., Whittingham, D. G. 1973. The metabolism of specifically labelled lactate and pyruvate by two-cell mouse embryos. *J. Reprod. Fert.* 33:207–22

136. Wales, R. G., Whittingham, D. G. 1974. Further studies on the accumulation of energy substrates by two-cell mouse embryos. *Aust. J. Biol. Sci.* 27:519–29

137. Warner, C. M., Versteegh, L. R. 1974. In vivo and in vitro effect of α-amanitin on preimplantation mouse embryo RNA polymerase. *Nature London* 248:678–80

138. Weitlauf, H. M. 1974. Metabolic changes in the blastocysts of mice and rats during delayed implantation. *J. Reprod. Fert., Symp. Rep. No. 3* 213–25

139. Woodland, H. R., Graham, C. 1969. RNA synthesis during early development of the mouse. *Nature London* 221:327–32

140. Zotin, A. I., Faustov, V. S., Radzinskaya, L. I., Ozernyuk, N. D. 1967. ATP level and respiration of embryos. *J. Embryol. Exp. Morphol.* 18:1–12

INFLUENCES OF MOVEMENT DETECTORS ON PYRAMIDAL TRACT NEURONS IN PRIMATES

❖1145

R. Porter

Department of Physiology, Monash University, Clayton, Victoria, Australia 3168

INTRODUCTION

In his Ferrier Lecture, Phillips (42), commenting on the report by Evarts (12) that pyramidal tract neuron discharge in the conscious monkey was more related to the force to be generated in particular muscle groups than to other aspects of movement performance, noted:

> One may hazard the speculation that the increased discharge of the PT (pyramidal tract) cell [when more force was required to produce a particular displacement], was in response to a signal of mismatch between "intended" and actual displacement. Whether this signal is a crude one from the muscle spindles, or whether the mismatch has been computed by the cerebellum is still unknown; nor, in this experiment, can the contribution of joints, skin and vision be assessed. But however "instructed", the CM (cortico-motoneuronal) projection would transfer the "instruction" for increased force to the alpha motoneurons with maximum directness. If the CM projection is indeed part of a control loop, new sense is made of the old observation that "voluntary" movements of a monkey's arm are grossly impaired by deafferentation (31), when responses to cortical stimulation are unaffected (40, 51). It may well be that the most important function of fusimotor co-activation in the case of the hand is to maintain the inflow of information of muscle length to the cortex and cerebellum.

This speculation raises a number of questions concerning the function of pyramidal tract neurons and other precentral cells in movement performance. Recent evidence related to this concept of involvement of feedback about movement performance in modifying the "pyramidal command" for movement (Houk 28) is reviewed here. Situated as they are, only one or a few synapses removed from the motoneurons whose orderly recruitment is required for skilled movement, pyra-

121

midal tract neurons could be sites of convergence for a variety of signals relevant to motoneuron output.

But, in evaluating the concept of adjustment of the pyramidal tract output of a control system for movement performance in the light of feedback information about that performance (derived from peripheral receptors in the moving part or from vision), it is necessary not only to demonstrate that the feedback converges onto the pyramidal tract neurons, but that it is effective and appropriate for the required adjustments. Phillips (42) focused attention on the possibility that muscle spindles play a dominant role in a transcortical servo-loop, and some progress has been made toward evaluating that concept. Other experimental work has attempted to examine the "compensation" that results from a disturbance of movement performance (15, 38).

This review examines the progress made in collecting the evidence necessary for the thorough evaluation of the concept propounded by Phillips and quoted above. Only a few of the relevant pieces of scientific work have been selected for inclusion in the commentary. These selected investigations are representative of the studies relating to the problem posed in the opening paragraph. The reader may find it more useful to examine these in some depth, rather than to attempt to cope with a relatively undigested list of all the papers recently published on this topic. A more extensive bibliography can be compiled readily, using the work examined here as a source of references.

A number of separate questions may be extracted from the paragraph quoted from Phillips.

1. Does information from muscle spindles (possibly about mismatch between "intended" and actual displacement) have access to pyramidal tract neurons whose activity is associated with that displacement?
2. Do other systems capable of detecting or measuring movement or displacement (afferents from joints, skin, and vision) also converge onto these same pyramidal tract neurons?
3. By which central nervous pathways does this information reach the pyramidal tract neurons?
4. What changes in pyramidal tract output are produced by purposely disturbing an intended movement (and so activating detectors of position and movement)? Are these changes in an appropriate direction for maintaining the intended movement in spite of the disturbance? Do the changes occur early enough to be useful to the animal in the normal performance of a smooth natural movement? Can normal performance be carried out in the absence of these changes?

A number of these questions have been examined in a variety of animal species. Often the assumption has been made that the detection of a response to a disturbance indicated a competent feedback loop operating in servo-compensation for the disturbance. Yet the nature of the experiment itself invalidated that conclusion because no compensation occurred or because no relation between feedback and compensation was established. In the present review, the examples are drawn almost exclusively from experiments on primates; only occasional reference is made to the important studies on afferent projections to pyramidal tract neurons of the cat or other animals (see 5).

PROJECTIONS TO PYRAMIDAL TRACT NEURONS FROM MUSCLE SPINDLE AFFERENTS

Evoked potentials may be recorded on the surface of both pre- and postcentral cortex when deep tissue is stimulated (1, 37), or when muscle nerves are activated with weak shocks (4). But these evoked potentials could have been generated in zones removed from the recording site. Studies of the discharges of individual neurons in the monkey's cerebral cortex led Powell & Mountcastle (45) to suggest that the buried cortex between the principally "motor" precentral gyrus and the principally "sensory" postcentral gyrus was a region of transition that received "a heavy projection from deep tissues." This view has since received strong support from the studies of Phillips, Powell & Wiesendanger (43). In baboons anesthetized with nitrous oxide and oxygen together with chloralose, stimuli were delivered to muscular branches of nerves supplying the hand and forearm, while the cerebral cortex both in front of and behind the central sulcus was explored with microelectrodes. Both the evoked "field" potentials and the discharges of individual neurons responding to these muscle nerve shocks were localized within area 3a. The majority of units discharged between 5 and 10 msec after the group I volley, set up by weak stimulation of the nerves, entered the spinal cord along dorsal roots. Neurons in area 3a responded to a brief pull on muscle tendons or to brief periods of vibration of tendons. No such early responses were recorded in area 4. Weak shocks applied to muscle nerves did not evoke field potentials or cause the discharge of neurons in area 4, and stimulation of neurons in area 3a did not alter the thresholds for minimal muscle responses caused by intracortical microstimulation in area 4 (43).

The conclusion must be that, under the particular anesthetic conditions used in these baboons, no short-latency powerful excitatory projection from muscle spindles could be demonstrated to influence neurons in area 4. It is also of interest to note that the cells in area 3a, activated by group I volleys in muscle nerves, were not pyramidal tract neurons (they were not sending their axons out of the cortex through the pyramidal tracts). So, area 3a itself was not the reflex center of a long-loop reflex for adjustment of pyramidal tract output to the mismatch between intended and actual muscle length that could be detected by muscle spindles.

But other evidence existed for a projection of influences from muscle receptors to individual neurons in the precentral motor cortex. Albe-Fessard & Liebeskind (3) described influences on motor cortex cells from peripheral stimuli. They noted that a large majority of motor cortex cells could be driven by passive movements of limbs (not by light tactile stimulation of the skin). These effects were considered to arise in muscles because traction on muscle tendons and light pressure on denuded muscles influenced the cells in the cortex. The monkeys used in these experiments were also anesthetized with chloralose. The latencies of the responses of motor cortex neurons could not be measured accurately in these experiments, nor could it be concluded that the recordings were from neurons destined to send their axons into the spinal cord.

Further evidence for the muscular origin of some of the influences projected to the motor cortex was obtained by Albe-Fessard, Lamarre & Pimpaneau (2). These authors stimulated fusimotor fibers to the semitendinosus muscle of critically curarized monkeys. Under these conditions, the dose of d-tubocurarine was adjusted so that stimulation of muscle nerves could still activate the more resistant intrafusal fibers of muscle spindles, even though neuromuscular transmission to extrafusal muscle fibers was totally paralyzed and no overt contractions of the muscle occurred. The stimulation therefore activated muscle spindle afferents without causing muscle contraction or movement of joints. It also produced discharge of neurons in the motor cortex.

Wiesendanger (60) examined the responses of precentral neurons in baboons and monkeys anesthetized with nitrous oxide and oxygen together with chloralose. He was able to demonstrate that electrical stimulation of muscle nerves caused excitation of proven pyramidal tract neurons in the precentral gyrus. Although a few "minimal" responses were obtained with stimuli at 1.4 times group I threshold, most units studied required repetitive shocks of 2–3 times group I threshold, and the unit could be driven by one or more muscle nerves. The mean response latencies of pyramidal tract cells measured from the first peak of the compound action potential entering the spinal cord along dorsal root fibers were of the order of 20–25 msec, although nonpyramidal tract cells could be activated at shorter latencies.

Wiesendanger also found, in contrast to Albe-Fessard and her colleagues, considerable convergence onto individual pyramidal tract cells from both muscle nerve afferents and skin nerve afferents when these were activated by electrical shocks (Albe-Fessard et al had reported their observation for natural stimulation). He reasoned that the strong stimulation of muscle nerves required to activate pyramidal tract cells, the long latencies of the responses, and the insensitivity of the discharges of these pyramidal tract neurons to intravenous injections of succinylcholine which excites primary endings indicated that afferents from secondary, rather than from primary, endings of muscle spindles must be responsible.

Passive manipulation of the finger and wrist joints was an adequate stimulus for discharge of pyramidal tract neurons, and it was reported (60) that the discharges produced by passive manipulation of joints were tonic in character, similar to those reported by Albe-Fessard & Liebeskind (3). These movements could also have activated muscle afferents, and the tonic responses were considered to be consistent with an input from afferent fibers of secondary endings in muscle spindles.

Hore et al (27) recorded from neurons in both area 3a and area 4 of the chloralose anesthetized baboon while they delivered ramps of stretch to hindlimb muscles. The results of their experiments suggest a convergence of inputs from both primary and secondary endings of muscle spindle receptors onto cells in these two regions. Units with the greatest sensitivity to length changes in the muscle were found in area 4, whereas units in area 3a often had little or no "static" response to maintained length of the muscle. Velocity sensitivity, as detected by the dynamic index of the cortical unit when the muscle was subjected to different rates of stretch, was measurable for both units in area 4 and in area 3a, although the latter cells tended to have the greatest velocity sensitivity.

In summary, pyramidal tract neurons and other cells in area 4 of the motor cortex have been shown to be influenced [excited in most experiments, but inhibited in some of the observations of Hore et al (27)] by afferent signals projecting to the central nervous system from muscles. This input reaches the motor cortex later than it is available to cells in area 3a and appears to have a more sustained effect on cells in area 4.

PROJECTIONS FROM RECEPTORS OTHER THAN THOSE IN MUSCLE

Although the experimental work described above establishes that projections from muscle afferents can influence pyramidal tract and other precentral neurons, a contribution from joint afferents, from tendon organs, or from skin receptors could have been involved in producing some of the responses observed. Fetz & Baker (20) examined the responses of a large population of precentral neurons in the "leg" area of conscious monkeys and found that 85% of these responded in a reliable and reproducible way to movement of one or more joints of the contralateral leg. Only a very small proportion of cortical neurons could be shown to be influenced by natural stimulation of the skin.

Fetz et al (22) recorded the discharges of precentral neurons in relation to both active and passive movements of the elbow of conscious monkeys. About half of the cells studied responded only to one direction of passive movement (flexion or extension) and about one-third responded to movement in both directions. Cells that discharged during passive movement of the elbow in only one direction also responded when the animal performed active movements. Roughly one third of these cells discharged most strongly when the active movement was made in the same direction as the passive movement to which the cell responded. For roughly one third, the active movement with which the strongest discharge was associated was in the opposite direction and, for the rest, strong discharge of the cell occurred during active movements in both directions. The suggestion was made that there must be "a variety of input-output relations for precentral cells" receiving projections from elbow afferents (22).

In the conscious cooperating animal, it has not been possible to dissect the contributions of muscle, tendon, skin, or joint afferents to the responses being studied. An impression gained from published work, as well as from observations in the author's own laboratory, is that when natural stimuli such as passive finger flexion are used, more definite, sustained, and reproducible responses of pyramidal tract and other precentral neurons are recorded in the conscious animal, compared with those reported for chloralose anesthetized monkeys. Interaction of influences from a variety of receptors in the moving part may occur more readily at a number of levels in the nervous system and produce a more pronounced effect in the absence of depression produced by anesthetic agents. It is certainly possible that the effects reported by Fetz and his colleagues represent additional influences of joint afferents (over and above those caused by stretching muscles) on precentral neurons.

Evidence for a contribution of peripheral influences, other than those from the prime-mover muscles, in the natural discharges of pyramidal tract neurons came from the studies of Lewis & Porter (34), in which local anesthesia at the wrist was used to reduce the input from skin and joint receptors of the hand (and from the small muscles of the hand), while all the feedback from muscles in the forearm operating about the joints of the hand was left intact. For a small population of pyramidal tract neurons (roughly 10% of the total number studied), selected because they showed clear changes in activity with changes in the load to be moved, as well as a distinct relationship of their bursts of discharge to the timing of contraction of the prime-mover muscles, partial local anesthesia at the wrist produced an increase in activity of pyramidal tract neurons in relation to the same movement performance. But the cell could still change its firing with a change in load (so feedback for this must either have come from intact receptors such as those in muscles or have been internal feedback related to the program of movement). Also the relationship between the cell's activity and the timing of muscle contraction generally was preserved; there was, however, a tendency for a longer period to elapse between the beginning of pyramidal tract discharge and the beginning of movement after the hand had been partially anesthetized.

Goldring, Aras & Weber (23) drew attention to the fact that the afferent projections to the motor cortex are different in different animals and show differential sensitivity to anesthetic agents. They used transcortical recording of evoked potentials in order to localize the inputs from peripheral nerves in the cat [see also the detailed analysis of inputs to cat PT cells by Towe & Tyner (59)], squirrel monkey, and man, and they compared observations made in the awake and the anesthetized states. More responses and a greater variety of influences were detected in the waking monkey than in the anesthetized monkey. Inputs from limited contralateral receptive fields (preserved in the anesthetized state) as well as long latency inputs from large fields, from ipsilateral zones, and of a "polysensory" nature (suppressed by anesthesia) could be defined.

In man, studied with the same evoked potential methods, the responses were variable. In general, however, the afferent projections to the motor cortex of man were more limited and mostly contralateral. No responses to auditory stimuli were found in man or the monkey (although these were readily recorded in the cat). No evoked responses to visual stimuli were observed in any of the three species.

A very limited number of observations have been made on the responses of individual precentral neurons in conscious man during active and passive limb movements (24). The majority of cells discharged only in association with active voluntary movements of the contralateral hand (opening or closing the fist on command), but a few discharged with active movement of either hand. Those cells showing a change in firing that preceded voluntary movement were also excited by the same movement when carried out passively by the observer. This observation held true also for cells whose discharge was related to movements of both hands— these cells had bilateral receptive domains for passive movement. None of the cells was influenced by tactile stimulation (with a light cotton wisp) or by auditory stimulation (with a click). Goldring & Ratcheson (24) concluded from their study of a limited number of cortical units in man that the significant projection to the hand area of motor cortex in man differed from that in animals by being from the restricted region involved in the movement and by being concerned exclusively with movement detection. They concluded: "It appears that, in man, the function of processing diverse sensory inputs from the periphery, a function characterizing the motor cortex of the cat and, to a lesser extent, that of the macaque, has been relegated elsewhere" (24). These observations deserve prominence because they have been made in subjects most able to cooperate, to carry out a variety of movement tasks on command, to relax during passive manipulation, and to attempt exact copies of posture and movement without complex and prolonged training schedules. But the limited number of observations that can be made requires that conclusions be accepted with caution and that additional evidence for these conclusions be sought in further experimental work.

The absence of short-latency responses to visual stimuli of precentral neurons in the monkey and man is consistent with Evart's (16, 17) report that when monkeys were conditioned to make the same movement response to a visual signal or to a perturbation of the handle held by the animal, the responses of pyramidal tract neurons began much earlier following the mechanical stimulus to the hand (an interval of as little as 25 msec) than after the visual signal; the latency was then about 100 msec. The nature of the receptors responsible for the short-latency responses to a mechanical perturbation of the hand to be moved could not be deduced. But from the different responses evoked by different directions of the perturbation [push or pull of the hand (15)] and from the influence of prior instruction on the nature of these short-latency responses (18), it might tentatively be concluded that stretch of muscles by the perturbation was in part responsible for the early effects. A contribution from joint afferents was also possible.

The important conclusion from the experiments of Evarts & Tanji (18) was that, in the conscious animal, even the short-latency influences on pyramidal tract neurons of a small passive movement of the hand could be remarkably modified by the training and instruction regarding the movement performance to be executed after delivery of this perturbation. Such modifications could have occurred by changes in fusimotor drive to spindle receptors or they could have resulted from alterations in central sensitivity to spindle influences. They could also account for variability in the direction of the responses of different individual neurons in a class behaving uniformly in other respects [as in relation to the one direction of active movement performance (22)].

Short-latency influences produced by small perturbations of movement performance by the arm or hand have been reported by Evarts (15), Porter & Rack (48), and Conrad et al (10). The movement performance and its disturbance were quite different in each of these cases, yet the usual latency of the response of pyramidal tract neurons was remarkably similar (of the order of 25 msec as a minimum). This latency is also very similar to that reported from muscle nerve stimulation in anesthetized animals. As in those experiments, nonpyramidal tract neurons could be found that responded earlier to the disturbance. In all cases, the disturbance could have influenced muscle, joint, and skin receptors. The fact that pyramidal tract and other precentral neurons are influenced by a disturbance of movement performance as early as 25 msec after this disturbance is produced could mean that feedback about movement accomplishment plays a part in the modification of pyramidal tract output during movement execution and while the movement is still in progress. Other experiments will be required to demonstrate whether this early influence of peripheral receptors does exert a significant effect on the evolution of a movement once it has been initiated.

PATHWAYS INVOLVED IN PROJECTIONS FROM PERIPHERAL RECEPTORS TO PYRAMIDAL TRACT NEURONS

Although there is a wealth of evidence for connections to the motor cortex from thalamic nuclei, the role of projections from the spinal cord through these, either directly or via the cerebellum, has not been evaluated adequately in attempts to account for the results in primates reported above. Moreover, the contributions that cortico-cortical connections make to the afferent influences on pyramidal tract neurons have received little attention. In particular, it is not clear whether—and by what route—the very early influences of activation of primary afferents from muscle spindles on neurons in area 3a of the cerebral cortex are then relayed from that zone of cortex to pyramidal tract neurons in area 4.

Asanuma & Fernandez (6, 7) studied the receptive fields of individual neurons in the ventrolateral nucleus of the thalamus in cats. A proportion of these cells could be shown to project to the motor cortex. The receptive fields differed markedly from those in the ventrobasal complex. No neuron in the ventrolateral nucleus could be activated from a circumscribed skin area localized on the contralateral side of the body. About half could be activated by pressure somewhere on the contralateral body surface, and it was suggested that the receptors responsible for this activation were located in deep structures. There was often no localized receptive field, but the authors reported their impression that about 90% of the cells that could be activated were influenced by twisting or pressing one or more joints of the contralateral limbs. The other 10% could be influenced by pressure applied to any part of the body surface. The neurons in the ventrolateral nucleus of the cat were shown to project diffusely to the motor cortex [see also Strick (54)] or to project only to a narrow focus (7).

Evidence has been produced suggesting that some cells of the ventrolateral nucleus of the thalamus alter their discharge in relation to movement performance in the monkey and that they may demonstrate characteristic changes in their firing before the beginning of movement (13). But the relationship of peripheral afferent influences to this firing has not been evaluated adequately in primates. Joffroy & Lamarre (29) studied the responses of neurons in the ventrolateral complex of the conscious monkey. About half the cells from which they recorded could be influenced by peripheral stimuli and most of the responsive cells were located in the ventral parts of the complex. (Cells in the dorsal part of the ventrolateral nucleus were not responsive.) The responding cells could be activated by sharp pressure on deep tissues or by taps on tendons or muscles in one or several limbs "either contralateral or homolateral" (29). The latency of some of the responses to sharp taps on muscle was found to be 15–20 msec, and these cells increased their discharge in advance of spontaneous movements.

A recent preliminary study has been made of the effects of a sudden postural disturbance of the fingers on the discharges of ventrolateral nucleus neurons in conscious monkeys (P. Chau and R. Porter, 1975, unpublished observations). About half of a very small sample of neurons situated in the anterior division of the ventrolateral nucleus showed a clear response to a sudden small passive movement of the fingers. None of these responsive units exhibited changes in firing with the muscular activity and the development of force in the postural task itself. The sudden passive movement of the fingers could be controlled, so that a latency of response of each cell in the anterior division of the ventrolateral nucleus of the thalamus could be calculated; these latencies were all between 15 and 30 msec. Therefore some of these responses could have occurred before the activation of pyramidal tract cells in the motor cortex, first seen 20 or more msec after a similar disturbance under the same experimental conditions (48).

The possibility exists, then, that there are cells in the ventrolateral complex of the thalamus that receive inputs from receptors capable of detecting disturbances of movement performance. These cells could be transmitting this information to pyramidal tract neurons after the effect of the disturbance has been "computed by the cerebellum" (42). But more exact information about the connections and precise responses to peripheral stimuli of the thalamic neurons is required to assess this possibility. Moreover, the differential connections of different parts of the ventrolateral complex (32) need to be evaluated because the observations made so far seem to indicate that different populations of neurons behave in quite different ways in relation to movement or its disturbance.

Meyer-Lohmann et al (39) found that reversible cooling of the dentate nucleus had no effect on early precentral responses to sudden displacements imposed on a learned elbow movement being carried out by monkeys. It seems unlikely therefore that a direct pathway from the cerebellar cortex through the dentate nucleus and ventrolateral nucleus of the thalamus is involved in the early response to perturbations of movement. Moreover, although recordings have been made in the cerebellum during movement (57, 58) and during drug induced tremor (33), recordings of the activities of cells in the cerebellar nuclei following sudden disturbances of movement have not been made in primates. The possible contributions of a number of alternative and parallel pathways from peripheral detectors of movement to the motor cortex in producing the early responses of pyramidal tract neurons must be evaluated.

Both pre- and postcentral neurons have been shown to change their firing during active movement performance, although the latter, on average, respond later than the former (14). Moreover, postcentral neurons responded to passive movements of the limb (52) in the conscious cooperating monkey. The short latency of responses of postcentral neurons to peripheral stimuli, the topographical organization of these projections, and the highly organized interconnections between pre- and postcentral regions of cortex in the monkey (41) would seem to suggest a function for postcentral neurons in the feedback to pyramidal tract cells related to movement performance or its disturbance.

Cortical regions other than area 3a could be concerned in the receipt of information from deep structures and subsequent projection of this to output neurons in the precentral gyrus. Powell & Mountcastle (45) reported that, while a majority of cells in area 3 of the postcentral gyrus were activated by cutaneous stimuli, 90% of the cells in area 2 were influenced by activation of receptors in deep tissues (fascia and joints). More recently, Burchfiel & Duffy (9) found cells in area 2 influenced by stimulation of muscles as well as joints. Cells in area 2 had limited receptive domains and were influenced by movement of one joint only, sometimes through a part of its range of movement.

Neurons in area 5 could also be influenced by joint movement (11) but, in their case, the receptive domain included a number of joints, as though these cells were engaged by convergent influences from other neurons, perhaps in area 2. Because area 4 in the precentral gyrus and area 6 and 8 in front of it are sent projections from the regions in receipt of inputs from peripheral receptors (both on the skin and in deep tissues), it is possible that corticocortical connections could subserve the delivery of information from movement detectors to the output pyramidal tract neurons (30). Although Sperry (53) indicated that interruptions of corticocortical connections by multiple transections of the sensorimotor cortex did not disrupt movement performance, refinements of motor skills could be contributed by corticocortical influences.

Recently, Haaxma & Kuypers (25) produced direct behavioral evidence for a function of corticocortical connections between visual receiving areas and the motor cortex in the "visual steering" of relatively independent hand and finger movements. Animals were required to orient the hand so that the thumb and forefinger could be inserted into a pair of grooves leading to a food well in a board. The appropriate grooves were painted white to distinguish them from other radially oriented grooves around the food well. All except these "correct" grooves ended blindly, and the orientation of the correct grooves could be changed from trial to trial, requiring changes in the attitude of the hand and the orientation of the finger and thumb if the food reward was to be retrieved. Following division of occipitofrontal connections, the animal's hand could be brought accurately to the general area of the target, but could not be adapted to the correct orientation of the white grooves without tactile exploration of the field. Yet the animal had no visual discrimination defect. The defect was one of *movement control,* appropriately orienting the hand and fingers to the target under visual control.

EFFECTIVENESS OF AFFERENT DISCHARGE PRODUCED BY DISTURBANCES OF VOLUNTARY MOVEMENT

When a voluntary movement such as flexion of the terminal phalanx of the thumb is unexpectedly obstructed, a human subject will demonstrate increased activity in the flexing muscles to overcome the obstruction—an appropriate and effective output reaction. This had been conceived as a simple spinal reflex response to the obstruction until the experiments of Marsden, Merton & Morton (38) demonstrated that the delay between the disturbance and the response was considerably longer (of the order of 50 msec for the human thumb movement) than would have been expected for a simple stretch reflex. The longer latency could have allowed afferent signals about the disturbance of movement to be transmitted to higher levels of the central nervous system, perhaps including the motor cortex, and for the output of these centers to be changed appropriately for increasing the force of muscle contraction. Marsden, Merton & Morton assembled the evidence on which a long-loop response through the cerebral cortex might be implicated in this situation (38).

That the response was much more complicated than a stretch reflex was also demonstrated by the observation that local anesthesia of the skin and joints of the moving thumb, without in any way affecting the action of the prime mover muscle or its muscle spindle afferents, abolished the response to sudden perturbations of the learned movement. To be effective then, the input system for detecting the disturbance of movement had to include information coming from the moving joint as well as information returning to the central nervous system from the operating muscles. Without this information, the subjects reported that more conscious effort was required to start a movement.

Some authors have interpreted the observations made on pyramidal tract cells of monkeys in the light of the above findings in man. The discharges of cortical neurons that occurred with short latencies after a disturbance of a trained movement were described as part of a "load compensation" reflex (10). But it is not clear in all these cases that load compensation occurred, nor has the role of pyramidal tract neurons in load compensation been demonstrated. Animals could still be trained in a force development task after pyramidal tract section (26). The destinations of the pyramidal tract neurons from which recordings were made in the experiments involving disturbances of movement could not be discovered; they were assumed to be related to output centers in the appropriate region of the spinal cord.

If the relationship between the discharge of pyramidal tract neurons and the development of force in recognizable and particular muscles was always as clearly proportional as for some of the small number of cells reported by Evarts (12), then an increase in firing of those cells following a disturbance of movement might be closely related to an increase in force to overcome the disturbance. But it is clear that such a relationship holds for only a small proportion of pyramidal tract cells (50) and that a more complicated relation is likely to exist between the discharges of most precentral cells and the force output of a group of contracting muscles. This makes it impossible to equate a burst of discharge in sampled pyramidal tract neurons with a load compensation response.

Moreover, the direction of the effect (excitation or inhibition) exerted on individual pyramidal tract cells has not been shown to be related directly to the direction of movement with which the cell's firing was associated in active movement. This could be caused by the very complex nature of most of the movement tasks used, involving as they do co-contraction of very large numbers of widely distributed muscle groups. Alternatively, it could be that the relationship between discharge of cortical neurons and the movement is "plastic" (49). Then inputs from the periphery about the movement being executed might also be expected to vary with repeated performances, changing conditions, and previous responses. Schmidt, Jost & Davis

(49) reported that approximately one third of precentral motor cortex cells had a changing (plastic) relationship with a stereotyped movement task. This plasticity may have been concealed in many of the observations made by others in which less attention was paid to trial by trial modifications in firing and more to overall patterns of activity as detected by averaging nerve cell discharges over many repetitions of a stereotyped task. But, under these conditions, others have concluded that the average responses of pyramidal tract neurons in the conscious monkey occur in fixed temporal relationship to the movement task and presumably to the contractions of some muscle groups involved in that task (46, 47). Certainly some pyramidal tract neurons discharge in a very regular and reproducible manner in association with every repetition of a stereotyped motor task, and with well-defined temporal relationship to muscle contractions in that task. This relationship is preserved without change through very large numbers of repetitions.

The evaluation of the effectiveness and appropriateness of inputs to the motor cortex must be influenced by the modifiability of the discharges recorded from cells in this zone. Fetz & Finocchio (21) demonstrated that the relationship between cell firing and muscle contraction could be influenced by operant conditioning in the monkey. But, even so, some correlations were more resistant to change than others, and it might be concluded that, if the correct pairing of pyramidal tract cell and muscle (or collection of motor units) were examined, strict and relatively fixed correlations between these perhaps rare but potentially important tightly coupled pairs could be demonstrated. Tight coupling between some pyramidal tract neurons and some motoneurons exists through the corticomotoneuronal system (8, 44).

Modifiability of the influences of peripheral feedback concerning disturbances of movement has also been demonstrated and referred to above (18). Depending upon the direction of the movement required to be made by the animal following a sudden disturbance of the hand and arm, responses of pyramidal tract cells to this disturbance could be enhanced or suppressed. Even when the animals had not been trained to carry out some movement performance following the peripheral disturbance (48), it may still have made a particular response that was not observed, or it may inadvertently have been conditioned to produce changes of cortical cell firing (19). With appropriate conditions for reward, monkeys may change the firing of precentral cortical neurons, including pyramidal tract cells, without overt responses in muscles whose electrical activity is being sampled (19, and E. Fetz, personal communication).

One of the greatest problems in the assessment of the responses of motor cortex cells to feedback from peripheral detectors of movement lies in the passive manipulation of the limb and the activation of movement detectors in conscious monkeys. Even with prolonged periods of training, it is difficult to achieve relaxation of the animal's limb to a degree at which the movements could really be called "passive." Moreover, it is very difficult to assess small changes in muscle tone or subtle adjustments of posture that the animal may produce in association with the manipulations of the limb. These self-initiated adjustments may be as potent as the passive movements in causing changes in firing of the precentral neurons. Such effects are much less likely to influence the short-latency responses to sudden, unexpected, and randomly timed disturbances of the position of the limb. But they could influence the more prolonged, sustained, later responses that have been shown to be modified by reversible interruption of pathways transversing the dentate nucleus (39).

The need for peripheral feedback about movement accomplishment has been challenged by the observation that tasks requiring graded performance of force development could be learned and performed after section of dorsal root fibers conveying input from the limb to the central nervous system (55). But when a trained rapid flexion movement of the forearm of a squirrel monkey was analyzed in detail before and after dorsal root section, the results left "no doubt that the normal patterning of the motor output to the agonist and antagonist is strictly dependent on sensory input data, at least during fast ballistically initiated movements. In particular, they exclude that even for a learned motor task the output to the agonist and antagonist is pre-programmed centrally" (56). Experiments of this sort do not yet provide information about the central nervous level at which the dorsal root input influences the pattern of muscle contraction involved in the task and they do not indicate whether the cerebellum or cerebral cortex are involved.

The EMG changes that resulted from dorsal root section could have been caused in large part by alterations in excitability at a spinal cord level. But the fact that modifications were evident even in a very rapid ballistic movement must argue for some influence of peripheral receptors. In a slowly evolving skilled movement, comparison between actual and intended movement may be even more important. A more significant evaluation of the function of peripheral feedback in the performance of movement is likely to be obtained by limited interference with particular aspects of potential movement detection (such as blocking of joint afferents) than by section of dorsal roots.

One must presume that both central direction and peripheral feedback are involved in normal movement performance. The peripheral feedback may be complicated in its origin and it may produce generalized or localized effects (or both simultaneously). Although most experimental work has concentrated on the excitatory effects of activation of peripheral receptors, inhibitory actions have also been revealed and these could be extremely important in a localizing function for the influences that reach pyramidal tract cells from peripheral receptors. But the relationship between movement and sensation of movement may be one of the most important factors to control in assessing the influence of peripheral feedback. The effect produced may depend very largely on whether the animal is truly passive during the manipulation of its limb or whether it assists or opposes this movement with some active muscle contraction. Just as different sensations may result from the same moving stimulus, depending on whether the stimulus is moved or whether the stimulus is stationary and the receiving surface is moved actively past it, so cells in the motor cortex may respond differently to the same peripheral stimulus under passive or active conditions. In many experiments, these conditions cannot completely be controlled.

A number of the observations that relate stimulation of receptors in the periphery to the presumed functional relationship between pyramidal tract cells and movement appear to suggest a positive feedback effect. A number of investigators have reported that passive movement of a limb or joint in a given direction is effective in causing discharge of a pyramidal tract cell when the displacement is made in the same direction as that with which the cell's firing was associated during active movement. That this may be the case for only some precentral cortical cells is suggested by the findings of Fetz et al (22). But the proposal of a positive feedback from movement detectors deserves further examination.

In one special instance, positive feedback from peripheral receptors seems to play an important functional role. Lund & Lamarre (36) examined the discharges of neurons in the lateral parts of the precentral cortex during jaw movements which occurred rhythmically as monkeys chewed food. They found that cells in this region could be related to the movement performance and also responded to passive movements of the jaw; loads that aided jaw opening increased the discharge of units that fired with active jaw opening movements. Some "jaw closing" cells seemed to receive inputs from receptors within the mouth and were responsive to pressure on the teeth. It was suggested that these neurons might participate in the control of force of jaw closure when this closure was opposed by a resistance between the teeth.

Lund & Lamarre (35) reasoned that if cortical neurons controlling the force of contraction of jaw closing muscles receive positive feedback from receptors in the periodontal membrane, then elimination of this feedback should reduce the force of voluntary biting. This possibility was tested in a group of human subjects whose bite was monitored with a strain gauge between the teeth and with electromyograms. After infiltration of local anesthetic around the roots of the upper and lower premolar teeth on one side, there was a fall in the voluntary applied force that could be developed in the bite on that side. This then recovered as the local anesthetic effect declined. Control injections around contralateral teeth not involved in the bite did not affect the force development.

In this case then, some detectors of the movement performance (probably receptors in the periodontal membrane) could have been involved in positive reinforcement of the movement performance by stimulating increased activity of cortical neurons associated with biting. The reinforcement could have had an appropriate and effective influence because removal of it by local anesthesia in the vicinity of the receptors led to a reduction in the capacity to produce a maximum voluntary force output.

Further analysis of this important question of the function of peripheral feedback will require more evidence on a number of matters referred to above. We are not able to give a quantitative account of the stream of information that flows into the central nervous system during the execution of a simple movement such as flexing the index finger. The contributions made to this information by different classes of receptors and its significance at spinal or supraspinal levels are, at present, largely speculative. But methods exist for the experimental study of movement detection. The intelligent application of these should lead to a better understanding of the relevance of movement detectors for movement performance.

Literature Cited

1. Adey, W. R., Porter, R., Carter, I. D. 1954. Temporal dispersion in cortical afferent volleys as a factor in perception; an evoked potential study of deep somatic sensibility in the monkey. *Brain* 77:325–44
2. Albe-Fessard, D., Lamarre, Y., Pimpaneau, A. 1966. Sur l'origine fusoriale de certaines afférences somatiques atteignant le cortex moteur du Singe. *J. Physiol. Paris* 58:443–44
3. Albe-Fessard, D., Liebeskind, J. 1966. Origine des messages somato-sensitifs activant les cellules du cortex moteur chez le singe. *Exp. Brain Res.* 1:127–46
4. Albe-Fessard, D., Liebeskind, J., Lamarre, Y. 1965. Projection au niveau du cortex somatomoteur du singe d'afférences provenant des récepteurs musculaires. *C. R. Acad. Sci.* 261:3891–94
5. Asanuma, H. 1973. Cerebral cortical control of movement. *The Physiologist* 16:143–66
6. Asanuma, H., Fernandez, J. J. 1974. Organization of projection from the thalamic relay nuclei to the motor cortex in the cat. *Brain Res.* 71:515–22
7. Asanuma, H., Fernandez, J. J. 1975. Characteristics of projections from the nucleus ventralis lateralis to the motor cortex in the cat: an anatomical and physiological study. *Exp. Brain Res.* In press
8. Bernhard, C. G., Bohm, E., Petersen, I. 1953. Investigations of the organization of the corticospinal system in monkeys (*Macaca mulatta*). *Acta Physiol. Scand.* 29:Suppl. 106, 29:79–105
9. Burchfiel, J. L., Duffy, F. H. 1972. Muscle afferent input to single cells in primate somatosensory cortex. *Brain Res.* 45:241–46
10. Conrad, B., Matsunami, K., Meyer-Lohmann, J., Wiesendanger, M., Brooks, V. B. 1974. Cortical load compensation during voluntary elbow movements. *Brain Res.* 71:507–14
11. Duffy, F. H., Burchfiel, J. L. 1971. Somatosensory system: organizational hierarchy from single units in monkey area 5. *Science* 172:273–75
12. Evarts, E. V. 1968. Relation of pyramidal tract activity to force exerted during voluntary movement. *J. Neurophysiol.* 31:14–27
13. Evarts, E. V. 1971. Activity of thalamic and cortical neurons in relation to learned movement in the monkey. *Int. J. Neurol.* 8:321–26

14. Evarts, E. V. 1972. Pre- and postcentral neuronal discharge in relation to learned movement. In *Corticothalamic Projections and Sensorimotor Activities,* ed. T. Frigyesi, E. Rinvick, M. D. Yahr, 449–58. New York: Raven
15. Evarts, E. V. 1973. Motor cortex reflexes associated with learned movement. *Science* 179:501–3
16. Evarts, E. V. 1974. Sensorimotor cortex activity associated with movements triggered by visual as compared to somesthetic inputs. In *The Neurosciences, Third Study Program,* ed. F. O. Schmidt, F. G. Worden, 327–37. Cambridge, Mass: MIT Press
17. Evarts, E. V. 1974. Precentral and postcentral cortical activity in associated with visually triggered movement. *J. Neurophysiol.* 37:373–81
18. Evarts, E. V., Tanji, J. 1974. Gating of motor cortex reflexes by prior instruction. *Brain Res.* 71:479–94
19. Fetz, E. E. 1975. Operant control of single unit activity and correlated motor responses. In *Perspectives in the Brain Sciences, Vol. 2. Operant Control of Brain Activity,* ed. M. H. Chase. Los Angeles: Brain Information Service
20. Fetz, E. E., Baker, M. A., 1971. Response properties of precentral neurons in awake monkeys. *The Physiologist* 12:223
21. Fetz, E. E., Finocchio, D. V. 1971. Operant conditioning of specific patterns of neural and muscular activity. *Science* 174:431–35
22. Fetz, E. E., Finocchio, D. V., Baker, M. A., Soso, M. J. 1974. Responses of precentral motor cortex cells during passive and active joint movements. *Abstr. Soc. Neurosci. Fourth Ann. Meet.,* p. 208
23. Goldring, S., Aras, E., Weber, P. C. 1970. Comparative study of sensory input to motor cortex in animals and man. *Electroencephalogr. Clin. Neurophysiol.* 29:537–50
24. Goldring, S., Ratcheson, R. 1972. Human motor cortex: Sensory input data from single neuron recordings. *Science* 175:1493–95
25. Haaxma, R., Kuypers, H. G. J. M. 1974. Role of occipitofrontal corticocortical connections in visual guidance of relatively independent hand and finger movements in rhesus monkeys. *Brain Res.* 71:361–66

26. Hepp-Reymond, M. C., Wiesendanger, M. 1972. Unilateral pyramidotomy in monkeys: effect on force and speed of a conditioned precision grip. *Brain Res.* 36:117–31

27. Hore, J., Preston, J. B., Durkovic, R. G., Cheney, P. D. 1974. Response patterns of precentral neurons to ramp stretch of some hindlimb muscles in the baboon. *Abstr. Soc. Neurosci. Fourth Ann. Meet.,* p. 259

28. Houk, J. C. 1972. On the significance of various command signals during voluntary control. *Brain Res.* 40:49–53

29. Joffroy, A. J., Lamarre, Y. 1974. Single cell activity in the ventral lateral thalamus of the unanaesthetized monkey. *Exp. Neurol.* 42:1–16

30. Jones, E. G., Powell, T. P. S. 1970. An anatomical study of converging sensory pathways within the cerebral cortex of the monkey. *Brain* 93:793–820

31. Knapp, H. D., Taub, E., Berman, A. J. 1963. Movements in monkeys with deafferented forelimbs *Exp. Neurol.* 7:305–15.

32. Kievit, J., Kuypers, H. G. J. M. 1972. Fastigial cerebellar projections to the ventrolateral nucleus of the thalamus and the organization of the descending pathways. In *Corticothalamic Projections and Sensorimotor Activities,* ed. T. Frigyesi, E. Rinvik, M. D. Yahr, 91–114. New York: Raven

33. Lamarre, Y., Dumont, M. 1972. Activity of cerebellar and lower brain stem neurons in monkeys with harmaline-induced tremor. In *Medical Primatology,* Pt. 2, ed. E. I. Goldsmith, J. Moor-Jankowski, 274–81. New York: Karger

34. Lewis, M. McD., Porter, R. 1974. Pyramidal tract discharge in relation to movement performance in monkeys with partial anaesthesia of the moving hand. *Brain Res.* 71:345–51

35. Lund, J. P., Lamarre, Y. 1973. The importance of positive feedback from periodontal pressoreceptors during voluntary isometric contraction of jaw closing muscles in man. *J. Biol. Buccale* 1:345–51

36. Lund, J. P. Lamarre, Y. 1974. Activity of neurons in the lower precentral cortex during voluntary and rhythmical jaw movements in the monkey. *Exp. Brain Res.* 19:282–99

37. Malis, L. I., Pribram, K. H., Kruger, L. 1953. Action potentials in "motor" cortex evoked by peripheral nerve stimulation. *J. Neurophysiol.* 16:161–67

38. Marsden, C. D., Merton, P. A., Morton, H. B. 1972. Servo action in human voluntary movement. *Nature* 238: 140–43

39. Meyer-Lohmann, J., Conrad, B., Matsunami, K., Brooks, V. B. 1975. Effects of dentate cooling on precentral unit activity following torque pulse injections into elbow movements. *Brain Res.* 94: 237–51

40. Mott, F. W., Sherrington, C. S. 1895. Experiments upon the influence of sensory nerves upon movement and nutrition of the limbs. Preliminary communication. *Proc. R. Soc. B* 57:481–88

41. Pandya, D. N., Kuypers, H. G. J. M. 1969. Cortico-cortical connections in the rhesus monkey. *Brain Res.* 13: 13–36

42. Phillips, C. G. 1969. The Ferrier Lecture, 1968. Motor apparatus of the baboon's hand. *Proc. R. Soc. B* 173: 141–74

43. Phillips, C. G., Powell, T. P. S., Wiesendanger, M. 1971. Projection from low-threshold muscle afferents of hand and forearm to area 3a of baboon's cortex. *J. Physiol.* 217:419–46

44. Phillips, C. G., Porter, R. 1964. The pyramidal projection to motoneurones of some muscle groups of the baboon's forelimb. In *Progress in Brain Research: Physiology of Spinal Neurons,* ed. J. C. Eccles, J. P. Schade, 222–42. Amsterdam: Elsevier

45. Powell, T. P. S., Mountcastle, V. B. 1959.Some aspects of the functional organization of the cortex of the postcentral gyrus of the monkey: a correlation of findings obtained in a single unit analysis with cytoarchitecture. *Johns Hopkins Hosp. Bull.* 105:133–62

46. Porter, R., Lewis, M. McD. 1975. Relationship of neuronal discharges in the precentral gyrus of monkeys to the performance of arm movements. *Brain Res.* In press

47. Porter R., Lewis, M. McD. 1975. Orderly discharge of precentral neurons in relation to movement performance. *Brain Res.* In press

48. Porter, R., Rack, P. M. H. 1974. The response of neurones in the pre-central cortex to an unexpected disturbance of finger positions. *J. Physiol.* 241:95–96P

49. Schmidt, E. M., Jost, R. G., Davis, K. K. 1974. Plasticity of cortical cell firing patterns after load changes. *Brain Res.* 73:540–44

50. Schmidt, E. M., Jost, R. G., Davis, K. K. 1975. Reexamination of the force

relationship of cortical cell discharge patterns with conditioned wrist movements. *Brain Res.* 83:213–23

51. Sherrington, C. S. 1931. Quantitative management of contraction in lowest level coordination. *Brain* 54:1–28

52. Soso, M., Fetz, E. E. 1973. Responses of postcentral cells during active and passive joint movements. *Abstr. Soc. Neurosci. Third Ann. Meet.,* p. 318

53. Sperry, R. W. 1947. Cerebral regulation of motor coordination in monkeys following multiple transection of sensorimotor cortex. *J. Neurophysiol.* 10:275–94

54. Strick, P. L. 1973. Light microscopical analysis of the cortical projection of the thalamic ventrolateral nucleus in the cat. *Brain Res.* 55:1–23

55. Taub, E., Berman, A. J. 1968. Movement and learning in the absence of sensory feedback. In *The Neuropsychology of Spatially Oriented Behavior,* ed. J. Freedman, 173–92. Homewood, Illinois: Dorsey

56. Terzuolo, C. A., Soechting, J. F., Ranish, N. A. 1974. Studies on the control of some simple motor tasks. V. Changes in motor output following dorsal root section in squirrel monkey. *Brain Res.* 70:521–26

57. Thach, W. T. 1970. Discharge of cerebellar neurons related to two maintained postures and two prompt movements. I. Nuclear cell output. *J. Neurophysiol.* 33:527–36

58. Thach, W. T. 1970. Discharge of cerebellar neurons related to two maintained postures and two prompt movements. II. Purkinje cell output and input. *J. Neurophysiol.* 33:537–47

59. Towe, A. L., Tyner, C. F. 1971. Cortical circuitry underlying the mixed receptive fields of certain pyramidal tract neurons. *Exp. Neurol.* 31:239–57

60. Wiesendanger, M. 1973. Input from muscle and cutaneous nerves of the hand and forearm to neurones of the precentral gyrus of baboons and monkeys. *J. Physiol.* 228:203–19

GATING IN SODIUM
CHANNELS OF NERVE

❖1146

Bertil Hille

Department of Physiology and Biophysics, University of Washington School of Medicine, Seattle, Washington 98195

SOME QUESTIONS

During the period 1937–1952 the study of electrical excitability mechanisms in axons matured from discoveries of membrane impedance changes to a complete kinetic description of ionic permeability changes in the squid giant axon (35). There followed a period of relative stagnation while the results on squid were rechecked and new voltage clamp methods were developed for other excitable systems. Then in the 1960s a new movement developed whose philosophy underlies the substantial activity and rate of progress characteristic of the field today. The new movement may be traced to the discovery of the specific blocking action of tetrodotoxin (TTX). TTX was shown to block the transient Na^+ permeability of axon membranes with no effects on K^+ permeability (47, 52, 53), and it was concluded that Na^+ and K^+ permeability are mediated by separate and discrete sites, now called Na channels and K channels. Very soon, techniques were developed to count the number of TTX binding sites and hence the number of Na channels. These events finally replaced the idea of a homogeneous membrane endowed with diffuse ionic permeability by the idea of discrete molecular pores, the ionic channels. Arguments for molecular pores have been reviewed (3, 21, 28, 65, 66).

The new molecular viewpoint has fostered efforts to count channels, to measure the permeability of single open channels, to measure their pore size and internal topography, to modify them chemically, and even to isolate them. Conceptually the channel is considered to have two fundamental properties: excitability and permeability. Excitability means the ability to react to changes in the membrane potential and is loosely attributed to an electric field sensor coupled to gates that open or close the channel. Permeability includes the ability to let ions cross the membrane and the ability to discriminate among different ionic species. Permeability is presumed to be explainable in terms of the morphology and chemical nature of the pore revealed when the gates of the channel are open. Recent advances in explaining ionic permeability have just been reviewed (3, 21, 31, 32, 65); therefore this review turns

139

instead to some of the pressing questions in excitability. Nearly all the work discussed was done by the voltage clamp method on squid giant axons or frog myelinated nerve fibers. Examples are cited selectively rather than comprehensively. The common features of voltage-dependent permeability changes in sodium and potassium channels suggest that the sensing-gating mechanisms of the two channels work on the same principles. Nevertheless, the review is restricted to the conventional activation and inactivation processes in sodium channels.

As it turns out, we seem to be near the stage where a major clarification of the gating mechanism might occur. There are several new observations that settle certain fundamental questions and other provocative ones that need explanation. At the same time, the new approaches of fluctuation analysis and gating current measurement promise to give an entirely new look at gating mechanisms. This review summarizes some of the major new observations and conclusions that should contribute to the forthcoming synthesis.

So little is understood about the molecular basis of voltage sensing and gating that the major questions to be answered today are, at least conceptually, quite simple ones: Is the sensor-gate mechanism entirely built into the channel and associated parts of the membrane or are soluble cofactors, such as ions or small molecules, essential participants? Can individual channels open in a partial or graded way or is each opening an all-or-nothing process? How many different states of closed channel are there? What mechanisms can give rise to the extraordinarily steep voltage dependence of opening that, in the extreme, can increase sodium permeability tenfold with only a 9 mV change of membrane potential? Are the activation and subsequent inactivation of depolarized sodium channels independent parallel processes as originally described in the Hodgkin-Huxley model, or are they somehow interacting or even strictly sequential events? Despite their apparent simplicity, these fundamental questions have nonetheless been difficult to attack experimentally.

RESULTS

Dissolved Ions and Molecules as Gates or Sensors

CALCIUM   It has long been known that increasing the concentration of free calcium bathing nerves or muscles increases the critical depolarization required to reach firing threshold (11). In terms of the Hodgkin-Huxley (35) model of permeability, calcium concentration changes shift the voltage dependence of activation and inactivation along the voltage axis as if the voltage sensing processes experience some hidden bias (23). This observation has been interpreted by two different types of theory. Gordon & Welsh (27) proposed that the Ca^{2+} cation is pulled into the membrane by the inwardly directed electric field at rest and released into the bathing medium as the inward field is reduced by depolarization. In more modern terminology, their theory supposes that Ca^{2+} ions can plug pores, acting simultaneously as the field sensor and the gate. This simple idea has been the basis of a long list of speculative models for excitability. Unfortunately, no quantitative model based on the calcium plug idea agrees with observations and many observations directly contradict the idea. For example, it is now known that Ca^{2+} ions can pass through open sodium channels and not through closed ones (8, 46). At the same time, excitability can be preserved for tens of minutes in solutions containing calcium-chelating agents (6), and in calcium-free solutions the voltage dependence of opening of sodium channels remains as steep as before (33). Finally, a weakly voltage-dependent block of sodium channels by Ca^{2+} ions has been detected in frog nerve and muscle (33, 68; D. T. Campbell and B. Hille, in preparation). A rough estimate of the percentage of channels blocked by this mechanism at rest in normal frog Ringers is only 10–33%, far too small a value to account for the minute permeability to Na^+ ions at rest. Hence the theory that Ca^{2+} ions are the voltage-dependent gate must be abandoned.

An alternative explanation (23) of how calcium affects the depolarization needed to open channels has recently been subjected to a full quantitative test (12, 24, 33, 48–51). The fit with theory is so successful that the basic features may be accepted as proven. Briefly, the nerve membrane is envisioned as having many negatively charged groups, such as ionized carboxylic acid or phosphate groups, at its outer surface. Of necessity, monovalent and divalent cations are attracted toward these groups as counterions. Some ions may even bind to the surface charges. Within the membrane substance, where the sensors of the excitability mechanisms may lie, there is an electric field compounded from at least three sources: the conventional potential difference between internal and external media, the local field from fixed negative surface charges, and the local field from the excess counterions attracted to the surface. Thus the sensors are biased by local fields not detectable by electro-physiological electrodes, and these biasing fields depend on the number and type of ions in the bathing medium. The quantitative properties of such a system are well known in surface chemistry and are described by the so-called Gouy-Chapman-Stern theory of ionic double layers. The quantitative theory was first successfully applied to voltage shifts with changes of monovalent, divalent, and hydrogen ion concentrations on potassium channels (12, 24, 48–51) and then equally successfully to sodium channels (14, 33). Evidently, the primary role of Ca^{2+} ions is neither as a sensor nor as a gate, but rather more simply as a counterion to surface charges. Nevertheless, this is an important role, as it directly modifies the firing threshold of the cell.

OTHER DISSOLVED IONS AND MOLECULES   Several nonphysiological ions can give voltage- and time-dependent plugging and unplugging of channels in a manner resembling gating [e.g. (2)]. However, all evidence speaks against such a mechanism for normal gating in sodium channels. Axons have been perfused inside and outside with an extraordinary variety of organic and inorganic ions without seriously com-promising the time course of opening and closing of sodium channels during a depolarization (15, 29, 30). The internal perfusion can flow hundreds of volumes of pure salt solutions through the axon and certainly would wash out any readily soluble small molecules and ions. There seems to be no indispensable ingredient in the internal or external solutions. Therefore, sensors and gates must be intrinsic components of the axon membrane, and no soluble cofactors or sources of metabolic energy are needed for their operation. The sensing-gating processes would then be ascribed to conformational changes of macromolecules in the membrane.

All-or-Nothing Opening of Channels

Research papers in axonology today are generally written with the tacit assumption that channels have only two states of permeability: open and closed. All changes in membrane ionic permeability are then ascribed to changes in the number of conducting channels. There is no direct proof of this proposition, but there are qualitative arguments in its favor, the most direct having to do with ionic selectivity. For the sake of argument, consider that individual channels open in a graded or multistep fashion such that the macroscopic changes of membrane sodium permeability are due to variations in the graded opening of all channels. Such channels might be designed in two ways. Either there is a pore with a permanent selectivity filter and, in series with this, a gradually opening gating mechanism, or the selectivity filter and gate are the same structure and gradually open. Quite clearly, the ionic selectivity would vary during the time course of opening in the second type of channel, as selectivity must be a sensitive reflection of the structure, size, and electric fields of the selectivity filter. Less obviously, selectivity should also vary with opening in the first type of channel. With fully open gates, selectivity will take place at the selectivity filter, but consider when the gates are only 10% open. Then the rate-limiting step for passage through the channel would be to pass by the gating region, where the ionic selectivity would take place. The most careful relevant experiments are those of Chandler & Meves (15–18). They looked, for example, at ionic currents in sodium channels in giant axons perfused internally with K^+ ions and externally with Na^+ ions. Here the reversal potential is a direct index of Na-K selectivity. They found that the reversal potential does not vary during the transient activation and inactivation of sodium channels. Indeed, the time course of permeability change seems to be the same for all monovalent metal and organic cations accepted by sodium channels (15–18, 29, 30). Hence graded opening is unlikely.

Another argument against graded opening of single channels relates to the very steep relation between peak sodium permeability and membrane potential. As a general principle of equilibrium thermodynamics, a steep voltage dependence of a conformational change means that the energy difference between open and closed states is itself steeply voltage dependent. Indeed, using the Boltzmann relation, Hodgkin & Huxley (35) proved that the extreme tenfold activation of sodium permeability for 9 mV of depolarization requires an energy difference equivalent to moving a hexavalent particle across the entire potential drop in the membrane for every unit of conductance activated. This large electrical energy difference is for a simple two-state closed-open channel. If instead a graded channel opening takes place through a long sequence of states of increasing permeability A-B-C-D . . . , the electrical energy difference between successive states will need to remain as large as before. The total energy difference between the closed state and the final open state will become extremely large and, with enough states, difficult to account for physically. Put another way, a theory with a long sequence of partially open steps makes either the voltage dependence of permeability too small or the charge (or dipole) equivalent of the conformational changes too large. Hence the number of open states is small. The above argument does not apply to the case where there are several open states, but transitions among them are not voltage dependent. In the ultimate analysis, even the transitions of a two-state channel cannot be instantaneous; on an exceedingly fast time scale, each transition would appear as a continuous change of permeability.

Finally, a new technique, *fluctuation analysis,* can test if each channel opens in a graded way with voltage. When observed at high enough gain, the ionic current recorded in a voltage clamp always has a fluctuating "noisy" component, some of which is produced by random fluctuations of the gating processes in channels. Techniques for analyzing conductance fluctuations and results to date have been reviewed (62, 63, 67). The technique and theory are difficult but hold much promise for the future. In principle it will be possible to distinguish among numerous possible microscopic mechanisms of opening by comparing predicted and measured frequencies and amplitudes of the noise. At least in simple systems both the size of unitary conductance steps and the time constants associated with their appearance and disappearance can be measured.

In the rest of this review the conventional assumption is made that channels have only two major permeability states. At the same time it still seems most probable that closed and even open channels may exist in several forms with similar conductance but with different probabilities of making a transition to the other permeability state.

Relation of Inactivation to Activation

Depolarization of axon membranes opens and then closes sodium channels. In the Hodgkin-Huxley model (35) this sequence is explained by the simultaneous and independent relaxation of an activation h and an inactivation process, both of which must be in a permissive state for the channel to be open. The permissive state m^3 of the activating process rises with a sigmoid time course, and simultaneously the permissive state h of the inactivation process falls with an exponential time course during a maintained depolarization. Hence the open state m^3h of the channel rises and falls in probability. These concepts have given rise to terms like "h gate" and "m" or "m^3 gate" and statements such as "the m gate opens and the h gate closes."

The postulated independence of inactivation from activation is now being questioned. Indeed, from a molecular viewpoint the possibility of making many parallel independent rearrangements in one macromolecular system seems unlikely, particularly when these rearrangements are all supposed to govern a single endpoint, the opening of a molecular pore. Instead, the probability of any given internal transition might well be influenced by which other transitions had already occurred. Hence kinetic interactions between activation and inactivation would not be surprising.

KINETICS IN NORMAL AXONS   During the past five years, the onset and recovery from inactivation with voltage clamp steps have been found to deviate from the simple exponential time course of the Hodgkin-Huxley (35) model. The measurements are made from long series of double-pulse experiments as done by Hodgkin & Huxley (34). In squid, the marine worm *Myxicola,* and frog, the time course of inactivation is definitely sigmoid, showing an initial lag before the most rapid rate of change (1, 25, 57–59). In addition, the rate constant and the degree of inactivation seem to vary with the method used to measure them (22, 26, 36). These deviations have been interpreted as evidence for tightly coupled models where channels must be activated before inactivation may proceed. While such models may be correct, the evidence obtained shows primarily that inactivation is not a simple first order process and does not go far towards demonstrating any causal relation to the degree of activation. For example, most observations might be explained by assuming that there are four states of the inactivation system rather than two. These states could be connected in linear sequence A-B-C-D, where A and B are permissive states and C and D are not. At very negative potentials the system is in state A and at positive potentials, state D. Transitions would show second or third order properties, and rates would depend on initial conditions.

KINETICS IN DRUG-TREATED AXONS   Several pharmacological treatments hold sodium channels open longer than usual. Detailed analysis of the kinetics of sodium current in these treated axons reveals that some drug actions can be described as quite selective modifications of inactivation or activation processes. The clearest case is internal perfusion of a squid giant axon with the proteolytic enzyme(s) pronase (7). After a few minutes of treatment, sodium inactivation disappears. Sodium channels then open upon depolarization and close again only when the axon is repolarized. The time course of currents is the same as that expected if an unaltered activation mechanism were the only factor controlling permeability. However, the size of current is smaller than expected. In the Hodgkin-Huxley model, inactivation begins to develop as soon as the membrane is depolarized so that by the time the sodium current reaches a peak, half the channels are already inactivated. Therefore eliminating inactivation ought to reveal a maximum value of sodium permeability twice the peak value seen in the normal axon. The peak permeability is not increased by pronase treatment, however. Some of the discrepancy is removed by supposing again that sodium inactivation normally develops along a sigmoid time course with an initial lag. In any case, pronase effects prove that inactivation is not an inseparable feature of activation.

Other treatments vastly slow the kinetics of sodium inactivation with either small or no effect on the time course of activation and with small or no increase in peak sodium permeability. These include internal perfusion of squid axons with NaF (16–18) or frog nodes with iodate (61a) and external application of toxins of *Leiurus* scorpion to frog nodes (40, 41), of *Buthus* scorpion to squid axons (55), and of *Condylactis* anemone to crayfish axons (54). Only *Condylactis* toxin increases peak sodium permeability, and that by less than 20%. Each of these treatments makes sodium inactivation incomplete so that sodium channels can remain open for hundreds of milliseconds during a depolarization. Detailed measurements of the complexities of inactivation with internal NaF have been successfully described by a three-state linear model B-C-D with B and D as permissive states (16–18). They would therefore also fit the four-state model A-B-C-D mentioned earlier, if the treatment were imagined to convert normally nonpermissive state D to a permissive state.

One pharmacological treatment is known to change activation significantly with just minor effects on inactivation: external application of *Centruroides* scorpion venom to nodes of Ranvier (13). There the voltage dependence of activation in some channels is shifted by 50 mV to more negative voltages so that sodium current flows at the resting potential. Hyperpolarizing pulses shut off this component of current reversibly with the fast kinetics expected from a severely shifted activation system. Depolarizing pulses shut it off reversibly with the slower kinetics expected from a normal inactivation system. The observed increase of sodium permeability seen when a depolarizing pulse is shut off is unique to the literature. It is the first case that can successfully be described as a removal of inactivation from channels that are already activated (13). Also for the first time, the time course of inactivation can be measured directly from the time course of the current rather than having to be inferred from amplitudes in a series of multiple-pulse experiments. No evidence of deviation from a single exponential was reported, but the point should be reinvestigated more completely. The alkaloids aconitine and batrachotoxin also shift sodium activation of some channels by roughly 50 mV to more negative potentials but, since, in addition, the channels do not inactivate, a reversal of inactivation cannot be studied (39a, 60).

A different kinetic feature of some drug treatments is that the drug may modify or block channels only when the channel is in a certain state. In all examples known, the channel is more reactive in the depolarized state than in the resting state. The drugs include local anesthetics and derivatives (19, 64), strychnine (61), Maculotoxin (20), *Centruroides* venom (13), and sulfhydryl reagents (42). In some of these cases there is evidence for interference between closing of the channel and departure of the drug from its receptor (19, 61, 64). Further exploitation of these techniques might give new insight into how many states channels may take and help in elucidating if inactivation and activation interact.

Gating Current

Potentially the most important new result in the study of gating is the discovery of gating current (4, 37). Thermodynamically there is no way for channels to continue to open and close millions of times without direct input of energy into the sensing-gating process on every cycle. Arguments have already been presented against direct contributions from conventional metabolic sources or from the ion gradient. The only remaining source of energy is the electric field. The field must do electric work on the sensor-gate by moving some charges through the intramembrane field. Hence, while the work is being done a small membrane current reflecting these internal rearrangements will flow. The name *carrier current* was originally coined for this current by Hodgkin & Huxley (34, 35). More recently it has been called *gating current* (28) although, as discussed below, the intramembrane charge movement need not coincide in time with the opening or closing of gates.

When should gating current flow and how large is it expected to be? From a thermodynamic point of view, the only restriction on timing is that the energy be injected into the system at least by the time it is used. A step depolarization could in principle inject, within a few microseconds, energy that is stored mechanically and liberated over the next few milliseconds to send channels through a cycle of activation and inactivation. At the other extreme, the electrical work might be done exactly in synchrony with the opening and closing of gates. How large the current is depends on two factors: how many channels there are to open and how much electrical work must be done to open a channel. As has already been discussed, the steep voltage dependence of sodium activation requires a gating charge movement equivalent to at least six electrons flowing from the outside of the membrane to the axoplasmic side for each channel activated. With this background, the observations can be discussed.

Gating currents are detected by voltage clamp experiments designed to reduce interference from ionic currents, conventional capacity currents, and noise. The axon is perfused inside and out with solutions of impermeant ions and channel-blocking agents. Carefully matched positive and negative voltage clamp pulses are applied and the resulting currents are added so that exactly symmetrical capacity and leakage currents will cancel, leaving only any asymmetrical component of current. The pulses are repeated many times, and the result is accumulated in a computer of averaged transients. Several groups have reported finding asymmetrical components of current, which they attribute in part to gating current for activating sodium channels (4, 5, 9, 10, 37–39, 43–45, 56). Typical examples are given in Figure 1, comparing small observed asymmetrical currents when ionic channels are mostly blocked (a and c) with large sodium currents in the unblocked axon (b and d). During depolarization to 0 mV, sodium channels become activated over a 1 msec period and an outward net asymmetry current is found. When the axon is repolarized, sodium channels close quickly and an equally fast inward asymmetry current is found. For these short depolarizations the total asymmetric charge movement (area of the current transient) is the same at the on and the off of the depolarizing pulse (5, 38, 43). The equality argues against a conventional ionic current flow and in favor of the expected kind of intramembrane polarization. What fraction of these charge movements is related to gating?

No definitive criterion is yet available to distinguish true gating current from other unrelated membrane rearrangements. Indeed, slow changes in many macromolecules might be expected when a membrane is polarized. Nevertheless the polarization currents now being studied probably include significant contributions from gating processes. As required thermodynamically, the charge movements occur at least by the time sodium channels open. The sodium permeability and charge movements are decreased irreversibly by internal perfusion with 30 mM glutaraldehyde (43) and reversibly by internal perfusion with 10 mM $ZnCl_2$ (5) or external perfusion with 1% procaine (38). Armstrong & Bezanilla (5, 9) found that sodium permeability and charge movement are also reduced by preceding depolarizations sufficient to produce conventional or long-term sodium inactivation. Then permeability and charge movement recover in parallel on repolarization with the time course appropriate for recovery from conventional or long-term inactivation.

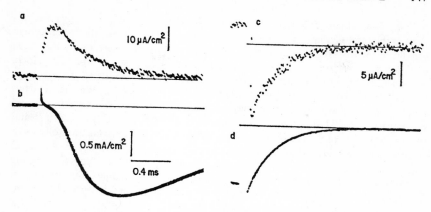

Figure 1 Asymmetrical membrane charge movements compared with sodium currents during turn-on and turn-off of sodium permeability at 2°C. Charge movements are the sum of currents flowing during (*a*) and immediately after (*c*) 50 positive and 50 negative steps of 70 mV amplitude from a holding potential of −70 mV. Tris seawater with tetrodotoxin outside and mixture of CsF, KF, and sucrose inside. (*b*) Sodium current measured during a step from −100 mV to 0 mV. Sodium seawater outside and a mixture of CsF, KF, and sucrose inside. (*d*) Sodium-current on return to −70 mV after a 700 μsec pulse to 0 mV. Sodium seawater outside and a mixture of KF, tetraethylammonium bromide, and sucrose inside. *a* and *b* from one axon, *c* and *d* from another. [From Armstrong & Bezanilla 1974 (5). Reprinted with permission.]

Similarly, when the experiment of Figure 1 is repeated with 5 msec depolarizing pulses to +50 mV, sodium channels are inactivated by the end of each pulse and the rapid off charge movement is reduced to one third the value obtained with shorter pulses (10). Pretreatment with pronase eliminates both the sodium inactivation and the development of the concomitant reduction of charge movements (10). These strong correlations with sodium inactivation are unexpected and imply that inactivation restricts the ability of channels to undergo submillisecond conformational changes (such as "*m* gate" transitions) when the membrane potential is changed. Hence, like the original voltage clamp studies (34), the charge movement experiments show that there are at least two forms of closed channels. Perhaps even a third closed form is evident from the observation that on depolarization more than half of the putative gating current flows before half the channels open, implying that an unopened intermediate form precedes the open form during a depolarization. Upon repolarization after short depolarizations, the off charge movement has exactly the same time course as the closing of sodium channels (Figure 1). Neither this similarity of time courses nor the interactions of charge movements with inactivation are expected from the simplest interpretations of the Hodgkin-Huxley model. Tetrodotoxin evidently has no effect on any of the charge movements.

Gating current cannot be analyzed definitively until reliable procedures are found to separate gating current from extraneous components of asymmetrical polarization currents. Then the various components of gating current will need to be peeled apart as well. Keynes & Rojas (38) and Meves (43) have given quantitative descriptions of the total asymmetrical current of squid axons. The current after each voltage step decays with a roughly exponential time course with time constants in the range 0.05–1.0 msec, depending on voltage, temperature, and past history. The voltage dependence of the time constant has some of the qualitative features of the voltage dependence of the Hodgkin-Huxley activation time constant τ_m. With large depolarizations the charge movement may saturate with 1500–2500 electron charges moving per μm^2. Half of the charge is moved by depolarizations to –20 mV and the steepest slope of the charge movement could be fitted by a two-state Boltzmann theory with an energy difference equivalent to moving single "particles" of 1.3 electron charges across the membrane. If all the charge movement goes for opening sodium channels at the equivalent of six electrons per channel, the number of channels is 250–400/μm^2, and if the opening is accomplished by several independent particles of charge 1.3 moving across the entire membrane to the permissive position, there must be at least five such particles. However, the charge per particle and the number of particles participating depend on the model used for interpretation, and the particle idea should probably be regarded as just an electrically equivalent representation of protein conformational changes involving movements of charged or dipolar residues. As extraneous currents are separated from the total current, the number of channels will necessarily be revised downward and the detailed interpretation of the remaining gating current may change. Keynes, Rojas & Rudy (39) and Meves (43) did not confirm that long depolarization inactivates the charge movement they have studied. This must mean that their methods emphasized different components of the total charge movement than those studied by Armstrong & Bezanilla. A similar analysis on total asymmetric charge movements in myelinated nerve fibers of the frog gives an upper limit of 1.6×10^5 channels at one node of Ranvier (56).

CONCLUSIONS

In recent years the problem of explaining excitability of membrane permeability has been rephrased as the problem of finding the molecular basis of voltage sensors and gates in ionic channels. The sensing-gating process has been shown not to involve direct participation of Ca^{2+} ions nor to require any particular monovalent ions, soluble small molecules, or sources of metabolic energy. All of the energy required for cyclic opening must come from the electric field across the membrane, and the sensing-gating processes would involve conformational changes of macromolecules attached to or buried in the membrane. The permeability of individual channels probably has only two states, open and closed, but the closed state, at least, has several forms. Somewhere in the sequence of transitions from closed to open there are conformational changes involving rather large rearrangements of charged moieties. Current flows corresponding to such rearrangements have now been detected and will give new constraints on possible models. As yet, however, our understanding of this voltage sensing aspect of excitability is not far advanced from the concept of moving six charges introduced 23 years ago by Hodgkin & Huxley (35).

The distinction between activation and inactivation processes is now less clear than in the Hodgkin-Huxley model. On the one hand, several pharmacological treatments seem to separate the two processes cleanly. On the other hand, several investigators favor strong coupling between inactivation and activation because the time course of currents in multiple-pulse experiments does not fit Hodgkin-Huxley kinetics. Probably the most striking argument for coupling is the disputed effect of long depolarization on gating currents. These ideas require a new level of experimental sophistication in reviewing the question of how many states a sodium channel can take and how the states are kinetically interrelated.

The nature of gates is entirely unresolved. Simply by analogy with most other sophisticated biological machinery, the channel, gates, and sensors may be envisioned as a multisubunit assembly of proteins stretching from one side of the membrane to the other. Attempts to pin down the location of gates or sensors by the location of action of applied agents will be difficult if, as expected, the assembly is highly interacting. For example, inactivation is eliminated by internal pronase and severely changed by external scorpion venoms. Both of these are large molecules unable to cross membranes. Indeed, internal application of scorpion venom has no effect (55). However, the sum of many kinds of evidence does favor locating gating towards the axoplasmic end of the channels. Each channel might have several gates in series allowing it to have several closed forms, or there may only be one gate with the multiple forms occurring in the sensor and other apparatus that instructs the gate. Hence there may not be separate "m gates" and "h gates." Gating itself might be a pure mechanical block like the closing of the garden gate or, alternatively, it could be an electrostatic block as in a field effect transistor. To give an overspecific example, the closing of a channel might involve a conformation change that brings a large number of positively charged residues close enough to the pore to repel cations from the pore. Unlike other possible models this one would accomplish voltage sensing, "gating charge movement," and gating all in one event. We can hope that, during the next five years, many of the questions raised in this review will be more clearly resolved.

ACKNOWLEDGMENTS

I thank Doctors W. Almers, T. Begenisich, and D. T. Campbell for discussions and for reading the manuscript and Susan A. Morton for invaluable secretarial help. Preparation of this review and some of the cited experimental work were supported by grant NS 08174 from the National Institutes of Health.

150   HILLE

Literature Cited

1. Armstrong, C. M. 1970. Comparison of g_K inactivation caused by quaternary ammonium ion with g_{Na} inactivation. *14th Ann. Meet. Biophys. Soc.,* 185a (Abstr.)
2. Armstrong, C. M. 1971. Interaction of tetraethylammonium ion derivatives with the potassium channels of giant axons. *J. Gen. Physiol.* 58:413–37
3. Armstrong, C. M. 1974. Ionic pores, gates, and gating currents. *Quart. Rev. Biophys.* 7:179–210
4. Armstrong, C. M., Bezanilla, F. 1973. Currents related to movement of the gating particles of the sodium channels. *Nature* 242:459–61
5. Armstrong, C. M., Bezanilla, F. 1974. Charge movement associated with the opening and closing of the activation gates of the Na channels. *J. Gen. Physiol.* 63:533–52
6. Armstrong, C. M., Bezanilla, F. M., Horowicz, P. 1972. Twitches in the presence of ethylene glycol bis (β-amino ethyl ether)-N,N'-tetraacetic acid. *Biochim. Biophys. Acta* 267:605–8
7. Armstrong, C. M., Bezanilla, F., Rojas, E. 1973. Destruction of sodium conductance inactivation in squid axons perfused with pronase. *J. Gen. Physiol.* 62:375–91
8. Baker, P. F., Hodgkin, A. L., Ridgway, E. B. 1971. Depolarization and calcium entry in squid giant axons. *J. Physiol. London* 218:709–55
9. Bezanilla, F., Armstrong, C. M. 1974. Gating currents of the sodium channels: Three ways to block them. *Science* 183:753–54
10. Bezanilla, F., Armstrong, C. M. 1975. Inactivation of gating charge movement. *19th Ann. Meet. Biophys. Soc.,* 163a (Abstr.)
11. Brink, F. 1954. The role of calcium ions in neural processes. *Pharmacol. Rev.* 6:243–98
12. Brismar, T. 1973. Effects of ionic concentration on permeability properties of nodal membrane in myelinated nerve fibres of *Xenopus laevis*. Potential clamp experiments. *Acta Physiol. Scand.* 87:474–84
13. Cahalan, M. D. 1975. Modification of sodium channel gating in frog myelinated nerve fibres by *Centruroides sculpturatus* scorpion venom. *J. Physiol. London* 244:511–34
14. Chandler, W. K., Hodgkin, A. L., Meves, H. 1965. The effect of changing the internal solution on sodium inactivation and related phenomena in giant axons. *J. Physiol. London* 180:821–36
15. Chandler, W. K., Meves, H. 1965. Voltage clamp experiments on internally perfused giant axons. *J. Physiol. London* 180:788–820
16. Chandler, W. K., Meves, H. 1970. Sodium and potassium currents in squid axons perfused with fluoride solutions. *J. Physiol. London* 211:623–52
17. Chandler, W. K., Meves, H. 1970. Evidence for two types of sodium conductance in axons perfused with sodium fluoride solution. *J. Physiol. London* 211:653–78
18. Chandler, W. K., Meves, H. 1970. Rate constants associated with changes in sodium conductance in axons perfused with sodium fluoride. *J. Physiol. London* 211:679–705
19. Courtney, K. R. 1975. Frequency-dependent inhibition of sodium currents in frog myelinated nerve by the lidocaine derivative GEA 968. *J. Pharmacol. Exp. Ther.* In press
20. Dulhunty, A., Gage, P. W. 1971. Selective effects of an octopus toxin on action potentials. *J. Physiol. London* 218:433–45
21. Ehrenstein, G., Lecar, H. 1972. The mechanism of signal transmission in nerve axons. *Ann. Rev. Biophys. Bioeng.* 1:347–68
22. Frankenhaeuser, B. 1963. A quantitative description of potassium currents in myelinated nerve fibres of *Xenopus laevis*. *J. Physiol. London* 169:424–30
23. Frankenhaeuser, B., Hodgkin, A. L. 1957. The action of calcium on the electrical properties of squid axons. *J. Physiol. London* 137:217–43
24. Gilbert, D. L., Ehrenstein, G. 1969. Effect of divalent cations on potassium conductance of squid axons: Determination of surface charge. *Biophys. J.* 9:447–63
25. Goldman, L., Schauf, C. L. 1972. Inactivation of the sodium current in *Myxicola* giant axons. Evidence for coupling to the activation process. *J. Gen. Physiol.* 59:659–75
26. Goldman, L., Schauf, C. L. 1973. Quantitative description of sodium and potassium currents and computed action potentials in *Myxicola* giant axons. *J. Gen. Physiol.* 61:361–84
27. Gordon, H. T., Welsh, J. H. 1948. The role of ions in axon surface reactions to

toxic organic compounds. *J. Cell. Comp. Physiol.* 31:395–419

28. Hille, B. 1970. Ionic channels in nerve membranes. *Progr. Biophys. Mol. Biol.* 21:1–32

29. Hille, B. 1971. The permeability of the sodium channel to organic cations in myelinated nerve. *J. Gen. Physiol.* 58:599–619

30. Hille, B. 1972. The permeability of the sodium channel to metal cations in myelinated nerve. *J. Gen. Physiol.* 59:637–68

31. Hille, B. 1975. Ionic selectivity of Na and K channels of nerve membranes. In *Membranes—A Series of Advances,* ed. G. Eisenman, 3:255–323. New York: Dekker

32. Hille, B. 1975. Ionic selectivity, saturation, and block in sodium channels: A four barrier model. *J. Gen. Physiol.* In press

33. Hille, B. Woodhull, A. M., Shapiro, B. I. 1975. Negative surface charge near sodium channels of nerve: Divalent ions, monovalent ions, and pH. *Philos. Trans. R. Soc.* In press

34. Hodgkin, A. L., Huxley, A. F. 1952. The dual effect of membrane potential on sodium conductance in the giant axon of *Loligo. J. Physiol. London* 116:496–506

35. Hodgkin, A. L., Huxley, A. F. 1952. A quantitative description of membrane current and its application to conduction and excitation in nerve. *J. Physiol. London* 117:500–44

36. Hoyt, R., Adelman, W. 1970. Sodium inactivation: Experimental test of two models. *Biophys. J.* 10:610–17

37. Keynes, R. D., Rojas, E. 1973. Characteristics of the sodium gating current in the squid axon. *J. Physiol. London* 233:28–30P

38. Keynes, R. D., Rojas, E. 1974. Kinetics and steady-rate properties of the charged system controlling sodium conductance in the squid giant axon. *J. Physiol. London* 239:393–434

39. Keynes, R. D., Rojas, E., Rudy, B. 1974. Demonstration of a first-order voltage-dependent transition of the sodium activation gates. *J. Physiol. London* 239:100–1 P

39a. Khodorov, B. I., Peganov, E. M., Revenko, S. V., Shishkova, L. D. 1975. Sodium currents in voltage clamped nerve fiber of frog under the combined action of batrachotoxin and procaine. *Brain Res.* 84:541–46

40. Koppenhöfer, E., Schmidt, H. 1968. Die Wirkung von Skorpiongift auf die Ionenströme des Ranvierschen Schnürrings. I. Die Permeabilitäten P_{Na} und P_K. *Pfluegers Arch.* 303:133–49

41. Koppenhöfer, E., Schmidt, H. 1968. Die Wirkung von Skorpiongift auf die Ionenströme des Ranvierschen Schnürrings. II. Unvollständige Natrium Inaktivierung. *Pfluegers Arch.* 303:150–61

42. Marquis, K. K., Mautner, H. G. 1974. The effect of electrical stimulation on the action of sulfhydryl reagents in the giant axon of squid; suggested mechanisms for the role of thiol and disulfide groups in the electrically-induced conformational changes. *J. Membr. Biol.* 15:249–60

43. Meves, H. 1974. The effect of holding potential on the asymmetry currents in squid giant axons. *J. Physiol. London* 243:847–67

44. Meves, H. 1975. Asymmetry currents in intracellularly perfused squid giant axons. *Philos. Trans. R. Soc.* In press

45. Meves, H., Shaw, T. I., Vogel, W. 1974. Asymmetry currents in squid giant axons. *Pfluegers Arch.* 347:R33

46. Meves, H., Vogel, W. 1973. Calcium inward currents in internally perfused giant axons. *J. Physiol. London* 235:225–65

47. Moore, J. W., Narahashi, T. 1967. Tetrodotoxin's highly selective blockage of an ionic channel. *Fed. Proc.* 26:1655–63

48. Mozhayeva, G. N., Naumov, A. P. 1970. Effect of surface charge on the steady state potassium conductance of modal membrane. *Nature* 228:164–65

49. Mozhayeva, G. N., Naumov, A. P. 1972. Effect of surface charge on stationary potassium conductivity of Ranvier node membrane. I. Change of pH of exterior solution. *Biofizika* 17:412–20

50. Mozhayeva, G. N., Naumov, A. P. 1972. Effect of surface charge on stationary potassium conductivity of Ranvier node membrane. II. Change of ionic strength of external solution. *Biofizika* 17:618–22

51. Mozhayeva, G. N., Naumov, A. P. 1972. Effect of surface charge on stationary potassium conductance of Ranvier node membrane. III. Effect of divalent cations. *Biofizika* 17:801–8

52. Narahashi, T. 1974. Chemicals as tools in the study of excitable membranes. *Physiol. Rev.* 54:813–89

53. Narahashi, T., Moore, J. W., Scott, W. R. 1964. Tetrodotoxin blockage of sodium conductance increase in lobster

giant axons. *J. Gen. Physiol.* 47:965–74

54. Narahashi, T., Moore, J. W., Shapiro, B. I. 1969. Condylactis toxin: Interaction with nerve membrane ionic conductances. *Science* 163:680–81

55. Narahashi, T., Shapiro, B. I., Deguchi, T., Scuka, M., Wang, C. M. 1972. Effects of scorpion venom on squid axon membranes. *Am. J. Physiol.* 222:850–57

56. Nonner, W., Rojas, E., Stämpfli, R. 1975. Displacement currents in the node of Ranvier: Voltage and time dependence. *Pfluegers Arch.* 354–18

57. Peganov, E. M. 1973. Kinetics of the process of inactivation of sodium channels in the node of Ranvier of frogs. *Bull. Exp. Biol. Med. USSR* 11:5–9

58. Peganov, E. M., Timin, E. N., Khodorov, B. I. 1973. Interrelationship between the processes of sodium activation and inactivation. *Bull. Exp. Biol. Med. USSR* 10:7–11

59. Schauf, C. L. 1974. Sodium currents in *Myxicola* axons: Nonexponential recovery from the inactive state. *Biophys. J.* 14:151–54

60. Schmidt, H., Schmitt, O. 1974. Effect of aconitine on the sodium permeability of the node of Ranvier. *Pfluegers Arch.* 349:133–48

61. Shapiro, B. I., Wang, C. M., Narahashi, T. 1974. Effects of strychnine on ionic conductances of squid axon membrane. *J. Pharmacol. Exp. Ther.* 188:66–76

61a. Stämpfli, R. 1974. Intraaxonal iodate inhibits sodium inactivation. *Experientia* 30:505–8

62. Stevens, C. F. 1972. Inferences about membrane properties from electrical noise measurements. *Biophys. J.* 12:1028–47

63. Stevens, C. F. 1975. Principles and applications of fluctuation analysis: A nonmathematical introduction. *Fed. Proc.* 34:1364–69

64. Strichartz, G. R. 1973. The inhibition of sodium currents in myelinated nerve by quaternary derivatives of lidocaine. *J. Gen. Physiol.* 62:37–57

65. Taylor, R. E. 1974. Excitable membranes. *Ann. Rev. Phys. Chem.* 25:387–405

66. Ulbricht, W. 1974. Ionic channels through the axon membrane: A review. *Biophys. Struct. Mech.* 1:1–16

67. Verveen, A. A., DeFelice, L. J. 1974. Membrane noise. *Progr. Biophys. Mol. Biol.* 28:189–265

68. Woodhull, A. M. 1973. Ionic blockage of sodium channels in nerve. *J. Gen. Physiol.* 61:687–708

NEUROTRANSMITTER RECEPTORS IN THE BRAIN: BIOCHEMICAL IDENTIFICATION

Solomon H. Snyder and James P. Bennett, Jr.

Departments of Pharmacology and Experimental Therapeutics and Psychiatry
and the Behavioral Sciences, Johns Hopkins University School of Medicine,
Baltimore, Maryland 21205

INTRODUCTION

Until very recently, studies of neurotransmitter receptors in the brain have relied almost exclusively on neurophysiologic techniques. Indeed, the major criterion for the identity of a compound as a neurotransmitter, that it mimic the actions of the natural transmitter, implies neurophysiologic approaches (117). However, neurophysiologic studies have some inherent limitations. For instance, when a substance is injected iontophoretically, the investigator does not know the exact concentration utilized and it is difficult to compare the concentrations of two administered compounds because the amount released from the micropipette depends on the electrical charge of the compound, its concentration within the pipette, and a constant unique to each micropipette, the transport number. Examining large numbers of drugs and multiple concentrations is much more readily accomplished with typical biochemical protocols permitting 100 or more assays in a day. In iontophoretic investigations, it is difficult to work with drugs that are uncharged or only weakly ionic.

GENERAL PRINCIPLES IN BIOCHEMICAL LABELING OF NEUROTRANSMITTER RECEPTORS

Recent successes in biochemical identification of neurotransmitter receptors in the brain derive from satisfactory solutions to certain technical issues. Labeling usually involves binding radioactive forms of the neurotransmitter itself, the agonist, or of a suitable antagonist to brain membrane preparations. However, most radioactive chemicals bind to biological membranes in a relatively nonspecific fashion, presumably due to ionic attractions, hydrophobic interactions, and van der Waal's forces. Because the density of neurotransmitter receptors in the brain appears to be in the

153

range of $10-100$ pmol g^{-1} and the concentration of nonspecific binding sites is virtually infinite, it is difficult to attain binding to the specific receptor in amounts that exceed nonspecific binding by a significant margin. Success in overcoming this problem derives in part from the use of ligands with high receptor affinity labeled to high specific radioactivity and therefore employed in low concentrations that should manifest very little nonspecific binding. This approach must be used with caution, however, as high affinity binding can take place to materials that have no relation to biological receptor function. Thus Cuatrecasas & Hollenberg (26) found that insulin binding to talcum powder has an affinity in the nanomolar range, not dissimilar to the affinity of insulin for the insulin receptor itself.

In our own laboratory, we encountered such a potential artifact in studies of the opiate receptor. The major feature of pharmacologic responses to opiates is that they are stereospecific, elicited usually by levorotatory [(−)] isomers much more than by dextrorotatory [(+)] isomers. Accordingly, as a routine screen for opiate receptor binding, one measures stereospecific binding of radioactive opiates. We found that certain glass filters bind opiates stereospecifically with a preference for the pharmacologically more potent (−) isomer (84). Similarly, the ubiquitous lipid, cerebroside sulfate (69), binds opiates stereospecifically. Accordingly, to ensure specificity one must show that a fairly extensive series of drugs, hormones, or neurotransmitter analogs bind to the putative receptor sites with affinity that parallels their biological effects.

Even when using very low concentrations of ligand, nonspecific binding can often exceed biologically relevant binding. It is usually obligatory to wash tissue preparations to remove nonspecifically bound ligand. However, if the dissociation rate of the ligand from the biological receptor is sufficiently rapid, it will also wash away. For instance, the half-life for dissociation of strychnine from the glycine receptor is about $30-45$ sec, even at low temperatures, so that vigorous washing of membranes washes away both specifically and nonspecifically bound strychnine; strychnine binding to the glycine receptor must routinely be measured under conditions in which membranes are not washed (127–129). For ligands with slower dissociation rates, extensive washing of membrane preparations can be accomplished without dissociating the ligand if the membranes with bound ligand are trapped on a filter under reduced pressure so that the membranes and filter can be washed several times with substantial volumes of fluid in only a few seconds. Another effective technique involves centrifugation of membranes with bound ligand through multilayer gradients composed of liquids only slightly more dense than water. In this way, ligand bound to membrane is rapidly separated from unbound ligand, and "washing" layers can be placed in the gradients to reduce nonspecific binding.

Although biological and binding activity ideally should be measured in the same tissue under in vitro conditions where molar concentrations can be precisely specified, this goal is difficult to realize in the brain, where the biological responses to neurotransmitters cannot usually be measured in membrane fragments employed for binding. However, in the case of the dopamine receptor, the affinity of dopamine analogs and dopamine receptor antagonists for a dopamine-sensitive adenylate cyclase in membrane fragments reflects reasonably well in their in vivo properties (21, 47, 56, 59, 74, 75). Accordingly, it has been possible to directly compare binding of numerous drugs and dopamine analogs to the dopamine receptor of the corpus striatum (16) with the reported influence of these agents on the striatal dopamine-sensitive adenylate cyclase. In peripheral neural tissues, such comparisons are much easier. Thus biological and binding potencies of muscarinic cholinergic agents can be readily compared in the guinea pig ileum whose contractions in vitro in response to cholinergic agonists can be monitored (123). Changes in sodium fluxes in microsacs of membrane fragments of electric organs from the electric eel or *Torpedo* in response to nicotinic cholinergic agonists correlate with the affinity of these agents for binding sites in the same tissue preparations (57).

Several other criteria are important in identifying transmitter receptors. For instance, binding of ligands should be saturable, indicating a limited number of sites, with a reasonably high affinity paralleling the biological activity of the ligand used. Binding ought also be restricted to tissues and species that respond physiologically to the agonist.

Binding can be studied with either agonists or antagonists. For many neurotransmitters, certain antagonists seem to have substantially greater affinity for receptor sites than the agonists and, accordingly, are especially useful for studies of receptor binding. In the central nervous system, such antagonists have been used to label the muscarinic cholinergic (6, 37, 41, 42, 100, 121, 124, 125) and glycine receptors (127–129). However, receptor sites for gamma-aminobutyric acid (GABA) (34, 35, 130) and dopamine (16) have been identified by the binding of the neurotransmitters (agonists) themselves, and efforts to demonstrate binding of appropriate receptor antagonists have failed. For the opiate receptor, which has characteristics in common with neurotransmitter receptors, binding of both agonists and antagonists is readily demonstrable (90, 104, 113). The postsynaptic serotonin receptor in the brain can be labeled with serotonin (11, 107) and also with LSD (8, 10), which appears to behave as a mixed agonist-antagonist neurophysiologically (1).

Although biochemical identification of receptors in the central nervous system is only in its infancy, the information already accumulated has proved useful in several different areas. But first, we should define what is meant by "identifying biochemically neurotransmitter receptors."

As Werman has pointed out (116), measuring changes in membrane conductance is probably the most specific neurophysiologic criterion for quantifying neurotransmitter-receptor interactions. This methodology has been used in studying the postsynaptic responses of invertebrate neurons to GABA (110), and vertebrate spinal motoneurons to glycine (118). However, much other valuable information about the postsynaptic receptors of these and other neurotransmitters in the brain has been derived from studying higher order responses such as changes in membrane potentials or firing rates. In any event, all of these neurophysiologic changes are the end products of at least two processes, receptor recognition and binding to a site, and transduction of this information into ionic conductance or analogous alterations. Whether the same or separate molecules mediate recognition and ion conductance change is not clear, although they are probably closely linked. Almost by definition, biochemical binding studies label primarily the recognition sites; for the purposes of this review, these are the receptors that are identified biochemically. A receptor is considered to be specifically labeled only after a number of criteria have been met to ensure that the measured binding represents the physiologically relevant receptor site. Some workers may consider that biochemical identification requires solubilization of the receptor, its purification to homogeneity, and its complete chemical characterization. While this is an ideal goal, it has not been met for any central neurotransmitter receptors. Moreover, an extensive body of functionally important information can be accumulated simply by studying binding to receptors in intact membranes. Indeed, from the experience available with the nicotinic receptor, it appears that interaction of the receptor with several ligands changes substantially when the receptor is solubilized, so that binding to membranes may provide the most biologically meaningful data about receptor function.

The ability to quantitate the affinity of numerous agonists and antagonists can clarify the structural specificity of the receptor. Novel influences of drugs may have therapeutic relevance, perhaps even suggesting the directions for developing more potent analogs, and may also provide new tools for the neurophysiologist in clarifying synaptic dynamics. Receptor interactions of agonists, antagonists, and ions have suggested some alternative models to explain the transduction of receptor recognition into alterations in ionic permeability.

THE OPIATE RECEPTOR: A MODEL FOR NEUROTRANSMITTER RECEPTOR FUNCTION

The notion that opiates exert their pharmacologic activities via a specific "opiate receptor" derives from several features of opiate pharmacology. Certain rigid opiates, such as etorphine, can exert pharmacologic effects at vanishing low doses, smaller than those required by the potent hallucinogenic drug LSD. Opiate action is stereospecific so that for most opiates virtually all pharmacologic activity resides in the (–) isomer. Moreover, opiate antagonists exist which, in very low doses, can completely prevent the actions of opiate agonists although they themselves produce no pharmacologic responses and hence are "pure" antagonists. Identification of opiate receptor binding has been possible by using tritiated opiate agonists or antagonists of high specific activity and trapping the bound opiate by centrifugation or filtration (83, 90, 104, 113). Under optimal conditions, upwards of 80 or 90% of ligand binding takes place to the opiate receptor so that nonspecific binding is minimal. The affinity of large numbers of opiate agonists and antagonists for binding sites parallels their pharmacologic potency in vivo (90, 104, 113). For opiates, the guinea pig ileum provides a tissue in which binding and biological response can be measured together. Morphine and other opiate agonists inhibit electrically induced contractions of the guinea pig ileum at low concentrations and in a fashion that parallels their analgetic potency (25, 62). Both binding and biological potencies of an extensive series of opiate agonists and antagonists are very closely correlated in this tissue (25). Besides showing that binding labels the pharmacologically relevant receptor, these data shed light on an important concept in receptor theory. Indirect evidence utilizing irreversible antagonists had suggested that for certain neurotransmitters, classically exemplified by acetylcholine in the guinea pig ileum, only a small proportion of the total number of receptors need be occupied to elicit a maximal biological response. However, direct binding studies reveal that the concentrations of opiate agonists and antagonists occupying 50% of binding sites correspond precisely to concentrations required for 50% of a maximal pharmacologic response, indicating that "spare receptors" are not involved in this receptor.

Studies of the regional distribution of the opiate receptor in human and monkey brain have provided clues about the normal function of the opiate receptor (43, 66). Receptor density is highest in medially located areas associated with the paleospinothalamic and spinoreticulodiencephalic pathways, which are thought to mediate the affective component of pain perception. Examples include the high density of opiate receptors in the periaqueductal gray of the midbrain, where lesions produce analgesia (72), electrical stimulation appears to cause pain (81, 106), and implantation of small amounts of morphine selectively relieves pain (88). Autoradiographic studies confirm these findings derived from regional dissections and biochemical assays, and further emphasize the selective localization of the opiate receptor (89). Thus autoradiographic grains that label the opiate receptor are highly concentrated in the zona compacta of the substantia nigra but are relatively sparse over the closely adjacent zona reticulata of the substantia nigra. Similarly, grains are heavily concentrated over the locus coeruleus but not over adjacent brain stem regions. Interestingly, the zona compacta of the substantia nigra contains exclusively cell bodies for dopamine neurons, but the zona reticulata does not contain dopamine cells. Similarly, the locus coeruleus consists almost entirely of norepinephrine cell bodies. The selective labeling of the opiate receptor on these nuclei fits well with the abundant pharmacological evidence that biogenic amines, including dopamine and norepinephrine, play a role in mediating pharmacologic actions of opiates.

Direct evidence for an endogenous morphinelike factor (MLF) has been obtained in two ways. Hughes (50) showed that brain extracts possess a substance that, like morphine, inhibits electrically induced contractions of the mouse vas deferens. Specificity was shown by the fact that low concentrations of the pure opiate antagonist naloxone reverse the effects of this brain extract. Another approach involves demonstrating that brain extracts inhibit opiate receptor binding (85, 114). Properties of the MLF assayed by each of these techniques are the same. The regional distribution of this substance parallels that of the opiate receptor in both assay systems, and the material behaves like an opiate agonist physiologically and biochemically. The MLF appears to be a small peptide, as its activity is decreased by carboxypeptidase A treatment (50, 85). It may contain aromatic amino acids, because it is sensitive to digestion by chymotrypsin (85), which selectively degrades peptide bonds of aromatic amino acids. It probably does not contain peptide bonds linked to lysine or arginine, because it is resistant to high concentrations of trypsin, which attacks these bonds selectively (50, 85). Its behavior in a series of gel columns and membrane filters suggests a molecular weight of about 1000 (85). Limited evidence from subcellular fractionation experiments suggests that it may be contained within osmotically sensitive subcellular compartments, probably synaptosomes (pinched-off nerve terminals).

The possibility that the MLF may be a peptide neurotransmitter is interesting in light of recent findings suggesting that several small peptides are neurotransmitters in the brain. Substance P satisfies the criteria to be expected of the primary afferent neurotransmitter in the spinal cord (109). The distribution (82), iontophoretic (96), and brain receptor (17) properties of thyrotropin releasing hormone (TRH) indicate that, besides its endocrine effects, TRH is probably a neurotransmitter. Potent central actions of angiotensin II suggest a possible transmitter role for this peptide as well (101).

If the MLF is a normally occurring neurotransmitter substance, there should exist central neurons that respond selectively and specifically to morphine and similar opiates. Such neurophysiologically identified opiate receptor responses should demonstrate the same pharmacological specificity of the pharmacological effects of opiates. This direct evidence has been provided recently by Herz and his collaborators (99), who demonstrated consistent inhibition of cell firing in the cerebral cortex in response to iontophoretically administered morphine. The iontophoretic effects of morphine are antagonized by the opiate antagonist naloxone and are displayed by the analgetically active levorphanol but not by its inactive (+) isomer, dextrorphan. Interestingly, animals chronically treated with morphine, who are pharmacologically tolerant to its analgetic effects, also display a lessened response of these cerebral cortical cells to iontophoretically administered morphine. Thus if the MLF is a neurotransmitter, it would most likely function as an inhibitory transmitter on these cerebral cortical cells. The ionic mechanism whereby morphine slows the firing rate of cerebral cortical cells has not been worked out. However, studies of ionic influences on opiate receptor binding suggest a possible mechanism.

Concentrations of sodium as small as 1 mM enhance receptor binding of opiate antagonists and decrease binding of opiate agonists to a corresponding extent (91). The influence of sodium is selective; it can be reproduced to a lesser extent by lithium, but is not manifested by potassium, rubidium, or cesium (91). Binding of mixed agonist-antagonist drugs, some of which have less addicting potential than pure opiate agonists, is affected by sodium in a fashion intermediate between agonists and antagonists. Thus, at a practical level, the influence of sodium on opiate receptor binding provides a tool to determine whether a given drug is a pure antagonist such as naloxone, an antagonist "contaminated" with some agonist activity such as nalorphine, a mixed agonist-antagonist, or a pure agonist.

At a theoretical level, the influence of sodium suggests a model for opiate receptor function that has implications for general mechanisms of synaptic transmission. Applying the allosteric model of enzyme function to receptors (55, 76), one can conceive of the opiate receptor as existing in two interconvertible conformational states, an antagonist form in the presence of sodium and an agonist form in the absence of sodium. Antagonists have high and low affinities respectively for the sodium and nonsodium forms of the receptor, whereas agonists have preferential high affinity for the nonsodium receptor conformation. In some classic formulations of drug-receptor interactions, the effects of antagonists are attributed to their binding to receptor sites, but the antagonists lack the intrinsic activity to elicit whatever secondary response is necessary for pharmacological effects. In the present formulation, a drug has intrinsic activity, hence agonist activity, only when it binds to the agonist, nonsodium state of the receptor. By binding to the sodium state of the receptor, antagonists shift the equilibrium between the two forms of the receptor so that there are fewer nonsodium states available for agonist binding.

Presumably, interconversion of opiate receptor states involves conformational changes that might be altered by protein modifying reagents and enzymes. Consistent with this notion is the finding that protein modifying reagents and enzymes such as trypsin, chymotrypsin, and phospholipase A change the sensitivity of the opiate receptor to sodium, so that binding of opiate agonists is decreased more by sodium than in the normal membrane preparations (86, 119).

Assuming that the opiate receptor is in fact a neurotransmitter receptor, these data can represent a general model for synaptic transmission. A major question in neurobiology deals with how transmitter recognition is transduced into an alteration in ion conductance. In the model presented here, one would postulate that the ion whose conductance is selectively affected binds preferentially to one of the two states of the receptor. The transition of antagonist to agonist state of the receptor caused by the endogenous neurotransmitter could be associated with a change in binding of the ion whose conductance is altered. The selective influence of sodium suggests that this may be the ion whose conductance is affected in the opiate receptor. If the MLF neurotransmitter were to hyperpolarize receptive cells by influencing sodium conductance, one would have to assume that it decreases sodium conductance. It is interesting that the hyperpolarizion by norepinephrine of Purkinje cells (103) and spinal motoneurons (33) has been postulated to involve decreases in sodium conductance.

All the available data on receptor binding of opiates and various neurotransmitters in the brain are also consistent with a slightly different model in which agonists and antagonists bind to distinct portions of the receptor that are not interconvertible, but interact in a cooperative fashion, perhaps through interposed membrane structures (55). In this way, binding of antagonists or a particular ion to one subunit of the receptor would alter the binding of agonists to another subunit. This model, in which agonist and antagonist sites on the receptor are distinct, is especially attractive for receptors in which agonists and antagonists are of markedly different chemical structures; it would thus be unnecessary to assume that the receptor could sufficiently alter conformation to accommodate, on different occasions, agonists and antagonists. The model in which the receptor is interconvertible between agonist and antagonist conformations is attractive for opiates because opiate agonists and antagonists are extremely similar chemically.

The preceding models assume that the endogenous MLF is a neurotransmitter for the opiate receptor. The selective iontophoretic influences of morphine on single units in the brain are consistent with this postulate. Rigorous proof that the MLF is a transmitter substance requires demonstration that naturally occurring inhibitory transmission and inhibition resulting from application of pure MLF to morphine-responsive cells be as sensitive to blockade by opiate antagonists as is the influence of morphine itself. Whether or not MLF is a true neurotransmitter, the properties of the opiate receptor provide valuable insights into the functioning of other transmitter receptors.

THE GLYCINE RECEPTOR

Glycine appears to be a major inhibitory neurotransmitter in the spinal cord and brain stem and has been demonstrated to be the natural transmitter mediating postsynaptic inhibition (27, 30, 118). Both glycine and GABA hyperpolarize motoneurons in the spinal cord by increasing chloride conductance with reversal potentials similar to those of the natural inhibitory transmitter. Because the effects of iontophoretically administered glycine and the natural inhibitory transmitter in the spinal cord and brain stem are potently antagonized by strychnine, whereas GABA inhibition is much less sensitive to strychnine, most workers have concluded that glycine is the natural inhibitory transmitter in these areas (29, 30, 63, 118). This neurophysiologic evidence is supported by an abundance of neurochemical data. Neurophysiologically, glycine is a potent inhibitor in the spinal cord and brain stem with much weaker actions in the cerebral cortex, where GABA is a potent inhibitor (24, 27, 60, 64). Similarly, endogenous glycine levels in spinal cord and brain stem are 2–3 times higher than levels at more rostral portions of the central nervous system (2). The extent to which glycine levels in the spinal cord and brain stem exceed those in the cerebral cortex suggests that half or more of endogenous glycine in the brain stem and spinal cord is concerned with the neurotransmitter functions of glycine. However, for amino acid transmitter candidates, it is important to discriminate between neurotransmitter and general metabolic pools of the compound. This has been possible by taking advantage of selective high affinity uptake systems of neurotransmitters.

It appears likely that almost all neurotransmitters are inactivated after synaptic release by uptake into the nerve endings that released them and, possibly, uptake into glia that surround the synapse (51). Acetylcholine appears to be the one major exception to the rule, as no appropriate reuptake system has been identified for acetylcholine, and the activity of acetylcholinesterase can account for termination of its synaptic effects. Amino acids are accumulated by almost all cells in the body via uptake systems of relatively low affinity with apparent Michaelis-Menton constants in the millimolar range (22).

Selective nerve terminal uptake of putative neurotransmitter amino acids can be differentiated from the generalized transport of these compounds, because the former process has substantially higher affinity (100–1000-fold) and greater sodium dependence than the latter (5, 9, 68, 79). In the spinal cord, the only amino acids with high affinity sodium-dependent transport systems into nerve terminal preparations are glycine, GABA, and glutamic and aspartic acids, all neurotransmitter candidates (9, 68, 79). In the cerebral cortex, where glycine is probably not a neurotransmitter, there is no high affinity sodium-dependent uptake for glycine (9); such uptake systems can still be demonstrated for GABA (71), and glutamic and aspartic acids (9). A unique population of synaptosomes, which accumulate glycine only under conditions of the high affinity sodium-dependent uptake, can be separated from the general population of synaptosomes in the spinal cord (3), suggesting that the uptake system labels glycine-specific neurons.

In addition to specific presynaptic uptake, a neurotransmitter should be released upon neuronal depolarization. In the brain, it is difficult to study a single neuronal pathway selectively, and field stimulation of brain preparations may provoke nonspecific release (58). Nonetheless, the fact that potassium depolarization of spinal cord, but not of cerebral cortex slices, releases [^{3}H]glycine only if it has been accumulated under high affinity sodium-dependent conditions (40, 46, 78), is consistent with a neurotransmitter role for glycine. Moreover, the selectivity of this release is indicated by the failure of potassium depolarization under these conditions to release any amino acids in the spinal cord other than glycine, GABA, and glutamic and aspartic acids (78).

The accumulation of neurophysiologic and neurochemical evidence supporting glycine as a major inhibitory transmitter in the spinal cord prompted investigations attempting to demonstrate the glycine receptor biochemically. The glycine receptor has been labeled by the binding of [^{3}H]strychnine to synaptic membrane preparations of the spinal cord and brain stem (127–129). Numerous amino acids compete with [^{3}H]strychnine for binding sites in proportion to their ability to mimic the synaptic effects of glycine. Strychnine binding is highest in gray matter within the spinal cord and brain stem, and decreases as one ascends the neuraxis, paralleling the distribution of endogenous glycine, high affinity glycine uptake into unique synaptosomes, and the ability of glycine to mimic the natural inhibitory transmitter.

Several features of the glycine receptor are consistent with the general model described above for neurotransmitter receptor functioning. Glycine and strychnine do not appear to bind to identical sites (129). Thus treatment of spinal cord synaptic membrane preparations with protein modifying reagents such as N-ethylmaleimide impairs the ability of glycine to displace [^{3}H]strychnine binding without affecting the ability of unlabeled strychnine to displace bound [^{3}H]strychnine. The glycine and strychnine sites appear to interact in a cooperative fashion. The Hill coefficient for the displacement of [^{3}H]strychnine by glycine is 1.7, indicating some degree of positive cooperativity; the displacement of [^{3}H]strychnine by strychnine provides a Hill coefficient of 1.0, indicating a noncooperative process. When synaptic membrane preparations are treated with certain protein modifying reagents, the cooperativity of glycine's displacing bound [^{3}H]strychnine is decreased, whereas the normally noncooperative displacement of bound [^{3}H]strychnine by strychnine is unchanged. This binding suggests even more strikingly the existence of two separate binding sites for glycine and strychnine, which interact cooperatively. Unfortunately, we have not yet been able to demonstrate specific glycine binding to its recognition site and cannot test the hypothesis in the reverse direction.

Presumably, glycine binds to the glycine recognition site of the receptor. What is the role of the strychnine binding site? In physiological concentrations, chloride and other anions inhibit strychnine binding in close proportion to their ability to reverse inhibitory post synaptic potentials of spinal motoneurons (128). In other words, the ability of anions to mimic the role of chloride in mediating the conductance changes associated with glycine-induced synaptic inhibition correlates closely with their potency in inhibiting strychnine binding. To a certain extent, the influence of anions on strychnine binding is related to their hydrated radius and the closeness of this radius to that of chloride, hence the ability of the anions to "fit" the chloride pore in the synaptic membrane. However, formate has a somewhat larger hydrated radius, yet is able to reverse inhibitory postsynaptic potentials and to inhibit strychnine binding. These data support a formulation in which the antagonist or strychnine state of the receptor is closely related to the ion conductance mechanism. Whether ions also affect glycine binding is not clear, because, as previously mentioned, it has not been possible to measure directly the binding of glycine to the glycine receptor.

The cooperativity evident in the displacement of strychnine by glycine may be related to the observed cooperativity in the neurophysiological effects of glycine in some systems (116, 118). Neurophysiologically, cooperativity is usually detected by sigmoid rather than hyperbolic membrane polarization or conductance changes in response to increasing amounts of neurotransmitter. The allosteric two-state model is not the only possible explanation for observed cooperativity. Cooperativity, when considered in the most general sense as any reaction of order higher than one, can exist without any interactions between subunit sites. Such an independent subunit model was proposed by Hodgkin & Huxley (44) to explain the sigmoid ionic conductance changes observed in giant squid axon action potentials. An important restriction of noninteracting, independent subunit models is that, although the processes may yield a Hill slope greater than one, the number must always be integral (92). In contrast, for allosteric two-state or multistate models where interactions can take place between different receptor conformations, the Hill coefficient may approach limiting values of either integral or nonintegral values (23, 92). Unfortunately, the limited neurophysiological data on synaptic cooperativity do not discriminate among alternative models based on Hill slopes. Thus approximately integral values ($n = 2$) for limiting Hill coefficients have been reported for the actions of glycine and GABA in some systems (110, 116). In another report, the actions of iontophoretically applied glycine on spinal neurons were clearly cooperative with respect to both membrane polarization and conductance changes, but a Hill plot was not performed (118).

CHOLINERGIC RECEPTORS

The most extensive biochemical investigations of neurotransmitter receptors have involved the nicotinic cholinergic receptor of the electric organ of various invertebrates (20, 32, 77, 80, 94). In the brain, neurophysiologic studies suggest that the majority of cholinergic synapses are muscarinic. Biochemically, several laboratories have identified both peripheral (6, 14, 15, 38, 39, 87, 123) and central (6, 37, 41, 42, 100, 121, 122, 124, 125) muscarinic cholinergic receptor binding. Much less extensive studies have been performed for the central nervous nicotinic receptors (13, 36, 77, 98, 100).

The most successful approach to labeling muscarinic receptors in the brain has utilized radioactive antagonists (6, 37, 41, 42, 98, 121, 122, 124, 125). Reversible ligands have included [^{3}H]atropine (37, 100), [^{3}H]quinuclidinyl benzilate (QNB) (121, 122, 124, 125), [^{3}H]benzetimide, and [^{3}H]dexetimide (6). In the guinea pig ileum and in the brain, it has also been feasible to label the muscarinic receptor with an irreversible alkylating agent related to the antagonist benzilyl choline (14, 38, 41, 42). These two classes of ligands have their individual merits and faults. For instance, with irreversible labels, it is difficult to evaluate competition by unlabeled drugs. If incubations are performed to equilibrium, as each molecule of the nonradioactive drug dissociates, it will be replaced by the radiolabeled irreversible ligand so that, even at a concentration of the nonradioactive drug which occupies virtually all the receptor sites, no inhibition of [^{3}H]-ligand binding will be demonstrable. Kinetic studies, especially of dissociation rates, cannot be performed with irreversible ligands. On the other hand, an irreversible ligand is useful in solubilization studies, as even drastic treatment with detergents will not dissociate the ligand from the receptor. However, the physical properties of the receptor labeled with an irreversible ligand may not be the same as those of the native receptor.

In several studies, binding of muscarinic antagonists to brain tissue has been demonstrated to be associated with the muscarinic receptor; the abilities of muscarinic agonists and antagonists to inhibit this binding parallel their pharmacologic potency, whereas nicotinic and noncholinergic drugs do not affect binding. Moreover, the regional distribution of [^{3}H]QNB binding to monkey brain membranes parallels cholinergic markers such as endogenous levels of acetylcholine, the activity of choline acetyltransferase, and high affinity sodium-dependent choline uptake, which selectively labels cholinergic neurons (121). Some discrepancies in these correlations may shed light on the relative proportion of muscarinic and nicotinic synapses in different parts of the brain. Thus six different areas of the cerebral cortex of the monkey have essentially the same density of muscarinic receptors and similar levels of choline acetyltransferase and choline uptake, except for the pyriform cortex whose choline uptake and choline acetyltransferase are about three times higher than any other areas of the cerebral cortex. Perhaps in the pyriform cortex, an important portion of cholinergic synapses are nicotinic. Similarly, the interpeduncular nucleus appears to be the brain region richest in cholinergic nerve terminals that may derive from cell bodies in the habenula. The very high levels of choline acetyltransferase and choline uptake in the interpeduncular nucleus are abolished after discrete lesions in the habenula. Because the interpeduncular nucleus has low levels of muscarinic receptor binding, synapses here may also be nicotinic. The fact that, in most brain regions, there is a close correlation between cholinergic markers and muscarinic receptor binding confirms the neurophysiologic evidence that the majority of cholinergic synapses in the brain are muscarinic (63).

Studies correlating biological and binding potency for muscarinic receptors in the guinea pig ileum provide evidence that, like other neurotransmitter receptors, the muscarinic receptor may function according to an allosteric model. For pure antagonists, relative potencies in inhibiting acetylcholine induced contractions and in competing for [^{3}H]QNB binding sites are essentially the same (123). For pure agonists, biological potencies are 10–100 times greater than potency in inhibiting binding of the antagonist [^{3}H]QNB. According to the allosteric model, antagonists would compete directly with [^{3}H]QNB for binding to the antagonist conformation of the receptor, explaining their similar biological and binding potencies. Agonists effect the biological response by binding to the agonist state of the receptor, but to inhibit [³H]QNB binding, they must indirectly decrease the number of available antagonist receptors by shifting the equilibrium between unoccupied antagonist and agonist receptor conformations. If the interconversion of agonist and antagonist receptor states were extremely facile, agonists might be as potent in inhibiting [³H]QNB binding as in contracting the guinea pig ileum. However, if there were energy constraints on this interconversion, agonists should be less potent in inhibiting receptor binding of an antagonist than in eliciting a biological response themselves.

Thus, like the glycine receptor, the muscarinic receptor appears to possess separate binding sites for agonist and antagonist drugs. Neurophysiologic studies indicate that muscarinic excitation is associated with the reduction in potassium permeability, whereas inhibition arises from an increase in potassium permeability (63). However, potassium and numerous other cations examined do not influence the binding of [³H] antagonists to the muscarinic receptor or the potency of muscarinic drugs in inhibiting this binding.

To evaluate dynamic changes in receptor functioning under various physiological and pharmacologic conditions, it would be desirable to label neurotransmitter receptors in vivo. With intravenously administered [³H]QNB, it has been possible to label the muscarinic receptor in vivo (122). The number of binding sites and their regional distribution determined in this way are similar to the in vitro findings. Moreover, by labeling the muscarinic receptor in vivo, it is possible to visualize the receptor by autoradiography under the light microscope and thereby to map the distribution of muscarinic receptors throughout the brain (120). Much of the success in elucidating a function of central nervous catecholamines and serotonin stems from the development of histochemical techniques in mapping neuronal systems that use these compounds as neurotransmitters. Histochemical localization of cholinergic neurons has not been accomplished with comparable success. Hopefully, the ability to visualize muscarinic receptor sites in the brain may stimulate progress in brain cholinergic research.

Neurophysiologic studies indicate that Renshaw cells in the spinal cord have both nicotinic and muscarinic receptors (63). In the rest of the central nervous system, neurophysiologic evidence for nicotinic synapses is equivocal. Attempts to label the nicotinic receptors in the brain with ligands such as [³H]nicotine (100) and radiolabeled bungarotoxin (13, 98) have not been clear-cut. The most convincing studies have utilized [³H]bungarotoxin and demonstrated some drug specificity in inhibiting ligand binding (36). Some interesting differences in drug potencies exist between apparent rat brain nicotinic receptor sites studied by [³H]bungarotoxin binding and the much better characterized nicotinic receptor of *Electrophorus* microsacs (36).

POSTSYNAPTIC SEROTONIN RECEPTORS

For serotonin, dopamine, and possibly for other neurotransmitters there appear to be presynaptic or *autoreceptors* in addition to conventional postsynaptic receptors

(1, 12, 18). Interaction of these autoreceptors with the neurotransmitter serves to inhibit firing of the presynaptic neuron. The autoreceptors apparently provide a mechanism to regulate neuronal firings so that, after synaptic release, the neurotransmitter tells the autoreceptor, "I have done my job, now stop firing." It has not been possible to label autoreceptors for any neurotransmitter. The postsynaptic serotonin receptor can be labeled by the agonist [^{3}H]serotonin (11, 107) itself as well as by [^{3}H]LSD (8, 10). The binding of both agents appears to be postsynaptic, as lesions of the midbrain raphe nuclei, which provide the major serotonin presynaptic input to the forebrain, fail to alter the binding of both [^{3}H]serotonin and [^{3}H]LSD. For serotonin, neurophysiologic studies of various agents at postsynaptic receptor sites are limited so that it is difficult to correlate binding and biological potency for many compounds. However, competition for [^{3}H]serotonin or [^{3}H]LSD binding sites by several agents parallels their known influence at serotonin postsynaptic receptors (G. Aghajanian, personal communication). LSD appears to be a mixed agonist-antagonist at postsynaptic serotonin receptors, so that it presumably binds to both postulated agonist and antagonist states of the receptor. In any event, there are differences in the potencies of agents in inhibiting LSD and serotonin binding. Pure tryptamine agonists related to serotonin are 10–100 times more potent in inhibiting serotonin than LSD binding, whereas classical pure serotonin antagonists are more potent in inhibiting LSD than serotonin binding (11). Analogs of LSD and other psychedelic drugs, which are thought to be mixed agonist-antagonists, are approximately equally potent in inhibiting LSD and serotonin binding (11, 107). Thus binding to the serotonin receptor is consistent with a two-state model. Whereas displacement of [^{3}H]LSD by nonradioactive LSD has a Hill coefficient of 1.0, displacement of [^{3}H]LSD by serotonin shows a Hill coefficient of about 0.5, suggesting negative cooperative interaction (10).

Although LSD binds with substantial affinity to the postsynaptic receptor, this effect appears unrelated to the psychedelic actions of this drug. LSD is thought to exert its psychedelic effects by behaving as a pure agonist mimicking serotonin at the presynaptic autoreceptors, hence slowing the firing of serotonin neurons (1). 2-bromo-LSD is essentially ineffective as a psychedelic agent and is very weak in its effect on presynaptic autoreceptors, but is as potent as LSD on postsynaptic receptors in both neurophysiologic (G. Aghajanian, personal communication) and binding studies (10).

GAMMA-AMINOBUTYRIC ACID RECEPTORS

Quantitatively, gamma-aminobutyric acid (GABA) is probably the major inhibitory neurotransmitter in the brain. Evidence for its neurotransmitter effects derives from neurophysiologic studies showing that its reversal potential and other synaptic characteristics mimic those of the natural transmitter (60, 64, 112), and that bicuculline (28, 61, 70, 111) and picrotoxin (61, 93, 112) inhibit both natural synaptic inhibition and the inhibitory influences of GABA.

The postsynaptic GABA receptor has been labeled by direct binding of [^{3}H]GABA (34, 35, 130). Numerous amino acids compete for [^{3}H]GABA binding sites in proportion to their ability to mimic the neurophysiologic effects of GABA. Bicuculline is a potent inhibitor of [³H]GABA binding (35, 130). In the monkey, but not in the rat, the regional distribution of GABA receptor binding parallels endogenous GABA levels (34). Studies to date have not revealed cooperativity in GABA binding or its inhibition by GABA agonists or antagonists (35, 130). However, the inability to demonstrate GABA receptor binding with radiolabeled antagonists has prohibited a thorough examination for such interactions. Without both antagonist and agonist ligands, it is difficult to obtain evidence for or against an allosteric model for the GABA receptor.

Studies of GABA receptor binding illuminate problems encountered in labeling neurotransmitter receptor sites. In the presence of sodium, GABA binds avidly to brain membranes, but the substrate specificity of this binding indicates that it does not involve the postsynaptic GABA receptor. This sodium-dependent GABA binding appears to label primarily a GABA transport site, perhaps involving glia (35). Only by extensively washing membranes to remove sodium and by subjecting them to a freezing and thawing process that decreases this sodium-dependent binding and enhances the sodium-independent receptor binding, can postsynaptic receptor be demonstrated.

THE DOPAMINE RECEPTOR

Dopamine neuronal pathways in the brain have substantial clinical importance, because degeneration of the nigrostriatal dopamine pathway is associated in part with the pathophysiology of Parkinson's disease (48), and blockade of other dopamine receptors in the brain seems to explain the therapeutic actions of antischizophrenic drugs (19, 108). Neurophysiologically, dopamine is primarily inhibitory (63). The demonstration of a dopamine-sensitive adenylate cyclase in areas of the brain enriched in dopamine nerve terminals has suggested that cyclic AMP (cAMP) may be a second messenger in the synaptic actions of dopamine (21, 47, 56, 59, 74, 75). In most parts of the body, cAMP acts by stimulating the phosphorylation of specific proteins. In the brain, cAMP enhances phosphorylation of certain membrane proteins (115); this has been postulated to be the mechanism for synaptic actions of dopamine. The nature of a possible association between such membrane phosphorylation and a change in ionic permeability is unclear. Neurophysiologic studies are inconclusive, but suggest that dopamine may hyperpolarize cells by increasing potassium conductance or, more likely, by decreasing sodium conductance (63). Sodium conductance could be lowered either by closing sodium pores or by activating the outward pumping of sodium.

Recently, binding of [³H]dopamine to the dopamine receptor in the corpus striatum of mammalian brain has been demonstrated directly (16). The competition of catecholamines for the binding sites parallels their known neurophysiologic effects on the dopamine receptor, as does the influence of a number of antischizophrenic phenothiazines and related drugs. The molar affinities of these drugs for the [³H]dopamine binding sites are almost exactly the same as their affinities for the dopamine-sensitive adenylate cyclase in similar tissue preparations. Thus the dopamine receptor may provide one of the few cases in the brain in which receptor binding can be correlated in the same tissue preparation with a bioassay. It has been suggested that the dopamine-sensitive adenylate cyclase is the dopamine receptor. This raises the question of whether the adenylate cyclase and the dopamine recognition site are contained on the same molecule. Evidence from a variety of hormone-stimulated adenylate cyclase systems favors an alternative model (7) in which dopamine and other neurotransmitter and hormone receptor complexes migrate through the synaptic membrane surface by lateral diffusion and periodically collide with adenylate cyclase molecules. According to this model, activation of the adenylate cyclase occurs only if the receptor is complexed with the neurotransmitter at the time of collision.

RECEPTOR EFFECTS OF NOREPINEPHRINE

Synaptic actions of norepinephrine also appear to be associated with AMP. In brain slices from particular regions of certain species, norepinephrine enhancement of cAMP accumulation is antagonized by α-noradrenergic receptor blockers (49); in other regions, particularly the cerebellum, β-blockers are more potent (49, 95). Thus there appear to be two classes of norepinephrine receptors in the brain, α and β.

It has been possible to label the β-receptor of turkey and frog red blood cells with potent β-antagonists (4, 67). The substrate specificity of these binding sites is closely similar to known physiological properties of β-norepinephrine receptors. Recently, it has proved feasible to label β-adrenergic receptors in the brain (D. B. Bylund and S. H. Snyder, in preparation) with [^{3}H]alprenolol, a β-receptor blocker that has been used to demonstrate β-receptor binding in frog red blood cells (67).

The most detailed neurophysiologic studies are those of Bloom and co-workers (103), characterizing the norepinephrine pathway with cell bodies in the locus coeruleus and terminals upon the Purkinje cells of the cerebellum. Stimulation of the locus coeruleus and iontophoretic administration of norepinephrine to Purkinje cells both cause a hyperpolarization associated with an increase in membrane resistance. Natural stimulation of the pathway as well as application of norepinephrine are antagonized by β-receptor blockers. Thus norepinephrine mimics the effects of the natural transmitter substance. As with the dopamine receptor, the effects of norepinephrine in the cerebellum appear to be mediated by a cAMP. Iontophoretically applied cAMP can mimic the effects of norepinephrine, and the actions of both are enhanced by inhibitors of the cAMP degrading enzyme phosphodiesterase (103). Moreover, stimulation of the locus coeruleus elicits an enhanced histochemical fluorescence of cAMP over the Purkinje cells (102).

The ionic mechanism of norepinephrine effects on Purkinje cells in the cerebellum appears to involve a decrease in sodium conductance, as has been suggested for dopamine receptors. Whether this results from a closing of sodium pores or from increased outward pumping of sodium is not clear.

GLUTAMIC ACID RECEPTORS

Quantitatively, GABA and glycine, the two major inhibitory transmitters, probably account for about half of all the synapses in the brain (45, 52). Biogenic amines, serotonin, norepinephrine, dopamine, and acetylcholine account for only a small portion. What might be the major excitatory transmitters? The dicarboxylic amino acids glutamate and aspartate are among the best candidates, although evidence supporting a transmitter role for them is less strong than for the other transmitters already discussed.

A direct demonstration that glutamate is contained in specific neurons utilizes the cerebellum of hamsters treated with a virus that selectively destroys cerebellar granule cells. With 90% destruction of the granule cells, there is a 40% decline in endogenous levels of glutamate with no change in any other amino acid (126). High affinity sodium-dependent glutamate and aspartate uptake is reduced 85% in these virus-treated animals, but uptake of other amino acids is not lowered. As the number of glial cells is normal in these animals, the possibility that glutamate uptake occurs into glia can be excluded. Thus the transmitter of the granule cells, known from neurophysiological studies to be excitatory, is probably glutamate. Moreover, about 40% of the endogenous glutamate in the cerebellum appears to be contained in the transmitter pool in granule cells.

Neurophysiologically, it is difficult to establish glutamate definitively as a neuro-transmitter. Its excitatory actions are virtually universal (27, 54) so that it is difficult to discriminate nonspecific excitation from effects relevant to normal synaptic trans-mission. Moreover, no potent selective antagonists of glutamate and natural excita-tory transmission have been demonstrated. In neurophysiologic studies, some neurons respond more to glutamate and others more to aspartate (31, 53). Specifi-cally, spinal interneurons are more sensitive to glutamate than aspartate, whereas the reverse is true for Renshaw cells (31).

Although glutamate is not yet conclusively established as a neurotransmitter, it already appears possible to label brain membranes with kainic acid (105), a potent glutamate agonist, with binding and displacement parameters consistent with known postsynaptic glutamic responses. Binding of radiolabeled glutamate itself to brain membranes does not fulfill as rigorously the structure-activity requirements of the postsynaptic glutamate receptor and may be associated instead with presynap-tic neuronal or glial uptake site (73, 97, 105). Kainic acid, which is 1–2 orders of magnitude more potent than glutamate at glutamate-specific cells in the spinal cord, binds to central nervous system membrane preparations with high specificity, sug-gesting that it involves the glutamate receptor (105). Kainic acid itself has about 50 times the affinity of L-glutamate of binding sites. The only other compound that competes potently with kainic acid is quisqualic acid, which itself is 1–2 orders of magnitude more potent than glutamate in exciting central neurons and has about 25 times the affinity of glutamate for the kainic acid binding sites. L-glutamate has about 50 times the affinity for L-asparate for the receptor sites. Receptor binding is stereospecific, as D-glutamate has essentially no affinity. No other amino acids, drugs, or transmitter candidates compete successfully with kainic binding sites, which are thus highly specific. Kainic acid binding is mostly enriched in the corpus striatum, where binding is almost twice that in the cerebellum, hypothalamus, cerebral cortex, and hippocampus; midbrain, thalamus, and medulla-pons have only about one fifth the binding of the corpus striatum. These regional differences do not parallel regional variations in endogenous glutamic acid, which is not altogether surprising, as the major portion of endogenous glutamate in most brain regions, with the possible exception of the cerebellum (126), does not appear to be associated with a neurotransmitter pool. Because of the preferential affinity of glutamate for kainic acid binding sites, labeling appears to involve the specific glutamate receptor. Glutamate has been advanced as the transmitter of primary afferent neurons to the spinal cord, although substance P may be a more promising candidate (109). On the basis of localization in different parts of the spinal cord, aspartate has been suggested as the transmitter of excitatory interneurons in the spinal cord. Studies of the detailed localization of kainic acid binding sites might help to clarify the identity of the glutamate-specific synapses.

COMPARATIVE PROPERTIES OF RECEPTORS AND CONCLUSION

A valuable feature of biochemical measurement of receptors is the ability to measure the actual concentration of receptor sites in the brain. The densities of serotonin, dopamine, GABA, and glycine receptors, as well as the density of muscarinic cholinergic receptors, are all fairly similar, ranging from 10 to 100 pmol g^{-1} wet wt. This is surprising, because the numbers of neurons that use each of these substances as transmitters vary tremendously. Thus, while up to 50% of synapses in some brain regions are GABAnergic, serotonin accounts for less than 0.1% of brain synapses (65). How does one explain the similar total numbers of their receptor sites? Conceivably, cells may bear receptors for transmitters that they never encounter. This is unlikely in light of the similar regional distribution of transmitter levels and receptor density. More likely is the possibility that while a cell must receive input from a transmitter to possess a receptor for it, receptor density is "all or none" and not proportional to the number of nerve terminals synapsing upon the cell. Thus although the hypothalamus possesses more than 10 times higher endogenous levels of serotonin than the cerebral cortex, both brain regions have similar numbers of serotonin receptors (11). Histochemical studies show that though the density of serotonin terminals is much less in the cerebral cortex than in the hypothalamus, almost every cell in the cerebral cortex receives some serotonin innervation.

In the hypothalamus, the percentage of cells receiving serotonin terminals is probably no greater than in the cerebral cortex, but hypothalamic cells receiving serotonin terminals bear much larger numbers of terminals than comparable cells in the cerebral cortex. By this reasoning, one would expect to find approximately the same serotonin receptor density in areas both heavily and sparsely innervated by serotonin terminals.

The conformational state of a receptor may determine the apparent number of receptor sites labeled by a particular ligand. If postulated agonist and antagonist conformations of a receptor interconvert rapidly, saturating concentrations of radiolabeled agonists or antagonists should label all receptor sites regardless of their conformation at the beginning of the incubation. This is probably the case with the opiate receptor, as the total number of receptor sites calculated is the same whether measured with a labeled agonist or antagonist. However, if interconversion of receptor conformations is not energetically favorable, a given ligand will label only receptor states for which it has high affinity. In the case of the serotonin receptor, the number of LSD binding sites in the brain appears to be two times the number of serotonin binding sites, for most major brain regions (11). Assuming that LSD binds equally to agonist and antagonist conformations, this suggests that there are approximately equal numbers of agonist and antagonist states of the serotonin receptor.

In summary, it is now possible to study biochemically the receptor sites for most of the known neurotransmitters in the central nervous system. Although work in this field is in its infancy, receptor binding properties can be related to physiological functions of the associated synapses. The most promising insights have to do with the apparent two-state properties of synaptic receptors and their alteration by ions whose conductance changes are involved in synaptic transmission. The question of how neurotransmitter recognition is translated into a change in ion conductance or conceivably some other "second messenger" is one of the key problems in neurobiology. Receptor binding studies summarized here will hopefully provide a means to elucidate the molecular mechanism of this translation.

ACKNOWLEDGMENTS

This work was supported by USPHS Fellowship 5T01GM0062414 and a summer fellowship from the Epilepsy Foundation of America to JPB and USPHS grant DA-00266 and RSDA Award MH-33128 to SHS, and by the Benevolent Foundation of Scottish Rite Freemasonry, Northern Jurisdiction, USA.

Literature Cited

1. Aghajanian, G. K., Haigler, H. J., Bloom, F. E. 1972. Lysergic acid diethylamide and serotonin direct actions on serotonin-containing neurons. *Life Sci. Pt. I Physiol. Pharmacol.* 17:615–22
2. Aprison, M. H., Shank, R. P., Davidoff, R. A. 1969. A comparison of the concentration of glycine, a transmitter suspect, in different areas of the brain and spinal cord in seven different vertebrates. *Comp. Biochem. Physiol.* 28:1345–55
3. Arregui, A., Logan, W. J., Bennett, J. P., Snyder, S. H. 1972. Specific glycine-accumulating synaptosomes in the spinal cord of rats. *Proc. Nat. Acad. Sci. USA* 69:3485–89
4. Aurbach, G. D., Fedak, S. A., Woodard, C. J., Palmer, J. S., Hauser, D., Troxler, F. 1974. β-Adrenergic receptor: stereospecific interactions of iodinated β-blocking agent with high affinity site. *Science* 186:1223–24
5. Balcar, V. J., Johnston, G.A.R. 1972. The structural specificity of the high-affinity uptake of L-glutamate and

L-aspartate by rat brain slices. *J. Neurochem.* 19:2657–66
6. Beld, A. J., Ariens, E. J. 1974. Stereospecific binding as a tool in attempts to localize and isolate muscarinic receptors. Part II. Binding of (+)-benzetimide, (–)-benzetimide and atropine to a fraction from bovine tracheal smooth muscle and to bovine caudate nucleus. *Eur. J. Pharmacol.* 25:203–9
7. Bennett, G. V., O'Keefe, E., Cuatrecasas, P. 1975. Mechanisms of action of cholera toxin and the mobile receptor theory of hormone receptor-adenylate cyclase interactions. *Proc. Nat. Acad. Sci. USA* 72:33–37
8. Bennett, J. L., Aghajanian, G. K. 1974. D-LSD binding to brain homogenates: possible relationship to serotonin receptors. *Life Sci.* 15:1935–44
9. Bennett, J. P. Jr., Logan, W. J., Snyder, S. H. 1973. Amino acids as central nervous transmitters. The influence of ions, amino acid analogues, and ontogeny on transport systems for L-glutamic and L-aspartic acids and glycine into central

nervous synaptosomes of the rat. *J. Neurochem.* 21:1533–50

10. Bennett, J. P., Snyder, S. H. 1975. Stereospecific binding of D-lysergic acid diethylamide (LSD) to brain membranes: relationship to serotonin receptors. *Brain Res.* 94:523–44

11. Bennett, J. P., Snyder, S. H. 1975. [³H]-Serotonin binding to postsynaptic serotonin receptors in rat brain. *Mol. Pharmacol.* In press

12. Bloom, F. E. 1975. Physiological assessment of pre- and postsynaptic receptors. In *Pre- and Postsynaptic Receptors,* ed. E. Usdin, W. E. Bunney Jr., 67–87. New York: Dekker. 337 pp.

13. Bosmann, H. B. 1972. Acetylcholine receptor. I. Identification and biochemical characterization of a cholinergic receptor of guinea pig cerebral cortex. *J. Biol. Chem.* 247:130–45

14. Burgen, A. S. V., Hiley, C. R. 1974. Two populations of acetylcholine receptors in guinea pig ileum. *Brit. J. Pharmacol.* 51:127P

15. Burgen, A. S. V., Hiley, C. R., Young, J. M. 1974. The binding of [³H]-propylbenzilylcholine mustard by longitudinal muscle strips from guinea pig small intestine. *Brit. J. Pharmacol.* 50:145–51

16. Burt, D. R., Creese, I., Enna, S. J., Snyder, S. H. 1975. Binding of [³H]-dopamine to the postsynaptic dopamine receptor of rat striatal membranes. *Proc. Nat. Acad. Sci. USA.* In press

17. Burt, D. R., Snyder, S. H. 1975. Thyrotropin releasing hormone (TRH): apparent receptor binding in rat brain membranes. *Brain Res.* In press

18. Carlsson, A., Kehr, W., Lindquist, M., Magnusson, T., Atack, C. U. 1972. Regulation of monoamine metabolism in the central nervous system. *Pharmacol. Rev.* 24:371–84

19. Carlsson, A., Lindquist, M. 1963. Effect of chlorpromazine or haloperidol on formation of 3-methoxytyramine and normetanephrine in mouse brain. *Acta Pharmacol. Toxicol.* 20:140–44

20. Changeux, J. P., Kasai, M., Lee, C. Y. 1970. Use of a snake venom toxin to characterize the cholinergic receptor protein. *Proc. Nat. Acad. Sci. USA* 67:1241–47

21. Clement-Cormier, Y. C., Kebabian, J. W., Petzold, G. L., Greengard, P. 1974. Dopamine-sensitive adenylate cyclase in mammalian brain: a possible site of action of antipsychotic drugs. *Proc. Nat. Acad. Sci. USA* 71:1113–17

22. Cohen, S. R., Lajtha, A. 1972. Amino acid transport. In *Handbook of Neurochemistry, Vol. 7,* ed. A. Lajtha, 543–72. New York: Plenum

23. Colquhoun, D. 1973. The relation between classical and cooperative models for drug action. In *Drug Receptors,* ed. H. P. Rang, 149–82. London: Univ. Park Press. 321 pp.

24. Crawford, J. M., Curtis, D. R. 1964. The excitation and depression of mammalian cortical neurons by amino acids. *Brit. J. Pharmacol. Chemother.* 23: 313–29

25. Creese, I., Snyder, S. H. 1975. Opiate receptor binding and pharmacological activity in the guinea pig intestine. *J. Pharmacol. Exp. Ther.* 94:205–19

26. Cuatrecasas, P., Hollenberg, M. D. 1975. Binding of insulin and other hormones to non-receptor materials: saturability, specificity and apparent "negative cooperativity." *Biochem. Biophys. Res. Commun.* 62:31–41

27. Curtis, D. R. 1970. Amino acid transmitters in the mammalian central nervous system. *Proc., 4th Int. Congr. Pharmacol.,* ed. R. Eigenbrann, 9–31. Basel, Switzerland: Schwabe

28. Curtis, D. R., Duggan, A. W., Felix, D., Johnston, G. A. R., McLennan, H. 1971. Antagonism between bicuculline and GABA in the cat brain. *Brain Res.* 33:57–73

29. Curtis, D. R., Duggan, A. W., Johnston, G. A. R. 1971. The specificity of strychnine as a glycine antagonist in the mammalian spinal cord. *Exp. Brain Res.* 12:547–65

30. Curtis, D. R., Hösli, L., Johnston, G. A. R. 1968. The hyperpolarization of spinal motorneurons by glycine and related amino acids. *Exp. Brain Res.* 5:235–58

31. Duggan, A. W. 1974. The differential sensitivity to L-glutamate and L-aspartate of spinal interneurons and L-aspartate of spinal interneurons and Renshaw cells. *Exp. Brain Res.* 19:522–28

32. Eldefrawi, M. E., Britten, A. G., Eldefrawi, A. T. 1971. Acetylcholine binding to Torpedo electroplax: relationship to acetylcholine receptor. *Science* 173:338–40

33. Engberg, I., Marshall, K. C. 1971. Mechanisms of noradrenaline hyperpolarization in spinal cord motorneurons of the cat. *Acta Physiol. Scand.* 83: 142–44

34. Enna, S. J., Kuhar, M. J., Snyder, S. H. 1975. Regional distribution of postsynaptic receptor binding for γ-

aminobutyric acid (GABA) in monkey brain. *Brain Res.* In press

35. Enna, S. J., Snyder, S. H. 1975. Properties of γ-aminobutyric acid (GABA) receptor binding in rat brain synaptic membrane fractions. *Brain Res.* In press

36. Eterović, V. A., Bennett, E. L. 1974. Nicotinic cholinergic receptor in brain detected by binding of α-[³H]bungarotoxin. *Biochim. Biophys. Acta* 362:346–55

37. Farrow, J. T., O'Brien, R. D. 1973. Binding of atropine and muscarome to rat brain fractions and its relation to the acetylcholine receptor. *Mol. Pharmacol.* 9:33–40

38. Fewtrell, C., Rang, H. P. 1971. Distribution of bound ³H-benzilylcholine mustard in subcellular fractions of smooth muscle from guinea pig ileum. *Brit. J. Pharmacol.* 43:417–18

39. Gill, E. W., Rang, H. P. 1966. An alkylating derivative of benzilycholine with specific and long-lasting parasympatholytic activity. *Mol. Pharmacol.* 2:284–97

40. Hammerstad, J. P., Murray, J. E., Cutler, R. W. P. 1971. Efflux of amino acid neurotransmitters from rat spinal cord slices. II. Factors influencing the electrically induced efflux of [¹⁴C]glycine and [³H]GABA. *Brain Res.* 35:357–67

41. Hiley, C. R., Burgen, A. S. V. 1974. The distribution of muscarinic receptor sites in the nervous system of the dog. *J. Neurochem.* 22:159–62

42. Hiley, C. R., Young, J. M., Burgen, A. S. V. 1972. Labeling of cholinergic receptors in subcellular fractions from rat cerebral cortex. *Biochem. J.* 127:86P

43. Hiller, J. M., Pearson, J., Simon, E. J. 1973. Distribution of stereospecific binding of the potent narcotic analgesic, etorphine, in the human brain: predominance in the limbic system. *Res. Commun. Chem. Pathol. Pharmacol.* 6:1052–62

44. Hodgkin, A. L., Huxley, A. F. 1952. A quantitative description of membrane current and its application to conduction and excitation in nerve. *J. Physiol. London* 117:500–44

45. Hökfelt, T., Ljundahl, A. 1971. Light and electron microscopic autoradiography on spinal cord slices after incubation with labeled glycine. *Brain Res.* 32:189–94

46. Hopkin, J., Neal, M. J. 1971. Effect of electrical stimulation and high potassium concentrations of the efflux of [¹⁴C]glycine from slices of spinal cord. *Brit. J. Pharmacol.* 42:215–23

47. Horn, A. S., Cuello, A. C., Miller, R. J. 1974. Dopamine in the mesolimbic system of the rat brain: endogenous levels and the effects of drugs on the uptake mechanism and stimulation of adenylate cyclase activity. *J. Neurochem.* 22:265–70

48. Hornykiewicz, O. 1972. Neurochemistry of Parkinsonism. In *Handbook of Neurochemistry, Vol. 7*, ed. A. Lajtha, 465–501. New York: Plenum

49. Huang, M., Ho, A. K. S., Daly, J. W. 1973. Accumulation of adenosine cyclic 3',5'-monophosphate in rat cerebral cortical slices. Stimulating effect of *alpha* and *beta* adrenergic agents after treatment with 6-hydroxydopamine, 2,3,5-trihydroxyphenethylamine, and dihydroxytryptamines. *Mol. Pharmacol.* 9:711–17

50. Hughes, J. 1975. Search for the endogenous ligand of the opiate receptor. In *Neurosciences Research Program Bulletin, Vol. 13: Opiate Receptor Mechanisms*, ed. S. H. Snyder, S. Matthyse, 55–58. Boston, Mass: Neurosci. Res. Prog. 166 pp.

51. Iversen, L. L. 1971. Role of transmitter uptake mechanisms in synaptic neurotransmission. *Brit. J. Pharmacol.* 41:571–91

52. Iversen, L. L., Bloom, F. E. 1972. Studies on the uptake of ³H-GABA and ³H-glycine in slices and homogenates of rat brain and spinal cord by electron microscopic autoradiography. *Brain Res.* 41:131–43

53. Johnston, G. A. R., Curtis, D. R., Davies, J., McCulloch, R. M. 1974. Spinal interneurone excitation by conformationally restricted analogues of L-glutamic acid. *Nature London* 248:804–5

54. Johnson, J. L. 1972. Glutamic acid as a synaptic transmitter in the nervous system. A review. *Brain Res.* 37:1–19

55. Karlin, A. 1967. On the application of "a plausible model" of allosteric proteins to the receptor for acetylcholine. *J. Theor. Biol.* 16:306–20

56. Karobath, M., Leitich, H. 1974. Antipsychotic drugs and dopamine-stimulated adenylate cyclase prepared from corpus striatum of rat brain. *Proc. Nat. Acad. Sci. USA* 71:2915–18

57. Kasai, M., Changeux, J. P. 1971. *In vitro* excitation of purified membrane fragments by cholinergic agonists. *J. Membr. Biol.* 6:1–23

58. Katz, R. I., Chase, T. N., Kopin, I. J. 1969. Effect of ions on stimulus-induced release of amino acids from mammalian brain slices. *J. Neurochem.* 16:961–67

59. Kebabian, J. W., Petzold, G. L., Greengard, P. 1972. Dopamine-sensitive adenylate cyclase in caudate nucleus of rat brain, and its similarity to the "dopamine receptor." *Proc. Nat. Acad. Sci. USA* 69:2145–49

60. Kelly, J. S., Krnjević, K., Morris, M. E., Yim, G. K. W. 1969. Anionic permability of cortical neurons. *Exp. Brain Res.* 7:11–31

61. Kelly, J. S., Renaud, L. P. 1971. Postsynaptic inhibition in the cuneate blocked by GABA antagonists. *Nature New Biol.* 232:25–26

62. Kosterlitz, H. W., Waterfield, A. A., Berthood, V. 1973. Assessment of the agonist and antagonist properties of narcotic analgesic drugs by their actions on the morphine receptor in the guinea pig ileum. In *Advances in Biochemical Psychopharmacology, Vol 8. Narcotic Antagonists.* ed. M. C. Braude, L. S. Harris, E. L. May, J. P. Smith, J. E. Villarreal, 319–34. New York: Raven

63. Krnjević, K. 1974. Chemical nature of synaptic transmission in vertebrates. *Physiol. Rev.* 54:418–540

64. Krnjević, K., Schwartz, S. 1967. The action of γ-aminobutyric acid on cortical neurons. *Exp. Brain Res.* 3:320–36

65. Kuhar, M. J., Aghajanian, G. K. 1973. Selective accumulation of ³H-serotonin by nerve terminals of raphe neurons: an autoradiographic study. *Nature New Biol.* 241:187–89

66. Kuhar, M. J., Pert, C. B., Snyder, S. H. 1973. Regional distribution of opiate receptor binding in monkey and human brain. *Nature* 245:447–50

67. Lefkowitz, R. J., Mukherjee, C., Coverstore, M., Caron, M. G. 1974. Stereospecific [³H](–)-alprenolol binding sites, β-adrenergic receptors, and adenylate cyclase. *Biochem. Biophys. Res. Commun.* 60:703–9

68. Logan, W. J., Snyder, S. H. 1972. High affinity uptake systems for glycine, glutamic and aspartic acid in synaptosomes of rat central nervous tissues. *Brain Res.* 42:413–31

69. Loh, H. H., Cho, T. M., Wu, Y.-C., Way, E. L. 1974. Stereospecific binding of narcotics to brain cerebrosides. *Life Sci.* 14:2231–45

70. McLennan, H. 1971. The pharmacology of inhibition of mitral cells in the olfactory bulb. *Brain Res.* 29: 177–84

71. Martin, D. L., Smith, A. A. 1972. Ions and the transport of gamma-aminobutyric acid by synaptosomes. *J. Neurochem.* 19:841–55

72. Melzack, R., Stotler, W. A., Livingston, W. K. 1958. Effects of discrete brainstem lesions in cats on perception of noxious stimulation. *J. Neurophysiol.* 21:353–67

73. Michaelis, E. K., Michaelis, M. L., Boyarsky, L. L. 1974. High affinity glutamic acid binding to brain synaptic membranes. *Biochim. Biophys. Acta* 367:338–48

74. Miller, R. J., Horn, A. S., Iversen, L. L. 1974. The action of neuroleptic drugs on dopamine-stimulated adenosine cyclic 3',5'-monophosphate production in rat neostriatum and limbic forebrain. *Mol. Pharmacol.* 10:759–66

75. Mishra, R. K., Gardner, E. L., Katzman, R., Makman, M. H. 1974. Enhancement of dopamine-stimulated adenylate cyclase activity in rat caudate after lesions in substantia nigra: evidence for denervation supersensitivity. *Proc. Nat. Acad. Sci. USA* 71:3883–87

76. Monod, J., Wyman, J., Changeux, J. P. 1965. On the nature of allosteric transitions: a plausible model. *J. Mol. Biol.* 12:88–118

77. Moore, W. J., Loy, N. J. 1972. Irreversible binding of a Krait neurotoxin to membrane proteins from eel electroplax and hog brain. *Biochem. Biophys. Res. Commun.* 46:2093–99

78. Mulder, A. H., Snyder, S. H. 1974. Potassium-induced release of amino acids from cerebral cortex and spinal cord slices of the rat. *Brain Res.* 76:297–308

79. Neal, M. J., Pickles, H. G. 1969. Uptake of ¹⁴C-glycine by spinal cord. *Nature London* 222:679–80

80. O'Brien, R. D., Gilmour, L. P., Eldefrawi, M. E. 1970. A muscarone binding material in electroplax and its relation to the acetylcholine receptor. II. Dialysis assay. *Proc. Nat. Acad. Sci. USA* 65:438–45

81. Olds, M. E., Olds, J. 1963. Approach-avoidance analysis of rat diencephalon. *J. Comp. Neurol.* 120:259–95

82. Oliver, C., Eskay, R. L., Ben-Jonathan, N., Porter, J. C. 1974. Distribution and concentration of TRH in the rat brain. *Endocrinology* 95:540–46

83. Pasternak, G. W., Snyder, S. H. 1974. Opiate receptor binding: effects of en-

zymatic treatments. *Mol. Pharmacol.* 10:183–93

84. Pasternak, G. W., Snyder, S. H. 1975. See Ref. 50, p. 27

85. Pasternak, G. W., Snyder, S. H. 1975. An endogenous morphine-like factor (MLF) in brain. *Life Sci.* 16:1765–69

86. Pasternak, G. W., Wilson, H. A., Snyder, S. H. 1975. The opiate receptor: differentiation of agonist and antagonist states by enzymatic treatments. *Mol. Pharmacol.* In press

87. Paton, W. D. M., Rang, H. P. 1965. The uptake of atropine and related drugs by intestinal smooth muscle of the guinea pig in relation to acetylcholine receptors. *Proc. R. Soc. Ser. B* 163:1–44

88. Pert, A., Yaksh, T. 1974. Sites of morphine induced analgesia in the primate brain: relation to pain pathways. *Brain Res.* 80:135–40

89. Pert, C. B., Kuhar, M. J., Snyder, S. H. 1975. Autoradiographic localization of opiate receptors in rat brain. *Life Sci.* In press

90. Pert, C. B., Snyder, S. H. 1973. Properties of opiate-receptor binding in rat brain. *Proc. Nat. Acad. Sci. USA* 70:2243–47

91. Pert, C. B., Snyder, S. H. 1974. Opiate receptor binding of agonists and antagonists affected differentially by sodium. *Mol. Pharmacol.* 10:868–79

92. Podleski, T. R. 1973. Cooperativity of the electroplax membrane. In *Drug Receptors,* ed. H. P. Rang, 135–48. London: Univ. Park Press. 321 pp.

93. Precht, W., Yoshida, M. 1971. Blockade of caudate-evoked inhibition of neurons in the substantia nigra by picrotoxin. *Brain Res.* 32:229–33

94. Raftery, M. A., Schmidt, J., Clark, D. G. 1972. Specificity of α-bungarotoxin binding to *Torpedo california* electroplax. *Arch. Biochem. Biophys.* 152:882–26

95. Rall, T. W. 1972. Role of adenosine 3',5'-monophosphate (cyclic AMP) in actions of catecholamines. *Pharmacol. Rev.* 24:399–409

96. Renaud, L. P., Martin, J. B. 1975. Thyrotropin releasing hormone (TRH): depressant action on central neuronal activity. *Brain Res.* 86:150–54

97. Roberts, P. J. 1974. Glutamate receptors in the rat central nervous system. *Nature* 252:399–401

98. Salvaterra, P. M., Moore, W. J. 1973. Binding of [^{125}I]-α-bungarotoxin to particulate fractions of rat and guinea pig brain. *Biochem. Biophys. Res. Commun.* 55:1311–18

99. Satoh, M., Zieglgänsberger, W., Fries, W., Herz, A. 1974. Opiate agonist-antagonist interaction at cortical neurons of naive and tolerant/dependent rats. *Brain Res.* 82:378–82

100. Schleifer, L. S., Eldefrawi, M. E. 1974. Identification of the nicotinic and muscarinic acetylcholine receptors in subcellular fractions of mouse brain. *Neuropharmacol.* 13:53–63

101. Severs, W. B., Severs, A. B.-D. 1973. Effects of angiotensin on the central nervous system. *Pharmacol. Rev.* 25: 415–49

102. Siggins, G. R., Bottenberg, E. F., Hoffer, B. J., Bloom, F. E. 1973. Noradrenergic stimulation of cyclic adenosine monophosphate in rat Purkinje neurons: an immunocytochemical study. *Science* 179:585–88

103. Siggins, G. R., Hoffer, B. J., Bloom, F. E. 1971. Studies on norepinephrine-containing afferents to Purkinje cells of rat cerebellum. III. Evidence for mediation of norepinephrine effects by cyclic 3',5'-adenosine monophosphate. *Brain Res.* 25:535–53

104. Simon, E. J., Hiller, J. M., Edelman, I. 1973. Stereospecific binding of the potent narcotic analgesic [^{3}H]etorphine to rat brain homogenate. *Proc. Nat. Acad. Sci. USA* 70:1947–49

105. Simon, J. R., Contrero, J. F., Kuhar, M. J., 1975. Specific [^{3}H]-kainic acid binding to brain membranes: evidence for association with the L-glutamate receptor. *J. Neurochem.* In press

106. Skultety, F. M. 1963. Stimulation of periaqueductal gray and hypothalamus. *Arch. Neurol.* 8:608–20

107. Snyder, S. H., Bennett, J. P. Jr. 1975. Biochemical identification of the postsynaptic serotonin receptor in mammalian brain. In *Pre- and Postsynaptic Receptors,* ed. E. Usdin, W. E. Bunney Jr., 191–206. New York: Dekker. 337 pp.

108. Snyder, S. H., Banerjee, S. P., Yamamura, H. I., Greenberg, D. 1974. Drugs, neurotransmitters, and schizophrenia. *Science* 184:1243–53

109. Takahashi, T., Otsuka, M. 1975. Regional distribution of Substance P in the spinal cord and nerve roots of the cat and the effect of dorsal root section. *Brain Res.* 87:1–11

110. Takeuchi, A., Takeuchi, N. 1967. Anion permeability of the inhibitory postsynaptic membrane of the crayfish

neuromuscular junction. *J. Physiol.* 191:575–90

111. Tebécis, A. K., Hösli, L., Haas, H. 1971. Bicuculline and the depression of medullary reticular neurones by GABA and glycine. *Experientia* 27:548

112. Ten Bruggencate, G., Engberg, I. 1971. Iontophoretic studies in Deiters' nucleus of the inhibitory actions of GABA and related amino acids and the interactions of strychnine and picrotoxin. *Brain Res.* 25:431–48

113. Terenius, L. 1973. Characteristics of the "receptor" for narcotic analgesics in synaptic plasma membrane fractions from rat brain. *Acta Pharmacol. Toxicol.* 33:377–84

114. Terenius, L., Wahlström, A., 1974. Inhibitor(s) of narcotic receptor binding in brain extracts and cerebrospinal fluid. *Acta Pharmacol. Toxicol. Suppl.* 35:55 (Abstr.)

115. Ueda, T. Maeno, H., Greengard, P. 1973. Regulation of endogenous phosphorylation of specific proteins on synaptic membrane fractions from rat brain by adenosine 3':5'monophosphate. *J. Biol. Chem.* 248:8295–8305

116. Werman, R. 1969. An electrophysiological approach to drug-receptor mechanisms. *Comp. Biochem. Physiol.* 30: 997–1017

117. Werman, R. 1972. CNS cellular level: membranes. *Ann. Rev. Physiol.* 34: 337–74

118. Werman, R., Davidoff, R. A., Aprison, M. H. 1968. Inhibitory action of glycine on spinal neurons in the cat. *J. Neurophysiol.* 31:81–95

119. Wilson, H. A., Pasternak, G. W., Snyder, S. H. 1975. Differentiation of opiate agonist and antagonist receptor binding by protein modifying reagents. *Nature* 253:448–50

120. Yamamura, H. I., Kuhar, M. J. 1975. Light autoradiographic localization of cholinergic muscarinic receptors in rat brain by specific binding of a potent antagonist. *Nature* 253:560–61

121. Yamamura, H. I., Kuhar, M. J., Greenberg, D., Snyder, S. H. 1974. Muscarinic cholinergic receptor binding: regional distribution in monkey brain. *Brain Res.* 66:541–16

122. Yamamura, H. I., Kuhar, M. J., Snyder, S. H. 1974. *In vivo* identification of muscarinic cholinergic receptor binding in rat brain. *Brain Res.* 80:170–76

123. Yamamura, H. I., Snyder, S. H. 1974. Muscarinic cholinergic receptor binding in the longitudinal muscle of the guinea pig ileum with [³H]quinuclidinyl benzilate. *Mol. Pharmacol.* 10:861–67

124. Yamamura, H. I., Snyder, S. H. 1974. Muscarinic cholinergic binding in rat brain. *Proc. Nat. Acad. Sci. USA* 71:1725–29

125. Yamamura, H. I., Snyder, S. H. 1974. Postsynaptic localization of muscarinic cholinergic receptor binding in rat hippocampus. *Brain Res.* 78:320–26

126. Young, A. B., Oster-Granite, M. L., Herndon, R. M., Snyder, S. H. 1974. Glutamic acid: selective depletion by viral induced granule cell loss in hamster cerebellum. *Brain Res.* 73:1–13

127. Young, A. B., Snyder, S. H. 1973. Strychnine binding associated with glycine receptors of the central nervous system. *Proc. Nat. Acad. Sci. USA* 70:2832–36

128. Young, A. B., Snyder, S. H. 1974. The glycine synaptic receptor: evidence that strychnine binding is associated with the ionic conductance mechanism. *Proc. Nat. Acad. Sci. USA* 71:4002–5

129. Young, A. B., Snyder, S. H. Strychnine binding in rat spinal cord membranes associated with the synaptic glycine receptor: cooperativity of glycine interactions. *Mol. Pharmacol.* 10:790–809

130. Zukin, S. R., Young, A. B., Snyder, S. H. 1974. Gamma-aminobutyric acid binding to receptor sites in the rat central nervous system. *Proc. Nat. Acad. Sci. USA* 71:4802–7

NEUROTROPHIC RELATIONS ❖1148

E. Gutmann

Institute of Physiology, Czechoslovak Academy of Sciences, Prague, Czechoslovakia

INTRODUCTION

Reviews reflecting the growing interest in neurotrophic relations are being published in increasing numbers. They stress different aspects of the topic, e.g. the evidence from denervation and regeneration studies (113); the neural regulation of acetylcholine (ACh) sensitivity, of acetylcholinesterase (AChE), of properties of "red" and "white" muscle (106); the differentiating capacity of the motoneuron as demonstrated by cross-union of nerves (157); and the "inductive functions" involved in maintaining synaptic connections (135). Neurotrophic aspects are also discussed comprehensively in studies on development and regeneration in the nervous system (155, 160). The wide scope of assumed neurotrophic interactions was demonstrated in a recent symposium that included studies ranging from trophic effects observed in tissue culture and limb regeneration, to use and disuse and dynamic properties of slow and fast muscles (65). Evidently, the term *neurotrophic relations and functions* ought to be restricted, and this is in fact increasingly done by defining it as long-term maintenance regulations not mediated by nerve impulses (121, 135, 234). The maintenance of synaptic connections (135) and the interactions between nerves and other cells which initiate or control molecular modification in the other cell (107) should be discussed with respect to this restriction.

We are in fact dealing with a component of complex intercellular relationships. The phenomena that regulate communication between individual cells range from cell-to-cell contact interactions, implied in growth control under culture conditions increasingly studied at the molecular level, to cell interactions operating in formation and maintenance of differentiation during development and adult life. No single mechanism can be expected to operate in each case. That diffusable and not "impulse related" agents and/or mechanisms are effective in relations between neuronal and non-neuronal cells seems to be established especially with respect to tissue culture work (54, 135, 202). However, it remains to be seen whether and to what extent this long-term (non-impulse) maintenance function of the neurons operates under normal conditions in vivo in the adult organism. Nerve-muscle cell relations have been the favorite object of such studies because of the relative ease of observing the effects of the neurotransmitter, and the distinct character of synaptic cell contact. Because of the comprehensiveness of a previous review (135), the present one

177

restricts itself to the neurotrophic relation between nerve and muscle cell and its differentiation from other intercellular mechanisms. Throughout this report, the motor nerve cell is envisaged as a neurosecretory cell that mediates to the muscle cell long-term information pertinent for maintenance of structure and metabolism of the postsynaptic cells and not directly connected with transmitter release and related impulse activity.

The concept that the dependence of muscle on nerve cannot be explained solely by neuronal activity related to transmitter release has been strengthened by observations on (a) release of both proteins and neurotransmitters (240, 291); (b) neurosecretion, with a trend to visualize the neuronal properties of neurosecretory cells (15, 186, 280); (c) axoplasmic transport of proteins moving with slow and fast rates (214, 215, 246), and apparently involved in the synthesis and renewal of a wide population of synaptic proteins serving different functions (18, 70); (d) the complex nature of the synaptic apparatus, involving complex mechanisms in synthesis and release of vesicles, in surface recognition, and in synthesis of membrane receptors increasing importance being attributed to glycoproteins in intercellular communications (18, 29, 276); (e) metabolic effects of the distal nerve stump after nerve section, dependent on the length of the peripheral nerve stump (128, 216); (f) growth promoting influences of nerves in amphibian limb regeneration independent of impulse conduction (288); (g) neurotrophic effects mediated by afferent nerves (248, 338); (h) specific changes in muscle after nerve section, affecting stability of membrane and intercellular constituents (3, 107, 113, 307); (i) trophic effects of neurons on muscle in tissue culture without synaptic transmission and even without contact between nerve and muscle cell (54, 136, 202); (j) possible transfer of neural constituents to the postsynaptic cell (182, 190).

The properties of muscle cells are, of course, regulated by different (neural and non-neural) mechanisms, not only by long-term neurotrophic actions. Differentiation of neural non-impulse (neurotrophic) activities from other components participating in the multiple regulation of muscle will become increasingly difficult. A critical choice of adequate parameters for testing neurotrophic actions is a prerequisite for such a differentiation.

THE MULTIPLE REGULATION OF MUSCLE

Myogenic Mechanism

Muscles and muscle fibers manifest differences in structural, contractile, metabolic, and membrane characteristics (46, 106, 115, 157, 221) that apparently reflect primarily differences between the motoneurons that innervate them (33, 113, 143). This has been substantiated by (a) the close correlation of physiological and histochemical properties of nerve and muscle cells constituting a motor unit (37), (b) the description of a homogeneous histochemical profile of a given motor unit (76), related to a specific muscle fiber pattern of different muscles, and (c) the considerable plasticity of muscle properties induced by the motoneuron during development and in adult life (46, 107).

However, primary myogenic mechanisms are also involved. Myofibers mature in the total absence of innervation, but neural influences are necessary for the maintenance of differentiation and postnatal growth (91). Myoblasts in tissue culture segregate and fuse, exhibiting a selective segregation (331), an inverse relationship between DNA and myofilament synthesis (26), and an electrical coupling via close junctions during early stages of fusion of myoblasts (269). ACh receptors appear about the same time that myoblasts begin to fuse and to synthesize contractile proteins (84)—before innervation and before the myoblasts appear to function in myogenesis. The coordinated development of ACh sensitivity and elaboration of contractile proteins suggest a control at the level of genetic information (83).

The evidence for primarily encoded myogenic properties that may be reflected in the emergence of different muscle fiber types is, however, not consistent so far. The electrophoretic pattern of light chains of embryonic myosin is the same as that of adult fast white muscle (296). However, the light chains of myosin (which differ in fast and slow mammalian muscles) change from a three- to a two-band pattern in the slow soleus muscle during early postnatal development (123). The clear association of different myosin molecules with specific muscle types, especially in primary structure of the heavy and light chains (258), the probability that they are coded by specific messenger ribonucleic acid (mRNA) (279), the phenotypic heterogeneity of myogenic clones (151), and the biphasic development of embryological muscle fiber type development (8) and its reproduction in postnatal regeneration of muscle (122) suggest the importance of primary myogenic mechanisms. Many properties of muscle are controlled primarily at the myogenic level as, for instance, are sensitivity to androgens (132) and to ACh (83), both of which are modified by neural influences at later stages of development. However, histochemical differentiation into reciprocally staining muscle fiber types was not observed in tissue culture (10), and characteristic features with respect to ATPase activity are established and maintained in cultured and regenerating rat muscle before differentiation of distinct histochemical fiber type occurs with innervation (9). Differentiation of different muscle fiber types is apparently controlled to a considerable degree by neural influences, as evidenced by cross-union (CU) (106) and regeneration of muscle (42) studies.

Dependence on neural influences appears to increase in phylogenesis. Early ultrastructural development and differentiation of striated muscle is observed in aneurogenic limbs of *Ambystoma* (319) and in denervated insect muscles from the stage of diapausing pupa until after ecdysis of the adult (243). However, the aneurogenic muscle fibers are not maintained and show progressive atrophy at later stages. Thus myogenic, apparently genetic, mechanisms initially operate without neural influences; the latter progressively exhibit their effects in maintenance and differentiation.

Nerve Impulse Activity

Increased use and disuse affect synaptic functions and metabolism of muscle (274, 285). Different methods have been used to produce excessive use or disuse in order to demonstrate long-term changes in the efficacy and maintenance of the neuromuscular synapse and metabolism of muscle and the participation of non-impulse-dependent mechanisms. Evidence for the latter is looked for throughout this review. At this point, a critical evaluation of the methods used, and the parameters of neurotrophic functions applied, appears necessary. Observations on excessive use by stimulation of muscle in tissue culture (88), organ culture (267), in vitro (114), and in vivo (32, 212, 230) may not always be reproducible under normal conditions. Electrical stimulation of muscle in tissue (51) and organ cultures (267) and of denervated muscle in vivo decreased the sensitivity to ACh (67, 170, 213) and prevented appearance of extrajunctional ACh sensitivity (211). Chronic stimulation of denervated muscle resulted in shortening of contraction time (212, 230). Long-term stimulation of muscles through implanted electrodes to the nerve resulted in a change of speed of contraction (260, 277) and an increase of succinic dehydrogenase (SDH) activity (260), as well as changes in Ca^{2+} activated ATPase activity, the pattern of light chains of myosin (297), and the pattern of sarcoplasmic reticulum proteins (268). The frequency pattern was apparently a decisive factor in the transformation of the muscle with respect to properties of the contractile proteins in stimulation experiments of both denervated (212) and normal (260, 268, 277, 297) muscle.

No such clear-cut results are obtained in exercise-training experiments in which normal increased motor activity is experimentally induced. The increase in activity of oxidative enzymes is consistent, regardless of the type of exercise or muscle used (181, 298). However, shortened contraction time and increased number of fibers with high ATPase activity (116, 298), or no change of contraction speed (16), was observed.

Compensatory hypertrophy, observed after section of the tendon of a synergistic muscle, has been used extensively as a model of excessive use. It results in increase of protein synthesis and amino acid transport and in decrease of protein degradation (99, 100). However, the marked effect of stretch on protein synthesis and contractile behavior, also observed in denervated muscle (125), and the complex concomitant changes, including activation of satellite (133) interstitial cells (281), make this model of excessive use a doubtful one (220).

Disuse has been studied in muscles innervated by an isolated (quiescent) spinal segment (315), by fixation of the limb (90, 274), or by temporary blockade of nerve impulse activity by local anesthesia (114, 211, 275) and tenotomy (241). The quiescent spinal segment method affects motor neurons and is not suited for controlled studies. Little change in extrajunctional ACh sensitivity, no change in junctional ACh sensitivity, little change in spontaneous transmitter release, and shortening of contraction time (CT) in the soleus muscle were observed in immobilized ("pinning of joints") muscles, which showed almost complete neuromuscular inactivity (89, 274). Shortening of CT was also observed after tenotomy in some (320), but not in other, experiments (241). Peripheral changes independent of neural influences may, however, induce changes in synthesis of proteins, number of sarcomeres, and CT (101, 125, 230).

Dissociation experiments, in which blockade of either nerve impulse (211) or non-impulse activity (axonal transport) is achieved, are gaining interest (4, 148,

211). They provide evidence for the importance and interaction of both neuronal mechanisms (65). Continuous chronic infusion of anesthetics around the sciatic nerve does not result in breakdown of axonal terminals, in early atrophy, or in increase of DNA accompanying denervation (113). Chronic anesthetic nerve cuff in rabbits did not result in ACh hypersensitivity or fibrillation of muscle (275); however, in other experiments on rats the whole membrane became sensitive to ACh after this procedure (211). The additional effects of anesthetic cuffs, interference with fast axonal transport, and even degeneration and partial denervation (30), have to be considered. Extrajunctional chemosensitivity was found to develop in muscles to whose nerves silastic cuffs containing colchicine or vinblastine were applied. Propagation of action potentials was not abolished, but axoplasmic transport was apparently arrested, and denervation-like changes developed (4, 148). Spontaneous and evoked transmitter release remained unaltered or even increased in these experiments, strong evidence that trophic substances are released from the nerve and that their release, which differs basically from transmitter release itself, mediates neurotrophic effects on muscle (4, 179). Colchicine and vinblastine appear to inhibit axoplasmic transport, which is in some way dependent upon microtubules; it also affects structures other than microtubules (254), and may affect membrane properties of muscle (39). However, extrajunctional sensitivity to ACh, tetrodotoxin-(TTX) resistant action potentials, and membrane depolarization were recorded in the "drug-cuffed," but not in the "sham-cuffed," leg (179).

Observations that botulinum toxin blocks impulse activity to muscle, selectively interferes with spontaneous transmitter release, and results in denervation-like changes (especially hypersensitivity to ACh) (306) originally suggested the identity of transmitter and neurotrophic agents (64). However, the relationship between spontaneous transmitter release and ACh sensitivity is not yet clear, as indicated by the discrepancies in findings of muscle atrophy after denervation or immobilization (274) and after blocking of impulse activity (211) or axoplasmic flow (4). Many factors are apparently involved in control of ACh sensitivity (171). Neurotrophic control of ACh sensitivity is, however, shown in vivo (234) and in culture (136).

Changes in contractile properties and/or histochemical muscle fiber spectrum apparently do not afford adequate parameters for neurotrophic functions. The relatively late onset of changes in contractile properties of denervated muscle (205, 303), the independence of the changed dynamic properties of denervated muscle on the length of sectioned nerve (124), the changes in speed of contraction induced by long-term stimulation of innervated (260, 277) and denervated (212, 230) muscle suggest that impulse activity is the decisive factor determining dynamic properties of muscle. Atrophy and hypertrophy are certainly controlled by neural influences, but this control may be mediated independently of dynamic properties (206). Moreover, there is a differential course of contractile changes in fast and slow denervated muscles (205, 303), and the changes of properties of stretched innervated and denervated muscles (125, 300) suggest the importance of peripheral factors.

The neural regulation of muscle fiber type is apparently mediated primarily by impulse activity. Contraction properties are closely coupled to myosin ATPase activity (46) and related histochemical muscle fiber type [low in Type I activity, high in Type II, according to ATPase (79)]. The basic subdivision of muscles and muscle fibers into fast and slow ones has been successfully applied. However, it has been complemented by differentiation of muscles and muscle fibers with respect to predominance of oxidative ("red") or glycolytic ("white") enzyme activities (72). In response to different demands of adaptation, three basic types, fast glycolytic, fast oxidative, and slow oxidative fibers are best distinguished. The description of three types parallels biochemical and physiological findings (17, 37). Intrafusal fibers also exhibit three distinct types (162).

The histochemical fiber pattern with respect to ATPase activity can be changed in a denervated muscle by stimulation (212, 230), or in compensatory hypertrophy (110). Very rapid changes in oxidative enzymes are induced after endurance exercise (181). The histochemical fiber pattern is apparently primarily controlled by impulse activity. Thus, changes in dynamic properties of muscle, histochemical fiber pattern, and even ACh sensitivity have to be considered carefully and may not provide adequate parameters for testing neurotrophic influences.

Hormonal Mechanisms

Most hormones have a regulatory action on some phases of growth, development, and maintenance of muscle and may have effects similar to other growth promoting factors. However, the effects are especially marked in target cells endowed with specific receptors. Such muscles are relatively rare, but allow the study of differentiation and interaction of neuronal and hormonal mechanisms. The broad spectrum of degree of interdependences is demonstrated especially in metamorphosis of some highly hormone-sensitive insect muscles basically controlled by interaction of the juvenile and the moulting hormone. Absence of juvenile hormone results in a hormonally induced, but neurally triggered (cessation of nervous impulses), complete and rapid breakdown of the intersegmental abdominal muscles in the adult silk moth (209); the cytolytic reaction is related to membrane changes and lysosomal activation in the muscle fiber (208). The rapidity of the hormonally induced breakdown contrasts with the slow process of denervation changes. Similar complete postnatal involution in the androgen-dependent levator ani (LA) muscle of the female rat is observed (45), but the muscle can be maintained after testosterone administration and temporarily after perinatal denervation (35), as the hormone has a relative nerve-independent effect during early stages of development. In the adult animal, interaction of hormonal and neural influences in this highly hormone-sensitive muscle (187) is indicated by the lack of activation of protein (35) and glycogen (255) synthesis after denervation. The different effect of hormonal and neural influences could be demonstrated in cross-union experiments of nerves to the LA muscle after castration and testosterone administration. The myotropic hormonal influence on the target muscle results in increase of weight and muscle fiber size, but not in reversal of muscle fiber pattern, which is affected by "foreign" innervation (131).

Moreover, testosterone influences synthesis of cholinacetyltransferase (ChAc), most of which is localized in the intramuscular nerve endings (141, 316), and of AChE. This occurs markedly only in the target (LA) muscle in which castration results in a 50% decrease (127) and testosterone administration leads to almost complete restoration of enzyme activity (191). Considering the direct action of testosterone on receptors in the target muscle (172), modulation of transmitter synthesis may operate by a feedback system from the muscle fiber. The small effect on nontarget muscles is probably a result of concomitant decrease or increase of motor activity with castration or testosterone administration, respectively.

However, hormonal actions, especially neurosecretory ones, have been most helpful in envisaging the route and mechanisms of neurotrophic communications. The hypothalamo-neurohypophysial system, with its neural secretion of peptides, transport of bound hormones along the related pathways, and their release in response to action potentials by exocystosis, has served as a model for secretory neurons acting on remote target cells (186). In view of the great variety in the chemical structure of hormones, no single cellular mechanism can be expected. Some hormones, including amino acid derivatives and peptides, interact with receptors on the cell surface, whereas steroid hormones interact with intracellular protein receptors (227). However, the mechanisms utilized by the classical "peptidergic" neurons of Scharer and Bargmann and a number of aminergic systems are very similar indeed, and the neuron is gaining further general recognition as a secretory cell (159, 291).

Humoral Mechanisms

No complete review on the various humoral mechanisms that may affect nerve-muscle cell interactions can be expected: only a few examples are mentioned here. Developmental changes in blood flow, with resulting changes in substrate supply, may be an important factor in differentiating metabolic muscle types (154). The importance of metabolic effects of satellite cells and of the Schwann cell in the process of regeneration and reinnervation of muscle (111, 332) and in auxillary ACh release (62) is increasingly realized. Agents (probably lytic enzymes) released by dividing cells appear to participate in the development of denervation hypersensitivity to ACh (171). Glial cells release agents, thus inducing differentiation in neuroblastic cells (238). The differentiation of muscle fiber types by immune fluorescent methods (104) indicates a role of the immune response. The latter is an important model for cellular maturation and differentiation. Immune responses may participate, for example, in rejection of hyperinnervation, or they may explain the changed immunochemical behavior of denervated muscle (150). These examples may suffice to point out the necessity of keeping in mind the different components affecting nerve muscle cell interactions.

EVIDENCE FOR NEUROTROPHIC FUNCTIONS

Tissue Cultures

Strong evidence for the existence of neurotrophic actions is supplied by tissue culture work (54, 135, 202, 312), which, in time, should make it simpler to define the chemical nature of neurotrophic agents than is the case of in vivo studies, which are hampered by the interference of additional cell-to-cell interactions. Intrinsic mechanisms are exhibited by cultured muscle cells, e.g. in the relation between synthesis of DNA and myofilaments (26), and in the profound biochemical changes at the time of fusion of myoblasts. The latter include increase of ChE activity (92), acquisition of ACh receptors and ACh sensitivity (84, 253), modification of the type of action potential (183), decrease of DNA synthesis, and increase of protein synthesis. This sequence may occur even after a suggested complete inhibition of RNA and stable mRNA (43). The fusion of myoblasts is triggered by Ca^{2+} ions (284). The later establishment of neurotrophic action is probably exhibited by regulation of gene expression. The evidence indicating that trophic effects are independent of nerve impulse transmission has been reviewed comprehensively (54, 135, 202). Specific and nonspecific effects, and effects mediated by contact or diffusion of agents, can be distinguished. Cultures of spinal cord and muscle fragments can develop synaptic transmission in the presence of curare (50, 53), and neuromuscular connections can be formed after such procedures and after chronic exposure of cord-muscle explants to hemicholinium-3(HC-3) (53). Muscle atrophy in long-term culture is prevented by explantation into a spinal cord–ganglion culture; recovery and differentiation proceed even after months of isolation of cultured muscle cells (54). In complex cultures of spinal cord and suspension of embryonic chicken muscle cells, no neuromuscular contact was formed when the spinal preparation had been stripped from the meningeal cover (312). The Schwann cells are thought to be of great importance here. Extirpation of the spinal cord portion (denervation in vitro) results in atrophy, but the muscle fiber can at least be maintained in the initial stages by addition of dorsal root or sympathetic ganglia, which provide an initial "unspecific" trophic stimulus to early phases of regeneration (54).

"Presentation" of sympathetic ganglion chains to a culture medium, supplemented with the nerve growth factor (NGF) to enhance outgrowth of the sympathetic neurons, could also retard atrophy in "cord-denervated" muscle fibers and even muscle contraction could be evoked (54), the latter resembling effects of sympathetic fibers cross-innervating a denervated skeletal muscle (231). Clonal cell lines from neuroblastoma can form neuromuscular contacts with cloned lines of skeletal muscle cells (136) after toxin-binding to ACh receptors and after the nerve cells had depleted their stores of ACh and could not be activated by ACh (253). Neither ACh release from nerve nor the presence of functional ACh receptors is a necessary precondition of nerve-muscle synapse formation (135). The rate of decline of ChE activity occurring in organ-cultured limbs of newt can be retarded by nerve explants or extracts (202). Especially marked is the effect of sensory ganglia explants that retard the disappearance of junctional folds and loss of sole plate ChE (202). A similar effect, achieved by additional adenosine 3', 5'-monophosphate (cyclic AMP), suggests a mediation of trophic effects via cyclic AMP (200). It remains to be seen what mechanism mediates the effect of activity on sensitivity to ACh in cultured muscle cells (51). It appears that, in addition to their sensitivity to non-neural growth promoting agents such as α-globulin (312), muscle cells in tissue cultures are also very sensitive to trophic agents released from other (dorsal ganglion and sympathetic) neurons, which may affect specialization of the postsynaptic cell. The NGF, which enhances outgrowth of nerve fibers from sensory and sympathetic ganglion cells (204) and even the development of specific sensory evoked synaptic networks (55), is, on the other hand, a specific growth promoting agent. Specialization of the postsynaptic cell can apparently be mediated by non-impulse activities and even by diffusable substances (202). An increasingly specific dependence of muscle cell on motoneuron influences is apparently involved in later developmental stages. The exact developmental squences of functional and metabolic changes in complex cultures are not yet known, as complex cultures have been made with very different systems. The ultrastructural findings of dense core vesicles in nerve terminals (thought to be neurosecretory) (250) and the marked pinocytic activity at developing neuromuscular junctions (NMJ) (161) signify a most active phase in intercellular communication.

Development and Regeneration

The developmental aspects of neuromuscular interactions have been reviewed comprehensively (155, 160, 333). The analogy to embryonal induction, operating in early development, has been stressed. Originally, it concerned the induction of differentiation of the nervous system in the overlying ectoderm by chordomesodermal material in amphibians (294). The basic observations implied an alteration in synthetic activities of cells following interaction with another inducer tissue; their capacity to respond to an inducer, i.e. their "competence," is limited to a restricted developmental stage. The inducing agents are assumed to be macromolecular diffusible substances, probably involved in derepression of specific genetic information in the target cell (14). In neurotrophic relations, however, the reciprocal effects of nerve and muscle cells are of great importance, as demonstrated by the marked developmental dependence of neurons on peripheral connections (130). Moreover, the responding undifferentiated cell is already endowed with certain genetically fixed potentialities, expressed at different stages of development (105). Many properties of the muscle cell are induced by distinct molecules, as in enzyme induction, which possibly inhibits the repressor gene. Neurotrophic effects are apparently more easily detected in maintenance functions than in formation of cell communications.

Evidence for neurotrophic mechanisms during development is found or suggested especially in studies of development of the NMJ and of neuromuscular receptors, during limb regeneration in amphibians, in insect metamorphosis, and in regeneration of muscle.

The embryogenesis of the NMJ undergoes successive stages before complete specialization of pre- and postsynaptic structure is achieved (146, 203, 305, 333). Many observations suggest the operation of neurotrophic influences. The first sign of formation of the NMJ is an increase of thickness of the muscle plasma membrane, which occurs when approaching nerve fibers are separated from the muscle by a gap of 2000–3000 Å. The nerve terminals contain vesicles similar to those in mature nerve terminals (146). Ach sensitivity, Ach receptors (82), and synthesis of ChE (304) appear before innervation. The frequency of miniature endplate potentials (min. epp's) increases in the rat about a hundredfold from day 17 of gestation to maturity (63), accompanied by a less pronounced decrease of extrajunctional Ach sensitivity. A secondary distribution of Ach receptors (AchR) occurs in which innervation is related to a marked increase of frequency of min. epp's and their quantal content (203). The association of high Ach sensitivity with nerve–muscle contact—the localization of receptors—is, of course, a decisive event in nerve–muscle cell interaction. The operation of neurotrophic mechanisms is suggested, but their nature remains unclear (299). The junctional region at the NMJ has a higher sensitivity to Ach and a greater density of receptors than do the extrajunctional parts of the muscle even after denervation, suggesting a more direct influence of the nerve terminals than only induction by impulse activity (194). The occurrence of dense core, neurosecretory vesicles, which may contain an active substance involved in trophic functions (291), is an interesting feature of developing or regenerating nerve terminals (146, 161, 250). They are also observed in invertebrate terminals (11, 126). Development of the NMJ was not arrested by immobilization of the muscle (174), but colchicin and vinblastine, assumed to block the intratubular axoplasmic transport systems, did result in arrest of development of NMJ (173). Structural differentiation of the NMJ seems to be related to mechanisms of axoplasmic transport and diffusion rather than to neuromuscular transmission and/or muscular activity (152, 175, 304).

Strong evidence for the importance of neurotrophic effects on development of end organs is supplied by studies on sensory innervation and sensory mechanoreceptors; such effects are a priori independent of impulse activity. Neuromuscular spindles —stretch receptors consisting of encapsulated, structurally specialized intrafusal muscle fibers—are primarily dependent on sensory innervation during their development (337, 338). No differentiation of spindles was observed after deafferentation by nerve section (337) or reinnervation (339) after nerve crush at birth in rats, whereas differentiation was not affected by de-efferentation (342). Thus a morphogenetic influence of sensory terminals mediated by release and uptake of a trophic substance at the synaptic junction could be assumed. The observation of dense core vesicles in sensory terminals (199) and of coated invaginations and vesicles and occasional exocytosis (341) favor this possibility. Taste buds degenerate after denervation and are reestablished after reinnervation (225, 335). In fact, such observations led to the first postulations of the flow of a hormone-like substance from the cell body of the neuron to its terminations (225), as did those on onset of atrophy in another sensory organ, the lateral line organ. Atrophy after section of the lateral line nerve was found to depend on length of the distal nerve stump (252). The regenerating taste fibers reestablish and maintain new taste buds in characteristic tongue locations. They are reestablished by both the central and the peripheral process of the gustatory ganglion cell (335), but do not cause taste buds to form in non-gustatory epithelia (336). However, transplantation of the circumvallate papilla can also result in the formation of taste buds in abnormal locations (336). Non-taste sensory and motor nerve fibers growing into the tongue are physiologically responsive to stimuli; they do not, however, reform new, or maintain existing, taste buds (244). Incompatibility between non-taste fiber and receptor cell precursor was assumed.

Neurotrophic phenomena are well demonstrated in limb regeneration in amphibians. Regeneration of limbs after amputation has been studied, especially in the newt; the sequence in regeneration repeats the phases of limb embryogenesis (309). The importance of nerves for newt limb regeneration was reported very early and has been extensively studied. The neurotrophic phenomenon revealed was that non-specific chemical agents, which can also be extracted from the brain, mediate regeneration of limbs (289). Motor, sensory, or central neurons can supply the neurotrophic agent, and a threshold number of nerve fibers (amount of neuroplasm) at the amputation surface is necessary (288). In vertebrates, the nervous supply may be threshold inadequate and limb regeneration can indeed be induced in the frog by augmenting the nervous supply of the amputation wound (289). Many factors, including species, critical phase of regeneration, and time of denervation, affect the process (309). Aneurogenic grafted salamander limbs do regenerate whether allowed to become innervated or not, but become dependent on their new nerves for regeneration (310). The factors responsible for the acquisition of nerve dependency are not known. Aneurogenic limb muscles of *Ambystoma* show normal early development and differentiation of muscles, but this differentiated stage is only maintained for two weeks before breakdown ensures (319).

In insects, a dependence on nerves and hormones for the development of muscles has been shown (242). During development—pre- and/or postnatal, according to the degree of maturation of the motor system at birth—the characteristic differences in contraction properties and muscle fiber pattern between fast and slow phasic and between phasic and slow tonic muscles are progressively established (46, 123). The process of differentiation with respect to contractile behavior is complex and may be related to a change of intrinsic force velocity properties and myosin ATPase activity and to a change in activity of sarcoplasmic reticulum (47, 66). After fetal denervation, myofibrillogenesis and sarcotubular differentiation are at first basically unchanged; however, the differential changes of the various fiber types are prevented by fetal denervation (134). The differentiation of fiber types is apparently related to the postnatal differentiation of distinct types of NMJ (249).

Denervation

A wide spectrum of changes in muscle following denervation has been described, reviewed (65, 106, 107, 112, 113, 135), and discussed (106, 107, 115, 135). The changes of greatest interest are those in membrane properties, ACh sensitivity and receptors, synthesis and degradation of proteins, structure, metabolites and enzymes related to excitation-contraction coupling, and energy supply and utilization. The different changes indicate dependencies on the neuron, but of course not necessarily on its neurotrophic function. The changes in membrane properties are the reduction in resting membrane potential (3, 270), appearance of tetrodotoxin- (TTX) resistant action potential and changes of the action potential (AP) (307), fibrillation potentials observed to start from spontaneous membrane potential oscillations (266, 308), anode break excitation (224), increase in specific membrane resistance (3), and centrifugal spread of ACh sensitivity from the junctional region (98). Early membrane depolarization (3 hr after denervation) is of special interest, as the onset of this initial response of the postsynaptic membrane occurs before any change in min. epp's, depends on the length of sectioned nerve (3), and can be produced by suppression of the axoplasmic flow (4, 179). The mechanism of denervation hypersensitivity is still not clear. The extrajunctional spreading (or exposure) of acetylcholine receptors (AChR) and increased ACh sensitivity (12, 98, 233) is reminiscent of conditions found in early stages of development (63), and a return of the denervated muscle to an early stage of development has been suggested (97). This does not, however, answer the question of the mechanism involved, especially with respect to a possible loss of neurotrophic control. The many data on development of ACh sensitivity and differentiation in embryonic muscle and in cultured cells, even in the presence of neurotoxins, carbamylcholine, or tubocurarine (53, 83, 139, 299), indicate intrinsic mechanisms in muscle cells whose nature is still unclear.

Moreover, direct electrical stimulation was found to prevent or reduce the onset of development of extrajunctional hypersensitivity of denervated muscle in vivo (67, 170, 211, 213), and of extrajunctional ACh sensitivity and fibrillation activity in muscle organ culture (267), but a temporary hypersensitivity also developed in a muscle on which a piece of degenerating nerve was placed (171). Release of agents from proliferating Schwann cells or phagocytic elements, e.g. proteolytic enzymes, might expose receptors normally present in the muscle fiber membrane (170, 218). Change in immunobiological behavior of denervated muscle (150) in connection with the appearance of diffuse receptors also suggests changes in the immune response. Junctional and extrajunctional sensitivities may be controlled by different processes, as even denervated endplate sensitivity remained above extrajunctional levels in a denervated stimulated muscle (213).

Structural changes in denervated muscle are easily described, but the significance and comparability of such changes are increasingly questioned. Decrease of fiber diameter is seen in most denervated vertebrate muscles; it is missing, however, in the crayfish opener muscle after immobilization or denervation, but not after tenotomy. The maintenance of this muscle is apparently more dependent on length (or passive tension) than on neurotrophic factors (27). Transient hypertrophy of denervated slow tonic avian diaphragm (85, 300) and of the mammalian diaphragm (300) is apparently also caused by stretching and can be avoided by prevention of stretch (168, 300). It is possible that only stretched muscles exhibit hypertrophy following denervation (300). Indeed, proteosynthetic capacity of isolated ribosomes increases in the denervated hemidiaphragm (318), but decreases in the denervated gastrocnemius muscle (185). However, there is a temporary absolute increase of DNA and RNA (113), observed also ultrastructurally (95); a temporary increase in potassium content and glycogen (113); and an initial early increase of mitochondrial mass, observed in morphometric ultrastructural studies (301). The nature of these initial temporary changes is not yet clear. Denervation atrophy reveals a change in control of breakdown and synthesis of proteins and is characterized by increase of lysosomal enzymes and degradation of proteins (99, 100, 113, 193, 228, 262), decrease of synthesis of proteins (99), and increase of incorporation of amino acids into proteins of denervated muscle in vivo (113) caused by increased substrate supply. There is a shift from synthesis of contractile proteins to synthesis of sarcoplasmic proteins (239). These observations are progressively complemented by studies of the denervation changes in different cell compartments. The transient increase of calcium uptake by the sarcoplasmic reticulum (SR) (295), found only in the slow soleus muscle by others (222), corresponds to the proliferation of the SR (95, 256). The enhanced synthesis of SR membrane proteins is a striking occurrence in denervated muscle, but is observed also in senescent muscle (118). It has not yet been possible to define specific ultrastructural changes in denervated muscle. Histochemically, a preferential atrophy of Type II (high ATPase activity—"white" fibers) (79) and a shift to a more homogeneous population of "red" fibers (95) are characteristic features. There is a loss of ratios of oxidative to glycolytic enzymes in denervation, not found in disuse atrophy (19).

Incorporation of [^{14}C]leucine into the proteolipid peak in the denervated diaphragm is increased; this has been correlated with enhanced synthesis of ACh receptors (184). The accumulation of free ribosomes in the subsarcolemmal sarcoplasma was also related to increase of size of receptor area (94). The physiological and structural significance of the release of ACh quanta from Schwann cells (62), normally suppressed by the axon (25), and of the DNA increase (113) is not yet clear. The latter may also result from activation of interstitial cells (334).

There is a rapid decrease of junctional AChE activity (by 50%) in denervated muscle (106, 107). The nerve is apparently essential for stimulating AChE at the endplate (287, 343). De novo synthesis occurs in normally innervated muscle poisoned with DFP, but not in denervated ones (87). If ACh triggers AChE synthesis by a process of substrate induction (287), it could do so by diffusion (202). However, the observation that AChE activity increases in cultured cells (140) remains to be explained. Little change in AChE activity occurs during tenotomy or immobilization (107).

Contraction properties differ in fast and slow denervated twitch muscles (115, 180, 206, 303), but there are species differences, and only the slowing of CT in fast denervated muscles is consistent. The changes of CT and muscle fiber pattern (212, 230) suggest a primary regulation of these properties by impulse activity.

Some of the denervation features such as the spread of ACh sensitivity and AChR and the contracture response of phasic muscles have often been interpreted as a reversal of denervated muscle to early developmental features (97, 158, 221) and may be related to a loss of neurotrophic control.

Strong evidence for neurotrophic mechanisms is supplied by analysis of the time of appearances of changes following nerve sections made at various distances from the muscle, since impulse activity is a priori eliminated as a responsible factor. These changes have been listed in recent reviews (135, 215) and concern presynaptic and postsynaptic events. For instance, degeneration of terminal axons (128), failure of transmission and disappearance of min. epp's (236), ChAc activity (316), fibrillation of muscle and hypersensitivity to ACh (216), increase of proteolytic activity (114), decrease of glycogen synthesis (128), decrease of resting membrane potential (3), appearance of TTX-resistant AP (137), and other disturbances appear earlier in the muscle with a shorter nerve stump. These findings suggest a progressive depletion of trophic substances occurring earlier in the shorter piece of nerve.

Interpretation of denervation changes and of differentiation from disuse is often difficult because of the interaction of neurotrophic and impulse activities of the neurons. Elimination or replacement strategies (107) have been used. The first type of approach concerns, for example, experiments in which botulinum toxin has been used to block ACh release and has reproduced many denervation changes. On the basis of such experiments, it was postulated that ACh is the only neurotrophic agent (64, 65). There are many arguments against this contention (106, 115). Colchicine and vinblastine, which block axoplasmic transport (and thus presumably eliminate the neurotrophic substances carried by this system), result in a spread of ACh sensitivity and development of TTX-resistant potentials (4, 148). Replacement experiments, for instance, concern changes in denervated muscle observed after stimulation. Some membrane changes developing in denervated muscle can indeed be prevented, i.e. extrajunctional sensitivity to ACh, fibrillation, and acceptance of additional innervation. The problems involved have been discussed before.

Reinnervation

Self-reinnervation (innervation by the original nerve) of muscle results in restoration of the specialized NMJ (333), metabolism (113, 115), membrane characteristics (226), enzyme muscle fiber pattern (292), and contractile behavior of muscle (46). The shift in control of protein metabolism is characterized by progressive increase of proteosynthesis (no longer due to increase of substrate supply) and decrease of DNA content to original levels (113). These complex processes must be coupled with the process of axonal regeneration and transport of material, transported also in nonregenerating neurons to replace proteins and glycoproteins lost by different mechanisms and necessary for maintenance of the axon (see 109). One would expect an accentuated axonal transport of macromolecules during regeneration. This is indicated by regeneration experiments (103, 111, 192) and in collateral regeneration. Slow axoplasmic flow, which moves with rates similar to those found in neuronal growth, is also faster during early development (see 215). In spite of discrepancies in axoplasmic flow rates in regenerating nerve fibers (215), the assumption of a close coupling of axonal transport and regeneration as an intraneural "maintenance" mechanism for neurotrophic maintenance of muscle is most probable.

Neuromuscular connections after nerve repair in higher vertebrates differ from those developing in embryogenesis; the former lose the correct correspondence between neuron and muscle and fail to achieve a perfect functional result (160, 223). At an early stage of regeneration, axons are in contact with muscle fibers without neuromuscular transmission. This was observed in limb regeneration of the salamander, revealing a nontransmitting phase in which axon terminals spontaneously released transmitter without evoking an endplate potential (59). A nontransmitting stage exerting trophic effects on muscle was observed in mammalian (129), avian (23), and frog muscle (61, 62, 232), with a failure of AP propagation in the regenerating neuron proximal to the endplate region (60). At this stage, some junctions respond to nerve stimulation with only subthreshold endplate potentials (60).

The restoration of the NMJ shows a sequence of events suggesting the operation of different mechanisms and differs according to level of lesion (129). Axons return to the site of the original NMJ, if the distance of the lesion from the muscle is small (22, 129, 232). If reinnervation is delayed, endplates may be formed de novo (129).

Accordingly, the picture of the NMJ will differ and reinnervation of the preserved subneural apparatus (22, 217), or an induction of infoldings of the sarcolemma as in ontogenesis (22, 217), will be observed. The incidence of formation of NMJ outside the original one increases with delay of reinnervation, and recovery of the release of ACh (quantal content of min. epp's) is delayed in such cases (314). Low lesions are thus more adequate for a study of the sequence of events (226). Frequency of min. epp's is very low in immature junctions (226). Min. epp's reappear 9 days after nerve crush and their frequency is very low; membrane potential increases at the same time; and the contraction response to caffeine in the EDL muscle, which appears after denervation, is lost 4 days after reinnervation. On the other hand, the decrease of extrajunctional ACh sensitivity occurs very slowly, long after the return of spontaneous and evoked transmitter release (226).

The existence of a nontransmitting phase, synapse formation even in the presence of bungarotoxin (80), the development of NMJ in the presence of d-tubocurarine (50), and the regeneration of forelimbs of the newt, in spite of specific cholinergic blockade (see 289), suggest the operation of neurotrophic mechanisms in the regeneration process. An interesting feature of regenerating axons is the occurrence of dense core vesicles (201, 217, 257) resembling those found in developing NMJ (305, 333), which are possible related to neurotrophic agents.

Collateral Sprouting

Collateral sprouting (CS) of axons may occur anywhere along the whole axon, sometimes at a distance from an injury, sometimes near the muscle with formation of new NMJ. It can be defined as a compensatory response of the neuron, functioning to establish new contacts, and is apparently a general event both in the peripheral and central nervous system (CNS). Its importance is now stressed; it may represent a normal replacement mechanism of the NMJ (see 75, 135), a general mechanism of recovery by growth of residual intact fibers after lesions in the CNS (207, 219), and even a basic mechanism of CNS plasticity (75). The literature has been comprehensively reviewed (109, 135). The functional significance of CS is demonstrated after section of a cutaneous nerve, when neighboring axons sprout and extend into the denervated area, resulting in considerable recovery of sensation (327). Normally, an innervated muscle will not accept new innervation (2), but after denervation (129) or muscle fiber injury (2), new NMJ are found. The spread of ACh sensitivity, e.g. after injury (178), may be one of the conditions for additional acceptance of innervation. The newly formed NMJ resemble those in early development, but no indication of a normal replacement in adult muscle fibers was found at later developmental stages (333). However, "hyperneurotization," i.e. formation of additional NMJ by implantation of a "foreign" nerve, could be obtained if the muscle were temporarily denervated and reinnervated (93, 117), if the nerve were blocked by application of a cuff containing a local anesthetic (163), or if botulinum toxin were injected into the muscle (149), but this leads to sprouting at the NMJ (74). The operation of neurotrophic mechanisms in this process was suggested by the effects of "preimplantation" into an innervated muscle (86), but this was not confirmed (56).

Neurotrophic mechanisms are, however, indicated by experiments in which, after application of colchicine onto a salamander, nerve sprouting in neighboring axons and enlargement of peripheral motor and sensory fields begin despite continued impulse function of the treated nerve (1). Neuronal impulse and non-impulse activities apparently interact, as blocking of impulse activity also resulted in hyperinnervation and could be largely reduced by direct stimulation of the muscle (163). However, once the new neuromuscular contact is established, it induced an increase of proteosynthetic capacity of free ribosomes (36), hypertrophy (86, 117), change in contracture response (117), and transformation of contractile and histochemical properties (36). The latter transformations are apparently a result of impulse activities of the additional neuron.

Heteroinnervation

Heteroinnervation, i.e. cross-union of the motor neurons to fast and slow muscle fibers or implantation of a foreign nerve into a denervated muscle, results in a reversal of a wide range of muscle properties. Since the basic findings of reversal of contractile characteristics after cross-union (CU) of nerves (33), much work has been concentrated on this problem of transformation of muscle and has been repeatedly reviewed (46, 106, 116, 135). Force-velocity properties (46); myosin ATPase activities (34); myosin subunits (278); histochemical (73), biochemical (68), and ultrastructural properties of muscle (169, 340); contracture response to caffeine (78, 117); sensitivity to ACh (237) and other properties are apparently transformed according to the type of innervating neuron. The experiments raise questions on the mechanism by which the nerve exerts the differentiating influence upon muscle fibers, on the specifity of this neural influence, and on possible genetic aspects involved in this transformation. The first studies (33) suggested the operation of neurotrophic effects. Moreover, contracture response is transformed before neuromuscular transmission is restored (78). However, with respect to the wide range of changes induced by the foreign nerve, multiple mechanisms can be assumed.

The most detailed work concerns the CU studies of the phasic, focally innervated posterior latissimus dorsi (PLD) and the tonic, multiply innervated anterior latissimus dorsi (ALD) muscles of the chicken, which differ profoundly in ultrastructural and contractile behavior. The basic condition for the transformation appears to be the formation of a foreign type of NMJ (147, 188), which, in a successful CU, mediates the characteristics of the foreign neuron. Thus, for example, after a CU of the slow ALD nerve to the PLD muscle, low efficacy of neuromuscular transmission, low quantal content (323), and ACh sensitivity (322) are recorded. Properties of the motor neuron after CU remain essentially unchanged or are redifferentiated to their original state after recovery from the changes after nerve section (33, 196), suggesting that the nerve plays an almost exclusive role in muscle transformation.

The operation of myogenic factors is, however, indicated by some CU studies of adult avian muscles. The ALD and PLD muscle fibers showed the original innervation pattern (distribution of cholinergic receptors and of AChE) and sensitivity distribution to ACh after CU in adult chickens. It was concluded that the pattern of reinnervation of mature vertebrate muscles is determined by muscle itself (23).

However, when CU experiments were performed at hatching, both the type and the pattern of innervation were changed according to the foreign nerve supply (24). Refractoriness of the membrane to further synapse formation over a particular distance was suggested as the neural mechanism that determines the innervation pattern. The existence of a neurotrophic influence was suggested, since denervation supersensitivity was reduced before the nerve terminal could elicit muscular contraction (23). Successful transformation is apparently achieved if the CU is performed in newly hatched chickens and combined with transposition of the muscle, which facilitates transformation by inducing degeneration and regeneration of the muscle fibers and therefore allows transformation (redifferentiation) of the muscle cells (169, 340). Enhanced conversion of cross-innervated muscles was also obtained, apparently for the same reasons, when the preexisting muscle fibers had been injured (273). A different degree of transformation of structure of muscle fibers after CU in newly hatched chickens (169) suggests a different plasticity of muscle cells and myogenic factors, respectively. However, the type of NMJ was always found to correspond to the foreign neuron. Transformation of contraction properties after foreign innervation in chicken muscle was achieved, when performed in newly hatched (166), but not in adult, chickens (147).

Peripheral factors may also be important, as tenotomy also results in ultrastructural transformation of avian muscles (144). In addition, species differences may be important. Thus the slow graded response to stimulation by KCl or ACh in slow tonic muscle fibers of frog (78, 235), but not of the toad (48), is lost after reinnervation with fast phasic nerve fibers. Myogenic mechanisms may be more, and consequently plasticity less, active in the latter case.

CU experiments may not have fulfilled the high expectations held for them with respect to analysis of neurotrophic mechanisms. Moreover, myogenic, inherent muscle factors are indicated by incomplete transformation of muscle, repeatedly referred to (33, 46), and CU experiments have not allowed a clear differentiation of myogenic factors. However, CU experiments have demonstrated a very high degree of neuronal specifity, which induces transformation of properties of muscle.

CU studies suggest that the nerve influences gene expression in the muscle cell. The genetic interpretations have been discussed (108, 115) and are justified only if a qualitative change in synthesis of specific proteins is demonstrated. A selective expression of genetic information may be indicated by changes in the myosin light-chain components of muscle after a cross-union (278), or during development of the soleus muscle of the guinea pig, which, at birth, is a fast muscle (with three bands and a mixed histochemical pattern) and changes to a slow muscle [with two bands of light chains and a uniform histochemical fiber pattern (123)]. The change in proteosynthetic capacity of isolated ribosomes in a slow muscle induced by implantation of a fast nerve results in a differential change of enzyme activities; this may be affected by different mRNAs (36).

Regeneration of Muscle

Since the first description of regeneration of entire muscles from minced fragments of muscle tissue (302), transplantation of muscle (minced or free grafts) has proved to be a potent tool in the study of nerve–muscle relationships. The morphogenetic process in the regenerating muscle following the primary degeneration after mincing, injury, or free grafting has been reviewed (40). Neural influences do not significantly affect the early stages of regeneration, but differentiation without innervation is deficient from the myotube stage onwards (344, 345). Neurotrophic influences are postulated, as recovery proceeds during early reinnervation before restoration of neuromuscular transmission (345). Contractile properties (41) and the histochemical fiber pattern in the rat (42, 272) progressively differentiate from a slow to a fast muscle type as they do during ontogenetic development in the rat. Complete restoration of the muscle fiber pattern was observed in the fast, but was deficient in the slow, avian muscle (145). In minced grafts, the first contractile reactions can already be observed in 7 day regenerates. These contractions are caused by myotubes, which synthesize myofilaments without innervation (41). However, spontaneous min. epp's are not present in regenerates before 11–14 days, and evoked endplate potentials usually are not seen (21). Successful cross-transplantation of fast and slow muscles can be observed in which contractile and histochemical properties change according to the foreign nerve supply (42). The transformation is in fact more complete than that usually observed after CU of nerves. Degeneration with succeeding regeneration of muscle fibers can also be achieved with a local anesthetic (methylbupivacaine), which leaves the nerve terminals intact. Very fast recovery of spontaneous min. epp's (167) and restoration of a normal NMJ as early as 14 days after injection (165) are observed. The rapid formation of the NMJ follows the pattern observed during ontogenesis, the axonal terminals containing dense core vesicles.

THE TROPHIC FUNCTIONS OF AFFERENT NERVE

Afferent nerves may mediate two main trophic functions: the direct morphogenetic effect on innervated tissue, and the regulatory feedback functions mediated by (probably non-impulse) signals ascending the nerve. The direct neurotrophic morphogenetic effect is well demonstrated by: 1. the maintenance of taste buds by gustatory nerves through a specific trophic action, which can be transmitted by both the axons and the dendrites of the ganglion (335), but which needs a specific gustatory epithelium for its full expression (336); 2. the stimulation of amphibian limb regeneration (288, 289) —sensory supply can sustain regeneration, probably via a relatively nonspecific growth promoting agent unrelated to known chemical transmitters (289); 3. the differentiation and maintenance of intrafusal muscle fibers (338, 341, 342). Regulatory trophic functions of afferent nerves must be assumed during the earliest phases of blastema development; during the early stages of development of neuromuscular communications in the adult.

Morphogenetic cell death is a general occurrence in early embryogenesis and has been followed in detail in the motor neurons of the ventral horn (155, 264). Some of it is, however, part of a genetic program and takes place before innervation (44). The subsequent wave of histogenetic cell death appears, however, to depend only on formation of neuromuscular contacts and retrograde signals respectively. Ablation or enlargement of the peripheral field affects the number of nerve cells (see 155, 264, 265).

Histogenetic cell death appears to involve neurons that fail to establish contact with the periphery. Critical periods in embryonic development are of special importance for death of cells lacking peripheral contact (see 264, 265). However, studies on embryonic development of chick ciliary ganglion showed that preganglionic fibers form functional synapses prior to cell death (197) and also that peripherally deprived neurons may differentiate normally. Information from the periphery was found not to be required for ganglion cell synapse formation per se (198).

Two retrograde mechanisms or signals are thus important in maintenance of neurons and are also basically involved in the so-called chromatolytic reaction of neurons. The two signals that can apparently be distinguished are either from axon to soma or from muscle to neuron. These mechanisms have been studied in detail in mature neurons. Section of a nerve results in characteristic changes in the nerve cell including an increase in RNA and protein synthesis (31, 324), loss of synaptic boutons (28), decrease in conduction velocity, and changes in excitability of the neuron (195). The anabolic reaction is described in detail in amphibian (265) and mammalian (326) motor neurons. It is independent of nerve impulse transmission or afferent nerves (see 114). Loss of boutons on rat hypoglossal neurons does not occur after prolonged blocking of the AP, but when lost after axotomy they are not restored until nerve-muscle contact has been made again (57). Thus we must deal with an intra-axonal afferent signal system.

Besides an axon-soma signal, which affects synthesis and turnover of neuronal nucleic acids and proteins and is related to axonal growth, a second signal (from muscle to neuron) exists, which is related to establishment of synaptic transmission. These two signals have been demonstrated and differentiated (325, 326). The nature of the signal for chromatolysis has been discussed; electrical phenomena, loss of axoplasm, retrograde axonal transport, and depletion of neuronal repressor substances have been suggested as signals (52). The initial signal appears to be the loss, after axotomy, of proteins which are replaced by the regeneration process. Thus, crushing a nerve above nerve section, i.e. induction of regeneration, prevents, to a considerable degree, decrease of fiber diameter and of conduction velocity, normally observed in the proximal stump of the sectioned nerve (113, 114). However, the basic mechanisms are apparently related to retrograde axonal transport (214). The chromatolytic reaction can be reproduced by blocking transport without affecting nerve conduction (57, 261). Axonotomy apparently induces nonspecific retrograde signal. However, retrograde axonal transport may show high selectivity, as demonstrated in retrograde transport of the nerve growth factor (NGF) and its effects on induction of enzymes in adrenergic neurons (251).

THE NEUROTROPHIC AGENT

The chemical nature of neurotrophic agents is unknown, and therefore indirect approaches and hypothetical considerations are unavoidable. The candidates for neurotrophic agents should comply with conditions of mediating long-term effects, acting relatively independently of impulse activity, and controlling protein synthesis in the innervated tissue. Observations that substances with neurotrophic actions are released or can be extracted from nervous tissue raise the question of the chemical nature of the neurotrophic agent. There is increasing evidence for substances released from nerve terminals after stimulation, such as glutamic acid (330) and proteins binding ACh (240). Some substances, for instance ATP (286), substance P, and other polypeptides, have excitatory actions (see 153, 194). Clonal nerve cells release a number of proteins (283). Substances released from nerve maintain cultured muscle cells (313) and increase their oxygen uptake (142). The physiological significance of these substances is not clear.

Substances mediating neurotrophic effects in muscle are of special interest. AChE activity of cultured muscle fibers is increased by addition of brain-spinal cord extract to the culture medium (247). Nerve homogenates infused into denervated limbs of newts stimulate protein synthesis (see 289). A diffusible factor released from nerve explants, sensory ganglia, and nerve homogenates affects maintenance of ChE in organ culture (202) and may also be involved in the localization process of AChR in culture (299).

The neurotrophic agent evidently does affect synthesis of DNA, RNA, and proteins. In fact, accentuation of anabolic processes has been considered the main mechanism of neurotrophic regulation, as indicated by disturbances in resynthesis of proteins and different metabolites after stimulation of a denervated muscle (112). The lack of a growth promoting agent in the nerve results in a reduction of synthesis of DNA, RNA, and protein in a regenerating amphibian limb (69), or in insect muscles after ecdysis (243). These effects are apparently nonspecific and act in early development, whereas more specific effects appear to be mediated postnatally, e. g. in regulation of mitosis of taste buds (336). The possibility of a derepressive influence of the nerve on part of the muscle genome in denervated muscle is suggested by the increase of DNA and of proteolytic activity (see 114) and by prevention of extrajunctional ACh receptors after blocking DNA-dependent RNA synthesis (see 307).

With respect to the great range of effects on end organs, the existence of a single neurotrophic agent appears improbable, although such a claim has been made for the cholinergic neurotransmitter (64). The evidence rests particularly on the reproduction of denervation effects by agents that eliminate ACh release; these effects include changes in histochemical and contractile properties, ChE, axonal sprouting, and hyperneurotization (65). The evidence against the sole neurotrophic action of ACh release has been summarized repeatedly (106, 114, 135). The appearance of extrajunctional sensitivity to ACh in muscle that responds to nerve stimulation while axoplasmic transport is blocked (4, 148) supports the notion that trophic agents other than the transmitter regulate the muscle membrane. Impulse-directed ACh release does, of course, affect many properties of muscle. This review does not deal primarily with this regulation. However, spontaneous quantal release (176) and/or nonquantal release of the transmitter without the production of muscle depolarization (263) may still be a factor in neurotrophic actions.

Macromolecules may be involved in neurotrophic regulation. They are synthesized in the neuron, transported along the axon, released, and replaced. Axonal migration of macromolecules and renewal of synaptic proteins (18, 70) are increasingly studied especially with respect to maintenance of axons and nerve endings (see 109). Only few studies discuss or are concerned with the interaction of these mechanisms in neurotrophic communication (29, 71, 291). The assumption that macromolecules transported intra-axonally have a postsynaptic function (29, 291) may best be met by a concept ascribing neurotrophic functions to a neurosecretory mechanism (113). In many respects, the differences between "neurons with glandular activity" (15) or "neurosecretory cells with neuronal properties" (259) are becoming less rigid. Thus the existence of polypeptides secreted by the neuron and operating in control of proteosynthesis appears possible.

AXOPLASMIC TRANSPORT AND TRANSSYNAPTIC TRANSFER

The existence of axoplasmic flow is now generally recognized and its importance for neurotrophic relations is repeatedly stressed. Recent reviews concern particularly its importance in maintenance of axon, nerve terminal, and innervated tissue, the differentiation of fast and slow flow, the factors affecting it, and the analysis of the molecular mechanisms involved in initiation and blocking of axonal transport (58, 71, 109, 215, 246). Axonal flow was first described as a slow process of transport related to migration of axoplasm from cell body to periphery (329). The slow flow, probably consisting mainly of soluble proteins, has a velocity of about 1 mm/day, which corresponds to the rate of axon regeneration. The relationships between the slow axonal transport and growth are indicated, but have still to be elucidated (103, 215). Axonal transport however, occurs also in nonregenerating neurons and replaces proteins, glycoproteins, and other material lost by local breakdown, exocytosis into the synaptic cleft, retrograde migration to the cell body, and synaptic turnover. The replacement occurs apparently in the neural perikaryon as local synthesis plays only a minor role (109, 215). Replacement can be accomplished by fast flow moving with much higher velocity, i.e. of about 400 mm/day (245, 246). Axonal flow is now considered to be a bidirectional process (214, 215) related to axonal migration of a multitude of material, enzymes, neurotransmitters, and macromolecules moving at different rates. A rapid axonal transport (245) with high dependence on energy metabolism may indeed be expected for material essential for impulse conduction and transmission, a slower one for material essential for long-term neurotrophic maintenance, not only of axon (109), but also of innervated tissue.

The characteristics of axoplasmic flow can be envisaged after interruption of continuity of axons by accumulation, time course of development of changes at synapses and innervated cells, progress of Wallerian degeneration, and time course of transport of labeled precursors after injection into neurons. With respect to neurotrophic relations, the accumulation and transport of neurosecretory material, norepinephrine (58), ChAc and AChE (316, 317), glycoproteins, and/or synaptic proteins (71), are of special interest (see 215). The rate of axonal transport of ChAc proceeds five times more slowly than that of AChE in the central stump of a sectioned nerve (317).

The importance of axoplasmic flow for maintenance of the axon is indicated by the proximodistal spread of Wallerian degeneration after nerve section, its velocity varying from 10–270 mm/day according to thickness of the axon (215). Trophic substances maintaining axonal terminals (128) and synaptic transmission (236) migrate at a comparable velocity. The much earlier onset of degeneration of axonal terminals than of axons (311) suggests specific conditions for maintenance of axonal terminals. Central effects of axotomy may be due to interruption of retrograde axoplasmic transport. Onset of chromatolytic changes appears to depend on the distance from the lesion (324); no exact rates have been reported, however (215).

Axonal migration can be detected and measured, and its importance for maintenance of muscle analyzed by the time of appearance of membrane and metabolic disturbances after nerve section made at various distances from the innervated cells. The related velocities are listed in a recent review (215). The velocities, at which presumed trophic factors responsible for or participating in maintenance functions move, differ. The calculations indicate a velocity of 20 mm/day for decrease of synthesis of glycogen and increase of proteolytic activity (114, 128), 320 mm/day for disappearance of min. epp's (236), 113 mm/day for decrease of ChAc activity (316) in the rat, and 48 mm/day for fibrillation and hypersensitivity to ACh in the cat (216). Very fast rates have been suggested for onset of early muscle membrane changes (3, 137), suggesting that different neurotrophic agents move to the muscle cell with different rates.

A different rate of transport can be expected for proteins; their rate of migration is proportional to their molecular weight (6). Studies on transport of protein to the presynaptic calices of the avian ciliary ganglion demonstrate fast moving proteins (288 mm/day), assigned to renewal of various membrane components, and slowly moving proteins (1.0–10 mm/day), which start migrating after a time lag. The latter are thought to replace axoplasmic components (71). Convincing evidence of the slow flow and the time relations of fast and slow flow waves was thus provided. Glycoproteins are transported in the fast component of axonal transport (71). Longitudinally oriented structures and interactions between microtubules and membranes of vesicles are apparently operant in fast flow (246, 282), whereas the slow flow may be a large extent be related to soluble proteins (see 215). The functional significance of fast and slow flow with respect to impulse conduction and transmission and to maintenance functions is repeatedly discussed (71, 109, 215), and their differentiation will be of great interest. Fast flow continues after nerve section, is not directly dependent on protein synthesis, is highly dependent on oxygen, and is temperature dependent (see 215, 246). The slow flow is apparently related to axonal growth and maintenance and appears to be increased in early development. The arrest of axoplasmal flow after application of colchicine is generally attributed to disassembly of microtubules. Such blocking of the axoplasmic flow resulted in denervation-like changes (4, 148) and suggested the operation of neurotrophic mechanisms. The development of membrane changes despite increase of frequency of min. epp's after colchicine application is of special interest (179). The relationships between microtubules and axoplasmic flow need further elucidation with respect to the complex action of plant alkaloids (254).

The possibility of transfer of neurotrophic agents from presynaptic terminals to postsynaptic structures is evidently of basic importance and has been raised by observations on the entry of labeled material from motor nerves into muscle (182, 190) and on transsynaptic transfer of labeled axonal material in the CNS (102) and into utricular neuroepithelium (5). The mechanism of such a transfer could imply direct transfer of macromolecules, diffusion of substances, or complex changes at the synapse. Among the latter are synthesis and release of synaptic macromolecules which might also participate in synthesis of neurotransmitters and their storage in or release from vesicles, and exocytosis and pinocytotic activity of the muscle cell membrane (18, 29). The possibilities of direct transfer at the NMJ are suggested by observations of radioactive neuronal proteins reaching the muscle (189) and of a selective transfer of distinct neural proteins (electrophoretically separated) into muscle in succeeding waves (7). Scintillation studies do not, however, eliminate the possibility that radioactive proteins found in the muscle are confined to nerve terminals. High resolution autoradiography of the avian ciliary ganglion has shown that very small amounts of label are found in the postsynaptic cell after inhibition of protein synthesis, indicating that even in such a gap junction only a restricted number of labelled proteins or peptide molecules could be transferred from the presynaptic sites (71). Transsynaptic effects can, however, be observed in developing NMJ (333), and "passageways" connecting adjoining cells at membrane regions of high permeability have been observed and may allow passage of larger molecules (210).

Diffusion of neurotrophic agents, well documented especially in tissue and organ cultures, would concern smaller molecules; transfer of macromolecules probably occurs by pinocytic mechanisms, described especially in development and regeneration. Synaptic transfer of macromolecules is, however, not yet proved. The transsynaptic control of protein synthesis by neurotrophic (and not only impulse) neuronal mechanisms appears, however, to be established.

The complexities of the modulation of functional connections by pre- and postsynaptic membranes are being closely studied (18, 290). Observations on interactions between surface glycotransferases and their cell surface glycosol acceptors (276) and production of glycoproteins in neurons and their rapid transport along the axons to nerve endings (20) suggest that glycoproteins have a special role in cell recognition and communication (29).

REGULATION OF RECEPTOR PROPERTIES

New methods have been introduced to study distribution and turnover of AChR with the help of labeled neurotoxin and autoradiography; AChR in clonal cell cultures; and specificity of the AchR and definition of its biochemical nature (see 82, 135, 153). These approaches have allowed a more concrete analysis of several aspects of the regulation of AChR: the different reaction of junctional and extrajunctional AChR, the process of localization of AChR at the NMJ, and denervation supersensitivity. These questions are of special interest for the study of neurotrophic relations, as the nature of neural control of AChR is generally related to impulse or non-impulse activities.

There is, however, new strong evidence for a multiple regulation of AChR synthesis and distribution. AChR develop during myogenesis at the time of fusion of myoblasts (84) and increase in density with maturation of myotubes (138) without innervation. Inherent myogenic events are also indicated by observations on differentiation of muscle cells during blockade of the receptors (84, 139), on development of ACh sensitivity even before organization of myofilaments into myofibrils (84), and on ChE activity in myoblasts and myotubes (140). The site of contact between nerve cell and myotube is associated with a small area of increased sensitivity to ACh (136). However, in nerve-muscle cell cultures, localization of AChR occurs even after their occlusion by d-tubocurarine or α-neurotoxins; this has strengthened the conclusion that neither receptor activation nor ACh release is basically involved and that some diffusible factor released (but not ACh) may be responsible in this interaction (299). The process of restriction of sensitivity to ACh or localization, studied in postnatal development clearly indicates the neural influence (63), as does the spread of sensitivity (97, 98) and the marked increase in AChR sites (82) after denervation.

Following denervation, spread of sensitivity to ACh occurs (97). The reappearance of extrajunctional receptors suggests either synthesis of new receptors that can indeed be blocked by inhibition of protein synthesis (82) or exposition of preexisting ones (178, 218). Receptor density again increases from 6–635 per μm^2 in rat diaphragm muscle fibers (81), a revised estimate differing from previous histoautoradiographic studies. The junctional receptor density, however, remains much higher at the NMJ and considerable evidence for different reactions of junctional and extrajunctional receptors does exist (213, 299).

Evidence that impulse activity is involved in control of AChR rests on observations of prevention or reduction of ACh sensitivity in chronically stimulated denervated muscle (67, 170, 211, 213) and in stimulated non-innervated chick myotubes (51). It is interesting, however, that no change in sensitivity of junctional ACh sensitivity was observed after stimulation of denervated muscle (213).

The evidence that regulation by neurotrophic agents is involved rests on observations of spread of ACh sensitivity after colchicine blocks (4, 148, 179), i.e. after blocking axoplasmic flow only. Moreover, onset of increase of sensitivity to ACh in a denervated muscle depends on the length of sectioned nerve stump (216). Observations in cell cultures (135, 136, 299) also indicate the importance of non-impulse, neurotrophic regulation of AChR. Degradation and synthesis of AChR receptors can, however, also be affected by other factors. Increased ACh sensitivity occurs in injured muscle fibers (178) and may also be caused by substances released from dividing cells that increase ACh sensitivity (171). Changes in the immune response may be involved. This is also indicated by the immunochemical change of denervated muscle. Molecules identified with antisera as histocompatibility antigens affect cell interactions (177), which are profoundly changed in denervated muscle.

Thus although both impulse and non-impulse neuronal activities control ACh sensitivity, degradation, and/or synthesis of AChR, other factors also participate. Hence regulation of ACh receptors is a complex process and differentiation of the components of regulation is not yet achieved.

SPECIFICITY OF NEUROTROPHIC AGENTS

The question of whether neuronal specificity applies also to neurotrophic functions remains open. The concept of "neuronal specificity" is used to account for the formation of specific nerve connections in the developing (and regenerating) nervous system. It is based especially on observations of the visual system. Mechanisms of intercellular recognition that exhibit selective biochemical affinities and establish neuronal "phenotypic specificity" of a more or less fixed type are assumed to exist (96, 160). With respect to neuromuscular connections, phenotypic specificity would imply a high neuronal specificity exhibited during development, regeneration, selective reinnervation of NMJ, and transformation of muscle in heteroinnervation. Connections made during embryogenesis generally exhibit a correct correspondence between motoneurons and muscles.

A correct correspondence between nerve and muscle appears to be lost in reinnervation of muscle after nerve repair in higher vertebrates. Specific reinnervation after nerve section is still observed in muscles of invertebrates (49) and teleost fish (223), indicating a high degree of "intercellular recognition" and replication of the pattern of embryogenesis. The importance of polyneural innervation of skeletal muscle fibers, also found as a developmental stage in some mammalian muscles (13), is stressed in this connection with respect to the polyneural innervation of fish muscle (223). Selective reinnervation of adult mammalian muscles, which would imply a mechanism of "neurotropism" (i.e. "chemotrophic attractions") was envisaged by Cajal (38). The evidence is far from conclusive, however (see 135, 333). Mechanical (contact) random guidance (328) rather than chemotactic guidance is suggested. However, preferential reinnervation of the original endplates has been repeatedly observed (22, 188, 333). The trend of regenerating nerves to grow back into their own muscles, which may preferentially accept innervation of their own type, was considered, especially in CU experiments performed at early stages of development (340). Further examples of selective reinnervation are quoted in a recent review (135). Other factors, such as a different rate of regeneration of axons or a different sensitivity of different muscles to ACh, may operate and might explain the faster reinnervation of the soleus muscle after interruption of the sciatic nerve (156, 164). The problem of neurotropism in reinnervation is not yet solved.

A high degree of neuronal specificity is indicated in the formation of a specified type of NMJ after cross-union of nerves (24, 147, 188). Neuronal specificity is conclusively demonstrated in the transformation of muscle after cross-union or cross-transplantation of nerves; the transformation, however, is modified or limited by some primary myogenic specifications. Heteroinnervation is essentially an experimental test of degree of specificity of the neuron and of the muscle plasticity induced by the neuron. Nerve cells and muscle cells that they innervate are matched by analogous properties, especially exhibited by the histochemical homogeneity of motor units (76). The genetic implications are discussed (108, 115) and imply that, next to nonspecific neurotrophic functions promoting growth and affecting protein synthesis, the neuron also exerts a specific influence on gene expression. Nonspecific and specific neurotrophic influences apparently interact and are, for instance, contrasted in limb regeneration of amphibian on the one hand (288) and specific reinnervation of taste buds on the other (244, 336).

FUNCTIONAL ROLE OF NEUROTROPHIC FUNCTIONS

The close coupling of impulse and neurotrophic, non-impulse activities of the neuron and the lack of direct biochemical identification of neurotrophic agents make considerations on their functional role difficult or premature. However, the existence of two different communication systems appears to be generally accepted and the functional significance of long-term neurotrophic functions is mainly discussed with respect to maintenance of synaptic contacts (75, 135), plasticity or modifiability of the NMJ, especially with regard to use and disuse (274, 285), and functional recovery after lesions of the nervous system (77, 111, 332). Neuronal maintenance functions concern pre- and postsynaptic sites and the effector organ and are discussed primarily with respect to relation of mediator release and availability of receptors (135, 213, 274).

Neurotrophic mechanisms are apparently operating and/or cooperating in processes of regeneration, maintenance of synaptic contact, collateral regeneration, and modification or plasticity of contact. Spontaneous neuronal degeneration has been described postnatally in mammalian nerves (271) and in central neurons concurrent with regeneration (293), suggesting a process of continuous remodeling of axonal terminals. The significance of such spontaneous processes is unclear; however, they may gain increasing importance in regeneration and sprouting as possible mechanisms for functional recovery (77, 109). Considerable changes occur in the NMJ during its initial formation, such as the reduction of the number of terminal axons (13), increase of quantal transmitter release and frequency of min. epp's, and restriction of sensitivity to ACh (63, 203). Spontaneous degeneration and replacement of NMJ throughout life has been suggested, but this has not been confirmed (333).

Spontaneous changes in the maintenance of synaptic contact occur in muscles of senescent (118–120) and hibernating animals (229). In senescent muscles the very marked reduction in synthesis of neuronal proteins, ChAc, and spontaneous transmitter release is not accompanied by an increase of ACh sensitivity. It does, however, result in a random loss of muscle fibers, which explains why only the size, but not the number, of motor units is affected. The often extreme atrophy of senescent muscle fibers (with absence of axonal degeneration) is related not to the decrease of neurotransmitter release, but apparently to lack of undefined neurotrophic agents (321). Collateral sprouting, but not formation, of new NMJ is observed in senescent muscles. The loss of maintenance of synaptic connections (resulting finally in a loss of muscle fibers) is a characteristic feature of old age; two stages—(relatively) "silent synapses," with still intact contact, and "silent axon terminals," retracted from the disrupted infoldings of the muscle membrane and heralding muscle fiber disintegration—could be distinguished (119). Silent terminals are also observed in insect muscles undergoing complete developmental involution (126). Muscles of hibernating animals show marked reduction in frequency of min. epp's and a twofold increase in ACh sensitivity (229).

Collateral sprouting after lesions in the CNS is now studied in detail (see 77, 109, 135) and has been shown to be functionally effective (219). However, information about the adequate stimulus for sprouting and the nature of synapses that may normally remain silent is missing. Collateral sprouts do form functional NMJ in mammalian muscle under conditions described before. In eye muscles of fish, collateral NMJ can be induced from antagonistically acting nerves. They are, however, functionally repressed after innervation of the muscle by its original nerve (223). This is not the case in collateral reinnervation of mammalian muscle, in which the foreign nerve maintains functional connections (36, 93, 117).

The existence of silent, nontransmitting, and activated synapses is suggested by studies of collateral sprouting. These questions are necessarily discussed with respect to the role of liberation of ACh and receptor availability. The evidence for neurotrophic mechanisms in control of synapse formation in muscle has been discussed before. Modifications and plasticity of synapses are discussed with respect to continuous processes of axonal growth and regrowth especially in central synapses (75) and with respect to use and disuse at the NMJ especially in connection with changes in transmitter release and receptors (274). The factors affecting the efficacy of synaptic transmission may relate to increases in quantal size or quantal content or to changes in the postsynaptic availability of receptors. However, these relations are not always clear (153). Concerning long-term effects that may affect plasticity at the NMJ, evidence for operation of both neurotrophic- and transmitter release-directed mechanisms is presented (274). Disuse, produced by anesthetic cuff (211) or by limb immobilization (90), results in normal or increased frequency of quantal release. However, extrajunctional ACh sensitivity can be reduced by muscle stimulation (67, 170, 211, 213). Quantum content is not decreased by immobilization, and changes in transmitter release, if noted, are present and remain unchanged only after 3–5 days of disuse (274). On the other hand, frequency of min. epp's and sensitivity to ACh is also increased after blocking axoplasmic flow (179). Thus it is not yet possible to identify the mechanisms of synaptic modulation with respect to use and disuse, especially when judged by transmitter release and receptor change only. However, plasticity of other muscle properties induced by neural influences is very marked indeed and is apparently affected by both impulse and non-impulse activities.

CONCLUSION

Increasing evidence for the existence of neurotrophic (non-impulse) mechanisms, especially in nerve-muscle cell relations, has been discussed. Studies on axoplasmic transport, release of agents (other than transmitter) from the nerve, and possible transfer of macromolecules at the NMJ and on differentiation of impulse and non-impulse (neurotrophic) activities have advanced, but not solved, the basic questions. Progress has been slowed because often less than adequate indicators of neurotrophic functions have been used and because only a single neurotrophic agent was generally assumed. Neurotrophic actions are best understood as components of multiple regulation in the context of general intercellular relations. The analysis of neurotrophic regulations will become clear only after chemical definition of the neurotrophic agents. Until then, study of the differentiation and interaction of neuronal impulse and non-impulse activities is, and will remain, an important problem for an understanding of the plasticity of the NMJ and muscle.

Literature Cited

1. Aguilar, C. E., Bisby, M. A., Diamond, J. 1972. Impulses and the transfer of trophic factors in nerves. *J. Physiol. London* 226:60–61P
2. Aitken, J. T. 1950. Growth of nerve implants in voluntary muscle. *J. Anat.* 84:38–49
3. Albuquerque, E. X., Schuh, F. T., Kaufman, F. C. 1971. Early membrane depolarization of the fast mammalian muscle after denervation. *Pfluegers Arch.* 328:36–50
4. Albuquerque, E. X., Warnick, J. E., Tasse, J. R., Sansone, F. M. 1972. Effects of vinblastine and colchicine on neural regulation of fast and slow skeletal muscles of the rat. *Exp. Neurol.* 37:607–34
5. Alvarez, J., Püschel, M. 1972. Transfer of material from efferent axons to sensory epithelium in the goldfish vestibular system. *Brain Res.* 37:265–78
6. Anderson, L. E., McClure, W. O. 1973. Differential transport of proteins in axons: Comparison between the sciatic nerve and dorsal columns of cats. *Proc. Nat. Acad. Sci. USA* 70:1521–25
7. Appeltauer, G. S. L., Korr, I. M. 1975. Axonal delivery of soluble, insoluble and electrophoretic fractions of neuronal proteins to muscle. *Exp. Neurol.* 46:132–46
8. Ashmore, C. R., Robinson, D. W., Rattray, P., Doerr, L. 1972. Biphasic development of muscle fibres in the fetal lamb. *Exp. Neurol.* 37:241–55
9. Askanas, V., Hee, D. 1973. Histochemistry of cultured, embryonic and regenerating rat muscle. *J. Histochem. Cytochem.* 21:785–93
10. Askanas, V., Shafiq, S. A., Milhorat, A. T. 1972. Histochemistry of cultured aneural chick muscle. Morphological maturation without differentiation of fiber types. *Exp. Neurol.* 37:218–30
11. Atwood, H. L., Luff, A. R., Morin, W. A., Sherman, R. G. 1971. Dense-cored vesicles at neuromuscular synapses of arthropods and vertebrates. *Experientia* 27:816–17
12. Axelsson, J., Thesleff, S. 1959. A study of supersensitivity in denervated mammalian skeletal muscle. *J. Physiol. London* 149:178–93
13. Bagust, J., Lewis, D. M., Westerman, R. A. 1973. Polyneuronal innervation of kitten skeletal muscle. *J. Physiol. London* 229:241–55
14. Balinsky, B. I. 1965. *An Introduction to Embryology.* Philadelphia: Saunders. 673 pp.
15. Bargmann, W.- 1966. Neurosecretion. *Int. Rev. Cytol.* 19:183–201
16. Barnard, R. J., Edgerton, V. R., Peter, J. B. 1970. Effect of exercise on skeletal muscle. *J. Appl. Physiol.* 28:767–70
17. Barnard, R. J., Edgerton, V. R., Furukawa, T., Peter, J. B. 1971. Histochemical, biochemical and contractile properties of red, white and intermediate fibers. *Am. J. Physiol.* 220:410–14
18. Barondes, S. H. 1974. Synaptic macromolecules: identification and metabolism. *Ann. Rev. Biochem.* 43:147–68
19. Bass, A., Gutmann, E., Hanzlíková, V., Hájek, I., Syrový, I. 1969. The effect of castration and denervation upon contraction properties and metabolism of the levator ani muscle of the rat. *Physiol. Bohemoslov.* 18:177–92
20. Bennett, G., Di Giamberardino, L., Koenig, H. L., Droz, B. 1973. Axonal migration of protein and glycoproteins in nerve endings of chicken ciliary ganglion after intracerebral injection of ³H fucose and ³H glucosamine. *Brain Res.* 60:129–46
21. Bennett, M. R., Florin, T., Woog, R. 1974. The formation of synapses in regenerating mammalian striated muscle. *J. Physiol. London* 238:79–92
22. Bennett, M. R., McLachlan, E. M., Taylor, R. S. 1973. The formation of synapses in reinnervated mammalian

striated muscle. *J. Physiol. London* 233:481–500

23. Bennett, M. R., Pettigrew, A. G., Taylor, R. S. 1973. The formation of synapses in reinnervated and cross-innervated adult avian muscles. *J. Physiol. London* 230:331–57

24. Bennett, M. R., Pettigrew, A. G. 1974. The formation of synapses in reinnervated and cross-reinnervated striated muscle during development. *J. Physiol. London* 241:547–73

25. Bevan, S., Miledi, R., Grampp, W. 1973. Induced transmitter release from Schwann cells and its suppression by actinomycin D. *Nature* 241:85–86

26. Bischoff, R., Holtzer, H. 1969. Mitosis and the process of differentiation of myogenic cells in vitro. *J. Cell Biol.* 41:188–200

27. Bittner, G. D. 1973. Trophic dependence of fibre diameter in a crustacean muscle. *Exp. Neurol.* 41:38–53

28. Blinzinger, K., Kreutzberg, G. 1968. Displacement of synaptic terminals from regenerating motoneurons by microglial cells. *Z. Zellforsch. Mikrosk. Anat.* 85:145–57

29. Bloom, F. E., Iversen, L. L., Schmitt, F. 1970. Macromolecules in synaptic function. *Neurosci. Res. Progr. Bull.* 8:329–449

30. Blunt, R. J., Jones, R., Vrbová, G. 1975. The use of local anaesthetics to produce prolonged motor nerve blocks in the study of denervation hypersensitivity. *Pfluegers Arch.* 355:189–204

31. Brattgard, S.-O., Edström, J.-E., Hydén, H. 1957. The chemical changes in regenerating neurons. *J. Neurochem.* 1:316–25

32. Brown, M. D. 1973. Role of activity in the differentiation of slow and fast muscles. *Nature* 244:178–79

33. Buller, A. J., Eccles, J. C., Eccles, R. M. 1960. Interactions between motoneurons and muscles in respect to the characteristic speeds of their responses. *J. Physiol. London* 150:417–39

34. Buller, A. J., Mommaerts, W. F. H. M., Seraydarian, K. 1969. Enzymic properties of myosin in fast and slow twitch muscles of the cat following cross-innervation. *J. Physiol. London* 205:581–97

35. Burešová, M., Gutmann, E., Hanzlíková, V. 1972. Differential effects of castration and denervation on protein synthesis in the levator ani muscle of the rat. *J. Endocrinol.* 54:3–14

36. Burešová, M., Hanzlíková, V., Gutmann, E. 1975. Changes of muscle

properties after implantation of fast nerve into denervated and into self reinnervated slow soleus muscle of the rat. *Pfluegers Arch.* 360:95–108

37. Burke, R. E., Levine, D. N., Tsairis, P., Zajac, F. E. 1973. Physiological types and histochemical profiles in motor units of the cat gastrocnemius. *J. Physiol. London* 234:723–48

38. Cajal, S. R. 1929. *Studies in Vertebrate Neurogenesis.* Transl. 1960 by L. Guth. Springfield, Ill.: Thomas. 432 pp.

39. Cangiano, A. 1973. Acetylcholine supersensitivity: the role of neurotrophic factors. *Brain Res.* 58:255–59

40. Carlson, B. M. 1973. The regeneration of skeletal muscle—a review. *Am. J. Anat.* 137:119–50

41. Carlson, B. M., Gutmann, E. 1972. Development of contractile properties of minced muscle regenerates in the rat. *Exp. Neurol.* 36:239–49

42. Carlson, B. M., Gutmann, E. 1974. Transplantation and "cross" transplantation of free muscle grafts in the rat. *Experientia* 30:1292–94

43. Celoti, L., Furlan, D., Levis, A. G. 1973. Relationships between protein and nucleic acid synthesis during muscle differentiation in vitro. *Acta Embryol. Exp. Palermo* 2:123–44

44. Čihák, R. 1972. Ontogenesis of the skeleton and intrinsic muscles of the human hand and foot. *Adv. Anat. Cell. Biol.* 46:8–189 pp.

45. Čihák, R., Gutmann, E., Hanzlíková, V. 1970. Involution and hormone-induced persistence of the M. sphincter (levator) ani in female rats. *J. Anat.* 106:93–110

46. Close, R. I. 1972. Dynamic properties of mammalian skeletal muscles. *Physiol. Rev.* 52:129–97

47. Close, R. I. 1974. Specialization among fast-twitch muscles. In *Exploratory Concepts in Muscular Dystrophy,* ed. A. T. Milhorat, 2:309–16. Amsterdam: Excerpta Medica, Elsevier

48. Close, R., Hoh, J. F. Y. 1968. Effects of nerve cross union on fast twitch and slow-graded muscle fibres in the toad. *J. Physiol. London* 198:103–25

49. Cohen, M. J. 1974. Trophic interactions in excitable systems of invertebrates. *Ann. NY Acad. Sci.* 228: 364–80

50. Cohen, M. W. 1972. The development of neuromuscular connexions in the presence of d-tubocurarine. *Brain Res.* 41:457–63

51. Cohen, S. A., Fischbach, G. D. 1973. Regulation of muscle acetylcholine sen-

sitivity by muscle activity in cell culture. *Science* 181:76–78
52. Cragg, B. G. 1970. What is the signal for chromatolysis? *Brain Res.* 23:1–21
53. Crain, S. M., Peterson, E. R. 1971. Development of paired explants of fetal spinal cord and adult skeletal muscle during chronic exposure to curare and hemicholinium. *In Vitro* 6:373
54. Crain, S. M., Peterson, E. R. 1974. Development of neural connections in culture. *Ann. NY Acad. Sci.* 228:6–34
55. Crain, S. M., Peterson, E. R. 1975. NGF-enhanced development of specific sensory-evoked synaptic networks in fetal mouse ganglion-cord-brain stem cultures. *Anat. Rec.* 181:339
56. Crockett, J. L., Edgerton, V. R. 1974. Responses of normally innervated soleus muscle to supplementary nerve implantation. *Exp. Neurol.* 43:207–15
57. Cull, R. E. 1974. Role of nerve-muscle contact in maintaining synaptic connections. *Exp. Brain Res.* 20:307–10
58. Dahlström, A. 1971. Axoplasmic transport (with particular respect to adrenergic neurons). *Philos. Trans. Soc. B* 261:325–58
59. Dennis, M. J. 1975. Physiological properties of junctions between nerve and muscle developing during salamander limb regeneration. *J. Physiol. London* 244:683–702
60. Dennis, M. J., Miledi, R. 1974. Characteristics of transmitter release at regenerating neuromuscular junctions. *J. Physiol. London* 239:571–94
61. Dennis, M. J., Miledi, R. 1974. Nontransmitting neuromuscular junctions during an early stage of end plate reinnervation. *J. Physiol. London* 239:553–70
62. Dennis, M. J., Miledi, R. 1974. Electrically induced release of acetylcholine from denervated Schwann cells. *J. Physiol. London* 237:431–52
63. Diamond, J., Miledi, R. 1962. A study of foetal and new-born rat muscle fibres. *J. Physiol. London* 162:393–408
64. Drachman, D. B. 1967. Is acetylcholine the trophic neuromuscular transmitter? *Arch. Neurol.* 17:206–18
65. Drachman, D. B., ed. 1974. Trophic functions of the neuron. *Ann. NY Acad. Sci.* 228:423 pp.
66. Drachman, D. B., Johnston, D. M. 1973. Development of a mammalian fast muscle: dynamic and biochemical properties correlated. *J. Physiol. London* 234:29–42
67. Drachman, D. B., Witzke, F. 1972. Trophic regulation of acetylcholine sensitivity of muscle: Effect of electrical stimulation. *Science* 176:514–16
68. Drahota, Z., Gutmann, E. 1963. Long term regulatory influence of the nervous system on some metabolic differences in muscles of different function. *Physiol. Bohemoslov.* 12:339–48
69. Dresden, M. H. 1969. Denervation effects on newt limb regeneration: DNA, RNA and protein synthesis. *Develop. Biol.* 19:311–20
70. Droz, B. 1973. Renewal of synaptic proteins. *Brain Res.* 62:383–94
71. Droz, B., Koenig, H. L., Di Giambardino, L. 1973. Axonal migration of protein and glycoprotein to nerve endings. I. Radioautographic analysis of the renewal of protein in nerve endings of chicken ciliary ganglion after intracerebral injection of ^{3}H lysine. *Brain Res.* 60:93–127
72. Dubowitz, V., Pearse, A. G. 1960. A comparative study of oxidative and phosphorylase activity in skeletal muscle. *Histochemie* 2:105–17
73. Dubowitz, V., Newman, D. L. 1967. Change in enzyme pattern after cross-innervation of fast and slow skeletal muscle. *Nature* 214:840–41
74. Duchen, L. W. 1972. Motor nerve growth induced by botulinum toxin as a regenerative phenomenon. *Proc. R. Soc. Med.* 65:1967–97
75. Eccles, J. C. 1974. Trophic interactions in the mammalian central nervous system. *Ann. NY Acad. Sci.* 228:406–22
76. Edström, L., Kugelberg, E. 1968. Histochemical composition, distribution of fibers and fatiguability of single motor units. *J. Neurol. Neurosurg. Psychiat.* 31:424–33
77. Eidelberg, E., Stein, D. G. 1974. Functional recovery after lesions of the nervous system. *Neurosci. Res. Progr. Bull.* 12:195–303
78. Elul, R., Miledi, R., Stefani, E. 1970. Neural control of contracture in slow muscle fibres of the frog. *Acta Physiol. Lat. Am.* 20:194–226
79. Engel, W. K. 1962. The essentiality of histo and cytochemical studies of skeletal muscle in the investigation of neuromuscular disease. *Neurology* 12:778–84
80. Essen, D. Van, Jansen, J. K. S. 1974. Reinnervation of rat diaphragm during perfusion with bungarotoxin. *Acta Physiol. Scand.* 91:571–73
81. Fambrough, D. M. 1974. Revised estimates of extrajunctional receptor den-

sity in denervated rat diaphragm. *J. Gen. Physiol.* 64:468–72

82. Fambrough, D. M., Hartzell, H. C., Powell, J. A., Rash, J. E., Joseph, N. 1974. On the differentiation and organization of the surface membrane of a postsynaptic cell—the 'skeletal muscle fibre. In *Synaptic Transmission and Neuronal Interaction,* ed. M. V. L. Bennett, 285–313. New York: Raven

83. Fambrough, D., Hartzell, H. C., Rash, J. E. 1974. Receptor properties of developing muscle. *Ann. NY Acad. Sci.* 228:47–62

84. Fambrough, D., Rash, J. E. 1971. Development of acetylcholine sensitivity during myogenesis. *Develop. Biol.* 26:55–68

85. Feng, T. P., Lu, D. K. 1965. New lights on the phenomenon of transient hypertrophy in the denervated hemidiaphragm of the rat. *Scientia Sin.* 14:1172–84

86. Fex, S., Jirmanová, I. 1969. Innervation by nerve implants of "fast" and "slow" skeletal muscles of the rat. *Acta Physiol. Scand.* 76:257–69

87. Filogamo, G., Gabella, G. 1967. The development of neuromuscular correlations in vertebrates. *Arch. Biol. Liège* 78:9–60

88. Fischbach, G. D., Cohen, S. A., Henkart, M. P. 1974. Some observations on trophic interaction between neurons and muscle fibers in cell culture. *Ann. NY Acad. Sci.* 228:35–46

89. Fischbach, G. D., Robbins, N. 1969. Changes in contractile properties of disused soleus muscle. *J. Physiol. London* 201:305–20

90. Fischbach, G. D., Robbins, N. 1971. Effects of chronic disuse of rat soleus neuro-muscular junctions on postsynaptic membrane. *J. Neurophysiol.* 34:562–69

91. Fischman, D. A. 1972. Development of striated muscle. In *The Structure and Function of Muscle,* ed. G. H. Bourne, I/1:75–148. London: Academic

92. Fluck, R. A., Strohman, R. C. 1973. Acetylcholinesterase activity in developing skeletal muscle cell in vitro. *Develop. Biol.* 33:417–28

93. Frank, E., Jansen, J. K. S., Lømo, T., Westgaard, R. 1974. Maintained function of foreign synapses on hyperinnervated skeletal muscle fibres in the rat. *Nature* 247:375–76

94. Gauthier, G. F., Schaeffer, S. F. 1973. Ultrastructural and cytochemical manifestations of protein synthesis in the peripheral sarcoplasm of denervated and newborn skeletal muscle fibres. *J. Cell. Sci.* 14:113–37

95. Gauthier, G. F., Dunn, R. A. 1973. Ultrastructural and cytochemical features of mammalian skeletal muscle fibres following denervation. *J. Cell. Sci.* 12:525–47

96. Gaze, R. M. 1974. Neuronal specificity. *Br. Med. Bull.* 30:116–21

97. Ginetzinski, A. G. 1970. *Chemical Transmission of the Nerve Impulse in the Evolution of the Muscle Fibre.* Leningrad: Nauka. 202 pp. (in Russian)

98. Ginetzinski, A. G., Shamarina, N. M. 1942. The tonomotor phenomenon in denervated muscles. *Usp. Sovrem. Biol.* 15:283–94 (in Russian)

99. Goldberg, A. L. 1972. Mechanisms of growth and atrophy of skeletal muscle. In *Muscle Biology,* ed. R. G. Cassens, Vol. 1:81–118. New York: Dekker

100. Goldberg, A. L., Jablecki, C., Li, J. B. 1974. Effects of use and disuse on amino acid transport and protein turnover in muscle. *Ann. NY Acad. Sci.* 228:190–201

101. Goldspink, G., Tabary, C., Tabary, J. C., Tardieu, C., Tardieu, G. 1974. Effect of denervation on the adaptation of sarcomere number and muscle extensibility to the functional length of the muscle. *J. Physiol. London* 236:733–42

102. Grafstein, B. 1971. Transneuronal transfer of radioactivity in the central nervous system. *Science* 172:177–79

103. Grafstein, B. 1971. Role of slow axonal transport in nerve regeneration. *Acta Neuropathol. Suppl.* 5:144–52

104. Gröschel-Stewart, U., Meschede, K., Lehr, I. 1973. Histochemical and immunochemical studies on mammalian striated muscle fibres. *Histochemie* 33:79–85

105. Gurdon, J. B. 1974. *The Control of Gene Expression in Animal Development.* Cambridge,· Mass.: Harvard Univ. Press. 260 pp.

106. Guth, L. 1968. "Trophic" influences of nerve on muscle. *Physiol. Rev.* 48:645–87

107. Guth, L. 1969. "Trophic" effects of vertebrate neurons. *Neurosci. Res. Progr. Bull.* 7:1–73

108. Guth, L. 1971. A review of the evidence for the neural regulation of gene expression in muscle. In *Contractility of Muscle Cells and Related Processes,* ed. R. J. Podolsky, 189–201. New Jersey: Prentice-Hall

109. Guth, L. 1974. Axonal regeneration and functional plasticity in the central nervous system. *Exp. Neurol.* 45: 606–54
110. Guth, L., Yellin, H. 1971. The dynamic nature of the so-called "fibre types" of mammalian skeletal muscle. *Exp. Neurol.* 31:277–300
111. Gutmann, E. 1958. *Die funktionelle Regeneration der peripheren Nerven.* Berlin: Akademie Verlag. 262 pp.
112. Gutmann, E., ed. 1962. *The Denervated Muscle.* Prague: Czechoslov. Acad. Sci. 479 pp.
113. Gutmann, E. 1964. Neurotrophic relations in the regeneration process. *Progr. Brain Res.* 13:72–112
114. Gutmann, E. 1969. The trophic function of the nerve cell. *Scientia* 104:1–20
115. Gutmann, E. 1973. Critical evaluation and implications of denervation and reinnervation studies of cross striated muscle. *Methods Neurochem.* 5:189–254
116. Gutmann, E. 1973. The multiple regulation of muscle fibre pattern in cross striated muscle. *Nova Acta Leopold.* 38:193–218
117. Gutmann, E., Hanzlíková, V. 1967. Effects of accessory nerve supply to muscle achieved by implantation into muscle during regeneration of its nerve. *Physiol. Bohemoslov.* 16:244–50
118. Gutmann, E., Hanzlíková, V. 1972. *Age Changes in the Neuromuscular System.* Bristol, Engl.: Scientechnica. 195 pp.
119. Gutmann, E., Hanzlíková, V. 1975. Fast and slow motor units in aging. *Gerontologia.* In press
120. Gutmann, E., Hanzlíková, V., Vyskočil, F. 1971. Age changes in cross striated muscle of the rat. *J. Physiol. London* 219:331–43
121. Gutmann, E., Hník, P. 1962. Denervation studies in research of neurotrophic relationships. See Ref. 112, 13–56
122. Gutmann, E., Melichna, J. 1975. Biphasic development of contractile and histochemical properties in regeneration of slow muscle. In preparation
123. Gutmann, E., Melichna, J., Syrový, I. 1974. Developmental changes in contraction time, myosin properties and fibre pattern of fast and slow skeletal muscles. *Physiol. Bohemoslov.* 23:19–27
124. Gutmann, E., Melichna, J., Syrový, I. 1975. Changes in contraction properties of denervated mammalian muscle dependent on length of nerve stump. *Physiol. Bohemoslov.* In press
125. Gutmann, E., Schiaffino, S., Hanzlíková, V. 1971. Mechanism of compensatory hypertrophy in skeletal muscle of the rat. *Exp. Neurol.* 31:451–64
126. Gutmann, E., Srihari, T., Hanzlíková, V. 1974. Persistance des axones au cours des derniers stages d'involution des muscles du vol chez Acheta domestica. *C.R. Acad. Sci. Paris* 279:570–73
127. Gutmann, E., Tuček, S., Hanzlíková, V. 1969. Changes in cholinacetyltransferase and cholinesterase activities in the levator ani muscle of rats following castration. *Physiol. Bohemoslov.* 18:195–203
128. Gutmann, E., Vodička, Z., Zelená, J. 1955. Changes in cross striated muscle after nerve interruption depending on the length of the nerve stump. *Physiol. Bohemoslov.* 4:200–4 (in Russian)
129. Gutmann, E., Young, J. Z. 1944. The reinnervation of muscle after various periods of atrophy. *J. Anat. London* 78:15–43
130. Hamburger, V., Levi-Montalcini, R. 1949. Proliferation, differentiation and regeneration in the spinal ganglia of the chick embryo under normal and experimental conditions. *J. Exp. Zool.* 111:457–501
131. Hanzlíková, V., Gutmann, E. 1972. Effect of foreign innervation on the androgen-sensitive levator ani muscle of the rat. *Z. Zellforsch. Mikrosk. Anat.* 135:165–74
132. Hanzlíková, V., Gutmann, E. 1974. The absence of androgen-sensitivity in the grafted soleus muscle innervated by the pudendal nerve. *Cell. Tissue Res.* 145:121–29
133. Hanzlíková, V., Macková, E. V., Hník, P. 1975. Satellite cells of the rat soleus muscle in the process of compensatory hypertrophy combined with denervation. *Cell. Tissue Res.* 160:411–21
134. Hanzlíková, V., Schiaffino, S. 1973. Studies on the effect of denervation in developing muscle. III. Diversification of myofibrillar structure and origin of myofibrillar structure and origin of the heterogeneity of muscle fibre types. *Z. Zellforsch. Mikrosk. Anat.* 147:75–85
135. Harris, A. J. 1974. Inductive functions of the nervous system. *Ann. Rev. Physiol.* 36:251–305
136. Harris, A. J., Heinemann, S., Schubert, D., Tarakis, H. 1971. Trophic interaction between cloned tissue culture lines of nerve and muscle. *Nature* 231:296–301

137. Harris, J. B., Thesleff, S. 1972. Nerve stump length and membrane changes in denervated skeletal muscle. *Nature* 236:60–61

138. Hartzell, H. C., Fambrough, D. M. 1973. Acetylcholine receptor production and incorporation into membranes of developing muscle fibers. *Develop. Biol.* 30:153–65

139. Harvey, A. L., Dryden, W. F. 1974. Differentiation of cultured muscle in the presence of α-bungarotoxin. *Experientia* 30:613–15

140. Harvey, A. L., Dryden, W. F. 1974. The development and distribution of cholinesterases in cultured skeletal muscle with and without nerve. *Differentiation* 2:237–47

141. Hebb, C. O., Krnjević, K., Silver, A. 1964. Acetylcholine and choline acetyltransferase in the diaphragm of the rat. *J. Physiol. London* 171:504–13

142. Heller, I. H., Hesse, S. 1964. The activating substances in peripheral nerves. *Exp. Neurol.* 10:133–39

143. Henneman, E., Olson, C. B. 1965. Relations between structure and function in the design of skeletal muscle. *J. Neurophysiol.* 28:581–98

144. Hikida, R. S. 1972. Morphological transformation of slow to fast muscle fibres after tenotomy. *Exp. Neurol.* 35:265–73

145. Hikida, R. S., Lombardo, J. A. 1974. Regeneration of pigeon fast and slow muscle fibre types after partial excision and mincing. *J. Cell Biol.* 61:414–26

146. Hirano, H. 1967. Ultrastructural study on the morphogenesis of the neuromuscular junction in the skeletal muscle of the chick. *Z. Zellforsch. Mikrosk. Anat.* 79:189–208

147. Hník, P., Jirmanová, I., Vyklický, L., Zelená, J. 1967. Fast and slow muscles of the chick after nerve cross-union. *J. Physiol. London* 193:309–25

148. Hofmann, W. W., Thesleff, S. 1972. Studies on the trophic influence of nerve in skeletal muscle. *Eur. J. Pharmacol.* 20:256–60

149. Hofmann, W. W., Thesleff, S., Zelená, J. 1964. Innervation of botulinum poisoned skeletal muscles by accessory nerves. *J. Physiol. London* 169:12P

150. Hollán, S. R., Novák, E., Koszeghy, S., Stark, E. 1965. Immunochemical study of denervated muscle proteins. *Life Sci.* 4:1779–83

151. Holtzer, H., Rubinstein, J., Chi, J., Dienstman, S., Biehl, J. 1974. The phenotypic heterogeneity of myogenic clones and what cells synthesize which molecules. See Ref. 47, 3–14

152. Hsu, L., Lentz, T. L. 1973. Effect of colchicin on the fine structure of the neuromuscular junction. *Z. Zellforsch. Mikrosk. Anat.* 135:439–48

153. Hubbard, J. 1973. Microphysiology of vertebrate neuromuscular transmission. *Physiol. Rev.* 53:674–723

154. Hudlická, O. 1973. *Muscle Blood Flow.* Amsterdam: Swets & Zeitlihger. 219 pp.

155. Hughes, A. F. W. 1968. *Aspects of Neural Ontogeny.* London: Logos. 249 pp.

156. Ip, M. C., Vrbová, G. 1973. Motor and sensory reinnervation of fast and slow mammalian muscles. *Z. Zellforsch. Mikrosk. Anat.* 146:261–79

157. Itina, N. A. 1973. The effect of motoneurones on the functional characteristics of vertebrate muscle. Denervation and cross-union effects. *Usp. Sovrem. Biol.* 75:419–40

158. Itina, N. A., Nasledov, G. A., Skorobnitzik, N. F. 1969. New data on distribution of acetylcholin receptors on muscle fibres *Zh. Evol. Biochem. Physiol.* 5:98–105 (in Russian)

159. Iversen, L. L. 1974. Neuropharmacology of peptides. *Nature* 252:630

160. Jacobson, M. 1970. *Developmental Neurobiology.* New York: Holt, Rinehart & Winston. 465 pp.

161. James, D. W., Tresman, R. L. 1969. An electron microscopic study of de novo formation of neuromuscular junction in tissue culture. *Z. Zellforsch. Mikrosk. Anat.* 100:126–140

162. James, N. T. 1971. The histochemical demonstration of three types of intrafusal muscle fiber in rat muscle spindles. *Histochem. J.* 3:457–62

163. Jansen, J. K. S., Lomo, T., Nicolaysen, K., Westgaard, R. 1973. Hyperinnervation of skeletal muscle fibers: Dependence on muscle activity. *Science* 181:559–61

164. Jaweed, M. M., Herbison, G. J., Dituno, J. F. 1975. Reinnervation of "fast" and "slow" muscles: A histochemical study in rats. *Exp. Neurol.* In press

165. Jirmanová, I. 1975. Ultrastructure of motor endplates during pharmacologically induced degeneration and subsequent regeneration of skeletal muscle. *J. Neurocytol.* 4:141–55

166. Jirmanová, I., Hník, P., Zelená, J. 1971. Implantation of "fast" nerve into slow muscle in young chickens. *Physiol. Bohemoslov.* 20:199–204

167. Jirmanová, I., Thesleff, S. 1972. Ultrastructural study of experimental degeneration and regeneration in the adult rat. *Z. Zellforsch. Mikrosk. Anat.* 131: 77–97

168. Jirmanová, I., Zelená, J. 1970. Effect of denervation and tenotomy on slow and fast muscles of the chicken. *Z. Zellforsch. Mikrosk. Anat.* 106:333–47

169. Jirmanová, I., Zelená, J. 1973. Ultrastructural transformation of fast chicken muscle fibres induced by nerve cross union. *Z. Zellforsch. Mikrosk. Anat.* 146:103–21

170. Jones, R., Vrbová, G. 1970. Effect of muscle activity on denervation hypersensitivity. *J. Physiol. London* 210:144–45P

171. Jones, R., Vrbová, G. 1974. Two factors responsible for denervation hypersensitivity. *J. Physiol. London* 236:517–38

172. Jung, I., Baulieu, E. E. 1972. Testosterone cytosol "receptors" in the rat levator ani muscle. *Nature New Biol.* 237:24–26

173. Juntunen, J. 1973. Effects of colchicine and vinblastine on neurotubules of the sciatic nerve and cholinesterases in the developing myoneural junction of the rat. *Z. Zellforsch. Mikrosk. Anat.* 142:193–204

174. Juntunen, J. 1973. Morphogenesis of the myoneural junctions after immobilization of the muscle in the rat. *Z. Anat. Entwicklungsgesch.* 143:1–12

175. Juntunen, J. 1974. Morphological studies on the induction of the postsynaptic membrane of the myoneural junction. *Acta Inst. Anat. Univ. Helsinki* Suppl. 7:9–32

176. Katz, B. 1966. *Nerve, Muscle and Synapse.* New York: McGraw. 193 pp.

177. Katz, D. H., Benacerraf, B. 1975. The function and interrelationships of T-cell receptors in genes and other histocompatibility gene products. *Transplant. Rev.* 22:175–95

178. Katz, B., Miledi, R. 1964. The development of acetylcholine sensitivity in nerve-free segments of skeletal muscle. *J. Physiol. London* 170:389–96

179. Kaufman, F. C., Warnick, J. E., Albuquerque, E. X. 1974. Uptake of ^{3}H colchicine from silastic implants by mammalian nerves and muscles. *Exp. Neurol.* 44:404–6

180. Kean, C. J. C., Lewis, D. M., McGarrick, J. D. 1974. Dynamic properties of denervated fast and slow twitch muscle of the cat. *J. Physiol. London* 237:103–13

181. Keul, J., Doll, E., Keppler, D. 1969. *Muskelstoffwechsel.* München: Barth. 240 pp.

182. Kerkut, G. A., Shapira, A., Walker, R. J. 1967. The transport of ^{14}C labelled material from CNS to muscle along a nerve trunk. *Comp. Biochem. Physiol.* 23:729–59

183. Kidoroko, Y. 1973. Development of action potential in a clonal skeletal muscle cell line. *Nature:* 241:158–59

184. Kimura, M., Kimura, I. 1973. Increase of nascent protein synthesis in neuromuscular junction of rat diaphragm induced by denervation. *Nature* 241: 114–15

185. Klemperer, H. G. 1972. Lowered proportion of polysomes and decreased amino acid incorporation by ribosomes from denervated muscle. *FEBS Lett.* 28:169–72

186. Knowles, F. G. W., Bern, H. A. 1966. The function of neurosecretion in endocrine regulation. *Nature* 210:271–72

187. Kochakian, C. D. 1960. Regulation of muscle growth by androgens. In *Physiology and Biochemistry of Muscle as a Food,* ed. E. J. Briskey, R. C. Cassens, J. C. Trautmann, 1:81–112 Madison: Univ. Wisconsin Press

188. Koenig, J. 1970. Contribution à l'étude de la morphologie des plaques motrices des grands dorsaux antérieur et postérieur du poulet après innervation croisée. *Arch. Anat. Microsc. Morphol. Exp.* 59:403–26

189. Korr, I. M., Appeltauer, G. S. L. 1974. The time course of axonal transport of neuronal proteins to muscle. *Exp. Neurol.* 43:452–63

190. Korr, I. M., Wilkinson, P. N., Chornock, F. W. 1967. Axonal delivery of neuroplasmic components to muscle cells. *Science* 155:342–45

191. Koštířová, D., Tuček, S., Gutmann, E., Dupalová, H. 1975. The effect of testosterone on the activity of cholinacetyltransferase and cholinesterase in the rat levator ani and soleus muscle. *Physiol. Bohemoslov.* 24:63–64

192. Kreutzberg, G. W., Schubert, P. 1971. Changes in axonal flow during regeneration of mammalian motor nerves. *Acta Neuropathol.* (suppl.) 5:70–75

193. Krishnamoorthy, R. V. 1973. Increased lysozyme activity in muscular atrophy of denervated frogs. *Enzymologia* 43: 353–58

194. Krnjevic, K. 1974. Chemical nature of synaptic transmission in vertebrates. *Physiol. Rev.* 54:418–540

195. Kuno, M., Miyata, Y., Munoz-Martinez, E. J. 1974. Differential reaction of fast and slow motoneurones to axotomy. *J. Physiol London.* 240:725–39

196. Kuno, M., Miyata, Y., Munoz-Martinez, E. J. 1974. Properties of fast and slow motoneurones following motor reinnervation. *J. Physiol. London* 242:273–88

197. Landmesser, L., Pilar, G. 1974. Synaptic transmission and cell death during normal ganglionic development *J. Physiol. London.* 241:737–49

198. Landmesser, L., Pilar, G. 1974. Synapse formation during embryogenesis on ganglion cells lacking periphery. *J. Physiol. London* 241:715–36

199. London, B. N. 1972. The fine structure of the equatorial regions of developing muscle spindles in the rat. *J. Neurocytol.* 1:189–210

200. Lentz, T. L. 1972. A role of cyclic AMP in a neurotrophic process. *Nature* 238:154–55

201. Lentz, T. L. 1967. Fine structure of nerves in the regenerating limb of the newt Triturus. *Am. J. Anat.* 121:647–70

202. Lentz, T. L. 1974. Neurotrophic regulation at the neuromuscular junction. *Ann. NY Acad. Sci.* 228:323–37

203. Letinsky, M. S. 1974. The development of nerve-muscle junctions in Rana catesbiana tadpoles. *Develop. Biol.* 40:129–53

204. Levi-Montalcini, R., Angeletti, R. H., Angeletti, P. U. 1972. The nerve growth factor. In *The Structure and Function of Nervous Tissue*, ed. C. H. Bourne, 5:1–38. London: Academic

205. Lewis, D. M. 1972. The effect of denervation on the mechanical and electrical properties of fast and slow mammalian twitch muscle. *J. Physiol London.* 222:51–75

206. Lewis, D. M., Kean, C. J. C., McGarrick, J. D. 1974. Dynamic properties of slow and fast muscle and their trophic regulation. *Ann. NY Acad. Sci.* 228:105–20

207. Liu, C. N., Chambers, W. W. 1958. Intraspinal sprouting of dorsal root axons. *Arch. Neurol. Psychiat.* 79:46–61

208. Lockshin, R. A., Baulton, J. 1974. Programmed cell death. Cytochemical evidence for lysosomes during the normal break down of intersegmental muscles. *J. Ultrastruct. Res.* 46:43–63

209. Lockshin, R., Williams, C. M. 1965. Programmed cell death. III. Neural control of the break down of the inter-segmental muscles of silk moths. *J. Inst. Physiol.* 11:601–10

210. Loewenstein, W. R. 1968. Communication through cell junctions. Implications in growth control and differentiation. *Develop. Biol. Suppl.* 2:151–83

211. Lømo, T., Rosenthal, J. 1972. Control of ACh sensitivity by muscle activity in the rat. *J. Physiol London.* 221:493–513

212. Lømo, T., Westgaard, R. H., Dahl, H. A. 1974. Contractile properties of muscle: Control by pattern of muscle activity in the rat. *Proc. R. Soc. London Ser. B* 187:99–103

213. Lomo, T., Westgaard, R. H. 1975. Further studies on the control of ACh sensitivity by muscle activity in the rat. *J. Physiol. London.* In press

214. Lubińska, L. 1964. Axoplasmic streaming in regenerated and in normal fibres. *Progr. Brain Res.* 13:1–71

215. Lubińska, L. 1975. On axoplasmic flow. *Int. Rev. Neurobiol.* 17:241–96

216. Luco, J. V., Eyzaguirre, C. 1955. Fibrillation and hypersensitivity to ACh in denervated muscle. Effect of length of degenerating nerve fibres. *J. Neurophysiol.* 18:65–73

217. Lüllmann-Rauch, R. 1971. The regeneration of neuromuscular junctions during spontaneous re-innervation of the rat diaphragm. *Z. Zellforsch. Mikrosk. Anat.* 121:593–603

218. Lunt, G. G., Stephani, E., De Robertis, E. 1971. Increased incorporation of G-^{3}H leucine into possible "receptor" proteolipid in denervated muscle in vivo. *J. Neurochem.* 18:1545–53

219. Lynch, G., Deadwyler, S., Cotman, C. 1975. Postlesion axonal growth produces permanent functional connections. *Science* 180:1364–66

220. Macková, E., Hník P. 1973. Compensatory muscle hypertrophy induced by tenotomy of synergists is not true working hypertrophy. *Physiol. Bohemoslov.* 22:43–49

221. Magazanik, L. G., Nasledov, G. A., ed. 1974. *Evolution of the Contractile Behaviour of the Skeletal Muscle.* Leningrad: Nauka. 335 pp.

222. Margreth, A., Salviati, G., Di Mauro, S., Turati, G. 1972. Early biochemical consequences of denervation in fast and slow skeletal muscles and their relationship to' neural control over muscle differentiation. *Biochem. J.* 126:1099–1110

223. Mark, R. F. 1974. Selective innervation of muscle. *Br. Med. Bull.* 30:122–25

224. Marshall, M. W., Ward, M. R. 1974. Anode break excitation in denervated rat skeletal muscle. *J. Physiol. London* 236:413–20

225. May, R. M. 1925. The relation of nerves to degenerating and regenerating taste buds. *J. Exp. Zool.* 42:371–410

226. McArdle, J. J., Albuquerque, E. X. 1973. A study of the reinnervation of fast and slow mammalian muscles. *J. Gen. Physiol.* 61:1–23

227. McEwen, B. S., Denef, C. J., Gerlach, J. L., Papinger, L. 1974. Chemical studies of the brain as a steroid hormone target tissue. In *Neurosciences,* ed. F. O. Schmitt, F. G. Worden, 3:599–620. Cambridge, Mass.: MIT Press

228. McLaughlin, J., Abood, L. G., Bosmann, H. B. 1974. Early elevations of glycosidase, acid phosphatase, and acid proteolytic enzyme activity in denervated skeletal muscle. *Exp. Neurol.* 42:541–54

229. Melichar, I., Brožek, G., Janský, L., Vyskočil, F. 1973. Effect of hibernation and noradrenaline on acetylcholine release and action at neuromuscular junction of the golden hamster (Mesocriatus auratus). *Pfluegers Arch.* 345:107–22

230. Melichna, J., Gutmann, E. 1974. Stimulation and immobilization effects on contractile and histochemical properties of denervated muscle. *Pfleugers Arch.* 352:165–78

231. Mendez, J., Arana, L. C., Luco, J. V. 1970. Antifibrillary effect of adrenergic fibers on denervated striated muscles. *J. Neurophysiol.* 33:882–90

232. Meledi, R. 1960. Properties of regenerating neuromuscular synapses in the frog. *J. Physiol. London* 154:190–205

233. Meledi, R. 1960. Junctional and extrajunctional acetylcholine receptors in skeletal muscle fibres. *J. Physiol. London* 151:24–30

234. Miledi, R. 1963. An influence of nerve not mediated by impulses. In *The Effect of Use and Disuse on Neuromuscular Functions,* ed. E. Gutmann, P. Hnik, 35–40. Amsterdam, London, New York: Elsevier. 576 pp.

235. Miledi, R., Orkand, P. 1969. Effect of a "fast" nerve on "slow" muscle fibres in the frog. *Nature* 209:717–18

236. Miledi, R., Slater, C. R. 1970. On the degeneration of rat neuro-muscular junctions after nerve section. *J. Physiol. London* 207:507–28

237. Miledi, R., Stefani, E., Zelená, J. 1968. Neural control of acetylcholine sensitivity in rat muscle fibres. *Nature* 220:497–98

238. Monard, D., Solomon, F., Rentsch, M., Gysin, R. 1973. Glia-induced morphological differentiation in neuroblastoma cells. *Proc. Nat. Acad. Sci. USA* 70:1894–97

239. Muscatello, U., Margreth, A., Aloisi, M. 1965. On the differential response of sarcoplasm and myoplasm to denervation in frog muscle. *J. Cell Biol.* 27:1–24

240. Musick, J., Hubbard, J. I. 1972. Release of protein from mouse motor nerve terminals. *Nature* 237:279–81

241. Nelson, P. G. 1969. Functional consequences of tenotomy in hind limb muscles in the rat. *J. Physiol. London* 221:493–513

242. Nüesch, H. 1968. The role of the nervous system in insect morphogenesis and regeneration. *Ann. Rev. Entomol.* 13:27–44

243. Nüesch, H., Bienz-Isler, G. 1972. Die Entwicklung denervierter Imaginalmuskeln bei Anthera polyphemus (Lep.) und die Frage der entwicklungsfördernden Nervenwirkung. *Zool. Jb. Anat.* 89:333–50

244. Oakley, B. 1974. On the specification of taste neurons in the rat tongue. *Brain Res.* 75:85–96

245. Ochs, S. 1972. Fast transport of materials in mammalian nerve fibers. *Science* 176:252–60

246. Ochs, S. 1974. Systems of material transport in nerve fibers (axoplasmic transport) related to nerve function and trophic control. *Ann. NY Acad. Sci.* 228:202–23

247. Oh, T., Johnson, D. D., Kim, S. U. 1973. Neurotrophic effect on isolated chick embryo muscle in culture. *Science* 178:1298–1300

248. Olmsted, J. M. D. 1920. The nerve as a formative influence in the development of taste buds. *J. Comp. Neurol.* 31:465–68

249. Padykula, H. A., Gauthier, G. F. 1970. The ultrastructure of neuromuscular junctions of mammalian red, white and intermediate skeletal muscle fibres. *J. Cell Biol.* 46:27–41

250. Pappas, G. D., Peterson, E. R., Masurovsky, E. B., Crain, S.M. 1971. Electron microscopy of the in vitro development of mammalian motor end plates *Ann. NY Acad. Sci.* 183:33–45

251. Paravicini, U., Stoeckel, K., Thoenen, H. 1975. Biological importance of retrograde axonal transport of nerve growth

factor in adrenergic neurons. *Brain Res.* 84:279–91

252. Parker, G. H. 1932. On the trophic impulse, so called, its rate and nature. *Am. Natur.* 60:147–58

253. Patrick, J., Heinemann, S. F., Lindström, J., Schubert, D., Steinbach, J. H. 1972. Appearance of acetylcholine receptors during differentiation of a myogenic cell line. *Proc. Nat. Acad. Sci. USA* 69:2762–66

254. Paulson, J. C., McClure, W. O. 1974. Microtubules and axoplasmic transport. *Brain Res.* 73:333–37

255. Pellegrino, C., Bergamini, E., Pagni, R. 1970. Interference of denervation on testosterone effects on glycogen synthesis in levator ani muscle. *Abstr. int. Congr. Horm. Steroids, Hamburg. Exc. Med. Found., 3rd,* ed. L. Martini, Int. Congr. Ser. No. 210: 163 pp.

256. Pellegrino, C., Francini, C. 1963. An electron microscope study of denervation atrophy in red and white skeletal muscle fibres. *J. Cell Biol.* 17:327–49

257. Pellegrino de Iraldi, A., de Robertis, E. 1968. The neurotubular system of the axon and the origin of granulated and non-granulated vesicles in regenerating nerves. *Z. Zellforsch. Mikrosk. Anat.* 87:330–44

258. Perry, S. V. 1974. Variation in the contractile and regulatory proteins of the myofibril with muscle type. See Ref. 47, 319–28

259. Petersen, O. H. 1974. Cell membrane permeability change: an important step in hormone action. *Experientia* 30: 1105–7

260. Pette, D., Smith, M. E., Staudte, H. W., Vrbová, G. 1973. Effects of long-term electrical stimulation on some contractile and metabolic characteristics of fast rabbit muscles. *Pfluegers Arch.* 338:257–72

261. Pilar, G., Landmesser, L. 1972. Axotomy mimicked by localized colchicine application. *Science* 177:1116–18

262. Pollock, M. S., Bird, J. W. C. 1968. Distribution and particle properties of acid hydrolase in denervated muscle. *Am. J. Physiol.* 215:716–22

263. Potter, L. T. 1970. Synthesis, storage and release of ^{14}C acetylcholine in isolated rat diaphragm muscle. *J. Physiol. London* 206:145–66

264. Prestige, M. C. 1974. Axon and cell numbers in the developing nervous system. *Br. Med. Bull.* 107–11

265. Price, D. L. 1974. The influence of the periphery on spinal motor neurons. *Ann. NY. Acad. Sci.* 228:355–63

266. Purves, D., Sakmann, B. 1974. Membrane properties underlying spontaneous activity of denervated muscle fibres. *J. Physiol. London* 239:125–53

267. Purves, D., Sakmann, B. 1974. The effects of contractile activity on fibrillation and extrajunctional acetylcholine-sensitivity in rat muscle maintained in organ culture. *J. Physiol. London* 237: 157–82

268. Ramirez, B. U., Pette, D. 1974. Effects of long term electrical stimulation on sarcoplasmic reticulum of fast rabbit muscle. *FEBS Lett.* 49:188–90

269. Rash, J. E., Fambrough, D. 1973. Ultrastructural and electrophysiological correlates of cell coupling and cytoplasmic fusion during myogenesis in vitro. *Develop. Biol.* 30:166–86

270. Redfern, P., Thesleff, S. 1971. Action potential generation in denervated rat skeletal muscle. I. Quantitative aspects. *Acta Physiol. Scand.* 81:557–64

271. Reier, P. J., Hughes, A. 1972. Evidence for spontaneous axon degeneration during peripheral nerve maturation. *Am. J. Anat.* 135:147–52

272. Riley, D. A. 1973. Histochemical changes in ATPase activity during regeneration of adult skeletal muscle fibres. *Exp. Neurol.* 44:690–704

273. Riley, D. A. 1974. Factors affecting the conversion of cross-reinnervated skeletal muscles. *Am. J. Anat.* 140:609–15

274. Robbins, N. 1974. Long-term maintenance and plasticity of the neuromuscular junction. See Ref. 227, 953–59

275. Robert, E. D., Oester, J. T. 1970. Absence of supersensitivity to acetylcholine in innervated muscle subjected to a prolonged pharmacological block. *J. Pharmacol. Exp. Ther.* 174:133–40

276. Roth, S. 1973. A molecular model for cell interactions. *Q. Rev. Biol.* 48: 541–63

277. Salmons, S., Vrbová, G. 1969. The influence of activity on some contractile characteristics of mammalian fast and slow muscle. *J. Physiol. London* 201: 535–49

278. Samaha, F. J., Guth, L., Albers, R. W. 1970. The neural regulation of gene expression in the muscle cell. *Exp. Neurol.* 27:276–82

279. Sarkar, S. 1974. Purification, translation and characterization of messenger ribonucleic acid for myosin heavy chain. See Ref. 17, 172–84

280. Scharrer, E. 1965. The final common path in neuroendocrine integration. *Arch. Anat. Microscop. Morphol. Exp.* 54:359–70

281. Schiaffino, S., Pierobon Bormioli, S., Aloisi, M. 1972. Cell proliferation in rat skeletal muscle during early stages of compensatory hypertrophy. *Virchows Arch. B* 11:268–73

282. Schmitt, F. O. 1968. Fibrous proteins-neuronal organelles. *Proc. Nat. Acad. Sci. USA* 60:1092–1101

283. Schubert, D. 1973. Protein secretion by clonal glial and neuronal cell lines. *Brain Res.* 56:387–91

284. Schudt, C., Van der Bosch, J., Pette, D. 1973. Inhibition of muscle cell fusion by Mg^{2+} and K^+ ions. *FEBS Lett.* 32:296–98

285. Sharpless, S. K. 1964. Reorganization of function in the nervous system—use and disuse. *Ann. Rev. Physiol.* 26:357–88

286. Silinsky, E. M., Hubbard, J. I. 1973. Release of ATP from rat motor nerve terminals. *Nature* 243:404–5

287. Silver, A. 1974. *The Biology of Cholinesterases.* Amsterdam: North-Holland. 596 pp.

288. Singer, M. 1952. The influence of the nerve in regeneration of the amphibian extremity. *Q. Rev. Biol.* 27:169–200

289. Singer, M. 1974. Neurotrophic control of limb regeneration in the newt. *Ann. NY Acad. Sci.* 308–21

290. Singer, S. J., Rothfield, L. I. 1973. Synthesis and turnover of cell membranes. *Neurosci. Res. Progr. Bull.* 11:7–86

291. Smith, A. D. 1971. Summing up: some implications of the neuron as a secreting cell. *Philos. Trans. R. Soc. London B* 261:423–37

292. Smith, V. 1965. Changes in the enzyme histochemistry of skeletal muscle during denervation and reinnervation. *J. Neurol. Neurosurg. Psychiat.* 28:99–103

293. Sotello, C., Palay, S. L. 1971. Altered axons and axon terminals in the lateral vestibular nucleus of the rabbit. *Lab. Invest.* 25:653–71

294. Spemann, H. 1936. *Experimentelle Beiträge zu einer Theorie der Entwicklung.* Berlin: Springer. 296 pp.

295. Sreter, F. A. 1970. Effect of denervation on fragmented sarcoplasmic reticulum of white and red muscle. *Exp. Neurol.* 29:52–64

296. Sreter, F. A., Holtzer, S., Gergely, J., Holtzer, H. 1972. Some properties of embryonic myosin. *J. Cell Biol.* 55:586–94

297. Sreter, F. A., Gergely, J., Salmons, S., Romanul, F. 1973. Synthesis by fast muscle of myosin light chain characteristic of slow muscle in response to long term stimulation. *Nature* 241:17–19

298. Staudte, H. W., Exner, G. U., Pette, D. 1973. Effects of short term, high intensity (sprint) training on some contractile and metabolic characteristics of fast and slow muscle of the rat. *Pfluegers Arch.* 344:159–68

299. Steinbach, J. H., Heinemann, S. 1974. Nerve-muscle interactions in clonal cell cultures. See Ref. 47, 161–69

300. Stewart, D. M., Sola, O. M., Martin, A. W. 1972. Hypertrophy as a response to denervation in skeletal muscle. *Z. Physiol.* 76:146–67

301. Stonnington, H. H., Engel, A. G. 1973. Normal and denervated muscle. *Neurology* 23:714–24

302. Studitsky, A. N. 1959. *Experimental Surgery of Muscles.* Moscow: Akad. Nauk SSSR (in Russian)

303. Syrový, I., Gutmann, E., Melichna, J. 1972. The effect of denervation on contraction and myosin properties of fast and slow rabbit and cat muscles. *Physiol. Bohemoslov.* 21:353–61

304. Tennyson, V. M., Brzin, M., Slotwiner, P. 1971. The appearance of acetylcholinesterase in the myotome of the embryonic rabbit. An electron microscopic cytochemical and biochemical study. *J. Cell Biol.* 51:703–21

305. Teräväinen, H. 1968. Development of the myoneural junction in the rat. *Z. Zellforsch. Mikrosk. Anat.* 87:249–65

306. Thesleff, S. 1960. Supersensitivity of skeletal muscle produced by botulinum toxin. *J. Physiol. London* 151:598–607

307. Thesleff, S. 1974. Physiological effects of denervation of muscle. *Ann. NY Acad. Sci.* 228:89–103

308. Thesleff, S., Ward, M. R. 1975. Studies on the mechanism of fibrillation potentials in denervated muscle. *J. Physiol. London* 244:313–23

309. Thornton, C. S. 1970. Amphibian limb regeneration and its relation to nerves. *Am. Zool.* 10:113–18

310. Thornton, C. S., Thornton, M. T. 1970. Recuperation of regeneration in denervated limbs of *Amblystoma* larvae. *J. Exp. Zool.* 173:293–300

311. Titeca, J. 1935. Etude des modifications fonctionelles du nerf au course de la dégénerescence wallérienne. *Arch. Int. Physiol.* 41:1–56

312. Tolar, M. 1973. *Development of the*

Neuromuscular System in vitro. Prague: Avicenum. 111 pp. (in Czech)

313. Tolar, M., Hanzlíková, V., Gutmann, E. 1974. The effect of external factors on development of the chick skeletal muscle tissue in vitro. *Physiol. Bohemoslov.* 23:182–83

314. Tonge, D. A. 1974. Physiological characteristics of re-innervation of skeletal muscle in the mouse. *J. Physiol. London* 241:141–53

315. Tower, S. S. 1937. Function and structure in the chronically isolated lumbosacral spinal cord of the dog. *J. Comp. Neurol.* 67:109–32

316. Tuček, S. 1973. Choline acetylase activity in skeletal muscles after denervation. *Exp. Neurol.* 4:23–35

317. Tuček, S. 1975. Transport of choline acetyl transferase and acetylcholinesterase in the central stump and isolated segments of a peripheral nerve. *Brain Res.* 86:259–70

318. Turner, L. V., Manchester, K. L. 1973. Effects of denervation hypertrophy in rat diaphragm muscle on the activity of ribosomes and sap fractions in protein synthesis. *Biochim. Biophys. Acta* 299:612–20

319. Tweedle, C. D., Popiela, H., Thornton, C. S. 1974. Ultrastructure of the development and subsequent breakdown of muscle in aneurogenic limbs *(Ambystoma). J. Exp. Zool.* 190:155–66

320. Vrbová, G. 1963. The effect of motoneurone activity on the speed of contraction of striated muscle. *J. Physiol. London* 169:513–26

321. Vyskočil, F., Gutmann, E. 1969. Spontaneous transmitter release from motor nerve endings in muscle fibres of castrated and old animals. *Experientia* 25:945–46

322. Vyskočil, F., Vyklický, L. 1974. Acetylcholine sensitivity of the chick fast muscle after cross-union with the slow muscle nerve. *Brain Res.* 72:158–61

323. Vyskočil, F., Vyklický, L., Huston, R. 1971. Quantum content at the neuromuscular junction of fast muscle after cross-union with the nerve of slow muscle in the chick. *Brain Res.* 26:443–45

324. Watson, W. E. 1968. Observations on the nucleolar and total cell body nucleic acid of injured nerve cells. *J. Physiol. London* 196:655–76

325. Watson, W. E. 1970. Some metabolic responses of axotomized neurones to contact between their axons and denervated muscle. *J. Physiol. London* 210:321–43

326. Watson, W. E. 1974. Cellular responses to axotomy and to related procedures. *Br. Med. Bull.* 30:112–15

327. Weddell, G., Guttmann, L., Gutmann, E. 1941. The local extension of nerve fibres into denervated areas of skin. *J. Neurol. Psychiat.* 4:206–25

328. Weiss, P. 1934. In vitro experiments on the factors determining the course of the outgrowing nerve fibre. *J. Exp. Zool.* 68:393–448

329. Weiss, P., Hiscoe, H. B. 1948. Experiments on the mechanism of nerve growth. *J. Exp. Zool.* 107:315–95

330. Wheeler, D. D., Boyarsky, L. L., Brooks, W. H. 1966. The release of amino acids from nerve during stimulation. *J. Cell. Comp. Physiol.* 67:141–48

331. Yaffe, D. 1969. Cellular aspects of muscle differentiation. *Curr. Top. Develop. Biol.* 4:37–77

332. Young, J. Z. 1944. The functional repair of nervous tissue. *Physiol. Rev.* 22:318–74

333. Zacks, S. I. 1973. *The Motor Endplate.* Huntington, New York: Krieger. 495 pp.

334. Zak, R., Grove, D., Rabinowitz, M. 1969. DNA synthesis in the rat diaphragm as an early response to denervation. *Am. J. Physiol.* 216:647–54

335. Zalewski, A. A. 1969. Regeneration of taste buds after reinnervation by peripheral or central fibers of vagal ganglia. *Exp. Neurol.* 25:429–37

336. Zalewski, A. A. 1972. Regeneration of taste buds after transplantation of tongue and ganglia grafts to the anterior chamber of the eye. *Exp. Neurol.* 35:519–28

337. Zelená, J. 1957. The morphogenetic influence of innervation on the ontogenetic development of muscle spindles. *J. Embryol. Exp. Morphol.* 5:283–92

338. Zelená, J. 1964. Development, degeneration and regeneration of receptor organs. *Progr. Brain Res.* 13:175–213

339. Zelená, J., Hník, P. 1960. Absence of spindles in muscles of rats reinnervated during development. *Physiol. Bohemoslov.* 9:373–81

340. Zelená, J., Jirmanová, I. 1973. Ultrastructure of chicken slow muscle after nerve cross union. *Exp. Neurol.* 38:272–85

341. Zelená, J., Soukup, T. 1973. Development of muscle spindles deprived of fusimotor innervation. *Z. Zellforsch. Mikrosk. Anat.* 144:435–52

342. Zelená, J., Soukup, T. 1974. The differentiation of intrafusal fibre types in

rat muscle spindles after motor denervation. *Cell. Tissue Res.* 153:115–36

343. Zelená, J., Szentágothai, J. 1956. Ver-
lagerung der Lokalisation spezifischer
Cholinesterase während der Entwicklung der Muskelinnervation. *Acta Histochem.* 3:284–96

344. Zhenevskaya, R. P. 1954. Development
of innervation of muscle, restored by
means of the transplantation of minced
muscle tissue. *Dokl. Akad. Nauk SSSR*
96:217–20 (in Russian)

345. Zhenevskaya, R. P. 1974. *Neurotrophic
Regulation of Plastic Activity of Muscle
Tissue* Moscow: Nauka. 239 pp. (in
Russian)

HIGHER FUNCTIONS OF THE NERVOUS SYSTEM

❖1149

P. Buser

Laboratoire de Neurophysiologie Comparée, Université Paris VI, Paris, France

INTRODUCTION

The field covered by higher brain functions is as yet ill defined. In principle, it should extend to all functions that are not strictly sensory receptive or motor projective and which, according to traditional psychology, are somehow artificially divided into attention, perception, voluntary activity, higher integrations, learning, memory, etc. Having to make a choice—unavoidably oriented by personal biases and interests— I decided to concentrate on cognitive and elaborative mechanisms. The emphasis is on electrophysiological data, but ablation and stimulation studies also remain indispensable tools whose results deserve consideration here. Neurochemical and neuropharmacological investigations are not included as, up to now, they do not seem to have provided many new ideas in this field. Finally, due to the conciseness of this study, no specific section is devoted to memory, which, owing to its complexity, would require special attention.

ELECTROPHYSIOLOGICAL CORRELATES OF ATTENTION

To the neurophysiologist who tries to search for specific signs of attention, the operational criteria for such signs stand within a narrow "safety margin." Cells in various structures that selectively respond to complex categories of stimuli (objects, situations) (see below) in fact represent feature detectors of very high order and thus belong to perceptual mechanisms, unless it is demonstrated that their modality of response varies with attention shifts. Moreover if one searches for changes of response patterns caused by peripheral or central intercurrent stimuli, these changes must be short term; otherwise they belong to learning processes. Finally, one of the greatest problems to be overcome in attention studies is the difficulty of distinguishing between unspecific arousal effects (intensive aspect of attention) and the process of selection that eliminates irrelevant stimuli (its selective aspect) (8).

The often suggested hypothesis that selection of relevant stimuli is made at the input stage has been discussed. Theoretical studies (8, 50, 154, 210) have questioned this viewpoint; in fact, adequate filtering requires complex discrimination, likely to

217

be the privilege of the higher levels. Attention may instead be a multistaged process with selectivity pervading throughout the cognitive continuum from input to output, with parallel channels facilitating or inhibiting it. Evidence of controls in the sensory channels presents merely a partial aspect of the problem, as other controls may also come into play in later stages of integration and elaboration, in the form of "response sets" rather than "stimulus sets" (8, 15, 169). Although mainly speculative, these views may well be of use in preventing physiologists' tendencies to "hyperlocalize" the level at which attention-related changes may occur. Finally, another problem, often confused with but not identical to the preceding one, is whether attention is governed by a particular structure. The favorite candidate has been and still remains the reticular formation, but other systems may also come into play. Given these complex theoretical aspects, it is not surprising that data on attention mechanisms are rather heterogeneous.

1. The specific difference between arousal and selectivity was sought (89) by testing the excitability of the lateral geniculate body and visual cortex in cats pressing a lever in response to sound or light-stimuli: the excitability did not change during intense visual attention, but its reduction during intense auditory attention suggested a switching-off of the visual system. Not many other reports on similar specific changes are available from recent studies [see (201) for previous results].

Reticular influences on the sensory systems have long been under study and with varying results. It was thus found that auditory cortex cells responding to complex sounds in squirrel monkeys were unaffected by reticular activation (136), whereas in macaques, such cells changed responses depending on the level of arousal (127). During moderate inattention, tactile, auditory, and reticular stimulation facilitated transmission through the monkey lateral geniculate nucleus (LGN), but not at the visual cortex and not when the animal was fully awake (5). LGN thus seems to be a strategic structure in the reticular control of visual input with relation to shifts of attention (44). It was also reported that reticular influences act similarly on the various functional classes of cells identified in the visual system (4). However, a specific effect at the cortical level should also be considered (59). In the moderately alert cat, reticular stimulation affected neither the LGN responses to flicker nor the critical flicker-fusion (CFF) threshold, while facilitation occurred at low levels of arousal. Moreover, spontaneous facilitations were observed, which were not accompanied by changes in the overall reticular activity; this was taken as evidence that sensory selection may not be effected by reticular formation, but rather by other structures such as the thalamus. (73).

A somewhat different approach to selective attention showed that, in awake cats or monkeys, distinct discrete thalamocortical systems can independently develop rhythmic activities that appear localized over either the somatic or visual cortex. These rhythms are provoked by a shift of attention from the corresponding sensory domain (172). These "sectorized" thalamocortical synchronizations may be at the same time an index of and a basis for the mechanism of selective attention, as thalamocortical systems in a given pathway may be available for integration only when they are not engaged in clustered firing (94, 123, 171).

Going a step further into basic mechanisms, the question is posed as to the nature of the neuronal processes involved in selection. Recurrent inhibition has been suggested (210), but this hypothesis was criticized as an oversimplification (60). Exploration of the fundamental processes has been thorough in lower forms. Interesting and penetrating studies on habituation and sensitization at the synaptic level (22) may indeed provide explanations for the neuronal mechanisms of selection; they would require special review.

2. Another valuable approach to attention and cognitive processes is to investigate event-related phenomena, i.e. responses to sensory stimulations in simple [evoked potentials (EPs)] or complex [contingent negative variations (CNVs)] paradigms in animals and through averaging techniques of scalp recording in humans.

Evoked Potentials

Before weighing experimental findings, some things ought to be said about both the method's validity and its limitations.

EPs measure sensory transmission in the brain, but whether they represent processes that mediate subjective sensory experience remains disputable, especially for their early components (197). In cats, the visual detectability of stimuli has been shown to be accompanied by changes in the early response components in the lateral geniculate body (LGN) and the midbrain reticular formation (MRF), but not in the striate cortex; this was considered an indication that early detection may be subcortical (203). In humans, whether the least detectable scalp EP is related to the perceptual threshold remains unsettled (160, 183). Cortical stimulation in conscious humans also placed in question the perceptive value of early components (107).

In spite of valid efforts (see e.g. 27), the neuronal mechanisms underlying EPs are insufficiently known so that their behavioral correlates remain only at a descriptive level. The time may come when this difficulty is surmounted, lending a new heuristic value to EP studies.

In contrast to other periods, only a very few behavioral correlates of EPs have been reported recently in animals (see below). On the other hand, fairly stable correlations have been established between psychological variables and the attention and cognitive domains in humans, based on consideration of the latencies and polarities of the components of the scalp-averaged EPs. To summarize older findings (e.g. 197 for review), when attention was drawn to the source of stimulation (by giving precise instructions to the subject) an increase in EP amplitude ensued, whereas distraction or habituation often reduced EPs (after all other sources of change had been eliminated, such as artifactual reduction of input or changes in the background EEG). The following is a brief summary of recent studies in the field:

1. Auditory scalp EPs in response to brief sounds or clicks displayed not less than 15 distinct components (86, 152, 179): attention instructions left unchanged the first 11 (indicating absence of gating at early stations of the pathway) while increasing the negative N1 peak (80 millisec latency) and in certain cases the subsequent positive P2 (160 msec). Nonspecific effects of arousal and effects of predictability of the stimuli (217) were carefully ruled out.

2. More substantial increases occurred for the late positive component of EPs in response to various stimuli [called P3 or P300, given its peak latency (40), or "association potential" (163)] in connection with the information content of the eliciting stimulus (108).

Nevertheless, the categories of independent variables of the stimulus remain uncertain: P300 increases when unpredictable shifts occur in an ongoing repetitive series of stimuli (63), but also increases in response to stimuli implying significance, decision making, selective attention, etc (40, 42, 85, 86, 205). However, P300 was smaller with words than with nonsense sounds of equivalent physical properties, which again indicates the importance of novelty over significance (118, 184). To resolve the contradiction thus implied, two P3 components have been proposed that differ in topography and latency: P3a (240 msec), which is enhanced by unpredictability, and P3b (>300 msec), which subtends processing in active attention (190).

Briefly, it is plausible that, whereas an early component such as N1 represents an early stage of processing, which admits all sensory inputs having any one attribute in common, but which blocks irrelevant ones, P3 underlies the subsequent stages of processing sensory information and of comparison with "memorized templates."

Contingent Negative Variations

Another family of scalp potentials was discovered when a standard paradigm was employed, designated hereafter as S1-S2-R, where S1 is a warning stimulus followed after $\sim$ 1 sec by the S2 imperative stimulus by which the subject is requested to perform a standard task (push a button, press a lever, etc). A slow negative wave, CNV (contingent negative variation), develops in the interval S1–S2, then quickly returns to baseline after the motor performance (*CNV resolution*). One debate centered about the determination of the exact psychological variable involved. Because CNVs can develop when no motor task is performed (39), they cannot belong to "motor potentials" developing before self-paced movements (see below). Beyond this fact, no definite conclusion has been reached; nevertheless the following categories of variables have been proposed: holding readiness, preparing perceptual judgment, anticipating a reinforcer, preparing a cognitive decision, and conceptualizing a movement (85, 198), but not regulating the finer details of its execution, which probably accounts for the loose correlation between CNV amplitude and the reaction time of the task after S2 (114, 159). Finally, expectancy of S2 was considered more important than the intention to respond to it (24, 168). CNVs were, at one time, thought to include several components: a rolandic ("central") one more strictly linked to task performance and a frontal shift depending upon the uncertainty of the subject. This multiplicity of components (such as those of EPs) may indeed explain some of the contradictions that have arisen regarding the determining variables (93).

CNV resolution calls for some discussion. Some variables have been shown to accelerate the return to baseline; moreover, this return actually initiates a positive poststimulus deflection whose identity with the P3 EP component in response to the imperative stimulus has been postulated and refuted (38, 42, 211, 216, 218). Using complex tasks and complex paradigms with three stimuli, it could be shown (211) that CNV resolution is not dependent on the overt response, nor on the final decision, but possibly on a coarse sensory recognition of the stimulus.

Even more than EPs, the physiological mechanisms of CNVs remain almost completely unknown and CNVs therefore tend to be ignored by analysts. It is true that slow shifts were recorded in animals in various conditions at several brain sites including the subcortex (13, 41). However, whether these shifts are of dendritic origin or due to glial ionic exchanges or to vascular changes remains unknown (118, 158), in spite of results illustrating correspondences between negative slow potentials and unit firing in the thalamus and cerebral cortex (165).

PERCEPTUAL MECHANISMS

According to traditional associative thinking, the levels of complexity in cortical operations are spatially segregated. Sensory reception is performed in primary fields while perceptual or "encoding" processes occur in "association areas" lying in their vicinity.

The following examples may serve to indicate whether recent investigations favor this conceptualization.

The Monkey Visual System

Visual agnosia is one of the symptoms of the Klüver-Bucy syndrome after temporalectomy; later studies have confirmed that, in the monkey, temporal areas participate in visual discrimination (212). Since then, new data have accumulated and deserve comment.

Anatomically (79, 212), the monkey's higher visual system includes the following elements: (a) striate area (area 17, V1); (b) areas 18 (V2) and 19 (V3), which form the *circumstriate belt* (CSB); and (c) the inferotemporal cortex (IT). V1 is cortico-cortically projected to CSB, then to IT, presumably through an intermediate area called the *prelunate gyrus*. V1 receives point-to-point retino-geniculate projections, and V2–V3 and IT receive projections from the pulvinar nucleus. The latter in turn receives fibers from the superior colliculus and V1. It then projects to pulvinar, to the superior colliculus and to limbic nuclei (amygdala) and basal ganglia. The flow diagram thus clearly indicates that CSB and IT receive information from multiple sources: cortico-cortical from V1 and CSB, subcortical from the superior colliculus through the pulvinar nucleus, and transhemispheric from contralateral IT.

ABLATION STUDIES   Ablation studies have thoroughly documented the functional differences between the various areas. (a) After extensive ablation of V1, it is not only the sensitivity to total flux that is retained (Klüver's original conclusions), but also some space localization, some brightness, color, and even shape discrimination that pose the problem of takeover of function [partly solved by demonstrating the role of the accessory optic tract (146)]. (b) Ablation of CSB (176) had variable effects: discrimination impairments were observed by some authors but not by others. (c) Regarding IT lesions, a distinction is now made between those of the posterior part (near CSB), which affect attention to and perception of stimuli and those of the more anteriorly situated cortex, which elicit a true retrograde amnesia in visual perception (agnosia, as commonly understood) (30, 31). In all cases, the basic visual performances were left intact. (*d*) Pulvinar (202) and collicular lesions (see below) also impaired visual discrimination.

SINGLE UNIT EXPLORATIONS   The characteristics of the feature detectors in V1 and CSB of monkeys are well known, but in lesser detail, than in the cat, regarding segregation among simple, complex, and hypercomplex cells. IT cells were recently found (79) to exhibit specific properties: long latency following the onset of light; large receptive fields, all of which included the fovea; reaction of some cells to moving slits, some to colors, and some to significant objects. The transitional area between CSB and IT was shown (232) to contain a high percentage of cells sensitive to movement, and it was suggested that this area feeds information on movement into the superior colliculus.

These data raise a variety of questions that extend far beyond the particular case: (*a*) The picture that begins to emerge is that of a mosaic of cortical areas with spatial segregation between simple and more sophisticated operations (156, 232). The "wiring" is even more complex, however, since subcortical projections also participate. Much remains to be investigated to clarify the functional importance of this complex interplay of redundant channels. Unit explorations in the pulvinar (124) revealed neurons with receptive field properties fairly similar (but not identical) to those at IT. An interesting observation was that pulvinar lesions increased the size of receptive fields in IT, which implies a modulating influence of the subcortical route. (*b*) The cortico-cortical pathway V1—→IT does not preserve topographical organization; this "break" in the point-to-point correspondence may be considered prerequisite to a system that should be capable of extracting or transferring any message configuration (18). (*c*) A further stage of complex integration would consist of intermodality operations. At this step, very little is yet known on the monkey; IT exploration did not reveal plurimodality, and data on other cortical fields were obtained essentially under chloralose anesthesia, except for some recent data (see below). (*d*) It also remains to be decided whether cortical areas here represent end stations or if they transfer messages to subcortical structures, by either feed-forward (to basal ganglia or limbic structures) or feedback (into the ascending visual route) (156).

The Auditory System (Cat and Monkey)

The mechanism for recognition of sound patterns is seemingly not as amply documented as that for vision. The traditional theory (36, 52) of tuning curves with bandwidth narrowing from the brain-stem level through the medial geniculate body (MGN) with tonotopic organization at the acoustic cortex appears fairly obsolete now. Studies on unanesthetized animals have revealed neurons in the MGN and acoustic cortex and even in the inferior colliculus that display a variety of complex response patterns, a thorough catalog of which is not possible here (2, 12, 195). Besides cells responding to complex stimuli (frequency- or amplitude-modulated sounds, temporal tone sequences, etc), the most interesting data concern cells in the squirrel monkey and macaque auditory cortices that respond specifically to vocalization features of their own species (66, 127, 135, 220, 221, 227). Some general remarks can be made: (*a*) It seems that the auditory pathway, as opposed to the visual system, displays complex feature extraction early in its ascending route (inferior colliculus). (*b*) As yet no clear indication exists of further processing in association areas. (*c*) One condition for observing complex feature extraction seems to be the absence of anesthesia.

The Cat Suprasylvian Cortex

In the cat, several cortical areas may be considered "associative" by classic definitions: in particular, the suprasylvian cortex, where sensory projections of various modalities could be identified and where a large number of cells were found to be polymodal, especially under chloralose anesthesia. In the visual domain, suprasylvian cells were characterized by their large receptive fields, low degree of orientation specificity, and responsiveness to movement regardless of direction (45); in the auditory domain, cells had broad and relatively shallow tuning curves, which again indicated poor specificity (213). The source of these sensory activations has been only partially studied; it may be either direct from the primary cortices or from the subcortex, chiefly lateralis posterior-pulvinar, as recently confirmed (161).

Ablations of the suprasylvian gyrus have been more or less inconclusive to date with regard to visual brightness or form discrimination. At most, they have been effective only in animals previously deprived of visual cortex, indicating that the gyrus might be involved in the residual discrimination of these cats (223). Ablation of all the cortex surrounding the primary acoustic cortex also failed to impair complex sound discrimination (99). It may well be that adequate tests have not yet been developed for investigating the feline association areas separately, or that the function of these areas is not sufficiently differentiated to allow independent analysis.

THE MOTOR ELABORATION SYSTEMS

New concepts (borrowed mainly from system analysis) have greatly altered older theories that organized movements are primarily a chain of reflexes. The flow chart of a motor act now introduces operational loops and blocks (some of which had indeed been proposed long ago, but in dispersed order) into logical systems (program, comparator, external feedback, open-loop action, internal feedback, corollary discharge, etc) (90). The present selection of data is restricted to problems relating to purposive motion in general and includes some fundamental concepts of higher elaboration (omitting the more specific aspects of movement organization irrelevant to this review).

Preparation of Somatic Movements

The concept of a "preparatory" or decision-making phase of movement, when electrophysiological changes are shown to occur before the movement begins, seems to be the outcome of various recent experiments. Data from both humans and animals are considered.

Scalp recordings aided by averaging techniques led to the discovery of human scalp potentials that develop when the subject performed a self-paced movement (32, 207). 1. Given a precisely timed, unilateral localized (e.g. index) movement, several successive components were distinguishable: (*a*) a slow negative shift starting 800 msec before the electromyographic sign of motion [Bereitschaftspotential (BP), readiness potential (RP), or N1 component]; (*b*) a "premotion positivity" (PMP or P1) preceding the movement by ~80 msec; (*c*) a negative motor potential (MP or N2) 50 msec before the movement; (*d*) a mainly positive deflection that immediately follows the movement [Reafferenzpotential (RAP) or P2]. 2. RP is bilateral over rolandic and parietal sectors; PMP is bilateral parietal, whereas MP is generated only contralaterally to the performed movement (96). 3. It is agreed that RP (N1) precedes movement initiation, while RAP certainly follows it (as it stems from afferent information triggered by the movement); researchers disagree on whether PMP and MP precede movement (33, 104) or coincide with its initiation (207). 4. RPs tend to increase as motivation and attention are intensified [significance of the task, emotional load, certainty of a go-stimulus (113, 173)]. The functional meaning of these potentials, beyond showing that "something" happens almost 1 sec before a self-paced movement is performed, remains undetermined and therefore merely speculative.[1]

Single-neuron analysis in cats and monkeys performing stereotyped movements pointed to the existence in various structures of cells that discharge before the initiation of the movements. 1. In monkeys, such "anticipatory" cells were found in the precentral cortex, but not in the postcentral gyrus; in a reaction-time task, anticipation was particularly clear when the animal was visually triggered. With a kinesthetic triggering (passive stretch), precession was very short in contrast, suggesting in that case a "cortical reflex" rather than a preparatory process (see below) (56, 57, 112, 178). In still another study, where the animals were "instructed" concerning a forthcoming perturbation in the grasped handle, motor cortex cells changed activity soon after the instruction, much before the perturbation (58). 2. Other structures were shown to participate directly in voluntary movement in the monkey; some of these displayed cells that anticipated its initiation [n. ventralis lateralis (94, 123), putamen, pallidum (33), cerebellar cortex, dentate, and interpositus cerebellar nuclei (200)], but others, like the caudate nucleus, did not (19).

The functional meaning of these precessions remains to be explored. These activities logically underlie the preparation of the movement, but they may more precisely correspond to distinct mechanisms. Indeed, some may represent higher level integration before movement; others may more directly subtend a presetting of spinal mechanisms or the postural preparation of the movement (58, 123).

Motor Program

The question of whether the sequence and characteristics of contractions in a given movement are predetermined or if they are servo-controlled during execution is of

[1]Motor potentials present the same difficulties as other slow phenomena: they are not easily interpreted in terms of active neuronal substrate.

considerable general interest. Many interesting contributions to this discussion cannot reasonably be considered herein (see 145).

Information on preprogramming generally relies on the observation that one or another parameter of the movement—force, velocity, acceleration—is determined at its initiation, as a function of the required final goal or performance. This was shown, for instance, in monkeys (17) and humans (125). Although it would be naive to think of any particular structure as a program generator, the hypothesis (104) that fast ballistic movements are preprogrammed in the cerebellum and slow ramp ones are organized in the basal ganglia has found some support: cells in the monkey putamen were shown to fire only in connection with slow movements of the animal (33). In addition, eye saccades were affected by cerebellar lesions (104). However, it is likely that the cerebellum, especially the dentate nucleus, is involved in the preprogramming of all kinds of limb movements (122) as shown in experiments with cryogenic blockade of the dentate in monkeys (17).

An interesting case of interaction between reflex-regulated and programmed movement was reported after studying eye-head coordination in head turning in the monkey. Eye-head coordination is normally regulated by the labyrinth and so would be of reflex origin. On the other hand, labyrinthectomized animals can learn a new strategy with preprogrammed compensatory eye movement, which illustrates the shift from reflex control to internal programming (35). Finally, it is likely that the alternative thus formulated is largely oversimplified, and that servo-control and preprogramming (with subroutines) may be intricately combined at any time during movement. The ability to shift permanently from one mode to the other may be one expression of functional plasticity.

Feedback Loops in Movements

In order to determine the importance of feedback in motor operations, well-known behavioral approaches were carried out to "open the loop." Animals that had been prevented from birth from seeing their limbs moving could display (82, 84) visual placing on a broad surface; precise visuomotor guidance, however, required previous visual experience of a limb in motion. The problem of whether somatic feedback is indispensable for correct performance of movement after visual deprivation has also been recently investigated (14). The fact that there was recovery after transection of the dorsal roots in the monkey forelimb suggested the possible role of internal feedback loops of a type recalling corollary discharge. Recently, through electrophysiological analysis, several control circuits have been identified or suggested.

THE SOMATIC CORTICAL LOOP   Starting with the fact that low threshold muscle afferents project on to the motor cortex, it was proposed that a "cortical servo-loop" directly controls motor elaboration by Ia afferents from a given muscle acting on colonies of pyramidal tract cells that command the muscle of origin itself (55, 150). Also, in humans (120) it was indirectly proved that some stretch "reflexes" can in fact pass via the cerebral cortex. However, the cortical loop is probably more complicated than initially supposed, first of all because it seems to involve multiple parallel input channels (132) and, second, because recently Ia projections were not found in area 4 but in the neighboring somatic sector 3a (151, 215, see also 231), which would suppose a transcortical route. The main criticism of this hypothesis is that it represents at first glance a rather mechanistic and rigid concept of motor cortex operations. Consequently, it is of interest that data have been reported indicating that the loop can be gated on and off or modulated by instructions and learning as shown in experiments on monkeys (58).[2]

EXAMPLES OF COROLLARY DISCHARGES   One current hypothesis concerning motor control organization is that afferent inputs are controlled during motor execution through an internal loop. The cat dorsal column nucleus has repeatedly been shown to be one of the strategic sites at which this internal loop control may be exercised in the somatic domain (26, 72). Changes in somatic EPs to hand stimulation either during active voluntary clenching of the hand being stimulated (106) or on decreases of conscious perception of an electrical stimulus before or during voluntary finger flexion (25) were interpreted as signs of corollary blocking actions in the somatic pathway in humans.

Passing to eye movements, traditionally it has been similarly inferred that the excitability of the visual pathway is modified during ballistic eye movements ("saccadic suppression"). Such modifications were sought in lateral geniculate nucleus (LGN) and visual cortex. They were found in cat LGN, but proved to be linked to the properties of the retinal network (1, 139, 140), and not to a corollary action. The monkey LGN displayed no changes, but a neighboring area (pregeniculate nucleus) did so (20). The cat visual cortex, on the other hand, showed a feasible corollary facilitation (1).

THE CIRCUITRY FOR VISUOMOTOR GUIDANCE   The problem of the visual guidance of movements covers a number of distinct analytical aspects, two of which are briefly considered here.

1. The first aspect involves how the motor cortex can, in fact, guide limb movements. While visual projections to the cat's associative areas are now generally accepted, those to motor cortex remain controversial, as results obtained initially under chloralose anesthesia were difficult to confirm in other types of preparations. These discrepancies will have to be explained before we can know how those visuomotor strategies, which necessarily implicate the pyramidal tract, are organized. Data from chloralose studies involving visual receptive field mappings have recently shown that (69, 100, 170, 199) (a) visual inputs converge with preference upon units receiving somatic afferents from the body axis; such cells may also receive vestibular inputs; (b) visual fields are very large, each including fovea; (c) 50% of the cells display movement sensitivity, part of them directionally sensitive. In one of these studies (100), no movement-sensitive cells were found. A related problem concerns the pathway by which the motor cortex is steered visually; the traditional view of a cortico-cortical route from the visual cortex in monkeys was recently upheld by behavioral experiments after surgery (80). Electrophysiological investiga-

[2]More complex loops such as those through the cerebellum are not considered here.

tions have favored instead (18) a complex pathway through subcortical relays, including the superior colliculus, and are reinforced by data on the role of this latter structure (see below). Theoretical speculations, partly strengthened by clinical data, have postulated the cerebellum or basal ganglia as intermediary, assuming that cortico-cortical reflexes do not exist (104).

2. The superior colliculus probably represents one of the most interesting structures, since it combines sensory reception and motor integration. The physiological studies on its receptive fields are almost inseparable from those dealing with its role in visually guided operations: eye-head fixation and visual attention [see (116) for reviews].

The characteristics of collicular cell responses have been investigated in the cat and in various species of monkey (28, 74, 75, 166, 206, 214, 228, 229). (a) The retinotopic organization was largely confirmed; receptive fields tended to be larger with eccentricity; cells in the deeper layers had very large fields. Most units were binocularly driven; they were very sensitive to moving stimuli but displayed poor (or no) shape specificity (thus contrasting with the visual cortex), indicating only coarse visual discrimination capacities. Cats, but not monkeys, displayed direction selectivity; in primates this property is possibly transferred to the temporal cortex (see above). (b) Collicular cell firings hinted at a close relationship with the oculomotor system: in monkeys some cells in the superficial layers increased firing when the stimulus became the target for a saccade. Cells in deeper layers were found to discharge prior to a saccade, regardless of the stimulus used for eliciting it. The background activity of other cells became inhibited during spontaneous eye movements, even in the dark. On the other hand, no neurons discharged in relation to head movements. (c) Collicular cells (mainly the deeper ones) are under the close control of the visual cortex (as shown by ablation or cooling experiments) (162, 177); the visual cortex $\longrightarrow$ superior colliculus pathway is essentially excitatory and clearly organized such that superior colliculus and visual cortex cells with receptive fields overlapping in the visual field are interconnected (117). (d) Indices of complex sensory integration in the colliculus were also found in relation to visual attention and tracking: first, cells that respond to a novel stimulus appearing in the field and become quickly habituated with repetition; second, cells that respond to objects approaching the animal's head (77) or that discharge in relation to the animal's attention to a target in the visual field, or, third, cells that exhibit polymodal responses to auditory and somatic stimuli. In cats (77), audiovisual cells required moving stimuli and preferred the same direction for both modalities; somatovisual cells were "fovea-face" or "periphery-forelimb." Visuovestibular interactions were also described (9).

Collicular ablations have led to rather different results in cats and monkeys, presumably indicating the relative loss of their importance in primates. Cats (189) had reduced eye movements after bilateral superior collicular ablation, losing their ability to scan adequately; the learning of pattern discrimination was impaired whereas discrimination learned preoperatively was only slightly affected. It was therefore suggested that distinct neural structures served in initial learning and engram storing and that learning was impaired because of a lack of coordination between retinal input and limb-movement information. After section of the chiasma, relearning of dark-light discrimination through the ipsilateral eye was impaired in cats when the ipsilateral colliculus was lesioned after ablation of the cortex, but not when only the colliculus was lesioned (222). It was also interesting to compare the development of visual behavior in the kitten (orienting to stimulus in visual field at 16 days of age, and other visual guidances at 25 days) with the ontogeny of collicular receptive fields (which acquire their adult properties between 15 and 35 days) (141). At least partial visual neglect was observed in monkeys as well (98), with brightness discrimination influenced, but not as severely as when tectal and cortical lesions were combined (219). These and other results clearly indicate that the colliculus may play a role in gaze focusing (229) on a given area of the visual field, but they also cast doubt on the well-developed theory of a dichotomy in the visual system, one system serving localization (where?) and the other for shape discrimination and recognition (what?). The close cortical control of the superior colliculus together with the fact that functional compensation can occur between the superior colliculus and the visual cortex refute this oversimplified view. A theory of visual guidance that would more accurately define the contributions of the visual cortex and the colliculus is still lacking.

CIRCUITRY FOR SOUND LOCATION   A possible parallel to the visual system has been attempted regarding a "what-where" dichotomy in the auditory system. According to recent data based on older anatomical findings, a division might exist between the ventral pathway (ventral cochlear nucleus, trapezoid body, superior olive) subserving head and eye responses to sound ("auditory reflexes") and the dorsal pathway (dorsal cochlear nucleus, lateral lemniscus, inferior colliculus, medial geniculate body, auditory cortex) involved in auditory discrimination (53). The ventral nucleus has uncomplicated excitatory sound responses with restricted tuning curves, whereas the dorsal nucleus responds with complex frequency distribution (54). Nevertheless this view suffers from the same weaknesses as that of the visual pathway because higher levels of the auditory pathway also display directionally selective cells (48, 51, 185). Moreover, cells were found in the cat visual cortex that responded to sounds; their participation in audiovisual localization in space was suggested (62).

HIGHER LEVELS OF INTEGRATION

Beyond studies on perception or volitional movements, two other aspects of higher brain operations have been explored. The first is in the context of the localizationist view of analyzing areas that have long since been known, both from clinical work on humans and from experimental studies on monkeys and apes, to govern the highest integrations. The other represents a more holistic approach to cognitive functions whose immense interest–split-brain animals and commissurotomized patients–has been widely recognized.

The Prefrontal Cortex

The defects after lesions in the dorsolateral prefrontal granular cortex in monkeys are well known (see e.g. 192). Corresponding to these data, cells were recorded in this area during various tasks requiring spatial cues and/or delays. In a delayed response (DR) paradigm, cells were found that increased firing long before the motor response; some of them fired during the delay period after cue presentation. These were interpreted either as expressing attention related to stored information ("short-term memory cells") (67) or as specifically involved in the kinetic task with visual cue (105). In a delayed alternation (DA) paradigm (137, 138), cells were also mainly characterized as discharging in relation to the visual guidance of the motor task. In a visually guided task with no delay, it was confirmed that some of the cells were activated in connection with the visuomotor operation itself [such cells were not fired by just the visual stimulus nor by just pressing (174) whereas other cells were activated prior to any movement, and still others while the monkey was waiting for the light signal. Cells discharging to light were shown to have large receptive fields (125). The evidence regarding the role of the prefrontal cortex is far from conclusive; a recent study concerning its cryogenic blockade again suggested that it ensures purposive attention to cues (and not simply to the spatial features of the stimuli) (68).

The Parietal Cortex

The effects of lesions of the posterior parietal cortex in the nondominant hemisphere have been well described in human (apraxia for dressing, constructional apraxia, disorders of the topographical sense, etc). Monkeys with lesions of Brodmann's areas 5 and 7 also display a complex deficit, probably with a cognitive component (defect of tactual perception of complex objects) and a more praxic one (defect of stereotactic exploration and orientation within the surrounding extrapersonal space) (81, 130). This region receives cortico-cortical projections from area SI and, in the sensory domain, cells in area 5, with large receptive fields, were shown to be excited by non-noxious joint rotations or by light mechanical deformations of skin and deep tissues. The most puzzling elements were those driven maximally by contact between two separate body parts (175). More recent recordings (130) in monkeys performing motor reaching tasks showed cells in area 5 that only discharged when the animal explored its extrapersonal space to reach a given goal, regardless of whether the cue was somesthetic or visual. Area 7 exhibited some cells with still higher processing properties; they fired in connection with visual attention directed to the surroundings (visual fixation, visual tracking) (91, 130).

Split-Brain Studies and Hemispheric Dominance

Animal investigations on the standard split preparation with all three commissures —anterior commissure (AnC), corpus callosum (CC), and posterior commissure (PC)—and massa intermedia cut, and optic chiasm divided are perhaps now less numerous than in preceding periods. Recent studies mainly set out to define the particular roles of AnC vs CC or to define which tasks still exhibit contralateral generalization after commissurotomy, indicating organization at lower untransected levels. Delayed alternation and delayed response tasks learned unilaterally could still be transferred after commissurotomy in monkey (230) (because they are based upon memories of body postures) while a go-no-go visual discrimination or manually learned skills (based on exteroceptive cueing) could not. In cats, the visual interhemispheric transfer seems to be carried out by CC alone; in monkeys both AnC and CC (splenium) participate with functional equivalence or possibly with some differences, depending on the task imposed (193, 194, 204).

Split-brain experiments also provided insight into the problems of hemispheric asymmetry and specialization: indications of left-hand predominance were reported in monkeys that had not been operated upon (21); predominance of the right hemisphere was shown in monkeys with split brain, although preference could be shifted by differential rewarding (71); cats with split brain (167) exhibited greater efficiency in pattern discrimination in one hemisphere (depending on the animal). The prefrontal dominance in delayed response tasks was shown to be the result of initial training in monkeys (191). Whether all observed lateralizations in animals are due to early training remains to be seen.

Finally, the "dynamic" aspect of commissural influences was considered in animals with a sectioned chiasma; the AnC or CC splenium was spared but still prepared for interruption (43). Evidence is that the untrained hemisphere could accomplish a learned task so long as the splenium was uncut, suggesting that no spontaneous crossing of the engram into the untrained side had occurred during learning and that the splenium was active during readout of the engram. These observations point out the necessity of clearly distinguishing between transfer during learning and readout of stored engrams during retrieval and performance.

Patients having undergone complete section of CC, AnC, and probably PC, with some possible interruption of massa intermedia of the thalamus, were carefully examined (128, 134, 187). Routine speech, calculation, motor coordination, verbal reasoning, and recall abilities were not impaired. On the other hand, studies with lateralized tests have revealed some distinct capacities of the left and right hemispheres. To grossly simplify (and noting that all patients were right handed): 1. The left hemisphere performed all language skills (naming or writing words presented in right visual half-field, etc). 2. The right hemisphere displayed limited verbal comprehension. Naming or writing objects or colors in the left visual field required prolonged presentation; subjects did not obey orders flashed in this field; tactile stimuli from either half-body were recognized verbally, but the direction of a tactile stimulus when moved toward the left was not perceived (133). 3. The right hemisphere performed better than the left hemisphere in a variety of nonverbal tasks such as perceiving and manipulating spatial relationships, conceptualizing a complete stimulus configuration from spatial data, etc. 4. The right hemisphere also proved to be superior in comprehending auditory verbal input and in tactile verbal recognition. To briefly sum up these ideas, the dominant hemisphere analyzes the inputs sequentially for details while the minor hemisphere deals with data in terms of overall patterns and spatial relationships. Finally, tests or activities tending to focus hemispheric activities into a general motor attitude or posture, overall attention, or emotional response failed to yield evidence for specific lateralization because of either bilateral representation or participation of unifying lower brain-stem structures.

Hemispheric Dominance in Humans

A related problem concerns hemispheric dominance in normal human subjects as investigated through behavioral or electrophysiological indices. From experiments on normal subjects, it has been established that: 1. Spoken digits are best perceived with the ear opposite to the speech-dominant hemisphere and nonverbal material (musical input) by the other ear (16). 2. Right-handed subjects, measured for their reaction times, confirmed right visual field superiority for speed of response to letters and of left for recognition of faces (164). It has also been suggested (101) that visual information of low association value, as opposed to that of high association value, does not readily traverse the corpus callosum.

Speech dominance and hand preference have usually been considered correlative, with left-speech dominance in right-handed subjects. In reality the problem is more complex (128, 187); clinical results obtained with the Wada amytal test indicate that: 1. Only 92% of right-handed individuals possess left-speech dominances. 2. Instances are known of right-handed persons with right-speech dominance. 3. In left-handed and ambidextrous patients, the pattern of speech dominance is hard to predict; it is not an exact reversal of that in right-handers. 4. Left-handed individuals are more likely to have left-speech dominance than right-speech dominance, as left-handedness is far more common than right-speech dominance. 5. In left-handed or ambidextrous individuals who suffered left hemispheric damage early (before age 6), a majority possessed right-speech dominance, indicating that reorganization had probably occurred.

Given these facts, it could be expected that indices of speech dominance would be found by using asymmetries in gross potentials (the practical reason is to avoid usage of the amytal test); the general assumption is that verbal processing is localized in the left hemisphere and visuospatial functions in the right hemisphere (in left-speech dominant subjects). Let us briefly consider these data, which, as is seen later, lead to conflicting and still unclear conclusions. 1. EPs compared when produced by verbal or nonverbal auditory stimuli showed differences in some cases, as N1-P2 were larger on the left hemisphere in response to verbal stimuli. Asymmetry seemed more generally the rule however, because it occurred also with auditory stimuli that were meaningful but nonverbal (126) or with visually presented stimuli (208). In fact, even coherence studies showed the predominance of auditory EPs in the dominant hemisphere and of visual EPs in the minor hemisphere (29). Other studies on the P300 component using verbal vs nonverbal stimuli came to the opposite conclusion, that is, no asymmetry was detected (64, 65, 184). 2. CNV asymmetries were also explored: Marsh & Thompson (121) failed to demonstrate significant hemispheric differences in verbal or nonverbal discrimination tasks, whereas CNVs were almost always larger than those with nonverbal stimuli. On the contrary, greater CNVs were found in the dominant hemisphere during performances using numerical imperative stimuli in arithmetic operations or when using meaningful polysyllabic words. On the other hand, CNVs in commissurotomized patients, once a unilateral expectancy was created, were identical in both hemispheres, with no difference between the "warned" and the "unwarned" side (85). 3. Concerning the "motor potentials," which were previously discussed, two somewhat different findings were reported: these were of slightly but significantly larger amplitude in right-handed subjects, over the dominant hemisphere (whatever side the movement was performed), while no such preponderence could be found in left-handed subjects. But it had also been observed that, in the majority of cases, motor potentials in response to words were larger than those to simple vocalization on the left hemisphere only (see 32). A summary of the most recent data in this field should soon appear (34).

LEARNING AND PLASTICITY

One of the most promising approaches to our understanding of higher brain operations rests on studies on progressive changes as a consequence of experience. Two aspects are considered here. One is traditional, since it concerns neurophysiological investigations of learning in a broad sense, i.e. how a "connection" can be progressively established such that a signal stimulus determines a response. The second is a rather new approach that may answer an old problem, i.e. how far progressive changes can occur in the brain during ontogeny as a result of early experience.

Learning

Electrophysiological indices of the learning process were sought at various levels using coarse or single unit activity. Two sets of data were obtained through gross recording from various brain sites in cats being trained with a conditional stimulus-unconditional stimulus (CS-US) paradigm (95). After a steady CS had been repeatedly paired with an intermittent US, its application would determine anticipated electrophysiological rhythms at US frequency. With an intermittent CS, EPs that developed at each CS had a late component, if and only if the conditioned response (CR) were going to be performed (an observation somewhat relevant to those on P300 in human). In both groups of data, it was stressed that the observed "labeled phenomena" (frequency-specific rhythms or late EP components) were recorded from numerous brain sites, thus giving the picture of a holistic process (6). These phenomena were not due to unspecific effects such as arousal, but merely represented the sign of a "readout process" in a specific memory system.

Relatively few additional studies have been reported on specific changes of EPs during learning (in contrast with previous periods). A study on monkeys (78) has shown that while they were acquiring visual discrimination, the most significant changes in EPs were observed in area 18 (CSB) (see above) and pulvinar, whereas, after reaching the criterion, the main differences in EPs were seen in the primary pathway at the lateral geniculate nucleus and V1, suggesting that distinct groups of structure may operate at different stages of learning.

A group of investigations on rats (37, 103, 109, 110, 143, 180–182) was based on integration of single unit activity during short-term learning of discrimination (auditory CS$^+$ for pellet and CS$^-$ not reinforced). An attempt was made to separate the possibly specific signs of "rerouting" of nerve impulses at onset of CS$^+$ from side effects due to nonspecific arousal, elaboration of motor response, motivational factors, etc. Two features were considered: the temporal course of the changes (early or late) of a structure's firing as learning went on, and the latency (short or long) of the newly appearing responses (relative to the CS$^+$). To sum up: 1. Several structures developed short latency accelerations to CS only (neocortex, hippocampus), others displayed nonspecific changes (reticular formation, posterior thalamus), and still others (midline thalamus, somatic, and visual pathways) were unaffected. Cells in the ventral forebrain showed inhibition to CS$^+$, most likely in relation to arousal. 2. In the course of learning, the ventral brain stem, ventral thalamus, and dentate gyrus were involved first, then the posterior thalamus, and only then the cortex. This finding does not confirm the older claim that the cortex plays a primary role early in learning. Various other single unit recordings during learning should also be mentioned, one of which (142) indicates that, during training, changes occur in the overall spontaneous activity of cells (not only in time-locking to CS); in another study, observations were made on changes of amygdala unit firing by simple pairing of sensory stimuli of distinct modalities [the preparation was paralyzed to avoid overt response (7)].

Significant changes in the cat motor cortex were demonstrated by various tests during a training procedure with double auditory CSs [click, producing a blink; hiss, eliciting nose twitch (49, 224)]. After training, the CS evoked a response of greater magnitude (more cells firing and at a higher rate) than after extinction. Another result was that the threshold of the cortical cells commanding the target muscle was progressively lowered due to increased synaptic bombardment (225). In other words, sensory projections onto the motor cortex can be modulated when the stimulus acquires significance (i.e. when it becomes a CS$^+$), indicating that sensory fields in this area display plasticity. It was also shown that a bilateral ablation of the motor area permanently impaired acquisition of the conditioned blink, while UC blinks were not affected (226).

These findings recall older studies that led to indecisive results and confused discussions regarding the importance of the cortex in the learning processes. This is certainly an oversimplification of the matter, since obviously not all types of learning are equivalent. Because the possibilities of a new "link" or "rerouting" are manifold due to redundancy and hierarchical superimposition of sensorimotor circuits, the final results from surgical cortical ablation may be quite unpredictable. Either (a) the cortex is indispensable, or (b) it simply operates a permanent control over the (indispensable) subcortical circuits, or (c) it really does not play a role. The fact that a learned performance is permanently lost after ablation logically implies case a, whereas quick recovery after ablation is usually interpreted in favor of c; in reality, it could also mask a b-type cortical action. The validity of b could then only be determined by using transitory cryogenic or pharmacological blockade (see 18).

Plasticity

After brain lesions, some functions may recover while others do not, which may explain the extreme positions expressed in the past, ranging from strict localization to equipotentiality in the brain (with every degree of intermediate stance). At least three groups of factors may account for these differences and discrepancies: 1. A given function may depend on a complex system, possibly neurochemically specific, which extends throughout several brain levels rather than being strictly localized. 2. Redundancy probably exists with only secondary and minute differences between parallel channels. 3. Functional reorganization may occur after lesions, due to the plasticity of the neuronal network (3). Given the multiplicity of what are probably intermingled factors, each particular case of functional recovery is likely to need special investigation, especially when the function in play belongs to integrations of a higher order.[3] Space precludes discussion of accumulated histological data that show the occurrence of reorganization of connectivity with demonstrated functional synapses in neural structures even in the adult (see 47). From the functional point of view, some of the conditions for recovery have been known a long time and have recently been discussed (47, 97): recovery is easier in, but is not the exclusive privilege of, early life; it is greatly facilitated by forced usage (23), and, above all, when lesions are performed in two or more stages instead of in a single stage (61, 196). Two examples may, however, illustrate the danger of hasty generalizations: infant monkeys showed no deficiency one year after a frontal lesion (in either delayed alternation or delayed response tests) because of compensation by the caudate nucleus; this subcortical takeover of function was no longer possible in the adult (192). On the other hand, pyramidotomized monkeys (of any age) recovered fine finger movements if and only if the parallel (redundant) extrapyramidal pathways (which terminate along with the pyramidal fibers) were left intact (Kuypers in 47).

The most recent and perhaps most interesting aspect of plasticity, which cannot be overlooked here since it implies some of the essential aspects of brain functioning, concerns the ontogenetic development of feature detectors in the cat visual pathways (visual cortex and superior colliculus). The fundamental problem, which for a long time opposed nativistic to empiricist views, has suddenly acquired new interest; it poses the question whether these detectors are indeed innate or if they depend on early experience for their characteristics. Hubel & Wiesel's original observation (see 10) that cells in the visual cortex of kittens with no visual experience, besides being binocular, already displayed orientation selectivity and that "prewiring" was thus present prior to experience was later challenged: 1. Visual cortex cells in dark-reared kittens were poorly or not at all orientation- and direction-selective (92, 148); a few hours of normal visual experience were sufficient to create specific receptive fields (92). 2. After kittens were reared in a selective environment—fixed stripes of given orientation (10, 149) or stripes moving in a given direction (205)—visual cortex cells

---

[3]This multiplicity of possible factors has for instance been mentioned as accounting for residual visual function after lesions of the central visual pathway in humans (153).

also displayed biases in their orientation or direction selectivity; the period of maximum sensitivity was 3–14 weeks of age and 1 hr visual exposure again was sufficient. 3. Monocular deprivation (one eye sutured) led to dominance of visual cortex cells by the experienced eye; the deprived eye activated practically no cortical neurons. This effect was shown to be only somewhat reversible (70). A brief period of monocular deprivation at 5–14 weeks was sufficient to bring about this dominance (11); a brief exposure of one eye in binocularly deprived kittens (88, 147) had a similar effect. The monocular deprivation mainly affects the "Y" indirect pathway from the lateral geniculate nucleus to the visual cortex presumed to act secondarily upon the superior colliculus. 4. Monocular differential rearing (vertical stripes before one eye, horizontal before the other) determined visual cortex cells selectively activated by the "vertical eye" and others by the "horizontal eye" ("environmental surgery"); this monocular training could, however, be corrected later by a period of binocular viewing (87). This led to the conclusion that units which have achieved specificity in selective rearing are immune to further changes, but that new classes of cells with other receptive fields can be added through later experience; this type of plasticity may well be present throughout life (188).

Twenty years ago, Riesen had already described the behavioral deficiencies of the kitten deprived of pattern visual stimulation from birth (lack of visual placing, disorientation, etc), all of which disappeared after several hours of normal exposure (see 83). Further studies have tended to analyze this complex series of defects: monocular training in visually deprived animals required twice as many trials to reach criterion as did normals, but interocular transfer was excellent (see 83). Animals reared in specific environments showed good scores when tested with the experienced stimuli and failed to respond to perpendicular lines (70, 87). Finally, cats having undergone 4 months of selective deprivation in their early life were tested in adulthood and proved to still exhibit sequelae in their acuity (131). The predominance of early experience over endogenous properties thereby demonstrated suggested a theoretical model to explain how a self-organizing network with initially random connections could be taught specificity from experience (119).

Optokinetic nystagmus (OKN) was also shown to be influenced to a certain extent by specific rearing: kittens dark-reared with no visual experience displayed OKN (to stripes moving in any direction except downward), indicating a preexisting ability to respond to movement; animals reared in a moving environment, however, exhibited a better OKN for stripes moving in the opposite direction to which they had been exposed (209).

CONCLUDING REMARKS

One of the difficulties encountered in reviewing physiological investigations on behavioral mechanism and higher brain functions lies in the fact that psychologists have long proposed theories regarding each function that cannot be ignored by neurophysiologists, and yet bridging the gap is difficult. Psychologists, developing very subtle and elaborate molar approaches and theoretical viewpoints sometimes tend to simplify excessively when using data from physiological investigations in order to work out mechanistic explanations. The danger is just as great that physiological approaches to complex processes start from over-reduced theories or rather naive interpretations of psychological facts. Space limitations, as well as this author's limited competence have of course excluded review and adequate discussion of these borderline problems.

Most attempts to explore higher brain functions using neurophysiological methodology have implied common principles: (a) general reductionism, postulating that complex processes can be analyzed in elementary components; (b) localizationism, assuming that each function has a localized substrate; (c) reflexology, extrapolating from the basic stimulus-response (S-R) model to complex situations. This review is not the place to discuss the validity of these fundamental attitudes. In this context, some general aspects may nevertheless be underlined, to conclude this brief—and certainly incomplete—survey of "cognitive" brain operations.

1. Within the visual system, at least, recent studies have soundly confirmed associationist hypotheses claiming that distinct cortical areas subserve operations of different complexities. However, no extension to other systems is possible at this time: on the contrary, the present data indicate that, in the auditory system, complexity is processed within the primary pathway itself with no identified participation of nonprimary fields. The somatic domain is again different, as higher level tactual integrations now appear to be closely associated with praxic elaboration.

2. One may wonder to what degree all the parts of the sensory systems generally adopt a reductionist approach of analyzing shapes in simple terms, or whether one should foresee cells highly specialized at detecting certain complex features and even "object specific" cells. Complex gnosis has been hypothesized to be subserved by "gnostic units" that store perceptual features and, where component analysis is no longer possible, lend a holistic or gestalt view of perception and elaboration (102, 130).

3. It is likely, however, that the traditional view of cortico-cortical processes underlying this passage toward complexity will have to be revised, since the growing importance of information carried through subcortical routes to nonprimary areas is beginning to be recognized. The functional meaning of this redundancy still awaits its logical formulation.

4. The comments above also concern the value of localizationism in general. The debate is somewhat prejudiced, since factors such as redundant pathways or plasticity may mimic a holistic process. It is not unreasonable to believe that the extreme positions will eventually find a common denominator (111, 157).

5. Another problem not yet sufficiently explored is whether receptive or cortical fields display a transfer function such that output to subcortical centers is time locked to input, or whether they benefit from more sophisticated, dynamic input-output laws, with the possibility of a kind of "holding" process between the input and the output stages.

6. One would have expected a review on higher functions to be more specifically centered around neurophysiological exploration of the learning mechanisms themselves. In reality, only a limited number of new electrophysiological investigations seem to have been performed in recent years in this field; however, more and more

attention is being directed to distinguishing between the acquisition of learning and the retention of a well-established learned performance. It is likely that in the future an even more thorough investigation of the dynamic stages of acquisition will provide new insight into the underlying neuronal mechanisms.

A surprising contradiction now tends to pop up when one confronts the molar with the physiological approaches to higher brain operations, and it deserves a final mention. On the one hand, learning studies remain strictly in the behavioristic line, which ignores consciousness and mental states. On the other, more and more studies of events occurring within the brain reintroduce terms and designate functions that were ignored, rejected, or forbidden in S-R models. It seems as if behavioristic rejection of the language of conscious experience is becoming outmoded and that some of the mentalistic terminology is even being carried over to animal studies. Indeed several books and reviews have dealt with these mainly philosophical problems (46, 76, 115, 144, 155, 186).

Literature Cited

1. Adey, W., Noda, H. 1973. Influence of eye movements on geniculostriate excitability in the cat. *J. Physiol. London* 235:805–21
2. Aitkin, L., Prain, S. 1974. Medial geniculate body: unit responses in the awake cat. *J. Neurophysiol.* 37:512–21
3. Bach y Rita, P. 1975. Plastic brain mechanisms in sensory substitution. In *Cerebral Localization,* ed. P. Zülch. Berlin: Springer. In press
4. Bartlett, J., Doty, R. 1974. Influence of mesencephalic stimulation on unit activity in striate cortex of squirrel monkey. *J. Neurophysiol.* 37:642–52
5. Bartlett, J., Doty, R., Pecci-Saavedra, J., Wilson, P. 1973. Mesencephalic control of lateral geniculate nucleus in primates. III. Modifications with state of alertness. *Exp. Brain. Res.* 18:214–24
6. Bartlett, F., John, E. R. 1973. Equipotentiality quantified: The anatomical distribution of the engram. *Science* 181:764–67
7. Ben-Ari, Y., Le Gal La Salle, G., Champagnat, J. C. 1974. Lateral amygdala unit activity: I. Relationship between spontaneous and evoked activity. *Electroencephalogr. Clin. Neurophysiol.* 37:449–62
8. Berlyne, D. E. 1970. Attention as a problem in behavior theory. *Attention: Contemporary Theory and Analysis.* ed D. I. Mostofsky, 25–49 New York: Appleton-Century-Crofts. 447 pp.
9. Bisti, S., Maffei, L., Piccolino, M. 1974. Visuovestibular interactions in the cat superior colliculus. *J. Neurophysiol.* 37:146–55
10. Blakemore, C. 1974. Developmental factors in the formation of feature extracting neurons. *The Neurosciences, 3rd Study Program,* ed. F. O. Schmitt, F. G. Worden, 105–13. Cambridge: Mass: MIT Press, 1107 pp.
11. Blakemore, C., Van Sluyters, R. 1974. Reversal of the physiological effects of monocular deprivation in kittens: further evidence for a sensitive period. *J. Physiol. London* 237:195–216
12. Bock, G. R., Webster, W., Aitkin, L. 1972. Discharge patterns of single units in inferior colliculus of alert cat. *J. Neurophysiol.* 35:265–77
13. Borda, R. P. 1973. The relationship of CNV to behavior in animals *Electroencephalogr. Clin. Neurophysiol.* Suppl. 33:249–56
14. Bossom, J. 1974. Movement without proprioception. *Brain Res.* 71:285–96
15. Broadbent, D. E. 1970. Stimulus set and response set: two kinds of selective attention. See Ref. 8, 51–60
16. Broadbent, D. E. 1974. Division of function and integration of behavior. See Ref. 10, 31–41
17. Brooks, V. B. 1974. Some examples of programmed limb movements. *Brain Res.* 71:299–308
18. Buser, P., Angyan, L., Kitsikis, A., Mitova, L., Richard, D., Wiesendanger, M. 1972. Liaisons fonctionnelles entre cortex visuel et cortex moteur chez le chat: Bases neurophysiologiques de la coordination visuo-motrice. *Rev. Can. Biol.* Suppl. 31:103–14
19. Buser, P., Pouderoux, G., Mereaux, J. 1974. Single unit recording in the cau-

date nucleus during sessions with elaborate movements in the awake monkey. *Brain Res.* 71:337–44

20. Buttner, A., Fuchs, B. 1973. Influence of saccadic eye movements on unit activity in simian lateral geniculate and pregeniculate nuclei. *J. Neurophysiol.* 36:127–41

21. Butler, O. R., Francis, A. C. 1973. Specialization of left hemisphere in baboon. Evidence from directional preferences. *Neuropsychologia* 11:351–54

22. Carew, T., Kandel, E. 1974. The simplified model: studies on molluscs. In *Synaptic Transmission and Neuronal Interaction,* ed. M. V. L. Bennett, 339–83. New York: Raven

23. Chow, K. L., Stewart, D. L. 1972. Reversal of structural and functional effects of long term visual deprivation in cats. *Exp. Neurol.* 34:409–33

24. Cohen, J. 1973. The C.N.V. and visual recognition. *Electroencephalogr. Clin. Neurophysiol.* Suppl. 33:201–4

25. Coquery, J. M., Coulmance, M., Leron, M. C. 1972. Modifications des potentiels évoqués corticaux somesthésiques durant des mouvements actifs et passifs chez l'homme. *Electroencephalogr. Clin. Neurophysiol.* 33:269–76

26. Coulter, J. D. 1974. Sensory transmission through lemniscal pathway during voluntary movement in the cat. *J. Neurophysiol.* 37:831–45

27. Creutzfeldt, O., Kuhnt, U. 1973. Electrophysiology and topographical distribution of visual evoked potentials in animals. *Handbook of Sensory Physiology,* ed. R. Jung 7:595–646. Berlin: Springer

28. Cynader, M., Berman, N. 1972. Receptive field organization of monkey superior colliculus. *J. Neurophysiol.* 35:187–201

29. Davis, A., Wada, J. 1974. Hemispheric asymmetry: frequency analysis of visual and auditory evoked responses to nonverbal stimuli. *Electroencephalogr. Clin. Neurophysiol.* 37:1–9

30. Dean, P. 1974. The effect of inferotemporal lesions on memory for visual stimuli in rhesus monkeys. *Brain Res.* 77:451–69

31. Dean, P., Weizkrantz, L. 1974. Loss of preoperative habits in rhesus monkeys with inferotemporal lesions; recognition feature or relearning deficit? *Neuropsychologia* 12:299–311

32. Deecke, L., Becker, W., Grözinger, B., Scheid, P., Kornhuber, H. 1973. Human brain potentials preceding voluntary limb movements. *Electroenceph-*

alogr. Clin. Neurophysiol. Suppl. 33: 87–94

33. De Long, M. R., Strick, P. L. 1974. Relation of basal ganglia, cerebellum and motor cortex units in ramp and ballistic limb movements. *Brain Res.* 71:327–35

34. Desmedt, J. E. 1975. *Recent Developments in the Psychobiology of Language: The Cerebral Evoked Potential Approach.* Oxford: Oxford Univ. Press. In press

35. Dichgans, J., Bizzi, E., Morasso, P., Tagliasco, V. 1974. The role of vestibular and neck afferents during eye-head coordination in the monkey. *Brain Res.,* 71:225–32

36. Dickson, J., Gerstein, G. 1974. Interactions between neurons in auditory cortex of the cat. *J. Neurophysiol.* 37: 1239–61

37. Disterhoft, J., Olds, J. 1972. Differential development of conditioned unit changes in thalamus and cortex of rat. *J. Neurophysiol.* 35:665–79

38. Donald, M., Goff, W. 1973. Contingent negative variation and sensory evoked responses: their interaction and relationship to auditory discrimination. *Electroencephalogr. Clin. Neurophysiol.* Suppl. 33:109–18

39. Donchin, E., Gerbrandt, L., Leifer, L., Tucker, L. 1973. Contingent negative variations and motor responses. *Electroencephalogr. Clin. Neurophysiol.* Suppl. 33:187–90

40. Donchin, E., Kubovy, M., Kutas, M. 1973. Graded changes in evoked response (P300) amplitude as a function of cognitive activity. *Percept. Psychophysiol.* 14:319–24

41. Donchin, E., Otto, D., Gerbrandt, L., Pribram, K. 1973. Studies on the physiology of the CNV. *Electroencephalogr. Clin. Neurophysiol.* Suppl. 33:257–62

42. Donchin, E., Tueting, P., Ritter, W., Kutas, M., Heffley, E. 1975. On the independence of the CNV and P300 components of the human averaged evoked potential. *Electroencephalogr. Clin. Neurophysiol.* 38:449–61

43. Doty, R., Negrao, N., Yamago, K. 1973. The unilateral engram. *Acta Neurobiol. Exp.* 33:711–28

44. Doty, R., Wilson, P., Bartlett, J., Pecci-Saavedra, J. 1973. Mesencephalic control of LGN in primates. I. Electrophysiology. *Exp. Brain Res.* 18:189–203

45. Dow, B. M., Dubner, R. 1971. Single-unit response to moving stimuli in the

middle suprasylvian gyrus of the cat. *J. Neurophysiol.* 34:47–55

46. Eccles, J. C. 1973. *The Understanding of the Brain.* New York/London: McGraw Hill. 238 pp.

47. Eidelberg, E., Stein, D. G. 1974. Functional recovery after lesions of the nervous system. *Neurosci. Res. Prog.* 12:191–303

48. Eisenman, L. 1974. Neural encoding of sound location: an electrophysiological study in auditory cortex (A 1) of the cat using free field stimuli. *Brain Res.* 75:203–14

49. Engel, J., Woody, C. D. 1972. Effects of character and significance of stimulus on unit activity of coronal-precruciate cortex of cat during performance of conditioned motor response. *J. Neurophysiol.* 35:220–29

50. Erdelyi, M. H. 1974. A new look at the new look. Perceptual defense and vigilance. *Psychol. Rev.* 81:1–25

51. Erulkar, S. D. 1972. Comparative aspects of spatial localization of sounds. *Physiol. Rev.* 52:237–360

52. Evans, E. F. 1974. Neural processes for the detection of acoustic patterns and for sound localization. See Ref. 10, 131–45

53. Evans, E., Nelson, P. 1973. The responses of single neurons in the cochlear nucleus of the cat as a function of their location and the anaesthetic state. *Exp. Brain Res.* 17:402–27

54. Evans, E., Nelson, P. 1973. On the functional relationship between the dorsal and ventral divisions of the cochlear nucleus of the cat. *Exp. Brain Res.* 17:428–42

55. Evarts, E. V. 1973. Motor cortex reflexes associated with learned movement. *Science* 179:501–3

56. Evarts, E. 1974. Sensorimotor cortex activity associated with movements triggered by visual as compared to somesthetic inputs. See Ref. 10, 327–37

57. Evarts, E. 1974. Precentral and postcentral cortical activity in association with visually triggered movement. *J. Neurophysiol.* 37:373–81

58. Evarts, E. V., Tanji, J. 1974. Gating of motor cortex reflexes by prior instruction. *Brain Res.* 71:479–94

59. Feeney, D., Orem, J. 1972. Modulation of visual cortex inhibition during reticular evoked arousal. *Physiol. Behav.* 9:805–8

60. Feeney, D., Pittman, J., Wagner, H. 1974. Lateral inhibition and attention: comments on the neuropsychological theory of Walley and Weiden. *Psychol. Rev.* 81:536–39

61. Finger, S., Walbran, B., Stein, D. 1973. Brain damage and behavioral recovery: serial lesion phenomena. *Brain Res.* 63:1–18

62. Fishman, M., Michael, C. R. 1973. Integration of auditory information in the cat's visual cortex. *Vision Res.* 13:1415–19

63. Friedman, D., Hakerem, G., Sutton, S., Fleiss, J. 1973. Effect of stimulus uncertainty on the pupillary dilation response and the vertex evoked potential. *Electroencephalogr. Clin. Neurophysiol.* 34:475–84

64. Friedman, D., Simson, R., Ritter, W., Rapin, I. 1975. Cortical evoked potentials elicited by real speech words and human sounds. *Electroencephalogr. Clin. Neurophysiol.* 38:13–19

65. Friedman, D., Simson, R., Ritter, W., Rapin, I. 1975. The late positive component (P300) and information processing in sentences. *Electroencephalogr. Clin. Neurophysiol.* 38:255–62

66. Funkenstein, H., Winter, P. 1973. Responses to acoustic stimuli of units in the auditory cortex of awake squirrel monkeys. *Exp. Brain Res.* 18:464–88

67. Fuster, J. M. 1973. Unit activity in prefrontal cortex during delayed-response performance: neuronal correlates of transient memory. *J. Neurophysiol.* 36:61–78

68. Fuster, J., Bauer, R. 1974. Visual short-term memory deficit from hypothermia of frontal cortex. *Brain Res.* 81:393–400

69. Garcia-Rill, E., Dubrovsky, B. 1974. Responses of motor cortex cells to visual stimuli. *Brain Res.* 82:185–94

70. Ganz, L., Haffner, M. 1974. Permanent perceptual and neurophysiological effects of visual deprivation in the cat. *Exp. Brain Res.* 20:67–87

71. Gazzaniga, M. S. 1971. Changing hemisphere dominance by changing reward probability in split-brain monkeys. *Exp. Neurol.* 33:412–19

72. Ghez, C., Pisa, M. 1972. Inhibition of afferent transmission in cuneate nucleus during voluntary movement in the cat. *Brain Res.* 40:145–51

73. Gijsbers, K. J. 1973 Visual discrimination during reticular stimulation in the alert cat. *Exp. Neurol.* 38:286–94

74. Goldberg, M., Wurtz, R. 1972. Activity of superior colliculus in behaving monkey. II. Effect of attention on neu-

ronal responses. *J. Neurophysiol.* 35: 560–74
75. Goldberg, M. E., Wurtz, R. 1972. Activity of superior colliculus in behaving monkey. I. Visual receptive fields of single neurons. *J. Neurophysiol.* 35:542–59
76. Goodfield, J. 1972. The problem of reduction in biology. A conference report. *Nature* 240:446–48
77. Gordon, B. 1973. Receptive fields in deep layers of cat superior colliculus. *J. Neurophysiol.* 36:157–78
78. Gould, J., Chalupa, L., Lindsley, D. 1974. Modifications of pulvinar and geniculo-cortical evoked potentials during visual discrimination learning in monkeys. *Electroencephalogr. Clin. Neurophysiol.* 36:639–49
79. Gross, C. G., Bender, D. B., Rocha-Miranda, C. E. 1974. Inferotemporal cortex. A single-unit analysis. See Ref. 10, 229–38
80. Haaxma, R., Kuypers, H. 1974. Role of occipito-frontal cortico-cortical connections in visual guidance of relatively independent hand and finger movements in rhesus monkeys. *Brain Res.* 71: 361–66
81. Hartje, W., Ettlinger, G. 1974. Reaching in light and dark after unilateral posterior parietal ablations in the monkey. *Cortex* 9:346
82. Hein, A. 1974. Prerequisite for development of visually guided reaching in the kitten. *Brain Res.* 71:259–63
83. Held, R. 1968. Dissociation of visual functions by deprivation and rearrangement. *Psychol. Forsch.* 31:338–48
84. Held, R., Bauer, J. 1974. Development of sensorially-guided reaching in infant monkeys. *Brain Res.* 71:265–71
85. Hillyard, S. A. 1973. The C.N.V. and human behavior. Event related slow potentials of the brain. *Electroencephalogr. Clin. Neurophysiol.* Suppl. 33: 161–71
86. Hillyard, A., Hink, R., Schwent, V., Picton, T. 1973. Electrical signs of selective attention in the human brain. *Science* 182:177–79
87. Hirsch, H. 1972. Visual perception in cats after environmental surgery. *Exp. Brain Res.* 15:405–23
88. Hoffmann, K., Sherman, S. 1974. Effects of early monocular deprivation on visual input to cat superior colliculus. *J. Neurophysiol.* 37:1276–86
89. Horn, G., Wiesenfeld, Z. 1974. Attention in the cat: electrophysiological and behavioural studies. *Exp. Brain Res.* 21:67–82

90. Houk, J. C. 1972. On the significance of various command signals during voluntary control. *Brain Res.* 40:49–53
91. Hyvärinen, J., Poranen, A. 1974. Function of the parietal associative area 17 as revealed from cellular discharges in alert monkeys. *Brain* 97:673–92
92. Imbert, M., Buisseret, P. 1974. Receptive field characteristics and plastic properties of visual cortical cells in kittens reared with or without visual experience. *Exp. Brain Res.* 22:25–36
93. Järvilehto, T., Fruhstorfer, H. 1970. Differentiation between slow cortical potentials associated with motor and mental acts in man. *Exp. Brain Res.* 11:309–17
94. Joffroy, A., Lamarre, Y. 1974. Single cell activity in the ventral lateral thalamus of the unanesthetized monkey. *Exp. Neurol.* 42:1–16
95. John, E. R., Bartlett, F., Shimokochi, M., Kleinman, D. 1973. Neural readout from memory. *J. Neurophysiol.* 36:893–924
96. Jones, J., Beck, C. 1975. Motor potentials and the timing of muscular activity. *Electroencephalogr. Clin. Neurophysiol.* 38:273–79
97. Kasamatsu, T., Adey, W. R. 1974. Recovery in visual cortical neurons following total visual deafferentation. *Brain Res.* 74:105–17
98. Keating, E. 1974. Impaired orientation after primate tectal lesions. *Brain Res.* 67:538–41
99. Kelly, J. 1974. Polysensory cortical lesions and auditory temporal pattern discriminations in the cat. *Brain Res.* 80:317–27
100. Kitsikis, A., Mitova, L., Richard, D. 1969. Identification des champs récepteurs visuels des cellules du cortex moteur chez le chat. *J. Physiol. Paris* 61:325–26
101. Kleinman, K. M., Little, R. W. 1973. Inter-hemispheric transfer of meaningful visual information in normal human subjects. *Nature* 241:55–57
102. Konorski, J. 1967. *Integrative Activity of the Brain. An Interdisciplinary Approach.* Chicago/London: Univ. Chicago Press. 530 pp.
103. Kornblith, C., Olds, J. 1973. Unit activity in brain stem reticular formation of the rat during learning. *J. Neurophysiol.* 36:489–501
104. Kornhuber, H. 1974. Cerebral cortex, cerebellum and basal ganglia. An introduction to their motor functions. See Ref. 10, 267–80

105. Kubota, K., Iwamoto, T., Suzuki, H. 1974. Visuokinetic activities of primate prefrontal neurons during delayed-response performance. *J. Neurophysiol.* 37:1197–1212

106. Lee, R. G., White, D. G. 1974. Modification of the human somatosensory evoked response during voluntary movement. *Electroencephalogr. Clin. Neurophysiol.* 36:53–62

107. Libet, B., Alberts, E., Wright, E., Feinstein, B. 1972. Cortical and thalamic activation in conscious sensory experience. In *Neurophysiology Studied in Man*, ed. G. Somjen, 157–68. Amsterdam: Excerpta Medica. 255 pp.

108. Lindsley, D., Scales, D., Wilson, G. 1973. Changes in the late components of visual evoked potentials with visual information processing. *Soc. Neurosci. Abstr.* 3:422

109. Linseman, M. A. 1974. Inhibitory unit activity of the ventral forebrain during both appetitive and aversive Pavlovian conditioning. *Brain Res.* 80:146–51

110. Linseman, M. A., Olds, J. 1973. Activity changes in rat hypothalamus, preoptic area and striatum associated with Pavlovian conditioning. *J. Neurophysiol.* 36:1038–50

111. Luria, A. R. 1973. *Restoration of Function After Brain Injury.* New York: Macmillan. 277 pp.

112. Luschei, E. S., Garthwaite, C. R., Armstrong, M. E. 1971. Relationship of firing patterns of units in face area of monkey precentral cortex to conditioned jaw movements. *J. Neurophysiol.* 34:552–61

113. McAdam, D. W. 1973. Physiological mechanisms. A review. *Electroencephalogr. Clin. Neurophysiol.* Suppl. 33: 79–86

114. McCallum, W., Papakostopoulos, D. 1973. The CNV and relation time in situations of increasing complexity. *Electroencephalogr. Clin. Neurophysiol.* Suppl. 33:179–86

115. McGuigan, F. J., Schoonover, R. A. 1973. *The Psychophysiology of Thinking–Studies of Covert Processes.* New York: Academic. 512 pp.

116. McIlwain, J. T. 1972. Central vision: visual cortex and superior colliculus. *Ann. Rev. Physiol.* 34:291–314

117. McIlwain, J. T. 1973. Retinotopic fidelity of striate cortex-superior colliculus interactions in the cat. *J. Neurophysiol.* 36:702–10

118. McSherry, J. 1973. Physiological origins. A review. *Electroencephalogr. Clin. Neurophysiol.* Suppl. 33:53–62

119. Malsburg, C. Von der. 1973. Self organization of orientation sensitive cells in the striate cortex. *Kybernetik* 14:85–100

120. Marsden, C. D., Merton, P. A., Morton, H. B. 1973. Latency measurements compatible with a cortical pathway for the stretch reflex in man. *J. Physiol. London* 230:58P–59P

121. Marsh, G. R., Thompson, L. 1973. Effects of verbal and non verbal psychological set on hemispheric asymmetries in the CNV. *Electroencephalogr. Clin. Neurophysiol.* Suppl. 33:195–200

122. Massion, J. 1973. Intervention des voies cérébello-corticales et cortico-cérébelleuses dans l'organisation et la régulation du mouvement. *J. Physiol. Paris* 67:117–70

123. Massion, J., Smith, A. M. 1973. Activity of ventrolateral thalamic neurones related to posture and movement during a modified placing reaction in the cat. *Brain Res.* 49:489

124. Mathers, L. H., Rapisardi, S. C. 1973. Visual and somatosensory receptive fields of neurons in the squirrel monkey pulvinar. *Brain Res.* 64:65–83

125. Maton, B., Bouisset, S. 1975. Motor unit activity and preprogramming of movement in man. *Electroencephalogr. Clin. Neurophysiol.* 38:658–60

126. Matsumiya, Y., Tagliasco, V., Lombroso, C., Goodglass, H. 1972. Auditory evoked responses: meaningfulness of stimuli and interhemispheric asymmetry. *Science* 175:790–92

127. Miller, J., Beaton, R., O'Connor, T., Pfingst, B. 1974. Response pattern complexity of auditory cells in the cortex of unanesthetized monkeys. *Brain Res.* 69:101–13

128. Milner, B. 1974. Hemispheric specialization scope and limits. See Ref. 10, 75–89

129. Mohler, C., Goldberg, M., Wurtz, R. 1973. Visual receptive fields of frontal eye field neurons. *Brain Res.* 61:385–89

130. Mountcastle, V. B. 1975. The view from within: pathways to the study of perception. *The Johns Hopkins Med. J.* 136:109–31

131. Muir, D., Mitchell, D. 1975. Behavioral deficits in cats following early selected visual exposure to contours of a single orientation. *Brain Res.* 85:459–77

132. Murphy, J. T., Wong, Y. C., Kwan, H. C. 1974. Distributed feedback sys-

tems for muscle control. *Brain Res.* 71:495–505

133. Nebes, R. D. 1973. Perception of spatial relationships by the right and left hemispheres in commissurotomized man. *Neuropsychologia* 11:285–89

134. Nebes, R. 1974. Hemispheric specialization of commissurotomized man. *Psychol. Bull.* 81:1–14

135. Newman, J., Wollberg, Z. 1973. Multiple coding of species-specific vocalizations in the auditory cortex of squirrel monkeys. *Brain Res.* 54:287–304

136. Newman, J., Semmes, D. 1974. Arousal effects on unit responsiveness to vocalizations in squirrel monkey auditory cortex. *Brain Res.* 78:125–38

137. Niki, H. 1974. Prefrontal unit activity during delayed alternation in the monkey. I. Relation to direction of response. *Brain Res.* 68:185–96

138. Niki, H. 1974. Prefrontal unit activity during delayed alternation in the monkey. II. Relation to absolute versus relative direction of response. *Brain Res.* 68:197–204

139. Noda, H. 1975. Sustained and transient discharges of retinal ganglion cells during spontaneous eye movements of cats. *Brain Res.* 84:515–29

140. Noda, H., Adey, W. 1974. Retinal ganglion cells of the cat transfer information on saccadic eye movements and quick target motion. *Brain Res.* 70: 340–45

141. Norton, T. 1974. Receptive field properties of superior colliculus cells and development of visual behavior in kittens. *J. Neurophysiol.* 37:674–90

142. O'Brien, J., Packham, S., Brunnhoelzl, W. 1973. Features of spike train related to learning. *J. Neurophysiol.* 36: 1051–61

143. Olds, J., Disterhoft, J., Segal, M. 1972. Learning centers of rat brain mapped by measuring latencies of conditioned unit responses. *J. Neurophysiol.* 35:202

144. Ornstein, R. 1972. *The Psychology of Consciousness.* San Francisco: Freeman. 247 pp

145. Paillard, J., Massion, J. 1974. Motor aspects of behaviour and programmed nervous activities. A symposium. *Brain Res.* 71:189–575

146. Pasik, P., Pasik, T. 1973. Extrageniculostriate vision in the monkey. V. Role of accessory optic system. *J. Neurophysiol.* 36:450–57

147. Peck, C., Blakemore, C. 1975. Modification of single neurons in the kitten's visual cortex after brief periods of monocular visual experience. *Exp. Brain Res.* 22:57–68

148. Pettigrew, J. 1974. The effect of visual experience in the development of stimulus specificity by kitten cortical neurons. *J. Physiol. London* 237:49–74

149. Pettigrew, J., Garey, L. 1974. Selective modification of single neuron properties in the visual cortex of kittens. *Brain Res.* 66:160–64

150. Phillips, C. G. 1968. Motor apparatus of the baboon's hand. *Proc. R. Soc. Ser. B* 173:141–74

151. Phillips, C. G., Powell, T. P. S., Wiesendanger, M. 1971. Projection from low-threshold muscle afferents of hand forearm to area 3a of baboon's cortex. *J. Physiol. London* 217:419–46

152. Picton, T. W., Hillyard, S. A. 1974. Human auditory evoked potentials. II. Effects of attention. *Electroencephalogr. Clin. Neurophysiol.* 36:191–99

153. Pöppel, E., Held, R., Frost, D. 1973. Residual visual function after brain wounds involving the central visual pathways in man. *Nature* 243:295–96

154. Posner, M., Boies, S. 1971. Components of attention. *Psychol. Rev.* 78:391–408

155. Powers, W. T. 1973. *Behavior. The Control of Perception.* Chicago: Aldine. 296 pp.

156. Pribram, K. H. 1974. How is it that sensing so much we can do so little? See Ref. 10, 249–61

157. Pribram, K. H., Nuwer, M., Baron, R. J. 1974. The holographic hypothesis of memory structure in brain function and perception. In *Contemporary Developments in Mathematical Psychology,* ed. R. C. Atkinson, D. H. Krantz, R. C. Luce, P. Suppes, 416–57. San Francisco: Freeman

158. Rebert, C. S. 1973. Elements of a general cerebral system related to CNV genesis. *Electroencephalogr. Clin. Neurophysiol. Suppl.* 33:63–68

159. Rebert, C., Tecce, J. 1973. A summary of CNV and reaction time. *Electroencephalogr. Clin. Neurophysiol. Suppl.* 33:173–78

160. Regan, D. 1972. *Evoked Potentials in Psychology, Sensory Physiology and Clinical Medicine.* London: Chapman & Hall. 328 pp.

161. Richard, D., Angyan, L., Buser, P. 1972. Contrôle, par le cortex visuel, du groupe thalamique latéral postérieur chez le chat. *Exp. Brain Res.* 15:386–404

162. Richard, D., Thiery, J. C., Buser, P. 1973. Cortical control of the superior

colliculus in awake non-paralyzed cats. *Brain Res.* 58:524–28

163. Ritter, W., Simson, R., Vaughan, H. 1972. Association cortex potentials and reaction time in auditory discrimination. *Electroencephalogr. Clin. Neurophysiol.* 33:547–55

164. Rizzolatti, G., Umilta, C., Berlucchi, G. 1971. Opposite superiorities of the right and left cerebral hemispheres in discriminative reaction time to physiognomical and alphabetical material. *Brain* 94:431–42

165. Robert, C. 1973. Slow potential correlates of neuronal population responses in the cat's lateral geniculate nucleus. *Electroencephalogr. Clin. Neurophysiol.* 35:511–15

166. Robinson, D., Jarvis, C. 1974. Superior colliculus neurons studied during head and eye movements of the behaving monkey. *J. Neurophysiol.* 37:533–40

167. Robinson, J. S., Voneida, T. J. 1973. Hemisphere differences in cognitive capacity in the split-brain cat. *Exp. Neurol.* 38:123–34

168. Roth, W., Kopell, B., Trinklenberg, J. 1975. The contingent negative variation during a memory retrieval task. *Electroencephalogr. Clin. Neurophysiol.* 38:171–74

169. Rothblat, L., Pribram, K. H. 1972. Selective attention: input filter or response selection? *Brain Res.* 39:427–36

170. Roucoux-Hanus, M., Boisacq-Schepens, N., Crommelinck, M. 1974. Organisation d'afférences périphériques et interhémisphériques et relation avec l'efférence pyramidale au niveau du cortex moteur du chat. *Arch. Ital. Biol.* 112:199–223

171. Rougeul, A., Buser, P. 1974. Inhibition interne de Pavlov et états transitionnels de vigilance. *Rev. Electroencephalogr. Neurophysiol.* 4:69–78

172. Rougeul, A., Corvisier, J., Letalle, A. 1974. Rythmes électrocorticaux caractéristiques de l'installation du sommeil naturel chez le chat. Leurs rapports avec le comportement moteur. *Electroencephalogr. Clin. Neurophysiol.* 37:41–57

173. Rubin, E., McAdam, D. 1972. Slow potential concomitants of the retrieval process. *Electroencephalogr. Clin. Neurophysiol.* 32:84–86

174. Sakai, M. 1974. Prefrontal unit activity during visually guided lever pressing reaction in the monkey. *Brain Res.* 81:297–309

175. Sakata, H., Takaoka, Y., Kawarasak, A., Shibutani, H. 1973. Somatosensory properties of neurons in the superior parietal cortex (area 5) of the rhesus monkey. *Brain Res.* 64:85–102

176. Schilder, P., Pasik, P., Pasik, T. 1972. Extrageniculostriate vision in the monkey. III "Circle vs triangle" "and red vs green" discrimination. *Exp. Brain Res.* 14:436–48

177. Schiller, P., Stryker, M., Cynader, M., Berman, N. 1974. Response characteristics of single cells in the monkey superior colliculus following ablation or cooling of visual cortex. *J. Neurophysiol.* 37:181–94

178. Schmidt, E. M., Jost, R. G., Davis, K. K. 1974. Cortical cell discharge patterns in anticipation of a trained movement. *Brain Res.* 75:309–11

179. Schwent, V., Hillyard, S. 1975. Evoked potential correlates of selective attention with multichannel auditory inputs. *Electroencephalogr. Clin. Neurophysiol.* 38:131–38

180. Segal, M. 1973. Dissecting a short-term memory circuit in the rat brain. I. Changes in entorhinal unit activity and responsiveness of hippocampal units in the process of classical conditioning. *Brain Res.* 64:281–92

181. Segal, M. 1973. Flow of conditioned responses in limbic telencephalic system of the rat. *J. Neurophysiol.* 36:840–54

182. Segal, M., Olds, J. 1972. Behavior of units in hippocampal circuit of the rat during learning. *J. Neurophysiol.* 35:680–90

183. Shagass, C. 1972. *Evoked Brain Potentials in Psychiatry.* New York: Plenum. 274 pp.

184. Shelbourne, E. 1973. Visual evoked responses to language stimuli in normal children. *Electroencephalogr. Clin. Neurophysiol.* 34:135–43

185. Sovijärvi, A., Hyvärinen, J. 1974. Auditory cortical neurons in the cat sensitive to the direction of sound source movement. *Brain Res.* 73:455–71

186. Sperry, R. W. 1970. An objective approach to subjective experience. Further explanation of a hypothesis. *Psychol. Rev.* 77:585–90

187. Sperry, R. W. 1974. Lateral specialization in the surgically separated hemisphere See Ref. 10, 5–19

188. Spinelli, D., Hirsch, H., Phelps, R., Metzler, J. 1972. Visual experience as a determinant of the response characteristics of cortical receptive fields in cats. *Exp. Brain Res.* 15:289–304

189. Sprague, J., Berlucchi, G., Rizzolatti, G. 1973. The role of the superior colliculus and pretectum in vision and visually guided behavior. See Ref. 27, 27–101

190. Squires, N., Squires, K., Hillyard, S. 1975. Two varieties of long latency positive waves evoked by unpredictable auditory stimuli in man. *Electroencephalogr. Clin. Neurophysiol.* 38:387–401

191. Stamm, J. S., Gadotti, A., Rosen, S. C. 1975. Interhemispheric functional differences in prefrontal cortex of monkeys. *J. Neurobiol.* 6:39–49

192. Stamm, J. S., Rosen, S. C. 1973. The locus and crucial time of implication of prefrontal cortex in the delayed response task. *Psychophysiology of the Frontal Lobes,* ed. K. Pribram A. Luria, 139–53. New York: Academic

193. Sullivan, M. V., Hamilton, C. R. 1973. Interocular transfer of reversed and nonreversed discriminations via the anterior commissure in monkeys. *Physiol. Behav.* 10:355–59

194. Sullivan, M., Hamilton, C. 1973. Memory establishment via the anterior commissure of monkeys. *Physiol. Behav.* 11:873–79

195. Swarbrick, L., Whitfield, I. C. 1972. Auditory cortical units selectively responsive to stimulus "shape." *J. Physiol. London* 224: 68P–69P

196. Tanaka, D. 1974. Sparing of an escape response following serial prefrontal decortication in the monkey. *Brain Res.* 65:195–201

197. Tecce, J. 1970. Attention and evoked potentials in man. See Ref. 8, 331–65

198. Tecce, J. 1972. Contingent negative variation (CNV) and psychological processes in man. *Psychol. Bull.* 77:73–108

199. Teyler, T., Shaw, C., Thompson, R. 1972. Unit responses to moving visual stimuli in the motor cortex of the cat. *Science* 176:811–13

200. Thach, W. T. 1972. Cerebellar output: properties, synthesis and uses. *Brain Res.* 40:89–97

201. Thompson, R., Bettinger, L. 1970. Neural substrates of attention. See Ref. 8, 367–401

202. Thompson, R., Myers, R. E. 1971. Brain stem mechanisms underlying visually guided responses in the rhesus monkey. *J. Comp. Physiol. Psychol.* 74:479–512

203. Thorn, F. 1974. Electrophysiological correlates of visual detection in the cat. *Brain Res.* 65:53–64

204. Tieman, S. B., Hamilton, C. R. 1974. Interhemispheric communication between extraoccipital visual areas in the monkey. *Brain. Res.* 67:279–87

205. Tretter, F., Cynader, M., Singer, W. 1975. Modification of direction selectivity of neurons in the visual cortex of kittens. *Brain Res.* 84:143–49

206. Updyke, B. 1974. Characteristics of unit responses in superior colliculus of the cebus monkey. *J. Neurophysiol.* 37:896–909

207. Vaughan, H., Ritter, W. 1973. Physiologic approaches to the analysis of attention and performance. In *Attention and Performance,* ed. S. Kornblum, 129–54. New York: Academic

208. Vella, E., Butler, A., Glass, A. 1972. Electrical correlates of right hemisphere function. *Nature New Biol.* 236: 125–26

209. Vital-Durand, F., Jeannerod, M. 1974. Maturation of the kinetic response: genetic and environmental factors. *Brain Res.* 71:249–57

210. Walley, R. E. Weiden, T. D. 1973. Lateral inhibition and cognitive masking. A neuropsychological theory of attention. *Psychol. Rev.* 80:284–302

211. Weinberg, H. 1973. The contingent negative variation: its relation to feedback and expectant attention. *Electroencephalogr. Clin. Neurophysiol.* Suppl. 33: 219–28

212. Weiskrantz, L. 1974. The interaction between occipital and temporal cortex in vision. An overview. See Ref. 10, 189–204

213. Wester, K., Irvine, D., Thompson, R. 1974. Acoustic tuning of single cells in middle suprasylvian cortex of cat. *Brain Res.* 76:493–502

214. Westheimer, G., Blair, S. 1972. Mapping the visual sensory onto the visual motor system. *Invest. Opthalmol.* 11: 490–96

215. Wiesendanger, M. 1972. Effects of electrical stimulation of peripheral nerves to the hand and forearm on pyramidal tract neurones of the baboon and monkey. *Brain Res.* 40:193–97

216. Wilkinson, R. T., Ashby, S. 1974. Selective attention, contingent negative variation and the evoked potential. *Biol. Psychol.* 1:167–79

217. Wilkinson, R., Lee, M. 1972. Auditory evoked potentials and selective attention. *Electroencephalogr. Clin. Neurophysiol.* 33:411–18

218. Wilkinson, R. T., Spence, M. 1973. Determinants of the post-stimulus reso-

lution of the contingent negative variation (CNV) *Electroencephalogr. Clin. Neurophysiol.* 35:503–9

219. Wininger, J., Pasik, P., Pasik, T. 1973. Effect of superior colliculus lesions on discrimination of luminous flux-equated figures by monkeys deprived of striate cortex. *Soc. Neurosci. Abstr.* 2:100

220. Winter, P., Funkenstein, H. 1973. The effect of species specific vocalization on the discharge of auditory cortical cells in the awake squirrel monkey (Saimiri sciureus). *Exp. Brain Res.* 18:489–504

221. Wollberg, Z., Newman, J. D. 1972. Auditory cortex of squirrel monkey: response patterns of single cells to species specific vocalization. *Science* 175:212–14

222. Wood, B. 1975. Monocular relearning of a dark-light discrimination by cats after unilateral cortical and collicular lesions. *Brain Res.* 83:156–62

223. Wood, C., Spear, P., Braun, J. 1974. Effects of sequential lesions of suprasylvian gyri and visual cortex on pattern discrimination in the cat. *Brain Res.* 66:443–66

224. Woody, C., Engel, J. 1972. Changes in unit activity and threshold to electrical microstimulation at coronal precruciate cortex of cats with classical conditioning of different facial movements. *J. Neurophysiol.* 35:230–41

225. Woody, C., Yarousky, P. 1972. Conditioned eye blink using electrical stimulation of coronal-precruciate cortex as conditional stimulus. *J. Neurophysiol.* 35:242–56

226. Woody, C., Yarousky, P., Owens, J., Black-Cleworth, P., Crow, T. 1974. Effects of lesions of cortical motor areas on acquisition of conditioned eye blink in the cat. *J. Neurophysiol.* 37:385–94

227. Worden, F., Galambos, R. 1972. Auditory processing of biologically significant sounds. *Neurosci. Res. Progr. Bull.* 10:1–119

228. Wurtz, R. H., Goldberg, M. E. 1972. Activity of superior colliculus in behaving monkey. III. Cells discharging before eye movements. *J. Neurophysiol.* 35:575–86

229. Wurtz, R., Goldberg, M. 1972. Activity of superior colliculus in behaving monkey. IV. Effects of lesions on eye movements. *J. Neurophysiol* 35:587–96

230. Yamaguchi, S., Myers, R. 1973. Prefrontal lobe functions and the neocortical commissures in monkeys. *Exp. Brain Res.* 18:119–30

231. Yumiya, H., Kubota, K., Asanuma, H. 1974. Activities of neurons in area 3a of the cerebral cortex during voluntary movements in the monkey. *Brain Res.* 78:169–77

232. Zeki, S. M. 1974. Functional organization of a visual area in the posterior bank of the superior temporal sulcus of the rhesus monkey. *J. Physiol. London* 236:549–73

IONS AND INOTROPY[1]

W. Barry Van Winkle and Arnold Schwartz

Department of Cell Biophysics, Division of Myocardial Biology, Baylor College of Medicine, and the Fondren-Brown Cardiovascular Research and Training Center of The Methodist Hospital, Houston, Texas 77025

> We have seen that a perfect contraction can be obtained with a neutral circulating fluid composed of saline solution with a minute trace of calcium chloride and potassium chloride.
>
> Sidney Ringer, 1883

INTRODUCTION

An inotropic effect [from the Greek *ino-*($\iota\nu\epsilon\sigma$), fiber or muscle, and *tropos* ($\tau\rho o\pi o\sigma$), turn] represents a change in the rate of development of force of contraction of the myocardium usually expressed as dT/dt, dF/dt, or dP/dt, depending on the means of measuring such parameters. (T = tension; F = force; P = pressure) (4). Because we tend to associate the term *inotropic* with an increase of contraction, this review is confined to the ionic factors that may operate during the positive inotropic effect and to the possible chemical mechanisms by which such responses are produced.

The original observations of Ringer, nearly 100 years ago (102), showed clearly that the contraction of the heart depends on an external supply of calcium (Ca^{2+}). Ringer observed that a frog heart stopped beating in the absence of Ca^{2+}, and Mines (76) showed that excitability was retained under these conditions. Consequently, extracellular Ca^{2+} appears to be necessary to specifically maintain cardiac contractility. There has been a sustained interest (as evidenced by numerous articles and reviews) in the role of Ca^{2+} and other ions in cardiac contractility and in how changes in the distribution and affinities of these ions may augment the contractility of the heart. It is now universally accepted that Ca^{2+} is a vital link in the process of contraction and relaxation (91).

Although many questions concerning molecular mechanisms remain unanswered, it is generally accepted that an interaction between a specific subunit of the

[1]The studies cited from the authors' laboratory were supported by HL 17269, HL 05435, HL 07906, Contract NIH 71–2493, and American Heart Association, Houston Chapter, Texas Affiliate.

regulatory protein, troponin, and Ca^{2+} somehow leads to muscle contraction (35, 93, 94). The source of this modulating (or activator) Ca^{2+} and its regulation will become clear when we understand the molecular organization of biological membranes of excitable tissues and the dynamic electrochemical events associated with these membranes.

The reader is cautioned that revelations into specific mechanisms by which sodium, potassium, magnesium, and calcium modulate the inotropic state of the myocardium, do not appear in this discussion; instead, a mechanistic formulation of what is known and what needs to be known is presented.

Ultrastructure of the Sarcolemma

In thin section, the cardiac sarcolemma appears as two distinct entities: a 50–80 nm thick amorphous outer region and a 9 nm trilamellar plasma membrane (71). The role of the amorphous mucopolysaccharide coat, which stains with either ruthenium red (66) or lanthanum (57), may be that of maintaining an external membrane store of Ca^{2+} bound to the ionized carboxyl groups of sialic acid (57, 58, 119). Of possible significance in the dynamic role of this "coat" is that not only does it appear thicker in developing cells than in adult cells (58), but it becomes thicker in hibernating animals (105). This could reflect an increase in storage capacity for Ca^{2+}.

If, as suggested by Langer (55), this coat represents a superficial store of rapidly exchangeable Ca^{2+}, further study of the composition, development, and species differences may yield an understanding of the role of this "fuzzy layer" in excitation-contraction coupling.

Invaginations of the sarcolemma [the transverse (T) system of mammalian cardiac (31) and skeletal muscle] (107) have been implicated in the transmission of depolarization to the sarcoplasmic reticulum, which then results in a release of Ca^{2+} for contraction (24). Further support for the role of the T system in excitation-contraction coupling is provided by the findings that decreases in contractility (but not action potential conduction velocities) by ryanodine have been observed only in the myocardium of adult mammals containing a well-developed T system, and not in fetal mammalian or toad myocardium. The latter two do not possess a well-developed T system. These decreases in contractility appear to correlate with the ryanodine-induced, disrupted T-system tubules (89, 90).

The anastomosing network of membranes, which courses over the surface of the contractile apparatus in cardiac sarcomeres, the sarcoplasmic reticulum (SR), is found to be less extensive in heart than in most skeletal muscle systems (28, 126). Although the SR has been shown to be the physiological "muscle relaxing factor," it may also be a source of "releasable Ca^{2+}" for contraction. This aspect is discussed later with special emphasis on the junctional or subsarcolemmal portions of the SR as possible sites for additional stores of releasable Ca^{2+}.

Newer techniques in specimen preparation in electron microscopy, as well as recent applications of physical methods such as X-ray diffraction, nuclear magnetic resonance, and electron spin resonance, have provided a more detailed image of the macromolecular architecture of the plasmalemma. This membrane acts not only as a semipermeable, ion-selective barrier, but may serve as a matrix for numerous enzyme complexes, such as $Na^+-K^+-ATPase$ and adenylate cyclase, whose possible link with changes in cardiac contractility is also reviewed here. Before hormonal and neural induced alteration of ion flux in control of cardiac contractility can be completely understood, a more thorough knowledge of the physiochemical structure of the plasmalemma is required.

In the past few years, the static unit membrane theory (103) has been replaced by a more dynamic model based on thermodynamic consideration of the hydrophobic and hydrophilic interactions of membrane components. This "fluid mosaic" membrane (124) is composed of a lipid bilayer or matrix into which globular proteins are intercalated. In addition to these "integral" proteins, there are "peripheral" proteins, which may serve as initial binding sites for ligands (123). The freeze-fracture method has led to interesting interpretations of membrane surfaces. This procedure has enabled investigators to observe variations in distribution of membrane protein particles in external and internal surfaces of biological membranes (87), changes in protein distribution and population associated with the developmental changes in SR (130), and ion transport systems (51). Results from lipid-depletion studies on freeze-fractured SR and mitochondrial membranes indicate a dynamic role for phospholipids in membrane structure and function rather than merely an inert support for proteins (87).

Rash & Ellisman (97) have recently observed macromolecular aggregates of particles in freeze-fractured surfaces of skeletal muscle sarcolemmas. The particles may represent components of sodium (Na^+), potassium (K^+), and calcium (Ca^+) channels. Although the freeze-fracture method, applied to cardiac muscle, has confirmed previous findings of a continuation between the sarcolemma and the T system (60), detailed examination of cardiac sarcolemmal membranes with respect to their relation to ion translocation has not yet been carried out.

Membrane Currents and Ion Fluxes

The total ionic membrane current was first described by Hodgkin & Huxley (42), using a voltage clamp procedure developed by Cole (18) for the squid axon. The formulation involving the sum of three kinetically different components has become the basis for studies on excitation. The currents are carried by sodium (I_{Na}), potassium (I_K), and a small, time-independent component referred to as leakage (I_L). Each of the components was expressed by Hodgkin & Huxley (42) as the product of conductance (G_i) and the electromotive driving force. The latter is the difference between membrane potential (E_m) and the ion equilibrium potential (E_i). Each of the current components is expressed as: $I_i = G_i(E_m - E_i)$ for the specific ions. The currents described by the equation above are linear functions of the driving forces only after instantaneous changes in E_m, when G_i is already activated. If not, the currents would be nonlinear, because conductance depends on both membrane potential and time.

In 1957 Hodgkin & Keynes (43), measured tracer fluxes, and in 1970 Baker, Hodgkin & Ridgeway (3), used the photoprotein aequorin injected into axons, and identified two possible "phases" of a Ca^{2+} inward movement: an early rapid one, sensitive to tetrodotoxin (TTX), which may represent Ca^{2+} using a Na^+ channel;

and a second delayed component dependent on external Ca^{2+}. The second component has features that agree with a Hodgkin-Huxley system—voltage- and time-dependent activation and inactivation. (This component is also insensitive to TTX and sensitive to external magnesium, manganese, and verapamil.)

It was not known from these studies if the ions traverse the membrane through pores or by some type of carrier system. In addition, the studies of Hodgkin & Huxley (42) did not provide information about the nature of the "gating" processes that clearly must modulate ion permeation in response to changes in membrane potential. The voltage clamp method is still the best way of monitoring channel activity, as very rapid changes of membrane voltage (V_m), may be observed. Membrane potential is the main determinant of the dynamic state of the channels. Unfortunately, ionic current data yield information only on the fraction of the channels that is open (as functions of V_m and time) and conducting at a specific time, and tell almost nothing about the gates or gating currents that open and close channels. Each Na^+ channel is controlled by two gating factors:

Na^+ ACTIVATION AND INACTIVATION.   Armstrong (2), used techniques for measuring gating current, and deduced that there are two sets of separate Na^+ and K^+ channels and that the Na^+ channels are controlled by two separate gating factors. The following chemical data substantiated this concept and, incidentally, added support for the pore rather than the carrier hypothesis: Tetraethylammonium ion (TEA) eliminated I_K, leaving a current that looks like I_{Na}; TTX eliminated I_{Na}, leaving I_K; and pronase destroyed only the inactivation gates of the Na^+ channel one by one, which suggests that each Na^+ channel has its own inactivation gate. Therefore, Na^+ and K^+ channels or "pores" are probably separate, although it is still possible that a single set of pores exists that can be converted into different ion-specific conformers (80). Each Na^+ channel may have two gates, activation and inactivation, and the latter can be destroyed without an effect on the former. The destruction of the inactivation mechanism by the proteolytic enzyme pronase implies that the inactivation mechanism is probably a protein structure. Armstrong (2) has provided evidence, using derivatives of TEA, of the existence of K^+ pores of particular dimensions (2.6–3.0 Å), possessing a narrow "bridge" structure and a larger portion. The selectivity mechanism of a pore, according to Armstrong (2), involves exclusion of an impermeant ion rather than a preferential binding of an ion to a carrier. Hille (41) has suggested that the walls of the pore are lined with oxygen atoms and are hydrophilic. Although the composition of such pores or charged structures remains hypothetical, a recent model predicting the amino acid sequence of such a channel has been proposed. Based on known binding conditions for the Na^+ channel toxins and their sites of action with regard to surfaces of the membranes, this β-pleated sheet may fulfill many of the requirements for a Na^+ channel (127). As further evidence for ion pores, the insoluble peptide fragment T(is) derived from glycophorin by trypsin treatment from the membrane-penetrating glycoprotein (glycophorin) of human erythrocytes increases $^{42}K^+$ flux in artificial membranes, perhaps similar to a pore, or by local perturbation in the lipid ordering of the membrane (59). It is thought that hydrogen bonding plays an important role in transport. The mechanism by which a pore of approximately 3×5 Å distinguishes between Na^+ and K^+, which have crystal diameters of 1.8 and 2.66 Å, respectively, is unknown, however.

The gates of the pores open and close in response to V_m, which means that parts of the gates are charged. The movement of gating charge, or gating current, has recently been approached by Armstrong (2). The gating current is slow and nonlinear and, as indicated above, is part of the total capacitive current. The absence of a TTX effect on gating current suggests that the TTX receptor is separate from the gate and is consistent with the notion that the pore is a stable structure possessing a movable gate inside and a TTX binding receptor outside (pronase applied to the inside of the membrane destroys Na^+ inactivation; TTX blocks only from the outside without interfering with the activation gate; a TEA derivative cannot block the K^+ channel unless the activation gate is open). The nexus of the intercalated disc has been suggested as the site of low resistance for the conductivity of impulses in adjacent cardiac cells (70). In support of this supposition, Weingart (140) has observed that the nexal membrane is 2×10^4 times more permeable to TEA than is the sarcolemma and that the pore size in this region is at least 10 Å, much larger than the 3×5 Å pores just described. However, selectivity studies for ions in this region have not been completed.

Finally, Ca^{2+} is not a gating particle, and its effect on Na^+ permeability (a tenfold reduction in Ca^{2+} shifts the threshold potential equivalent to a 15 mV depolarization) is probably a result of entrance via the sodium pore. Such concepts of ion pore proteins in excitable membranes fit well within the framework of a "fluid mosaic" model, whose membrane-spanning proteins may be energized by special gating currents or other external influences resulting in ion influx or efflux (see Figure 1).

Cardiac Membrane Potentials

The electrophysiological analysis of the action potential of cardiac muscle initiated by Draper & Weidmann (22) (Purkinje fibers, frog and mammalian contracting ventricle and atria) has required, within recent years, the use of voltage clamp techniques (32, 77, 100). All of the variations of clamp procedures, including the use of short cardiac Purkinje fibers and two microelectrodes, a single sucrose gap, double sucrose gap technique, and a hybrid-type of sucrose gap in which the free end of the muscle preparation is attached to a tension transducer, are designed to approximate the "homogeneous clamp" produced with nerve preparations. The heterogeneity and complexity of cardiac muscle often result in spatial and temporal nonuniformity of the distribution of potential and this, unfortunately, can lead to difficulties in interpretation, a problem emphasized by Johnson & Lieberman (46) and clearly recognized by investigators employing these methods.[2] The information

---

[2]As Weidmann (139) has emphasized, the cable nature of the heart precludes an ideal "space clamp." If, however, one tries to optimize geometry and take precautions to avoid strong current flow for more than a few milliseconds, then a minimum of artifact in recording the rapid inward current can be accomplished. Weidmann has also advised that an addition of a small quantity of calcium chloride to the sucrose solution used in the voltage clamp procedure will prevent "uncoupling" at the site of the intercalated discs. This should limit the continuous increase in internal longitudinal resistance frequently encountered with the sucrose gap techniques.

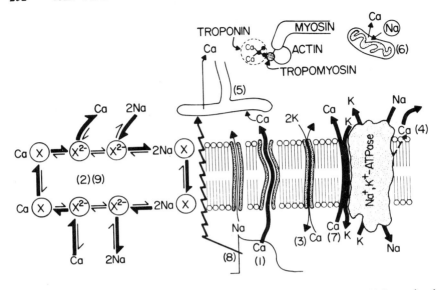

Figure 1 This representation of a fluid mosaic membrane of a lipid bilayer with intercalated modules as ionic pores, enzyme complexes, or carriers indicates suggested routes by which Ca^{2+} may enter the cardiac cell and become available for interaction with troponin: 1. electrogenic, Phase 2 Ca^{2+} slow channel, 2. electroneutral $Na^+:Ca^{2+}$ exchange carrier, 3. electroneutral $K^+:Ca^{2+}$ exchange carrier, 4. Na^+, K^+-ATPase-phospholipid:Ca^{2+} "carrier," 5. Ca^{2+}-induced Ca^{2+} release from SR, 6. mitochondrial Ca^{2+} release by Na^+, 7. Na^+, K^+-ATPase pump-linked $Ca^{2+}:K^+$ exchange, 8. release of SR Ca^{2+} by signal from depolarized T system or sarcolemma associated with spike of action potential. Ca^{2+} efflux from the cell may be accomplished by 9. possible release of Ca^{2+} from SR, which may activate the $Na^+:Ca^{2+}$ carrier in the reverse direction of route 2.

obtained, however qualitative, particularly with respect to ionic characteristics of contraction, is important as a basis for understanding the control of cellular activity.

It is generally believed that the height of the action potential plateau (Phase 2) in a variety of cardiac tissues is much less sensitive to Na^+ than are the fast upstroke phase and initial spike. A slow phase or component of depolarization that includes the plateau is relatively insensitive to $(Na)_O$. External Ca^{2+}, La^{3+}, Mn^{2+}, Co^{2+}, and Ni^{2+} decrease the plateau with variable (increase, decrease, or none) effects on $(dV/dt)_{max}$ and the initial spike; TTX decreases $(dV/dt)_{max}$ and the initial spike with no effect on the plateau; epinephrine increases the plateau height and has no effect on the fast upstroke (100). The results of numerous studies (7, 8, 73, 83, 84, 100, 101, 131, 139, 142) indicate that two inward currents exist: a fast initial phase described as an inward Na^+ current responsible for the upstroke and spike, and a second slow inward current that may be carried by Na^+ and/or Ca^{2+}. Such a dual-ion slow channel has been found in some species such as the frog (106), and more recently in tissue culture cells (69) and cardiac cell aggregates (68). In addition, Na^+ slow channels in chick embryonic cells are blocked by verapamil, but those acquired during cell culture are not (69). From these results, Sperelakis and his colleagues (69, 120) have concluded that, in regard to the slow current, verapamil does not block Ca^{2+} alone, but may also block certain Na^+ slow channels as well. Also, Van der Kloot & Kita (134) found that Na^+ and K^+ conductance changes in frog sartorius muscle were depressed by verapamil. In addition, Ba^{2+}, Sr^{2+}, and Mg^{2+} can increase the current of this slow phase (52). The slow inward current is therefore probably carried through a conductance channel, and the contribution of Na^+ and Ca^{2+} ions to this current depends upon the concentrations of these ions in the external solution, the selectivity of the conductance channels for the two ions (100), and the species and the stage of development (110). Fast Na^+ channels detected by their insensitivity to TTX appear to be absent in young embryonic hearts (110). The action potential is Na^+ dependent in the chick and Ca^{2+} dependent in the rat embryonic heart (110). Cells from "older" embryonic hearts, which are TTX sensitive when placed in cell cultures, rapidly revert to an early embryonic-like state by becoming insensitive to TTX (110). Using an isolated guinea pig heart, Schneider & Sperelakis (110) studied the slow current by depolarizing with 27 mM KCl (–40 mV) and adding isoproterenol to induce excitability (88). The action potential of this preparation is similar to the plateau phase of the normal action potential, but the $(dV/dt)_{max}$ is generally slow (6–12 V sec^{-1}). Methylxanthines mimicked catecholamines but were not blocked by propranolol. The slow responses were blocked by Ca^{2+}–free solutions, Mn^{2+}, or verapamil. Sodium was also required, however. Cyclic AMP also induced the slow responses, which were not blocked by propranolol. Hypoxia and ischemia blocked the slow responses. It was concluded that the slow current is dependent on both Ca^{2+} and Na^+ and that verapamil is not a specific blocker of Ca^{2+} current, but rather blocks the slow response. It is of interest that inactivation of the slow response mechanism by poisons, hypoxia, or ischemia, results in (or is accompanied by) electromechanical uncoupling. Reuter (100) indicated that the slow inward current component in Purkinje fibers is activated along a sigmoid curve in the potential range –60 to +10 mV, but admits that the kinetic properties have not been worked out well. The instantaneous current-voltage relationship of the slow inward current is linear between –90 and –20 mV; above –20 mV it is difficult to measure because of the increasing outward current.

All of these and other experiments carried out using heart tissue from sheep, calf, guinea pig, pig, rat, cat, and frog clearly emphasize the presence and importance of two separable inward current components: a rapid one that is TTX sensitive and dependent on external Na^+, and a slow one that is TTX insensitive and dependent at least in part on Ca^{2+} and is abolished by verapamil, D-600 (a verapamil-like compound), and lanthanum. The Ca^{2+} influx during the plateau phase has been implicated as a main influence of contractile tension (8, 63, 129), but the accompanying small rise in internal Ca^{2+} concentration by this route appears insufficient for the complete activation of contraction (84, 101). Instead, it has been suggested that the Ca^{2+} influx "refills" emptied intracellular stores (30, 143) or refills and subsequently releases Ca^{2+} from specialized portions of the SR to initiate the contractile event (84). This "trigger" Ca^{2+}, responsible for larger release of bound Ca^{2+} from intracellular stores, has been suggested as a control for both skeletal (23) and cardiac muscle (25). Deposits of intracellular Ca^{2+} may be located in the SR adjoining the plasmalemma (126) or T system in cardiac cells. The kinetics of the slow Ca^{2+} current are extremely complex, but important because of the obvious relationship to control of cardiac contractility. If the energy for Ca^{2+} transport across the cell membrane is derived solely from the electrochemical gradient for Ca^{2+}, contraction should be related to this gradient, E_{Ca}. The Nernst equation gives an approximation of E_{Ca} as follows:

$$E_{Ca} = \frac{RT}{2F} \ln \frac{(Ca)_O}{(Ca)_i}.$$

If it is assumed that $(Ca)_O$ is about 2×10^{-4} M and $(Ca)_i$ is about 5×10^{-8} or 10^{-7} M (these values are, of course, only an approximation, as intracellular concentrations have not been accurately determined in muscle), then $E_{Ca} = 104$ mV. The "calcium current," I_{Ca}, is given by

$$I_{Ca} = g_{Ca}(E_{Ca} - V_{max}),$$

where (I_{Ca}) = transmembrane Ca^{2+} current; g_{Ca} = conductance of the membrane to Ca^{2+}; $(E_{Ca} - V_{max})$ = electromotive force for Ca^{2+} movement). Morad & Goldman (77), using frog heart and a hybrid sucrose gap voltage clamp method, found a near linear relationship between clamp potential and tension in the range of the calculated E_{Ca}. Therefore, at least in the frog ventricle, it appears that activator Ca^{2+} may not be transported solely by its electrochemical gradient (at E_{Ca} no net electrochemical force for the Ca^{2+} movement should exist, and hence no tension should develop if this were the only mechanism by which Ca^{2+} reaches the contractile elements). Reuter (100) has considered whether I_{Ca} is large enough to significantly alter activator intracellular Ca^{2+}, and he and Bassingthwaighte (5) concluded that

> there has to be a rather small distribution space for calcium ions close to the membrane in order to account for the large changes of E_r (the reversal potential of the slow inward calcium current) . . . though the gain in $(Ca)_i$ during the flow of I_{Ca} may be too small for appreciable activation of the contractile proteins during a single depolarization, repetitive action potentials may cause accumulation of calcium in the internal stores (sarcolemmal clefts and cisternae of the sarcoplasmic reticulum) from where it can be released during depolarization.

The amount of Ca^{2+} that is moved across the membranes with each action potential in picomoles per square centimeter per impulse, depending on $(Ca)_O$ and possibly on species, varies from 0.13–1.1 (100). This amount is clearly not enough to appreciably affect contraction directly but, as discussed below, may initiate important regenerative changes involved in the contractile process.

How May Ca^{2+} Be Involved in the Control of Contraction?

Within the excitation-contraction-relaxation-recovery cycle, it is probable that the cardiac muscle cell, with respect to Ca^{2+}, must maintain net steady-state total cell content, and some type of directional control (i.e. influx and efflux coupled with the mechanical and electrical activity). In addition net electroneutrality must be maintained.

The various sinks that may control activator Ca^{2+} have been considered in detail (112, 114). Briefly, these are the cell membrane (see above), mitochondria, and SR. Only the SR has been closely implicated in the contraction-relaxation cycle, with the emphasis on cardiac relaxation. The SR, in mammalian ventricle, has the capacity to remove Ca^{2+} from troponin to effect relaxation. The problem of Ca^{2+} delivery to troponin and the problem of Ca^{2+} egress from the cell are of major concern. With respect to the measurement of contraction, there are two basic parameters that reflect contraction: the instantaneous rate of force development, which is a measure of the intensity of the active state, and the time period during which active force is developed, which represents the duration of the active state. The intensity is probably proportional to the maximal rate of tension development $(dP/dt)_{max}$, and the time to peak tension (TPT) of isometric contraction, an index of active state duration. The concentration of Ca^{2+} at a given moment at the myofilaments (i.e. troponin) and the length of time a particular concentration (or activity) of Ca^{2+} remains at the contractile sites must determine $(dP/dt)_{max}$; an augmented amount of Ca^{2+} to troponin per unit time would increase the intensity of the active state and the velocity of contraction. It is probable that the amount of Ca^{2+} available in storage sites prior to excitation controls intensity. The factors that may affect Ca^{2+} on the storage sites are as follows: extracellular Ca^{2+}, extracellular K^+ (a reduction causes an increase in $(dP/dt)_{max}$, extracellular Na^+ (a reduction causes an increase in Ca^{2+} influx), intracellular Na^+ (an increase may stimulate a Na^+:Ca^{2+} carrier), intracellular K^+ (perhaps involved in a Ca^{2+}:K^+ carrier), the Na^+,K^+–ATPase (a Ca^{2+} component may be present), and the SR (regenerative Ca^{2+} release?). The result of all of the above perturbations would be an augmented $(dP/dt)_{max}$ and a decrease in TPT, reflecting a mechanism involving intensity of active state. Cardiac glycosides produce a similar mechanical response. In terms of duration of active state, there is evidence in favor of a membrane "gate" control such that as long as depolarization is maintained above mechanical threshold, Ca^{2+} would continue to enter the cell and hence would favor a prolonged TPT.

Let us discuss some of the factors listed above in terms of modulation of cellular activator Ca^{2+}. With regard to the supply side, there are two major concepts that have evolved: the cell membrane superficial Ca^{2+} theory of Langer (55) and the regenerative intracellular release mechanism described by Endo (23), Ford & Podolsky (29), and others. The Langer concept (55) has been published in detail and therefore is not reviewed extensively here.

The existence of a rapidly exchangeable Ca^{2+} associated with the sarcolemma has been postulated by investigators based on (a) results from ^{45}Ca exchange experiments (16, 53), (*b*) La³⁺ staining of the amorphous coat, and (*c*) displacement of bound Ca^{2+} by La^{3+} and other ions (Mn^{2+}, Cd^{2+}, Zn^{2+}) (58). The importance of this rapidly exchanging Ca^{2+} pool in excitation-contraction coupling has been emphasized by Langer and his colleagues (58, 121). This pool not only may serve as a store for Ca^{2+} following its efflux from the cell, but also may supply Ca^{2+} for the slow electrogenic channel in the plateau phase of the action potential and as a source for Ca^{2+} influx coupled to Na^+ efflux (see Figure 1 for these sources and their possible relationships).

From studies of the effects of ouabain on ^{45}Ca exchange in guinea pig atria, Carrier et al (16) have concluded that a fast exchangeable Ca^{2+} fraction is located on or in the plasmalemma facing the extracellular environment. These investigators calculated the rates of Ca^{2+} exchange and concluded that all of the Ca^{2+} required for the control of beat-to-beat contraction of the heart can be supplied from this pool. This concept would not require the Ca^{2+}-induced Ca^{2+} release or trigger effect mentioned earlier. Nayler (82) has also suggested the presence of a superficial membrane store of Ca^{2+} directly involved in excitation-contraction coupling. As attractive as such hypothetical stores of Ca^{2+} may be, however, as yet no one has proposed how the Ca^{2+}-membrane complex may be altered so that the Ca^{2+} can be rapidly transported into the interior of the cell. Also, there are certain problems with the action of La^{3+} (an ion that has been used extensively as a membrane probe) with regard to tissue specificity and sensitivity, membrane effects (stabilization), or even cellular penetration of La^{3+}, which require resolution (44, 49, 140, 141). Silber (122) pointed out, for example,

> The chemistry of the lanthanide ion is fundamentally different from . . . Ca^{2+} when the dielectric constant is less than that for water. Under these conditions, a lanthanide ion will exhibit nonspecific binding with . . . polar regions of the macromolecule.

The binding of La^{3+} depends upon the hydrophilicity of the binding region. Silber concluded that La^{3+} cannot bind when the environment surrounding the region is hydrophobic, whereas Ca^{2+} can bind to sites in hydrophobic regions.

The isolated sarcolemma from skeletal muscles can apparently bind Ca^{2+} (72, 128) and the binding is inhibited by La^{3+} (128) and ruthenium red (72). The conclusion of Madiera & Atunes-Madiera (72) that Ca^{2+} does not bind to sarcolemmal phospholipids is in disagreement with that of Carrier et al (16) and with the recent results of Gervais et al (36) in this laboratory that up to 80 nmoles of Ca^{2+} can bind to phospholipids associated with purified Na^+,K^+–ATPase.

Langer (55), used arterially perfused interventricular mammalian preparations and a novel compartment kinetic analysis and identified several "pools" or "phases" of Ca^{2+}, only one of which appears to be directly involved in the beat-to-beat control of contraction. The model he constructed is of a "one-way street" variety and can be summarized as follows: the source of "activator Ca^{2+}" is located on or near the sarcolemma and T system, and the amount that can be released is sufficient to effect full contraction [this amount is unknown but probably ranges from 12–25 μmoles

kg^{-1} wet weight heart (33, 125)].[3] The control of this Ca^{2+} pool may be through a Na^+:Ca^{2+} exchange system. The Bowditch or staircase effect of increased contractility is observed in most hearts (except the rat) when the frequency of stimulation is progressively increased. Niedergerke (85) concluded that the strength of the contractions depends upon changes in Ca^{2+} concentration within the cell. Using increased frequency of stimulation as the inotropic stimulus, Langer has postulated that the net K^+ loss that occurs is a secondary osmotic response to the primary small net gain in intracellular Na^+. Sodium influx temporarily exceeds Na^+ efflux causing a stimulation of the Na^+,K^+–ATPase and an adjustment to the demand. Calcium influx is also stimulated, and this occurs via a Na^+ efflux-Ca^{2+} influx exchange system. Cardiac glycoside administration and cooling inhibits the Na^+,K^+ pump, leading to a rise in intracellular Na^+ and stimulation of the Na^+:Ca^{2+} exchange. The $(Na)_i$:$(Na)_O$ ratio would then control the influx of Ca^{2+}. With digitalis and temperature drop, $(Na)_i$ increases because the Na^+,K^+–ATPase is inhibited, and with increased heart rate, $(Na)_i$ would increase because of the increased demand. In any event, these interventions all result in a greater proportion of Na^+ transport being coupled to Ca^{2+}. The involvement of a Na^+:Ca^{2+} exchange [adapted from experiments on squid axon by Baker et al (3) and from the studies of Goddard & Robinson (37) in brain synaptosomes] in positive inotropy has also gained support from the findings of Horackova & Vassort (45) that the veratrine alkaloids increase Na^+ influx during the cardiac action potential and cause a positive inotropic response. In addition, Brace et al (12) concluded that the positive inotropic effect resulting from myocardial hypokalemia in dogs may be a manifestation of increased intracellular Na^+ produced by the inhibition of Na^+,K^+–ATPase by low external K^+. After interacting with troponin, the Ca^{2+} is then removed by the SR and somehow returned to the interstitial space, ". . . perhaps through a specific route" (55). There is no question that a pool of Ca^{2+} exists that is rapidly exchangeable with extracellular Ca^{2+} and displaceable by La^{3+}, and that the sites are probably superficially located. The unsolved problems include; the amount of Ca^{2+} made available from these sites with each excitation event, the universality of the hypothesis and the

---

[3]There are numerous complexities in the accurate determination of the actual intracellular Ca^{2+} concentration. Scatchard analysis has revealed, for instance, that Ca^{2+} may bind to cardiac myofibrils at two classes of sites, one having a binding constant of 6×10^5 M^{-1} and a maximal binding of 0.56 μmoles g^{-1} of myofibrils, the second having a binding constant of 6.3×10^3 M^{-1} and a maximal binding of 8.4 μmoles g^{-1} myofibrils. Measurements of ATPase and tension suggested that the activation process is more closely related to the first site than to the total amount of Ca^{2+} bound. It also appears that ATP alters the affinity of Ca^{2+} at the first site (125). Troponin (TnC) appears to have two classes of Ca^{2+}-binding sites with different affinities (35, 39, 94, 144) and can be (TnI) phosphorylated by cyclic AMP–dependent protein kinase (118). A recent suggestion has been made that this phosphorylation may alter the reactivity of cardiac actomyosin ATPase to Ca^{2+} (108). In addition, Potter (93) has recently reported that Mg^{2+} (0.3 mM) decreases the myosin affinity for Ca^{2+} binding from 5×10^6 to 7×10^4 M^{-1}, but that the "physiological significance of this Ca^{2+} binding to myosin and its regulation by Mg^{2+} is unclear."

mechanism of Ca^{2+} extrusion, which, if a major component of influx is electroneutral, must likewise be neutral. It is not easy to reconcile the electroneutral influx of Ca^{2+} (according to Langer) with some kind of one-way street transport, or perhaps pump, on or through the longitudinal SR, cisterna, and out through the T system (55).

Reviewing the ways in which Ca^{2+} enters the cell, there appears to be at least two components of flux across the sarcolemma: an electrogenic influx during depolarization described as the slow inward flow of current (see above) and an electroneutral coupled exchange of Ca^{2+} for Na^+ that occurs during diastole and possibly during systole. Figure 2, reproduced from a paper by Jundt et al (47), describes both an influx and efflux system. Two Na^+ ions and one Ca^{2+} ion compete for "carrier" X^{2-} at both sides of the membrane. When the X is unoccupied, it moves slowly or not at all. When ligands interact with the molecule, the carrier moves more quickly; the equation below the figure gives the respective distribution ratios at equilibrium. Reuter (100, 101) has concentrated on a Na^+-dependent Ca^{2+} efflux system that is insensitive to cardiac glycosides. Because the cardiac cell membrane is permeable to Ca^{2+}, if there were no efflux of Ca^{2+} the cell would become overloaded with Ca^{2+} and oxidative phosphorylation would be uncoupled, which would lead to a severe loss of ATP and cell death. It appears that at least 80% of Ca^{2+} efflux depends

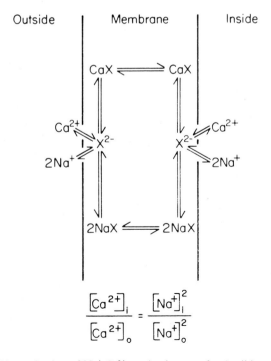

$$\frac{[Ca^{2+}]_i}{[Ca^{2+}]_o} = \frac{[Na^+]_i^2}{[Na^+]_o^2}$$

Figure 2   Possible mechanism of Na^+:Ca^{2+} carrier (see text for details).

on the presence of external Na^+ and Ca^{2+}. Two Na^+ ions and one Ca^{2+} ion compete for one transport molecule (47). The exchange system has a Q_{10} of 1.35 and is not poisoned by metabolic inhibitors. Hence, this has the characteristics of an efficient cell Ca^{2+} depleter. Furthermore, Jundt et al (47) suggested that this carrier system has a higher affinity for Ca^{2+} than does troponin, although the rate of this carrier-mediated Ca^{2+} efflux is too slow to account for relaxation alone. If Reuter's concept (electroneutral) is correct, the Langer suggestion that internal Na^+ controls influx of Ca^{2+} (electroneutral) is not entirely clear. Internal Na^+ should be high at end-systole, which should result in an increase in Ca^{2+} influx at this point; during the recovery phase (diastole), Na^+ should be low, which should cause Ca^{2+} to egress. This would not be consistent with a function for Ca^{2+} in contraction. It is clear that many more molecular details are required for a clear understanding of Ca^{2+} movements coupled to electrical and mechanical events.

The problem is how sequestered Ca^{2+}, after relaxation (SR located), is moved from the SR to the outside. Is it possible that most of the sequestered Ca^{2+} is released intracellularly during the next excitation event and only the small fraction that enters the cell with each depolarization is extruded by the exchange system? The ability of the muscle to contract after the previous excitation event is fully available only if the membrane potential is allowed the time (about 100 msec) to repolarize to at least –70 mV; the restoration is a sigmoid function of the E_m. It appears that activation and restoration of contraction occur over the same potential range as activation and inactivation of Ca^{2+} conductance (101a) and both processes, as described above, are voltage and time dependent. Also, the time courses of recovery of the inward slow Ca^{2+} current from the inactivation process and the time course of contraction recovery are very close at each E_m, which suggests that both processes are related (101a). Reuter (101) suggested that the Na^+ gradient, which is maintained by the Na^+,K^+–ATPase, provides the primary energy for Ca^{2+} extrusion in the heart. If this is so, digitalis would act by inhibiting the Na^+,K^+–ATPase (117), causing a gain in intracellular Na^+. If internal Na^+ is increased according to the distribution ratio (Figure 2), it would cause a significant increase in intracellular Ca^{2+}.

Morad & Greenspan (78), as discussed above, used a modified voltage clamp procedure on frog heart. They reported that the observed inward currents are inactivated within the first 100 msec of depolarization, during which time no tension was developed. Furthermore, the voltage-tension relation was linear in the range –5 to +80 mV with no maximum. This would be inconsistent with an E_{Ca} of about +100 mV. Therefore Morad and co-workers have proposed another hypothesis for the excitation control of contraction (with the assumption that activator Ca^{2+} does not enter the cell electrogenically). He invokes a membrane carrier system that is linked to the efflux of K^+ during the plateau; the electrochemical gradient for K^+ would provide the energy to drive the carrier. No net inward current is required if more than two K^+ are transported for each Ca^{2+}. According to Morad, this process is attractive because it links repolarization with Ca^{2+} entry. Also, a linear and direct relation between the action potential duration (APD) and contraction, the voltage-tension relation and the influx of Ca^{2+} at, near, or above E_{Ca} would all be consistent with the hypothesis. The rate of carrier turnover would thus depend on P_K, and

E_K, and $(Ca)_O$. In an attempt to add some evidence in favor of the Ca-K exchange hypothesis, Morad & Greenspan (78) treated a frog ventricular strip with 5×10^{-6} M acetylstrophanthidin. Increased $(dP/dt)_{max}$ was measured concomitant with a decrease in the duration of the action potential plateau (78):

> ... increased permeability would shorten the APD which in turn would depress developed tension. However, the Ca^{2+}/K^+ hypothesis predicts an increased rate of Ca^{++} influx and rate of tension development (dp/dt) secondary to increased K^+ efflux. The final twitch tension is determined by the interplay between dp/dt and APD ... and for the cardiac glycosides, the dp/dt effect predominates, resulting in increased twitch tension.

The effects also occurred in the presence of TTX, which blocked over 95% of fast Na^+ inward current. Apparently toxicity was also associated with a marked shortening of the APD, but with a depolarization of E_m and contraction as well. These investigators argue that with "progressive toxicity, the decreased rate of relaxation may result from the high Ca^{++} influx and the impaired uptake of Ca^{++} by the SR" (78). "Inhibition of the Na^+,K^+-ATPase causes the cell to lose K^+ and gain Na^+" (78). There are a number of significant problems with this study. The concentration of glycoside used was high; the shortened APD was probably indicative of a toxic effect (104) and therefore the loss of K^+ might simply have been due to the inhibition of the Na^+,K^+-ATPase and not to a $Ca^{2+}:K^+$ exchange system. The authors cited the work of Lee & Choi (62b) on the effect of glycosides on Ca^{2+} uptake of SR as evidence to support the idea of progressive toxicity. This is incorrect, since Lee and his co-workers (62, 62b) suggested that they were studying a therapeutic action. In any case, there is very little to support an action of digitalis in any concentration on the SR (117). The $Ca^{2+}:K^+$ "carrier" idea is still attractive, but it is more likely to be associated with the Na^+,K^+-ATPase (65). Recently, Poole-Wilson & Langer (92a, b) reduced the K^+ leak-efflux component by producing a respiratory acidosis; under this condition, digitalis still produced a positive inotropic effect. These studies, however, still do not remove the possibility that a small compartment of K^+ exchanges with Ca^{2+}. The recent development (61) of a microelectrode technique for measuring cardiac intracellular activities of Na^+ and K^+ should be of value in solving this and other problems associated with ion movements.

We questioned the universality of the Langer $Na^+:Ca^{2+}$ hypothesis (56, 67). A decrease in contractility of perfused rabbit hearts was produced by us by pretreatment with verapamil. Upon increased stimulation frequencies, conversion from the normal positive to a negative inotropic response was observed. This appeared to be caused by the verapamil block of Ca^{2+} influx during systole. Verapamil also delayed the ouabain-induced positive inotropic response but did not decrease the eventual magnitude of the response. Therefore the staircase (treppe) and digitalis effects must occur by different mechanisms, with the former probably closely associated with plateau Ca^{2+} (100) and the latter involving the Na^+,K^+-ATPase receptor (117).

Vassort (135) observed that the slow Ca^{2+} current was not affected during glycoside-induced inotropism in frog ventricle, and Morad & Greenspan (78) suggested that the slow inward current in frog ventricle does not appear to be an activator of contraction.

We would like to suggest in additional possibility: a pool of available Ca^{2+} at the sarcolemmal surface associated with the Na^+,K^+-ATPase transport system. Gervais et al (36) have found that calcium 45 binds to the phospholipids of purified Na^+,K^+-ATPase. Treatment of the enzyme with ouabain caused an increase in affinity so that under physiological conditions enough Ca^{2+} would theoretically be made available to cause an increase in contractile force (36). Figure 1 depicts diagrammatically our current understanding of possible ways in which Ca^{2+} can enter the cell. The model does not describe intracellular mechanisms involved in supplying enough Ca^{2+} to troponin, but merely the mechanism of availability of extracellular Ca^{2+} to the cell.

This brings us to a further consideration: the possible function of the SR as an intracellular site for activator Ca^{2+}. In 1970 Endo et al (23) observed repetitive contractions in skinned fibers (the cell membrane is absent) induced by caffeine, Ca^{2+}, and chelating agents and suggested that intracellular Ca^{2+} release is a regenerative process in which small amounts of Ca^{2+} cause the release of a large quantity of Ca^{2+} from the SR. Ford & Podolsky (29) reported essentially the same phenomenon. Similar events have recently been observed in sarcolemma-free disrupted heart cells (26, 50). However, Fabiato & Fabiato (26) noted that preloading with Ca^{2+} was necessary to demonstrate the regenerative release process in ventricular tissue of mammalian species other than the rat. Moreover, regenerative release could not be found in frog heart. They concluded that ". . . regenerative release . . . may be important in mammalian atria and rat ventricle, less important in the ventricle of other mammalian species . . . and absent in frog" (26). Kerrick & Best (50) noted that when Cl^- was substituted for proprionate as the major anion in the medium bathing the heart cells (a situation analogous to electrical depolarization), a contraction occurred. Endo & Nakajima (24) showed recently that depolarization of the SR of skinned skeletal fibers induces the release of Ca^{2+}, and suggested that regenerative release may not occur physiologically because the concentration of Ca^{2+} required may be too high. Recently, Baylor & Oetliker (6) have interpreted a portion of a three-component birefringent signal from skeletal muscle as a voltage change across the SR (during Ca^{2+} transport), which is regulated by changes in membrane potentials of the sarcolemma and T system. From voltage clamp studies of frog skeletal muscle, Schneider & Chandler (111) postulated that movement of charged groups during depolarization and repolarization may serve, by their displacement in the T-system membrane, as signals transmitted to the SR to regulate the release of Ca^{2+}. Cardiac mitochondria constitute a large portion of nonmyofibrillar content of cardiac cells and can actively accumulate large quantities of Ca^{2+}. These observations have generated interest in the possibility that mitochondria may constitute uptake and release sites for contractile Ca^{2+} (14, 15, 21, 133). Carafoli et al (15) recently reported that, in addition to a possible Ca^{2+} uptake store, cardiac mitochondria may also function in the release of Ca^{2+} under certain ionic conditions. However, the rates of Na^+-induced release of Ca^{2+} from the mitochondria (15) were not measured, and it is not known if under physiological conditions the Na^+ influx during the spike of the action potential is large enough to raise the internal Na^+ concentration in the cytosol around the mitochondria to the 20–50 mM concentrations required (in the absence of the ruthenium red used to inhibit rebinding of released Ca^{2+} in these authors' studies) for the subsequent release of Ca^{2+} for contraction. In addition, the amount of Ca^{2+} removed from the myofibrils by mammalian mitochondria was calculated by Scarpa & Graziotti (109) from stopped-flow kinetic studies, and found to be only 0.9–1.3 nm Ca^{2+} g^{-1} wet weight of myocardium, presumably less than the amount required for relaxation. In mechanically disrupted cardiac tissue, Bloom et al (10) determined from contractility studies that the mitochondria, might function in the maintenance of resting tension, but could not function in the Ca^{2+} regulation of contractility, which appears to be modulated more by the SR. Thus cardiac mitochondria may serve as a Ca^{2+} sink, but compelling evidence for their participation in the beat-to-beat control of contraction of the heart is lacking.

Cardiac Glycosides and Positive Inotropy

Although the cardiac glycoside-induced positive inotropic action has been known for some time (17), the precise ion-related mechanism by which this effect is produced is not completely understood. Lee & Klaus (62) recently presented an extensive overview of the numerous sites of action that have been proposed for cardiac glycosides. In spite of a considerable amount of evidence indicating that the Na^+, K^+-ATPase may be a receptor for these drugs, direct involvement of this enzyme in the mechanism of action of digitalis is not accepted by all investigators. The recent review by Schwartz, Lindenmayer & Allen (117) of the Na^+,K^+-ATPase includes discussions of the possible relationship between Na^+,K^+-ATPase, cardiac glycosides, and inotropism. It is pertinent here, however, to include recent findings in this important and controversial area, especially in considering the role of increased $(Ca)_i$ concentration as possibly related to Na^+,K^+-ATPase in production of inotropy (55, 117).

Besch et al (9) found that the increased $(dP/dt)_{max}$ in canine myocardium produced by infusion of ouabain was related to the inhibition of the isolated Na^+,K^+-ATPase. More recently, Akera and his colleagues (1, 54) have observed a relationship between the onset and loss of glycoside-induced inotropy in isolated guinea pig atria and glycoside binding to Na^+,K^+-ATPase activity in homogenates. In contrast, others have reported an apparent dissociation of glycoside-induced inotropy and inhibition of Na^+,K^+-ATPase (81, 86, 92). The dissociation reported by Okita et.al (86), who worked with isolated perfused rabbit hearts, was questioned by Schwartz et al (113) who compared ouabain-induced inotropy and the activity of subsequently isolated Na^+,K^+-ATPase in rabbit ventricles with that in the cat, a species that appears to be very sensitive to digitalis (117). These authors pointed out that the levels of activity of isolated Na^+,K^+-ATPase reported by Okita et al (86) prior to, during, and following glycoside-induced inotropy were low, rendering comparison difficult. Furthermore, the fast rate of disappearance of ouabain from the isolated, perfused rabbit heart increases the difficulty of measuring the supposed Na^+,K^+-ATPase inhibition. Schwartz et al (113) observed a temporal correlation between inotropy and Na^+,K^+-ATPase inhibition in the cat, but not in the rabbit. The stability of the in vitro–and ex vivo–formed glycoside-Na^+,K^+-ATPase complex was much greater in cat heart than in the in vitro–formed complex with a rabbit ventricle Na^+,K^+-ATPase.

Ku et al (54) questioned the conclusion of Peters, Rohen & Wasserman (92) that inotropy may not be related to Na^+,K^+-ATPase inhibition. Peters, Rohen & Wasserman (92) used isolated guinea pig atria to study the rate of disappearance of inotropy, but used calf ventricle to measure the dissociation of the in vitro–formed glycoside-Na^+,K^+-ATPase complex. The use of the alkylating derivative of cassaic acid mustard in the study by Peters, Rohen & Wasserman (92) may be of questionable value since the alkylating derivative of strophanthidin, strophanthidin 3-bromoacetate, is a poor probe for Na^+,K^+-ATPase activity because of its lack of specificity in alkylation and its rapid dissociation from binding sites (117). The relationship between inhibition of the Na^+,K^+-ATPase and increase in Ca^{2+} influx has been discussed in detail earlier. The interesting possibility that ouabain may influence contraction by a direct effect on a calcium binding component of Na^+,K^+-ATPase, has been discussed above (36).

Catecholamines

Epinephrine increases the slow Ca^{2+} (and Na^+) current of the action potential in frog atria (136), cardiac contractility (74, 75, 99), and heart rate and glycogenesis (98).

Two theories concerning the role of epinephrine in augmenting Ca^{2+} flux (98) are presented here briefly: a direct effect of epinephrine on Ca^{2+} influx leading to positive inotropy, and a stimulation of adenylate cyclase leading to increased intracellular levels of cyclic AMP, which somehow mediates the contractile response. A possible combination of the two yields a biphasic effect: an increase in Ca^{2+} influx for trigger release of internal stores or for contractile Ca^{2+} alone (16), and a concomitant stimulation of cyclic AMP formation, which could increase Ca^{2+} accumulation by SR, resulting in increased rate of relaxation (48, 114).

Meinertz, Naurath & Scholz (75) observed an epinephrine and/or dibutyryl cyclic AMP stimulation of ^{45}Ca exchange in rat atria. After modifying the original method for ^{45}Ca exchange, Meinertz, Naurath & Scholz (74) concluded that epinephrine causes an increased Ca^{2+} flux. Dibutyryl cyclic AMP appears to act in the same manner, although the data do not preclude an effect of cyclic AMP on the SR function described earlier (48, 115). Similarly, Tsien (132) recently found that cyclic AMP, but not its breakdown product 5'-AMP, administered intracellularly to canine cardiac Purkinje fibers increased the plateau and decreased the action potential duration, effects that are identical to those of epinephrine. Results of Watanabe & Besch (137, 138) appear to indicate a dual function of the catecholamine-β-receptor interaction in isolated perfused guinea pig ventricles. Verapamil pretreatment (presumably blocking the Ca^{2+} slow channel) prevented the isoproterenol-induced positive inotropic response in these preparations, but adenylate cyclase activity was still stimulated. The authors suggested that stimulation of the β-receptor occurs prior to the activation of the Ca^{2+} slow channels (see Addendum).

Brandt, Reiter & Seibel (13) have interpreted the tyramine-produced increase of the positive inotropic effect of epinephrine on isolated guinea pig papillary muscles as a possible antagonism of the shortened plateau phase of the action potential (Ca^{2+} flux) produced by norepinephrine. This would result in a longer plateau, hence a greater influx of external Ca^{2+}. In addition, both Brandt, Reiter & Seibel (13) and Reiter (99) concluded that the inotropic effect of norepinephrine may be limited by its effect on relaxation time, and that tyramine antagonism may reduce this action to allow higher internal accumulation of free Ca^{2+}.

The shortened relaxation time of cardiac muscle observed with epinephrine or norepinephrine (79) may be attributed to catecholamine-cyclic AMP mediated changes in cardiac SR that increase Ca^{2+} sequestration (24a, 48, 115). Removal of sarcolemma from cardiac fibers enabled Fabiato & Fabiato (27) to examine the effects of cyclic AMP directly on the SR. They suggested that cyclic AMP increases relaxation by enhancing the capacity and rate of SR Ca^{2+} accumulation and that the release of this "extra" Ca^{2+} may contribute to the inotropic effect of catecholamines.

In contrast, acetylcholine (ACh) produced a negative inotropic effect in isolated dog and rabbit atria in a few seconds following administration (96), concomitant with a loss of the action potential Ca^{2+} plateau. The authors attribute this effect to an ACh block of Ca^{2+} influx, which prevents refilling of internal release stores. In addition, the authors observed that manganese, which is known to displace Ca^{2+} from cardiac cells and produce uncoupling (58), also produced an ACh-like, negative inotropic action. The mechanism of ACh-induced negative inotropic action is by no means clear, however. Recently, George et al (34) showed quite clearly that the decrease in tension produced by ACh in isolated rabbit atria was preceded by a rise in intracellular cyclic GMP (over 200%) without a change in cyclic AMP content.

Other Inotropic Agents

THYROXINE   Short-term administration of thyroxine in guinea pigs produced an increase in dT/dt 24 hours after one dose (38). This response persisted following β-blockade, indicating that cardiac catecholamine was not involved in the effect. Administration of thyroxine for 8–21 days resulted in a 30% increase in myosin ATPase activity concomitant with a decreased time to peak tension, but no such changes in ATPase activity or speed of shortening in short-term treated animals were observed. According to the authors, short-term thyroxine treatment may result in a change in excitation-contraction coupling, which produces an increased internal Ca^{2+} concentration. However, no measurements of ion concentration or flux were made. Contrary to the report of Goodkind, Dambach et al (38), Rovetto et al (106a) found that injection of large doses of thyroxine did not increase cardiac myosin ATPase of rats.

ANGIOTENSIN   The action of angiotensin, once thought to be mediated by catecholamines, appears to have a more direct positive inotropic effect on the myocardium. Using extrinsic cardiac denervated cats to remove the possibility of catecholamine effect, Dempsey et al (20) observed increased dP/dt concomitant with a prolonged plateau phase of action potential. A similar prolongation of the plateau was reported by Bonnardeaux & Regoli (11) following administration of angiotensin II and its analogs. Thus it appears that an increased Ca^{2+} current during the action potential in response to angiotensin may be directly or indirectly responsible for the positive inotropy observed.

IONOPHORES   Recent studies of certain antibiotics have revealed interesting and potentially useful ion carrier characteristics (95). Of particular interest, with respect to cardiac muscle, is the ionophore X537A, now coded RO 2-2985, which has the ability to bind Ca^{2+} as well as Na^+ and a wide spectrum of cations. Increased force of contraction has been observed in rat diaphragm and rabbit atria following addition of X537A to the media (64). Similarly, Schwartz and his colleagues (116) and de Guzman & Pressman (19) have examined the positive inotropic effects of RO 2-2985 on intact dog heart and on isolated cat and rabbit atria. The mechanism of this interesting effect is still unknown (40).

Conclusions

It is reasonable to conclude that the increased availability of internal Ca^{2+} increases contractility in the myocardium. This increase may occur by a number of mechanisms and the Ca^{2+} may be derived from various sources of cellular or bound external Ca^{2+}. Theories about Ca^{2+} and contraction are generally based on physiological and/or pharmacological interventions that produce alterations of ion distribution. It is difficult to formulate a unified hypothesis because of differences in species studied, drugs employed, assay conditions, and other methodological variables. The complexity of biological membranes, their composite subunits and characteristics, is another source of difficulty in the interpretation of what may appear to be straightforward results.

Further progress in understanding the molecular organization and interaction of membrane components and the forces that act upon them should be of great benefit in the interpretation and evaluation of data in this expanding field. We are thus left with a number of very significant problems in the physiology of inotropy: (a) the molecular mechanism(s) by which Ca^{2+} interacts with membrane sites and is transported into the cell; (b) the quantitative aspects of Ca^{2+} delivery to troponin (superficial sites, SR involvement via regenerative release or electrical activity); and (c) mechanism of Ca^{2+} efflux from the cell.

To solve these problems we need to know:
1. The precise chemical nature of the cardiac membranes;
2. The specific sites or regions on membranes with which ions interact;
3. Microarchitectural changes in the membranes that reversibly precede each contraction and are dependent on ions;
4. Microarchitectural changes that occur during relaxation.

ADDENDUM

Recent reports by Reuter (101a) and Lefkowitz et al (62a), regarding the possible localization and characteristics of the β-adrenergic receptor, came to our attention after the completion of this manuscript, and are included here because of their relevance to the role of catecholamines in augmentation of intracellular Ca^{2+}.

Reuter (101a) observed that the iontophoretic application of norepinephrine to cardiac Purkinje cells accelerated pacemaker activity by a shift in I_{K2} (K^+ current responsible for pacemaker activity). Norepinephrine also increased the slow inward Ca^{2+} current, I_{Ca}, an effect associated with the elevated action potential plateau, lengthened APD, and increased isometric tension in isolated trabeculae and papillary muscles. Dibutyryl cyclic AMP produced the same qualitative effects as the catecholamine, but presumably only after the derivative penetrated the cell and was converted to cyclic AMP, results consistent with those reported by Tsien (132) and Watanabe & Besch (137, 138). Intracellular administration of norepinephrine was ineffective on Purkinje fibers, whereas intracellular iontophoresis of cyclic AMP accelerated pacemaker activity and elevated the plateau (132). Reuter concluded from these and other studies that the β-adrenergic receptors are located on the external surface of cardiac cell membranes and that the positive inotropic effect of norepinephrine, mediated in part via intracellular production of cyclic AMP, is observed only after the drug produces an increase in I_{Ca}. The mechanism by which limiting Ca^{2+} conductance of the membrane is altered is still unknown. Lefkowitz et al (62a), using a labeled specific β-adrenergic antagonist ([^{3}H]alprenolol) on red cell and heart membranes, suggested that their data are consistent with a membrane location of the β-adrenergic receptor.

Literature Cited

1. Akera, T., Baskin, S. I., Tobin, T., Brody, T. M. 1973. Ouabain: Temporal relationship between inotropic effect and the in vitro binding to, and dissociation from (Na$^+$ + K$^+$)-activated ATPase. *Arch. Pharmacol.* 277:151–62
2. Armstrong, C. M. 1975. Ionic pores, gates and gating currents. *Quart. Rev. Biophys.* 7:179–210
3. Baker, P. F., Hodgkin, A. L., Ridgway, E. B. 1970. Two phases of calcium entry during the action potential in giant axons of *Loligo. J. Physiol. London* 208:80–82P
4. Barnes, G. E., Bishop, V. S., Horwitz, L. D., Kaspar, R. L. 1973. The maximum derivatives of left ventricular pressure and transverse internal diameter as indices of the inotropic state of the left ventricle in conscious dogs. *J. Physiol. London* 235:571–90
5. Bassingthwaighte, J. B., Reuter, H. 1972. Calcium movements and excitation-contraction coupling in cardiac cells. *Electrical Phenomena of the Heart*, 353–95. New York: Academic
6. Baylor, S. M., Oetliker, H. 1975. Birefringence experiments on isolated skeletal muscle fibres suggest a possible sig-

nal from the sarcoplasmic reticulum. *Nature* 253:97–101
7. Beeler, G. W., Reuter, H. 1970. Voltage clamp experiments on ventricular myocardial fibers. *J. Physiol. London* 207:165–90
8. Beeler, G. W., Reuter, H. 1970. Membrane calcium current in ventricular myocardial fibres. *J. Physiol. London* 207:191–209
9. Besch, H. R., Allen, J. C., Glick, G., Schwartz, A. 1970. Correlation between the inotropic action of ouabain and effects on subcellular enzyme systems from canine myocardium. *J. Pharmacol. Exp. Ther.* 171:1–21
10. Bloom, S., Brady, A. J., Langer, G. A. 1974. Calcium metabolism and action tension in mechanically disaggregated heart muscle. *J. Mol. Cell. Cardiol.* 6:137–47
11. Bonnardeaux, J. L., Regoli, D. 1974. Action of angiotensin and analogues on the heart. *Can. J. Physiol. Pharmacol.* 52:50–60
12. Brace, R. A., Anderson, D. K., Chen, W.-T., Scott, J. B., Haddy, F. J. 1974. Local effects of hypokalemia on coronary resistance and myocardial con-

tractile force. *Am. J. Physiol.* 227: 590–97

13. Brandt, W., Reiter, M., Seibel, K. 1972. "Supramaximal" enhancement of the inotropic effect of noradrenalin by tyramine. *Arch. Pharmacol.* 273:294–306

14. Carafoli, E. 1975. Mitochondria, Ca^{+2} transport and the regulation of heart contraction and metabolism. *J. Mol. Cell. Cardiol.* 7:83–89

15. Carafoli, E., Tiozzo, R., Lugli, G., Crovetti, F., Kratzing, C. 1974. The release of calcium from heart mitochondria by sodium. *J. Mol. Cell. Cardiol.* 6:361–71

16. Carrier, G. O., Lüllman, H., Neubauer, L., Peters, T. 1974. The significance of a fast exchanging superficial calcium fraction for the regulation of contractile force in heart muscle. *J. Mol. Cell. Cardiol.* 6:333–47

17. Clark, A. J. 1912. The influence of ions upon the action of digitalis. *Proc. R. Soc. Med.* 5:181–97

18. Cole, K. S. 1949. Dynamic electrical characteristics of the squid axon membrane. *Arch. Sci. Physiol.* 3:253–58

19. de Guzman, N. T., Pressman, B. C. 1974. The inotropic effects of the calcium ionophore X537A in the anesthetized dog. *Circulation* 49:1072–77

20. Dempsey, P. J., McCallum, Z. T., Kent, K. M., Cooper, T. 1971. Direct myocardial effects of angiotensin II. *Am. J. Physiol.* 220:477–81

21. Diculescu, I., Popescu, L. M., Ionescu, N., Butucescu, N. 1971. Ultrastructural study of calcium distribution in cardiac muscle cells. *Z. Zellforsch.* 121:181–98

22. Draper, M. H., Weidmann, W. 1951. Cardiac resting and action potentials recorded with an intracellular electrode. *J. Physiol. London* 115:74–94

23. Endo, M., Tanaka, M., Ogawa, Y. 1970. Calcium induced release of calcium from the sarcoplasmic reticulum of skinned skeletal muscle fibers. *Nature* 225:34–36

24. Endo, M., Nakajima, Y. 1973. Release of calcium induced by depolarization of the sarcoplasmic reticulum membrane. *Nature* 246:216–18

24a. Entman, M. L., Levey, G. S., Epstein, S. E. 1969. Mechanism of action of epinephrine and glucagon on the heart: Evidence for a cyclic 3',5'-AMP mediated increase in cardiac sarcotubular stores. *Circ. Res.* 25:429–38

25. Fabiato, A., Fabiato, F. 1972. Excitation-contraction coupling of isolated cardiac fibers with disrupted or closed sarcolemmas. Calcium-dependent cyclic and tonic contractions. *Circ. Res.* 31:293–307

26. Fabiato, A., Fabiato, F. 1973. Activation of skinned cardiac cells. *Eur. J. Cardiol.* 12:143–55

27. Fabiato, A., Fabiato, M. 1975. Relaxing and inotropic effects of cyclic AMP on skinned cardiac cells. *Nature* 253: 556–58

28. Fawcett, D. W., McNutt, N. S. 1969. The ultrastructure of the cat myocardium. I. Ventricular papillary muscle. *J. Cell Biol.* 42:1–45

29. Ford, L. E., Podolsky, R. 1970. Regenerative calcium release within muscle cells. *Science* 167:58–59

30. Forester, G. V., Mainwood, G. W. 1974. Interval dependent inotropic effects in the rat myocardium and the effect of calcium. *Pfluegers Arch.* 352:189–96

31. Forssmann, W. G., Girardier, L. 1970. A study of the T system of the rat heart. *J. Cell Biol.* 44:1–19

32. Fozzard, H. A., Gibbons, W. R. 1973. Action potential and contraction of heart muscle. *Am. J. Cardiol.* 31: 182–92

33. Fuchs, F. 1974. Chemical properties of the calcium receptor site of troponin as determined from binding studies. *Calcium Binding Proteins,* 1–27. Amsterdam: Elsevier

34. George, W. J., White, L. E., Paddock, R. J., Ignano, L. J. 1974. Effects of autonomic agents on contractile force and tissue levels of cyclic GMP in isolated rabbit atria. *Fed. Proc.* 33:344 (Abstr.)

35. Gergely, J. 1974. Some aspects of the role of the sarcoplasmic reticulum and the tropomyosin-troponin system in the control of muscle contraction by calcium ions. *Circ. Res.* 34/35(3):74–82

36. Gervais, A., Lane, L. K., Lindenmayer, G. E. 1975. Ouabain (Ou) effect on calcium (Ca^{++}) binding to purified sheep kidney Na^+,K^+-ATPase (E). *Fed. Proc.* 34:715 (Abstr.)

37. Goddard, G. A., Robinson, J. D. 1975. Calcium fluxes in rat brain synaptosomes. *Fed. Proc.* 34:715 (Abstr.)

38. Goodkind, M. J., Dambach, G. E., Thyrum, P. T., Luchi, R. J. 1974. Effect of thyroxine on ventricular myocardial contractility and ATPase activity in guinea pigs. *Am. J. Physiol.* 226:66–72

39. Greaser, M. L., Yamaguchi, M., Brekke, M., Potter, J. D., Gergely, J. 1972. Troponin subunits and their interactions. *Cold Spring Harbor Symp. Quant. Biol.* 37:235–49

40. Hanley, H. G., Lewis, R. M., Hartley, C. J., Franklin, D., Schwartz, A. 1975. Effects of an inotropic agent, RO 2-2985 (X-537A), on regional blood flow and myocardial function in chronically instrumented conscious dogs and anesthetized dogs. *Circ. Res.* 37:215–25
41. Hille, B. 1970. Ionic channels in nerve membranes. *Progr. Biophys. Mol. Biol.* 21:1–32
42. Hodgkin, A. L., Huxley, A. F. 1952. A quantitative description of membrane current and its application to conduction and excitation in nerve. *J. Physiol. London* 117:500–44
43. Hodgkin, A. L., Keynes, R. D. 1957. Movements of labelled calcium in squid axons. *J. Physiol. London* 138:253–81
44. Hodgson, B. J., Kidwai, A. M., Daniel, E. E. 1972. Uptake of lanthanum by smooth muscle. *Can. J. Physiol. Pharmacol.* 50:730–33
45. Horackova, M., Vassort, G. 1974. Excitation-contraction coupling in frog heart. Effect of veratrine. *Pfluegers Arch.* 352:291–302
46. Johnson, E. A., Lieberman, M. 1971. Heart: Excitation and contraction. *Ann. Rev. Physiol.* 33:479–532
47. Jundt, H., Prozig, H., Reuter, H., Stucki, J. W. 1975. The effect of substances releasing intracellular calcium ions on sodium-dependent calcium efflux from guinea-pig auricles. *J. Physiol. London* 246:229–53
48. Katz, A. M., Repke, D. I. 1973. Calcium-membrane interactions in the myocardium: Effects of ouabain, epinephrine and 3′,5′-cyclic adenosine monophosphate. *Am. J. Cardiol.* 31:193–201
49. Katzung, B. G., Reuter, H., Porzug, H. 1973. Lanthanum inhibits Ca inward current but not Na-Ca exchange in cardiac muscle. *Experientia* 29:1073–75
50. Kerrick, W. G., Best, P. M. 1974. Calcium release in mechanically disrupted heart cells. *Science* 183:434–37
51. Kirk, R. G., Tosteson, D. C. 1973. Cation transport and membrane morphology. *J. Membr. Biol.* 12:273–83
52. Kohlhardt, M., Haastert, H. P., Krause, H. 1973. Evidence of nonspecificity of the Ca channel in mammalian myocardium fibre membranes. Substitution of Ca by Sr, Ba, or Mg as charge carriers. *Pfluegers Arch.* 342:125–36
53. Kolbeck, R. C., Paradise, N. F., Visscher, M. B. 1975. Localization of rapidly exchangeable calcium in mammalian heart muscle. *Am. J. Physiol.* 228:345–51
54. Ku, D., Akera, T., Pew, C. L., Brody, T. M. 1974. Cardiac glycosides: Correlations among Na⁺,K⁺-ATPase, sodium pump and contractility in the guinea pig heart. *Arch. Pharmacol.* 285:185–200
55. Langer, G. A. 1974. Ionic movements and the control of contraction. *The Mammalian Myocardium,* 193–217. New York:Wiley
56. Langer, G. A. 1971. The intrinsic control of myocardial contraction-ionic factors. *N. Engl. J. Med.* 255:1056–71
57. Langer, G. A., Frank, J. S. 1972. Lanthanum in heart cell culture. Effect on calcium exchange correlated with its localization. *J. Cell Biol.* 54:441–55
58. Langer, G. A., Serena, S. D., Nudd, L. M. 1974. Cation exchange in heart cell culture: Correlation with effects on contractile force. *J. Mol. Cell. Cardiol.* 6:149–61
59. Lea, E. J. A., Rich, G. T., Segrest, J. P. 1975. The effects of the membrane-penetrating polypeptide segment of the human erythrocyte MN-glycoprotein on the permeability of model lipid membranes. *Biochim. Biophys. Acta* 382:41–50
60. Leak, L. V. 1970. Fractured surfaces of myocardial cells. *J. Ultrastruc. Res.* 31:76–94
61. Lee, C. O., Fozzard, H. A. 1974. Activities of potassium and sodium in rabbit heart muscle. *Fed. Proc.* 33:299 (Abstr.)
62. Lee, K. S., Klaus, W. 1971. The subcellular basis for the mechanism of inotropic action of cardiac glycosides. *Pharmacol. Rev.* 23:193–261
62a. Lefkowitz, R. J., Mukherjee, C., Coverstone, M., Caron, M. G. 1974. Stereospecific ³H-alprenolol binding sites, β-adrenergic receptors and adenylate cyclase. *Biochem. Biophys. Res. Commun.* 60:703–9
62b. Lee, K. S., Choi, S. J. 1966. Effects of the cardiac glycosides on the Ca uptake of cardiac sarcoplasmic reticulum. *J. Pharmacol. Exp. Ther.* 153:114
63. Leóty, C. 1974. Membrane currents and activation of contraction in rat ventricular fibres. *J. Physiol. London* 239:247–49
64. Levy, S. V., Cohen, J. A., Inesi, G. 1973. Contractile effects of a calcium ionophore. *Nature* 242:461–63
65. Lindenmayer, G. E., Schwartz, A. 1975. A kinetic characterization of calcium on Na⁺, K⁺-ATPase and its po-

tential role as a link between extracellular and intracellular events: Hypothesis for digitalis-induced inotropism. *J. Mol. Cell. Cardiol.* In press

66. Luft, J. L. 1971. Ruthenium red and violet. Its fine structural localization in animal tissues. *Anat. Rec.* 171:369–416

67. McCans, J. L., Lindenmayer, G. E., Munson, R. G., Evans, R. W., Schwartz, A. 1974. A dissociation of positive staircase (Bowditch) from ouabain-induced positive inotropism. Use of verapamil. *Circ. Res.* 35:439–47

68. McDonald, T. F., Sachs, H. G. 1974. Electrical activity in embryonic heart cell aggregates. Development aspects. *Pfluegers Arch.* 354:151–64

69. McLean, M. J., Schigenobu, K., Sperelakis, N. 1974. Two pharmacological types of slow Na+ channels as distinguished by verapamil. *Eur. J. Pharmacol.* 26:379–82

70. McNutt, N. S. 1970. Ultrastructure of intracellular junctions in adult and developing cardiac muscle. *Am. J. Cardiol.* 25:169–83

71. McNutt, N. S., Fawcett, D. W. 1974. Myocardial ultrastructure. *The Mammalian Myocardium,* 1–49. New York: Wiley

72. Madiera, V. M. C., Atunes-Madiera, M. C. 1974. Interaction of ruthenium red with isolated sarcolemma. *J. Membr. Biol.* 17:41–50

73. Mascher, D. 1970. Electrical and mechanical responses from ventricular muscle fibres after inactivation of the sodium carrying system. *Pfluegers Arch.* 317:359–72

74. Meinertz, T., Naurath, H., Scholz, H. 1973. Adrenaline, DB-C-AMP and myocardial 45Ca exchange. Comparative studies in rat and guinea-pig auricles. *Arch. Pharmacol.* 279:313–25

75. Meinertz, T., Naurath, H., Scholz, H. 1973. Stimulatory effects of DB-C-AMP and adrenaline on myocardial contraction and 45Ca exchange. Experiments at reduced concentration and low frequencies of stimulation. *Arch. Pharmacol.* 279:327–38

76. Mines, G. R. 1913. On the functional analysis of the action of electrolytes. *J. Physiol. London* 46:188–235

77. Morad, M., Goldman, Y. 1973. Excitation-contraction coupling in heart muscle. *Progr. Biophys. Mol. Biol.* 27:257–313

78. Morad, M., Greenspan, A. M. 1973. Excitation-contraction coupling as a possible site for the action of digitalis on heart muscle. *Cardiac Arrhythmias,* 479–89. New York: Greene & Stratton

79. Morad, M., Rolett, E. L. 1972. Relaxing effects of catecholamines on mammalian heart. *J. Physiol. London* 224:537–38

80. Mullins, L. J. 1968. A single channel or a dual channel mechanism for nerve excitation. *J. Gen. Physiol.* 52:550–53

81. Murthy, R. V., Kidwai, A. M., Daniel, E. E. 1974. Dissociation of contractile effect and inhibition of Na+,K+-adenosine triphosphatase by cardiac glycosides in rabbit myometrium. *J. Pharmacol. Exp. Ther.* 188:575–81

82. Nayler, W. 1973. An effect of ouabain on the superficially located stores of calcium in cardiac muscle cells. *J. Mol. Cell. Cardiol.* 5:101–10

83. New, W., Trautwein, W. 1972. Inward membrane currents in mammalian myocardium. *Pfluegers Arch.* 334:1–23

84. New, W., Trautwein, W. 1972. The ionic nature of slow inward current and its relation to contraction. *Pfluegers Arch.* 334:24–38

85. Niedergerke, R. 1956. The "staircase" phenomenon and action of calcium on the heart. *J. Physiol. London* 134:569–83

86. Okita, G. T., Richardson, F., Roth-Schechter, B. F. 1973. Dissociation of the positive inotropic action of digitalis from inhibition of sodium and potassium activated adenosine triphosphatase. *J. Pharmacol. Exp. Ther.* 185:1–11

87. Packer, L., Mehard, C. W., Meissner, G., Zahler, W. L., Fleischer, S. 1974. The structural role of lipids in mitochondrial and sarcoplasmic reticulum membranes. Freeze-fracture electron microscope studies. *Biochim. Biophys. Acta* 363:159–81

88. Pappano, A. J. 1970. Calcium dependent action potentials produced by catecholamines in guinea pig atrial muscle fibers depolarized by potassium. *Circ. Res.* 27:379–90

89. Penefsky, Z. 1974. Studies on mechanism of inhibition of cardiac muscle contractile tension by ryanodine. Mechanical response. *Pfluegers Arch.* 347:173–84

90. Penefsky, Z. 1974. Ultrastructural studies on the site of action of ryanodine on heart muscle. *Pfluegers Arch.* 347:185–98

91. Perry, S. V. 1974. Calcium ions and the function of the contractile proteins of muscle. *Biochem. Soc. Symp.* 39:115–32

92. Peters, T., Rahen, R. H., Wassermann, O. 1974. Evidence for a dissociation between positive inotropic effect and inhibition of the Na+,K+-ATPase by ouabain, cassaine, and their alkylating derivatives. *Eur. J. Pharmacol.* 26:166–74

92a. Poole-Wilson, P. A., Langer, G. A. 1975. Effect of pH on ionic exchange and function in rat and rabbit myocardium. *Am. J. Physiol.* In press

92b. Poole-Wilson, P. A., Langer, G. A. 1975. Glycoside inotropy in the absence of an increased K+ efflux. *Circ. Res.* 37:390–95

93. Potter, J. D. 1975. Effect of Mg++ on Ca++ binding to myosin. *Fed. Proc.* 34:671 (Abstr.)

94. Potter, J. D., Gergely, J. 1974. Troponin, tropomyosin and actin interactions in the Ca²⁺ regulation of muscle contraction. *Biochemistry* 13:2697–2703

95. Pressman, B. 1973. Properties of ionophores with broad range cation sensitivity. *Fed. Proc.* 32:1698–1703

96. Prokopczuk, A., Lewartowski, B., Czarnecka, M. 1973. On the cellular mechanism of the inotropic action of acetylcholine on isolated rabbit and dog atria. *Pfluegers Arch.* 339:305–16

97. Rash, J. E., Ellisman, M. H. 1974. Studies of excitable membranes. I. Macromolecular specializations of the neuromuscular junction and nonjunctional sarcolemma. *J. Cell Biol.* 63:567–86

98. Rasmussen, H., Goodman, D. B. P., Tenenhouse, A. 1972. The role of cyclic AMP and calcium in cell activation. *Crit. Rev. Biochem.* 1:95–148

99. Reiter, M. 1972. Differences in the inotropic cardiac effects of noradrenalin and dihydro-ouabain. *Arch. Pharmacol.* 275:243–50

100. Reuter, H. 1973. Divalent cations as charge carriers in excitable membranes. *Progr. Biophys. Mol. Biol.* 26:1–43

101. Reuter, H. 1974. Exchange of calcium in the mammalian myocardium. *Circ. Res.* 34:599–605

101a. Reuter, H. 1974. Localization of β-adrenergic receptors, and the effects of noradrenaline and tension in mammalian cardiac muscle. *J. Physiol. London* 242:429–51

102. Ringer, S. 1883. A further contribution regarding the influence of the different constituents of the blood on the contraction of the heart. *J. Physiol. London* 4:29–42

103. Robertson, J. E. 1959. The ultrastructure of cell membranes and their derivatives. *Biochem. Soc. Symp.* 16:1–43

104. Rosen, M. R., Hoffman, B. F. 1973. Brief Reviews: Mechanisms of action of antiarrhythmic drugs. *Circ. Res.* 32:1–8

105. Rosenquist, T. H. 1970. Ultrastructural changes in plasma membrane and sarcoplasmic reticulum of myocardial cells during hibernation. *Cryobiology* 4:14–17

106. Rougier, O., Vassort, G., Garnier, D., Gargonil, M., Caraboeuf, E. 1969. Existence and role of a slow inward current during the frog atrial action potential. *Pfluegers Arch.* 308:91–110

106a. Rovetto, M. J., Hjalmarson, A. C., Morgan, H. E., Barrett, M. J., Goldstein, R. A. 1972. Hormonal control of cardiac myosin adenosine triphosphate in the rat. *Circ. Res.* 31:397–409

107. Rubio, R., Sperelakis, N. 1972. Penetration of horseradish peroxidase into the terminal cisternae of frog skeletal muscle fibers and blockade of caffeine contraction by Ca++ depletion. *Z. Zellforsch.* 124:57–71

108. Rubio, R., Villar-Palasi, R. 1975. Effect of c-AMP dependent protein kinase on actomyosin ATPase control by calcium. *Fed. Proc.* 34:262 (Abstr.)

109. Scarpa, A., Graziotti, P. 1973. Mechanism for intracellular calcium regulation in heart. I. Stopped flow measurements of Ca++ uptake by cardiac mitochondria. *J. Gen. Physiol.* 67:756–72

110. Schneider, J. A., Sperelakis, N. 1975. Slow calcium and sodium responses induced by isoproterenol and methylxanthines in isolated perfused guinea pig hearts exposed to elevated potassium. *J. Mol. Cell. Cardiol.* 7:249–73

111. Schneider, M. F., Chandler, W. K. 1973. Voltage dependent charge movement in skeletal muscle: A possible step in excitation contraction coupling. *Nature* 242:244–46

112. Schwartz, A. 1974. Active transport in the mammalian myocardium. *The Mammalian Myocardium*, 81–104. New York: Wiley

113. Schwartz, A., Allen, J. C., Van Winkle, W. B., Munson, R. 1974. Further studies on the correlation between the inotropic action of ouabain and its interaction with the Na+,K+-adenosine triphosphatase: Isolated perfused rabbit and cat hearts. *J. Pharmacol. Exp. Ther.* 191:119–27

114. Schwartz, A., Entman, M. L., Bornet, E. P. 1974. Rapid kinetic studies of cardiac sarcoplasmic reticulum. Effect of

inhibitors, drugs, pH, dyes, ionophores: New possible therapeutic application for RO 2-2985/1 (X537A). *Calcium Binding Proteins,* 425–67. Amsterdam: Elsevier

115. Schwartz, A. et al 1975. A spectrophotometric analysis of the rate of calcium uptake into sarcoplasmic reticulum of cardiac muscle and skeletal muscle (slow, fast and mixed) stimulated by cyclic-AMP-dependent protein kinase and by phosphorylase b kinase: Relationship to phosphorylation. *Biochim. Biophys. Acta.* In press

116. Schwartz, A. et al 1974. Hemodynamic and biochemical effects of a new positive inotropic agent. Antibiotic ionophore RO 2-2985. *Circ. Res.* 34:102–11

117. Schwartz, A., Lindenmayer, G. E., Allen, J. C. 1975. The sodium potassium adenosine triphosphatase: Pharmacological, physiological and biochemical aspects. *Pharmacol. Rev.* 27:3–134

118. Schwartz, A., Reddy, Y. S. 1974. Protein kinase catalyzed phosphorylation of cardiac troponin: Possible regulation by actin and myosin. *Calcium Binding Proteins* 223–51. Amsterdam: Elsevier

119. Scott, J. E. 1968. Ion binding in solutions containing acid mucopolysaccharides. *Chemistry and Physiology of Mucopolysaccharides,* 171–87. Boston, Mass.:Little-Brown

120. Shigenobu, K., Schneider, J. A., Sperelakis, N. 1974. Verapamil blockade of slow Na^{++} and Ca^{++} responses in myocardial cells. *J. Pharmacol. Exp. Ther.* 190:280–88

121. Shine, K., Serena, S. D., Langer, G. A. 1971. Kinetic localization of contractile calcium in rabbit myocardium. *Am. J. Physiol.* 221:1408–17

122. Silber, H. B. 1974. A model to describe binding differences between calcium and the lanthanides in biological systems. *FEBS Lett.* 41:303–6

123. Singer, S. J. 1974. The molecular organization of membranes. *Ann. Rev. Biochem.* 43:804–33

124. Singer, S. J., Nicholson, G. L. 1972. The fluid mosaic model of the structure of cell membranes. *Science* 175:720–31

125. Solaro, R. J., Briggs, F. N. 1974. Calcium and the control of enzymatic and mechanical activity in muscle. *Calcium Binding Proteins,* 587–607. Amsterdam: Elsevier

126. Sommer, J. R., Johnson, E. A. 1970. Comparative ultrastructure of cardiac membrane specializations. A review. *Am. J. Cardiol.* 25:184–94

127. Smythies, J. R., Benington, F., Bradley, R. J., Bridges, W. F., Morin, R. D. 1972. Molecular structure of the sodium channel. *J. Theor. Biol.* 43: 29–42

128. Sulakhe, P., Drummond, G. I., Ng, D. C. 1973. Calcium binding by skeletal muscle sarcolemma. *J. Biol. Chem.* 248:4150–57

129. Thyrum, P. T. 1974. Inotropic stimuli and systolic calcium flow in depolarized guinea-pig atria. *J. Pharmacol. Exp. Ther.* 188:166–79

130. Tillack, T., Boland, R., Martonosi, A. 1974. The ultrastructure of developing sarcoplasmic reticulum. *J. Biol. Chem.* 249:624–33

131. Tritthart, H., Volkmann, R., Weiss, R., Fleckenstein, A. 1973. Calcium-mediated action potentials in mammalian myocardium. Alteration of membrane response as induced by changes of Ca_i or by promoters and inhibitors of transmembrane Ca inflow. *Arch. Pharmacol.* 280:239–52

132. Tsien, R. W. 1973. Adrenaline-like effects of intracellular iontophoresis of cyclic AMP in cardiac Purkinje fibers. *Nature New Biol.* 245:120–21

133. Ueba, Y., Ito, Y., Chidsey, C. A. 1971. Intracellular calcium and myocardial contractility. I. Influence of intracellular calcium. *Am. J. Physiol.* 220: 1553–57

134. Van der Kloot, W., Kita, H. 1975. The effects of the "calcium antagonist" verapamil on muscle action potentials in frog and crayfish and on neuromuscular transmission in the crayfish. *Comp. Biochem. Physiol.* 50:121–25

135. Vassort, G. 1973. Influence of sodium ions on the regulation of frog myocardial contractility. *Pfluegers Arch.* 339: 225–40

136. Vassort, G. et al 1969. Effects of adrenaline on membrane inward currents during the cardiac action potential. *Pfluegers Arch.* 309:70–81

137. Watanabe, A. M., Besch, H. R. Jr. 1974. Cyclic adenosine monophosphate modulation of slow calcium influx channels in guinea pig hearts. *Circ. Res.* 35:316–24

138. Watanabe, A. M., Besch, H. R. Jr. 1974. Subcellular myocardial effects of verapamil and D_{600}: Comparison with propranolol. *J. Pharmacol. Exp. Ther.* 191:241–51

139. Weidmann, S. 1974. Heart: Electrophysiology. *Ann. Rev. Physiol.* 36: 155–69

140. Weingart, R. 1974. The permeability to tetramethylammonium ions of the surface membrane and the intercalated discs of sheep and calf myocardium. *J. Physiol. London* 240:741–62

141. Weiss, G. B. 1974. Cellular pharmacology of lanthanum. *Ann. Rev. Pharmacol.* 14:234–354

142. Weiss, R., Tritthart, H., Walter, B. 1974. Correlation of Na-withdrawal effects on Ca-mediated action potentials and contractile activity in the cat myocardium. *Pfluegers Arch.* 350:299–307

143. Wood, E. H., Heppner, R. L., Weidmann, S. 1969. Inotropic effects of electric currents. I. Positive and negative effects of constant electric currents or current pulses applied during cardiac action potentials. II. Hypothesis. Calcium movements, excitation-contraction coupling and inotropic effects. *Circ. Res.* 24:409–45

144. Potter, J. D., Gergely, J. 1975. The calcium and magnesium binding sites on troponin and their role in the regulation of myofibrillar adenosine triphosphotase. *J. Biol. Chem.* 250:4628–33

BIOCHEMICAL ADAPTATIONS TO ENDURANCE EXERCISE IN MUSCLE

❖1151

John O. Holloszy and Frank W. Booth
Department of Preventive Medicine, Washington University School of Medicine,
St. Louis, Missouri 63110

INTRODUCTION

Two quite distinct adaptive responses can be induced in skeletal muscle by regularly performed, strenuous exercise. The nature of the exercise stimulus determines the type of adaptation. One type of adaptation involves hypertrophy of the muscle cells with an increase in strength; it is exemplified in its most extreme form by the muscles of weight lifters and body builders. The second type of adaptation involves an increase in the capacity of muscle for aerobic metabolism with an increase in endurance and is found in its most highly developed form in the muscles of competitive middle- and long-distance runners, long-distance cross-country skiers, bicyclists, and swimmers. Although many types of physical activity can bring about varying degrees of both types of adaptation in the same muscle, it does appear that these adaptations can occur quite independently of each other in their most extreme forms. For example, the hypertrophied muscles of weight lifters do not appear to have an increased respiratory capacity (45), whereas the muscles of rodents trained by prolonged daily running, which have a large increase in respiratory capacity, are not hypertrophied (56, 92) and show no increase in strength (12).

This review deals with the biochemical adaptations induced in skeletal muscle by the endurance type of exercise and with the physiological consequences of these adaptations.

BACKGROUND INFORMATION

Different Types of Skeletal Muscle Fiber

Most of the skeletal muscles in those mammalian species in which the chronic adaptive responses to exercise have been studied are a mixture of three different fiber types. In rodent muscles, these are the fast-twitch white fibers, which have a low respiratory capacity, a high glycogenolytic capacity, and high myosin ATPase

273

activity; the fast-twitch red fibers, which have a high respiratory capacity, a high glycogenolytic capacity, and high myosin ATPase activity; and the slow-twitch red fibers, which have a moderately high respiratory capacity, a low glycogenolytic capacity, low myosin ATPase activity, and are fatigue resistant (5, 7, 8, 33, 97). In many other mammalian species, including man, in contrast to rodents, the slow-twitch rather than the fast-twitch red fibers have the highest respiratory capacity (22, 30, 41).

The earlier studies of the biochemical adaptations of muscle to endurance exercise were performed on whole mixed muscles, such as the gastrocnemius, of rodents, and on biopsy specimens of mixed muscles in human subjects. In more recent studies, two approaches were used to evaluate the adaptive responses of various types of muscle fiber. One approach has been to evaluate the levels of various enzymes histochemically in rodent and human muscles by their staining intensity; this quali-tative approach has led to some problems in interpretation which are discussed later. In other studies on rodents, the soleus muscle, which consists predominantly of slow-twitch fibers, has been used for biochemical studies on slow-twitch red fibers. For biochemical studies on fast-twitch white fibers, the superficial portion of the whole quadriceps, or of the vastus lateralis of the rat has been used, as these consist essentially of white fibers. The deepest red portion, closest to the femur, of the whole quadriceps or of the vastus lateralis, which consist predominantly of fast-twitch red fibers in the rat were used for studies on fast-twitch red fibers, (5, 8, 9, 126, 130). It is much more difficult to study the different fiber types in human muscle biopsies because of the small amount of tissue and because the red and white fibers are closely intermingled in human muscle. However, biochemical studies on individual fibers are underway in a number of Scandinavian laboratories; portions of single fibers, dissected out of freeze-dried sections of biopsy specimens, are analyzed using mi-croanalytical methods (36).

In studies on rodents, running has been the most effective and commonly used form of training (11, 49, 56, 121). In one program used in numerous studies, young rats are trained to run for progressively longer periods on a motor-driven treadmill up an 8° incline until at the end of 12 weeks they are running at 31 meters per minute for two hours per day, five days per week. They are maintained at this work level for a few more weeks. This program produces a high level of training, with a large increase in endurance but no muscle hypertrophy (40, 56, 92). In rats, swimming is less effective than running for inducing adaptive changes in the skeletal muscles, as these animals do only the minimum work necessary to keep afloat. Six hours of daily swimming for 14 weeks produced only 35% as great an increase in the respiratory capacity of leg muscles in rats as does the running program just de-scribed (4).

MITOCHONDRIAL ADAPTATIONS TO ENDURANCE EXERCISE

Studies on muscle homogenates and on the mitochondrial fraction from muscle have shown that endurance exercise-training increases the capacity of skeletal muscle to oxidize pyruvate. This increase in the capacity to oxidize carbohydrate has been demonstrated in rats (5, 56), humans (86), and guinea pigs (11). Subsequent studies on muscle mitochondria (84) and on muscle homogenates (5, 84) showed that the capacity to oxidize long chain fatty acids is also increased in exercise-trained rats. The increase in muscle respiratory capacity varies with the duration and intensity of the exercise. In rats subjected to the treadmill running program described earlier, the capacities to oxidize fat and carbohydrate both increase twofold (5, 56, 84). The rates at which homogenates of leg muscles oxidize β-hydroxybutyrate and acetoacetate are also increased in trained rats (127). These adaptations involve all three types of muscle fiber (5, 126).

The mitochondria from the trained animals' muscles exhibit normal respiratory control and tightly coupled oxidative phosphorylation (11, 56, 84), providing evidence that the increases in the capacities to oxidize fat and carbohydrate are accompanied by a parallel rise in the capacity to generate ATP via oxidative phosphorylation.

Underlying the exercise-induced increase in the capacity of muscle to generate ATP from the oxidative metabolism of substrates are increases in the levels of the enzymes involved in the activation, transport, and β-oxidation of long chain fatty acids (58, 84), the enzymes involved in ketone oxidation (126, 127), the enzymes of the tricarboxylic acid (TCA) cycle (29, 47, 62), the components of the mitochondrial respiratory chain involved in the oxidation of DPNH and succinate (16, 56, 86, 124), and mitochondrial coupling factor 1 (88). These increases in the levels of activity of a wide range of mitochondrial enzymes appear to result from an increase in enzyme protein concentration. The increases in the concentrations of the cytochromes (14, 56, 62) and in the protein content of the mitochondrial fraction of skeletal muscle is in accord with this inference (56, 86). Electron-microscopic studies on human (65, 86) and on rat (49) skeletal muscles have provided evidence that increases in both the size and number of mitochondria are responsible for the increase in total mitochondrial protein. In addition to the increase in size and number, there is also an alteration in the composition of skeletal muscle mitochondria in rats that have adapted to endurance exercise (61, 62, 88, 126). For example, in rats adapted to the two-hour-long program of daily running described in the preceding section, a number of TCA cycle enzymes, including citrate synthase (62, 126), aconitase (58), NAD-specific isocitrate dehydrogenase (62), and succinate dehydrogenase (62), increased twofold, and others, including α-ketoglutarate dehydrogenase (62) and malate dehydrogenase (62, 83), increased 50–60%. The TCA cycle–related enzyme glutamate dehydrogenase increased only about 30% (62) and acetoacetyl-CoA thiolase increased approximately 50% (126, 127). A number of mitochondrial enzyme activities do not increase at all in muscle in response to training when expressed per gram of muscle and, because of the increase in mitochondrial protein, are decreased when expressed per milligram of mitochondrial protein; these enzymes include mitochondrial creatine kinase (88), adenylate kinase (88), and α-glycerophosphate dehydrogenase (61). Creatine kinase and adenylate kinase activities in the cytoplasm are also unchanged in gastrocnemius muscle (88).

The exercise-induced adaptive responses of a number of mitochondrial enzymes have been studied in all three types of skeletal muscle fibers in the rat. Of these, citrate synthase (5, 126), carnitine palmityltransferase (5), cytochrome oxidase (5), cytochrome c (F. W. Booth and J. O. Holloszy, unpublished data), and acetoacetyl-CoA thiolase (126) increased to roughly the same extent, on a percentage basis, in the three fiber types. In contrast, β-hydroxybutyrate dehydrogenase activity increased 2.6-fold in slow red muscle, and sixfold in fast red muscle, while changing from not detectable to just measurable in white muscle of rats subjected to the running program described earlier (126).

Mitochondria from normal mammalian tissues are impermeable to NADH; a number of mechanisms have been proposed to explain how NADH formed during glycolysis is oxidized (123). The best documented of these are the malate-aspartate and the α-glycerophosphate shuttles (123). Muscles of trained individuals appear to produce less lactate than those of untrained individuals, even at comparable rates of glycogenolysis (111). This finding suggests that the capacity to transfer reducing equivalents to the respiratory chain from cytoplasmic NADH might be increased in response to exercise. In studies designed to test this possibility, mitochondrial α-glycerophosphate dehydrogenase, expressed per gram of muscle, was unaffected in rat gastrocnemius muscle (61). In contrast, the enzymes of the malate-aspartate shuttle were increased in the mitrochondria and the cytoplasm of leg muscles of trained rats (57).

A pathway for pyruvate removal in skeletal muscle is conversion to alanine via the alanine transaminase reaction. The quantitative importance of this pathway has been demonstrated by Felig & Wahren (38). Alanine transaminase activity increases in both the mitochondria and cytoplasm of gastrocnemius muscles of endurance exercise-trained rats (83). This adaptation could result in conversion of a greater proportion of the pyruvate formed in muscle to alanine and less to lactate, and thus help protect against the development of acidosis in muscle during strenuous exercise.

There is evidence that hyperthyroidism is associated with an increase in mitochondria in many tissues (118), and there has been some interest in the possibility that thyroid hormones play a role in the increase in muscle mitochondria induced by exercise. Although thyroidectomized rats have lower levels of succinate dehydrogenase activity in their skeletal muscles than euthyroid animals, a highly significant increase in the level of this enzyme occurred in thyroidectomized animals in response to a program of running (48). Hypophysectomized rats also show an increase in succinate dehydrogenase in skeletal muscle in response to training (48). Euthyroid exercised rats do not have any increase in triiodothyronine (T_3) and thyroxin (T_4) concentrations in skeletal muscle (129). Prolonged, severe thyrotoxicosis induces only 40% as great an increase in mitochondria in rat gastrocnemius muscle as does a program of treadmill running (128). It seems clear from all these observations that the increase in muscle mitochondria induced by exercise is not mediated by thyroid hormones.

Skeletal muscles of protein-deficient and diabetic rats have lower levels of mitochondrial enzymes than normal controls, but also undergo large increases in mitochondrial content in response to endurance exercise (44, 66).

Effects of a Reduction in Contractile Activity on Muscle Mitochondria

Not surprisingly, some of the biochemical changes induced in skeletal muscle by a reduction in contractile activity run counter to those seen in response to a chronic increase in contractile activity. The magnitude of the changes brought about by immobilization depends on the extent to which contractile activity is reduced. Some techniques for producing immobilization are more effective in reducing contractile activity than others. For example, immobilization of both the knee and ankle joints reduces contractile activity more than does immobilization of the ankle joint alone (39). Also, immobilizing a muscle in a position shorter than its normal resting length produces greater atrophy than immobilizing it at at greater than normal resting length (116).

In one study, ten days of immobilization resulted in decreases in the capacities of rat plantaris and soleus muscles to oxidize β-hydroxybutyrate, palmitate, and glucose (104). This decrease was significant when expressed either per muscle or per gram of muscle (104). The weights of the soleus and plantaris muscles decreased to 70% and 60%, respectively, of control values after 10 days of immobilization (104). In addition, significant decreases in the respiratory control index and ADP/O ratio (81) and a significant increase in ATPase activity (82) of mitochondria from rat gastrocnemius muscles immobilized from one to nine days have been reported.

The decrease in the levels of mitochondrial enzymes during immobilization does not appear to be the same in the different types of skeletal muscle fiber. Cytochrome oxidase activity per gram of muscle was significantly reduced in fast-twitch red, but not in slow-twitch red or fast-twitch white, fibers in rats after four weeks of immobilization (19). The time course of the decrease in the levels of various mitochondrial enzymes in the same muscle varies considerably. It has been reported that in rat skeletal muscle, cytochrome oxidase and monoamine oxidase activities per milligram of mitochondrial protein are unchanged after nine days of immobilization, whereas mitochondrial malate dehydrogenase is significantly decreased after two days (103). It is not known whether the decrease in the capacity of immobilized muscle to generate ATP via aerobic metabolism plays a role in the development of muscle atrophy or just occurs concomitantly.

TRIGLYCERIDE METABOLISM

Endogenous triglyceride stores can contribute a considerable portion of the energy utilized by red skeletal muscle during exercise (6, 23, 43, 101). In a group of men trained by bicycling, the capacity of quadriceps muscle to incorporate fatty acids into triglycerides was increased (86). Intramuscular stores of triglycerides also appear to be increased in trained men (85). In rats trained by means of treadmill running, a significant increase occurred in the capacity of skeletal muscle to synthesize triglycerides by esterification of glycerol-3-phosphate (2).

Exercise can result in a reduction in serum triglyceride levels (64). There is evidence that serum triglycerides can be utilized by skeletal muscle (71). In this context, the finding in a recent study (21) that lipoprotein lipase activity is increased threefold in fast-red muscle, twofold in slow-red, and twofold in white muscle fibers in rats subjected to a 12 week long program of running is of considerable interest, as it suggests that the capacity to hydrolyze triglycerides to free fatty acids (FFA) may be increased by exercise-training.

MYOGLOBIN

In the skeletal muscles of land mammals, myoglobin content generally closely parallels respiratory capacity; muscles that are dark red in color are rich in mitochondria and myoglobin; white muscles have a low respiratory capacity and contain little myoglobin. Exercise-training can increase muscle myoglobin concentration (78, 92). In rats subjected to a program of running for 14 weeks, myoglobin increased approximately 80% in hindlimb muscles (92). Myoglobin increases the rate of O_2 diffusion through a fluid layer (52). It seems likely that myoglobin may also facilitate O_2 utilization in muscle by increasing the rate of its diffusion through the cytoplasm to the mitochondria.

PHYSIOLOGICAL CONSEQUENCES OF THE EXERCISE-INDUCED INCREASE IN THE CAPACITY OF SKELETAL MUSCLE FOR AEROBIC METABOLISM

Submaximal Exercise

Individuals who have adapted to endurance exercise derive more of their energy from fat and less from carbohydrate than untrained individuals during submaximal exercise (26, 54, 110). The term *submaximal exercise* is used here to mean work requiring less than the individual's maximum capacity to utilize O_2 (VO_2 max). Serial biopsies of the quadriceps muscle during standardized submaximal exercise, showed that men deplete their muscle glycogen stores less rapidly when they are trained than when they are untrained (54, 110, 111). Exercise-trained rats deplete both muscle and liver glycogen less rapidly than untrained animals during standardized exercise tests (4, 40). In a recent study (40), the total amount of glycogen utilized during a standardized bout of exercise was inversely related to the respiratory capacity of the rat's muscles; the magnitude of the increase in mitochondria in the animals' gastrocnemius muscles varied over a twofold range as a result of varying the duration of the different groups' daily exercise sessions between 10 and 120 minutes per day. There was a significant correlation between how long the animals could run before they became exhausted and the respiratory capacity of their muscles (40). It is also well documented that trained individuals have lower blood (35, 54, 105, 110, 111) and muscle (110, 111) lactate levels than untrained individuals during submaximal exercise.

For many years it was believed that the trained individual's lesser reliance on carbohydrate [as reflected in lower lactate levels, slower glycogen depletion, and a lower respiratory quotient (RQ) during submaximal exercise] and his greater endurance were a result of improved delivery of O_2 to the working muscles. This concept that trained individuals' muscles are better supplied with blood and O_2 and are therefore "less hypoxic" than muscles of untrained individuals during submaximal exercise now appears to have been invalidated by studies showing that blood flow per gram of working muscle is lower in trained than in untrained men at the same absolute work level (16, 27, 50, 124). The working muscles compensate for the lower blood flow in the trained state by extracting more O_2; this is reflected in a greater arteriovenous O_2 difference (35, 109). Muscle blood flow appears to be similar at the same relative work load, that is, at the same percentage of the individual's $\dot{V}O_2max$, in the trained and untrained states (50). Further evidence against improved O_2 delivery to hypoxic muscles is the finding that O_2 uptake at the same absolute work load is the same in the trained and untrained states (27, 109, 110). If the working muscles were hypoxic, and if their O_2 supply were increased by training, one would expect O_2 uptake to be higher in the trained state at the same submaximal work level. In this context, it appears likely that the skeletal muscles' increased content of mitochondria and myoglobin, rather than improved O_2 delivery, is responsible for the trained individual's lower lactate levels, slower glycogen depletion, and lower RQ during submaximal exercise.

The rate at which muscle cells consume oxygen during work is primarily determined by the frequency of contraction when load is constant; the O_2 uptake of muscle cells can therefore be varied over a wide range by varying the work rate (24, 42). The mechanism by which oxygen consumption is closely geared to work rate relates to the tight coupling of phosphorylation of ADP to electron transport. When O_2 and substrate are not limiting, the rate of respiration appears to be an inverse function of the ratio $ATP/(ADP + P_i)$ (79). When muscle contracts, ATP and creatine phosphate (CP) are split and the levels of ADP and P_i in the mitochondria rise, leading to an increase in the rate of respiration. The increase in mitochondrial ADP appears to follow a saturation curve and attains a steady-state level, which is determined by the frequency of contraction (68), and, in turn, is largely responsible for determining the rate of O_2 consumption (79). Once steady-state levels of mitochondrial ADP and O_2 consumption are attained in a muscle cell contracting at a frequency that results in a submaximal rate of O_2 uptake (i.e. aerobic work), the rate of ATP formation via oxidative phosphorylation during and between muscle contractions must be sufficiently great to balance the rate of ATP splitting during the contraction. In the period between the beginning of work and attainment of the steady state, before ATP hydrolysis is balanced by oxidative phosphorylation, the concentrations of CP and ATP fall in muscle until steady state is attained. Simultaneously, the concentrations of ADP and P_i must rise in the mitochondria until electron transport, O_2 consumption, and oxidative phosphorylation increase sufficiently to balance ATP breakdown.

Oxygen consumption is the same in the trained and untrained states at the same submaximal work rate (27, 109, 110). As muscle adapted to endurance exercise has up to twice as many mitochondrial cristae per gram as untrained muscle, the steady-state levels of intramitochondrial ADP and P_i required to attain the same submaximal rate of O_2 consumption at a given work rate must be lower in trained than in untrained muscle. This is so because, with more mitochondrial respiratory chains, the rate of electron transport and O_2 consumption per respiratory chain must be lower to attain the same total O_2 consumption. In other words, the greater the number of mitochondrial respiratory chains per gram of muscle, the lower must be the O_2 uptake per respiratory chain to maintain a given submaximal level of O_2 uptake per gram of muscle. In this context, it seems reasonable that, in the process of attaining a given steady-state level of O_2 consumption, CP and ATP levels must decrease less and ADP, P_i, and creatine levels must increase less in muscles of trained as compared to untrained individuals. Because muscle contains high levels of adenylate kinase, some of the ADP formed is converted to AMP, part of which is deaminated by the action of adenylate deaminase, resulting in formation of ammonia (80). With a smaller rise in ADP, it seems likely that AMP and ammonia levels may also be lower in trained muscles during submaximal exercise, although no information on this point is yet available.

The intracellular levels of ATP, CP, P_i, AMP, ADP, and ammonia play major roles in controlling the rate of glycolysis (76, 91, 122, 131). ATP and creatine phosphate inhibit phosphofructokinase, and this inhibition is counteracted by P_i, ADP, AMP, and ammonia (76, 91, 122, 131). Therefore, because of higher steady-state levels of ATP and CP and lower levels of P_i; ADP, and, possibly, of AMP and ammonia, glycolysis should occur at a slower rate in muscle adapted to endurance exercise than in untrained muscle at a given submaximal rate of work and O_2 utilization. This could, in part, explain the slower rates of muscle glycogen depletion and lactate formation seen in the trained as compared to the untrained state during submaximal exercise. Experimental evidence supporting this line of reasoning has come from studies on muscle biopsies obtained from exercising men (111). At the same submaximal levels of work and O_2 consumption, the decreases in the steady-state concentrations of CP and ATP, the rate of glycogen depletion, and the increase in lactate in quadriceps muscle were all lower in the trained as compared to the untrained state in the same individual (111).

Another factor that helps to account for the slower glycogen depletion and lactate production is the shift in the carbon source of the TCA cycle. As discussed earlier, the trained individual derives a greater percentage of his energy from fat oxidation than does the untrained during submaximal exercise. It seems reasonable to ask why this should be so, as endurance exercise induces comparable increases in the capacities of skeletal muscle to oxidize fat and carbohydrate (5, 56, 84). The answer probably lies in certain of the control mechanisms that regulate carbohydrate metabolism. Among these is the rate of fatty acid oxidation.

At a given metabolic rate, the rate of fatty acid oxidation by a tissue appears to be determined by two factors; the concentration of fatty acids (i.e. substrate availability) and the capacity of the tissue to oxidize fat. When the metabolic rate is constant at rest, or during steady-state exercise, the rate of fat oxidation increases linearly with fatty acid concentration; saturating concentrations of free fatty acids do not appear to have been attained in vivo (93, 95). Thus the availability of fatty acids to the mitochondria is probably the rate-limiting factor for fatty acid oxidation at any given respiratory rate, in vivo. However, at any concentration of fatty acids, the rate of fatty acid oxidation will be highest in those tissues with the greatest capacity to oxidize fat. For example, at the same fatty acid concentration, the heart will oxidize fatty acids more rapidly than will skeletal muscle, and red muscle will oxidize fat more rapidly than white. Because the rate at which a substrate is utilized is a function of the level of enzyme activity, regardless of whether or not substrate concentration is at a saturating level, the muscles of trained individuals, with their greater capacity for fat oxidation, could be expected to oxidize more fat at the same fatty acid concentration than those of untrained individuals. An increase in the oxidation of fatty acids results in a decrease in carbohydrate utilization brought about, in part, by a reduction in the rate of glycolysis and pyruvate oxidation (87, 94). This may be mediated by an increase in the concentration of citrate with inhibition of phosphofructokinase (87, 91). As plasma FFA levels tend to be lower in the trained than in the untrained state during submaximal exercise (69, 70, 102, 127), the greater rate of fat oxidation in trained individuals appears to be due entirely to the increase in the capacity of their muscles to oxidize fatty acids.

One factor implicated in the development of muscle fatigue during prolonged exercise, which forces an individual to stop or slow his pace, is depletion of muscle glycogen stores (1, 17). The adaptations induced in skeletal muscle by endurance exercise could, by the above mechanisms, be responsible for postponing depletion of muscle glycogen and thus increasing endurance. The accumulation of a high concentration of lactate may also play a role in the development of fatigue during brief, strenuous exercise (55, 72). Lactic acid concentrations are lower in skeletal muscle and blood in the trained, as compared to the untrained, state at the same submaximal work rate (35, 54, 105, 110, 111). This difference may be explained by a decrease in the rate of glycolysis by the mechanisms discussed earlier and perhaps by the increases in the capacities of alanine transaminase and of the malate-aspartate shuttle to compete with lactate dehydrogenase for pyruvate and NADH, respectively. A third factor that may limit endurance during prolonged exercise is the development of hypoglycemia (25, 100). Trained animals deplete their liver glycogen more slowly than untrained animals during submaximal exercise and are therefore protected against hypoglycemia (4, 40). Decreased utilization of glucose by trained muscle, probably as a result of increased fat oxidation, must play the major role in accounting for the slower depletion of liver glycogen (4, 40).

Maximum O_2 Uptake

Endurance exercise-training induces an adaptive increase in maximum cardiac output (34, 35, 107, 109), which implies an increase in the maximum capacity to supply O_2 to the working muscles. However, studies using the ^{133}Xe clearance method have shown that maximum flow to the working muscles, expressed as milliliters per gram of muscle per minute, is not increased in the trained state (16, 27, 50, 124). It would therefore appear that any increase in $\dot{V}O_2$ max brought about by an increase in maximum cardiac output is the result of delivery of O_2 to a larger mass of working muscle rather than to delivery of more O_2 to the individual muscle cells. Although considerable variability in response has been noted among individuals, on the average, an increase in maximum cardiac output appears to account for approximately 50% of the rise in $\dot{V}O_2$max that occurs in response to training (34, 35, 107–109).

The other 50% of the increase is accounted for by increased extraction of O_2 by the working muscles; this is reflected in an increased arteriovenous O_2 difference and a lower O_2 tension in venous blood (34, 35, 107–109). It is therefore not surprising that a number of investigators have found a good correlation between skeletal muscle respiratory capacity and $\dot{V}O_2$max (20, 65, 75).

There is no experimental information regarding the mechanism by which trained muscle cells extract more O_2 from the blood. However, if delivery of O_2 to the muscle cells during maximal exercise is the same in the trained and untrained states, as suggested by the ^{133}Xe clearance data, it seems reasonable to assume that O_2 tension in the muscle cells and, secondarily, in the capillaries must be lower in the trained state as a result of the greater number of muscle mitochondria and of the higher work rate required to attain $\dot{V}O_2$max.

ENZYMES OF GLYCOLYSIS, GLYCOGENOLYSIS, AND GLYCOGEN SYNTHESIS

Hexokinase is unique among the glycolytic enzymes in that its activity in different types of muscles varies with respiratory capacity (15), which is highest in the heart and lowest in white skeletal muscle. It is interesting in this context that exercise, which induces an increase in the mitochondrial content of skeletal muscle, also results in an increase in hexokinase activity (8, 13, 63, 77, 98). In rats subjected to a strenuous program of running, hexokinase activity increased 170% in fast-twitch red muscle, 52% in slow-twitch red muscle, and 30% in white muscle (8). As is discussed later, these differences in response may reflect the extent of involvement of the different types of muscle fibers in prolonged, submaximal exercise. Like exercise, insulin administration increases hexokinase to supernormal levels, whereas insulin deprivation decreases hexokinase in skeletal muscle (73). The effect of insulin on hexokinase may be mediated by increased entry of glucose into muscle (73). In keeping with this hypothesis is the finding that repeated muscle contraction also markedly increases muscle cell permeability to sugar (51, 59, 60). In contrast to the mitochondrial enzymes, which increase in response to prolonged bouts of exercise over a period of weeks, hexokinase activity increases in response to single bouts of prolonged exercise (77) or a few brief bouts of exercise (13).

In the rat, the other glycolytic enzymes undergo rather small changes in response to endurance exercise. In fast-red muscle, which has a high glycolytic capacity, a decrease of approximately 20% occurred in the levels of glycogen phosphorylase, phosphofructokinase, glyceraldehyde-3-phosphate dehydrogenase, pyruvate kinase, cytoplasmic α-glycerophosphate dehydrogenase, and lactate dehydrogenase in response to the running program described earlier (8). It has been reported that the decrease in lactate dehydrogenase is limited to the "M" isozyme of the enzyme (132). Slow-red muscle, which has a low glycogenolytic capacity, in contrast to fast-red muscle, underwent small increases in the above enzymes (8). In white muscle, the only change found in the glycolytic enzymes, other than hexokinase, was a 15% decrease in lactate dehydrogenase (8). In studies on mixed muscles such as the gastrocnemius and quadriceps, the exercise-induced decreases in the glycolytic enzymes in fast-red muscle are obscured by the increases in slow-red and the unchanged glycolytic enzyme levels in the white fibers (8, 63). Like endurance running, a program of sprinting has been reported to produce a small increase in glycolytic enzymes in soleus muscle; however, no changes were found in fast-red or fast-white muscle (112).

Some confusion exists regarding the response of phosphofructokinase (PFK) activity in human skeletal muscle to exercise-training. In a study in which subjects trained one leg by means of bicycle exercise while the other leg served as an untrained control, no significant changes were found in phosphorylase, PFK, aldolase, or pyruvate kinase in quadriceps muscle (86). In contrast, another group of investigators reported that a strenuous program of bicycle exercise results in a greater than twofold increase in PFK activity in the quadriceps (47). However, the same investigators reported that PFK activity in skeletal muscles of highly trained competitive bicyclists, distance runners, and swimmers is no higher than in sedentary controls (45).

The finding that muscle glycogen concentration is generally elevated in trained individuals (45, 47) has led to investigation of the effects of training on enzymes involved in glycogen synthesis. Total glycogen synthetase activity was increased in skeletal muscles of humans and rodents in response to exercise training (67, 86, 120). The magnitude of this increase varied between 30% and 100%. Glycogen branching enzyme activity was also increased in muscle with training (119). These findings suggest that there is an increased capacity for glycogen synthesis in trained muscles.

ADENINE NUCLEOTIDE CYCLE ENZYMES

Ammonia formed by muscle during work arises from deamination of AMP in the AMP deaminase reaction; the IMP thus formed may be reconverted to AMP by the adenylosuccinate synthetase and adenylosuccinase reactions (80). AMP deaminase closely parallels the activities of the glycolytic enzymes in the different types of muscle fibers; the highest AMP deaminase activity is seen in the white fibers and in the fast-red fibers; the slow-twitch red fibers have the lowest AMP deaminase activity of the three fiber types (130). In the rat, the fast-twitch red muscle, the only fiber type that undergoes a decrease in glycogenolytic capacity (8), is also the only type that shows a decrease in AMP deaminase activity (40%) in response to the running program described earlier (130). Adenylosuccinase activity is much lower than AMP deaminase activity in all three muscle fiber types and does not change significantly (130).

One suggestion regarding the physiological role of AMP deaminase is that this enzyme may regulate the rate of glycolysis by controlling the activity of PFK, as the ammonium ion activates this enzyme (80). The finding that there is a very high correlation between AMP deaminase activity and of PFK activity lends credence to the idea that one function of AMP deaminase may be to regulate flux through the glycolytic pathway (80, 130).

ACTOMYOSIN ATPASE

Slow muscle myosin and fast muscle myosin have different biochemical properties (10, 115). When a slow muscle and a fast muscle are cross-innervated, a reversal of contractile properties occurs if sufficient time is permitted to elapse (10). Concomitantly, the biochemical properties of myosin change as slow muscle myosin is replaced by fast myosin and vice versa (10). Conflicting reports have appeared regarding the adaptive response of skeletal muscle actomyosin to exercise. One group reported a 44% increase in actomyosin ATPase activity in gastrocnemius muscle of rats subjected to a program of exhausting bouts of swimming (125). Others have reported that no change occurs in actomyosin ATPase in mixed muscles of rats trained by means of either swimming (117) or running (3), or in *Galago senegalensis* (lesser bush baby) trained by means of running (31). The contractile properties of mixed muscles were also unchanged in trained animals (12, 31). On the other hand, a small but significant increase in actomyosin ATPase activity was found in soleus muscles of young rats subjected to a swimming program (117). In rats trained by means of the running program described earlier, actomyosin ATPase activity decreased 20% in fast-twitch red muscle and increased about 20% in slow-red soleus; no significant change in actomyosin occurred in white muscle (9). These responses are very similar in magnitude and direction to the changes seen in PFK, phosphorylase, and a number of other glycolytic enzymes (8, 9). There is also a remarkably close parallel between actomyosin ATPase activity and the capacity of the glycogenolytic-glycolytic pathway as reflected in PFK activity in the different types of muscle in trained and untrained animals (9). Thus there appears to be a constant relationship between the capacities of these major pathways for ATP generation and ATP utilization in muscle (9).

ADAPTIVE RESPONSES TO ENDURANCE EXERCISE IN THE DIFFERENT TYPES OF MUSCLE

In histochemical studies in which the staining intensities of succinate dehydrogenase, DPNH diaphorase, or malate dehydrogenase were used to distinguish the fiber types in rodent skeletal muscle, it appeared that the percentage of fibers with the staining characteristics of white muscle decreased, while the percentage of red-appearing fibers increased (11, 32, 37). This finding suggested that endurance exercise brings about the conversion of some white fibers to red. However, as reviewed above, biochemical studies have shown that although the respiratory capacity of white muscle increases, white fibers are not converted to red. On the contrary, some of the differences between the white and the red muscle fibers are accentuated in exercise-trained rodents (5, 8, 9, 126, 130). The stains for the respiratory enzymes, as generally used, are relatively insensitive and are inappropriate for quantitation of enzyme activity. They serve to distinguish fibers with a mitochondrial content above some critical level which makes them appear "red" from "white" fibers with a mitochondrial content below this level. Training apparently increases respiratory enzymes sufficiently in certain white fibers, perhaps those with the highest respiratory capacity initially, to reach the critical staining intensity needed to give a red appearance. The differences between red and white fibers are, however, maintained. Histochemical studies on the effects of exercise on human skeletal muscle, in which the fibers have been characterized only as fast or slow on the basis of actomyosin ATPase staining characteristics, have shown no evidence of interconversion of fiber types (47).

Information from cross-innervation studies (10, 106) and studies involving chronic electrical stimulation (99) suggest that skeletal muscle fibers may have the potential for conversion from one type to another. However, as reviewed above, normal endurance exercise does not appear to result in interconversion of fiber types. The white fibers (which have the lowest respiratory capacity and hexokinase activity, the highest glycogenolytic capacity and actomyosin ATPase activity, and therefore the greatest potential for exercise-induced adaptive change) undergo the smallest increase in respiratory capacity and hexokinase activity and little or no change in actomyosin ATPase or glycolytic enzyme activity. On the other hand, the fast-twitch red fibers, which have the highest respiratory capacity and hexokinase activity, somewhat surprisingly undergo the largest, absolute increase in oxidative capacity and hexokinase.

Because the extent of an adaptive response is usually related to the magnitude of the inducing stimulus, the small changes in enzyme levels in white muscles relative to red could reflect a lesser participation in endurance exercise. This possibility has been investigated using muscle glycogen depletion as an indicator of prior contractile activity. In rats subjected to a two-hour long bout of running such as was used in training studies that resulted in a twofold increase in muscle mitochondria (5, 126), glycogen concentration decreased approximately 5.6 mg per gram of muscle in fast-twitch red muscle, 2.7 mg per grain in slow-twitch red muscle, and only 0.3 mg per gram in white muscle (6). Muscle biopsy studies on humans have shown that exercise of an intensity that can be maintained continuously for prolonged periods results in glycogen depletion primarily in slow-twitch fibers with little involvement of the white fibers (46). It seems reasonable to conclude that a positive relationship exists between the magnitude of the habitual level of contractile activity, and the extent of the adaptive response. The finding that white muscle is minimally involved in endurance exercise, as evidenced by minimal glycogen depletion, helps to explain why the absolute increases in respiratory capacity and hexokinase activity are so much smaller in white than in red muscle. With a different exercise program that results in greater recruitment of the white fibers, larger adaptive responses may occur in white skeletal muscle.

In contrast to skeletal muscle, heart muscle does not undergo an adaptive increase in respiratory capacity in response to endurance exercise (89, 90, 113). The activities of a number of mitochondrial enzymes and the concentrations of cytochrome c and mitochondrial protein, expressed per gram of heart, are unchanged in hearts of trained animals (89, 90, 113). The heart hypertrophies in response to endurance exercise, so that trained animals have heavier hearts than untrained controls of the same body weight. There is evidence that myocardial contractility is enchanced by training (28, 96). The specific activity of actomyosin ATPase is increased in hearts of rats subjected to programs of swimming, this adaptation could play a role in increasing myocardial contracility (18, 125). There is also evidence that the hearts of trained animals have increased resistance to hypoxia (114).

Because heart muscle contracts continuously and has the highest capacity for aerobic metabolism of any mammalian muscle, it seems reasonable that the levels of activity of the enzymes for the generation of ATP and for the hydrolysis of ATP during muscle contraction are the optimal ones for continuous, vigorous contractile activity. The heart appears to obtain its energy essentially completely from aerobic metabolism, taking up lactate rather than forming it (53, 74). Skeletal muscle has specialized functions (such as maintenance of posture in the case of slow-muscle fibers and the performance of short bursts of intense work that exceed the muscles' capacity for aerobic metabolism in the case of fast-twitch muscle fibers) that preclude an enzyme pattern identical to that in heart. However, in response to endurance exercise-training, the slow-red and the fast-red types of skeletal muscle fibers become more like heart muscle in their enzyme patterns, with respect to (a) mitochondrial enzymes involved in the generation of ATP via aerobic metabolism (126), (b) glycolytic and glycogenolytic enzymes (8), and (c) actomyosin ATPase (9).

ACKNOWLEDGMENTS

We are grateful to Ms. Sandra Zigler for help in the preparation of this manuscript. Research in the authors' laboratory was supported by NIH Grants HD 01613 and AM 05341, and by a grant from the Muscular Dystrophy Associations of America. Dr. Booth was supported by a Research Fellowship from the Muscular Dystrophy Associations of America.

Literature Cited

1. Ahlborg, B., Bergström, J., Ekelund, L.-G., Hultman, E. 1967. Muscle glycogen and muscle electrolytes during prolonged physical exercise. *Acta Physiol. Scand.* 70:129–42
2. Askew, E. W., Huston, R. L., Dohm, G. L. 1973. Effect of physical training on esterification of glycerol-3-phosphate by homogenates of liver, skeletal muscle, heart, and adipose tissue of rats. *Metabolism* 22:473–80
3. Bagby, G. J., Sembrowich, W. L., Gollnick, P. D. 1972. Myosin ATPase and fiber composition from trained and untrained rat skeletal muscle. *Am. J. Physiol.* 223:1415–17
4. Baldwin, K. M., Fitts, R. H., Booth, F. W., Winder, W. W., Holloszy, J. O. 1975. Depletion of muscle and liver glycogen during exercise: protective effect of training. *Pfluegers Arch.* 354:203–12
5. Baldwin, K. M., Klinkerfuss, G. H., Terjung, R. L., Molé, P. A., Holloszy,

J. O. 1972. Respiratory capacity of white, red and intermediate muscle: adaptive response to exercise. *Am. J. Physiol.* 222:373–78
6. Baldwin, K. M., Reitman, J. S., Terjung, R. L., Winder, W. W., Holloszy, J. O. 1973. Substrate depletion in different types of muscle and in liver during prolonged running. *Am. J. Physiol.* 225:1045–50
7. Baldwin, K. M., Tipton, C. M. 1972. Work and metabolic patterns of fast and slow twitch skeletal muscle contracting in situ. *Pfluegers Arch.* 334:345–56
8. Baldwin, K. M., Winder, W. W., Terjung, R. L., Holloszy, J. O. 1973. Glycolytic enzymes in different types of skeletal muscle: adaptation to exercise. *Am. J. Physiol.* 225:962–66
9. Baldwin, K. M., Winder, W. W., Holloszy, J. O. 1975. Adaptation of actomyosin ATPase in different types of muscle to endurance exercise. *Am. J. Physiol.* 229:422–26

ADAPTATIONS TO EXERCISE   287

10. Bárány, M., Close, R. I. 1971. The transformation of myosin in cross-innervated rat muscles. *J. Physiol.* 213:455–74
11. Barnard, R. J., Edgerton, V. R., Peter, J. B. 1970. Effect of exercise on skeletal muscle. I. Biochemical and histochemical properties. *J. Appl. Physiol.* 28: 762–66
12. Barnard, R. J., Edgerton, V. R., Peter, J. B. 1970. Effect of exercise on skeletal muscle. II. Contractile properties. *J. Appl. Physiol.* 28:767–70
13. Barnard, R. J., Peter, J. B. 1969. Effect of training and exhaustion on hexokinase activity of skeletal muscle. *J. Appl. Physiol.* 27:691–95
14. Barnard, R. J., Peter, J. B. 1971. Effect of exercise on skeletal muscle. III. Cytochrome changes. *J. Appl. Physiol.* 31: 904–8
15. Bass, A., Brdiczka, D., Eyer, P., Hofer, S., Pette, D. 1969. Metabolic differentiation of distinct muscle types at the level of enzymatic organization. *Eur. J. Biochem.* 10:198–206
16. Bergman, H., Björntorp, P., Conradson, T. -B., Fahlén, M., Stenberg, J., Varnauskas, E. 1973. Enzymatic and circulatory adjustments to physical training in middle-aged men. *Eur. J. Clin. Lab. Invest.* 3:414–18
17. Bergström, J., Hermansen, L., Hultman, E., Saltin, B. 1967. Diet, muscle glycogen and physical performance. *Acta Physiol. Scand.* 71:140–50
18. Bhan, A. K., Scheuer, J. 1972. Effects of physical training on cardiac actomyosin adenosine triphosphatase activity. *Am. J. Physiol.* 223:1486–90
19. Booth, F. W., Kelso, J. R. 1973. Cytochrome oxidase of skeletal muscle: adaptive response to chronic disuse. *Can. J. Physiol. Pharmacol.* 51:678–81
20. Booth, F. W., Narahara, K. A. 1974. Vastus lateralis cytochrome oxidase activity and its relationship to maximal oxygen consumption in man. *Pfluegers Arch.* 349:319–24
21. Borensztajn, J., Rone, M. S., Babirak, S. P., McGarr, J. A., Oscai, L. B. 1975. Effect of exercise on lipoprotein lipase activity in rat heart and skeletal muscle. *Am. J. Physiol.* 229:394–97
22. Burke, R. E., Levine, D. N., Zajac, F. E., Tsairis, P., Engel, W. K. 1971. Mammalian motor units: Physiological-histochemical correlation in three types in cat gastrocnemius. *Science* 174: 709–12
23. Carlson, L. A., Ekelund, L. -G., Fröberg, S. O. 1971. Concentration of triglycerides, phospholipids, and glycogen in skeletal muscle and of free fatty acids and β-hydroxybutyric acid in blood in man in response to exercise. *Eur. J. Clin. Invest.* 1:248–54
24. Chapler, C. K., Stainsby, W. N. 1968. Carbohydrate metabolism in contracting dog skeletal muscle in situ. *Am. J. Physiol.* 215:995–1004
25. Christensen, E. H., Hansen, O. 1939. Hypoglykämie, Arbeitsfähigkeit und Ermudüng. *Skand. Arch. Physiol.* 81: 172–79
26. Christensen, E. H., Hansen, O. 1939. Respiratorischer Quotient und O_2-Aufnahme. *Skand. Arch. Physiol.* 81: 180–89
27. Clausen, J. P., Larsen, O. A., Trap-Jensen, J. 1969. Physical training in the management of coronary artery disease. *Circulation* 40:143–54
28. Crews, J., Aldinger, E. E. 1967. Effect of chronic exercise on myocardial function. *Am. Heart J.* 74:536–42
29. Dohm, G. L., Huston, R. L., Askew, E. W., Fleshood, H. L. 1973. Effects of exercise, training and diet on muscle citric acid cycle enzyme activity. *Can. J. Biochem.* 51:849–54
30. Dubowitz, V., Brooke, M. H. 1973. *Muscle Biopsy: A Modern Approach*, 50–60. London: Saunders. 475 pp.
31. Edgerton, V. R., Barnard, R. J., Peter, J. B., Gillespie, C. A., Simpson, D. R. 1972. Overloaded skeletal muscles of a nonhuman primate (*Galago senegalensis*). *Exp. Neurol.* 37:322–39
32. Edgerton, V. R., Gerchman, L., Carrow, R. 1969. Histochemical changes in rat skeletal muscle after exercise. *Exp. Neurol.* 24:110–23
33. Edgerton, V. R., Simpson, D. R. 1969. The intermediate muscle fiber of rats and guinea pigs. *J. Histochem. Cytochem.* 17:828–38
34. Ekblom, B. 1969. Effect of physical training on oxygen transport system in man. *Acta Physiol. Scand. Suppl.* 328:1–45
35. Ekblom, B., Åstrand, P.-O., Saltin, B., Stenberg, J., Wallström, B. 1968. Effect of training on circulatory response to exercise. *J. Appl. Physiol.* 24:518–28
36. Essén, B., Henriksson, J. 1974. Glycogen content of individual muscle fibres in man. *Acta Physiol. Scand.* 90:645–47
37. Faulkner, J. A., Maxwell, L. C., Brook, D. A., Lieberman, D. A. 1971. Adaptation of guinea pig plantaris muscle fibers

to endurance training. *Am. J. Physiol.* 221:291–97

38. Felig, P., Wahren, J. 1971. Amino acid metabolism in exercising man. *J. Clin. Invest.* 50:2703–14

39. Fischbach, G. D., Robbins, N. 1970. The different effect of neuromuscular inactivity and muscle atrophy on speed of contraction. *Exp. Neurol.* 28:189–90

40. Fitts, R. H., Booth, F. W., Winder, W. W., Holloszy, J. O. 1975. Skeletal muscle respiratory capacity, endurance and glycogen utilization. *Am. J. Physiol.* 228:1029–33

41. Fitts, R. H., Nagle, F. J., Cassens, R. G. 1973. Characteristics of skeletal muscle fiber types in the miniature pig and the effect of training. *Can. J. Physiol. Pharmacol.* 51:825–31

42. Folkow, B., Halicka, D. H. 1968. A comparison between "red" and "white" muscle with respect to blood supply, capillary surface area and oxygen uptake during rest and exercise. *Microvasc. Res.* 1:1–14

43. Fröberg, S. O. 1971. Effect of acute exercise on tissue lipids in rats. *Metabolism* 20:714–20

44. Fuge, K. W., Crews, E. L., Pattengale, P. K., Holloszy, J. O., Shank, R. E. 1968. Effects of protein deficiency on certain adaptive responses to exercise. *Am. J. Physiol.* 215:660–63

45. Gollnick, P. D., Armstrong, R. B., Saubert, C. W., Piehl, K., Saltin, B. 1972. Enzyme activity and fiber composition in skeletal muscle of untrained and trained men. *J. Appl. Physiol.* 33:312–19

46. Gollnick, P. D., Armstrong, R. B., Saubert, C. W., Sembrowich, W. L., Shepherd, R. E., Saltin, B. 1973. Glycogen depletion patterns in human skeletal muscle fibers during prolonged work. *Pfluegers Arch.* 344:1–12

47. Gollnick, P. D., Armstrong, R. B., Saltin, B., Saubert, C. W., Sembrowich, W. L., Shepherd, R. E. 1973. Effect of training on enzyme activity and fiber composition of human skeletal muscle. *J. Appl. Physiol.* 34:107–11

48. Gollnick, P. D., Ianuzzo, C. D. 1972. Hormonal deficiencies and the metabolic adaptations of rats to training. *Am. J. Physiol.* 223:278–82

49. Gollnick, P. D., King, D. W. 1969. Effect of exercise and training on mitochondria of rat skeletal muscle. *Am. J. Physiol.* 216:1502–9

50. Grimby, G., Häggendal, E., Saltin, B. 1967. Local xenon 133 clearance from the quadriceps muscle during exercise in man. *J. Appl. Physiol.* 22:305–10

51. Helmreich, E., Cori, C. F. 1957. Studies of tissue permeability. II. The distribution of pentoses between plasma and muscle. *J. Biol. Chem.* 224:663–79

52. Hemmingsen, E. A. 1963. Enhancement of oxygen transport by myoglobin. *Comp. Biochem. Physiol.* 10:239–44

53. Herman, M. V., Elliott, W. C., Gorlin, R. 1967. An electrocardiographic, anatomic, and metabolic study of zonal myocardial ischemia in coronary heart disease. *Circulation* 35:834–46

54. Hermansen, L., Hultman, E., Saltin, B. 1967. Muscle glycogen during prolonged severe exercise. *Acta Physiol. Scand.* 71:129–39

55. Hill, A. V., Kupalov, P. 1929. Anaerobic and aerobic activity in isolated muscle. *Proc. R. Soc. Ser. B* 105:313–22

56. Holloszy, J. O. 1967. Biochemical adaptations in muscle. Effects of exercise on mitochondrial oxygen uptake and respiratory enzyme activity in skeletal muscle. *J. Biol. Chem.* 242:2278–82

57. Holloszy, J. O., Booth, F. W., Winder, W. W., Fitts, R. H. 1975. Biochemical adaptation of skeletal muscle to prolonged physical exercise. *Metabolic Adaptation to Prolonged Physical Exercise,* ed. H. Howald, J. R. Poortmans, 438–47. Basel: Birkhauser Verlag. 488 pp.

58. Holloszy, J. O., Molé, P. A., Baldwin, K. M. Terjung, R. L. 1973. Exercise induced enzymatic adaptations in muscle. *Limiting Factors of Physical Performance,* ed. J. Keul, 66–80. Stuttgart: Thieme. 282 pp.

59. Holloszy, J. O., Narahara, H. T. 1965. Studies of tissue permeability. X. Changes in permeability to 3-methylglucose associated with contraction of isolated frog muscle. *J. Biol. Chem.* 240:3493–5500

60. Holloszy, J. O., Narahara, H. T. 1967. Enhanced permeability to sugar associated with muscle contraction: studies of the role of Ca^{++}. *J. Gen. Physiol.* 50:551–62

61. Holloszy, J. O., Oscai, L. B. 1969. Effect of exercise on α-glycerophosphate dehydrogenase activity in skeletal muscle. *Arch. Biochem. Biophys.* 130:653–56

62. Holloszy, J. O., Oscai, L. B., Don, I. J., Molé, P. A. 1970. Mitochondrial citric acid cycle and related enzymes: adaptive response to exercise. *Biochem. Biophys. Res. Commun.* 40:1368–73

63. Holloszy, J. O., Oscai, L. B., Molé, P. A., Don, I. J. 1971. Biochemical adaptations to endurance exercise in skeletal muscle. *Muscle Metabolism During Exercise,* ed. B. Pernow, B. Saltin, 51–61. New York: Plenum. 558 pp.
64. Holloszy, J. O., Skinner, J. S., Toro, G., Cureton, T. K. 1964. Effects of a six month program of endurance exercise on the serum lipids of middle-aged men. *Am. J. Cardiol.* 14:753–60
65. Hoppeler, H., Lüthi, P., Claassen, H., Weibel, E. R., Howald, H. 1973. The ultrastructure of normal human skeletal muscle. A morphometric analysis of untrained men, women and well-trained orienteers. *Pfluegers Arch.* 344:217–32
66. Ianuzzo, C. D., Lesser, M., Battista, F. 1974. Metabolic adaptations in skeletal muscle of streptozotocin-diabetic rats following exercise training. *Biochem. Biophys. Res. Commun.* 58:107–11
67. Jeffress, R. N., Peter, J. B., Lamb, D. R. 1968. Effects of exercise on glycogen synthetase in red and white skeletal muscle. *Life Sci.* 7:957–60
68. Jöbsis, F. F., Duffield, J. C. 1967. Oxidative and glycolytic recovery metabolism in muscle: fluorometric observations on their relative contributions. *J. Gen. Physiol.* 50:1009–47
69. Johnson, R. H., Walton, J. L., Krebs, H. A., Williamson, D. H. 1969. Metabolic fuels during and after severe exercise in athletes and non-athletes. *Lancet* 2:452–55
70. Johnson, R. H., Walton, J. L. 1972. The effect of exercise upon acetoacetate metabolism in athletes and non-athletes. *Q. J. Exp. Physiol.* 57:73–79
71. Jones, N. L., Havel, R. J. 1967. Metabolism of free fatty acids and chylomicron triglycerides during exercise in rats. *Am. J. Physiol.* 213:824–28
72. Karlsson, J., Saltin, B. 1970. Lactate, ATP, and CP in working muscles during exhaustive exercise in man. *J. Appl. Physiol.* 29:598–602
73. Katzen, H. M., Soderman, D. D., Wiley, C. E. 1970. Multiple forms of hexokinase: activities associated with subcellular particulate and soluble fractions of normal and streptozotocin diabetic rat tissues. *J. Biol. Chem.* 245:4081–96
74. Keul, J., Keppler, D., Doll, E. 1967. Lactate-pyruvate ratio and its relation to oxygen pressure in arterial coronary venous and femoral venous blood. *Arch. Int. Physiol. Biochem.* 75:573–78

75. Kiessling, K.-H., Pilström, L., Bylund, A.-Ch., Saltin, B., Piehl, K. 1974. Enzyme activities and morphometry in skeletal muscle of middle-aged men after training. *Scand. J. Clin. Lab. Invest.* 33:63–69
76. Krzanowski, J., Matschinsky, F. M. 1969. Regulation of phosphofructokinase by phosphocreatine and phosphorylated glycolytic intermediates. *Biochem. Biophys. Res. Commun.* 34:816–23
77. Lamb, D. R., Peter, J. B., Jeffress, R. N., Wallace, H. A. 1969. Glycogen, hexokinase, and glycogen synthetase adaptations to exercise. *Am. J. Physiol.* 217:1628–32
78. Lawrie, R. A. 1953. Effect of enforced exercise on myoglobin concentration in muscle. *Nature London* 171:1069–70
79. Lehninger, A. L. 1965. *The Mitochondrion,* 132–56. New York: Benjamin. 263 pp.
80. Lowenstein, J. M. 1972. Ammonia production in muscle and other tissues: the purine nucleotide cycle. *Physiol. Rev.* 52:382–414
81. Max, S. R. 1972. Disuse atrophy of skeletal muscle: loss of functional activity of mitochondria. *Biochem. Biophys. Res. Commun.* 46:1394–98
82. Max, S. R. 1973. Muscular atrophy: activation of mitochondrial ATPase. *Biochem. Biophys. Res. Commun.* 52:1278–84
83. Molé, P. A., Baldwin, K. M., Terjung, R. L., Holloszy, J. O. 1973. Enzymatic pathways of pyruvate metabolism in skeletal muscle: adaptations to exercise. *Am. J. Physiol.* 224:50–54
84. Molé, P. A., Oscai, L. B., Holloszy, J. O. 1971. Adaptation of muscle to exercise. Increase in levels of palmityl CoA synthetase, carnitine palmityltransferase and palmityl CoA dehydrogenase and in the capacity to oxidize fatty acids. *J. Clin. Invest.* 50:2323–30
85. Morgan, T. E., Short, F. A., Cobb, L. A. 1969. Effect of long-term exercise on skeletal muscle lipid composition. *Am. J. Physiol.* 216:82–86
86. Morgan, T. E., Cobb, L. A., Short, F. A., Ross, R., Gun, D. R. 1971. Effects of long-term exercise on human muscle mitochondria. See Ref. 63, 87–95
87. Neely, J. R., Morgan, H. E. 1974. Relationship between carbohydrate and lipid metabolism and the energy balance of heart muscle. *Ann. Rev. Physiol.* 36:413–59

88. Oscai, L. B., Holloszy, J. O. 1971. Biochemical adaptations in muscle. II. Response of mitochondrial adenosine triphosphatase, creatine phosphokinase, and adenylate kinase activities in skeletal muscle to exercise. *J. Biol. Chem.* 246:6968–72

89. Oscai, L. B., Molé, P. A., Brei, B., Holloszy, J. O. 1971. Cardiac growth and respiratory enzyme levels in male rats subjected to a running program. *Am. J. Physiol.* 220:1238–41

90. Oscai, L. B., Molé, P. A., Holloszy, J. O. 1971. Effects of exercise on cardiac weight and mitochondria in male and female rats. *Am. J. Physiol.* 220: 1944–48

91. Passonneau, J. V., Lowry, O. H. 1963. P-fructokinase and the control of the citric acid cycle. *Biochem. Biophys. Res. Commun.* 13:372–79

92. Pattengale, P. K., Holloszy, J. O. 1967. Augmentation of skeletal muscle myoglobin by a program of treadmill running. *Am. J. Physiol.* 213:783–85

93. Paul, P. 1970. FFA metabolism of normal dogs during steady-state exercise at different work loads. *J. Appl. Physiol.* 28:127–32

94. Paul, P., Issekutz, B., Miller, H. I. 1966. Interrelationship of free fatty acids and glucose metabolism in the dog. *Am. J. Physiol.* 211:1313–20

95. Paul, P., Issekutz, B. 1967. Role of extramuscular energy sources in the metabolism of the exercising dog. *J. Appl. Physiol.* 22:615–22

96. Penpargkul, S., Scheuer, J. 1970. The effect of physical training upon the mechanical and metabolic performance of the rat heart. *J. Clin. Invest.* 49:1859–68

97. Peter, J. B., Barnard, R. J., Edgerton, V. R., Gillespie, C. A., Stemple, K. E. 1972. Metabolic profiles of three fiber types of skeletal muscle in guinea pigs and rabbits. *Biochemistry* 14:2627–33

98. Peter, J. B., Jeffress, R. N., Lamb, D. R. 1968. Exercise: effects on hexokinase activity in red and white skeletal muscle. *Science* 160:200–1

99. Pette, D., Smith, M. E., Staudte, H. W., Vrbová, G. 1973. Effects of long-term electrical stimulation on some contractile and metabolic characteristics of fast rabbit muscles. *Pfluegers Arch.* 338:257–72

100. Pruett, E. D. R. 1970. Glucose and insulin during prolonged work stress in men living on different diets. *J. Appl. Physiol.* 28:199–208

101. Reitman, J., Baldwin, K. M., Holloszy, J. O. 1973. Intramuscular triglyceride utilization by red, white and intermediate skeletal muscle and heart during exhausting exercise. *Proc. Soc. Exp. Biol. Med.* 142:628–31

102. Rennie, M. J., Jennett, S., Johnson, R. H. 1974. The metabolic effects of strenuous exercise: a comparison between untrained subjects and racing cyclists. *Q. J. Exp. Physiol.* 59:201–12

103. Rifenberick, D. H., Gamble, J. G., Max, S. R. 1973. Response of mitochondrial enzymes to decreased muscular activity. *Am. J. Physiol.* 225:1295–99

104. Rifenberick, D. H., Max, S. R. 1974. Substrate utilization by disused rat skeletal muscles. *Am. J. Physiol.* 226: 295–97

105. Robinson, S., Harmon, P. M. 1941. The lactic acid mechanism and certain properties of the blood in relation to training. *Am. J. Physiol.* 132:757–69

106. Romanul, F. C. A., Van Der Meulen, J. P. 1967. Slow and fast muscles after cross innervation. Enzymatic and physiological changes. *Arch. Neurol.* 17:387–402

107. Rowell, L. B. 1971. Cardiovascular limitations to work capacity. *Physiology of Work Capacity and Fatigue,* ed. E. Simonson, 132–69. Springfield, Ill.: Thomas. 571 pp.

108. Rowell, L. B. 1974. Human cardiovascular adjustments to exercise and thermal stress. *Physiol. Rev.* 54:75–159

109. Saltin, B., Blomqvist, G., Mitchell, J. H., Johnson, R. L., Wildenthal, K., Chapman, C. B. 1968. Response to exercise after bedrest and after training. *Circulation* 38: Suppl. 7, 1–78

110. Saltin, B., Karlsson, J. 1971. Muscle glycogen utilization during work of different intensities. See Ref. 63, 289–99

111. Saltin, B., Karlsson, J. Muscle ATP, CP and lactate during exercise after physical conditioning. See Ref. 63, 395–99

112. Saubert, C. W., Armstrong, R. B., Shepherd, R. E., Gollnick, P. D. 1973. Anaerobic enzyme adaptations to sprint training in rats. *Pfluegers Arch.* 341: 305–12

113. Scheuer, J., Penpargkul, S., Bhan, A. K. 1974. Experimental observations on the effects of physical training upon intrinsic cardiac physiology and biochemistry. *Am. J. Cardiol.* 33:744–51

114. Scheuer, J., Stezoski, S. W. 1972. Effect of physical training on the mechanical and metabolic response of the rat heart to hypoxia. *Circ. Res.* 30:418–29

115. Streter, F. A., Seidel, J. C., Gergely, J. 1966. Studies on myosin from red and white muscles of the rabbit. I. Adenosine triphosphatase activity. *J. Biol. Chem.* 241:5772–76

116. Summers, T. B., Hines, H. M. 1951. Effect of immobilization in various positions upon the weight and strength of skeletal muscle. *Arch. Phys. Med.* 32:142–45

117. Syrový, I., Gutmann, E., Melichna, J. 1972. Effect of exercise on skeletal muscle myosin ATPase activity. *Physiol. Bohemoslov.* 21:633–38

118. Tata, J. R. 1974. Growth and developmental action of thyroid hormones at the cellular level. *Handb. Physiol., Sect. 7, Endocrinol.* 3:469–78

119. Taylor, A. W., Stothart, J., Booth, M. A., Thayer, R., Rao, S. 1974. Human skeletal muscle glycogen branching enzyme activities with exercise and training. *Can. J. Physiol. Pharmacol.* 52:119–22

120. Taylor, A. W., Thayer, R., Rao, S. 1972. Human skeletal muscle glycogen synthetase activities with exercise and training. *Can. J. Physiol. Pharmacol.* 50:411–15

121. Tipton, C. M. 1965. Training and bradycardia in rats. *Am. J. Physiol.* 209:1089–94

122. Uyeda, K., Racker, E. 1965. Regulatory mechanisms in carbohydrate metabolism. VII. Hexokinase and phosphofructokinase. *J. Biol. Chem.* 240:4682–88

123. Van Dam, K., Meyer, A. J. 1971. Oxidation and energy conservation by mitochondria. *Ann. Rev. Biochem.* 40:115–60

124. Varnauskas, E., Björntorp, P., Fahlén, M., Prérovský, I., Stenberg, J. 1970. Effects of physical training on exercise blood flow and enzymatic activity in skeletal muscle. *Cardiovasc. Res.* 4:418–22

125. Wilkerson, J. E., Evonuk, E. 1971. Changes in cardiac and skeletal muscle myosin ATPase activities after exercise. *J. Appl. Physiol.* 30:328–30

126. Winder, W. W., Baldwin, K. M., Holloszy, J. O. 1974. Enzymes involved in ketone utilization in different types of muscle: adaptation to exercise. *Eur. J. Biochem.* 47:461–67

127. Winder, W. W., Baldwin, K. M., Holloszy, J. O. 1975. Exercise-induced increase in the capacity of rat skeletal muscle to oxidize ketones. *Can. J. Physiol. Pharmacol.* 53:86–91

128. Winder, W. W., Baldwin, K. M., Terjung, R. L., Holloszy, J. O. 1975. Effects of thyroid hormone administration on skeletal muscle mitochondria. *Am. J. Physiol.* 228:1341–45

129. Winder, W. W., Heninger, R. W. 1971. Effect of exercise on tissue levels of thyroid hormones in the rat. *Am. J. Physiol.* 221:1139–43

130. Winder, W. W., Terjung, R. L., Baldwin, K. M., Holloszy, J. O. 1974. Effect of exercise on AMP deaminase and adenylosuccinase in rat skeletal muscle. *Am. J. Physiol.* 227:1411–414

131. Wu, R., Racker, E. 1959. Regulatory mechanisms in carbohydrate metabolism. III. Limiting factors in glycolysis of ascites tumor cells. *J. Biol. Chem.* 234:1029–35

132. York, J. W., Oscai, L. B., Penney, D. G. 1974. Alterations in skeletal muscle lactate dehydrogenase isozymes following exercise training. *Biochem. Biophys. Res. Commun.* 61:1387–93

EXCITATION-CONTRACTION COUPLING[1]

Setsuro Ebashi

Department of Pharmacology, University of Tokyo, Hongo, Bunkyo-ku, Tokyo 113, Japan

INTRODUCTION

The question of how electrical phenomena (that is, action potential or depolarization) induce muscle contraction had already been implied in Galvani's (53) epoch-making discovery in the late eighteenth century, but was left untouched for more than a century. Physiologists only recently became fully aware of the existence of an important field within physiology that must supply an answer to the above question. Great progress has since been made in this field, appropriately termed *excitation-contraction coupling* (E-C coupling) by Sandow in 1952 (105); consequently, in late 1960s we have reached the following, essentially accurate understanding of E-C coupling (cf 28): (*a*) The action potential at the sarcolemma is conducted into the interior of muscle fiber through the T system. (*b*) The depolarization of the T-system membrane thus induced releases stored Ca ion from the terminal cisternae of the sarcoplasmic reticulum (SR). (*c*) Ca ion thus released reaches troponin located in the thin filament to produce the contraction (i.e. the interaction of the thick filament and thin filament) by removing the depressive effect of Ca-free troponin located in the thin filament complex. (*d*) If the influence of depolarization ends, Ca ion is reaccumulated by the whole surface of the SR utilizing the energy of ATP; reduction of the Ca ion concentration thus induced releases Ca from troponin, and relaxation follows.

Step *b* is undoubtedly the most crucial one in E-C coupling, but it was the least understood in the 1960's. In fact, it appeared that an understanding of the processes involved in *b* would not be reached in the near future; some recent observations, however, seem to have opened up a new approach.

We have an excellent review by Fuchs (49) on striated muscle in Volume 36 of this series. Although Fuchs was concerned with the whole area of muscle physi-

---

[1]As this article does not cover the whole field of excitation-contraction coupling, but is concerned with a few selected subjects, the references cited have been limited to those papers most directly relevant.

ology, he allotted nearly half of the review to problems related to E-C coupling and reviewed the progress made in this field since Sandow's excellent review (107). Taking advantage of this, I do not cover the whole area of E-C coupling, but concentrate my efforts on illuminating new trends in this field.

Emphasis is on the recent findings concerning step *b*, i.e. the problem of how depolarization in the T system is transmitted to the SR with subsequent release of Ca. Reference to E-C coupling of muscles other than skeletal muscle is made only when directly relevant to a general mechanism.

T SYSTEM

Morphological Aspects

OPENING OF THE T SYSTEM   The monumental work of Huxley & Taylor (69, 70) in 1958 indicated that the space surrounded by the T-system membrane is directly connected with the extracellular space. However, for many years, morphological evidence for the existence of the opening of the T system at the surface membrane was not available for vertebrate skeletal muscles except in the case of some fish.

Recently, however, several investigators have reached a common understanding as to the peripheral structure of the T system, confirming the existence of such an opening (48). The failure to find this opening is perhaps because it is very small, similar to caveola in size and shape. In addition, the peripheral part of the T system near the opening contains various structures, which differ in size from the main part; the peripheral part occasionally appears to be constricted, but more frequently to be dilated.

In this connection, Zampighi et al (128) reported that the caveola, a membrane-bound component with a round profile forms the transition from the sarcolemma to the T system. This observation is further confirmed by the developmental process of the T system in the embryonic stage (40).

LONGITUDINAL OR LATERAL T SYSTEM   Recognition that portions of the T system run longitudinally was first made by Huxley (71). Eisenberg & Eisenberg (31) presented clear evidence for the presence of such structures, some of which run the whole length of the sarcomere. Their occurrence may not be so frequent as once postulated (101), i.e. less than 10% of the total T system, perhaps closer to 3% (30).

SPIRAL ARRANGEMENT OF THE T SYSTEM   Using a high-voltage electron microscope and very thick section, Peachey has shown that the T system can be followed through successive serial slices. As a result, the T system is shown to take a spiral course with a very small slope around the axis of the whole fiber (99). This finding is related not only to the problem of the T-system formation, but also to the important question of how the sarcomeres are arranged in the process of their formation. One of the physiological implications of the spiral structure is referred to later. The relationship of this structure to the lateral T system is not clear, but it is interesting that the long lateral T system often coincides with the part where the cross striations are out of register (47).

Excitability of the T System

The elegant work of Costantin (22) has clearly indicated that the T system is not merely a canal conducting the depolarization of the surface membrane electrotonically into the interior of a muscle fiber, but that its membrane system can produce regenerative conduction, as can the surface membrane. This finding has been further substantiated by the work of several investigators (14, 55, 100).

One important question remained to be solved: whether or not the action potential of the T system was necessary for normal muscle contraction. Bastian & Nakajima (10) answered this question by an ingenious experiment. Using a double sucrose-gap method (89), they applied a simulated action potential to a node of a muscle fiber in a sucrose gap rendered inexcitable by tetrodotoxin or by the lack of Na, and compared the contraction produced by this simulated potential with that produced by a real action potential. If the spread of the potential in the T system were passive, no difference should have been observed between the two. However, the ratio of the twitch height in the former to that in the latter was shown to be only about 0.3 at 20°C. Thus the excitability of the T system is shown to be necessary for physiological contraction.

It should also be pointed out that the ratio becomes more than 0.8 at 10°C, suggesting that the excitability of the T system has more importance to the contraction at higher temperature where the duration of the action potential is very short.

The experiment of Adrian et al (2), performed prior to that of Costantin, indicated the presence of delayed rectification in the T system. Thus the T system has qualitatively the same electrophysiological properties as the surface membrane.

From the quantitative point of view, however, the properties of the T-system membrane are distinctly different from those of the sarcolemma. First, the T system in the resting state has a very low Cl^- conductance (33), assumed to be about 1/36 that of the surface membrane in specific value (1), although its K^+ conductance is about one third that of the surface membrane (33). Second, the Na^+ and K^+ channels involved in the excitation process appear to be far less in the T system than in the surface membrane. Adrian & Peachy (1) have shown that the action potential can be satisfactorily reconstructed by assuming that the densities of Na and K channels in the T-system membrane would be 1/20 and 1/33, respectively.

"Detubulation" or Glycerol Treatment of Muscle Fibers

In the early sixties, Fujino et al (50) found that muscle fibers treated with hypertonic glycerol briefly (e.g. 0.4 M) and then returned to normal media, lose their contractility during the course of glycerol leakage from fibers despite retention of the excitability of the surface membrane. This finding has been connected by Eisenberg and his colleagues (31, 32, 52) and Howell & Jenden (67) to a lesion of the T system; the former group (31) has presented clear electron microscopic evidence that the glycerol treatment disrupts the T system [see also (49)].

Thus glycerol treatment is now widely used as a procedure to prepare muscle fibers without the T system. This is certainly a useful method, but the effects of glycerol should not be ascribed entirely to its T-system disrupting action.

Glycerol treatment abolishes E-C coupling in muscles lacking the T system [(51), see also (49)]. If muscle fibers are treated with a lower concentration of glycerol, the contractility of the inactivated fiber is restored on re-immersion in the glycerol solution used to inactivate the fibers (127), concomitant with the disappearance of large vacuoles, probably located in the T system (85). Furthermore, much of the T system remains unimpaired by the glycerol treatment for a short time, as judged by its electrical capacity, in spite of almost complete loss in contractility (25). Thus the situation is not so simple as first supposed. It is likely that the glycerol treatment, or glycerol removal, appears to affect primarily the E-C coupling mechanism and secondarily the T-system structure.

Propagating Contraction of Skinned Fibers

Natori (92–95) has demonstrated electrically induced propagating contraction in skinned fibers immersed in oil: the velocity of propagation ranges from 0.5 to 3 mm per sec. Because such a propagation contraction is eliminated by tetrodotoxin, ouabain, or Na deprivation (93, 95), it is reasonable to assume that the conduction is mediated by an excitable membrane other than the sarcolemma running along the axis of the muscle fiber. The longitudinal or lateral T system could be the mediator, but it is difficult to explain the propagating contraction on the basis of this system. The velocity of electrical conduction in the ordinary T system is too fast to account for the slowness of contraction velocity unless conduction in the longitudinal T system is unusually slow. The recent finding of Peachey (99) that the T system has a spiral structure with a very gentle slope explains in part the slow velocity of the propagating contraction.

COUPLING BETWEEN T SYSTEM AND SARCOPLASMIC RETICULUM

Morphological Considerations

The unique structural relationship between the T-system membrane and the projections, or "feet," of the terminal cisternae of the SR has been clarified mainly by Franzini-Armstrong (45–47). This structure is now widely accepted as playing a crucial role in the coupling between the T system and the SR, which is the most important step in E-C coupling.

The coupling of the sarcolemma and the SR (the so-called peripheral coupling), which has essentially the same structural relationship as that between the T system and SR, has been demonstrated not only in cardiac muscle, which has abundant subsurface cisterna structures (74), but also in adult skeletal muscle (114). Smooth muscle contains SR-like structures much more abundantly than expected, some of them forming structures similar to that just described (113).

Inactivation

In spite of continuous depolarization, muscle cannot remain in the contracted state; contraction is followed by relaxation. The responsiveness of relaxed muscle to the next depolarization cannot be restored immediately by abolishing the depolarization or hyperpolarization—its restoration requires some recovery time. This property, more noticeable in white fast muscle, was first clearly pointed out by Hodgkin and Horowicz (65), but they explained it as a result of activator exhaustion. By analogy to the inactivation process of the Na-carrying system, the term *inactivation* was used to explain the situation (27, 86), the relationship among the three states (resting, activated, and inactivated) and their mutual conversion are qualitatively very similar to those of the Na-carrying system (66).

In the early 1960's it was thought that the T system might play only a passive role in conducting the depolarization of the surface membrane, and therefore that the depolarization directly influences the SR to release Ca. Consequently, the inactivation of E-C coupling was assumed to be the inherent nature of the Ca-release mechanism of the SR (86). Further work revealed that the delayed rectification of muscle was relatively rapidly inactivated by a maintained depolarization (90), and thresholds for the delayed rectification and for the activation of the contractile process were shown to be similar to each other under various conditions (cf 29, 60, 61). It was gradually recognized that the T system could develop an active electrical process (49, cf 69). With this background, the T system was added to the list of candidates for the site of inactivation of E-C coupling (28, 29).

In view of recent various observations, including those mentioned in the next section, it is reasonable to assume that the site for the inactivation process is confined to the T system, including its junction with the SR. Although another inactivation process is conceivable in the Ca-release mechanism of the SR in view of some in vitro experiments (34a) there is no need to consider such a process at present.

Delayed rectification was once assumed to play a crucial role in E-C coupling. This assumption was based mainly on the apparent parallels between delayed rectification and activation of the contractile process (cf 29, 61). Further detailed comparison, however, has revealed some definite discrepancies between the two mechanisms (18, 60, 79), especially in the time course of their inactivation processes (as described in the next section), which indicate no causal interrelationship.

As pointed out first by Lüttgau (86) Ca^{2+} in the medium plays a role in the inactivation of the contractile process, as it does in the excitation mechanism (44); decreases in Ca^{2+} concentration markedly accelerates the inactivation process or retards recovery from the inactivated state.

Lüttgau's experiment is somewhat complicated by the effect of Ca^{2+} deprivation on the excitability of the surface membrane and T system. Addition of Mg to the medium can largely eliminate this complication. Under this condition, the absence of Ca^{2+} strongly depresses the slow plateau phase of K+ contracture, leaving the initial rapid phase of K+ contracture almost intact (115). This phenomenon was explained on the basis of presumed physiological role of Ca^{2+} influx, i.e. a minute amount of Ca^{2+} entry from the outer medium should trigger the Ca^{2+}-induced Ca^{2+} release. However because the twitch is not affected by the removal of Ca^{2+} from the bathing solution, it is more likely that the depression of K^+ contracture in the absence of Ca^{2+} is a result of enhanced inactivation.

Charge Movement Associated with Depolarization of the T System

One of the recent exciting observations in neurophysiology is the discovery of the "gating" current, which may represent the presence in the excitable membrane of molecules with a high dipole moment, probably related to the Na-activating process of the excitation mechanism [Armstrong & Bezanilla (8), Keynes & Rojas (83), see also Armstrong (7)].

A similar idea—that because the activation of the contractile system is strongly voltage dependent, the step in the activation mechanism should involve some unique voltage-dependent process—led Schneider & Chandler to discover the presence of a charge movement in the T system (110). Experiments were carried out in the presence of tetrodotoxin and tetraethylammonium ion to block the Na^+ and K^+ current. The membrane potential was clamped with three microelectrodes (3), and the investigators searched for an asymmetric component between the membrane currents induced by the positive and negative steps of the same size from respective holding potentials. The voltage-dependent charge movement thus discovered has the following properties (4, 6, 17, 18, 110): 1. The time course of the charge movement in muscle is 20–100 times slower than that found by Armstrong & Bezanilla (8) in the giant nerve of a squid. These findings imply that the former is not related to the latter, which is now believed to be the gating current for the Na^+ channel. 2. The amount of movable charge per unit area of surface and T-system membrane, is about three times that in the giant axon of squid.

Two questions are raised. (*a*) Is the charge movement confined to the T system? (*b*) Is the charge movement a gating current for the delayed rectification? The latter question has double-barreled implications because it was once assumed that the delayed rectification would play a crucial role in E-C coupling.

The evidence favoring an affirmative answer to the first question is that the glycerol treatment (see section on detubulation) decreases the amount of the charge movement more intensely than that of the capacitance of the T system (18); the latter is an index of the degree of disruption of the T system. If the glycerol treatment has no effects other than those described above, i.e. uncoupling between the T system and SR cisternae and disruption of the T system these effects may be taken as strong evidence that the charge movement is confined mainly to the T system.

The evidence against an affirmative answer to the second question is as follows: (*a*) The delayed rectification of a glycerol-treated fiber is practically unaffected in spite of a marked decrease in the amount of the charge movement (18). (*b*) The time course of the decay of the charge movement due to depolarization is always faster than that of delayed rectification, and the ratio between them differs from fiber to fiber. (*c*) In Na Ringer solution made hypertonic with sucrose, a small depolarization induces only charge movement, not delayed current.

Thus the charge movement is apparently located in the T system and is different from the gating current of the delayed rectification.

The next problem is the relationship between charge movement and Ca release from the SR or the activation of the contractile process. There is a good agreement between them as regards the time course as well as the threshold (6, 18, 110). Furthermore, both the charge movement and contractility are eliminated in the inactivated state induced by prolonged depolarization (4, 6). Adrian et al (4) have further pursued the problem of the inactivation by inquiring into the relationship between the repriming of the contractile response and the recovery of voltage-dependent charge movement. On the whole, there are good correlations between them, in their time course as well as in their temperature dependence, and so on; it is interesting that the recovery of contractility requires a threshold amount of charge movement (4). [The coincidence has also been observed between the repriming of the Na current and the reactivation of the inactivated Na-carrying system (7).]

All of the facts so far presented seem to favor the idea of Chandler and his collaborators (18, 110) that the charge movement is the crucial step in the coupling between the depolarization and the activation of the contractile process.

The densities of the maximum movable charges are 300 (110), 500–600 (17), or $800/\mu m^2$ (6), provided that the charges are located in the T system. The agreement of these figures with the density of the "feet" of the terminal cisternae around the T system i.e. 500–1000 (47), is not fortuitous, but is important evidence that the charge movement plays a vital role in E-C coupling (18, 110). Each charge movement should exert its effect on the corresponding "foot" and thus transmit the signal from the T system to the SR.

What is the role of charge movement in signal transmission from the T system to the terminal cisternae of the SR? Chandler et al have assumed that the movement of the charged molecule directly opens the Ca^{2+} channel located in the feet of the terminal cisterna (18). The important point of this model is that the site for Ca^{2+} release is confined only to the terminal cisternae, particularly to their feet. The problem lies in reconciling this scheme with the view that the electrical phenomenon, presumably associated with Ca^{2+} release, is derived from the whole area of the SR.

An interesting point, derived from the studies on charge movement and the fact that the T-system membrane has a low density of Na^+- and K^+-carrying system (1) and a low Cl^- conductance (32), is that the T-system membrane has distinctly different properties from those of the sarcolemma. It may reasonably be assumed that the peripheral coupling, the contact between the surface membrane and the feet of subsurface cisternae, has the charge movement. The question is then raised whether the SR can recognize the special part of the surface membrane in forming the contact, or if the property of surface membrane would be altered after formation of the contact with the SR.

So far, no agent, except formaldehyde, has been found that depresses this charge movement while concurrently abolishing E-C coupling. However, in view of the decoupling action of glycerol treatment between depolarization and contraction, which can be seen before detubulation, it is urgent to carry out pharmacological studies on charge movement with drugs known to affect E-C coupling.

Almers (5) has presented evidence that the charge movement does not follow first-order kinetics, i.e. it is too simple to assume that the charged molecule can exist in two positions related by simple rate constants. Moreover, a muscle fiber inactivated by depolarization, in which no charge movement can be observed under ordinary conditions, shows another type of charge movement under specified conditions, if one of the holding potentials is far more negative than the normal range (5). The physiological implication of the second type of charge movement is not yet known.

SARCOPLASMIC RETICULUM

Electrical Phenomena Associated with Ca^{2+} Release from SR

CHANGES IN OPTICAL PROPERTIES OF SR MEMBRANE AS A SIGN OF ELECTRICAL PHENOMENA   Electrical phenomena may be associated with the process of Ca^{2+} release from the SR, however, the usual electrophysiological techniques are not applicable to this system because of its minute size.

Stimulated by studies on the change in optical properties of nerve membrane associated with electrical activity (20, 21, 117), Bezanilla & Horowicz (13) and Baylor & Oetliker (11) applied the same techniques to the investigation of electrical phenomena in SR.

Bezanilla & Horowicz (13) determined the extrinsic fluorescence change of a muscle fiber stained with Nile Blue A, which is shown to have a relatively large fluorescence change per unit transmembrane potential (21). If muscle is stimulated, a transient increase in fluorescence occurs that starts in the falling phase of the action potential, i.e. slightly earlier than the onset of contraction. This fluorescence is increased by NO_3^- and depressed by D_2O, indicating the parallelism of this phenomenon with the release of Ca^{2+} from the SR. Tetrodotoxin does not affect the depolarization-induced fluorescence increase at all. The thresholds for tension development and fluorescence increase coincide well with each other.

Using the birefringence technique, Baylor & Oetliker (11) have found that the action potential produces a change in the birefringence signal of muscle membrane, which consists of three components. The first component, small in size, is undoubtedly related to the action potential. The second component is very large and behaves similarly to the fluorescence change just described. The current-passing experiment of Baylor & Oetliker (11) implies that the signal is unrelated to the depolarization of the T system (the third component is referred to below).

Based on these and other findings, Bezanilla & Horowicz (13) and Baylor & Oetliker (11) concluded that the optical changes mentioned above are associated with changes in electrical properties of the SR membrane.

The signal derived from the surface membrane is not observed by the fluorescence method (13) probably because of its small area compared with that of the SR membrane. However, the birefringence method allows a comparison of the signals derived from both kinds of membrane. Even if we take into account the large area of the SR membrane, the intensity of its birefringence change per unit area is about 50% larger than that of the surface membrane. If the ratio between the electric potential and optical changes is constant irrespective of the kind of membrane, the potential change of the SR should be much larger than 100 mV. This conclusion implies that the birefringence signal cannot be derived from a part of the SR such as the terminal cisternae, but is derived from its whole area.

On the other hand, the fluorescence study (13) has provided some estimates of electrophysiological properties of the SR membrane: Potassium resistance is almost the same as that of the surface membrane. The reduction of resistance associated with the change in transmembrane potential of the SR is very small, less than one fifth of the resting resistance. Although interesting, it is difficult to reconcile these estimates with the calculation of a greater than 100 mV change in the potential across the SR membrane.

The nature of the third component in the birefringence change is not yet known. It is possible that the component is identical with the change in birefringence suggested by Yanagida & Oosawa (126) to be associated with the conformational change of the thin filament induced by Ca^{2+}.

ELECTRICAL PHENOMENA OBSERVED WITH SKINNED FIBER   As described in a previous section, Natori (92–94) demonstrated the propagating contraction in skinned fibers. Furthermore, he recorded electrical potential associated with the propagating contraction (95). Because the early part of such an electrical change can be observed a little prior to the mechanical disturbances, it is very probable that the electrical sign thus observed represents events in the internal membrane system. Using intact fibers, Strickholm (116) has also observed some electrical change, probably derived from internal membranes. There is no doubt that the propagating contraction is induced by the propagating action potential in the T system. However, the area of the T system is very small compared to that of the SR. Therefore, it is rather likely that the detected electrical change is derived from the SR.

Ca Release from the SR

GENERAL ASPECTS   Ca release from the SR of the intact muscle fibers can be observed using murexide (75) or aequorin (9, 118) as intracellular indicators, but the observations thus made reflect the properties of the coupling between the T system and the SR as well those of the SR.

The introduction into this field of the skinned fiber preparation of Natori (91), particularly as modified for use in ordinary aqueous solution (38, 42), has contributed a great deal to our understanding of the Ca^{2+} release mechanism. Skinned cardiac muscle fibers can now be prepared by homogenization of muscle fibers so as to disrupt the sarcolemma (41). This technique has also been applied to mammalian skeletal muscle with some success (82).

Ca^{2+} accumulated in the SR is apt to be released under several conditions: (a) treatment with caffeine and related substances; (b) increase in Ca^{2+} concentration; (c) decrease in Mg^{2+} concentration; (d) sudden fall in temperature; (e) "depolarization," i.e. the procedure rendering the electric potential on the inside of the SR membrane more negative; (f) decrease in osmotic pressure. The first four conditions are interrelated, and thus are dealt with together in the next section.

Ca^{2+}-INDUCED Ca^{2+} RELEASE AND RELATED PHENOMENA The idea of Ca-induced Ca release, or Ca-dependent regenerative Ca release, was independently reached by two groups at almost the same time: the study by Endo's group (38) was based mainly on the effect of caffeine and the study by Podolsky's group (42) on that of lowered Mg^{2+} concentration. Caffeine is now classified a labilizer of the Ca^{2+}-induced Ca^{2+} release mechanism (35). Reduction of the Mg^{2+} concentration exerts essentially the same effect as caffeine on the SR.

The fact that even a low Ca^{2+} concentration, e.g. less than 10^{-5} M, induces Ca^{2+} release from the SR under certain circumstances (38) suggests that this mechanism may be involved in physiological E-C coupling. If the Ca^{2+} bound to the inner surface of the T-system membrane is released by depolarization, the coupling of electrical phenomena of the T system with the SR could be reasonably explained.

However, Endo (35, 36, 119) recently presented evidence against the idea that Ca^{2+}-induced Ca^{2+} release plays an essential role in the mechanism of E-C coupling: (a) procaine, a rather specific inhibitor of Ca^{2+}-induced Ca^{2+} release did not depress the contracture induced by K^+ as effectively as depolarization (63); (b) Ca-induced Ca release takes place only under the following conditions: 1. the SR is nearly maximally filled with Ca^{2+} and the Ca^{2+} in the milieu is 3×10^{-5} M, or 2. Ca^{2+} in the milieu is more than 3×10^{-4} M and loaded Ca^{2+} in the SR is one third the maximum. But the degree of saturation of the SR with Ca^{2+} in ordinary fibers is less than one third the maximum and it is almost impossible to obtain such a high concentration of Ca^{2+} if there is no source of Ca other than that bound to the T system.

Ca release from the SR due to sudden lowering of the temperature of the bathing solution in the presence of a subthreshold concentration of caffeine is another important property of the SR (103). Because this effect is antagonized by procaine, it may well be considered as somehow related to the Ca-induced Ca release. This release takes place in the complete absence of excitation so that it can be utilized for the assessment of the Ca store in the muscle if combined with caffeine under the condition in which Ca^{2+} entry is completely prevented (104).

ELECTRICALLY INDUCED Ca RELEASE Natori's skinned fiber, which was immersed in oil, showed various types of responsiveness to electrical stimulation (see below). Costantin & Podolsky (23) applied to a skinned fiber a droplet of a solution with a different composition of salts from the original composition in the sacroplasm of the fiber to change the electric potential across the membrane. They obtained essentially the same contractile response as with electrical stimulation. However, the presence of the T system makes the interpretation very complicated. The use of partially skinned fibers (37), in which the T system is exposed to a K^+-rich medium, can exclude the involvement of T system as an electrogenic source. In contrast to the skinned fiber in oil, it is almost impossible to produce by electrical stimulation an electrical gradient across the membrane of the SR sufficient to induce contraction of a skinned fiber in an aqueous solution. Perhaps the only procedure by which an electrical gradient can be produced across the SR membrane is the chemical procedure mentioned above.

Using these procedures, Endo & Nakajima (37) succeeded in inducing Ca^{2+} release from such a skinned fiber. Contraction of the skinned fiber is induced either when a large anion, for instance, methane sulfonate, is replaced by a more permeable anion, for example, Cl^-, or when the permeable cation such as K^+ is replaced with a less permeable cation, e.g. Li^+, Na^+, or Tris. That the same response is obtained by the two kinds of procedures using different salt compositions strongly suggests that Ca^{2+} release is not a result of specific actions of certain ions, but derives from a common state induced by the two different procedures, i.e. the state in which the inside of the SR membrane becomes more negative. Endo & Nakajima (37) termed this state *depolarization;* this usage is adopted in this article. *Electrical* is also used in this article to express a similar state.

The response of skinned fibers to electrical stimulation differs in nature from that of Ca^{2+}-induced Ca^{2+} release. Depolarization-induced Ca release is more or less independent of Mg^{2+} concentration, or the degree of saturation of the SR by Ca^{2+} and is not depressed by procaine (119).

It might be argued, however, that although the T system of the partially skinned fiber soaked in aqueous solution is depolarized, a transient potential difference might be induced across the T-system membrane when the solution is changed. This hypotheses, however, may be refuted by the experiment of Kasai & Miyamoto, in which the fragmented SR, (undoubtedly detached from the T system as shown by electron microscopy) shows Ca release by electrical stimulation (80). K^+ or Na^+ contained in the fragmented SR is also released together with osmotically induced Ca release, but the Ca release induced by depolarization is not accompanied by Na^+ or K^+, indicating the specific nature of depolarization-induced Ca release (81).

OSMOTICALLY INDUCED Ca^{2+} RELEASE   If the concentration of the abundant ion species in the bathing fluid, say K^+ or methane sulfonate is suddenly decreased several-fold, a definite Ca^{2+} release is observed (39). This effect is not inhibited by procaine. An increase in osmotic pressure inhibits the release of Ca^{2+}. Substitution of Cl- for methane sulfonate produces depolarization-induced Ca^{2+} release more easily than that from K^+ to Tris (37). This may be explained by assuming that the osmotic effect in these phenomena favors Ca^{2+} release in the former but not in the latter.

Problems Regarding Ca^{2+} Movement in the Sarcoplasm

Not all the problems related to Ca movement in the sarcoplasm are discussed here; only a few topics are described.

The efforts to establish aequorin as an intracellular indicator of Ca^{2+} in muscle cells are briefly summarized in a paper by Taylor, Rüdel & Blinks (118). These authors observed that the amount of Ca released during twitch or tetanus depends on the sarcomere length and that the relationship between them is, perhaps fortuitously, very similar to the well-known relationship between sarcomere length and tetanus tension (57).

There is no doubt that Ca^{2+} released from the SR is taken up solely by the SR, at least in white, fast skeletal muscle, and that this process is directly related to the relaxation process. The detailed mechanism of Ca uptake has been worked out by a number of investigators (24, 59, 72, 88, 120) and reasonable explanations for it are now available. As yet unanswered however is the question of why even the highest rate of Ca^{2+} uptake, thus far measured directly or calculated from Ca-dependent ATPase of fragmented SR, is too slow to explain the rapid time course of relaxation in living fibers (28). To explain it quanititatively, the rate of Ca^{2+} uptake by the SR should be nearly 10 times higher than that indicated by the best available data. This means that the SR has not yet been fully qualified as one of the most important devices in muscle. This question has fundamental importance to our understanding of E-C coupling and should be answered as soon as possible.

Another important problem is whether or not Ca^{2+} uptake by the SR is carried out during the same period in which Ca^{2+} is released from SR. No report to support or deny this possibility has been presented.

There is no doubt that in white, fast skeletal muscle, mitochondria plays no role in the relaxation process (54), but the situation is not clear in red slow muscle or in cardiac muscle. Gillis (54) has shown that if a relatively large amount of Ca^{2+} is topically applied to skinned fibers of red slow muscle, a considerable delay in the course of relaxation is observed in the presence of ruthenium red, a specific inhibitor of Ca^{2+} uptake of mitochondria, indicating a role of mitochondria in regulation of intracellular Ca^{2+}. On the other hand, Kitazawa (84) compared cardiac SR and mitochondria with respect to their Ca uptake rates and relaxing effects and reached the conclusion that, so far as contraction of cardiac muscle under physiological condition is concerned (i.e. about one fourth the maximum tension, requiring about 5×10^{-6} M Ca) mitochondria do not play a substantial role. This result agrees with that of Scarpa on the kinetics of mitochondrial Ca uptake (109). Mitochondria, however, may play a role if the Ca^{2+} concentration is elevated above a certain level.

The now classical work of Winegrad (123, 124), indicates that Ca^{2+} is released mainly from the terminal cisternae and is taken up by the whole surface of the SR. The question is then raised whether even fragmented SR has a functional differentiation according to its origin, i.e. the longitudinal part may show only Ca^{2+} accumulation and the cisternae may be mainly concerned with Ca^{2+} release. Responses of fragmented SR to caffeine as well as depolarization seem to favor the concept that there is no strict functional differention at this level, but the evidence is not yet conclusive. If we accept the idea that the optical change of the SR membrane is associated with Ca^{2+} release, we are led to the conclusion that the whole area of the SR releases Ca^{2+}, but the possibility remains that the optical change in the whole surface is a result of an electrotonic influence of deplorization of the terminal cisternae. Thus the final conclusion as to the functional differentiation of the SR membrane according to localization should be reserved until clearer evidence is presented.

PHARMACOLOGY OF EXCITATION-CONTRACTION COUPLING

Drugs are often crucial tools for revealing the secret of physiological functions. For instance, our present knowledge of the neuromuscular junction in skeletal muscle could not have been obtained without the aid of drugs specific for this site, such as eserine, curare, or α-bungarotoxin. Compared with this, E-C coupling has been a poor field from a pharmacological point of view.

However, the discovery of dantrolene has somewhat changed the situation. Although it is far from comparable to eserine or curare, dantrolene has brought hope that someday a potent drug specific for true E-C coupling will become available and will contribute to studies on the mechanism of E-C coupling.

CAFFEINE   That the SR is the site of action of caffeine was first indicated by Weber (121) using fragmented SR. She also showed that Ca^{2+} is required for the action of caffeine (121).

In the presence of a fairly high concentration of caffeine, skinned fibers undergo reversible contracture (38) and fragmented SR accumulates Ca^{2+} almost to its full extent (96). Furthermore, the amount and rate of Ca^{2+} uptake by skinned fibers at a low Ca^{2+} concentration is not affected by caffeine. In view of these observations, Endo et al (38) concluded that the effect of caffeine on the SR was to facilitate the Ca^{2+}-releasing mechanism of the SR, not to reduce the capacity of the SR to accumulate Ca^{2+}.

In accordance with the finding that Ca release of the SR is regenerative, the mode of action of caffeine is now interpreted as labilization of the Ca^{2+}-induced Ca^{2+} release mechanism, rather than augmentation of Ca^{2+} release from the SR (36).

Ca release by caffeine from fragmented SR does not take place at low concentrations of ATP or its substitutes (96, 122). In this connection an observation has been made that—in the presence of carbamyl phosphate, which has a much weaker affinity for the Ca-dependent ATPase than ATP—AMPOPCP (β,γ-methylene ATP), an nonhydrolyzable analog of ATP, induces the release of Ca^{2+} from fragmented SR (97). If caffeine is supplied and the fragmented SR is then filled with Ca^{2+} to the full extent, AMPOPCP effects the release of more than 80% of accumulated Ca^{2+} (97). This indicates that the whole area of the SR, at least the whole longitudinal part, is sensitive to caffeine.

The above description is based on the assumption that the site of action of caffeine is confined to the SR. However, caffeine may have another action on a site different from the SR, probably on the coupling between the T system and terminal cisternae. The finding described in the section on Mn action may reflect such a property of caffeine.

PROCAINE AND TETRACAINE   The antagonistic action of procaine against caffeine was noticed very long ago (111). In accord with the new interpretation of the caffeine effect, the mode of action of procaine is now explained as a stabilization, or inhibition, of the Ca^{2+}-induced Ca^{2+} release mechanism (43, 119).

Tetracaine at low concentrations shows essentially the same effect as procaine (15, 87), but lidocaine does not exert such an effect (15). (These results are obtained with intact fibers, but skinned fibers yield essentially the same results; cocaine has no effect either.) Perhaps this effect of procaine should not be taken simply as a facet of its local anesthetic action.

In addition to stabilization of the Ca-induced Ca^{2+} release mechanism, procaine has another effect in a range of concentration slightly higher than that used to antagonize Ca-induced Ca^{2+} release: The duration, or the slow phase, of the contracture induced by depolarization in the presence of tetrodotoxin is depressed. Procaine also greatly retards the repriming of the contractile response of a fiber inactivated by prolonged depolarization (62) and has essentially the same effect on K^+ contracture. This depressive effect is more pronounced in K^+ contracture of a bundle of muscle fibers than in a single fiber. A moderate concentration of tetracaine produces essentially the same effect as procaine (87). Higher concentrations of tetracaine completely abolish K^+ contracture (87), without an effect on the charge movement (6).

Because the inhibitory action of procaine on K^+ contracture is greater at high K^+ concentrations, the mechanism of this action is definitely different from that of dantrolene or Mn^{2+}, as seen below.

The effect of moderate concentrations of procaine or tetracaine on K^+ contracture is similar to that of removal of Ca^{2+} from the bathing solution (86), indicating that the mode of action of procaine involves facilitation of inactivation. The question of whether or not the effect of tetracaine at higher concentrations is fundamentally related to the inactivation mechanism deserves further investigation.

HEAVY WATER   Kaminer (77) has shown that if most H_2O in the bathing solution is replaced by D_2O, the twitch of muscle is considerably depressed; the degree of depression of K^+ contracture is less intense than that of twitch, but is fairly marked even at a high K^+ concentration (125). Under this condition, the contractility of both the myofibrils and the excitation mechanism is not impaired (26, 77), but in intact fibers the release of Ca^{2+} from the SR (78) and the associated fluorescence change of the SR are apparently depressed (13).

In skinned fibers as well as intact fibers, it was shown that the Ca^{2+}-releasing ability of the SR induced by Ca^{2+}, caffeine, or depolarization is somewhat depressed, but the extent of its inhibition is too small to be considered the primary action of D_2O (125). As a whole, the main site of action of D_2O may be true E-C coupling, i.e. the process in which the depolarization of the T system is transmitted to the SR, but its effects on other sites cannot be ignored (125).

DANTROLENE SODIUM (DANTRIUM)   Dantrolene (112) may be the first drug that exerts its effect on E-C coupling at so-called pharmacological concentrations [less than 10^{-6} M (34)]. In a single fiber it depresses twitch more intensely than K^+ contracture (34); K^+ contracture at low concentrations of K^+ is depressed, but that at high concentrations K^+ contracture is not affected (63), although the contracture of a fiber bundle is intensely depressed even at high K^+ concentration (102). In contrast to caffeine, dantrolene's effect is more pronounced on mammalian muscle than on amphibian muscle (34). Caffeine induces contracture of dantrolene-treated intact muscle fibers (34), but the threshold is increased (102). Depolarization- and caffeine-induced Ca^{2+} release from skinned fibers is not depressed by this drug.

This drug thus seems to affect the site in which the signal from the T system to the SR is transmitted. In this respect, it is more specific than D_2O.

MANGANESE ION   Although Mn^{2+} has a remarkable effect on cardiac and smooth muscle, it had been supposed to have no significant effect on skeletal muscle. However, Oota et al (98) have shown that a high concentration of Mn^{2+} (10 mM or more) abolishes the twitch as well as K^+ contracture. Although the caffeine contracture of intact fibers is significantly depressed, that of depolarized fiber is not affected. Using single fibers, Chiarandini & Stefani (19) have shown that 10 mM of Mn^{2+}, which decreases the size of twitch tension down to about 30% of the maximum, strongly depresses K^+ contracture at low but not high concentrations of K^+. Thus, the mode of action of Mn^{2+} is similar to dantrolene. The inhibitory action of Mn^{2+} on Ca^{2+} influx (58), considered to be the main cause of suppressed contractility in cardiac and smooth muscle, may not play an important role.

NITRATE AND RELATED ANIONS   Many years have passed since the discovery of the contraction-enhancing effect of simple anions (13, 76, 106), i.e. NO_3^-, I^-, and SCN^-, but the mechanism is not yet well understood. These anions may have two sites of action; one may be related to the true E-C coupling-enhancing action and the other to caffeine-like action. The assertion that the effect is related to the enhancement of delayed rectification (29) should be withdrawn, because UO_2^+, Zn^{2+}, and tetraethylammonium ion do not abolish E-C coupling in spite of their inhibitory action on delayed rectification (79; see also 108).

As described above, the fluorescence probably associated with the electrical phenomena of the SR is enhanced by NO_3^- (13). This is fascinating, but may require confirmation by the birefringence method on a single fiber (11).

SUCROSE AND OTHER SUGARS   It is well known that hypertonic sucrose solution abolishes E-C coupling (64). As mentioned in detail by Fuchs (49), a large part of the action can be attributed to the osmotic effect, and the subsequent increase in the concentration of sarcoplasmic electrolytes. The interaction of myosin and actin is weakened at high ionic strength, which accounts for the finding that hypertonic Na salt solutions show essentially the same action as sucrose (56). If the hypertonicity is less than 2.5 times that of normal bathing solution, Ca^{2+} release from the SR is not inhibited (118). However, if the sucrose concentration exceeds this limit, Ca^{2+} release is depressed (118). It is not yet known whether this depression is also due to the increase in the concentration of sarcoplasmic electrolytes, or to the direct effects of sucrose on the true E-C coupling. The size of the second component of the birefringence change decreases with increase in osmotic pressure (11).

Apart from the above, all sugars so far tested, including sucrose, have inhibitory action on depolarization-induced release of Ca^{2+} from skinned fibers (119). To see this inhibitory action definitely, a fairly high concentration, perhaps 40 mM, is required, but it cannot solely be explained by an osmotic effect (39). Effects of caffeine are not antagonized by this action.

OTHER AGENTS   Formaldehyde of a particular concentration irreversibly eliminates E-C coupling without affecting caffeine-induced release of Ca^{2+} from the SR (68). The charge movement in the T system is affected but not intensely (6). It is possible that this mild inhibition has physiological significance. Quinine is another drug traditionally used to induce contracture, but its mode of action on fragmented SR differs from that of caffeine (16). Its action on living fiber is not antagonized by procaine (73).

GENERAL COMMENTS   The results obtained with a bundle of muscle fibers are sometimes quite at variance with those obtained with a single fiber. This is more apparent for K^+ contracture than for twitch or tetanus. For instance, the contracture of a single fiber induced by a high K^+ concentration is not affected by dantrolene or Mn, whereas that of a bundle is intensely depressed as described above. In the case of contraction-potentiating anions, their effects appear to be augmented more in a bundle than in a single fiber. An experiment with a muscle bundle has its own significance, but one disadvantage is that it cannot discriminate between the two groups of drugs described below.

There are two kinds of inhibitors of the signal transmission from the T system to the terminal cisternae, or uncouplers acting between these two systems. The main action of dantrolene and perhaps of Mn^{2+} belongs to the first group. These agents depress twitch more than they depress K^+ contracture; the contracture induced by a low K^+ concentration is strongly depressed, but that induced by a high concentration is scarcely affected, i.e. the threshold for the activation is elevated but the full activation can be obtained. Perhaps their effect is more marked at higher temperatures.

The second group may be represented by Ca^{2+} deficiency and procaine. The former does not affect twitch, but intensely depresses the slow phase of K^+ contracture irrespective of K^+ concentrations; the latter's effect on twitch is distorted by its inhibitory effect on the excitation mechanism, but its influence on the contracture, induced by either depolarization or K^+, is essentially the same as that of the former. The action of this group may be explained on the basis of its facilitating effect on the inactivation process.

CONCLUDING REMARKS

As described in the introduction, attention has been focused on the studies dealing with the question of how depolarization of the T system induces the release of Ca^{2+} from the SR. This has resulted in a serious shortcoming of this article in that some important aspects of E-C coupling and many excellent papers relating to them have been omitted. On the other hand, I am convinced that some new facets are being explored and developed in the field of E-C coupling, in accordance with the rapid progress taking place in other fields of biological sciences.

It appears that three new fronts are emerging as possible approaches to a full understanding of the mechanism of coupling between depolarization and Ca^{2+} release: (a) The T system contains a charged particle that can undergo voltage-dependent movement; in many respects, the behavior of this movable charge coincides with the properties of the coupling between depolarization and contraction. (b) The entire surface of the SR seems capable of exhibiting an electrical phenomenon, probably associated with Ca^{2+} release. (c) The release of Ca^{2+} from the SR may be induced by the electrical potential change across the SR membrane; compared with this, the role of Ca^{2+}-induced Ca^{2+} release is minor or negligible.

ACKNOWLEDGMENT

I am very grateful to my colleagues in our laboratories for their invaluable assistance in writing this review.

Literature Cited

1. Adrian, R. H., Peachey, L. D. 1973. Reconstruction of the action potential of frog sartorius muscle. *J. Physiol. London* 235:103–31
2. Adrian, R. H., Chandler, W. K., Hodgkin, A. L. 1969. The kinetics of mechanical activation in frog muscle. *J. Physiol. London* 204:207–30
3. Adrian, R. H., Chandler, W. K., Hodgkin, A. L. 1973. Voltage-clamp experiments in striated muscle fibres. *J. Physiol. London* 208:607–44
4. Adrian, R. H., Chandler, W. K., Rakowski, R. F. 1975. Charge movement and mechanical repriming in skeletal muscle. *J. Physiol. London.* In press
5. Almers, W. 1975. Observations on intramembrane charge movements in skeletal muscle. *Philos. Trans. R. Soc. London Ser. B* 270:501–13
6. Almers, W., Adrian, R. H., Levinson, R. S. 1975. Some dielectric properties of muscle membrane and their possible importance for excitation-contraction coupling. *Ann. NY Acad. Sci.* In press
7. Armstrong, C. M. 1975. Ionic pores, gates and gating currents. *Q. Rev. Biophys.* 7:179–210
8. Armstrong, C. M., Bezanilla, F. 1973. Currents related to the movement of gating particles of the sodium channels. *Nature* 242:459–61
9. Ashley, C. C., Ridgway, E. B. 1970. On the relationships between membrane potential, calcium transient and tension in single barnacle muscle fibres. *J. Physiol. London* 209:105–30
10. Bastian, J., Nakajima, S. 1974. Action potential in the transverse tubules and its role in the activation of skeletal muscle. *J. Gen. Physiol.* 63:257–78
11. Baylor, S. M., Oetliker, H. 1975. Birefringence experiments on isolated skeletal muscle fibres suggest a possible signal from the sarcoplasmic reticulum. *Nature* 253:97–101
12. Bethe, A., Franke, F. 1925. Versuche über die Kalikontraktur. *Biochem. Z.* 156:190–200
13. Bezanilla, F., Horowicz, P. 1975. Fluorescence intensity changes associated with contractile activation in frog muscle stained with nile blue A. *J. Physiol. London* 246:709–35
14. Bezanilla, F., Caputo, C., Gonzalez-Serratos, H., Venosa, R. A. 1972. Sodium dependence of the inward spread of activation in isolated twitch muscle fibres of the frog. *J. Physiol. London* 223:507–23
15. Bianchi, C. P., Bolton, T. C. 1967. Action of local anesthetics on coupling systems in muscle. *J. Pharmacol. Exp. Therap.* 157:388–405
16. Carvalho, A. P. 1968. Calcium-binding properties of sarcoplasmic reticulum as influenced by ATP, caffeine, quinine, and local anesthetics. *J. Gen Physiol.* 52:622–42
17. Chandler, W. K., Rakowski, R. F., Schneider, M. F. 1975. A nonlinear voltage dependent charge movement in frog skeletal muscle. *J. Physiol. London.* In press
18. Chandler, W. K., Rakowski, R. F., Schneider, M. F. 1975. Effects of glycerol treatment and maintained depolarization on charge movement in skeletal muscle. *J. Physiol. London.* In press

19. Chiarandini, D. J., Stefani, E. 1973. Effects of manganese on the electrical and mechanical properties of frog skeletal muscle fibres. *J. Physiol. London.* 232:129–47

20. Cohen, L. B., Hille, B., Keynes, R. D. 1970. Changes in axon birefringence during the action potential. *J. Physiol. London* 211:495–515

21. Cohen, L. B., Salzberg, B. M., Dávila, H.V., Ross, W. N., Landowne, D., Waggoner, A. S., Wang, C. H. 1974. Changes in axon fluorescence during activity: Molecular probes of membrane potential. *J. Membr. Biol.* 19:1–36

22. Costantin, L. L. 1970. The role of sodium current in the radial spread of contraction in frog muscle fibers. *J. Gen. Physiol.* 55:703–15

23. Costantin, L. L., Podolsky, R. J. 1967. Depolarization of the internal membrane system in the activation of frog skeletal muscle. *J. Gen. Physiol.* 50:1101–24

24. Drabikowski, W., Strezelecka-Golaszewska, H., Carafoli, E., eds. 1974. *Calcium Binding Proteins.* Warsaw: PWN; Amsterdam: Elsevier, 281–642

25. Dulhunty, A. F., Gage, P. W. 1973. Differential effects of glycerol treatment on membrane capacity and excitation-contraction coupling in toad sartorius fibres. *J. Physiol. London* 234:307–408

26. Eastwood, A. B., Grundfest, H., Brandt, P. W., Reuben, J. P. 1975. Sites of action of D$_2$O in intact and skinned muscle fibres. *J. Gen. Physiol.* In press

27. Ebashi, S. 1963. Relaxing factor and excitation contraction coupling. *Seitai no Kagaku* 14:279–85 (In Japanese)

28. Ebashi, S., Endo, M. 1968. Calcium ion and muscle contraction. *Progr. Biophys. Mol. Biol.* 18:123–83

29. Ebashi, S., Endo, M., Ohtsuki, I. 1969. Control of muscle contraction. *Q. Rev. Biophys.* 2:351–84

30. Eisenberg, B. R. 1972. Three dimensional branching of the T-system in frog sartorius muscle. *J. Cell Biol.* 55:68a

31. Eisenberg, B., Eisenberg, R. S. 1968. Selective disruption of the sarcotubular system in frog sartorius muscle. *J. Cell Biol.* 39:451–67

32. Eisenberg, R. S., Gage, P. W. 1967. Frog skeletal muscle fibres: Changes in electrical properties after disruption of transverse tubular system. *Science* 158:1700–1

33. Eisenberg, R. S., Gage, P. W. 1969. Ionic conductances of the surface and transverse tubular membranes of frog

sartorius fibres. *J. Gen. Physiol.* 53:279–97

34. Ellis, K. O., Carpenter, J. F. 1972. Studies on the mechanism of action of dantrolene sodium. *Arch. Exp. Pathol. Pharmakol.* 275:83–94

34a. Endo, M. 1974. The mechanism of Ca release from the sarcoplasmic reticulum. *Heart* 6:1506–14 (In Japanese)

35. Endo, M. 1975. Conditions required for calcium-induced release of calcium from the sarcoplasmic reticulum. *Proc. Jpn. Acad.* 51:467–72

36. Endo, M. 1975. Mechanism of action of caffeine on the sarcoplasmic reticulum of skeletal muscle. *Proc. Jpn. Acad.* 479–84

37. Endo, M., Nakajima, Y. 1973. Release of calcium induced by "Depolarisation" of the sarcoplasmic reticulum membrane. *Nature New Biol.* 246:216–18

38. Endo, M., Tanaka, M., Ogawa, Y. 1970. Calcium induced release of calcium from the sarcoplasmic reticulum of skinned skeletal muscle fibres. *Nature* 228:34–36

39. Endo, M., Thorens, S. 1975. Release of calcium from the sarcoplasmic reticulum induced by hypotonic solutions. *J. Physiol. Soc. Jpn.* In press

40. Ezerman, E., Ishikawa, H. 1967. Differentiation of the sarcoplasmic reticulum and T-system in developing chick skeletal muscle in vitro. *J. Cell Biol.* 35:405–17

41. Fabiato, A., Fabiato, F. 1975. Techniques of skinned cardiac cells and of isolated cardiac fibres with disrupted sarcolemmas with reference to the effects of catecholamines and of caffeine. In *Recent Advances in Studies on Cardiac Structure and Metabolism,* ed. P. E. Roy, 6:1–31. Baltimore, London & Tokyo: Univ. Park

42. Ford, L. E., Podolsky, R. J. 1970. Regenerative calcium release within muscle cells. *Science* 167:58–59

43. Ford, L. E., Podolsky, R. J. 1972. Intracellular calcium movements in skinned muscle fibres. *J. Physiol. London* 223:21–33

44. Frankenhaeuser, B., Hodgkin, A. L. 1957. The action of calcium on the electrical properties of squid axons. *J. Physiol. London* 137:218–44

45. Franzini-Armstrong, C. 1970. Studies of the triad. I. Structure of the junction in frog twitch fibers. *J. Cell Biol.* 47:488–99

46. Franzini-Armstrong, C. 1972. Studies of the triad. III. Structure of the junc-

tion in fast twitch fibers. *Tissue Cell* 4:469–78

47. Franzini-Armstrong, C. 1973. Membrane systems in muscle fibers. *The Structure and Function of Muscle,* ed. G. H. Bourne, 2:531–619. New York: Academic

48. Franzini-Armstrong, C., Landmesser, L., Pilar, G. 1974. Size and shape of transverse tubule openings in frog twitch muscle fibers. *J. Cell Biol.* 64:493–97

49. Fuchs, F. 1974. Striated muscle. *Ann. Rev. Physiol.* 36:461–502

50. Fujino, M., Yamaguchi, T., Suzuki, K. 1961. Glycerol effect and the mechanism linking excitation of the plasma membrane with contraction. *Nature* 192:1159–61

51. Fujino, M., Yamaguchi, T., Fujino, S. 1972. "Glycerol effect" in various kinds of muscle. *Jpn. J. Physiol.* 22:477–89

52. Gage, P. W., Eisenberg, R. S. 1967. Action potentials without contraction in frog skeletal muscle fibers with disrupted transverse tubules. *Science* 158:1702–3

53. Galvani, L. 1791. De viribus electricitatis in motu musculari commentarius. *Ist. Sci. Orti Liberali Bologna* 7:363–418

54. Gillis, J. M. 1972. *Le Role du Calcium dans le Controle Intracellulaire de la Contraction Musculaire.* Louvain, Belgium: Vander

55. Gonzalez-Serratos, H. 1971. Inward spread of activation in vertebrate muscle fibres. *J. Physiol. London* 212:777–99

56. Gordon, A. M., Godt, R. E. 1970. Some effects of hypertonic solutions on contraction and excitation-contraction coupling in frog skeletal muscles. *J. Gen. Physiol.* 55:254–75

57. Gordon, A. M., Huxley, A. F., Julian, F. J. 1966. The variation in isometric tension with sarcomere length in vertebrate muscle fibres. *J. Physiol. London* 184:170–92

58. Hagiwara, S. 1973. Ca spike. *Adv. Biophys.* 4:71–102

59. Hasselbach, W. 1974. Sarcoplasmic membrane ATPase. In *The Enzymes* 10:431–67

60. Heistracher, P., Hunt, C. C. 1969. The relation of membrane changes to contraction in twitch muscle fibres. *J. Physiol. London* 201:589–611

61. Heistracher, P., Hunt, C. C. 1969. Contractile repriming in snake twitch mus-

cle fibres. *J. Physiol. London* 201:613–26

62. Heistracher, P., Hunt, C. C. 1969. The effect of procaine on snake twitch muscle fibres. *J. Physiol. London* 201:627–38

63. Hainaut, K., Desmedt, J. E. 1974. Effect of dantrolene sodium on calcium movements in single muscle fibres. *Nature* 252:728–30

64. Hodgkin, A. L., Horowicz, P. 1957. The differential action of hypertonic solutions on the twitch and action potential of a muscle fibre. *J. Physiol. London* 136:17p

65. Hodgkin, A. L., Horowicz, P. 1960. Potassium contractures in single muscle fibres. *J. Physiol. London* 153:386–403

66. Hodgkin, A. L., Huxley, A. F. 1952. A quantitative description of membrane current and its application to conduction and excitation in nerve. *J. Physiol.* 117:500–44

67. Howell, J. N., Jenden, D. J. 1967. T-tubules of skeletal muscle morphological alterations which interrupt excitation-contraction coupling. *Fed. Proc.* 26:553

68. Hutter, O. F. 1969. Potassium conductance of skeletal muscle treated with formaldehyde. *Nature* 224:1215–16

69. Huxley, A. F. 1971. The activation of striated muscle and its mechanical response. *Proc. R. Soc. London Ser. B* 178:1–27

70. Huxley, A. F., Taylor, R. E. 1958. Local activation of striated muscle fibres. *J. Physiol. London* 144:426–41

71. Huxley, H. E. 1964. Evidence for the continuity between the central elements of the triads and extracellular space in frog sartorius muscle. *Nature* 202:1067–71

72. Inesi, G. 1972. Active transport of calcium ion in sarcoplasmic membranes. *Ann. Rev. Biophys. Bioeng.* 1:191–210

73. Isaacson, A., Yamaji, K., Sandow, A. 1970. Quinin contractures and Ca movements of frog sartorius muscle as affected by pH. *J. Pharmacol. Exp. Therap.* 171:26–31

74. Jewett, P. H., Sommer, J. R., Johnson, E. A. 1971. Cardiac muscle: Its ultrastructure in the finch and hummingbird with special reference to the sarcoplasmic reticulum. *J. Cell Biol.* 49:50–65

75. Jöbsis, E. F., O'Connor, M. J. 1966. Calcium release and reabsorption in the sartorius muscle of the toad. *Biochem. Biophys. Res. Commun.* 25:246–52

76. Kahn, A. J., Sandow, A. 1950. The potentiation of muscular contraction by the nitrate-ion. *Science* 112:647–49
77. Kaminer, B. 1960. Effect of heavy water on different types of muscle and on glycerol-extracted psoas fibres. *Nature* 185:172–73
78. Kaminer, B., Kimura, J. 1972. Deuterium oxide: Inhibition of calcium release in muscle. *Science* 176:406–7
79. Kao, C. Y., Stanfield, P. R. 1970. Actions of some cations on the electrical properties and mechanical threshold of frog sartorius muscle fibers. *J. Gen. Physiol.* 55:620–39
80. Kasai, M., Miyamoto, H. 1973. Depolarization induced calcium release from sarcoplasmic reticulum membrane fragments by changing ionic environment. *FEBS Lett.* 34:299–301
81. Kasai, M., Miyamoto, H. 1974. The mechanism of Ca-release from the fragmented sarcoplasmic reticulum. *Abstr. Jpn. Biophys. Soc., 13th.* 219 pp. (In Japanese)
82. Kerrick, W. G., Brian, K. 1975. Disruption of the sarcolemma of mammalian skeletal muscle fibers by homogenization. *J. Appl. Physiol.*
83. Keynes, R. D., Rojas, E. 1974. Kinetics and steady-state properties of the charged system controlling sodium conductance in the squid giant axon. *J. Physiol. London* 239:393–434
84. Kitazawa, T. 1975. Physiological significance of Ca uptake by mitochondria in the heart in comparison with that by its sarcoplasmic reticulum. *J. Biochem.* In press
85. Krolenko, S. A. 1969. Change in the T-system of muscle fibers under the influence of the influx and efflux of glycerol. *Nature* 221:966–68
86. Lüttgau, H. C. 1963. The action of calcium ions on potassium contractures of single muscle fibers. *J. Physiol. London* 168:679–97
87. Lüttgau, H. C., Oetliker, H. 1968. The action of caffeine on the activation of the contractile mechanism in striated muscle fibres. *J. Physiol. London* 194:51–74
88. Martonosi, A. 1972. Biochemical and clinical aspects of sarcoplasmic reticulum function. *Current Topics in Membranes and Transport,* ed. F. Bronner, A. Kleinzeller, 3:83–197. New York: Academic
89. Nakajima, S., Bastian, J. 1974. Double sucrose-gap method applied to single muscle fiber of *Xenopus laevis. J. Gen. Physiol.* 63:235
90. Nakajima, S., Iwasaki, S., Obata, K. 1962. Delayed rectification and anomalous rectification in frog's skeletal muscle membrane. *J. Gen. Physiol.* 46:97–115
91. Natori, R. 1954. The property and contraction process of isolated myofibrils. *Jikeikai Med. J.* 1:119–26
92. Natori, R. 1955. Repeated contraction and conductive contraction observed in isolated myofibrils. *Jikeikai Med. J.* 2:1–5
93. Natori, R. 1965. Effects of Na and Ca ions on the excitability of isolated myofibrils. *Molecular Biology of Muscular Contraction.* ed. S. Ebashi, F. Oosawa, T. Sekine, Y. Tonomura, 9:190–96. Tokyo & Amsterdam: Igaku Shoin and Elsevier
94. Natori, R. 1965. Propagated contractions in isolated sarcolemma-free bundles of myofibrils. *Jikeikai Med. J.* 12:214–21
95. Natori, R. 1975. The electric potential change of internal membrane during propagation of contraction of skinned fibre of toad skeletal muscle. *Jpn. J. Physiol.* 25:51–63
96. Ogawa, Y. 1970. Some properties of fragmented frog sarcoplasmic reticulum with particular reference to its response to caffeine. *J. Biochem.* 67:667–83
97. Ogawa, Y., Ebashi, S. 1973. Ca^{2+} uptake and release by fragmented sarcoplasmic reticulum with special reference to the effect of β,γ -methylene adenosine triphosphate. *Organization of Energy-Transducing Membranes,* ed. M. Nakao, L. Packer, 127–40. Tokyo: Univ. Tokyo Press
98. Oota, I., Takauji, M., Nagai, T. 1972. Effect of manganese ions on excitation-contraction coupling in frog sartorius muscle. *Jpn. J. Physiol.* 22:279–392
99. Peachey, L. D. 1975. Structure and function of the T-system in skeletal muscle cells. *Seitai no Kagaku* 26:259–67 (In Japanese)
100. Peachey, L. D., Adrian, R. H. 1973. Electrical properties of the transverse tubular system. *Structure and Function of Muscle,* ed. G. Bourne, 3:1–30. New York: Academic
101. Peachey, L. D., Schild, R. F. 1968. The distribution of the T-system along the sarcomeres of frog and toad sartorius muscles. *J. Physiol. London* 194:249–58
102. Putney, J. W. Jr., Bianchi, C. P. 1974. Site of action of dantrolene in frog sar-

torius muscle. *J. Pharmacol. Exp. Therap.* 189:202–12

103. Sakai, T. 1965. The effects of temperature and caffeine on activation of the contractile mechanism in the striated muscle fibres. *Jikeikai Med. J.* 12:88–102

104. Sakai, T., Kurihara, S. 1974. The rapid cooling contraction of toad cardiac muscle. *Jpn. J. Physiol.* 24:649–66

105. Sandow, A. 1952. Excitation-contraction coupling in muscular response. *Yale J. Biol. Med.* 25:176–201

106. Sandow, A. 1965. Excitation-contraction coupling in skeletal muscle. *Pharmacol. Rev.* 17:265–320

107. Sandow, A. 1970. Skeletal muscle. *Ann. Rev. Physiol.* 32:87–138

108. Sandow, A. 1973. Electromechanical transforms and mechanism of excitation-contraction coupling. *J. Mechanochem. Cell Motil.* 2:193–207

109. Scarpa, A., Graziotti, P. 1973. Mechanism for intracellular calcium regulation in heart. I. Stopped-flow measurement of Ca^{++} uptake by cardiac mitochondria. *J. Gen. Physiol.* 62:756–72

110. Schneider, M. F., Chandler, W. K. 1973. Voltage dependent charge movement in skeletal muscle: a possible step in excitation-concentration coupling. *Nature* 242:244–46

111. Schüller, J. 1925. Warum verhindern die Lokalanästhetika die Coffeinstarre des Muskel? *Arch. Exp. Pathol. Pharmakol.* 105:225–37

112. Snyder, H. R. Jr., Davis, C. S., Bickerton, R. K., Halliday, R. P. 1967. 1-(5-Arylfurfurylidence) amino hydantoins. A new class of muscle relaxants. *J. Med. Chem.* 10:807–10

113. Somlyo, A. P., Somlyo, A. V. 1975. Ultrastructure of smooth muscle. *Methods in Pharmacology,* ed. A. Schwartz, Vol. 3:3–45. New York: Appleton-Century-Crofts

114. Spray, T. L., Waugh, R. A., Sommer, J. R. 1974. Peripheral couplings in adult vertebrate skeletal muscle. *J. Cell Biol.* 62:223–27

115. Stefani, E., Chiarandini, D. J. 1973. Skeletal muscle dependence of potassium contractures on extracellular calcium. *Pfluegers Arch.* 343:143–50

116. Strickholm, A. 1974. Intracellular generated potentials during excitation-contraction coupling in muscle. *J. Neurobiol.* 5:61–87

117. Tasaki, I., Watanabe, A., Sandlin, R., Carnay, L. 1968. Changes in fluorescence, turbidity, and birefringence associated with nerve excitation. *Proc. Nat. Acad. Sci. USA* 61:883–88

118. Taylor, S. R., Rüdel, R., Blinks, J. R. 1975. Calcium transients in amphibian muscle. *Fed. Proc.* 34:1379–81

119. Thorens, S., Endo, M. 1975. Calcium-induced calcium release and "depolarization"-induced calcium release: Their physiological significance. *Proc. Jpn. Acad.* 51:473–78

120. Tonomura, Y. 1972. *Muscle Proteins, Muscle Contraction, and Cation Transport,* 305–56. Tokyo: Univ. Tokyo Press

121. Weber, A. 1966. Energized calcium transport and relaxing factors. *Curr. Top. Bioenerg.,* 203–54

122. Weber, A., Herz, R. 1968. The relationship between caffeine contracture of intact muscle and the effect of caffeine on reticulum. *J. Gen. Physiol.* 52:750–59

123. Winegrad, S. 1965. Autoradiographic studies of intracellular calcium in frog skeletal muscle. *J. Gen. Physiol.* 48:455–79

124. Winegrad, S. 1965. The location of muscle calcium with respect to myofibrils. *J. Gen. Physiol.* 48:997–1002

125. Yagi, S., Endo, M. 1974. Effects of D_2O on excitation-contraction coupling. *J. Physiol. Soc. Jpn.* 36:332 (In Japanese)

126. Yanagida, T., Oosawa, F. 1975. Effect of myosin on conformational changes of F-actin in thin filament in vivo induced by calcium ion. *Eur. J. Biochem.* 56:547–56

127. Zachar, J., Zacharova, D., Adrian, R. H. 1973. Observation on "detubulated" muscle fibers. *Nature New Biol.* 239:153–55

128. Zampighi, G., Vergara, J., Ramón, F. 1974. On the connection between transverse tubules and the plasma membrane in frog semitendinosus skeletal muscle. *J. Cell Biol.* 64:734–40

CELLULAR THERMOGENESIS[1]   ❖1153

Jean Himms-Hagen[2]

Department of Biochemistry, University of Ottawa, Ottawa, Ontario, Canada K1N 9A9

INTRODUCTION

The term *thermogenesis* means simply the production of heat. In animal cells, heat is produced by the oxidation of foodstuffs, principally glucose, fatty acids, and amino acids, the major combustible fuels ingested. The principal purpose of the combustion of fuels by animal cells is not, however, usually the production of heat, but rather the provision of a readily usable form of energy, largely ATP, for work of various kinds. The amount of heat produced by a nonbiological furnace is generally regulated according to the need for heat by altering the rate of delivery of fuel or oxygen. On the other hand, a biological furnace is not normally regulated by alteration of its fuel supply. Normally, fuel is always available within the cells, but it is oxidized by way of many discrete steps; heat production is regulated by many different control mechanisms operating at a number of these steps.

This review considers mechanisms of heat production in mammalian cells with emphasis on their control mechanisms at the cellular level. Because of editorially imposed space limitations, a detailed survey has not been possible, and only sufficient references have been provided to give the reader access to the relevant literature. Additional information is available in the recent reviews on regulation of body temperature (54), on temperature acclimation in intact animals (27), on nonshivering thermogenesis (109), comparative aspects of thermogenesis (87, 88), and the evolution of endothermy (166).

PHYSIOLOGICAL SIGNIFICANCE OF CELLULAR THERMOGENESIS

The basal metabolic rate (BMR) is the rate of combustion under conditions of rest in the postabsorptive state and at thermoneutral temperatures; it represents the rate of combustion needed to provide energy for the metabolic processes involved in keeping cells alive and for the mechanical processes involved in keeping the mammalian body alive (contraction of the heart, movements of the muscles involved in

[1]Unpublished work described in this review was supported by a grant from the Medical Research Council of Canada.

[2]Associate of the Medical Research Council of Canada.

respiration). The rate is normally controlled by thyroid hormones in mammals and birds. An increase or decrease in BMR usually occurs slowly and is persistent. Only rarely do changes in BMR have any explicable physiological function. Indeed, of the eight conditions listed in Table 1, only hibernation has a known physiological role.

On the other hand, it is possible to increase the metabolic rate above the basal level in a number of circumstances. In marked contrast to the slowness of onset and persistence of changes in the BMR, such changes are rapidly switched on and off and frequently a physiological function can be recognized (see Table 1). Such a function is clear in the case of shivering or nonshivering thermogenesis, in which the body temperature must be maintained during exposure to low ambient temperatures. The greater part of the heat produced during exercise must be dissipated in

Table 1 Physiological significance of cellular thermogenesis

Category	Condition	Control of heat production	Physiological significance of heat produced
Basal metabolic rate	Rest and postabsorptive state	Thyroid (normal)	Maintenance of body T above ambient T
Changes in basal metabolic rate	Increase		
	Hyperthyroidism	Thyroid (abnormal)	None
	Severe trauma (flow phase)	Catecholamines (abnormal)	None
	Pheochromocytoma	Catecholamines (abnormal)	None
	Malignant tumors	Genetic (mutation ?)	None
	Luft hypermetabolic syndrome	Genetic (mutation ?)	None
	Fever	CNS regulation	None
	Decrease		
	Hypothyroidism	Thyroid (abnormal)	None
	Malnutrition	Protein turnover (insulin ?)	None
	Hibernation	CNS inhibition	Survival under adverse conditions
	Severe trauma (ebb phase)	CNS inhibition	Survival (?)
Thermogenesis switched on/off rapidly	Muscle activity		
	exercise	CNS	Some improves muscle function
	shivering	CNS	Maintenance of body T in cold
	Nonshivering thermogenesis		
	cold-acclimated animals	Catecholamines	Maintenance of body T in cold
	newborn animals	Catecholamines	Maintenance of body T in cold
	hibernating animals	Catecholamines	Maintenance of body T in cold
			Increase in body T during arousal
	Thermic effect of feeding		
	food and alcohol	Food intake	Normal maintenance of body T
	Malignant hyperthermia	Genetic (drug-induced)	None
Adaptive increases in capacity for thermogenesis	Exercise training	CNS	None
	Nonshivering thermogenesis	Catecholamines	Maintenance of body T in cold
	Combustion of food	Food intake	None
	Combustion of alcohol	Alcohol intake	None

order to prevent the animal from becoming overheated. However, a limited rise in temperature can actually improve muscle function. In the condition of malignant hyperthermia, not only does the heat produced serve no useful purpose, but the hyperthermia may be lethal.

Adaptive changes in the capacity for thermogenesis involve only the rapid on/off mechanisms for elevating the metabolic rate above basal. Of the four such changes shown in Table 1, in only one, nonshivering thermogenesis, does the altered capacity for heat production serve a physiological function, namely the maintenance of body temperature in the cold.

Among the changes in thermogenesis listed in Table 1, some are of physiological importance in that the extra production of heat is part of the normal thermoregulatory response to cold. Others are of clinical interest, for example, hyperthyroidism, pheochromocytoma, severe trauma, Luft hypermetabolic syndrome, and malignant hyperthermia. In some of these, the extremely high metabolic rate may render management of the patient difficult.

CONTROL OF CELL THERMOGENESIS

A variety of control mechanisms and adaptive mechanisms would be expected to underlie the variety of changes in heat production listed in Table 1.

Site of Heat Production

The concept generally accepted at present is that the mitochondrion is the major site of heat production in the cell (156, 157). Prusiner & Poe (156, 157) pointed out that virtually all heat production during oxidation of a fuel such as glucose, involves mitochondrial oxidation of other substrates, such as $NADH_2$ and succinate, which are derived from glucose. They also noted that only about 25% of the free energy released is conserved as ATP, and 75% appears as heat. They concluded that the mitochondrion is the major site of heat production even during tightly coupled respiration. However, recent studies by Wilson et al (208) suggest that the multistep reaction between $NADH_2$ and the phosphorylation of ADP is in near-equilibrium. Since the change in free energy for a reaction at equilibrium is zero, it follows that virtually all of the free energy of the reactants appears in the products and does not, therefore, appear as heat. Implicit in this statement is that there is 100% efficiency of coupling of oxidative phosphorylation. This would suggest that very little heat production occurs in the fully coupled mitochondrion; the heat must instead be liberated when the ATP is utilized and when any products into which some of the free energy of the ATP hydrolysis may be incorporated are in their turn degraded. This could occur in any part of the cell. It should be noted that the efficiency of coupling makes no difference to the basic heat producing mechanism, namely, the complete combustion of substrate, such as glucose, to CO_2 and water; ultimately virtually all of the free energy appears as heat. The rate of heat production depends solely on the rate of the overall process. However, the efficiency of coupling does make a difference to the intracellular site of heat production, i.e. the lower the efficiency of coupling, the greater the proportion of heat produced in mitochondria.

Control of Combustions in Mitochondria

The factors controlling the rate of oxidation of substrates by mitochondria vary according to the state of coupling of the mitochondria. In the tightly coupled state, the rate of respiration is regulated by the phosphorylation state ratio (148), $[ATP]/[ADP][P_i]$, or the availability of ions such as calcium for translocation (123). In the uncoupled state and in the loosely coupled state, in which oxidative phosphorylation occurs but does not control the rate of substrate oxidation, the primary controlling factor appears to be substrate availability. Nonphosphorylating alternate pathways of electron transport have also been suggested as heat-producing pathways in mitochondria (11, 159). However, there is little supporting evidence for their occurrence as a major route of electron transport in mammalian mitochondria.

Thus the control of the rate of mitochondrial combustions depends upon the state of coupling of the mitochondria, the phosphorylation state ratio, the availability of ions, and the availability of substrate, although not upon all of these at the same time.

Control of Combustions in Intact Cells

Control of cellular respiration is exerted entirely via the factors listed above. Thus any influence from outside the cell that results in a change in any one of these factors may result in a change in the rate of respiration and of heat production.

Factors implicated in the control of coupling include free fatty acids (FFA) [postulated to cause either loosening of coupling (29) or uncoupling (20) or to act as cation ionophores (210)], nucleotides (158), thyroid hormones (85, 86), histones (111), and a low molecular weight, heat-stable, "cytoplasmic metabolic factor" (117). The phosphorylation state ratio is influenced by any process that utilizes ATP and hence forms ADP and P_i. Specific ATPases, such as myosin ATPase, and ATPases associated with ion pumping fall into this category of process. So also do any synthetic pathways in which ATP is used (e.g. triglyceride synthesis from FFA and glycerol), particularly if coupled with the appropriate catabolic pathway (e.g. triglyceride cycle) to provide a futile cycle. The pumping of ions by mitochondria depends partly upon the availability of ions and partly on the permeability of the mitochondria to ions. Any factors that alter the intracellular availability of ions or the permeability of the mitochondria to ions can alter the rate of mitochondrial respiration.

In intact cells there is also the possibility of combusting fuel via nonmitochondrial pathways, for example, the metabolism of ethanol via the microsomal ethanol oxidizing system in liver (125, 126).

Control of Combustions in Intact Animals

Control of cell thermogenesis in intact animals is through processes that influence the control mechanisms operating in individual cells as described above. The control is mediated by the neuroendrocrine system (54); the principal hormones involved are thyroid hormones and catecholamines. These hormones act directly on cells to modify thermogenesis; the former has a slow and long-lasting action, the latter has a rapid action that ceases as soon as the hormone is removed. In the intact animal, the sympathetic nervous system and the catecholamines also mobilize fuel for thermogenesis from the stores; FFA from the triglyceride of white adipose tissue, glucose from liver glycogen, and, via gluconeogenesis in liver, from muscle protein (73, 76).

The environment influences the mechanisms controlling heat production in intact animals, modifying behavior (motor activity), thermoregulatory functions, and feeding activity. The response of an animal to changes in its environment by altered heat production depends upon its genetic makeup (e.g. a hamster will switch on nonshivering thermogenesis when exposed to cold and will eventually hibernate, whereas the rat, unless acclimated to cold, has very little capacity to switch on nonshivering thermogenesis and will not hibernate) and upon its adaptive experience (e.g. a cold-acclimated rat will switch on nonshivering thermogenesis when exposed to cold whereas a warm-acclimated rat has very little capacity to do this and will switch on shivering thermogenesis instead). Sometimes the control of heat-producing mechanisms becomes relatively independent of the environment, as in the Luft hypermetabolic syndrome, in the hypermetabolism of severe trauma, in hyperthyroidism, and in pheochromocytoma. In each of these there exists a disorder of one of the normal control mechanisms.

EXAMPLES OF CELLULAR THERMOGENESIS

Rather than classifying examples of cellular thermogenesis according to their biochemical mechanism, as has already been done by Prusiner & Poe (157), each example is discussed individually because few of these changes in thermogenesis are pure examples of a single type of biochemical mechanism (e.g. ATPase, loosening of coupling, ion pumping, etc) but most involve more than one type of mechanism.

Basal Metabolic Rate

The basal rate of fuel consumption should depend on ATP utilization (or substrate utilization) to provide energy for those synthetic, mechanical, and osmotic processes necessary to keep the body alive. Synthetic processes would include protein synthesis, gluconeogenesis, ureagenesis, activation of fatty acids, and synthesis of lipids. Mechanical processes include the muscle activity necessary for the beating of the heart, the maintenance of tone in blood vessels and muscles, and the movements of respiration. Osmotic processes include the pumping of ions to maintain their far from equilibrium distribution in normal cells and in cellular organelles, for reabsorption of ions in the kidney, and for recovery of cells from depolarization, such as occurs continuously in the nervous system even in the basal state. Thus the BMR of the intact animal is attributable to a wide variety of reactions occurring to a greater or lesser extent in all cells of the body and appears to be largely subject to control via the phosphorylation state ratio and, to a lesser extent, via ion pumping directly dependent on substrate utilization by mitochondria.

There is a remarkable correlation between protein turnover and the BMR (197); indeed protein synthesis may account for as much as 10–15% of the BMR. The reduced BMR in malnutrition can probably be attributed to the protein-sparing adaptation that occurs. During growth, the BMR is elevated, as is the protein turnover (197). The increased heat production in some malignant tumors can probably be attributed to increased energy requirements for growth (120).

A widely accepted concept is that the activity of the Na^+K^+-ATPase controls a major part of the BMR. This concept has more recently served as the basis of hypotheses for the mode of action of thyroid hormones (43), the evolution of endothermy (166), and nonshivering thermogenesis (43, 90, 91, 166). The nature of the evidence for this concept and the assumptions required for its interpretation is reviewed because of the central importance of the concept in current thinking about mechanisms of thermogenesis. Much of the evidence for the concept rests on studies in which ouabain or lack of Na^+ has been used to reduce the activity of the sodium pump. The presence of ouabain or the absence of Na^+ in the medium inhibits the respiration of brain and kidney slices by 35–50% (198, 199). Two major assumptions were made in arriving at the conclusion that 35–50% of respiration is driven by ADP derived from the operation of the Na^+ pump (see 192). These are 1. that ouabain and lack of Na^+ specifically block the Na^+ pump and have no other action that might modify respiration and 2. that the changes in ion composition consequent upon the inhibition of the pump do not themselves modify cellular respiration. However, inhibition of the Na^+ pump is not the only effect attributable to ouabain. In some tissues (e.g. white adipose tissue), ouabain inhibits adenylate cyclase (84), whereas in other tissues (e.g. heart) it does not (179); in some tissues (e.g. muscle and white adipose tissue), it exerts an insulin-like effect on glucose uptake (53). Metabolic processes modified by ouabain include lipolysis in white adipose tissue (inhibited), gluconeogenesis in kidney (stimulated), and gluconeogenesis in liver (inhibited). Thus respiration may be altered by ouabain because of a change in an energy-requiring process other than the Na^+ pump.

Because marked changes in ion composition are caused by ouabain (Na^+ repletion, K^+ depletion) and by lack of Na^+ (Na^+ and K^+ depletion) (137, 199), it is also necessary to consider metabolic consequences of these changes. Moreover, since ouabain may modify Ca^{2+} transport (118, 185), the consequences of altered Ca^{2+} availability must also be considered. Ouabain can be demonstrated to have little or no immediate effect on the respiration of normal liver (108, 110, 137), kidney, or skeletal muscle slices (211), even though the Na^+ pump is inhibited as indicated by the changing ion contents (137, 211). This observation would lead to the conclusion that ATP utilization by the Na^+ pump is of little importance in determining the rate of tissue respiration. However, as the ion changes become more marked, the respiration is progressively inhibited by 30–50% (137, 211). It seems likely that this inhibition is secondary to the K^+ depletion rather than to an inhibition of ADP production by the Na^+ pump. Cells contain two K^+ pumps, the Na^+K^+-ATPase in the plasma membrane and a K^+ pump in the mitochondrion; inhibition of the latter by K^+ depletion is known to inhibit cellular respiration (60). Moreover, K^+ is known to be required for controlled mitochondrial respiration, and its lack causes inhibition of respiration in mitochondria isolated from liver (12, 59) or brain (149). Maintenance of intracellular K^+ by incubation in a high K^+ medium practically prevents the inhibition of the respiration of liver slices by ouabain (191, 192) as does the provision of succinate (155), the oxidation of which is not influenced by K^+

depletion (59). It might then be concluded that the inhibition of respiration caused by prolonged incubation with ouabain is not due directly to inhibition of the Na^+ pump, but is secondary to depletion of cellular K^+. It must, however, be borne in mind that the anti-ouabain action of high K^+ might be directly attributable to prevention of blockade of the Na^+ pump rather than to maintenance of a high internal K^+ concentration. Moreover, maintenance of the K^+ content of diaphragm at a level close to normal did not alter the proportion of respiration of normal tissue attributable to the Na^+ pump (as estimated from the inhibition of respiration in a Na^+ free medium) (I.S. Edelman and Y. Asano, unpublished).

Another problem with the use of ouabain is that its effect is variable. It can even stimulate respiration in slices of brain (110, 178, 185, 211) and heart (211). This appears to be due to altered Ca^{2+} distribution and does not occur in a Ca^{2+}-free medium (178, 185). Although ouabain does not inhibit respiration of liver slices incubated with Ca^{2+}, as described above, it does cause an immediate inhibition of respiration in liver slices incubated in the absence of Ca^{2+} (137). The most probable explanation for this is that liver slices incubated in the absence of Ca^{2+} are K^+-depleted and Na^+-repleted and their respiration is inhibited (137), probably because of the K^+ depletion. The Na^+ pump would be stimulated by the high internal Na^+ concentration and thus its inhibition by ouabain causes an appreciable inhibition of respiration. The Ca^{2+}-induced maintenance of respiration of liver slices may be in part due to the maintenance of the internal K^+ concentration and in part to energy-requiring Ca^{2+} uptake by mitochondria (116).

In conclusion, it is not possible to ascribe with any certainty a numerical value to the proportion of cellular respiration controlled by the Na^+ pump. It seems likely, however, that for most normal tissues (liver, kidney, heart, skeletal muscle, brain) this proportion is relatively small since it can be demonstrated that their respiration is not affected by ouabain even when the Na^+ pump is inhibited. It can also be stated that ouabain is not always a useful tool for probing the dependence of cellular respiration on the operation of the Na^+ pump. It is essential to know the time course of ionic changes and of inhibition of respiration induced by ouabain in order to exclude the possibility of inhibition by K^+ depletion being interpreted as inhibition by withdrawal of the ADP supply generated by the Na^+ pump and to ensure that the ionic composition of the incubation medium does not modify the permeability of the tissue to Na^+ and K^+.

A final reservation about the role of the Na^+ pump as a pacemaker of cellular respiration is that another interpretation of the evidence suggests that the Na^+K^+-ATPase does not function as a Na^+ pump in the currently accepted fashion, but that specific and modifiable binding of ions to intracellular proteins maintains the internal ionic composition [the association-induction hypothesis of Ling (68, 130)]. The requirement for this and other pumps is postulated to be greater than the energy-producing capacity of the cell and to lead to "caloric catastrophe" (141).

Hyperthyroidism and Hypothyroidism

There are two principal hypotheses for the mechanism of increased heat production in hyperthyroidism, the second of which has largely displaced the first. The older of the two proposed an uncoupling of oxidative phosphorylation from electron transport by a direct action of the thyroid hormones (85). Such an effect was seen as an increase in state four respiration and a reduction in P/O ratios in liver mitochondria from thyroid hormone-treated animals (86). This could be correlated with thyroid hormone content of the mitochondria and reversed by treatment with albumin, which removed the bound thyroid hormone from the mitochondria (86). This hypothesis is currently in disfavor, largely because of the successful isolation of tightly coupled mitochondria from tissues of hyperthyroid animals [e.g. liver (181) and skeletal muscle (62)] and because hyperthyroidism does not decrease the output of cellular work as do uncouplers. However, it is as possible to prepare mitochondria recoupled by the isolation procedure from an uncoupled state in vivo as it is to prepare isolated mitochondria uncoupled by the isolation procedure from a coupled state in vivo.

The second of the two hypotheses proposes that thyroid hormones in some way increase the operation of the Na^+K^+-ATPase and that the increased ADP production results in an increased rate of respiration (43, 44). Control is thus exerted via changes in the phosphorylation state ratio. This hypothesis is based upon the Whittam concept (198) of an appreciable proportion of the cellular respiration being regulated by the Na^+K^+-ATPase and proposes an increase in this proportion in hyperthyroidism and, conversely, a decrease in hypothyroidism. There are five lines of evidence for this hypothesis (44): (a) The increase in oxygen uptake of liver, kidney (102), and muscle (101) slices from hyperthyroid rats is to a large extent inhibited by ouabain and by deficiency of Na^+, both of which inhibit the operation of the Na^+ pump. (b) The Na^+K^+-ATPase activity increases in these same tissues (102, 104) while ATP content decreases and ADP content increases (105). (c) Ion contents of heart and diaphragm change in the direction expected for decreased operation of the pump in hypothyroidism (increased Na^+, decreased K^+) and for increased operation of the pump in hyperthyroidism (decreased Na^+, increased K^+) (101, 103). (d) The time course of the increase in Na^+K^+-ATPase activity in liver after injection of thyroid hormone follows closely the time course of the increase in tissue respiration (104). (e) The changes are tissue specific. No change in either respiration or Na^+K^+-ATPase occurs in brain, whereas increases in both respiration and Na^+K^+-ATPase occur in liver, heart, skeletal muscle, kidney, and intestine.

Six possible mechanisms for the stimulation of Na^+K^+-ATPase activity are envisaged: 1. increased permeability of the tissue to Na^+, thus providing more substrate (internal Na^+) for the enzyme, 2. an uncoupling of the Na^+ pump so that less Na^+ and K^+ is pumped per unit of ATP used, 3. an increase in the availability of the other substrate (ATP), 4. a direct stimulatory action of thyroid hormone on the pump, 5. increased synthesis of more pumps or pump activators, and 6. an unmasking of pump sites already present. The observed changes in ion content and adenine nucleotide distribution in tissues of hyperthyroid rats would not be in keeping with postulates 1–3 and 4 would be unlikely since the increased ATPase activity persists in isolated plasma membrane. Thus current thinking is in favor of postulates 5 or 6 (43).

The basic assumptions underlying the Edelman hypothesis are similar to, but more extensive than, those underlying the Whittam hypothesis (see section on basal metabolic rate). They are that ouabain and lack of Na^+ specifically block the Na^+ pump and have no other action, that the changes in ion distribution consequent upon inhibition of the pump do not themselves modify cellular respiration, that mitochondrial respiratory control is not changed in the hyper/hypothyroid state but still exerted by the phosphorylation state ratio; and that the measured changes in Na^+K^+-ATPase reflect an altered operation of the enzyme in the cells.

Criticisms of the use of ouabain to estimate the contribution of the Na^+ pump to metabolic rate are outlined above (see section on basal metabolic rate). The major criticism is that ouabain does not induce an immediate inhibition of respiration of liver, kidney, or muscle—and may even stimulate respiration of brain and heart. Only later when ionic changes have occurred is respiration inhibited. The use of ouabain to estimate the proportion of the thyroid hormone-induced increase in tissue respiration attributable to the operation of the Na^+ pump is subject to the same criticism. However, since the thyroid hormone-induced increase in respiration of liver slices is inhibited by ouabain under conditions in which the basal respiration is not altered (9, 108), it can be concluded that, at least for isolated liver slices, a major portion of the thyroid-induced increase in respiration can be attributed to an increased operation of the Na^+ pump (101, 102, 104, 108). Because ouabain-insensitive respiration also increases in response to thyroid hormone (104), not all the increase in respiration of liver can be attributed to increased Na^+ pump operation.

The problem of tissue K^+ depletion as a consequence of pump inhibition has been circumvented in a different way by Edelman by use of a high K^+ medium to maintain tissue K^+ concentration at its normal level. Under such conditions, which can be demonstrated to prevent entirely the ouabain-induced inhibition of respiration of normal liver slices (191, 192) it can be shown that about 75% of the thyroid-hormone-induced increase in respiration of liver slices is due to increased Na^+ pump activity (I. S. Edelman, personal communication).

Another assumption is that mitochondrial respiratory control is still exerted by the phosphorylation state ratio in the hyper/hypothyroid state. As pointed out above, it now seems unlikely that mitochondria are uncoupled in vivo in the hyperthyroid state. They do, however, show a higher activity of the translocase responsible for moving ADP in and ATP out (5). It is therefore possible that an increased operation of the translocase makes more ADP available for oxidative phosphorylation and more ATP available for accelerated pump operation, thus promoting both processes. Part of the increased respiration in hyperthyroidism might be due to such an adaptive change (5).

Another assumption is that the measured changes in Na^+K^+-ATPase activity reflect an altered level of its functioning in the intact cell. It is possible to calculate from the activity of the Na^+K^+-ATPase, using an average P/O ratio of 2.8, the maximum oxygen uptake that could be attributed to the operation of the enzyme at V_{max}, and the rephosphorylation of the ADP formed from it. In the case of the liver, it can be shown that the change in ATPase could account for only about 40% of the observed increase in ouabain-sensitive oxygen uptake (102, 104, 108). This suggests either that a certain proportion of Na^+K^+-ATPase not functioning in the euthyroid state is brought into play in the hyperthyroid state or that some other mechanism is involved. A similar calculation for kidney (102) and muscle shows that the increase in Na^+K^+-ATPase is three to four times greater than needed to account for the observed increase in ouabain-sensitive tissue respiration. In this case the increase in ouabain-sensitive tissue respiration can be ascribed to the increase in Na^+K^+-ATPase activity, the enzyme presumably operating at less than V_{max} in the cell. In kidney the level appears to be correlated with changes in Na^+ excretion rather than with hyperthyroidism or hypothyroidism (113). Thus there is no stoichiometric correlation between changes in Na^+K^+-ATPase activity and changes in ouabain-sensitive oxygen consumption, although the two changes are always in the same direction.

A modification of Na^+K^+-ATPase activity has been suggested as an early action of thyroid hormone (43, 104), with the known mitochondrial changes (5, 62, 181, 209) occurring later. This suggestion is based upon the early changes in respiration (at 6 hours) and in Na^+K^+-ATPase (at 24 hours) (104) after administration of a single dose of thyroid hormone, changes that in general precede the observed mitochondrial changes. However, it is possible to observe a change in a liver mitochondrial enzyme (glycerol-3-phosphate dehydrogenase) as early as 6 hours after administration of a small dose of thyroid hormone (19) and it seems likely that thyroid hormone, by its action to modulate protein synthesis in both cytosol and mitochondria (see 180), modifies the simultaneous synthesis of a number of different proteins located eventually in mitochondrion, plasma membrane, and other cellular regions (see 43).

That the changes are tissue specific is also not generally applicable, since the thyroid-induced increase in respiration of white adipose tissue is not ouabain sensitive (47). Brown adipose tissue would also be of great interest in this regard; it might help to distinguish between the validity of the two hypotheses for thermogenesis in this tissue (see section on nonshivering thermogenesis in brown adipose tissue), but it appears not to have been studied.

That the increase in Na^+K^+-ATPase is due to the presence of more pump sites rather than to activation of enzyme already present is indicated by the increase in ATP^{32} and ouabain binding induced by the hormone (I. S. Edelman, personal communication). The physiological regulation of the amount and activity of the Na^+K^+-ATPase is not understood in any detail (6), but it seems unlikely that thyroid hormone is the sole or even major regulator. Apart from regulation by substrate and products (Na^+, K^+, ATP, ADP), the enzyme is subject to inhibition by Ca^{2+} (35), by prostaglandins (112), by cyclic AMP in heart and liver (127, 133, 188), by epinephrine and glucagon in liver (133), but not by epinephrine in heart (179). Some amino acids stimulate its activity (134) and insulin relieves the inhibition by epinephrine (133). Stimulation by norepinephrine has also been reported in the case of the enzyme from brown adipose tissue (72), leucocytes and mast cells (33), and brain (212). [In the case of brain, the stimulation has been attributed to a sequestering of Ca^{2+} under the influence of norepinephrine rather than to a direct effect of the norepinephrine on the enzyme (57).] The physiological significance, if any, of such phenomena is unknown, but it is clearly possible to construct speculative schemes for the regulation in vivo of the enzyme, and hence thermogenesis, by a number of hormones.

The amount of Na^+K^+-ATPase present in cells is normally correlated with the leakiness of the cells to Na^+ (6). That there may be fairly direct control of formation of pump sites by internal ions is suggested by the finding that in cultured HeLa cells, inhibition of the Na^+ pump leads to a protein synthesis-dependent increase in the number of pump sites (13). Thus at the local tissue level, the amount of Na^+K^+-ATPase may well be controlled at least in part by the internal ionic composition, itself controlled by the number of pump sites already available, by the presence of inhibitors or activators of the pump, and by agents that modify the passive permeability of the membrane to ions. The question then arises whether thyroid hormones are inhibitors of the Na^+K^+-ATPase. There is at present no information available on this point.

In conclusion, it may be stated that in some tissues (e.g. liver, heart, kidney, skeletal muscle) but not others (e.g. brain, white adipose tissue) at least a part of the thyroid hormone-induced increase in metabolic rate in slices in vitro can be ascribed to an increased operation of the Na^+ pump, as a consequence of an increased amount of enzyme present. The mode of action of thyroid hormones is not understood, but may be presumed to involve a direct or indirect action on Na^+K^+-ATPase synthesis. The exact proportion of the thyroid hormone-induced increase in respiration attributable to the increased pump operation is uncertain. Other mechanisms involved in the thermogenic effect of thyroid hormones are even less well understood. Increased synthesis of mitochondria, providing that they are coupled as they seem to be, would explain an altered capacity to respire but would not explain an increase in BMR. Other possible mechanisms such as ion pumping by mitochondria or loosening of coupling by fatty acids are discussed further in the section on other speculative mechanisms.

There are two other reservations to accepting the Edelman hypothesis as a primary explanation of the action of thyroid hormone. First, the Na^+K^+-ATPase of liver and the ouabain-sensitive respiration of liver slices are both increased, not only in hyperthyroidism, but also in acclimation to cold and in chronic alcoholism (see sections on nonshivering thermogenesis and on thermic effect of alcohol). However, only in hyperthyroidism is there an increase in BMR; in cold acclimation (74, 98) and in chronic alcoholism (186) there is not (possibly an increase in liver alone would not be detectable in this way). What then do the increased Na^+K^+-ATPase and ouabain-sensitive respiration explain if not an increase in BMR? The fact that epinephrine injection will within one hour increase ouabain-sensitive respiration in liver (10) suggests that some other process, unrelated to the BMR, may be responsible for the observed changes in liver slices in all three of these conditions (see section on calorigenic action of catecholamines). In all three conditions, an increased level of circulating catecholamines or an increased sensitivity to the actions of circulating catecholamines would be expected. Second, the Na^+K^+-ATPase of sarcolemma of skeletal muscle (175) and heart (174) is increased in dystrophic hamsters. However, the BMR of these hamsters is lower than normal (93; B. A. Horwitz, personal communication). Thus, again, an increase in Na^+K^+-ATPase is not associated with an increase in BMR. The basic membrane defect in muscular dystrophy may be an increased leakiness to K^+ (96), and the increase in pump activity may represent a compensatory increase. It is significant, however, that the presumed increased functioning of the Na^+ pump in the largest organ of the body (muscle) is not reflected in an increase in BMR.

Muscle Activity

Muscle activity has long been recognized as a major source of heat for the mammalian body (144). The maintenance of skeletal muscle tone and the continuous activity of the heart both contribute to the BMR, and exercise or shivering can increase the metabolic rate severalfold above the basal level. The mechanism underlying the heat production associated with muscle contraction is perhaps the best understood of all the mechanisms of cell thermogenesis although, even for this example, knowledge is far from complete. For skeletal muscle the mechanism involves stimulation via the motor nerve, depolarization of the muscle, and the release of Ca^{2+} from circumscribed intracellular stores, resulting in an activation of myosin ATPase and muscle contraction (144). The increased ADP supply in turn accelerates mitochondrial oxidations resulting in an increased rate of combustion of fuel. Thus muscle activity is a mode of thermogenesis in which control is primarily via changes in the phosphorylation state ratio.

Another process that must contribute to the increase in heat production during muscle activity, at least to a minor extent, is ion pumping. The restoration of the normal polarized state of the sarcolemma must involve pumping of ions by the Na^+K^+-ATPase. Relaxation also requires the removal of Ca^{2+} from the cytosol, principally via pumping by the Ca^{2+} ATPase of the sarcoplasmic reticulum. Both of these processes also accelerate respiration via alteration of the phosphorylation state ratio. Because mitochondria are capable of active uptake of Ca^{2+}, it is possible that some of the Ca^{2+} released into the cytosol will be taken up by the mitochondria. Ca^{2+} uptake by mitochondria has indeed been suggested as one of the steps involved in relaxation in cardiac and red skeletal muscle (123). If this were so, it is evident that some additional mechanism would be necessary for the release of Ca^{2+} from the mitochondria in response to nerve stimulation. Na^+ ions have been proposed to mediate Ca^{2+} release from mitochondria during excitation-contraction coupling (24), but there is at present no evidence for their serving such a role in the intact tissue. An acceleration of mitochondrial respiration in association with uptake of Ca^{2+} would represent a control of thermogenesis by ion availability rather than by the phosphorylation state ratio as in the other mechanisms discussed above. Because Ca^{2+} uptake takes precedence over ADP phosphorylation (123), this last mechanism would take precedence over the others. A cyclic AMP-dependent coupling between excitation and respiration also exists in muscle (37), but its mechanism is unknown.

The capacity of muscle to produce heat is not fixed, but can vary with the functional state of the muscle. Exercise-trained muscle has been shown to acquire more and larger mitochondria in the rat and larger mitochondria in man. The capacity of both red and white muscle for mitochondrial respiration is increased (see chapter by Holloszy in this volume). In exercise-trained muscle there is no change in the basic mechanism of heat production, but an adaptive increase occurs in all the elements involved in muscle activity such that the capacity for activity is increased. Exercise training also increases the capacity of rats for heat production by shivering (172), as would be expected for these two processes which share the same basic mechanism.

Thermic Effect of Food

Otherwise known as the specific dynamic action of food, the thermic effect of food refers to the increase in metabolic rate that occurs over several hours following feeding. It can be explained reasonably satisfactorily by the obligatory utilization of ATP in the metabolic disposal of the ingested material (e.g. storage, structure, or waste). Thus for carbohydrate, the use of 2–4 moles of ATP per mole of glucose, depending on whether it is stored as glycogen or as triglyceride, results in a thermic effect equivalent to 5–10% of the caloric value of the ingested carbohydrate. For lipid, the use of approximately 2 moles of ATP per mole of fatty acid derived from and reincorporated into triglyceride results in a thermic effect equivalent to 1.4–4.6% of the caloric value of the ingested lipid, depending on how many times the triglyceride is hydrolyzed and its components reesterified before final storage. For protein, the use per mole of amino acid of 4 moles of ATP for incorporation into protein, or roughly 4 moles of ATP for conversion to urea and glucose or ketone bodies, results in a thermic effect of about 20–30%, depending on the amino acid composition of the ingested protein (the amount is much larger for some amino acids, e.g. glycine, alanine, aspartic acid, than for others, e.g. leucine, isoleucine, phenylalanine). It can be concluded that the thermic effect of food is mainly an ATPase type of mechanism with control exerted via the phosphorylation state ratio.

A minor part of the thermic effect of food may also be attributable to the transport of its components across membranes. For example, energy for coupled transport of sugars and amino acids may be derived from ion gradients (164). Because the ions enter together with the transported molecules, ion pumping requiring ATP is necessary to restore the gradient.

In obesity the thermic effect of food is not reduced (187), although such a change has been suspected as a cause of obesity, and the BMR may be normal or slightly reduced. However, overfeeding of normal subjects does not, as has been shown experimentally, always result in the expected weight gain despite unaltered physical activity (139, 140). This apparent contradiction of the laws of thermodynamics is explicable only by supposing that more of the ingested calories appear as heat during overfeeding than during periods of normal food intake (135). The thermic effect of food is, however, identical in overfed and normally fed subjects at rest (140). The overfed subjects show a much larger thermic effect of feeding only when they exercise. There is thus an unexplained synergism between exercise and feeding in that heat production is greater when the two are combined than when the two occur separately. No studies on the details of the metabolic processes in overfed exercising subjects appear to have been made. One explanation that can be offered is that the hormonal balance appropriate for the storage of the excess food, induced by the overfeeding, is antagonized by the hormonal balance appropriate for the mobilization of stored fuels, induced by the exercise, and that futile cycling of glucose, fatty acids, and amino acids in and out of storage may occur to a much greater extent than during either exercise or overfeeding alone.

The concept of energy wastage of food as heat is an important one for the accurate determination of nutritional (caloric) requirements (69) and for the understanding of the etiology of obesity. It is not unlikely that a biochemical explanation of why overeating leads to increased heat production in many individuals will help to explain why only moderate overeating can lead to obesity in a few individuals.

Thermic Effect of Ethanol

The thermic effect of feeding ethanol is rather small in normal subjects (186). The usual route of ethanol metabolism involves two NAD-linked dehydrogenases in liver and the further metabolism in other tissues of the acetate produced by the liver (125). The rate of metabolism is normally limited by the rate of reoxidation of the reduced NAD via a mitochondrial shuttle (125). The only obligatory use of ATP occurs during the activation of the acetate, calculated to be responsible for a thermic effect of 11%.

In contrast, alcoholics have a much greater thermic response to administration of ethanol (186). The explanation probably lies in an altered pathway for the metabolism of the ethanol. An alternate pathway exists, which requires reduced NADP and uses oxygen, although there is at present some controversy about the exact nature of the enzymes involved in this pathway. Some workers ascribe the metabolism of ethanol via this pathway to a specific microsomal ethanol-oxidizing system (MEOS) utilizing reduced NADP and oxygen (125, 126), whereas others ascribe it to a microsomal $NADPH_2$ oxidase system producing hydrogen peroxide and working in conjunction with catalase (183). An increase in the capacity of this alternate pathway has been demonstrated in alcoholics and in alcohol-fed rats (125, 126), and ethanol is metabolized more rapidly than usual. Because the pathway actually uses oxygen, an immediate explanation for the increased oxygen consumption after ethanol in alcoholics is apparent. Moreover, because the reaction uses reduced NADP, it would be expected that reduction of the NADP produced would be enhanced, entailing, for example, accelerated oxidation of glucose via the pentose phosphate pathway. It can be calculated that the thermic effect of alcohol would increase to 28% if it were all metabolized via this pathway. There appears to be no physiological function for this "adaptive" increase in heat production in alcoholics.

Another change in the liver of chronically ethanol-fed rats is the development of what has been described as a functional hyperthyroid state (108). The oxygen consumption by liver slices from these animals is elevated, and numerous biochemical changes occur that are identical with those occurring in hyperthyroidism. These include a sensitivity of the increased respiration to ouabain, an increase in Na^+K^+-ATPase activity and in ion transport, and an increase in the size of the mitochondria and in mitochondrial glycerol-3-phosphate dehydrogenase (9, 108).

These changes are believed to be caused by an increased uptake of thyroid hormone by the liver during chronic alcohol intake (106, 107). However, a more direct effect of ethanol on the liver should not be excluded, since ethanol has been demonstrated to induce an increased number of Na^+ pump sites in cultured cells (129). In fact, ethanol has been demonstrated to inhibit the Na^+K^+-ATPase of sarcolemma (203) and to inhibit Na^+ and K^+ transport in liver slices (191). Because inhibition, for example by ouabain, of this enzyme in cultured cells increases the amount of Na^+ K^+-ATPase (13), it is possible that the effect of ethanol to increase liver Na^+K^+-ATPase might be secondary to the inhibition of the enzyme by ethanol.

If the intact liver in vivo behaves as do the liver slices in vitro, it follows that the increase in heat production by the liver in vivo could be due to a greater utilization of ATP for ion pumping. This has not been demonstrated directly. Indeed, the BMR of alcoholics is not elevated (186) although possibly an elevation in liver alone would be undetectable by this means. That an increased heat production and requirement for oxygen do indeed occur is suggested by the finding that, in ethanol-treated rats, the liver needs a greater than normal oxygen supply and that restriction of the supply leads to liver damage (106). The idea has been put forward by Israel et al that the greater oxygen demand of liver is due to a greater use of ATP for ion pumping; control is thus exerted via the phosphorylation state ratio (106). Another possibility is that the greater oxygen demand in vivo is caused by the increased oxygen requirement for metabolism of ethanol via the MEOS pathway. There would appear to be no adaptive value in increasing the heat production by the liver via an ATPase type of mechanism in response to ethanol, although the change may serve to accelerate electron transport and thus enhance the capacity of the liver to reoxidize reduced NAD and thereby to oxidize ethanol via the alcohol dehydrogenase pathway (108).

Nonshivering Thermogenesis

The increase in heat production that occurs when an animal is exposed to cold may in part be due to the muscle activity of shivering and in part due to other processes, described collectively as *nonshivering thermogenesis.* The term is sometimes taken to mean any heat-producing mechanism not caused by mechanical activity of muscle. In this discussion the term is applied to the increase in metabolic rate brought about by exposure to cold, which does not involve muscle contraction; it has essentially the same function as shivering thermogenesis, but has a different underlying mechanism. The switching on and off of nonshivering thermogenesis in response to cold is mediated by the sympathetic nervous system and the process can be mimicked by administration of catecholamines (see 78). The rapid switching on of heat production by catecholamines, their calorigenic action, is also included in this discussion on nonshivering thermogenesis. The calorigenic response to norepinephrine is always very much enhanced in animals exhibiting nonshivering thermogenesis.

The magnitude of nonshivering thermogenesis varies with animal species, being greater in smaller than in larger species, generally greater in hibernators than in nonhibernators, greater in newborn animals than in adult animals, and greater in cold-acclimated[3] animals than in warm-acclimated animals (70, 109). Thus the hamster and the ground squirrel, both hibernators, have a large capacity for non-shivering thermogenesis, whether acclimated to cold or not (154, 195), whereas the rat does not, unless it has undergone acclimation to cold whereby its capacity for nonshivering thermogenesis can be increased to several times its BMR (39). Most of the discussion that follows refers to the rat, unless another species is specified, because, for reasons of convenience, much of the research on the mechanism of nonshivering thermogenesis has been carried out on this species. It should, however, be borne in mind that various details of the mechanism and its control may vary from one species to another.

It should be emphasized that, despite an increased level of triiodothyronine in its plasma (162), the cold-acclimated rat is not hyperthyroid (97). At thermoneutral temperatures, its BMR is no different from that of rats of the same strain not acclimated to cold (74, 98) or is slightly increased (38). The cold-acclimated rat and the hyperthyroid rat also differ in their calorigenic response to norepinephrine. The cold-acclimated rat has an increase in the maximal capacity to respond, whereas the hyperthyroid rat has an increased sensitivity to the calorigenic action of norepinephrine without an increase in its maximal capacity to respond (99).

There are two main sites of nonshivering thermogenesis: skeletal muscle and brown adipose tissue (see 78). It seems likely that, because of its large mass, skeletal muscle is usually the major site, although sometimes, as in the newborn rabbit, brown adipose tissue may play the major role in nonshivering thermogenesis because of its bulk (100).

Brown adipose tissue is specialized for thermogenesis and is generally more abundant in those species and under those conditions in which nonshivering thermogenesis occurs (50, 165). However, in the cold-acclimated rat the size of the brown adipose tissue is relatively small, even though it does grow during acclimation to cold and has been calculated to contribute 6–13% of the heat of nonshivering thermogenesis (75). In experiments designed to estimate the quantitative contribution of brown adipose tissue to nonshivering thermogenesis, surgical removal of the interscapular brown adipose tissue (about one third of the total in the cold-acclimated rat) has had relatively little immediate effect upon the enhanced calorigenic response to norepinephrine in cold-acclimated rats (52, 74, 75), but in a number of independent studies, it has caused a delayed reduction of 40–60% after two to four days (66, 74, 75, 92, 95, 119, 121, 122). However, two recent studies have shown no greater reduction than in sham-operated animals (51, 52). Because the loss of the enhanced response is delayed and is greater than can be accounted for by the small size of the tissue removed, a permissive role for brown adipose tissue in the control of nonshivering thermogenesis in other tissues of cold-acclimated

[3]The term *cold acclimated* refers to animals that have lived for some time at a low temperature. Temperatures used experimentally vary, according to the species, from below 0° to about 15°; for the rat a temperature of 4°–6° is usually used. Control animals that have lived in their thermoneutral zone are referred to as warm-acclimated animals.

rats has been suggested (66, 74, 75, 119, 122). This role is discussed further below.

Thus nonshivering thermogenesis is a calorigenic response to catecholamines, and an understanding of its mechanism requires an understanding of the metabolic actions of catecholamines, discussed first below. Nonshivering thermogenesis occurs principally in skeletal muscle and in brown adipose tissue and its magnitude varies, determined both genetically and by environmental influences. Because the mechanisms of heat production in the two major sites are probably different, they are discussed separately.

CALORIGENIC ACTION OF CATECHOLAMINES   Metabolic effects of catecholamines in intact animals can be divided into three classes: 1. the mobilization of energy reserves, as usually measured by the rise in concentration of a variety of compounds in the blood, 2. the calorigenic effect (see 73, 76), and 3. a shift of ions across cell membranes. All three are composite effects in the sense that they represent the sum of a variety of actions of the catecholamines on the metabolism of different tissues. The mobilization of energy reserves includes not only actions on liver and white adipose tissue, resulting in mobilization of liver glycogen and amino acids as glucose and white adipose tissue triglyceride as free fatty acids, but also actions on cardiac and skeletal muscle and on brown adipose tissue, resulting in the mobilization of endogenous reserves of glycogen or triglycerides for internal use (see 76).

Ionic changes include a biphasic hyperkalemia followed by hypokalemia. Increased release of K^+ from liver, uptake by muscle, and eventual reuptake by liver occur (193). Direct actions on liver and muscle appear to be involved (26, 193).

The details of the mechanism of the calorigenic action of catecholamines in intact animals have proved most elusive (73). It seems likely that acceleration of a number of metabolic processes involving the utilization of ATP must contribute to the effect. These include gluconeogenesis, ureagenesis, triglyceride synthesis, and glycogen synthesis, all of which are accelerated during or after the action of catecholamines. They occur principally in liver and white adipose tissue. As the action of catecholamines always involves a change in the state of polarization of the plasma membrane, it is quite likely that increased ion pumping accompanies and is, to some extent, a cause of their calorigenic action. For example, a ouabain-sensitive increase in respiration of liver slices occurs one hour after the injection of epinephrine into rats (10). Whether this really represents a direct action of the epinephrine, which would no longer be expected to be present in vitro, or whether it represents an altered composition of endogenous substrates, also known to cause changes in membrane potential of liver (36), is uncertain. Because liver previously treated with catecholamines would have an altered ionic composition (25), it is quite likely that the increased oxygen uptake observed in vitro (10) represents the recovery phase after epinephrine in which normal ionic composition is being restored. Catecholamines have a direct action to hyperpolarize liver cells (65, 152) and increase K^+ efflux and membrane permeability to K^+ (65). Catecholamines and cyclic AMP have been shown to have a direct action to inhibit the Na^+K^+-ATPase of liver plasma membrane (188) and to inhibit reuptake of K^+ by K^+-depleted liver cells (7). Their action mimics that of ouabain, which also causes hyperpolarization of rat liver cells (202) and does not inhibit the hyperpolarizing action of the catecholamines (36, 65).

Catecholamines have also been demonstrated to cause depolarization in brown adipose tissue (56, 94, 200), either depolarization (β-receptors) or hyperpolarization (α-receptors) in salivary glands (153), and depolarization (41, 91, 182, 189), hyperpolarization (196), or a biphasic hyperpolarization followed by a depolarization (16, 58) in skeletal muscle, depending on the muscle studied (184). The different types of response reported for muscle may be a consequence of the type of muscle fiber studied, since different muscles have quite different fiber populations (4) and different fiber types have different resting membrane potentials (21). However, since change in state of membrane polarization usually accompanies actions of hormones on cell membranes (151), including hormones lacking marked calorigenic actions, it is unlikely that this is a major contributor to the calorigenic action of catecholamines.

The calorigenic action of catecholamines on brown adipose tissue is better understood than its action on other tissues and is discussed in detail in the next section.

There remains, however, a large component of the calorigenic action of the catecholamines in the intact animal that cannot be explained by the ATPase effects noted above nor by the action on brown adipose tissue—the component occurring in skeletal muscle. In adult nonhibernators it represents a fairly small part of the total calorigenic response to the catecholamines, but is enhanced during acclimation to cold, is already large in adult hibernators, and makes the major contribution to nonshivering thermogenesis.

NONSHIVERING THERMOGENESIS IN BROWN ADIPOSE TISSUE   The morphology of brown adipose tissue is in keeping with the specialized heat-producing function of this tissue. The rich sympathetic innervation and the frequent gap junctions between cells (163) provide an excellent mechanism for catecholamine-induced heat production. The cells are packed with mitochondria and lipid droplets and the mitochondria are packed with cristae (176). In nonhibernators the tissue grows during acclimation to cold (see 165) and the mitochondria become larger and acquire more closely packed cristae (176). In hibernators the brown adipose tissue undergoes less marked changes during acclimation to cold (3).

There are two distinct hypotheses for the mechanism of norepinephrine-stimulated heat production in brown adipose tissue (see 50). The first postulates that the fatty acids liberated as a result of catecholamine-induced lipolysis uncouple or loosen the control of oxidative phosphorylation so that the rate of oxidation of substrates is accelerated. This hypothesis requires that brown adipose tissue mitochondria be different from mitochondria of other tissues, which are also exposed to fatty acids, but do not behave in the same way. The second postulates that increased ion pumping across the plasma membrane, occurring as a consequence of interaction with norepinephrine, uses ATP and thereby promotes coupled respiration by increasing the ADP supply.

Mitochondria isolated from brown adipose tissue are usually uncoupled or loosely coupled (50), and their respiration (20) and adenine nucleotide transport (30) are inhibited. Relief of the inhibition is associated with expansion of the matrix, entry of ions, and osmotic swelling (147). Recoupling requires treatment with ATP and carnitine (22, 83) or with albumin (158), usually together with a purine nucleotide (22, 158), and appears to involve the removal or transfer of a small proportion of the fatty acids bound to the mitochondria. The mechanism of action of the purine nucleotide is uncertain, but may involve reorganization of mitochondrial structure (158) in a manner similar to the transition from orthodox to condensed conformation caused by the binding of a small amount of ADP in liver mitochondria (see 124).

The extrapolation of these observations of isolated mitochondria to the events that occur in the intact tissue in the animal exposed to cold or injected with norepinephrine is not easy. Mitochondria in their normal intracellular environment would be exposed to protein, carnitine, and purine nucleotides. In fact, electron micrographs of intact tissue show the mitochondria to be largely in the orthodox form with an expanded matrix, not characteristic of uncoupled mitochondria. The initiation of heat production involves an action of norepinephrine to stimulate adenylate cyclase and consequent cyclic AMP-mediated lipolytic and calorigenic effects. It is postulated that the fatty acids, or acyl CoA derived from them, loosen or uncouple the mitochondria so that the rate of oxidation increases. The increase persists until the stimulus (norepinephrine) is removed, lipolysis is slowed, and the fatty acids removed by oxidation, esterification, or release from the tissue. Recoupling then occurs under the influence of purine nucleotides. Generation of ATP, essential to ensure continued activation of fatty acids, is maintained by substrate level phosphorylation in the tricarboxylic acid cycle, itself accelerated under these conditions, and in glycolysis (158).

Brown adipose tissue mitochondria differ from mitochondria of other tissues in their extremely high permeability to protons (145) and monovalent cations (147), in their purine nucleotide requirement, as noted above, and in their high rate of leakage of the energy potential [the energy potential is generated by the primarily conserved energy and is normally utilizable for chemical (ATP synthesis), osmotic (ion transport), or electrochemical (generation of an electrochemical gradient) work (50)]. As fatty acids have been demonstrated to act as natural ionophores for monovalent cations, even in liver mitochondria, it is logical to attribute the difference in brown adipose tissue mitochondria to the presence of fatty acids and to an unusual sensitivity to this effect of the fatty acids (210).

A major difficulty with this hypothesis is that no increase in fatty acid level in cells (128) or in mitochondria (150) has been detected during norepinephrine- or cold-induced thermogenesis, and it is necessary to fall back on postulates of compartmentation of fatty acids or on a role for a specific fatty acid in order to reconcile the hypothesis with these observations. Moreover, mitochondria in tissue sections from norepinephrine-treated or cold-exposed newborn rats are swollen and have an expanded matrix (177, 190), a change not characteristic of fatty acid-treated uncoupled mitochondria (20). Although the hypothesis is logical in view of the available evidence, it may not be the entire explanation.

The alternate hypothesis for the mechanism of heat production in brown adipose tissue (90, 91) derives from Edelman's hypothesis for the role of Na^+K^+-ATPase in heat production in response to thyroid hormone. (see section on hyperthyroidism and hypothyroidism). It proposes that increased pumping of Na^+ and K^+ by the Na^+K^+-ATPase is responsible for a significant part of the increase in metabolic rate. The hypothesis is based on the observed membrane changes and ion fluxes in adipose tissue and on the depressing effects of inhibition of the Na^+ pump on the calorigenic action of norepinephrine. Norepinephrine depolarizes brown adipose tissue (56, 94, 200), increases membrane permeability to ions (89), and causes efflux of K^+ and influx of Na^+ (56). In addition to altering distribution of ions, which would by itself stimulate the Na^+ pump, norepinephrine (72) and cyclic AMP (91) directly stimulate Na^+K^+-ATPase activity in homogenates of brown adipose tissue. That the ion movements described above are an essential part of the calorigenic effect has been concluded (90, 91) from the complete inhibition of the calorigenic effect of norepinephrine by ouabain and by lack of K^+ (48, 71, 90). However, as ouabain also inhibits stimulation of cyclic AMP production by norepinephrine (48) and the lipolytic response to norepinephrine (48, 71, 201), it is obvious that the use of ouabain is not helpful in distinguishing between the two hypotheses; fatty acid production is also inhibited and fatty acids are an essential component in the uncoupling hypothesis. Moreover, ouabain also inhibits the increase in oxygen uptake caused by cyclic AMP, theophylline, or palmitic acid (90). These agents either do not depolarize brown adipose tissue (56, 94) or cause a very slow depolarization quite unlike that caused by norepinephrine (200). It is possible that K^+ depletion, consequent upon inhibition of the Na^+ pump by oubain, may be responsible to some extent for the depression of stimulated respiration under these conditions. K^+ is known to be required for norepinephrine-stimulated respiration in brown adipose tissue (161).

In conclusion, it can be stated with some certainty that part of the calorigenic response to norepinephrine in brown adipose tissue is caused by increased ATP utilization by the Na^+ pump ATPase. The proportion of the total due to this activity cannot be estimated accurately at present.

The two hypotheses for heat production in brown adipose tissue (the uncoupling hypothesis and the Na^+ pump hypothesis) appear to be mutually exclusive since, if it is postulated that loosening or uncoupling occurs in response to fatty acids, any increased ADP production by the Na^+ pump should not influence the rate of respiration. Conversely, regulation of respiration by the ATPase activity of the Na^+ pump requires that the mitochondria be coupled and controlled by the phosphorylation state ratio. Another possibility, which would permit a role for the two mechanisms, is that uncoupling does indeed occur in response to fatty acids and that respiration becomes dependent on substrate supply. Because substrate level phosphorylation in the tricarboxylic acid cycle and in glycolysis would be required to occur at an accelerated rate to provide the increased substrate supply, a means for regenerating the extra ADP required as substrate for these accelerated phosphorylations would be necessary. A stimulated Na^+K^+-ATPase could regenerate the ADP required and thus permit a greater rate of delivery of substrate to the loosely coupled mitochondria.

If the unusual properties of brown adipose tissue mitochondria are indeed related to the thermogenic function of the tissue, it would be expected that, when brown adipose tissue hypertrophies and the mitochondria undergo morphological changes in those species that adapt to cold, the mitochondria would also undergo adaptive functional changes. This is indeed the case. Whereas albumin alone is sufficient to restore the coupled state and respiratory control in brown adipose tissue mitochondria isolated from adult guinea pigs, a purine nucleotide together with albumin is required for mitochondria isolated from newborn guinea pigs, in which the brown adipose tissue is in a thermogenic state (158). In contrast, brown adipose tissue mitochondria from a hibernator, which do not change morphologically during acclimation to cold (3), always require a purine nucleotide (145). Moreover, the energy dissipation, as measured by state four respiration, is higher in brown adipose tissue mitochondria from cold-acclimated rats and guinea pigs than from warm-acclimated rats and guinea pigs, whereas the rate is always high in hamster brown adipose tissue mitochondria and does not change during acclimation to cold (146). There would thus appear to be adaptive changes in the mitochondria of brown adipose tissue in association with its altered capacity for heat production, which suggests that the altered properties of the mitochondria do underly the mechanism of heat production.

NONSHIVERING THERMOGENESIS IN SKELETAL MUSCLE   Known metabolic effects of catecholamines on skeletal muscle include stimulation of adenylate cyclase, activation of protein kinase, and acceleration of glycogenolysis (see 76). No mechanism is apparent for the calorigenic action of catecholamines on muscle, and a major obstacle to the study of this action is the inability to demonstrate this effect in vitro despite its unquestioned occurrence in the intact animal (138). It is this action of norepinephrine that may be presumed to be so greatly enhanced in cold-acclimated rats and to be already large in hamsters.

The muscle of the cold-acclimated rat is a useful model in which to study the mechanism of the calorigenic action of norepinephrine. Three possible locations for an adaptive alteration resulting in an increased capacity of the muscle to respond to norepinephrine in this animal can be envisaged: 1. the norepinephrine-sensitive receptor system (presumed to involve adenylate cyclase), 2. the link between the receptor system and the final metabolic response (presumed to involve cyclic AMP), and 3. the final metabolic response itself (presumed to occur in the mitochondria). No change in norepinephrine-sensitive adenylate cyclase occurs in muscle in association with the enhanced response to norepinephrine (80). There is also no change in the use of the adenylate cyclase system in the intact animal in the cold, as indicated by unaltered cyclic AMP excretion in cold-acclimated rats in the cold, compared with warm-acclimated rats in the cold. Thus there would appear to be an unchanged receptor system.

The nature of the link between the receptor system and the mitochondria is not known for skeletal muscle. However, in skeletal muscle, as in brown adipose tissue, there do appear to be adaptive changes in the mitochondria during acclimation to cold. The mitochondria are smaller and more numerous, as indicated by electron microscopy and by counting and measuring size distribution of isolated mitochondria (8, 79). This change is associated with the adaptive increase in capacity to respond to norepinephrine, since both phenomena disappear together during deacclimation to cold and the appearance of both is inhibited when rats are treated with oxytetracycline during acclimation to cold (8, 80). The altered mitochondria in muscle are not, however, uncoupled, as are the altered mitochondria of brown adipose tissue of the same animals. ADP/O ratios and respiratory control with ADP (80), Ca^{2+}/O ratios and respiratory control with Ca^{2+} (79) and Ca^{2+} binding sites (D. Greenway and J. Himms-Hagen, unpublished) are all normal. There is an increase in state three respiration and a smaller increase in state four respiration with some substrates (80), and the specific activities of some enzymes are changed [malate dehydrogenase, a matrix enzyme, is decreased; succinic dehydrogenase and cytochrome oxidase, two inner membrane enzymes, are unchanged; glycerol-3-phosphate dehydrogenase, an inner boundary membrane enzyme, is increased (8, 79)]. Thus the morphology and enzyme composition of the muscle mitochondria are altered in association with the increased capacity of the muscle to respond calorigenically to norepinephrine, but none of the changes so far found has provided an explanation for that increased capacity. The changes in muscle mitochondria during acclimation to cold (8, 79) differ from the proliferation and increased size of muscle mitochondria that occur in prolonged hyperthyroidism (62, 209).

The development and maintenance of the changes in both muscle and brown adipose tissue mitochondria in cold-acclimated rats would appear to involve altered mitochondrial protein synthesis because they are associated with a decreased half-life of some, but not all, mitochondrial proteins (81) and are inhibited by oxytetracycline, a known inhibitor of mitochondrial protein synthesis (81).

The postulated role of the interscapular brown adipose tissue in promoting the calorigenic response of muscle to norepinephrine in cold-acclimated rats (see section on nonshivering thermogenesis) has been suggested to involve heat directed at central heat receptors (the neural hypothesis) (92, 95) or a factor that influences the capacity of muscle to respond to norepinephrine with an increase in heat production (74, 75, 80). The neural hypothesis developed by Horwitz to explain the very large drop in capacity to respond to norepinephrine after removal of the interscapular brown adipose tissue or after tying Sulzer's vein (92, 95) is questionable because there is no immediate change in the response to norepinephrine after removal of the interscapular brown adipose tissue (74, 75) and because tying Sulzer's vein does not always lead to a drop in the response to norepinephrine (77). Thus the nature of the influence remains unexplained. It is tempting to speculate that it may involve the regulation of mitochondrial structure and function in skeletal muscle.

A mechanism involving increased activity of the Na^+K^+-ATPase under the influence of norepinephrine has also been proposed for the calorigenic action of norepinephrine on skeletal muscle of cold-acclimated rats (91) and for nonshivering thermogenesis (93, 166). This is based upon the observed depolarization by norepinephrine of fibers in gracilis and sartorius muscles of cold-acclimated hamsters (91) and upon increased ouabain-sensitive respiration of muscle from cold-acclimated hamsters (91) and mice (167). However, as already pointed out, there appears to be considerable variation in the effect of catecholamines on muscle plasma membrane, depending on muscle fiber type, species, and time studied, and more detailed information about ion fluxes and different muscles will be required. The meaning of an increased tissue respiration in vitro of muscle from cold-acclimated animals is uncertain since no increase in BMR occurs in such animals and it would be expected that such an in vitro change would be a reflection of an increased MBR. It is unlikely that it represents an in vitro action of norepinephrine, as norepinephrine should no longer be present in vitro and acting on the tissue. It is also unlikely that it is associated with the acclimation to cold, since it occurs in both cold-exposed warm-acclimated rats and in cold-exposed cold-acclimated rats (143).

Thus the mechanism of nonshivering thermogenesis in skeletal muscle is uncertain. Although altered pumping of ions is likely to occur in response to catecholamines, and has indeed been observed under some conditions (41), there is at present no evidence that this process contributes greatly to the calorigenic effect of norepinephrine or that the responsiveness of this system alters in the cold-acclimated rat in association with the enhanced calorigenic response to norepinephrine. That the mitochondria undergo adaptive changes when the capacity for nonshivering thermogenesis in muscle is increased during acclimation to cold suggests an alteration in mitochondrial involvement during the transition from shivering to nonshivering thermogenesis. Possible mechanisms are discussed in the section on other speculative mechanisms. One puzzling observation, which makes difficult the formulation of a hypothesis for muscle nonshivering thermogenesis, is that whereas shivering thermogenesis and exercise thermogenesis do not summate in warm-acclimated rats, nonshivering thermogenesis and thermogenesis caused by muscle activity do summate in cold-acclimated rats (64). As the mechanisms of heat production in shivering and exercise are identical, the lack of summation is understandable. However, the summation of nonshivering thermogenesis and thermogenesis caused by muscle activity suggests that these two processes have different mechanisms, capable of simultaneous operation, at the mitochondrial level.

NONSHIVERING THERMOGENESIS IN OTHER TISSUES   The liver is not a major contributor to the increased oxygen uptake in response to norepinephrine or to cold in cold-acclimated rats (38, 39), but does appear to be capable of some nonshivering thermogenesis (170). Part of this would presumably be due to increased energy demands for gluconeogenesis and ureagenesis.

It has also been suggested that the calorigenic effect of catecholamines on liver is mediated by stimulation of the Na^+ pump (10), and liver slices from cold-acclimated rats do have an increased, ouabain-sensitive respiration (167, 194) and a doubled activity of Na^+K^+-ATPase (194). It is not clear whether these phenomena are caused by a functional hyperthyroid state of the liver in these animals, by an increased level of circulating catecholamines, or by both. It is quite likely that the increased oxygen uptake in vitro represents the recovery phase during which the ion distribution is being restored after the action of catecholamines in vivo (see section on calorigenic action of catecholamines). It is not known whether, as is true of the same phenomenon in muscle, the increase in ouabain-sensitive respiration occurs both in cold-acclimated rats and in acutely cold exposed warm-acclimated rats. Thus is it not known whether the change is specific for the cold-acclimated state. As administration of epinephrine to warm-acclimated rats also results in an increase in ouabain-sensitive respiration of liver slices (10), it is unlikely that the change is specific for the cold-acclimated state, but probable that it represents an action of endogenous catecholamines that can occur equally well in cold- and warm-acclimated animals.

Severe Trauma

Following severe trauma such as burns, breaking of limbs, or major surgery there is an initial and transient decrease in heat production. This is followed by a more prolonged increase in heat production. The initial decrease, referred to as the *ebb phase* (34), appears to be associated with a change in the thermoregulatory function of the hypothalamus such that the critical temperature is lowered (168); cold-induced shivering thermogenesis (169) and nonshivering thermogenesis (171) are both inhibited during the ebb phase. The change is thus similar to that which occurs in hibernation. If the size of the injury is such that compensatory regulation is insufficient to maintain body temperature, the ebb phase is succeeded by the *terminal phase*, in which heat production progressively diminishes because of a fall in blood supply to the tissues, and death finally occurs.

In contrast, in surviving animals, the ebb phase is succeeded by the *flow phase* (34), a period of hypermetabolism in which heat production may rise to double the BMR. The degree of hypermetabolism depends on the severity of the initial trauma (115) and is often sufficient to cause marked weight loss. Although there is marked muscle wasting in such subjects, protein contributes only 12–22% of the caloric expenditure; the remainder comes principally from lipid (114). The hypermetabolism appears to be caused primarily by the calorigenic action of catecholamines secreted in excessive quantities (206), possibly because of disturbances of hypothalamic control (207). The mechanism of the increased heat production is not fully understood. It must in part be a consequence of the energy cost (ATP utilization) for the accelerated gluconeogenesis and ureagenesis (205). In addition, since the critical temperature is elevated during the flow phase, some of the extra heat production can come from shivering thermogenesis at an environmental temperature within the thermoneutral range for an uninjured individual. The remainder and largest part of the increased heat production can be ascribed to nonshivering thermogenesis, that is, to an unknown mechanism initiated by the action of catecholamines (see section on nonshivering thermogenesis).

The function of these changes in metabolic rate following trauma is not clear. In rats the fall in heat production during the ebb phase appears to have a protective function in that survival is enhanced when the decrease in heat production is allowed to occur and is impaired by treatments that increase heat production (168). The function, if any, of the increased heat production of the flow phase is not apparent.

Pheochromocytoma

The increase in BMR seen in many patients with pheochromocytoma appears to be caused by the calorigenic effect of the catecholamines secreted by the tumor (45).

Luft Hypermetabolic Syndrome

The Luft hypermetabolic syndrome is characterized by a very high metabolic rate (greater than +200%) that is not caused by hyperthyroidism. Only two cases have been described: one in Sweden (132) and one in Lebanon (1, 2). The most remarkable feature of this disease is the presence in skeletal muscle of an increased number of mitochondria, many of which are morphologically abnormal. The abnormal forms include giant mitochondria, mitochondria with densely packed cristae arranged in parallel rows or in circular whorls, and mitochondria with inclusion bodies. Isolated mitochondria have a very high rate of respiration and no respiratory control by ADP. In the case described by Luft, the P/O ratios were normal, and he concluded that the mitochondria were loosely coupled (46, 132). In the case described in Lebanon, some studies have shown low P/O ratios (1, 2), whereas others have shown normal P/O ratios with some substrates (40). The problem of whether all mitochondria in muscle are abnormal in this disorder has not been resolved. It is possible that there are two populations of mitochondria, one normal and one abnormal, and that the disorder is due to a pseudoneoplastic proliferation of some mitochondria in muscle, the new mitochondria lacking certain proteins necessary for the normal regulation of function (1). That there is indeed unusually rapid proliferation of mitochondria in this disease is suggested by the reduction in the elevated BMR and in the elevated mitochondrial mass in muscle after treatment with chloramphenicol (1, 2). Chloramphenicol is known to inhibit mitochondrial protein synthesis in mammals, particularly in tissues in which rapid proliferation of mitochondria is occurring, for example, regenerating rat liver (49).

Thus the most probable explanation for the tremendous increase in heat production in the Luft hypermetabolic syndrome is the presence in skeletal muscle of an abnormally large mass of uncoupled or loosely coupled mitochondria; in either case the respiration is not controlled by ADP in the usual manner and is therefore very high. The muscle is not deficient in ATP, since ATP is produced in oxidative phosphorylation, either by a diminished population of normal mitochondria (1) or by the loosely coupled mitochondria (130). However, although it is logical to conclude that the symptoms in the Luft hypermetabolic syndrome are caused by loosely coupled mitochondria in muscle, it should be remembered that there are numerous reports in the literature of other myopathies in which loosely coupled mitochondria have been isolated from muscle (e.g. see 55). The main difference between the Luft hypermetabolic syndrome and these other myopathies lies not in the loose coupling of the mitochondria, but in the excessively large mass of mitochondria in the former. Indeed, the other myopathies are all characterized by an unchanged BMR and muscle weakness.

It is not clear whether, like most other myopathies, the two unrelated cases of the Luft hypermetabolic syndrome are of genetic origin or whether they represent two examples of a pseudoneoplastic disorder of unknown etiology. It is quite possible that the protein defect is dissimilar in the two reported cases.

Malignant Hyperthermia

Malignant hyperthermia is a genetic defect, primarily affecting muscle, in which extreme muscle rigidity and hyperthermia are triggered by a variety of agents, the most common of which is inhalational anesthetics such as halothane. This disorder has been described in man and in certain strains of pig, but it seems likely that the molecular defect may be different in these two species. For a recent compendium of research on this subject, the reader is referred to a recent symposium (61).

The major defect is a failure of the muscles in the susceptible individuals to keep the concentration of Ca^{2+} in the cytosol at its usual low level, probably because of an increased sensitivity to inhibition by halothane of the sarcoplasmic reticulum uptake mechanism for Ca^{2+} (15). A defect in the mitochondria has also been suggested (15, 142). However, halothane inhibits muscle mitochondrial respiration, and such an inhibition is an unlikely explanation for an increase in metabolic rate (15, 142). What is more likely is that the mitochondria take up excessive amounts of Ca^{2+} and eventually become uncoupled because of the high concentration of Ca^{2+} in the cytosol. During halothane-induced hyperthermia, mitochondria in muscle of pigs do have the appearance of uncoupled mitochondria; they are swollen and have an expanded matrix (17), just as do isolated liver mitochondria that have taken up large amounts of Ca^{2+} (63).

The sequence of events leading to the marked hyperthermia apparently involves accumulation of Ca^{2+} in the cytosol because of failure of the normal sarcoplasmic reticulum uptake mechanism: excessive activation of myosin ATPase leads to muscle rigidity and heat production, excessive uptake of Ca^{2+} by the mitochondria provides more heat, and eventual uncoupling of the mitochondria leads to uncontrolled combustion of substrates. Glycogenolysis and glycolysis are both accelerated, the former because of Ca^{2+}-induced activation of phosphorylase b kinase (see 76) and the latter because of the increased supply of ADP and phosphate, and so there is excessive lactate and pyruvate production. Thus heat is produced by a combination of an uncoupling mechanism and an ATPase type of mechanism and is derived from both aerobic and anerobic metabolism. This combination probably represents the most effective heat-producing mechanism known to exist in the mammalian body. Unfortunately, it is a pathological rather than a physiological mechanism, and sufficient heat is produced to cause a lethal hyperthermia.

Hibernation

Entry into hibernation involves switching off the usual thermogenic mechanisms (shivering and nonshivering thermogenesis) and the usual heat-conserving mechanisms (cutaneous vasoconstriction) so that the body temperature falls to or near to ambient temperature. The control mechanism resides in the brain stem and appears to involve specific inhibitory influences arising from the limbic system (131). The thermogenic mechanisms switched off are those described in the sections on muscle activity and nonshivering thermogenesis. As body temperature falls, so also do the rates of those reactions contributing to the BMR, which reaches a new low basal level.

Arousal from hibernation involves a removal of the central inhibition, triggered in some unknown way by an environmental stimulus, and the initiation of shivering and nonshivering thermogenesis. The relative proportions of these two processes varies from one species to another (67). A large part of the nonshivering thermogenesis in hibernators usually takes place in brown adipose tissue.

Other Speculative Mechanisms of Cellular Thermogenesis

Other speculative mechanisms of cellular thermogenesis include those mechanisms that occur in isolated systems and even in vivo, but have not been demonstrated to contribute to any appreciable extent to the categories of heat production so far described. As there are considerable gaps in our understanding of these categories, some speculative suggestions are offered concerning additional mechanisms that may be involved.

FUTILE CYCLES   The operation of futile cycles involving pairs of enzymes or pairs of pathways operating simultaneously has frequently been suggested to underlie heat production. The operation of such cycles has been established, for example, for gluconeogenesis (31, 204), but it can be calculated that their quantitative contribution to overall thermogenesis is exceedingly small. Similar calculations for the operation of the phosphofructokinase-fructose 1,6-diphosphatase cycle in muscle of malignant hyperthermic pigs (32) indicate an extremely small percentage of overall thermogenesis. Thus while such phenomena are interesting, there is at present no evidence that futile cycles represent a major thermogenic process in mammalian tissues. However, an excellent example from the invertebrates is the warm-up of the flight muscle of the bumblebee (see 87).

CALCIUM PUMPING   The movement of Ca^{2+} across cell and organelle membranes is an energy-requiring process. Mitochondria in particular have a very high affinity for Ca^{2+}, and use of energy for Ca^{2+} uptake competes with use of energy for ADP phosphorylation (123). Indeed, Ca^{2+} uptake by mitochondria has been suggested as a thermogenic mechanism for brown adipose tissue (28, 82). A large part of the state four respiration of isolated liver mitochondria can be attributed to Ca^{2+} recycling (173). Whether this occurs in mitochondria in their normal intracellular environment and thus contributes to the BMR is unknown.

Until recently, a major difficulty in accepting such a mechanism for thermogenesis has been that no physiological device was apparent for the release of Ca^{2+} from mitochondria. It is now known that such commonly occurring substances as cyclic AMP (14, 136), Na^+ ions (24), and prostaglandins (23) can release Ca^{2+} from mitochondria and that K^+ is required for its uptake (42). It is possible, at least in theory, to envisage processes by which such agents might be involved in a calcium-pumping thermogenic mechanism triggered by catecholamines. The important role of Ca^{2+} in the regulation of metabolic processes in cells has been emphasized by Rasmussen (see 160), and thermogenesis may well be included in the multitude of cellular activities in which Ca^{2+} is involved.

POTASSIUM PUMPING   The uptake of K^+ by mitochondria is another energy-dependent process that derives energy directly from substrate oxidation and does not require ATP. It can be demonstrated to occur in intact cells and to result in an increase in oxygen uptake in the presence of an artificial ionophore, valinomycin (60). Because certain fatty acids have been shown to act as natural ionophores for monovalent cations in mitochondria (210), it is possible that such an energy-dissipating cycling of K^+ might serve as a thermogenic process. There is indeed evidence that such a mechanism may play a part in the thermogenic response of brown adipose tissue to lipolytic stimuli (161). That isolated brown adipose tissue mitochondria have a very high permeability to K^+ ions (147) would be in keeping with such a mechanism. The extent to which it might contribute to other heat-producing processes is unknown.

INTRACELLULAR PROTEINS REGULATING MITOCHONDRIAL FUNCTION
Mitochondrial structure and function have been shown to be modified by histones. Histones cause a transformation of mitochondria from the condensed to the orthodox state, an energy-dependent efflux of K^+ and an increase in coupled respiration (111). Whether this is of physiological significance is unknown.

The cytoplasmic metabolic factor of Kun (117) may also fall into this category, although there is some doubt as to whether or not it is a protein.

INTRACELLULAR MOVEMENTS OF ORGANELLES   In cells in culture, the organelles clearly are not static, but change continuously both in shape and position. This movement appears not to be a property of the organelles alone, but is rather due to an interaction between them and a network of filaments and microtubules by a "sliding organelle" process analogous to the sliding filament mechanism of muscle contraction (18). Such a process would be energy dependent, as is muscle contraction, and thus could be the basis for a thermogenic mechanism. Indeed, mitochondrial movement was suggested as a possible mechanism for thermogenesis some time ago (73). However, the extent and control of organelle movement in mammalian cells in vivo is completely unknown.

CONCLUSIONS AND SUMMARY

The principal conclusion presented in this review is that no single mechanism underlies any of the examples of basal or altered cellular thermogenesis. Both increased Na^+ pump operation and uncoupling may occur to a greater or lesser extent, as may other heat-producing mechanisms. There are areas in which further information is needed in order to explain fully the composite nature of the mechanisms involved in cellular thermogenesis. The control of mitochondrial oxidations in their natural habitat (i.e. inside cells) by regulatory proteins, fatty acids, ions (Ca^{2+}, Na^+, K^+), cyclic AMP, protein kinases, prostaglandins, purine nucleotides, and other factors must be elucidated. There is evidence for the participation of all of these substances in the control of cellular thermogenesis, but no scheme has been developed that takes them all into account. Further emphasis on the tissue-specific differences in the regulation of mitochondrial function is desirable. The regulation of the biogenesis of mammalian mitochondria is another area currently under intense study for which no clear hypothesis has as yet emerged. Information in this area is needed in order to understand the mechanism and role of mitochondrial adaptations associated with altered thermogenesis in hyperthyroidism, in acclimation to cold, and in exercise training, as well as the nature of altered mitochondrial biogenesis, such as appears to underlie the Luft hypermetabolic syndrome.

Literature Cited

1. Abu Haydar, N., Conn, H. L., Afifi, A., Wakid, N., Ballas, S., Fawaz, K. 1971. Severe hypermetabolism with primary abnormality of skeletal muscle mitochondria. Functional and therapeutic effects of chloramphenicol treatment. *Ann. Intern. Med.* 74:548–58
2. Afifi, A., Ibrahim, M. Z. M., Bergman, R. A., Abu Haydar, N., Mire, J., Bahuth, N., Kaylani, F. 1972. Morphologic features of hypermetabolic mitochondrial disease. A. Light microscopic, histochemical and electron microscopic study. *J. Neurol. Sci.* 15: 271–90
3. Ahlabo, I., Barnard, T. 1974. A quantitative analysis of triglyceride droplet structure in hamster brown adipose tissue during cold exposure and starvation. *J. Ultrastruct. Res.* 48:361–76
4. Ariano, M. A., Armstrong, R. B., Edgerton, V. R. 1973. Hindlimb muscle fiber populations of five mammals. *J. Histochem. Cytochem.* 21:51–55
5. Babior, B. M., Creagan, S., Ingbar, S. H., Kipnes, R. S. 1973. Stimulation of mitochondrial adenosine diphosphate uptake by thyroid hormone. *Proc. Nat. Acad. Sci. USA* 70:98–102
6. Baker, P. F. 1972. The sodium pump in animal tissues and its role in the control of cellular metabolism and function. *Metabolic Pathways*, ed. L. E. Hokin, 6:243–68. New York: Academic
7. Barnabei, O., Leghissa, G., Tomasi, V. 1974. Hormonal control of the potassium level in isolated rat liver. *Biochim. Biophys. Acta* 362:316–25
8. Behrens, W., Himms-Hagen, J. 1975. Alteration in skeletal muscle mitochondria of cold-acclimated rats: association with enhanced metabolic response to noradrenaline. *J. Bioenerg.* In press
9. Bernstein, J., Videla, L., Israel, Y. 1973. Metabolic alterations produced in the liver by chronic ethanol administration. Changes related to energetic parameters of the cell. *Biochem. J.* 134:515–21
10. Bernstein, J., Videla, L., Israel, Y. 1975. Hormonal influences in the development of the hypermetabolic state of the liver produced by chronic administration of ethanol. *J. Pharmacol. Exp. Ther.* 192:583–91
11. Beyer, R. E. 1963. Regulation of energy metabolism during acclimation of laboratory rats to a cold environment. *Fed. Proc.* 22:874–77
12. Blond, D. M., Whittam, R. 1964. Effects of Na and K on oxidative phosphorylation in relation to respiratory control by a cell-membrane ATPase. *Biochem. Biophys. Res. Commun.* 17: 120–24
13. Boardman, L., Huett, M., Lamb, J. F., Newton, J. P., Polson, J. M. 1974. Evidence for the genetic control of sodium pump density in HeLa cells. *J. Physiol. London* 241:771–94
14. Borle, A. 1974. Cyclic AMP stimulation of calcium efflux from kidney, liver and heart mitochondria. *J. Membr. Biol.* 16:221–36
15. Britt, B. A., Kalow, W., Gordon, A., Humphrey, J. G., Rewcastle, N. B. 1973. Malignant hyperthermia: an investigation of five patients. *Can. Anaesth. Soc. J.* 20:431–67
16. Brown, G. L., Goffart, M., Vianna Dias, M. 1950. The effects of adrenaline and of sympathetic stimulation on the demarcation potential of mammalian skeletal muscle. *J. Physiol. London* 111:184–94
17. Brucker, R. F., Williams, C. H., Popinigis, J., Galvex, T. L., Vail, W. J., Taylor, C. A. 1973. In vitro studies on liver mitochondria and skeletal muscle sarcoplasmic reticulum fragments isolated from hyperpyrexic swine. See Ref. 61, 238–70
18. Buckley, I. K. 1974. Subcellular motility: a correlated light and electron microscopic study using cultured cells. *Tissue Cell* 6:1–20
19. Bulos, B., Shukla, S., Sacktor, B. 1972. Effect of thyroid hormone on respiratory control of liver mitochondria from adult and senescent rats. *Arch. Biochem. Biophys.* 151:387–90
20. Bulychev, A., Kramar, R., Drahota, Z., Lindberg, O. 1972. Role of a specific endogenous fatty acid fraction in the coupling-uncoupling mechanism of oxidative phosphorylation of brown adipose tissue. *Exp. Cell Res.* 72:169–87
21. Campion, D. S. 1974. Resting membrane potential and ionic distribution in

fast- and slow-twitch mammalian muscle. *J. Clin. Invest.* 54:514–18

22. Cannon, B., Nicholls, D. G., Lindberg, O. 1973. Purine nucleotides and fatty acids in energy coupling of mitochondria from brown adipose tissue. *Mechanisms in Bioenergetics,* ed. G. F. Azzone, L. Ernster, S. Papa, E. Quagliarello, N. Siliprandi, 357–63. New York: Academic

23. Carafoli, E., Crovetti, F. 1973. Interactions between prostaglandin E_1 and calcium at the level of the mitochondrial membrane. *Arch. Biochem. Biophys.* 154:40–46

24. Carafoli, E., Tiozzo, R., Lugli, G., Crovetti, F., Kratzing, C. 1974. The release of calcium from heart mitochondria by sodium. *J. Mol. Cell. Cardiol.* 6:361–71

25. Castro-Tavares, J., Cardoso, W. 1974. Effects of adrenergic stimulant and blocking drugs on the release and uptake of potassium by the liver. *Arch. Int. Pharmacodyn.* 209:100–12

26. Castro-Tavares, J., Garrett, J. 1973. The role of skeletal muscle in the biphasic response of plasma potassium to epinephrine and norepinephrine. *Life Sci.* 12:497–504

27. Chaffee, R. R. J., Roberts, J. C. 1971. Temperature acclimation in birds and mammals. *Ann. Rev. Physiol.* 33:155–202

28. Christiansen, E. N. 1971. Calcium uptake and its effect on respiration and phosphorylation in mitochondria from brown adipose tissue. *Eur. J. Biochem.* 19:276–82

29. Christiansen, E. N., Drahota, Z., Duszynski, J., Wojtczak, L. 1973. Transport of adenine nucleotides in mitochondria from the brown andipose tissue. *Eur. J. Biochem.* 34:506–12

30. Christiansen, E. N., Grav, H. J., Wojtczak, L. 1974. Effect of tonicity of the medium on transport of adenine nucleotides and phosphate in brown adipose tissue mitochondria. *FEBS Lett.* 46:188–91

31. Clark, M. G., Bloxham, D. P., Holland, P. C., Lardy, H. A. 1974. Estimation of the fructose 1,6-diphosphatase-phosphofructokinase substrate cycle and its relationship to gluconeogenesis in rat liver *in vivo. J. Biol. Chem.* 249:279–90

32. Clark, M. G., Williams, C. H., Pfeifer, W. F., Bloxham, D. P., Holland, P. C., Taylor, C. A., Lardy, H. A. 1973. Accelerated substrate cycling of fructose-6-phosphate in the muscle of malignant hyperthermic pigs. *Nature* 245:99–101

33. Coffey, R. G., Hadden, J. W., Hadden, E. M., Middleton, E. 1971. Stimulation of ATPase by norepinephrine: an alpha-adrenergic receptor mechanism. *Fed. Proc.* 30:497(Abstr.)

34. Cuthbertson, D. P., Fell, G. S., Rahimi, A. G. Tilstone, W. J. 1973. Environmental temperature and metabolic response to injury. Protein, mineral and energy metabolism. *Adv. Exp. Biol. Med.* 33:409–16

35. Dahl, J. L., Hokin, L. E. 1974. The sodium-potassium adenosinetriphosphatase. *Ann. Rev. Biochem.* 43:327–56

36. Dambach, G., Friedmann, N. 1974. Substrate-induced membrane potential changes in the perfused rat liver. *Biochim. Biophys. Acta* 367:366–70

37. Dawson, M. J., Bianchi, C. P. 1975. Restoration of potassium-stimulated respiration of "glycerol-treated" muscle. *Eur. J. Pharmacol.* In press

38. Depocas, F. 1958. Chemical thermogenesis in the functionally eviscerated cold-acclimated rat. *Can. J. Biochem. Physiol.* 36:691–99

39. Depocas, F. 1960. The calorigenic response of cold-acclimated white rats to infused noradrenaline. *Can. J. Biochem. Physiol.* 38:107–14

40. DiMauro, S., Schotland, D. L., Lee, C. P., Bonilla, E., Conn, H. 1972. Biochemical and ultrastructural studies of mitochondria in Luft's disease: Implications for "mitochondrial myopathies." *Trans. Am. Neurol. Assoc.* 97:265–67 (Abstr.)

41. Dockry, M., Kerman, R. P., Tangney, A. 1966. Active transport of sodium and potassium in mammalian skeletal muscle and its modification by nerve and by cholinergic and adrenergic agents. *J. Physiol. London* 186:187–200

42. Dransfeld, H., Greeff, K. Schorn, A., Ting, B. T. 1969. Calcium uptake in mitochondria and vesicles of heart and skeletal muscle in presence of potassium, sodium, β-strophanthin and pentobarbital. *Biochem. Pharmacol.* 18:1335–45

43. Edelman, I. S. 1974. Thyroid thermogenesis. *N. Engl. J. Med.* 290:1303–8

44. Edelman, I. S., Ismail-Beigi, F. 1972. Role of ion transport in thyroid calorigenesis. *Environmental Physiology: Bioenergetics,* ed. R. Em. Smith, 67–70. Washington:FASEB

45. Engelman, K., Mueller, P. S., Sjoerdsma, A. 1964. Elevated plasma free fatty acid concentrations in patients

with pheochromocytoma. *N. Engl. J. Med.* 270:865–70

46. Ernster, L., Luft, R. 1963. Further studies on a population of human skeletal muscle mitochondria lacking respiratory control. *Exp. Cell Res.* 32:26–35

47. Fain, J. N. 1973. Biochemical aspects of drug and hormone action on adipose tissue. *Pharmacol. Rev.* 25:67–118

48. Fain, J. N., Jacobs, M. D., Clement-Cormier, Y. C. 1973. Interrelationship of cyclic AMP, lipolysis, and respiration in brown fat cells. *Am. J. Physiol.* 224:346–51

49. Firkin, F. C., Linnane, A. W. 1969. Biogenesis of mitochondria. 8. The effect of chloramphenicol on regenerating rat liver. *Exp. Cell Res.* 55:68–76

50. Flatmark, T., Pedersen, J. I. 1975. Brown adipose tissue mitochondria. *Biochim. Biophys. Acta* 416:53–103

51. Flattery, K. V., Sellers, E. A. 1972. Brown adipose tissue, catecholamines and survival in the cold. See Ref. 44, 141–44

52. Foster, D. O. 1974. Evidence against a mediatory role of brown adipose tissue in the calorigenic response of cold-acclimated rats to noradrenaline. *Can. J. Physiol. Pharmacol.* 52:1051–62

53. Friedrichs, D., Schoner, W. 1973. Stimulation of renal gluconeogenesis by inhibition of the sodium pump. *Biochim. Biophys. Acta* 304:142–60

54. Gale, C. C. 1973. Neuroendocrine aspects of thermoregulation. *Ann. Rev. Physiol.* 35:391–430

55. Gimeno, A., Trueba, J. L., Blanco, M., Gosalvez, M. 1973. Mitochondrial functions in five cases of human neuromuscular disorders. *J. Neurol. Neurosurg. Psychiatry* 36:806–12

56. Girardier, L., Seydoux, J. 1971. Le contrôle de la thermogenèse du tissu adipeux brun. *J. Physiol. Paris* 63:147–86

57. Godfraind, T., Koch, M.-C., Verbeke, N. 1974. The action of EGTA on the catecholamines stimulation of rat brain Na-K-ATPase. *Biochem. Pharmacol.* 23:3505–11

58. Goffart, M., Perry, W. L. M. 1951. The action of adrenaline on the rate of loss of potassium ions from unfatigued striated muscle. *J. Physiol. London* 112:95–101

59. Gomez-Puyou, A., Sandoval, F., Tuena de Gomez-Puyou, M., Pena, A., Chavez, E. 1972. Coupling of oxidative phosphorylation by monovalent cations. *Biochemistry* 11:97–102

60. Gordon, E. E., Nordenbrand, K., Ernster, L. 1967. Evidence for a new mechanism of respiratory stimulation and proteon ejection in Ehrlich ascites tumour cells dependent on potassium ions. *Nature* 213:82–85

61. Gordon, R. A., Britt, B. A., Kalow, W., eds. 1973. *Malignant Hyperthermia.* Springfield, Ill.: Thomas

62. Gustafsson, R., Tata, J. R., Lindberg, O., Ernster, L. 1965. The relationship between the structure and activity of rat skeletal muscle mitochondria after thyroidectomy and thyroid hormone treatment. *J. Cell Biol.* 26:555–78

63. Hackenbrock, C. R., Caplan, A. 1969. Ion-induced ultrastructural transformation in isolated mitochondria: the energized uptake of calcium. *J. Cell Biol.* 42:221–34

64. Hart, J. S., Jansky, L. 1963. Thermogenesis due to exercise and cold in warm- and cold-acclimated rats. *Can. J. Biochem. Physiol.* 41:629–34

65. Haylett, D. G., Jenkinson, D. H. 1972. Effects of noradrenaline on potassium efflux, membrane potential and electrolyte levels in tissue slices prepared from guinea pig liver. *J. Physiol. London* 225:721–50

66. Hayward, J. S., Davies, P. F. 1972. Evidence for the mediatory role of brown adipose tissue during nonshivering thermogenesis in the cold-acclimated mouse. *Can. J. Physiol. Pharmacol.* 50:168–70

67. Hayward, J. S., Lyman, C. P. 1967. Nonshivering heat production during arousal from hibernation and evidence for the contribution of brown fat. *Mammalian Hibernation III*, ed. K. C. Fisher, A. R. Dawe, C. P. Lyman, E. Schönbaum, F. E. South, Jr., 346–55. New York: Elsevier

68. Hazlewood, C. F. 1973. Accumulation and exclusion of ions in contractile tissue of developing animals. *Ann. NY Acad. Sci.* 204:593–606

69. Hegsted, D. M. 1974. Energy needs and energy utilization. *Nutr. Rev.* 32:33–38

70. Heldmaier, G. 1971. Relationship between nonshivering thermogenesis and body size. *Nonshivering Thermogenesis,* ed. L. Jansky, 73–81. Amsterdam: Swets & Zeitlinger

71. Herd, P. A., Hammond, R. P., Hamolsky, M. W. 1973. Sodium pump activity during norepinephrine-stimulated respiration in brown adipocytes. *Am. J. Physiol.* 224:1300–4

72. Herd, P. A., Horwitz, B. A., Smith, R. Em. 1970. Norepinephrine-sensitive Na+/K+ ATPase activity in brown adipose cells. *Experientia* 26:825–26

73. Himms-Hagen, J. 1967. Sympathetic regulation of metabolism. *Pharmacol. Rev.* 19:367–461

74. Himms-Hagen, J. 1969. The role of brown adipose tissue in the calorigenic effect of adrenaline and noradrenaline in cold-acclimated rats. *J. Physiol. London* 205:393–403

75. Himms-Hagen, J. 1970. Regulation of metabolic processes in brown adipose tissue in relation to nonshivering thermogenesis. *Adv. Enzyme Reg.*, ed. G. Weber, 8:131–51. New York: Pergamon

76. Himms-Hagen, J. 1972. Effects of catecholamines on metabolism. *Handbook of Experimental Pharmacology*, ed. H. Blaschko, E. Muscholl, 33:363–462. Berlin: Springer

77. Himms-Hagen, J. 1974. Interscapular location of brown adipose tissue: role in noradrenaline-induced calorigenesis in cold-acclimated rats. *Can. J. Physiol. Pharmacol.* 52:225–29

78. Himms-Hagen, J. 1975. Role of the adrenal medulla in adaptation to cold. *Handb. Physiol.*, Section 7, Vol. 6:637–65

79. Himms-Hagen, J., Behrens, W., Hbous, A., Greenway, D. 1975. Altered mitochondria in skeletal muscle of cold-acclimated rats: adaptation for nonshivering thermogenesis. *Depressed Metabolism and Cold Thermogenesis*, ed. X. T. Musacchia, L. Jansky. Springfield, Ill: Thomas. In press

80. Himms-Hagen, J., Behrens, W., Muirhead, M., Hbous, A. 1975. Adaptive changes in the calorigenic effect of catecholamines: role of changes in the adenyl cyclase system and of changes in the mitochondria. *Mol. Cell. Biochem.* 6:15–31

81. Himms-Hagen, J., Bukowiecki, L., Behrens, W., Bonin, M. 1972. Mechanism of nonshivering thermogenesis in rats. See Ref. 44, 127–33

82. Hittelman, K. J., Fairhurst, A. S., Smith, R. E. 1967. Calcium accumulation as a parameter of energy metabolism in mitochondria of brown adipose tissue. *Proc. Nat. Acad. Sci. USA* 58:697–702

83. Hittelman, K. J., Lindberg, O., Cannon, B. 1969. Oxidative phosphorylation and compartmentation of fatty acid metabolism in brown fat mitochondria. *Eur. J. Biochem.* 11:183–92

84. Ho, R. J., Jeanrenaud, B., Posternak, T. H., Renold, A. E. 1967. Insulin-like action of ouabain. II. Primary antilipolytic effect through inhibition of adenyl cyclase. *Biochim. Biophys. Acta* 144:74–82

85. Hoch, F. L. 1962. Thyrotoxicosis as a disease of mitochondria. *N. Engl. J. Med.* 266:446–54, 498–505

86. Hoch, F. L., Motta, M. V. 1968. Reversal of early thyroid hormone action on mitochondria by bovine serum albumin in vitro. *Proc. Nat. Acad. Sci. USA* 59:118–22

87. Hochachka, P. W. 1974. Regulation of heat production at the cellular level. *Fed. Proc.* 33:2162–69

88. Hochachka, P. W., Somero, G. N. 1973. *Strategies of Biochemical Adaptation.* Philadelphia: Saunders

89. Horowitz, J. M., Horwitz, B. A., Smith, R. Em. 1971. Effect in vivo of norepinephrine on the membrane resistance of brown fat cells. *Experientia* 27:1419–21

90. Horwitz, B. A. 1973. Ouabain-sensitive component of brown fat thermogenesis. *Am. J. Physiol.* 224:352–55

91. Horwitz, B. A. 1975. Pathways underlying nonshivering thermogenesis in peripheral tissues. *Int. Symp. Depressed Metab. Cold Thermogenesis, Prague, 1974.* Prague: Academia. In press

92. Horwitz, B. A., Detrick, J. F., Smith, R. Em. 1972. Norepinephrine-induced thermogenesis: effect of interscapular brown fat. *Experientia* 28:284–86

93. Horwitz, B. A., Hanes, G. E. 1974. Isoproterenol-induced calorigenesis of dystrophic and normal hamsters. *Proc. Soc. Exp. Biol. Med.* 147:392–95

94. Horwitz, B. A., Horowitz, J. M., Smith, R. Em. 1969. Norepinephrine-induced depolarization of brown fat cells. *Proc. Nat. Acad. Sci. USA* 64:113–20

95. Horwitz, B. A., Smith, R. Em. 1972. Function and control of brown fat thermogenesis during cold exposure. See Ref. 44, 134–40

96. Howland, J. L. 1974. Abnormal potassium conductance associated with genetic muscular dystrophy. *Nature* 251:724–25

97. Hsieh, A. C. L. 1962. The role of the thyroid in rats exposed to cold. *J. Physiol. London* 161:175–88

98. Hsieh, A. C. L. 1963. The basal metabolic rate of cold-adapted rats. *J. Physiol. London* 169:851–61

99. Hsieh, A. C. L., Pun, C. W., Li, K. M., Ti, K. W. 1966. Circulatory and meta-

bolic effects of noradrenaline in cold-adapted rats. *Fed. Proc.* 25:1205–9
100. Hull, D., Segal, M. M. 1965. The contribution of brown adipose tissue to heat production in the new-born rabbit. *J. Physiol. London* 181:449–57
101. Ismail-Beigi, F., Edelman, I. S. 1970. Mechanisms of thyroid calorigenesis: role of active sodium transport. *Proc. Soc. Nat. Acad. Sci. USA* 67:1071–78
102. Ismail-Beigi, F., Edelman, I. S. 1971. The mechanism of the calorigenic action of thyroid hormone. *J. Gen. Physiol.* 57:710–22
103. Ismail-Beigi, F., Edelman, I. S. 1973. Effects of thyroid status on electrolyte distribution in rat tissues. *Am. J. Physiol.* 225:1172–77
104. Ismail-Beigi, F., Edelman, I. S. 1974. Time-course of the effects of thyroid hormone on respiration and $Na^+ + K^+$ –ATPase activity in rat liver. *Proc. Soc. Exp. Biol. Med.* 146:983–88
105. Ismail-Beigi, F., Salibian, A., Kirsten, E., Edelman, I. 1973. Effect of thyroid hormone on adenine nucleotide content of rat liver. *Proc. Soc. Exp. Biol. Med.* 144:471–74
106. Israel, Y., Kalant, H., Orrego, H., Khanna, J. M., Videla, L., Phillips, J. M. 1975. Experimental alcohol-induced hepatic necrosis: suppression by propylthiouracil. *Proc. Nat. Acad. Sci. USA* 72:1137–41
107. Israel, Y., Videla, L., Fernandez-Videla, V., Bernstein, J. 1975. Effects of chronic ethanol treatment and thyroxine administration on ethanol metabolism and liver oxidative capacity. *J. Pharmacol. Exp. Ther.* 192:565–74
108. Israel, Y., Videla, L., MacDonald, A., Bernstein, J. 1973. Metabolic alterations produced in the liver by chronic ethanol administration. Comparison between the effects produced by ethanol and by thyroid hormone. *Biochem. J.* 134:523–29
109. Jansky, L. 1973. Non-shivering thermogenesis and its thermoregulatory significance. *Biol. Rev.* 48:85–132
110. Joanny, P., Corriol, J. 1967. Influence de ouabaïne sur les mouvements ioniques, la respiration et la glycolyse aérobic du cortex cérébral isolé de mammifère. *Arch. Sci. Physiol.* 18:325–37
111. Johnson, C. L., Goldstein, M. A., Schwartz, A. 1973. Biochemical and ultrastructural studies on the interaction of basic proteins with mitochondria: a primary effect on membrane configura-

tion. *Arch. Biochem. Biophys.* 157:597–604
112. Johnson, M., Ramwell, P. W. 1973. Prostaglandin modification of membrane-bound enzyme activity: a possible mechanism of action? *Prostaglandins* 3:703–19
113. Katz, A. I., Lindheimer, M. D. 1973. Renal sodium- and potassium-activated adenosine triphosphate and sodium reabsorption in the hypothyroid rat. *J. Clin. Invest.* 52:796–804
114. Kinney, J. M., Duke, J. H. Jr., Long, C. L., Gump, F. E. 1970. Tissue fuel and weight loss after injury. *J. Clin. Pathol. Suppl. R. Coll. Pathol.* 4:65–72
115. Kinney, J. M., Gump, F. E., Long, C. L. 1973. Energy and tissue fuel in human injury and sepsis. *Adv. Exp. Med. Biol.* 33:401–7
116. Kleineke, J., Stratman, F. W. 1974. Calcium transport in isolated rat hepatocytes. *FEBS Lett.* 43:75–80
117. Kun, E. 1972. Cytoplasmic regulation of mitochondrial bioenergetics by a specific cellular factor. *Biochemical Regulatory Mechanisms in Eukaryotic Cells*, ed. E. Kun, S. Grisolia, 303–53. New York: Wiley Interscience
118. Langer, G. A. 1974. Calcium in mammalian myocardium. Localization, control and the effects of digitalis. *Circulation Res.* 35(Suppl. 3):91–98
119. Laury, M. C., Portet, R. 1974. Effets de l'ablation partielle de la graisse brune et de l'administration de théophylline sur la réponse calorigénique à la noradrénaline chez le rat adapté au froid. *Rev. Can. Biol.* 33:15–25
120. Lawson, R. N., Chugtai, M. S. 1963. Breast cancer and body temperature. *Can. Med. Assoc. J.* 88:68–70
121. LeBlanc, J., LaFrance, L., Villemaire, A., Roberge, C., Vallières, J., Rousseau, S. 1972. Catecholamines and cold adaptation. See Ref. 44, 71–76
122. Leduc, J., Rivest, P. 1969. Effets de l'ablation de la graisse brune interscapulaire sur l'acclimatation au froid chez le rat. *Rev. Can. Biol.* 28:49–66
123. Lehninger, A. L. 1974. Ca^{2+} transport by mitochondria and its possible role in the cardiac contraction-relaxation cycle. *Circ. Res.* 35 (Suppl. 3):83–90
124. Lehninger, A. L. 1975. Linked transport and binding functions in the mitochondrial membrane. *Functional Linkage in Biomolecular Systems*, ed. F. O. Schmitt, D. M. Schneider, D. M. Crothers, 165–80. New York:Academic

125. Lieber, C. S. 1973. Liver adaptation and injury in alcoholism. *N. Engl. J. Med.* 288:356–62

126. Lieber, C. S., DeCarli, L. M. 1970. Hepatic microsomal ethanol-oxidizing system. *In vitro* characteristics and adaptive properties *in vivo*. *J. Biol. Chem.* 245:2505–12

127. Limas, C. J., Notargiacomo, A. V., Cohn, J. N. 1973. Effect of cyclic 3',5'-AMP on the (Na+K)-ATPase of myocardial sarcolemma. *Cardiovasc. Res.* 7:477–81

128. Lindberg, O., Bieber, L. L., Houstek, J. 1975. Brown adipose tissue metabolism: an attempt to apply results from in vitro experiments to intact tissue. See Ref. 79. In press

129. Lindsay, R. 1974. The effect of prolonged ethanol treatment on the sodium-plus-potassium ion-stimulated adenosine triphosphatase content of cultured human and mouse cells. *Clin. Sci. Mol. Med.* 47:639–42

130. Ling, G. N., Ochsenfeld, M. M. 1973. Control of cooperative adsorption of solutes and water in living cells by hormones, drugs and metabolic products. *Ann. NY Acad. Sci.* 204:325–36

131. Luecke, R. H., South, F. E. 1972. A possible model for thermoregulation during deep hibernation. *Hibernation-Hypothermia, Perspectives and Challenges*, ed. J. P. Hannon, J. R. Willis, E. T. Pengelley, N. R. Alpert, 577–604. Amsterdam: Elsevier

132. Luft, R., Ikkos, D., Palmieri, G., Ernster, L., Afzelius, B. 1962. A case of severe hypermetabolism of nonthyroid origin with a defect in the maintenance of mitochondrial respiratory control: a correlated clinical, biochemical and morphological study. *J. Clin. Invest.* 41:1776–1804

133. Luly, P., Barnabei, O., Tria, E. 1972. Hormonal control in vitro of plasma membrane-bound (Na$^+$-K$^+$)-ATPase of rat liver. *Biochim. Biophys. Acta* 282:447–52

134. Luly, P., Verna, R. 1974. Stimulation of (Na$^+$-K$^+$)-ATPase of rat liver plasma membrane by amino acids. *Biochim. Biophys. Acta* 367:109–13

135. Mann, G. V. 1974. The influence of obesity on health. *N. Engl. J. Med.* 291:178–85

136. Matlib, A., O'Brien, P. J. 1974. Adenosine 3':5'-cyclic monophosphate stimulation of calcium efflux from mitochondria. *Biochem. Soc. Trans.* 2:997–1000

137. McLaughlin, C. W. 1973. Control of sodium, potassium and water content and utilization of oxygen in rat liver slices, studied by affecting cell membrane permeability with calcium and active transport with ouabain. *Biochim. Biophys. Acta* 323:285–96

138. Mejsnar, J., Jansky, L. 1971. Means of noradrenaline action during non-shivering thermogenesis in a single muscle. *Int. J. Biometeorol.* 15:321–24

139. Miller, D. S., Mumford, P. 1967. Gluttony. 1. An experimental study of overeating low- or high-protein diets. *Am. J. Clin. Nutr.* 20:1212–22

140. Miller, D. S., Mumford, P., Stock, M. J. 1967. Gluttony. 2. Thermogenesis in overeating man. *Am. J. Clin. Nutr.* 20:1223–29

141. Minkoff, L., Damadian, R. 1973. Caloric catastrophe. *Biophys. J.* 13:167–78

142. Mitchelson, K. R., Hird, F. J. R. 1973. Effect of pH and halothane on muscle and liver mitochondria. *Am. J. Physiol.* 225:1393–98

143. Mokhova, E. N., Zorov, D. B. 1973. The effects of cold stress on respiration of diaphragm muscle. *J. Bioenerg.* 5:119–28

144. Needham, D. M. 1971. *Machina Carnis. The Biochemistry of Muscular Contraction in its Historical Development*. Cambridge, Engl.: Cambridge Univ. Press

145. Nicholls, D. G. 1974. Hamster brown-adipose-tissue mitochondria. The control of respiration and the proton electrochemical potential gradient by possible physiological effectors of the proton conductance of the inner membrane. *Eur. J. Biochem.* 49:573–83

146. Nicholls, D. G., Cannon, B., Grav, H. J., Lindberg, O. 1974. Energy dissipation in non-shivering thermogenesis. *Dynamics of Energy-Transducing Membranes*, ed. L. Ernster, R. W. Estabrook, E. C. Slater, 529–37. Amsterdam: Elsevier

147. Nicholls, D. G., Grav, H. J., Lindberg, O. 1972. Mitochondria from hamster brown-adipose-tissue. Regulation of respiration in vitro by variations in volume of the matrix compartment. *Eur. J. Biochem.* 31:526–33

148. Owen, C. S., Wilson, D. F. 1974. Control of respiration by the mitochondrial phosphorylation potential. *Arch. Biochem. Biophys.* 161:581–91

149. Ozawa, K., Seta, K. Araki, H., Handa, H. 1967. Rapid liberation of potassium

ions from brain mitochondria. *J. Biochem. Tokyo* 62:584–90

150. Pedersen, J. I., Grav, H. J. 1972. Physiologically-induced loose coupling of brown-adipose-tissue mitochondria correlated to endogenous fatty acids and adenosine phosphates. *Eur. J. Biochem.* 25:75–83

151. Petersen, O. H. 1974. Cell membrane permeability change: An important step in hormone action. *Experientia* 30: 1105–7

152. Petersen, O. H. 1974. The effect of glucagon on the liver cell membrane potential. *J. Physiol. London* 239:647–56

153. Petersen, O. H., Pedersen, G. L. 1974. Membrane effects mediated by alpha- and beta-adrenoceptors in mouse parotid acinar cells. *J. Membr. Biol.* 16:353–62

154. Petrovic, V. M., Markovic-Giaja, L. 1973. A comparative study of the calorigenic action of noradrenaline in the rat and ground squirrel adapted to different temperatures. *Experientia* 29: 1295–96

155. Primack, M. P., Buchanan, J. L. 1974. Control of oxygen consumption in liver slices from normal and T_4-treated rats. *Endrocrinology* 96:619–20

156. Prusiner, S., Poe, M. 1968. Thermodynamic considerations of mammalian thermogenesis. *Nature* 220:235–37

157. Prusiner, S., Poe, M. 1970. Thermodynamic considerations of mammalian heat production. *Brown Adipose Tissue,* ed. O. Lindberg, 263–82. New York: Elsevier

158. Rafael, J., Wiemer, G., Hohorst, H.-J., Burckhardt, W. 1974. Mitochondria from brown adipose tissue: influence of albumin, guanine nucleotides and of substrate level phosphorylation on the internal adenine nucleotide pattern. *Z. Physiol. Chem.* 355:341–52

159. Ramasarma, R., Susheela, L. 1974. A mechanism of thermogenesis by modification of succinate dehydrogenase. *Biomembranes. Architecture, Biogenesis, Bioenergetics and Differentiation,* ed. L. Packer, 261–77. New York: Academic

160. Rasmussen, H., Goodman, D. B. P., Tenenhouse, A. 1972. The role of cyclic AMP and calcium in cell activation. *Crit. Rev. Biochem.* 1:95–148

161. Reed, N., Fain, J. N. 1968. Potassium-dependent stimulation of respiration in brown fat cells by fatty acids and lipolytic agents. *J. Biol. Chem.* 243: 6077–83

162. Reichlin, S., Bollinger, J., Nejad, I., Sullivan, P. 1973. Tissue thyroid concentration of rat and man determined by radioimmunoassay: biologic significance. *Sinai J. Med.* 40:502–10

163. Revel, J. P., Yee, A. G., Hudspeth, A. J. 1971. Gap junctions between electrotonically coupled cells in tissue culture and in brown fat. *Proc. Soc. Nat. Sci. USA* 68:2924–27

164. Schultz, S. G., Curran, P. F. 1970. Coupled transport of sodium and organic solutes. *Physiol. Rev.* 50:637–718

165. Smith, R. E., Horwitz, B. A. 1969. Brown fat and theremogenesis. *Physiol. Rev.* 49:330–425

166. Stevens, E. D. 1973. The evolution of endothermy. *J. Theor. Biol.* 38:597–611

167. Stevens, E. D., Kido, M. 1974. Active sodium transport: a source of metabolic heat during cold adaptation in mammals. *Comp. Biochem. Physiol. A* 47: 395–97

168. Stoner, H. B. 1970. Energy metabolism after injury. *J. Clin. Pathol. Suppl. R. Coll. Pathol.* 4:47–55

169. Stoner, H. B. 1971. Effects of injury on shivering thermogenesis in the rat. *J. Physiol. London* 214:599–615

170. Stoner, H. B. 1973. The role of the liver in non-shivering thermogenesis in the rat. *J. Physiol. London* 232:285–96

171. Stoner, H. B. 1974. Inhibition of thermoregulatory non-shivering thermogenesis by trauma in cold-acclimated rats. *J. Physiol. London* 238:657–70

172. Strømme, S. B., Hammel, H. T. 1967. Effects of physical training on tolerance to cold in rats. *J. Appl. Physiol.* 23:815–24

173. Stucki, J. W., Ineichen, E. A. 1974. Energy dissipation by calcium recycling and the efficiency of calcium transport in rat liver mitochondria. *Eur. J. Biochem.* 48:365–75

174. Sulakhe, P. V., Dhalla, N. S. 1973. Alteration in the activity of cardiac Na^+-K^+-stimulated ATPase in congestive heart failure. *Exp. Mol. Pathol.* 18:100–11

175. Sulakhe, P. V., Fedelsova, M., McNamara, D. B., Dhalla, N. 1971. Isolation of skeletal muscle membrane fragments. Comparison of normal and dystrophic muscle sarcolemma. *Biochem. Biophys. Res. Commun.* 42:793–800

176. Suter, E. R. 1969. The fine structure of brown adipose tissue. I. Cold induced changes in the rat. *J. Ultrastruct. Res.* 26:216–41

177. Suter, E. R. 1969. The fine structure of brown adipose tissue. III. The effect of cold exposure and its mediation in newborn rats. *Lab. Invest.* 21:259–68

178. Swanson, P. D. 1968. Effects of ouabain on acid-soluble phosphate and electrolytes of isolated cerebral tissues in presence or absence of calcium. *J. Neurochem.* 15:57–67

179. Tada, M., Kirchberger, M. A., Lorio, J. A. M., Katz, A. M. 1975 Control of cardiac sarcolemmal adenylate cyclase and sodium, potassium-activated adenosinetriphosphatase activities. *Circ. Res.* 36:8–17

180. Tata, J. R. 1964. Biological action of thyroid hormones at the cellular and molecular levels. *Actions of Hormones on Molecular Processes,* ed. G. Litwack, D. Kritchevsky, 58–131. New York: Wiley

181. Tata, J. R., Ernster, L., Lindberg, O., Arrhenius, E., Pedersen, S., Hedman, R. 1963. The action of thyroid hormones at the cell level. *Biochem. J.* 86:408–28

182. Teskey, N., Horwitz, B., Horowitz, J. 1975. Norepinephrine-induced depolarization of skeletal muscle cells. *Eur. J. Pharmacol.* 30:352–55

183. Thurman, R. G., Ley, H. C., Scholz, R. 1972. Hepatic microsomal ethanol oxidation. Hydrogen peroxide formation and the role of catalase. *Eur. J. Biochem.* 25:420–30

184. Tomita, T. 1975. Action of catecholamines on skeletal muscle. *Handb. Physiol.* Section 7, Vol. 6, 537–52

185. Tower, D. B. 1968. Ouabain and the distribution of calcium and magnesium in cerebral tissues in vitro. *Exp. Brain Res.* 6:273–83

186. Trémolières, J., Carré, L. 1961. Etudes sur les modalités d'oxydation de l'alcool chez l'homme normal et alcoolique. *Rev. Alcool.* 7:202–27

187. Trémolières, J., Martineaud, M. 1963. Les dépenses caloriques dans l'obésité. *Probl. Actuels Endocrinol. Nutr.* 7:87–128

188. Tria, E., Luly, P., Tomasi, V., Trevisiani, A. 1974. Modulation by cyclic AMP in vitro of liver plasma membrane (Na$^+$-K$^+$)-ATPase and protein kinases. *Biochim. Biophys. Acta* 343:297–306

189. Turkanis, S. A. 1969. Some properties of the denervated anterior gracilis muscle of the rat. *Brit. J. Pharmacol.* 37:414–24

190. Vallin, I. 1970. Norepinephrine response in brown adipose tissue from newborn rats. *Acta Zool.* 51:129–39

191. Van Rossum, G. D. V. 1970. On the coupling of respiration to cation transport in slices of rat liver. *Biochim. Biophys. Acta* 205:7–17

192. Van Rossum, G. D. V. 1972. The metabolic coupling of ion transport. See Ref. 131, 191–218

193. Vick, R. L., Todd, E. P., Luedke, D. W. 1972. Epinephrine induced hyperkalemia: relation to liver and skeletal muscle. *J. Pharmacol. Exp. Ther.* 181:139–46

194. Videla, L., Flattery, K. V., Sellers, E. A., Israel, Y. 1975. Ethanol metabolism and liver oxidative capacity in cold acclimation. *J. Pharmacol. Exp. Ther.* 192:575–82

195. Vybiral, S., Jansky, L. 1974. Non-shivering thermogenesis in the golden hamster. *Physiol. Bohemoslov.* 23:235–43

196. Vyskocil, F., Moravec, J., Melichar, I. 1975. Effect of noradrenaline on neuromuscular functions in a hibernator. See Ref. 91. In press

197. Waterlow, J. C. 1968. Observations on the mechanism of adaptation to low protein intakes. *Lancet* 2:1091–97

198. Whittam, R. 1961. Active cation transport as a pace-maker of respiration. *Nature* 191:603–4

199. Whittam, R., Willis, J. S. 1963. Ion movements and oxygen consumption in kidney cortex slices. *J. Physiol. London* 168:158–77

200. Williams, J. A., Matthews, E. K. 1974. Effects of ions and metabolic inhibitors on membrane potential of brown adipose tissue. *Am. J. Physiol.* 227:981–86

201. Williams, J. A., Matthews, E. K. 1974. Membrane depolarization, cyclic AMP, and glycerol release by brown adipose tissue. *Am. J. Physiol.* 227:987–92

202. Williams, J. A., Withrow, C. D., Woodbury, D. M. 1971. Effects of ouabain and diphenylhydantoin on transmembrane potentials, intracellular electrolytes, and cell pH of rat muscle and liver in vivo. *J. Physiol. London* 212:101–15

203. Williams, J. W., Tada, M., Katz, A. M., Rubin, E. 1975. Effect of ethanol and acetaldehyde on the (Na$^+$+K$^+$)-activated adenosinetriphosphatase activity of cardiac plasma membranes. *Biochem. Pharmacol.* 24:27–32

204. Williamson, J. R., Jakob, A., Scholz, R. 1971. Energy cost of gluconeogenesis in rat liver. *Metabolism* 20:13–26

205. Wilmore, D. W. 1974. Nutrition and metabolism following thermal injury. *Clin. Plast. Surg.* 1:603–19
206. Wilmore, D. W., Long, J. M., Mason, A. D., Skreen, R. W., Pruitt, B. A. 1974. Catecholamines: mediator of the hypermetabolic response to thermal injury. *Ann. Surg.* 180:653–69
207. Wilmore, D. W., Orcutt, T. W., Mason, A. D., Pruitt, B. A. 1975. Alterations in hypothalamic function following thermal injury. *J. Trauma.* In press
208. Wilson, D. F., Stubbs, M., Oshino, N., Erecinska, M. 1974. Thermodynamic relationships between the mitochondrial oxidation-reduction reactions and cellular ATP levels in ascites tumor cells and perfused rat liver. *Biochemistry* 13:5305–11

209. Winder, W. W., Baldwin, K. M., Terjung, R. L., Holloszy, J. O. 1975. Effects of thyroid hormone administration on skeletal muscle mitochondria. *Am. J. Physiol.* 220:1341–45
210. Wojtczak, L. 1974. Effect of fatty acids and acyl-CoA on the permeability of mitochondrial membranes to monovalent cations. *FEBS Lett.* 44:25–30
211. Wollenberger, A. 1947. Metabolic action of the cardiac glycosides. I. Influence on respiration of heart muscle and brain cortex. *J. Pharmacol. Exp. Ther.* 91:39–51
212. Yoshimura, K. 1973. Activation of Na-K activated ATPase in rat brain by catecholamines. *J. Biochem. Tokyo* 74:389–91

REGULATION OF PANCREATIC INSULIN AND GLUCAGON SECRETION

♦1154

John E. Gerich

Metabolic Research Unit and Department of Medicine, University of California, San Francisco, California 94143

M. Arthur Charles

Metabolic Research Unit, University of California, San Francisco, California 94143 and Letterman Army Institute of Research, Presidio of San Francisco, California 94129

Gerold M. Grodsky

Metabolic Research Unit and Department of Biochemistry and Biophysics, University of California, San Francisco, California 94143

INTRODUCTION

Homeostatic regulation of metabolic fuels involves the generally opposing actions of insulin and glucagon. As most agents simultaneously affect secretion of both hormones, this review attempts, when possible, to discuss regulation of insulin and glucagon secretion as related events.

The effects of stimulators and inhibitors of insulin and glucagon secretion have been systematically investigated in vivo and in vitro (116, 208, 244, 287, 322). The underlying molecular mechanisms are usually studied by measurement of islet metabolites, cyclic nucleotides, ions, and macromolecules, but holistic interpretation of these data is complicated by: (a) difficulties in measuring changes with time; (b) the functional significance of cellular compartments; and (c) the limited number of parameters that can be measured simultaneously. These difficulties are compounded for glucagon because normal islets contain 15–30% A cells. Although islets comparatively rich in A cells derived from animals treated with alloxan or streptozotocin have been used to study A-cell secretory biology (31, 186, 257), these cells may not be normal, as they have been chronically subjected to a diabetic environment. This problem may be minimized by maintaining such islets in tissue culture—a procedure that retains the high A-cell population and its response to

353

certain secretagogues (4, 147). The physical/chemical separation of A from B cells of normal islets would appear advantageous, but methods for such separation are not perfected. Finally, because glucagon that is immunochemically and physiochemically identical to pancreatic glucagon can also originate from A-like cells located in the gastrointestinal tract (225, 327), in vitro pancreatic studies may provide only a partial explanation of glucagon secretion patterns in vivo.

The A and B cells may represent a syncytium wherein a signal specific to one cell type causes an indirect functional response of the other. Thus occasional gap junctions between A and B cells are observed (254), which are presumed to be of sufficient size to permit transport of nucleotides, energy metabolites, and ions (although no such transport has yet been demonstrated). Furthermore, secretion of both glucagon and insulin into the interstitial fluid of the islet may directly influence subsequent A- and B-cell function. Exogenous glucagon, in high concentration, directly stimulates insulin release (121, 319), but it is unlikely that insulin release is grossly affected by changes in glucagon bathing the islet because: (a) glucagon secretion does not precede insulin release when islets are stimulated by their mutual secretagogue, arginine or amino acids (91, 157, 258); and (b) glucose, a major regulator of both cell types in vivo and in vitro, stimulates insulin release during attendant inhibition of glucagon secretion (see below). A significant physiologic effect of insulin on A-cell function appears more likely. Acute insulin deficiency in man causes hyperglucagonemia (99, 324). This, as well as the hyperglucagonemia found in animals made diabetic by alloxan, streptozotocin, or pancreatectomy, can be suppressed by insulin administration or islet transplantation, suggesting that A-cell inhibition by glucose is insulin dependent or that insulin per se inhibits glucagon secretion (28, 37a, 267). In vitro, high concentrations of insulin enhance glucose suppression of glucagon release from islets of experimentally diabetic rats; little effect occurs in normal islets where endogenous insulin is available (31, 257). These concentrations of insulin have been justified on the basis that islets represent only 1% of pancreatic tissue (145), so insulin secreted from the pancreas may reflect a greater than 100-fold higher concentration in islet interstitial fluid (227). Whether the use of such high insulin concentrations is justified is unclear, as exogenous insulin levels required to suppress glucagon in diabetic animals and man in vivo are far lower (Figure 1) (28, 324). Moreover, comparison of endogenous insulin and glucagon secretion in vitro during amino acid/glucose stimulations shows large changes in insulin secretion that do not affect glucagon release (77, 91, 258). Thus if insulin alters glucagon secretion directly, the level of insulin for maximum effect is very low and is usually exceeded, except in cases of severe insulin deficiency.

EFFECTS OF SUBSTRATES ON INSULIN AND GLUCAGON SECRETION

Considering the importance of glucagon and insulin in the regulation of carbohydrate, lipid, and amino acid metabolism, it is not surprising that these metabolic fuels, especially glucose, are prime determinants of A- and B-cell function.

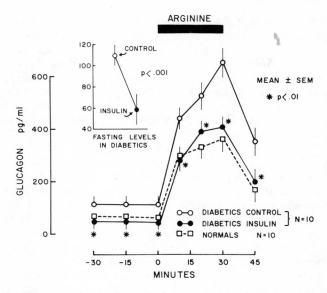

Figure 1 Normalization by insulin of fasting and arginine-induced glucagon secretion in juvenile-onset diabetic subjects. These subjects were studied on two separate occasions—once during the last hour of a 14-hr infusion of insulin (1 U/hr), which produced physiologic levels (25–35 μU/ml) of insulin, and once after withholding insulin for 24 hr. (Data from Gerich, J. E. et al 1975. Normalization of fasting hyperglucagonemia and excessive glucagon responses to intravenous arginine in human diabetes mellitus by prolonged infusion of insulin. *J. Clin. Endocrinol. Metab.* In press)

Glucose

Glucose causes multiphasic insulin release and monophasic inhibition of glucagon secretion (52, 91, 117, 124, 258). The glucose dose-response curve for both of these effects is sigmoidal. However, glucose inhibits A cells more effectively than it stimulates B cells: in vitro, the threshold, half-maximum, and maximum responses of the A cells to glucose occur at approximately 2.5, 5.0, and 10.0 mM glucose, whereas the corresponding values for stimulation of insulin secretion are 4.5, 8.0, and 25.0 mM. A rapid decrease in glucose concentration (< 3 mM) causes not only decreased insulin release but also a prompt, multiphasic glucagon release (331). Both hypoglycemia and cataglycemia stimulate glucagon secretion in vivo (1, 24, 26, 74, 86, 102, 223, 232, 252, 253, 259, 264, 328).

The comparatively high threshold for glucose-stimulated insulin secretion observed in vitro suggests that glucose alone does not regulate fasting insulin levels in vivo. However, many other agents, such as neuronal factors, glucagon (106, 249), gastrin (62, 136, 277), gut hormones, fatty acids, and arginine (16, 63, 65, 91, 197, 198, 258) elicit little insulin secretion alone but are more effective in the presence of low concentrations of glucose (5 mM). Thus an important action of nonstimulating levels of glucose in vivo is to modify insulin secretion in response to other stimuli. Although the fasting blood glucose level is in the effective range for glucagon suppression, in vitro experiments showing the low rates of basal glucagon secretion and the failure of glucopenia to cause sustained release in vitro suggest that other factors also regulate basal glucagon secretion in vivo. In view of the physiologic actions of insulin and glucagon, the reciprocal effects of glucose on A- and B-cell secretion may act to regulate the disposition of nutrients in vivo in accordance with the prevailing exogenous fuel supply and energy requirements (321).

POSSIBLE MECHANISMS OF ACTION OF GLUCOSE   The similarity of the sigmoidal dose-response curves for both phases of glucose-induced release of insulin (117, 171), insulin synthesis (200, 209), CO_2 production (7), calcium uptake (220), and islet cyclic adenosine 3',5'-monophosphate (cAMP) elevation (39, 115) indicates a single initiating signal by glucose on all of these processes. Whether this is the glucose molecule itself acting on a membrane receptor or the result of intracellular glucose metabolism is still unresolved, and all conclusions are based on indirect experiments.

The metabolic theory is supported by the following observations: (a) Metabolizable sugars including the triose, D-glyceraldehyde, stimulate insulin release, while nonmetabolizable ones are poorly active (9, 44, 119, 138). (b) Most (6, 154), although not all (229), reports indicate that glucose increases glycolytic intermediates in islets rapidly enough to account for stimulation of insulin secretion. (c) Chemical energy is required for insulin release, as dinitrophenol, oligomycin, and antimycin D are established inhibitors (44, 84, 130, 217). Adenosine triphosphate (ATP) levels spontaneously decline within five minutes in the absence of energy sources; however, glucose, glyceraldehyde, and other metabolizable carbohydrates maintain ATP (9). Maximal ATP is achieved by approximately 7–8 mM glucose, a level well below that causing maximal insulin release. Thus, although ATP is essential for insulin release, it does not appear to be the limiting factor in the glucose-sensitive signal. The maintenance of ATP levels may explain the ability of low levels of glucose to permit insulin secretion by other secretogogues (e.g. arginine and gut hormones) inactive in its absence. However, because different ATP pools exist in B cells (9, 84, 193), comparisons between insulin release and total ATP could be misleading.

Stimulation of release by glyceraldehyde has been interpreted as evidence that substrate oxidation produces reduced nucleotides that modulate insulin release (60, 139, 329). Glucose reduction to sorbitol may also contribute to glucose-stimulated insulin release (81). The significance of the pentose pathway has been previously discussed (116); however, this path is not appreciably increased by glucose (7).

The following indirect observations support the existence of a glucoreceptor: (a) The thiol blockers, iodoacetic acid and iodoacetamide, can dissociate insulin release from metabolic flux of glucose through the glycolytic pathway (228). However, these agents are nonspecific, and their action is exquisitely dose dependent. (b) Nonmetabolized amino acids elicit insulin release (42, 68). (c) Modification of plasma membranes with enzymes (182, 207) or surface sulfhydryl group-active agents (139) can either enhance or inhibit glucose-stimulated release, but whether these effects specifically involve glucose receptors or membrane-bound enzymes, ion pumps, etc (which also influence insulin release) is not clear. (d) Cytochalasin B stimulates both phases of insulin release (180) at concentrations that inhibit both glucose uptake and metabolism (199). (e) Other insulin secretogogues, such as the sulfonylureas, can act without entering the B cell (142). (f) The α-glucose anomer stimulates both phases of insulin release more effectively than the β anomer (125, 127, 247), even though islet glucose uptake and glycolysis do not favor the α anomer (155). At the moment, this seems one of the more compelling arguments favoring an α-stereospecific glucose receptor; however, understanding of anomer metabolism in islets is still incomplete and the information currently available would not exclude involvement of nonglycolytic metabolism, such as the sorbitol pathway (81). (g) Direct evidence for a glucose receptor has been suggested by experiments in which glucose, mannose, and fructose were shown to change the ultraviolet absorption spectra of a partially purified membrane fraction from islets while nonstimulating sugars were inactive (274). Purification of this fraction and characterization of the kinetics of binding may establish if the observations reflect specifically the receptor for insulin release or other glucose-sensitive sites (e.g. glucose transport).

The mechanism by which glucose suppresses glucagon secretion is unknown, but it may result in part from the possible interrelationships between the two cells and the dependence of the A cell on insulin secretion discussed above. Glucose can act directly, as A-cell suppression occurs at glucose levels too low to stimulate insulin release (24, 91, 258, 264). Glucagon release is enhanced by inhibitors of ATP synthesis and is inhibited by fatty acids and ketones, which are presumed to be acting as metabolic fuels (64). Because most secretory systems are energy requiring, it is possible that these observations may relate to ion or cyclic nucleotide metabolism in the A cell. Glucose may act through mechanisms independent of energy production, as α-glucose is more effective than the β anomer for suppressing glucagon release (125, 333a).

Amino Acids

Unlike glucose, which inhibits glucagon secretion and stimulates insulin release, amino acids stimulate release of both hormones (69, 91, 258) and in general are much more effective stimulators of glucagon than of insulin secretion. Individual amino acids differ in their ability to affect insulin and glucagon secretion, some being inactive. In the dog (282), tryptophan, leucine, aspartate, and isoleucine are the most potent stimulators of insulin release, whereas asparagine, glycine, and phenylalanine are most effective for glucagon secretion. In man, arginine, followed by lysine and leucine, are the most potent insulin stimulators (69). Arginine is the most active for glucagon secretion; alanine and glycine are less effective (239, 241, 332); and leucine, valine, and isoleucine are inactive. In vitro, in the absence of glucose, arginine and other amino acids generally stimulate multiphasic glucagon secretion and monophasic insulin release (91, 258). Addition of small amounts of glucose (4–5 mM) results in multiphasic secretion of both hormones (91, 258). Differences in secretory patterns, dose-response relationships, and islet metabolism of glucose and arginine [the latter is poorly metabolized (141)] indicate that these agents cause the release of pancreatic hormones via different actions. Nonmetabolizable analogs of leucine and arginine stimulate insulin and glucagon secretion, which suggests that amino acids may trigger islet hormone secretion via membrane receptors (67).

As physiologic concentrations of amino acids generally have little effect on insulin release in vitro but can cause abundant glucagon secretion, one might expect that, under physiologic conditions, amino acids might exert more control over the A than the B cell. However, because the presence of glucose augments insulin responses to amino acids (16, 63, 116, 157, 197, 198) while diminishing those of glucagon (91, 258), amino acids in conjunction with glucose have an important role in the differential release of both hormones. Insulin responses to a protein meal, for example, would result in hypoglycemia (and subsequent catabolism) were it not for concomitant glucagon secretion (325). This aminogenic glucagon release, by counteracting the effect of insulin on hepatic glucose output, could maintain normoglycemia and thus permit the anabolic action of insulin.

Free Fatty Acids and Ketone Bodies

Free fatty acids (FFA), β-hydroxybutyrate, and acetoacetate affect both insulin (12–14, 47, 135, 146, 206, 261, 297) and glucagon (5, 64, 96, 131, 205, 302) secretion, although their effects vary with different species and experimental conditions. In vitro, short chain fatty acids (octanoate, valerate, butyrate, and propionate), long chain fatty acids (oleate and palmitate), and ketone bodies stimulate insulin release from islets of various species in the presence of nonstimulatory concentrations of glucose (135). These agents also inhibit glucagon secretion as a function of their degree of metabolism (64). In vivo, ketone bodies stimulate insulin secretion in the dog and rat (12, 135, 206), but in other species, including man (13), inconsistent results have been found. Acute elevation of plasma FFA by infusion of oleate or a triglyceride emulsion plus heparin elevates plasma insulin levels in the dog (47, 206, 302). In man, such infusions have little effect on fasting insulin levels (14, 261, 297) but augment insulin responses to subsequent stimulation with glucose or tolbutamide (14). In similar experiments in the dog (205), duck (131), and man (5, 96), glucagon secretion is suppressed, an action which, unlike that of glucose, may not require insulin.

Acute lowering of plasma FFA levels by nicotinic acid lowers basal insulin secretion in the dog (205). In man, most but not all studies indicate that basal insulin secretion and responses to arginine are not affected, but that diminished responses to glucose, glucagon, and tolbutamide may occur (14). Transient elevation of glucagon levels after nicotinic acid administration have been observed in the dog (302) and man (5, 96). Whether these responses are the direct result of the decreased FFA levels or are responses to the associated stress is unclear.

The role of these fuels in the physiologic regulation of insulin and glucagon secretion requires further study. It has been proposed that these agents may be important during starvation to insure sufficient insulin release to prevent fatal ketoacidosis (302). Similarly, because glucagon is lipolytic and ketogenic, the inhibitory effect of these agents on glucagon secretion could act as part of a negative feedback system (96).

NEURAL INFLUENCES

Both the sympathetic and parasympathetic nervous systems may be important modulators of islet A- and B-cell function (95, 202–204, 208, 337). Nerves to the pancreas contain sympathetic fibers from the greater and middle splanchnic nerves, originating in the celiac and superior mesenteric plexuses, and parasympathetic fibers from the vagus nerve. Adrenergic and cholinergic terminals have been identified by light and electron microscopy within or, more commonly, at the periphery of islets. Although dopamine and serotonin have been demonstrated within islets (202, 337), they have not been found in nerve terminals (189, 202); accordingly, the effects of these agents are discussed in the section on hormonal influences.

Sympathetic Nervous System

The sympathetic nervous system may affect islet hormone secretion either neurally or by release of adrenomedullary catecholamines. Epinephrine, the major adrenomedullary hormone, inhibits glucose-induced insulin release (44, 172, 219) and augments glucagon secretion in vitro (158, 190) and in vivo (92, 95, 269, 271, 172). Insulin responses to glucagon, theophylline, dibutyryl-cAMP, tolbutamide, and, in some studies, amino acids are also inhibited by epinephrine (208). Norepinephrine, the adrenergic neurotransmitter, has similar effects on insulin and glucagon secretion (158, 273), whereas isoproterenol (a synthetic β-adrenergic agent) stimulates both glucagon and insulin release (95). Phentolamine, a specific α-adrenergic antagonist, reverses the inhibition of insulin secretion by epinephrine and norepinephrine (158, 269) as well as the suppression of glucagon secretion by methoxamine (95) (a relatively specific α agonist). Propranolol, a specific β-adrenergic receptor antagonist, abolishes the stimulation of insulin and glucagon secretion by isoproterenol (95). Thus both glucagon and insulin release are augmented by β- and inhibited by α-adrenergic receptor stimulation. In other tissues, epinephrine and norepinephrine stimulate both α- and β-adrenergic receptors, although norepinephrine primarily affects the former. As these catecholamines inhibit insulin and stimulate glucagon release, the B cells may have predominantly α-adrenergic receptors, whereas the A cells have a higher β-receptor population (95). In some instances, adrenergic receptor antagonists administered in vivo have, by themselves, affected fasting glucagon and insulin secretion: that is, phentolamine increases circulating insulin and glucagon levels, whereas propranolol diminishes insulin but does not affect glucagon levels, suggesting that adrenergic tone may modulate basal pancreatic hormone secretion (95, 156, 202–204, 269, 280).

Electrical stimulation of mixed pancreatic nerves containing cholinergic and adrenergic fibers enhances glucagon secretion and diminishes both basal insulin release and insulin responses to a glucose challenge in dogs pretreated with atropine (222, 270). Stimulation of splanchnic nerves increases both insulin and glucagon release (23, 167). The increase in insulin output may be due to stimulation of cholinergic fibers. Under these conditions α-adrenergic inhibition increases insulin release further, while not appreciably affecting glucagon release (167); β-adrenergic inhibition diminishes release of both hormones. These studies thus provide direct evidence for neural participation in adrenergic influence on pancreatic islet cell function.

Central nervous system modulation of pancreatic hormone secretion via the sympathetic system is also indicated, as electrical stimulation of hypothalamic areas (53), including the ventromedial nuclei (78) (the suspected hypothalamic sympathetic center), augments glucagon secretion and suppresses insulin release. Adrenalectomy reverses the latter but not the former, suggesting that, in these circumstances, glucagon release is due to direct innervation and that insulin release is inhibited by adrenomedullary catecholamines (78). Neuroglycopenia caused by 2-deoxy-D-glucose introduced into the lateral cerebral ventricle of rats causes systemic hyperglycemia and diminished insulin release. Because these effects are not modified by intraventricular infusion of phentolamine, propranolol (238), and 6-hydroxydopamine, or by systemic administration of atropine and propranolol, but are prevented by prior adrenal demedullation or intraperitoneal phentolamine, an α-adrenergic mechanism involving catecholamine release from the adrenal medulla is suggested (238). In calves treated with atropine, splanchnic nerve transection diminishes glucagon responses to neuroglycopenia induced by insulin, implying partial involvement of these nerves (24). In man, similar neuroglycopenia-induced glucagon responses are not affected by infusion of either propranolol or phentolamine (328); however, this may be due to the inability of these agents to antagonize neural stimulation. Destruction of the ventromedial hypothalamic nuclei in the rat leads to a chronic increase in circulating insulin levels, islet B-cell hypertrophy and hyperplasia, and obesity. Increased insulin levels have been observed prior to obesity, suggesting a direct hypothalamic effect rather than one secondary to hyperphagia (134, 224).

Parasympathetic Nervous System

Acetylcholine, a parasympathetic neurotransmitter, augments insulin (159, 219, 303) and glucagon (159) release in vitro. These effects appear to be muscarinic (303), as they are prevented by atropine, a cholinergic receptor antagonist (159, 219), and are augmented by eserine, a cholinesterase inhibitor (219). Methacholine increases fasting insulin levels in the dog (168) and man (163). Atropine lowers basal glucagon levels as well as glucagon responses to intravenous arginine in man (26) and diminishes responses to insulin-induced hypoglycemia in calves (24). Additionally, atropine has been reported to impair insulin responses to glucose administered orally but not to glucose given intravenously (318a).

In the dog, electrical stimulation of mixed pancreatic nerves results in transient insulin release, which is inhibited by atropine and thus is probably due to activation of parasympathetic fibers (222). Stimulation of the vagus nerve at various levels increases both insulin (54, 79, 169, 170) and glucagon (170) secretion in several species. Acute transection of the vagi decreases basal insulin release from the canine pancreas but does not affect the insulin responses to intravenous glucose (79). After chronic vagotomy, basal insulin and glucagon levels are not appreciably affected, but insulin responses to oral and intravenous glucose (133) and glucagon responses to hypoglycemia (26) have been reported to diminish.

Parasympathetic influences via the central nervous system also affect pancreatic hormone secretion. The ability to condition insulin release (335, 336) and to evoke insulin secretion by means of visual, olfactory, gustatory, and hypnotic stimuli (105, 260) is abolished by vagotomy or atropine. Electrical stimulation of the ventrolateral hypothalamic nuclei, the suspected hypothalamic parasympathetic regulating center, increases insulin levels (178), while bilateral destruction of this nucleus lowers circulating insulin levels (41). No comparable data are available for glucagon secretion, but presumably glucagon responses to hypoglycemia are mediated in part via central parasympathetic stimulation.

The role of neural mechanisms in the physiologic regulation of insulin and glucagon secretion is unclear. The autonomic nervous system may be important in islet responses to stress (22), mediated by both the sympathetic (↓insulin ↑glucagon) and parasympathetic (↑insulin ↑glucagon) systems. The parasympathetic system may coordinate insulin and glucagon responses to meals either directly or via certain gastrointestinal hormones (see below).

HORMONAL INFLUENCES

Various hormones can directly affect islet insulin and glucagon secretion, others are active only when administered in vivo and therefore presumably act indirectly (see Table 1). Some hormones possess little intrinsic activity, but modify insulin and glucagon responses to other stimuli (e.g. gastrin). In most studies, supraphysiologic concentrations of these hormones have been used, and whether these actions represent physiologic effects remains unclear.

Of the hypothalamic hormones, only somatostatin (growth hormone release-inhibiting factor) (33) has been shown to directly affect insulin and glucagon secretion in vitro (51, 93, 330). This agent inhibits the effects of all studied stimuli for both hormones and under certain conditions is a more effective inhibitor of glucagon than of insulin secretion (98). Its mode of action remains speculative (51, 98). Both radioimmunoassay and immunofluorescence indicate the presence of somatostatin-like activity within pancreatic islets (61, 201), suggesting that this agent acts as a local regulatory factor. Currently, synthetic somatostatin is being used as a research tool to evaluate the metabolic roles of insulin and glucagon (3, 88–90, 176a, 285a). In the future, a longer acting and more specific analog may find use in the treatment of insulinopenic diabetes mellitus, which is associated with excessive glucagon secretion.

Growth hormone, adrenocorticotropin (ACTH), and thyrotropin (TSH) affect islet cell function, but their major physiologic influence is probably indirect (21, 70, 208, 298, 326). Excessive insulin and glucagon secretion occur in acromegaly (107),

Table 1 Effect of various hormones on insulin and glucagon secretion[a]

Hormone	Insulin		References	Glucagon		References
Hypothalamic hormones						
somatostatin	↓	D	(51, 98)	↓	D	(98, 330)
luteinizing hormone releasing factor	0			0		
thyrotrophin-releasing factor	0			0		
Pituitary hormones						
growth hormone	↑	I	(208, 298)	↑	I	(21, 70, 107, 326)
adrenocorticotrophic hormone	↑	D I	(208, 298, 301)	↑	I	
follicle stimulating hormone	0			0		
luteotrophic hormone	0			0		
thyroid stimulating hormone	↑	D	(208)	?		
vasopressin	0			?		
oxytocin	0			?		
Thyroid hormones						
triiodothyronine	↓	I	(33a, 174a, 215,	↓	I	(277a, 298a)
thyroxine			220a, 277a,			
			298a, 302a)			
Gastrointestinal hormones						
secretin	↑	D	(62)	↓ or D		(291)
gastrin	↑	D	(62, 136, 277)	↑	D	(157)
pancreozymin	↑	D	(62, 113)	↑	D	(157)
enteroglucagon	↑	D	(292)	0		
VIP[b], GIP[c] incretin	↑	?	(30, 49, 286)	0		
Adrenal steroids						
cortisol	↑	I	(107, 262, 301,	↑	I	(221, 262, 333)
cortisone			333)			
aldosterone	?			?		
Gonadal hormones						
17 β-estradiol	0		(46, 132, 312)	?		
progesterone	↑	I	(46, 132, 165, 313)	?		
testosterone	?	I	(11)	?		
Miscellaneous						
parathyroid hormone	?			?		
calcitonin	?			?		
serotonin	↓ or ↓ D or I		(71, 189, 195, 202, 275a, 299)	?		
dopamine	↓	D	(189, 275a, 283)	↑	?	(85)
histamine	↑	I	(208)	?		
kalikrein	↑	I	(208)	?		
bradykinin	↑	I	(208)	?		
prostaglandins						
PGE$_1$	↑ D ↓ I		(162, 192, 279)	?		
PGE$_2$	↑	D	(162)	?		
PGE$_{2\alpha}$	↑	D	(162)	?		
·PGA$_1$	OD, ↓ I		(162, 285)	?		
Chorionic somatotropin	↑	I	(132, 216)	?		
Angiotensin	↓	I	(208)	?		

[a] ↓ = Decrease, ↑ = increase, 0 = no effect, ? = unknown, D = direct effect, I = indirect effect.
[b] Vasoactive intestinal peptide.
[c] Gastric inhibitory peptide.

Cushing's syndrome (333), and after administration of exogenous growth hormone (107) and glucocorticoids (221, 262, 333); conversely, diminished insulin release and normal or excessive glucagon secretion are found in hypopituitarism (326) and Addison's disease (301). Thyroid hormones have no direct effect on pancreatic islet cell function in vitro (215), but alterations in insulin and glucagon secretion can occur in experimental or spontaneous hyper- (33a, 220a, 298a) and hypothyroidism (174a, 277a, 302a).

Various gastrointestinal hormones have been implicated in explaining the observation that glucose or amino acids cause greater insulin responses when given orally than when given intravenously. Gastrin, secretin, and pancreozymin stimulate insulin release in vitro (in the presence of glucose) (116, 157); in vivo (62, 277), they may lower the threshold glucose concentration necessary for insulin release, thereby augmenting insulin responses to glucose. Gastrin is effective in vivo at near physiologic concentrations (277), but recent studies suggest that neither gastrin (136) nor pancreozymin (113) is important in augmenting insulin responses to meals. Pancreozymin and gastrin stimulate glucagon release in the dog (157) but not in man (252); variable results have been observed with secretin (252, 291). Insulin responses to meals are more likely mediated by peptides with as yet incompletely characterized effects: these include enteroglucagon (292), vasoactive intestinal peptide (286), gastric inhibitory polypeptide (30), and insulin-releasing peptide (49).

Changes in insulin and glucagon secretion occur during pregnancy (46, 55, 216, 294), the estrus cycle (11), and after the administration of oral contraceptives (312, 313). Estrogen and progesterone probably do not directly affect islets in vitro (46, 132, 216), but their long-term administration in vivo can cause increases in insulin secretion and B-cell size (46, 132, 165). No comparable data are available concerning glucagon secretion, but women respond to standard stimuli with greater release than do men (232). Progesterone administration elevates basal insulin levels and insulin responses to glucose (165, 313). In most studies, administration of physiologic amounts of estrogen (312) has not affected islet function. In one study, testosterone did not affect insulin responses after prolonged administration in the rat (11).

Glucocorticoids have no direct effect on islet cell function in vitro, but prolonged exposure to these hormones, either spontaneously [as in Cushing's syndrome (333)] or after exogenous administration (221, 262, 333), results in elevated basal and stimulated levels of insulin and glucagon. These may be due in part to an islet adjustment to peripheral antagonism induced by these hormones and also to the elevated plasma amino acid levels accompanying glucocorticoid excess.

Serotonin and dopamine occur in islets of several species (189, 202), suggesting that these amines may influence islet function. Conflicting results, which may be due to different intra- and extracellular actions of these agents (189, 202), leave their precise role unclear. Serotonin diminishes the insulin response to glucose in the golden hamster (275a), mouse (195), and rabbit (275a), but increases it or has no effect in the rat, dog (71), and man (71, 299). Serotonin antagonists (methysergide maleate) increase insulin release (275). Reserpine, which depletes catecholamine stores, reverses serotonin inhibition of insulin release, suggesting that serotonin may act indirectly by releasing catecholamines (275a). Dopamine—or the administration of L-dopa [β-(3,4-Dihydroxyphenyl)-L-alanine], which is subsequently converted to dopamine—has been reported to diminish insulin release in vitro (283) and to stimulate glucagon release in vivo (85). Whether dopamine acts by releasing catecholamines from local nerve endings, by a central nervous system action, or by a direct dopaminergic or other effect on islets is unresolved.

Prostaglandins have been reported to affect insulin release, but no data are available concerning glucagon secretion. PGE_1, PGE_2, and $PGE_{2\alpha}$ augment insulin responses to glucose in vitro in the rat (162). In vivo, inhibition (279) as well as stimulation (192) of insulin release has been observed with PGE_1 in dogs. PGA_1, while not affecting insulin release in vitro (162), diminishes insulin responses to glucose in vivo (285). Prostaglandins may affect insulin release by direct (cAMP; see below) and indirect means (release of catecholamines).

Chorionic somatotropin stimulates only transient insulin release in vitro (216, 298). Thus the augmented insulin secretion ascribed to it, observed during the third trimester of pregnancy, probably occurs via an indirect mechanism.

Various vasoactive hormones have been reported to alter insulin release (208). Angiotensin, a vasoconstrictor, diminishes release in vivo; histamine, kallikrein, and bradykinin, all vasodilators, augment insulin release in vivo. It is doubtful that they affect islet function significantly (123).

DEVELOPMENTAL AND NUTRITIONAL ASPECTS OF INSULIN AND GLUCAGON SECRETION

Pancreatic A and B cells are present early in fetal development (265), but functional maturity does not occur until after birth. Fetal islets are more responsive to amino acids and certain hormones (e.g. epinephrine and acetylcholine) than to glucose (103). Because responses to glucose are enhanced by theophylline or glucagon, the immaturity of the cAMP-adenylcyclase system rather than that of a glucose-sensing mechanism may be involved (161, 183). Plasma glucagon levels rise in the rat and human coincident with a fall in blood glucose levels at birth (102, 161, 226). Neonatal A cells are responsive to alanine and arginine (314, 334), but B cells are still refractory to glucose until the second or third day after birth (112, 309, 314). In children of diabetic mothers, insulin secretion is mature at birth, while glucagon secretion is suppressed. This may be due to hyperglycemia occurring in utero (25, 226).

The possible inductive effects of glucose on islet function (114) are pertinent to changes in insulin and glucagon secretion observed in over- and undernutrition. Basal serum insulin levels (1, 232) and insulin responses to glucose and amino acids (1, 218) are diminished after fasting, while basal glucagon levels and responses to hypoglycemia and amino acids are augmented (1, 93, 223, 232). In obesity, basal as well as stimulated insulin secretion is excessive (18, 173). Hyperinsulinism can be induced by experimental weight gain in man and reversed by weight loss, often trivial (306). Islets from obese animals are hyperplastic and hypertrophied. Dose-response studies indicate normal B-cell sensitivity to glucose in obesity (171), but an increase in the total targets of glucose action. Whether excessive insulin release results from an inductive effect of nutrients (114) or is a compensation for insulin resistance is unclear. Further, the relative importance of calories, as opposed to dietary carbohydrate, remains to be defined. Most (93, 111, 164), but not all (295, 332), reports indicate that basal glucagon levels are normal in obesity, but responses to arginine are excessive (93, 164). Observations of diminished responses to alanine (332) and normal responses to protein-containing meals (111) indicate the need for additional studies. Short-term manipulation of the relative proportion of protein and carbohydrate in isocaloric diets can alter both pancreatic A- and B-cell function (242).

KINETICS OF INSULIN AND GLUCAGON RELEASE

Secretion of insulin and glucagon is the ultimate result of a series of intracellular phenomena (116, 181, 254): synthesis of prohormone (160, 251, 263, 315a) in the endoplasmic reticulum; transport of prohormone to the Golgi apparatus (17, 191, 248, 251); formation and maturation of granules with attendant conversion of prohormone to hormone; and movement or transformation of secretory vesicles to a labile form available for release.

Glucose affects several of the B-cell processes. It increases proinsulin synthesis, both at transcriptional and translational levels (160, 263), and increases Golgi activity and granule formation in this organelle (17, 191). Emiocytosis appears established as the mechanism for insulin release (181, 254); however, in tolbutamide-depleted islets, a higher percentage of islet insulin is found in cytosol, suggesting that nongranular (soluble? microvesicular?) release should still be considered (48). Glucose stimulates secretion of stored hormone independently of its action on insulinogenesis (120, 266). In this latter regard, it appears to have a dual effect, causing instantaneous release and stimulating provision to, or potentiation of, the release system, thereby making more insulin available for secretion (35, 117, 124, 272).

The kinetics of insulin release have been recently reviewed in detail (118). In brief, the pancreas, when stimulated by a constant concentration of glucose or leucine (15, 185), secretes insulin multiphasically (Figure 2) (117). The two phases of insulin release reflect different, although probably related, phenomena: The second phase is inhibited by puromycin (52), dinitrophenol, oligomycin (130), diazoxide (196, 310), and dilantin (196) at selected concentrations that do not affect first-phase release. The first phase is selectively stimulated by sulfonylureas (52, 122, 310), potassium (109, 143), and secretin (194). Increased synthesis can be detected at the translational level within 15 min (263), but little de novo synthesized insulin is released from the pancreas before two hours (151, 237, 289, 290, 311, 318) and therefore does not account for second-phase release, although it could progressively contribute with extended glucose stimulation. The two phases may thus reflect different targets for glucose action. However, a single primary action of glucose on both is indicated, as the dose-response curve for both first- and second-phase insulin release is the same sigmoidal function of glucose concentration (117).

Characteristic kinetic responses of insulin secretion to glucose are summarized as follows: (a) Multiphasic release of a similar qualitative nature occurs at all rapid-

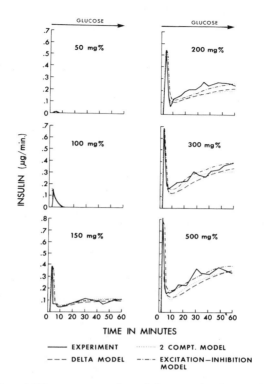

Figure 2 Effect of different concentrations of glucose on insulin secretion from the perfused pancreas of the rat. [Experimental data from (117); current development of models in collaboration with M. O'Connor and H. Landahl.]

step stimulations with glucose (Figure 2) (117). (*b*) If glucose (or arginine) is suddenly lowered to a less effective stimulatory concentration, a short refractory period or negative spike occurs (122, 197). (*c*) Prolonged glucose stimulation (one hour) augments insulin responses to a subsequent identical stimulation (35, 124, 272). (*d*) Brief stimulation by glucose, sufficient to elicit first-phase release, often causes a temporary refractory period (128, 310). (*e*) Glucose administered as a series of continuous, increasing steps ("staircase") produces a spike of insulin release at each step. By subtracting the slowly rising second phase and adding the areas under each spike, a dose-response curve for glucose is generated that is similar to the one derived from single-step experiments (117, 171). (*f*) If glucose is presented as a linear ascending ramp function, the first phase becomes less discernible with decreasing slope (117, 129). Both phases, however, may still contribute to the overall secretion pattern, although the overlap of the two may preclude their distinction. (*g*) The time required for first-phase release is finite (50), varies with the stimulating agent (comparatively slow for glucose: 1–3 min), and is decreased by prior infusion of a subthreshold concentration of glucose (184). (*h*) Certain combinations of non-glucose stimulators are both stimulatory and inhibitory, often producing a spike of insulin release (or off-response) after they are terminated (184). (*i*) Under special stimulatory circumstances, oscillations of insulin secretion occur, possibly due to microfilament activation or to periodicity of individual islets (20, 83, 125).

Conceptual Models

Originally multiphasic responses were ascribed to *stimulator-induced feedback inhibition* (122), wherein first-phase insulin secretion resulted from the relative levels of an exciter and inhibitor. The exciter was assumed to respond more quickly to new glucose concentrations than the inhibitor. Thus any step stimulation caused quick release followed by increased inhibition, a combination producing the insulin spike (Figure 2). Negative spikes and short-term refractory periods occur when the stimulator is rapidly decreased because of the temporarily high residual inhibitor. Second-phase insulin release can be controlled by a potentiation factor, which causes gradually increased islet sensitivity to continued glucose and could reflect membrane activation, or provision of additional insulin to the secretory system. Biologic parallels of this model are almost unlimited, as metabolic feedbacks by nucleotides, metabolic products, etc are well established. That the feedback inhibitor is secreted insulin is not supported by insulin perfusion studies (126). A similar schema for pancreatic function has been proposed in a whole-body model (33b).

Insulin may be stored in *compartments* or *pools,* which differ in lability to stimulating agents (117, 124, 196, 272). Glucose could affect both release of insulin from a small labile compartment and the provision of additional insulin to the secretory system (Figure 2). This provisional action could account for second-phase insulin release and the hypersensitivity after prolonged glucose. Because this model did not replicate spikes of insulin release at each concentration of glucose, a threshold or sensitivity distribution characteristic (117) was proposed whereby labile insulin (or a metabolic signal controlling insulin release) is not stored homogeneously but rather as packets with a Gaussian distribution of thresholds to glucose that respond in all-or-nothing fashion when their glucose threshold levels are exceeded. By incorporating a partial defect in final release, this model simulated the "delayed release" and subsequent hyperinsulinemia found in some forms of human diabetes (117). Compartmentalization of stored insulin is indicated by: (*a*) alignment of granules in trains associated with, or independent of, microtubules (179, 296); (*b*) association of granules with the microtubular-microfilamentous system (210); (*c*) variable degrees of bienesis among granules (80); (*d*) demonstration by cinematography of differential granular mobility (166); and (*e*) pulse-chase studies showing that the specific activity of secreted [^{3}H] insulin differs from the average specific activity of the stored hormone (151, 237, 289, 290, 311, 318). In these studies, channeling was indicated and mixing of newly formed insulin with total stored material was extremely slow (290). The observation that an increased number of B cells initiates action-potential discharges with increasing glucose concentrations suggested that threshold sensitivity characteristics could be among B cells rather than within a single cell (58).

Insulin release could result from a signal generated by the difference in concentration of a signal across a biologic barrier, the second phase of release being controlled by the same potentiating factor as for the other models. On stimulation, the differential (or delta) is positive, causing rapid secretion; as equilibrium occurs (within minutes), delta approaches zero and first-phase release is terminated (Figure 2). A sudden reduction in stimulation would produce a negative delta, accounting for negative spikes. This model may reflect an ion-membrane-electrical event known to be caused by secretogogues in islets (58, 256).

Each of these models can simulate most of the complicated release patterns observed when glucose is presented to the pancreas in a variety of ways, and some are being utilized in the development of artificial pancreases (75).

Multiphasic pancreatic hormone release was initially recognized as a forced response to deliberately nonphysiologic stimulations, important primarily to detect underlying mechanisms or to test for aberrations in clinical states. The recent demonstration that multiphasic release, particularly the fast response, may be important physiologically for anticipating glucose changes and conserving endogenous insulin requirements indicates that this phenomenon may be a vital function in total body homeostasis (2, 40).

Diphasic release of glucagon, similar in qualitative characteristics to that of insulin, can be produced by islet stimulation with arginine or amino acids or hypoglycemia (91, 157, 258, 331), suggesting that glucagon secretion may involve phenomena similar to those postulated for insulin release.

MOLECULAR INTERRELATIONSHIPS OF HORMONE SECRETION (Figure 3)

Cyclic nucleotides and calcium have been implicated in the macromolecular events associated with insulin and glucagon secretion (236, 317). The following discussion attempts to summarize critically the technical and conceptual aspects of these interrelationships.

Cyclic Nucleotides

Studies in vitro relating cyclic nucleotides to insulin and glucagon secretion have primarily been performed using isolated islets and islet homogenates. Islet perifusion appears more advantageous than static incubation, as simultaneous evaluation of dynamic hormone secretion and islet biochemical intermediates and regulators can be performed (37, 39, 43, 137, 153, 341). Although many cell types are present in most mammalian islets (e.g. A cells, D cells, fibroblasts, endothelial cells, and various parts of neurons), B cells comprise 70–85% of the cell population (152). Thus analyses of adenylate cyclase, phosphodiesterase, and islet cAMP levels presumably reflect B-cell changes and can be correlated with insulin secretion. Islets from animals treated with streptozotocin have been used for similar analyses of glucagon secretion, as A cells are the predominant cell type (147).

Measurements of islet cyclic nucleotides require careful controls because: (a) baseline levels can vary over a period of months in islets (39) as well as in other tissues (101); (b) the protein binding assay is sensitive to small changes in salt

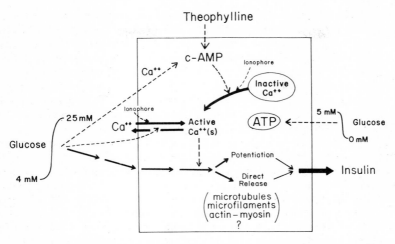

Figure 3   Theoretical schema showing interrelationships between nucleotides, Ca²⁺, and glucose as they affect insulin release. "Active Ca²⁺" is generally assumed to be cytosolic but in fact may represent different compartments of Ca²⁺ varying in their action on the secretion process.

concentration (100); (*c*) assays are not completely specific and additional controls confirming the identity of the measured cyclic nucleotides are required (37, 39, 100, 150); and (*d*) errors in cyclic guanosine 3',5'-monophosphate (cGMP) can result from the nonenzymatic conversion of guanosine triphosphate (GTP) to cGMP during the assay procedure (175). Effects of added cyclic nucleotides must also be interpreted cautiously because, at high concentrations (millimolar), cyclic nucleotides can have effects that may not reflect their physiologic action (104).

Exogenous cAMP stimulates insulin and glucagon secretion, whereas other nucleotides are relatively inactive (72, 161, 214, 316; G. Weir, personal communication). Both endogenous cAMP and cGMP are associated with positive modulation of insulin and glucagon secretion, even though opposing effects of these nucleotides have been emphasized in other systems (104). Both adenylate cyclase (10, 56, 108, 149, 177) and guanylate cyclase (150) have been found in islet homogenates. Hormone surface receptors occur in islets and appear related to cyclic nucleotide control. Receptors for glucagon, insulin, and various gastrointestinal peptides have been reported (56, 108, 149, 177). Binding of [¹²⁵I] glucagon to its islet receptor enhances membrane adenylate cyclase activity and has high affinity, specificity, reversibility, and a rapid association rate constant (108). Half-maximal activation of adenylate cyclase by glucagon is similar to that for [¹²⁵I] glucagon binding (nanomolar). Pharmacologic levels of insulin, presumably acting on an insulin receptor, decrease activity of islet adenylate cyclase (177) and cAMP content (341). Amine hormone and neurotransmitter receptors also appear present in islets, as α-adrenergic stimulation is associated with decreased islet adenylate cyclase activity, cAMP levels, and cAMP-dependent protein kinase activity as well as decreased insulin secretion (10,

149, 177, 234, 235, 320). β-Adrenergic stimulation appears to enhance islet adenylate cyclase and insulin secretion (10, 177). In islet preparations made deficient in B cells by streptozotocin, epinephrine increases adenylate cyclase activity and glucagon secretion (presumably a β-adrenergic effect) (147). Cholinergic receptors [muscarinic (303)] also appear present in B cells, as acetylcholine stimulates islet guanylate cyclase activity and insulin secretion (150). Prostaglandins also interact with the islet cyclic nucleotide regulatory molecules (162, 177). The above observations strongly implicate peptide hormones and amines as modulators of insulin and glucagon secretion through mechanisms involving cyclic nucleotides.

Agents that inhibit islet phosphodiesterase activity [e.g. theophylline, isomethylbutylxanthine (IMBX), and tolbutamide] elevate islet cAMP levels and insulin secretion (8, 27, 39, 43, 76, 115, 137, 234, 288, 320). The action of tolbutamide is more complex, as it may also stimulate adenylate cyclase (177). In islets deficient in B cells, theophylline also increases islet cAMP-dependent protein kinase activity and glucagon secretion (147). Imidazole, an islet phosphodiesterase stimulator (288), is associated with decreased glucose-induced insulin secretion (213). Although indirect experiments suggested that arginine caused insulin release via cAMP (66), direct islet cyclic nucleotide measurements indicate no change of cAMP or cGMP (M. A. Charles, J. Lawecki, A. Steiner, G. M. Grodsky, 1975. Adenosine 3',5'-monophosphate in pancreatic islets: Tolbutamide- and arginine-induced insulin release. Unpublished). Thus positive modulation of secretion may occur through mechanisms independent of cyclic nucleotides.

Most actions of cyclic nucleotides appear to be mediated by protein kinases. Islet homogenates contain cAMP- and cGMP-dependent protein kinases. The former is stimulated by glucagon, theophylline, and tolbutamide, inhibited by epinephrine, and unaffected by arginine (235); the latter kinase is stimulated by acetylcholine (150). In B-cell-deficient islets, epinephrine, theophylline, and dibutyryl-cAMP all enhance cAMP-dependent protein kinase activity and glucagon secretion (147).

Initially glucose was not thought to regulate cyclic nucleotides directly, as it did not alter adenylate cyclase, phosphodiesterase, islet cAMP levels, or cAMP-dependent protein kinase (8, 27, 56, 149, 177, 233–235, 288, 320). Several more recent studies (37, 39, 115, 137, 300, 339–341), but not all (43), indicate that glucose does elevate total islet cAMP levels. These studies indicate that glucose-induced cAMP elevation may be causally related to insulin secretion because (a) cAMP elevation occurs within seconds of stimulation, parallel with secretion (39, 115, 137, 339); (b) after the glucose stimulus is removed, both cAMP and secretion return to control with similar kinetics (115, 339); (c) dose-response curves for cAMP and insulin secretion are identical throughout the physiologic range of glucose concentrations (39, 115); (d) alloxan concomitantly inhibits glucose-induced cAMP elevation and insulin secretion (340); and (e) the α anomer of glucose enhances both cAMP elevation and secretion, whereas the β anomer is less effective for both events (115a).

The mechanism of glucose-induced acute elevation of islet cAMP is unclear. It is not due to the alteration of cAMP efflux from B cells (115) or to changes in adenylate cyclase and phosphodiesterase activities. That a glucose metabolite may enhance islet cAMP levels is supported by evidence that D-glyceraldehyde increases islet cAMP levels and insulin secretion even during alloxan-inhibited glucose stimulation (137, 340).

The relevance of cAMP to glucose-induced insulin secretion has been studied in detail. Theophylline, IMBX, and tolbutamide, when added alone or with low levels of glucose ($<$ 5 mM, a concentration approaching the threshold for glucose-induced cAMP elevation and insulin secretion), elevate islet cAMP much more than does maximal glucose, yet only transient or minimal insulin secretion ensues (37, 39, 115, 137). At levels of glucose greater than 5 mM, the same agents augment glucose-induced secretion, yet the elevated cAMP levels are only minimally increased compared with the levels observed with the phosphodiesterase inhibitor alone. Thus cAMP may not be a direct determinant of secretion but, rather, a positive modulator acting on a mechanism that directly mediates secretion. Glucose, by elevating cAMP may create a positive feed-forward modulation on its own mechanism of action that may be independent of cAMP (Figure 3) (39).

Cyclic Nucleotides and Calcium

The molecular details of cyclic nucleotide modulation of insulin and glucagon secretion are unknown. However, a cAMP/calcium interaction for insulin secretion similar to other secretory and nonsecretory systems has been suggested (29, 39, 174, 276, 317, 341). Based on calcium dynamics in islets, a hypothesis was proposed that alterations of intracellular calcium regulate insulin release. Consistent with this notion, glucose enhances cellular calcium influx and inhibits efflux (140, 211, 220), and cAMP augments secretion by enhancing mobilization of stored intracellular calcium (Figure 3) (29). Data from studies of isotopic calcium efflux are difficult to interpret with respect to shifts occurring in intracellular calcium compartments, as steady-state conditions were not defined and more than one compartment is probably involved. Nevertheless, other evidence combining pyroantimonate-fixed islets and X-ray microprobe analysis suggests that glucose indeed induces similar intracellular calcium shifts (144, 296).

The secretory role of extracellular calcium appears more complex than originally proposed. Thus although glucose-induced cAMP elevation and insulin secretion in islets are both dependent on near physiologic levels of extracellular calcium (39, 341), the action of theophylline is dependent upon extracellular calcium only for insulin secretion and not for cAMP elevation (39). These observations were critical for the viability of the above-mentioned hypothesis, as theophylline stimulates cellular calcium efflux at low extracellular calcium concentrations and it was not clear whether islet cAMP levels would be appropriately elevated. Further, the observed difference in calcium dependence suggested that different mechanisms exist for the elevation of cAMP induced by glucose and theophylline. Extracellular calcium appears to be involved in at least two sites of glucose-stimulated insulin secretion, one associated with the generation of cAMP by glucose and another regulating some process apparently distal to cAMP action (Figure 3). Investigations using perifused islets indicate that extracellular calcium (in the presence of theophylline and glucose) can regulate the kinetics of secretion independently of islet cAMP levels and that first-phase insulin secretion can occur in the virtual absence of bulk-phase (perifusion medium) extracellular calcium (39).

Studies using ionophores (molecules that either act as membrane carriers or create pores for ion transport regulated by electrochemical gradients) support the hypothesis that intracellularly active calcium elicits insulin secretion (38, 39, 45, 174, 338). A23187, a specific divalent cation carrier ionophore, promptly elicits secretion at physiologic levels of extracellular calcium in the absence of other insulin secretogogues (39, 174). The ionophore also induces insulin secretion at extracellular calcium concentrations of 0.05 mM (medium containing no extracellular calcium or magnesium) or at nanomolar levels ($^+$EGTA), suggesting that the ionophore also functions in intracellular membranes of organelles that store calcium (39). Secretion associated with A23187 and low extracellular calcium is not accompanied by an increase of islet cAMP or a change in subsequent responses to glucose once the ionophore is removed (39, 174). Transmission electron microscopy of islets that respond promptly to calcium after the addition of solubilized A23187 reveals no detectable destruction of microfilaments, microtubules, or secretory vesicle, mito-chondrial or plasma membranes (39). A23187 is also a carrier for magnesium; thus one must consider this cation's concentration before assuming that observed changes are due to calcium. Magnesium, at physiologic levels, also induces insulin secretion from perifused islets in the presence of the ionophore without extracellular calcium (39), but competes with calcium and inhibits glucose-induced secretion in the absence of the ionophore (19). This implies that the insulin secretory mechanism is sensitive to either divalent cation, but that calcium specificity under physiologic conditions may result from natural calcium ionophores in the membranes. These results are also consistent with neutralization of secretory vesicle surface charge being involved with exocytosis (57). Gramicidin, a sodium ionophore, induces insulin secretion in the presence of extracellular sodium (45). Whether this is due to direct effects of sodium or to the effects of sodium transport altering intracellular calcium levels is unclear. In summary, as shown in Figure 3, glucose and other agents may enhance intracellular calcium in an active compartment by more than one mechanism, and calcium may act as a direct regulator of secretion. Although fewer details are available for glucagon secretion, the positive modulation by cAMP and a probable (87), though complex (341a), requirement for calcium during stimulation indicate that similar underlying processes may be involved.

Macromolecular Nature of Islet Secretion

Dissection and reconstitution of the sarcolemmal and sarcoplasmic reticulum membranes, mitochondria, troponin, tropomyosin, actin, and myosin and their interactions with cAMP and calcium have elegantly clarified the molecular details of muscle contraction and its regulation (245). Similar dissection and reconstitution of islet macromolecular processes will enhance understanding of the molecular details of islet hormone secretion.

Several macromolecules may be involved in the secretory process. Microtubules have been implicated because: (a) they are observed in B cells by electron microscopy (179); (b) insulin secretion is inhibited by the alkaloid drugs colchicine and vincristine, which are stated to specifically bind tubulin (181); (c) microtubule fractions (brain) are phosphorylated by cAMP-dependent protein kinases (110, 307); and (*d*) microtubule activation (293) and polymerization (304) are affected by calcium. None of these arguments, however, clearly establishes the role of the microtubules in insulin secretion. First, in cell processes where microtubules have an unambiguous role [e.g. ciliary movement (293), cytoplasmic transport (284), or axoplasmic flow (308)], the microtubules have a distinct superstructure that is not consistently observed in B cells. Second, the alkaloid drugs are not specific and, in fact, vincristine at concentrations near that which inhibits insulin secretion also inhibits the actin activation of myosin ATPase (246). Third, phosphorylation of microtubules is difficult to interpret, as many proteins are substrates for cAMP-dependent protein kinases and phosphorylation of microtubules has not yet been associated with any biologic event. A more direct approach to microtubular involvement has been the measurement of islet tubulin by techniques that distinguish free from more highly polymerized tubulin thought to represent microtubules (268). These studies suggest that about 30% of total islet tubulin is in the polymerized form. Islets from fasted rats, which secrete less insulin and generate less cAMP (300), have a 50% decrease in polymerized tubulin when compared with controls, whereas islets from glucose-fed rats have levels 50% higher. It also appears that glucose acutely influences the level of polymerized tubulin in vitro.

Studies with cytochalasin B have implicated microfilaments with the B-cell secretory process (180, 212, 250). This agent alters islet microfilament structure and stimulates insulin release at concentrations that inhibit glucose uptake (231).

Because cytochalasin B has been shown to interact with the muscle contractile proteins, actin and myosin (315), studies are being conducted to assess the role of contractile proteins that may or may not be linked to microfilaments. Histochemical evidence suggests the presence of actin in cultured B-cell monolayers (82). Polyacrylamide gel electrophoresis of preparations from rat and fish islets and a human B-cell tumor also suggest the presence of actin as well as myosin with ATPase activity (36, 255). These observations do not, however, establish that contractile proteins are implicated with secretion. From theoretical considerations of secretory vesicle movement and cytoplasmic viscosity, it may be that microtubules and contractile proteins are unnecessary for the secretory process (230).

Studies of islet fractions rich in secretory vesicles indicated that these vesicles in themselves are insensitive to various insulin-release stimulators (148). Recently, freeze-fracture electron microscopy has emphasized exocytosis as a major mechanism of secretion, which implicates an interaction between plasma membrane and secretory vesicles (254). When secretory vesicle fractions are combined with B-cell plasma membrane fractions, insulin release occurs (188). This phenomenon appears to be B-cell, plasma membrane specific, as liver and pituitary membrane fractions do not enhance secretory vesicle release of insulin.

INSULIN AND GLUCAGON SECRETION IN DIABETES

Human diabetes mellitus exists as a spectrum ranging in severity from complete absence of insulin (ketosis-prone diabetes) to subtle abnormalities of insulin secretion with mild disturbances in glucose tolerance. Furthermore, rather than being a single disease entity, diabetes is probably a syndrome resulting from several possible environmental as well as genetic causes. In these conditions, abnormalities of glucagon secretion may be as important as those of insulin release.

Insulin Secretion

Insulin secretion is deficient in diabetes mellitus (34, 73, 176, 278, 305). However, many diabetics with impaired insulin responses to maximal stimulatory glucose challenges can still respond to other insulin secretogogues [tolbutamide, arginine, isoproterenol (59, 281)], suggesting that there may be a functional defect of the B cell due to hyporesponsiveness specific to glucose. Such a defect could explain diminished insulin secretion to stimuli whose responses depend on the presence of glucose (e.g. sulfonylureas, certain amino acids, fatty acids, and gastrointestinal hormones). Functional defects at various points within the sequence following B-cell recognition of a stimulus, such as abnormalities in the adenylcyclase-cAMP-calcium-microtubular system, might also underlie different forms of diabetes.

Glucagon Secretion

There is fasting hyperglucagonemia, either absolute ($>$ 200 pg/ml) or relative, in both juvenile-onset and adult-onset diabetes (32, 99, 323, 324). Higher levels are found in poorly controlled diabetes and in diabetic ketoacidosis (243). Studies using somatostatin, a hypothalamic peptide that inhibits glucagon secretion, indicate that this hyperglucagonemia contributes substantially to both fasting hyperglycemia (88) and excessive glucose responses after meals (97). Other abnormalities of pancreatic A-cell function found in diabetes include poor suppression following oral and intravenous glucose (323) or carbohydrate meals (240) and excessive responses to amino acids (94) and protein-containing meals (97). Hyperglucagonemia results shortly after acute insulin withdrawal from insulin-requiring human diabetics (99) and in animals made insulin deficient. This and excessive glucagon responses to arginine are reversed by reinfusion of insulin (Figure 1), but not as readily (324) as in experimentally diabetic animals (28). Whether diabetic A-cell abnormalities result solely from insulin lack is unclear. Hyperglucagonemia in the adult-onset human diabetic (323) and the db, db mouse (187) occurs with normal or elevated insulin levels. Impaired glucagon suppression during glucose perfusion of the pancreas of genetically diabetic, nonobese Chinese hamsters does not correlate with the concomitant decreased insulin release or pancreatic content of the two hormones (76, 77). With arginine alone as stimulant, hypernormal glucagon secretion was observed in the diabetic hamster pancreas without an attendant change in insulin release (77). Furthermore, suppression of glucagon by hyperglycemia may not require insulin (257). It has been suggested that human diabetes may be due to abnormal A- and B-cell sensitivity to glucose. This concept is supported by the fact that diabetic A cells fail to respond to hypoglycemia (94) as well as hyperglycemia. Recent studies using C-peptide to measure endogenous insulin in insulin-treated patients have indicated a correlation between the inability of the diabetic A cell to respond to decrements in glucose levels with the impaired ability of the diabetic B cell to respond to increments in glucose levels (278).

Literature Cited

1. Aguilar-Parada, E., Eisentraut, A. M., Unger, R. H. 1969. Effects of starvation on plasma pancreatic glucagon in normal man. *Diabetes* 18:717–23
2. Albisser, A. M. et al 1974. An artificial endocrine pancreas. *Diabetes* 23:389–96
3. Alford, F. et al 1974. Glucagon control of fasting glucose in man. *Lancet* 2:974–76
4. Andersson, A. et al 1973. Tissue culture of A_2 cell-rich pancreatic islets isolated from guinea pigs. *J. Cell Biol.* 57:241–47
5. Andrews, S. S., Lopez,-S., A., Blackard, W. G. 1975. Effect of lipids on glucagon secretion in man. *Metabolism* 24:35–44
6. Ashcroft, S. J. H., Capito, K., Hedeskov, C. J. 1973. Time course studies of glucose-induced changes in glucose-6-phosphate and fructose-1,6-diphosphate content of mouse and rat pancreatic islets. *Diabetologia* 9:299–302
7. Ashcroft, S. J. H., Randle, P. J. 1968. Glucose metabolism and insulin release by pancreatic islets. *Lancet* 1:278–79
8. Ashcroft, S. J. H., Randle, P. J., Täljedal, I. -B. 1972. Cyclic nucleotide phosphodiesterase activity in normal mouse pancreatic islets. *FEBS Lett.* 20:263–66
9. Ashcroft, S. J. H., Weerasinghe, L. C. C., Randle, P. J. 1973. Interrelationship of islet metabolism, adenosine triphosphate content and insulin release. *Biochem. J.* 132:223–31
10. Atkins, T., Matty, A. J. 1971. Adenyl cyclase and phosphodiesterase activity in the isolated islets of Langerhans of obese mice and their lean litter mates: The effect of glucose, adrenaline and drugs on adenyl cyclase activity. *J. Endocrinol.* 51:67–78
11. Bailey, C. J., Matty, A. J. 1972. Glucose tolerance and plasma insulin of the rat in relation to the oestrus cycle and sex hormones. *Horm. Metab. Res.* 4:266–70
12. Balasse, E., Couturier, E., Franckson, J. 1967. Influence of sodium beta-hydroxybutyrate on glucose and free fatty acid metabolism in normal dogs. *Diabetologia* 3:488–93
13. Balasse, E., Ooms, H. 1968. Changes in the concentration of glucose, free fatty acids, insulin and ketone bodies in the blood during sodium beta-hydroxybutyrate infusions in man. *Diabetologia* 4:133–35
14. Balasse, E. O., Ooms, H. A. 1973. Role of plasma free fatty acids in the control of insulin secretion in man. *Diabetologia* 9:145–51
15. Basabe, J. C., Farina, J., Chieri, R. A. 1975. Pancreatic beta cell glucose metabolism and glibenclamide-induced insulin release. *Horm. Metab. Res.* 7:10–15
16. Basabe, J. J., Lopez, N., Victoria, J., Wolff, F. 1971. Insulin secretion in the perfused rat pancreas. I. Effect of tolbutamide, leucine, arginine, their interaction with diazoxide and relation to glucose. *Diabetes* 20:449–56
17. Batts, A. 1959. Use of the golgi apparatus as an indicator of the level of activity of the cells of the islets of Langerhans. *Ann. NY Acad. Sci.* 82:302–18
18. Benedetti, A., Simpson, R. G., Grodsky, G. M., Karam, J. H., Forsham, P. H. 1967. Exaggerated insulin responses to glucagon in simple obesity. *Diabetes* 16:666–69
19. Bennett, L. L., Curry, D. L., Grodsky, G. M. 1969. Calcium-magnesium antagonism in insulin secretion by the perfused rat pancreas. *Endocrinology* 85:594–96
20. Bessman, S. P., Beigelman, P. M., Thomas, L. J. Jr. 1973. The periodicity of insulin secretion by islets of Langerhans shown by using a new apparatus. *Biochem. Med.* 7:97–102
21. Blackard, W. G., Andrews, S. S., Lazarus, E. J. 1973. Effect of growth hormone deficiency on glucagon secretion. *Proc. Soc. Exp. Biol. Med.* 143:1042–44
22. Bloom, S. R. 1973. Glucagon, a stress hormone. *Postgrad. Med. J.* 49 (Suppl.):607–11
23. Bloom, S. R., Edwards, A. V., Vaughan, N. J. A. 1973. The role of the sympathetic innervation in the control of plasma glucagon concentration in the calf. *J. Physiol. London* 233:457–66
24. Bloom, S. R., Edwards, A. V., Vaughan, N. J. A. 1973. The role of autonomic innervation in the control of glucagon release during hypoglycemia in the calf. *J. Physiol. London* 236:611–23
25. Bloom, S. R., Johnston, D. I. 1972. Failure of glucagon release in infants of diabetic mothers. *Br. Med. J.* 4:453–54
26. Bloom, S. R., Vaughan, N. J. A., Russell, R. C. G. 1974. Vagal control of glucagon release in man. *Lancet* 2:546–49

27. Bowen, V., Lazarus, N. R. 1973. Glucose-mediated insulin release: 3',5' cAMP phosphodiesterase. *Diabetes* 22:738–43

28. Braaten, J. T., Faloona, G. R., Unger, R. H. 1974. The effect of insulin on the alpha-cell response to hyperglycemia in long-standing alloxan diabetes. *J. Clin. Invest.* 53:1017–21

29. Brisson, G. R., Malaisse-Lagae, F., Malaisse, W. J. 1972. The stimulus-secretion coupling of glucose-induced insulin release. *J. Clin. Invest.* 51:232–41

30. Brown, J. 1974. Gastric inhibitory polypeptide (GIP). *Gastroenterology* 67:733–34

31. Buchanan, K. D., Mawhinney, W. A. A. 1973. Glucagon release from isolated pancreas in streptozotocin-treated rats. *Diabetes* 22:797–800

32. Buchanan, K. D., McCarroll, A. M. 1972. Abnormalities of glucagon metabolism in untreated diabetes mellitus. *Lancet* 2:1394–95

33. Burgus, R., Ling, N., Butcher, M., Guillemin, R. 1973. Primary structure of somatostatin, a hypothalamic peptide that inhibits secretion of pituitary growth hormone. *Proc. Nat. Acad. Sci. USA* 70:684–88

33a. Cavagnini, F. et al 1974. Impairment of growth hormone and insulin secretion in hyperthyroidism. *Eur. J. Clin. Invest.* 4:71–77

33b. Cerasi, E., Fick, G., Rudemo, M. 1974. A mathematical model for the glucose induced insulin release in man. *Eur. J. Clin. Invest.* 4:267–78

34. Cerasi, E., Luft, R. 1967. "What is inherited—what is added" hypothesis for the pathogenesis of diabetes mellitus. *Diabetes* 16:615–27

35. Cerasi, E., Luft, R., Efendic, S. 1972. Decreased sensitivity of the pancreatic beta cells to glucose in prediabetic and diabetic subjects. A glucose dose-response study. *Diabetes* 21:224–34

36. Charles, M. A., Clarke, M. 1975. Insulin secretion, calcium and B-cell contractile proteins. *Prog. Ann. Meet. Endocr. Soc., NY, 57th. June 18–20, 1975.* p. 90

37. Charles, M. A., Fanska, R., Schmid, F. G., Forsham, P. H., Grodsky, G. M. 1973. Adenosine 3',5'-monophosphate in pancreatic islets: Glucose-induced insulin release. *Science* 179:569–71

37a. Charles, A., Imagawa, W., Grodsky, G. 1975. In vitro insulin secretion from the isolated perfused liver containing islet isografts. *Diabetes* 24 (Suppl. 2):419 (Abstr.)

38. Charles, M. A., Lawecki, J., Manning, M., Grodsky, G. M. 1974. Cyclic AMP and insulin secretion: Sites and mechanisms of calcium control. *Clin. Res.* 22:128A (Abstr.)

39. Charles, M. A., Lawecki, J., Pictet, R., Grodsky, G. M. 1975. Insulin secretion: Interrelationships of glucose, cyclic adenosine 3',5'-monophosphate, and calcium. *J. Biol. Chem.* 250:6134–40

40. Cherrington, A. D., Kawamori, R., Pek, S., Vranic, M. 1974. Arginine infusion in dogs. Model for the roles of insulin and glucagon in regulating glucose turnover and fatty acid levels. *Diabetes* 23:805–15

41. Chlouverakis, C., Bernardis, L. 1972. Ventrolateral hypothalamic lesions in obese hyperglycemic mice (ob, ob). *Diabetologia* 8:179–84

42. Christensen, H. N. et al 1971. In vitro stimulation of insulin release by nonmetabolizable transport-specific amino acids. *Biochim. Biophys. Acta* 241:341–348

43. Cooper, R. H., Ashcroft, S. J. H., Randle, P. J. 1973. Concentration of adenosine 3':5'-cyclic monophosphate in mouse pancreatic islets measured by a protein-binding radioassay. *Biochem. J.* 134:599–605

44. Coore, H. G., Randle, P. J. 1964. Regulation of insulin secretion studied with pieces of rabbit pancreas incubated in vitro. *Biochem. J.* 93:66–78

45. Corkey, B. E., Mayhew, D. A. 1974. Ionophores and insulin secretion. *Diabetes* 23 (Suppl. 1):337 (Abstr.)

46. Costrini, N. V., Kalkoff, R. K. 1971. Relative effects of pregnancy, estradiol, and progesterone on plasma insulin and pancreatic islet insulin secretion. *J. Clin. Invest.* 50:992–99

47. Crespin, S. R., Greenough, W., Steinberg, D. 1969. Stimulation of insulin secretion by infusion of free fatty acids. *J. Clin. Invest.* 48:1934–43

48. Creutzfeldt, C., Track, N. S., Creutzfeldt, W. 1973. In vitro studies of the rate of proinsulin and insulin turnover in seven human insulinomas. *Eur. J. Clin. Invest.* 3:371–84

49. Creutzfeldt, W. 1974. Insulin-releasing factors of the gastrointestinal mucosa (incretin). *Gastroenterology* 67:748–50

50. Curry, D. L. 1971. Is there a common beta cell insulin compartment stimulated by glucose and tolbutamide? *Am. J. Physiol.* 220:319–23

51. Curry, D., Bennett, L. 1974. Reversal of somatostatin inhibition of insulin secretion by calcium. *Biochem. Biophys. Res. Commun.* 60:1015–19

52. Curry, D. L., Bennett, L. L., Grodsky, G. M. 1968. Dynamics of insulin secretion by the perfused rat pancreas. *Endocrinology* 83:572–84

53. Curry, D., Joy, R. 1974. Direct CNS modulation of insulin secretion. *Endocr. Res. Commun.* 1:229–37

54. Daniel, P. M., Henderson, J. R. 1967. The effect of vagal stimulation on plasma insulin and glucose levels in the baboon. *J. Physiol. London* 192:317

55. Daniel, R. R. et al 1974. Carbohydrate metabolism in pregnancy. XI. Response of plasma glucagon to overnight fast and oral glucose during normal pregnancy and in gestational diabetes. *Diabetes* 23:771–76

56. Davis, B., Lazarus, N. R. 1972. Insulin release from mouse islets: Effect of glucose and hormones on adenylate cyclase. *Biochem. J.* 129:373–79

57. Dean, P. M. 1974. Surface electrostatic-charge measurement on islet and zymogen granules: Effect of calcium ions. *Diabetologia* 10:427–30

58. Dean, P. M., Matthews, E. K. 1972. The bioelectrical properties of pancreatic islet cells: Effect of diabetogenic agents. *Diabetologia* 8:173–78

59. Deckert, T., Lauridsen, U., Madsen, S., Morgensen, P. 1972. Insulin response to glucose, tolbutamide, secretin, and isoprenaline in maturity-onset diabetes mellitus. *Dan. Med. Bull.* 19:222–26

60. Deery, D. J., Taylor, K. W. 1973. Effects of azaserine and nicotinamide on insulin release and nicotinamide-adenine dinucleotide metabolism in isolated rat islets of Langerhans. *Biochem. J.* 134:557–63

61. Dubois, M. 1975. Immunoreactive somatostatin is present in discrete cells of the endocrine pancreas. *Proc. Nat. Acad. Sci. USA* 72:1340–43

62. Dupre, J., Curtis, J., Unger, R. H., Waddell, R. W., Beck, J. C. 1969. Effects of secretin, pancreozymin, or gastrin on the response of the endocrine pancreas to administration of glucose or arginine in man. *J. Clin. Invest.* 48:745–57

63. Edgar, P., Rabinowitz, D., Merimee, T. J. 1969. Effects of amino acids on insulin release from excised rabbit pancreas. *Endocrinology* 84:835

64. Edwards, J. C., Taylor, K. W. 1970. Fatty acids and the release of glucagon from isolated guinea-pig islets of Langerhans incubated in vitro. *Biochim. Biophys. Acta* 215:310–15

65. Efendic, S., Cerasi, E., Luft, R. 1971. Role of glucose in arginine-induced insulin release in man. *Metabolism* 20:568–79

66. Efendic, S., Cerasi, E., Luft, R. 1972. Arginine-induced insulin release in relation to the cyclic AMP system in man. *J. Clin. Endocrinol. Metab.* 34:67–72

67. Fajans, S. S. et al 1971. Stimulation of insulin release in the dog by a nonmetabolizable amino acid. Comparison with leucine and arginine. *J. Clin. Endocrinol.* 33:35–41

68. Fajans, S. S., Christensen, H. N., Floyd, J. C. Jr., Pek, S. 1974. Stimulation of insulin and glucagon release in the dog by a nonmetabolizable arginine analog. *Endocrinology* 94:230–33

69. Fajans, S. S., Floyd, J. C. Jr. 1972. Stimulation of islet cell secretion by nutrients and by gastrointestinal hormones released during ingestion. In *Handb. Physiol. Endocrinology. Sec. 7, Vol. I,* ed. R. O. Greep, E. B. Astwood. Washington DC: Am. Physiol. Soc. 473–94

70. Farmer, R. W. et al 1971. Failure of growth hormone to stimulate glucagon secretion. *Proc. Soc. Exp. Biol. Med.* 138:491–93

71. Federspiel, G., Casara, D., Pedrazzoli, S., Sicolo, N., Scandellari, C. 1974. In vivo studies of 5-hydroxy-tryptomine and insulin secretion in dogs and in man. *Diabetologia* 10:13–17

72. Feldman, J. M., Jackson, T. B. 1974. Specificity of nucleotide-induced insulin secretion. *Endocrinology* 94:388–94

73. Fijita, Y., Herron, A., Seltzer, H. 1975. Confirmation of impaired early insulin response to glycemic stimulus in non-obese mild diabetics. *Diabetes* 24:17–28

74. Foa, P. P. 1972. The secretion of glucagon. See Ref. 69, 261–78

75. Foster, R. O., Soeldner, J. S., Tan, M. H., Guyton, J. R. 1973. Short term glucose homeostasis in man: A systems dynamics model. *J. Dyn. Syst. Meas. Control* September 1973:308–14

76. Frankel, B. J. et al 1974. Abnormal secretion of insulin and glucagon by the in vitro perfused pancreas of the genetically diabetic Chinese hamster. *J. Clin. Invest.* 53:1637–46

77. Frankel, B. J., Gerich, J. E., Fanska, R., Gerritsen, G. C., Grodsky, G. M. 1974. Responses to arginine of the perfused

pancreas of the genetically diabetic Chinese hamster. *Diabetes* 24:272–79

78. Frohman, L. A., Bernardis, L. L. 1971. Effect of hypothalamic stimulation on plasma glucose, insulin, and glucagon levels. *Am. J. Physiol.* 221:1596–603

79. Frohman, L. A., Ezdinli, E. Z., Javid, R. 1967. Effect of vagotomy and vagal stimulation on insulin secretion. *Diabetes* 16:443–48

80. Gabbay, K. H., Korff, J., Schneeberger, E. E. 1975. Vesicular binesis: Glucose effect on insulin secretory vesicles. *Science* 187:177–79

81. Gabbay, K. H., Tze, W. J. 1972. Inhibition of glucose-induced release of insulin by aldose reductase inhibitors. *Proc. Nat. Acad. Sci. USA* 69:1435–39

82. Gabbiani, G., Malaisse-Lagae, F., Blondel, B., Orci, L. 1974. Actin in pancreatic islet cells. *Endocrinology* 95:1630–35

83. Garcia-Hermida, O., Gomez-Acebo, J. 1974. Digitoxin, a multiple spike stimulator of insulin release in the perfused islets of the rat. *Biochem. Biophys. Res. Commun.* 58:1135–41

84. Georg, R. H., Sussman, K. E., Leitner, J. W., Kirsch, W. M. 1971. Inhibition of glucose and tolbutamide-induced insulin release by iodoacetate antimycin A. *Endocrinology* 89:169–76

85. George, D. T., Rayfield, E. J. 1974. L-dopa-induced plasma glucagon release. *J. Clin. Endocrinol. Metab.* 39:618–21

86. Gerich, J. E. et al 1974. Characterization of the glucagon response to hypoglycemia in man. *J. Clin. Endocrinol. Metab.* 38:77–82

87. Gerich, J. E. et al 1974. Calcium dependency of glucagon secretion from the in vitro perfused rat pancreas. *Endocrinology* 94:1381–85

88. Gerich, J. E. et al 1974. Effects of somatostatin on plasma glucose and glucagon levels in human diabetes mellitus: Pathophysiologic and therapeutic implications. *N. Engl. J. Med.* 291:544–47

89. Gerich, J. E. et al 1975. Evidence for a physiologic role of pancreatic glucagon in human glucose homeostasis: Studies with somatostatin. *Metabolism* 24:175–82

90. Gerich, J. E. et al 1975. Prevention of human diabetic ketoacidosis by somatostatin: Evidence for an essential role of glucagon. *N. Engl. J. Med.* 292:985–89

91. Gerich, J. E., Charles, M. A., Grodsky, G. M. 1974. Characterization of the effects of arginine and glucose on glucagon and insulin release from the in vitro perfused rat pancreas. *J. Clin. Invest.* 54:833–41

92. Gerich, J. E., Karam, J. H., Forsham, P. H. 1973. Stimulation of glucagon secretion by epinephrine in man. *J. Clin. Endocrinol. Metab.* 37:479–80

93. Gerich, J. E., Langlois, M., Noacco, C. 1973. Glucagon secretion in obesity. *Lancet* 1:1323

94. Gerich, J. E., Langlois, M., Noacco, C., Karam, J. H., Forsham, P. H. 1973. Lack of glucagon response to hypoglycemia in diabetes: Evidence for an intrinsic pancreatic alpha-cell defect. *Science* 182:171–73

95. Gerich, J. E., Langlois, M., Noacco, C., Schneider, V., Forsham, P. H. 1974. Adrenergic modulation of pancreatic glucagon secretion in man. *J. Clin. Invest.* 53:1441–46

96. Gerich, J. E., Langlois, M., Schneider, V., Karam, J. H., Noacco, C. 1974. Effects of alterations of plasma free fatty acid levels on pancreatic glucagon secretion in man. *J. Clin. Invest.* 53:1284–89

97. Gerich, J. E., Lorenzi, M., Karam, J. H., Schneider, V., Forsham, P. H. 1975. Abnormal pancreatic glucagon secretion and postprandial hyperglycemia in diabetes mellitus. *J. Am. Med. Assoc.* 234:159–65

98. Gerich, J. E., Lovinger, R., Grodsky, G. M. 1975. Inhibition by somatostatin of glucagon and insulin release from the perfused rat pancreas in response to arginine, isoproterenol, and theophylline: Evidence for a preferential effect on glucagon secretion. *Endocrinology* 96:749–54

99. Gerich, J. E., Tsalikian, E., Lorenzi, M., Karam, J. H., Bier, D. M. 1975. Plasma glucagon and alanine responses to acute insulin deficiency in man. *J. Clin. Endocrinol. Metab.* 40:526–29

100. Gilman, A. G. 1970. A protein binding assay for adenosine 3':5'-cyclic monophosphate. *Proc. Nat. Acad. Sci. USA* 67:305–12

101. Gilman, A. G., Minna, J. D. 1973. Expression of genes for metabolism of cyclic adenosine 3':5'-monophosphate in somatic cells. II. Effects of prostaglandin E_1 and theophylline on parental and hybrid cells. *J. Biol. Chem.* 248:6618–25

102. Girard, J. R. et al 1973. Fuels, hormones, and liver metabolism at term during the early postnatal period in the rat. *J. Clin. Invest.* 52:3190–200

103. Girard, J. R., Kervran, A., Soufflet, E., Assan, R. 1974. Factors affecting the secretion of insulin and glucagon by the rat fetus. *Diabetes* 23:310–17

104. Goldberg, N. D. 1974. Cyclic nucleotides and cell function. *Hosp. Pract.* 9 (May):127–42

105. Goldfine, I. D., Abraira, C., Gruenewald, D., Goldstein, M. S. 1970. Plasma insulin levels during imaginary food ingestion under hypnosis. *Proc. Soc. Exp. Biol. Med.* 133:274–76

106. Goldfine, I. D., Cerasi, E., Luft, R. 1972. Glucagon stimulation of insulin release in man: Inhibition during hypoglycemia. *J. Clin. Endocrinol. Metab.* 35:312–15

107. Goldfine, I. D., Kirsteins, L., Lawrence, A. M. 1972. Excessive glucagon responses to arginine in active acromegaly. *Horm. Metab. Res.* 4:97–100

108. Goldfine, I. D., Roth, J., Birnbaumer, L. 1972. Glucagon receptors in β-cells: Binding of ^{125}I-glucagon and activation of adenylate cyclase. *J. Biol. Chem.* 247:1211–18

109. Gomez, M., Curry, D. L. 1973. Potassium stimulation of insulin release by the perfused rat pancreas. *Endocrinology* 92:1126–34

110. Goodman, D. B. P., Rasmussen, H., DiBella, F., Guthrow, C. E. Jr. 1970. Cyclic adenosine 3':5'-monophosphate-stimulated phosphorylation of isolated neurotubule subunits. *Proc. Nat. Acad. Sci. USA* 67:652–59

111. Gossain, V. V., Matute, M. L., Kalkoff, R. F. 1974. Relative influence of obesity and diabetes on plasma alpha-cell glucagon. *J. Clin. Endocrinol. Metab.* 38:238–42

112. Grasso, S., Messina, A., Distefano, G., Vigo, R., Reitano, G. 1973. Insulin secretion in the premature infant: response to glucose and amino acids. *Diabetes* 22:349–53

113. Grayburn, J., Harvey, R., Jennings, R., Dowsett, L., Hartog, M. 1975. Relationship between changes in serum cholecystokinin-pancreozymin and serum insulin after different stimuli. *Diabetologia* 11:35–38

114. Grey, N. J., Goldring, S., Kipnis, D. M. 1970. The effect of fasting, diet, and actinomycin D on insulin secretion in the rat. *J. Clin. Invest.* 49:881

115. Grill, V., Cerasi, E. 1974. Stimulation by D-glucose of cyclic adenosine 3':5'-monophosphate accumulation and insulin release in isolated pancreatic islets of the rat. *J. Biol. Chem.* 249:4196–201

115a. Grill, V., Cerasi, E. 1975. Cyclic AMP and insulin response to different hexoses and mannoheptulose in islets of Langerhans from the rat. *Diabetologia* 11:345 (Abstr.)

116. Grodsky, G. M. 1970. Insulin and the pancreas. *Vitam. Horm. New York* 28:37–101

117. Grodsky, G. M. 1972. A threshold distribution hypothesis for packet storage of insulin and its mathematical modeling. *J. Clin. Invest.* 51:2047–59

118. Grodsky, G. M. 1975. The kinetics of insulin release. *Handb. Exp. Pharmacol.*, 32:1–16

119. Grodsky, G. M. et al 1963. Effects of carbohydrates on secretion of insulin from isolated rat pancreas. *Am. J. Physiol.* 205:638–44

120. Grodsky, G. M., Bennett, L. L. 1963. Insulin secretion from the isolated pancreas in the absence of insulinogenesis: Effect of glucose. *Proc. Soc. Exp. Biol. Med.* 114:769–71

121. Grodsky, G. M., Bennett, L. L., Smith, D. F., Schmid, F. G. 1967. Effect of pulse administration of glucose or glucagon on insulin secretion in vitro. *Metabolism* 16:222–33

122. Grodsky, G. M., Bennett, L. L., Smith, D., Nemechek, K. 1967. The effect of tolbutamide and glucose on the time release of insulin from the isolated perfused pancreas. In *Tolbutamide After Ten Years*, ed. W. Butterfield, W. Van Westering, 11–21. Amsterdam: Excerpta Medica

123. Grodsky, G. M., Curry, D., Bennett, L. L., Rodrigo, J. J. 1968. Factors influencing different rates of insulin release in vitro. *Acta Diabetol. Lat.* 5(Suppl. 1):140–61

124. Grodsky, G. M., Curry, D., Landahl, H., Bennett, L. 1969. Further studies on the dynamic aspects of insulin release in vitro with evidence for a two-compartmental storage system. *Acta Diabetol. Lat.* 6 (Suppl. 1):554–79

125. Grodsky, G. M., Fanska, R., Lundquist, I. 1975. Interrelationships between alpha and beta anomers of glucose affecting insulin and glucagon secretion. *Endocrinology* 97:573–80

126. Grodsky, G. M., Fanska, R., Schmid, F. G. 1973. Evaluation of the role of exogenous insulin on phasic insulin secretion. *Diabetes* 22:256–63

127. Grodsky, G. M., Fanska, R., West, L., Manning, M. 1974. Anomeric specificity of glucose-stimulated insulin release:

Evidence for a glucoreceptor. *Science* 186:536–38

128. Grodsky, G. M., Landahl, H., Curry, D., Bennett, L. L. 1970. A two-compartmental model for insulin secretion. In *Advances in Metabolic Disorders: Early Diabetes* (Suppl. 1), ed. R. A. Camerini-Davalos, H. S. Cole, 45–50. New York: Academic

129. Grodsky, G. M., Licko, V., Landahl, H. 1971. Variable sensitivity of the perfused rat pancreas to glucose. In *Recent Advances in Endocrinology*, ed. E. Mattar, G. B. Mattar, V. H. T. James, p. 421. Amsterdam: Excerpta Medica

130. Grodsky, G. M., Sando, H., Gerich, J., Karam, J., Fanska, R. 1974. Synthesis and secretion of insulin in dynamic perfusion systems. In *Advances in Metabolic Disorders*, Vol. 7, ed. R. Levine, R. Luft, 155–70. New York: Academic

131. Gross, R., Mialhe, P. 1974. Free fatty acid-glucagon feed-back mechanism. *Diabetologia* 10:277–83

132. Hager, D., Georg, R. H., Leitner, J. W., Beck, P. 1972. Insulin secretion and content of isolated rat pancreatic islets following treatment with gestational hormones. *Endocrinology* 91:977–81

133. Hakanson, R., Liedberg, G., Lundquist, I. 1971. Effect of vagal denervation on insulin release after oral and intravenous glucose. *Experientia* 27:461–62

134. Han, P. W., Yu, Y., Chow, S. L. 1970. Enlarged pancreatic islets of tube-fed hypophysectomized rats bearing hypothalamic lesions. *Am. J. Physiol.* 218:769–71

135. Hawkins, R. A., Alberti, K. G. M. M., Houghton, C. R. S., Williamson, D. H., Krebs, H. A. 1971. The effect of acetoacetate on plasma insulin concentration. *Biochem. J.* 125:541–44

136. Hayes, J., Ardill, J., Buchanan, K. 1975. Gastrin and insulin secretion. *Diabetologia* 11:89–92

137. Hellman, B., Idahl, L. -A., Lernmark, A., Täljedal, I. -B. 1974. The pancreatic β-cell recognition of insulin secretogogues: Does cyclic AMP mediate the effect of glucose? *Proc. Nat. Acad. Sci. USA* 71:3405–9

138. Hellman, B., Idahl, L. -A., Lernmark, A., Sehlin, J., Täljedal, I. -B. 1974. The pancreatic β-cell recognition of insulin secretogogues. Effects of calcium and sodium on glucose metabolism and insulin release. *Biochem. J.* 138:33–45

139. Hellman, B., Idahl, L. -A., Lernmark, A., Sehlin, J., Täljedal, I. -B. 1974. Membrane sulphydryl groups and the pancreatic beta cell recognition of insulin secretogogues. In *Diabetes. Proc. Congr. Int. Diabetes Fed. 8th*, ed. W. J. Malaisse, J. Pirart, 65–78

140. Hellman, B., Sehlin, J., Täljedal, I. -B. 1971. Calcium uptake by pancreatic β-cells as measured with the aid of ^{45}Ca and Mannitol-^3H. *Am. J. Physiol.* 221:1795–1801

141. Hellman, B., Sehlin, J., Täljedal, I. -B. 1971. Effects of glucose and other modifiers of insulin release on the oxidative metabolism of amino acids in micro-dissected pancreatic islets. *Biochem. J.* 123:513–21

142. Hellman, B., Sehlin, J., Täljedal, I. -B. 1973. The pancreatic β-cell recognition of insulin secretogogues. IV. Islet uptake of sulfonylureas. *Diabetologia* 9:210–16

143. Henquin, J. C., Lambert, A. E. 1974. Cationic environment and dynamics of insulin secretion. III. Effect of the absence of potassium. *Diabetologia* 10:789–94

144. Herman, L., Sato, T., Hales, C. N. 1973. The electron microscopic localization of cations to pancreatic islets of Langerhans and their possible role in insulin secretion. *J. Ultrastruct. Res.* 42:298–311

145. Hoftiezer, V., Carpenter, A. -M. 1973. Comparison of streptozotocin and alloxan-induced diabetes in the rat, including volumetric quantitation of the pancreatic islets. *Diabetologia* 9:178–84

146. Horino, M., Machlin, L., Hertelendy, F., Kipnis, D. M. 1968. Effect of short chain fatty acids on plasma insulin in ruminant and non-ruminant species. *Endocrinology* 83:118–28

147. Howell, S. L., Edwards, J. C., Montague, W. 1974. Regulation of adenylate cyclase and cyclic-AMP dependent protein kinase activities in A_2-cell rich guinea-pig islets of Langerhans. *Horm. Metab. Res.* 6:49–52

148. Howell, S. L., Fink, C. J. Lacy, P. E. 1969. Isolation and properties of secretory granules from rat islets of Langerhans. I. Isolation of a secretory granule fraction. *J. Cell Biol.* 41:154–76

149. Howell, S. L., Montague, W. 1973. Adenylate cyclase activity in isolated rat islets of Langerhans: Effects of agents which alter rates of insulin secretion. *Biochim. Biophys. Acta* 320:44–52

150. Howell, S. L., Montague, W. 1974. Regulation of guanylate cyclase in guinea-pig islets of Langerhans. *Biochem. J.* 143:379–84

151. Howell, S. L., Parry, D. G., Taylor, K. W. 1965. Secretion of newly synthesized insulin in vitro. *Nature New Biol.* 208:487

152. Hughes, H. 1956. An experimental study of regeneration in the islets of Langerhans with reference to the theory of balance. *Acta Anat.* 27:1–61

153. Idahl, L. -A. 1972. A micro perifusion device for pancreatic islets allowing concomitant recordings of intermediate metabolites and insulin release. *Anal. Biochem.* 50:386–98

154. Idahl, L. -A. 1973. Dynamics of pancreatic β-cell responses to glucose. *Diabetologia* 9:403–12

155. Idahl, L. -A., Sehlin, J., Täljedal, I. -B. 1975. Metabolic and insulin-releasing activities of D-glucose anomers. *Nature London* 254:75–77

156. Imura, H., Kato, Y., Ikeda, M., Morimoto, M., Yawato, M. 1971. Effect of adrenergic-blocking or -stimulating agents on plasma growth hormone, immunoreactive insulin and blood free fatty acid levels in man. *J. Clin. Invest.* 50:1069–77

157. Iversen, J. 1971. Secretion of glucagon from the isolated, perfused canine pancreas. *J. Clin. Invest.* 50:2123–36

158. Iversen, J. 1973. Adrenergic receptors and the secretion of glucagon and insulin from the isolated perfused canine pancreas. *J. Clin. Invest.* 52:2102–16

159. Iversen, J. 1973. Effect of acetyl choline on the secretion of glucagon and insulin from the isolated perfused canine pancreas. *Diabetes* 22:381–87

160. Jarrett, R. J., Keen, H., Track, N. S. 1968. Insulin biosynthesis and RNA metabolism studied in isolated islets of Langerhans. *Diabetologia* 4:394 (Abstr.)

161. Jarrousse, Cl., Rosselin, G. 1975. Interaction of amino acids and cyclic AMP on the release of insulin and glucagon by newborn rat pancreas. *Endocrinology* 96:168–77

162. Johnson, D. G., Fujimoto, W. Y., Williams, R. H. 1973. Enhanced release of insulin by prostaglandins in isolated pancreatic islets. *Diabetes* 22:658–63

163. Kajinuma, H., Kaneto, A., Kuzuya, T., Nakao, K. 1968. Effects of methacholine on insulin secretion in man. *J. Clin. Endocrinol. Metab.* 28:1384–88

164. Kalkhoff, R. K., Gossain, V. V., Matute, M. L. 1973. Plasma glucagon in obesity. *N. Engl. J. Med.* 289:465–67

165. Kalkhoff, R. K., Jacobson, M., Lemper, D. 1970. Progesterone, pregnancy and the augmented plasma insulin response. *J. Clin. Endocrinol. Metab.* 31:24–28

166. Kanazawa, Y., Kawazu, S., Kuzuya, T., Kosaka, K. 1974. Dynamic cytology of pancreatic β-cells in monolayer culture. Formation of β-granules, cellular alterations accompanying stimulation and inhibition of insulin release. *Eur. J. Clin. Invest.* 4:345

167. Kaneto, A., Kajinuma, H., Kosaka, K. 1975. Effect of splanchnic nerve stimulation on glucagon and insulin output in the dog. *Endocrinology* 96:143–50

168. Kaneto, A., Kajinuma, H., Kosaka, K., Kuzuya, T., Nakao, K. 1968. Stimulation of insulin secretion by parasympathetic agents. *Endocrinology* 83:651–58

169. Kaneto, A., Kosaka, K., Nakao, K. 1967. Effects of stimulation of the vagus nerve on insulin secretion. *Endocrinology* 80:530–36

170. Kaneto, A., Miki, E., Kosaka, K. 1974. Effects of vagal stimulation on glucagon and insulin secretion. *Endocrinology* 95:1005–10

171. Karam, J. H. et al 1974. "Staircase" glucose stimulation of insulin secretion in obesity: A measure of beta-cell sensitivity and capacity. *Diabetes* 23: 763–70

172. Karam, J., Grasso, S., Wegienka, L., Grodsky, G., Forsham, P. 1966. Effect of selected hexoses, of epinephrine, and of glucagon on insulin secretion in man. *Diabetes* 15:571–78

173. Karam, J. H., Grodsky, G. M., Forsham, P. H. 1963. Excessive insulin response to glucose in obese subjects as measured by immunochemical assay. *Diabetes* 12:197–204

174. Karl, R. C., Zawalich, W. S., Ferrendelli, J. A., Matschinsky, F. M. 1975. The role of calcium and cyclic $3'5'$-AMP in insulin release induced in vitro by the divalent cation ionophore A23187. *J. Biol. Chem.* In press

174a. Katsilambros, N. et al 1972. Intravenous glucose tolerance and insulin secretion in the rat after thyroidectomy. *Horm. Metab. Res.* 4:377–79

175. Kimura, H., Murad, F. 1974. Nonenzymatic formation of guanosine $3':5'$-monophosphate from guanosine triphosphate. *J. Biol. Chem.* 249:329–31

176. Kipnis, D. M. 1969. Insulin secretion in diabetes mellitus. *Ann. Intern. Med.* 69:891–901

176a. Koerker, D. J. et al. 1974. Somatostatin: Hypothalamic inhibitor of the endocrine pancreas. *Science* 184: 482–83

177. Kuo, W. -N., Hodgins, D. S., Kuo, J. F. 1973. Adenylate cyclase in islets of Langerhans: Isolation of islets and regulation of adenylate cyclase activity by various hormones and agents. *J. Biol. Chem.* 248:2705–11

178. Kuzuya, T. 1962. Regulation of insulin secretion by the central nervous system. II. The role of the hypothalamus and the pituitary gland upon insulin secretion. *J. Jpn. Soc. Intern. Med.* 51:65–74

179. Lacy, P. E., Howell, S. L., Young, D. A., Fink, C. J. 1968. New hypothesis of insulin secretion. *Nature London* 219:1177–79

180. Lacy, P. E., Klein, N. J., Fink, C. J. 1973. Effect of cytochalasin B on the biphasic release of insulin in perifused rat islets. *Endocrinology* 92:1458–68

181. Lacy, P. E., Malaisse, W. J. 1973. Microtubules and beta cell secretion. *Rec. Progr. Horm. Res.* 29:199–226

182. Lambert, A. E., Henquin, J. -C., Orci, L., Renold, A. E. 1974. Enzyme-induced modifications of beta cell function. I. Effect of pronase on insulin secretion. *Eur. J. Clin. Invest.* 4:459–68

183. Lambert, A. E., Jeanrenaud, B., Renold, A. E. 1967. Enhancement of caffeine of glucagon-induced and tolbutamide-induced insulin release from isolated fetal pancreatic tissue. *Lancet* 1:819–20

184. Landgraf, R., Brantburg, J., Matschinsky, F. 1971. Kinetics of insulin release from the perfused rat pancreas caused by glucose, glucosamine and galactose. *Proc. Nat. Acad. Sci. USA* 68:536–40

185. Landgraf, R., Landgraf-Leurs, M. M. C., Hörl, R. 1974. L-leucine and l-phenylalanine induced insulin release and the influence of D-glucose. Kinetic studies with the perfused rat pancreas. *Diabetologia* 10:415–20

186. Laube, H. et al 1971. Effects of tolbutamide on insulin and glucagon secretion of the isolated perfused rat pancreas. *Horm. Metab. Res.* 3:238–42

187. Laube, H., Fussgänger, R. D., Maier, V., Pfeiffer, E. F. 1973. Hyperglucagonemia of the isolated perfused pancreas of diabetic mice (db/db). *Diabetologia* 9:400–2

188. Lazarus, N. R., Davis, B. 1975. Model for extrusion of insulin β granules. *Lancet* 1:143–44

189. Lebovitz, H., Feldman, J. 1973. Pancreatic biogenic amines and insulin secretion in health and disease. *Fed. Proc.* 32:1797–802

190. Leclercq-Meyer, V., Brisson, G. R., Malaisse, W. J. 1971. Effect of adrenaline and glucose on release of glucagon and insulin in vitro. *Nature New Biol.* 231:248–49

191. Lee, J. C., Grodsky, G. M., Smith-Kyle, D. F., Craw, L. 1970. Ultrastructure of β-cells during the dynamic response to glucose and tolbutamide in vitro. *Diabetologia* 6:542–49

192. Lefebvre, P. J., Luyckx, A. S. 1973. Stimulation of insulin secretion after prostaglandin E_1 in the anesthetized dog. *Biochem. Pharmacol.* 22:1773–79

193. Leitner, J. W., Sussman, K. E., Vatter, A. E., Schneider, F. H. 1975. Adenine nucleotides in the secretory granule fraction of rat islets. *Endocrinology* 96:662–77

194. Lerner, R. L., Porte, D. 1970. Uniphasic insulin responses to secretin stimulation in man. *J. Clin. Invest.* 49:2276–80

195. Lernmark, A. 1971. The significance of 5-hydroxytryptamine for insulin secretion in the mouse. *Horm. Metab. Res.* 3:305–9

196. Levin, S. R., Charles, M. A., O'Connor, M., Grodsky, G. M. 1975. Use of diphenylhydantoin and diazoxide to investigate insulin secretory mechanisms. *Am. J. Physiol.* 229:49–54

197. Levin, S. R., Grodsky, G. M., Smith, D., Hagura, R., Forsham, P. 1972. Relationships between glucose and arginine in the induction of insulin secretion in the isolated perfused rat pancreas. *Endocrinology* 90:624–31

198. Levin, S., Karam, J., Hane, S., Grodsky, G., Forsham, P. 1971. Enhancement of arginine-induced insulin secretion in man by prior administration of glucose. *Diabetes* 20:171–76

199. Levy, J., Schoonheydt, J. 1974. Metabolic effects of cytochalasin B in isolated islets. *Diabetologia* 10:377

200. Lin, B. J., Nagy, B. R., Haist, R. E. 1972. Effect of various concentrations of glucose on insulin biosynthesis. *Endocrinology* 91:309–11

201. Luft, R., Efendic, S., Hokfelt, T., Johansson, O., Arimura, A. 1974 Immunochemical evidence for the localization of somatostatin-like immunoreactivity in a cell population of the pancreatic islets. *Med. Biol.* 52:428–30

202. Lundquist, I. 1971. Insulin secretion: Its regulation by monoamines and acid amyloglucosidase. *Acta Physiol Scand. Suppl.* 372:3–47

203. Lundquist, I. 1972. Interaction of amines and aminergic blocking agents with blood glucose regulation. I. β-adrenergic blockade. *Eur. J. Pharmacol.* 18:213–24

204. Lundquist, I. 1972. Interaction of amines and aminergic blocking agents with blood glucose regulation. II. β-adrenergic blockade. *Eur. J. Pharmacol.* 18:225–35

205. Luyckx, A. S., Lafebvre, P. J. 1970. Arguments for a regulation of pancreatic glucagon secretion by circulating plasma free fatty acids. *Proc. Soc. Exp. Biol. Med.* 133:524–28

206. Madison, L. L., Mebane, R., Unger, R. H., Lochner, A. 1964. The hypoglycemic action of ketones. II. Evidence for a stimulatory feedback of ketones on the pancreatic beta cell. *J. Clin. Invest.* 43:408–15

207. Maier, V., Schatz, H., Hinz, M., Pfeiffer, E. F., Blessing, J. 1973. Biosynthesis and secretion of insulin after treatment of pancreatic islets of mice with several glycosidases. *Endokrinologie* 62:269–78

208. Malaisse, W. J. 1972. Hormonal and environmental modification of islet activity. See Ref. 69, 237–60

209. Malaisse, W. J. et al 1973. The glucoreceptor mechanism in the pancreatic beta-cell. *Am. Zool.* 13:605–12

210. Malaisse, W. J. et al 1974. Dynamics of insulin release and microtubular-microfilamentous system. V. A model for the phase release of insulin. *Eur. J. Clin. Invest.* 4:313–18

211. Malaisse, W. J., Brisson, G. R., Baird, L. E. 1973. Stimulus-secretion coupling of glucose-induced insulin release. X. Effect of glucose on ^{45}Ca efflux from perifused islets. *Am. J. Physiol.* 224:389–94

212. Malaisse, W. J., Hager, D. L., Orci, L. 1972. The stimulus-secretion coupling of glucose-induced insulin release. IX. The participation of the beta cell web. *Diabetes* 21 (Suppl. 2):594–604

213. Malaisse, W., Malaisse-Lagae, F., King, S. 1968. Effects of neutral red and imidazole upon insulin secretion. *Diabetologia* 4:370–74 ·

214. Malaisse, W. J., Malaisse-Lagae, F., Mayhew, D. 1967. A possible role for the adenylcyclase system in insulin secretion. *J. Clin. Invest.* 46:1724–34

215. Malaisse, W. J., Malaisse-Lagae, F., McCaw, E. F. 1967. Effects of thyroid function upon insulin secretion. *Diabetes* 16:643–46

216. Malaisse, W., Malaisse-Lagae, F., Picard, C., Flament-Durand, J. 1969. Effects of pregnancy and chorionic growth hormone upon insulin secretion. *Endocrinology* 84:41–44

217. Malaisse, W., Malaisse-Lagae, F., Wright, P. H. 1967. A new method for the measurement in vitro of pancreatic insulin secretion. *Endocrinology* 80:99–108

218. Malaisse, W. J., Malaisse-Lagae, F., Wright, P. H. 1967. Effect of fasting upon insulin secretion in the rat. *Am. J. Physiol.* 213:843

219. Malaisse, W., Malaisse-Lagae, F., Wright, P. H., Ashmore, J. 1967. Effects of adrenergic and cholinergic agents upon insulin secretion in vitro. *Endocrinology* 80:975–78

220. Malaisse-Lagae, F., Malaisse, W. J. 1971. Stimulus-secretion coupling of glucose-induced insulin release. III. Uptake of ^{45}calcium by isolated islets of Langerhans. *Endocrinology* 88:72–80

220a. Maracek, R. L., Feldman, J. M. 1973. Effect of hyperthyroidism on insulin and glucose dynamics in rabbits. *Endocrinology* 92:1604–11

221. Marco, J. et al 1973. Hyperglucagonism induced by glucocorticoid treatment in man. *N. Engl. J. Med.* 288:128–31

222. Marliss, E. B. et al 1973. Glucagon release induced by pancreatic nerve stimulation in the dog. *J. Clin. Invest.* 52:1246–59

223. Marliss, E. B., Aoki, T. T., Unger, R. H., Soeldner, J. S., Cahill, G. F. 1970. Glucagon levels and metabolic effects in fasting man. *J. Clin. Invest.* 49:2256–70

224. Martin, J. M., Konijnendijk, W., Bouman, P. R. 1974. Insulin and growth hormone secretion in rats with ventromedial hypothalamic lesions maintained in restricted food intake. *Diabetes* 23:203–8

225. Mashiter, K. et al 1975. Persistent pancreatic glucagon but not insulin response to arginine in pancreatectomized dogs. *Endocrinology* 95:678–93

226. Masse-Benedetti, F., Falorni, A., Luyckx, A., Lefebvre, P. 1974. Inhibition of glucagon secretion in the human newborn by simultaneous administration of glucose and insulin. *Horm. Metab. Res.* 6:392–96

227. Matschinsky, F. M., Ellerman, J. E. 1968. Metabolism of glucose in the islets of Langerhans. *J. Biol. Chem.* 243:2730–36

228. Matschinsky, F. M., Ellerman, J. E. 1973. Dissociation of the insulin releasing and the metabolic functions of hexoses in islets of Langerhans. *Biochem. Biophys. Res. Commun.* 50:193–99

229. Matschinsky, F. M., Landgraf, R., Ellerman, J., Kotler-Brajtburg, J. 1972. Glucoreceptor mechanisms in islets of Langerhans. *Diabetes* 21 (Suppl. 2): 555–69

230. Matthews, E. K. 1970. Calcium and hormone release. In *Calcium and Cell Function,* ed. A. W. Cuthbert, 163–82. London: MacMillan

231. McDaniel, M. L., King, S., Anderson, S., Fink, J., Lacy, P. E. 1974. Effect of cytochalasin B on hexose transport and glucose metabolism in pancreatic islets. *Diabetologia* 10:303–8

232. Merimee, T. J., Fineberg, S. E. 1973. Homeostasis during fasting. II. Hormone substrate differences between men and women. *J. Clin. Endocrinol. Metab.* 37:698–702

233. Miller, E. A., Wright, P. H., Allen, D. O. 1972. Effect of hormones on accumulation of cyclic AMP-^{14}C in isolated pancreatic islets of rats. *Endocrinology* 91:1117–19

234. Montague, W., Cook, J.R. 1971. The role of adenosine 3':5'-cyclic monophosphate in the regulation of insulin release by isolated rat islets of Langerhans. *Biochem. J.* 122:115–20

235. Montague, W., Howell, S. L. 1973. The mode of action of adenosine 3':5'-cyclic monophosphate in mammalian islets of Langerhans: Effects of insulin secretogogues on islet-cell protein kinase activity. *Biochem. J.* 134:321–27

236. Montague, W., Howell, S. L. 1975. Cyclic AMP and the physiology of the islets of Langerhans. In *Advances in Cyclic Nucleotide Research, Vol. 6,* New York: Raven. In press

237. Morris, G. E., Korner, A. 1970. The effect of glucose on insulin biosynthesis by isolated islets of Langerhans of the rat. *Biochim. Biophys. Acta* 208:404–13

238. Müller, E. E., Frohman, L., Cocchi, I. D. 1973. Drug control of hyperglycemia and inhibition of insulin secretion due to centrally administered 2-deoxy-D-glucose. *Am. J. Physiol.* 224:1210–17

239. Müller, W. A., Aoki, T. T., Cahill, G. F. 1975. Effect of alanine and glycine on glucagon secretion in postabsorptive and fasting obese man. *J. Clin. Endocrinol. Metab.* 40:418–25

240. Müller, W. A., Faloona, G. R., Aguilar-Parada, E., Unger, R. H. 1970. Abnormal alpha-cell function in diabetes: Responses to carbohydrate and protein ingestion. *N. Engl. J. Med.* 283:109–15

241. Müller, W. A., Faloona, G. R., Unger, R. H. 1971. The effect of alanine on glucagon secretion. *J. Clin. Invest.* 50:2215–18

242. Müller, W. A., Faloona, G. R., Unger, R. H. 1971. The influence of the antecedent diet upon glucagon and insulin secretion. *N. Engl. J. Med.* 285:1450–54

243. Müller, W. A., Faloona, G. R., Unger, R. H. 1973. Hyperglucagonemia in diabetic ketoacidosis. *Am. J. Med.* 54: 52–57

244. Müller, W. A., Weir, G. C. 1974. Pathophysiology of glucagon secretion. *Pathobiol. Ann.* 4:263–87

245. Murray, J. M., Weber, A. 1974. The cooperative action of muscle proteins. *Sci. Am.* 230 (Feb.):59–71

246. Nicklas, W. J., Puszkin, S., Berl, S. 1973. Effect of vinblastine and colchicine on uptake and release of putative transmitters by synaptosomes and on brain actomyosin-like protein. *J. Neurochem.* 20:109–21

247. Niki, A., Niki, H., Miwa, I., Okuda, J. 1974. Insulin secretion by anomers of D-glucose. *Science* 186:150–51

248. Noe, B. D., Bauer, G. E. 1973. Further characterization of a glucagon precursor from angler fish islet tissue. *Proc. Soc. Exp. Biol. Med.* 142:210–13

249. Oakley, N. W., Harrigan, P., Kissebah, A. H., Kissin, E. A., Adams, P. W. 1972. Factors affecting insulin response to glucagon in man. *Metabolism* 21: 1001–7

250. Obberghen, E. van et al 1973. Dynamics of insulin release and microtubular-microfilamentous system. I. Effect of cytochalasin B. *J. Clin. Invest.* 52: 1041–51

251. O'Connor, K. J., Gay, A., Lazarus, N. R. 1973. The biosynthesis of glucagon in perfused rat pancreas. *Biochem. J.* 134:473–80

252. Ohneda, A. et al 1972. Plasma glucagon responses to blood glucose fall, gastrointestinal hormones and arginine in man. *Tohoku J. Exp. Med.* 107:241–51

253. Ohneda, A., Aguilar-Parada, E., Eisentraut, A. M., Unger, R. H. 1969. Control of pancreatic glucagon secretion by glucose. *Diabetes* 18:1–10

254. Orci, L. 1974. A portrait of the pancreatic B-cell. *Diabetologia* 10:163–87

255. Ostland, R. E., Kipnis, D. M. 1975. Identification of soluble myosin(s) in endocrine tissues. *Prog. Ann. Meet. Endocr. Soc. NY, 57th June 18–20, 1975,* p. 88 (Abstr.)

256. Pace, C. S., Price, S. 1972. Electrical responses of pancreatic islet cells to secretory stimuli. *Biochem. Biophys. Res. Commun.* 46:1557–63

257. Pagliara, A. S., Stillings, S. N., Haymond, M. W., Hover, B. A., Matschinsky, F. M. 1975. Insulin and glucose as modulators of the amino acid-induced glucagon release in the isolated pancreas of alloxan and streptozotocin diabetic rats. *J. Clin. Invest.* 55:244–55

258. Pagliara, A. S., Stillings, S. N., Hover, B., Martin, D. M., Matschinsky, F. 1974. Glucose modulation of amino acid-induced glucagon and insulin release in the isolated perfused rat pancreas. *J. Clin. Invest.* 54:819–32

259. Palmer, J., Ensinck, J. 1975. Stimulation of glucagon secretion by ethanol-induced hypoglycemia in man. *Diabetes* 24:295–300

260. Parra-Cavarrubias, A., Rivera-Rodriguez, I., Almaraz-Ugalde, A. 1971. Cephalic phase of insulin secretion in obese adolescents. *Diabetes* 20:800–2

261. Pelkonen, R., Miettinen, T., Taskinen, M., Nikkila, E. 1968. Effect of acute elevation of plasma glycerol, triglyceride and FFA levels on glucose utilization and plasma insulin. *Diabetes* 17:76–82

262. Perley, M., Kipnis, D. M. 1966. Effect of glucocorticoids on plasma insulin. *N. Engl. J. Med.* 274:1237–41

263. Permutt, M. A. 1974. Effect of glucose on initiation and elongation rates in isolated rat pancreatic islets. *J. Biol. Chem.* 249:2738–42

264. Persson, I., Gyntelberg, F., Heding, L. G., Boss-Nielson, J. 1971. Pancreatic glucagon-like immunoreactivity after intravenous insulin in normals and chronic-pancreatitis patients. *Acta Endocrinol.* 67:401–4

265. Pictet, R., Rutter, W. 1972. Development of the embryonic endocrine pancreas. See Ref. 69, 25–67

266. Pipeleers, D. G., Marichal, M., Malaisse, W. J. 1973. The stimulus-secretion of glucose-induced insulin release. XIV. Glucose regulation of insular biosynthetic activity. *Endocrinology* 93:1001–11

267. Pipeleers, D., Pipeleers-Marichal, M., Kipnis, D. 1975. Metabolic and morphologic studies of long-term islet transplanted rats. *Diabetes* 24 (Suppl. 2):420 (Abstr.)

268. Pipeleers, D. G., Pipeleers-Marichal, M. A., Kipnis, D. M. 1975. Physiological regulation of the microtubular system. *Prog. Ann. Meet. Endocr. Soc. NY 57th, June 18–20, 1975,* p. 88 (Abstr.)

269. Porte, D. 1967. A receptor mechanism for the inhibition of insulin release by epinephrine in man. *J. Clin. Invest.* 46:86–94

270. Porte, D., Girardier, L., Seydoux, J., Kanazawa, Y., Pasternak, J. 1973. Neural regulation of insulin secretion in the dog. *J. Clin. Invest.* 52:210–14

271. Porte, D., Graber, A., Kuzuya, T., Williams, R. 1966. The effect of epinephrine on immunoreactive insulin levels in man. *J. Clin. Invest.* 45:228–36

272. Porte, D., Pupo, A. A. 1969. Insulin responses to glucose: Evidence for a two-pool system in man. *J. Clin. Invest.* 48:2309–19

273. Porte, D., Williams, R. 1966. Inhibition of insulin release by norepinephrine in man. *Science* 152:1248–50

274. Price, S. 1973. Pancreatic islet cell membranes: Extraction of a possible glucoreceptor. *Biochim. Biophys. Acta* 318:459–63

275. Quickel, K. E., Feldman, J. M. Lebovitz, H. E. 1971. Enhancement of insulin secretion in adult-onset diabetics by methysergide maleate: Evidence for an endogenous biogenic amine mechanism as a factor in the impaired insulin secretion in diabetes mellitus. *J. Clin. Endocrinol. Metab.* 33:877–82

275a. Quickel, K. E., Feldman, J. M., Lebovitz, H. 1971. Inhibition of insulin secretion by serotonin and dopamine: Species variation. *Endocrinology* 89:1295–1302

276. Rasmussen, H., Goodman, D. B. P., Tenenhouse, A. 1972. The role of cyclic AMP and calcium in cell activation. *Crit. Rev. Biochem.* 1:95–150

277. Rehfeld, J. F., Stadil, F. 1973. The effect of gastrin on basal and glucose-stimulated insulin secretion in man. *J. Clin. Invest.* 52:1415–26

277a. Renould, A., Sverdlik, R. C., Andrade, L. L. 1974. Effects of hypothyroidism on serum immunoreactive insulin, free fatty acids and blood sugar in the dog as tested after oral glucose. *Horm. Metab. Res.* 6:137–41

278. Reynolds, C., Horwitz, D., Molnar, G., Rubinstein, A., Taylor, W. 1974. Abnormalities of endogenous insulin and glucagon in insulin-treated unstable and

stable diabetics. *Diabetes* 23 (Suppl. 1): 343

279. Robertson, R. P. 1974. In vivo insulin secretion: Prostaglandin and adrenergic interrelationships. *Prostaglandins* 6: 501–8

280. Robertson, R. P., Porte, D. 1973. Adrenergic modulation of basal insulin secretion in man. *Diabetes* 22:1–8

281. Robertson, R. P., Porte, D. 1973. The glucose receptor: A defective mechanism in diabetes mellitus distinct from the beta adrenergic receptor. *J. Clin. Invest.* 52:870–76

282. Rocha, D., Faloona, G. R., Unger, R. H. 1972. Glucagon-stimulating activity of twenty amino acids in dogs. *J. Clin. Invest.* 51:2346–51

283. Rossini, A. A., Buse, M. G. 1973. The effect of L-dopa on insulin release by isolated pancreatic islets of the rat. *Horm. Metab. Res.* 5:26–28

284. Rudzinska, M. A. 1967. Ultrastructures involved in the feeding mechanism of suctoria. *Trans. NY Acad. Sci.* 29 (4), ser. 2:512–25

285. Sacca, L., Rengo, F., Chiariello, M., Condorelli, M. 1973. Glucose intolerance and impaired secretion of insulin by prostaglandin A₁ in fasting anesthetized dogs. *Endocrinology* 92:31–34

285a. Sakaurai, H., Dobbs, R., Unger, R. 1974. Somatostatin-induced changes in insulin and glucagon secretion in normal and diabetic dogs. *J. Clin. Invest.* 54:1395–1402

286. Said, S. 1974. Vasoactive intestinal peptide (VIP). *Gastroenterology* 67:735–37

287. Samols, E., Tyler, J., Marks, V. 1972. Glucagon-insulin interrelationships. In *Glucagon Molecular Physiology. Clinical and Therapeutic Implications,* ed. R. Unger, P. Lefebvre, New York: Pergammon

288. Sams, D. J., Montague, W. 1972. The role of adenosine 3':5'-cyclic monophosphate in the regulation of insulin release: Properties of islet-cell adenosine 3':5'-cyclic monophosphate phosphodiesterase. *Biochem. J.* 129:945–52

289. Sando, H., Borg, J., Steiner, D. F. 1972. Studies on the secretion of newly synthesized proinsulin and insulin from isolated rat islets of Langerhans. *J. Clin. Invest.* 51:1476–85

290. Sando, H., Grodsky, G. M. 1973. Dynamic synthesis and release of insulin and proinsulin from perifused islets. *Diabetes* 22:354–60

291. Santeusanio, F., Faloona, G. R., Unger, R. H. 1972. Suppressive effect of secre-

tin upon pancreatic alpha cell function. *J. Clin. Invest.* 51:1743–49

292. Sasaki, H., Faloona, G., Unger, R. 1974. Enteroglucagon. *Gastroenterology* 67:746–48

293. Satir, P. 1974. How cilia move. *Sci. Am.* 231(4):45–52

294. Saudek, C. D., Finkowski, M., Knopp, R. H. 1975. Plasma glucagon and insulin in rat pregnancy. *J. Clin. Invest.* 55:180–87

295. Schade, D. S., Eaton, R. P. 1974. Role of insulin and glucagon in obesity. *Diabetes* 23:657–61

296. Schäfer, H.-J., Klöppel, G. 1974. The significance of calcium in insulin secretion: Ultrastructural studies on identification and localization of calcium in activated and inactivated B cells of mice. *Virchows Arch. A* 362:231–45

297. Schalch, D., Kipnis, D. 1965. Abnormalities in carbohydrate tolerance associated with elevated plasma nonesterified fatty acids. *J. Clin. Invest.* 44:2010–20

298. Schatz, H., Maier, V., Hinz, M., Nierle, C., Pfeiffer, E. F. 1973. Hypophysis and function of pancreatic islets. III. Secretion and biosynthesis of insulin in isolated pancreatic islets of intact and hypophysectomized rats in the presence of growth hormone, corticotropin, and human chorionic somatotrophin in vitro. *Horm. Metab. Res.* 5:29–33

298a. Seino, Y., Goto, Y., Taminato, T., Ikeda, M., Imura, H. 1974. Plasma insulin and glucagon responses to arginine in patients with thyroid dysfunction. *J. Clin. Endocrinol. Metab.* 38:1136–40

299. Seino, Y., Ikeda, M., Kuzuya, H., Sakurai, H., Imura, H. 1975. Effect of 5-hydroxytryptophan, L-dopa, and bethanidine on plasma insulin response to intravenous glucose loading in normal subjects. *Horm. Metab. Res.* 7:92–93

300. Selawry, H. et al 1973. A mechanism for glucose-induced insulin release. *Diabetes* 22 (Suppl. 1):295 (Abstr.)

301. Serrano-Rios, M. et al 1974. Insulin secretion in Addison's disease: Effect of hydrocortisone treatment. *Horm. Metab. Res.* 6:17–21

302. Seyffert, W. A., Madison, L. L. 1967. Physiologic effects of metabolic fuels on carbohydrate metabolism. I. Acute effect of elevation of plasma free fatty acids on hepatic glucose output, peripheral glucose utilization, serum insulin and plasma glucagon levels. *Diabetes* 16:765–76

302a. Shah, J., Cerchio, G. M. 1973. Hypoinsulinemia of hypothyroidism. *Arch. Intern. Med.* 132:657–61
303. Sharp, R., Culbert, S., Cook, J., Jennings, A., Burr, I. M. 1974. Cholinergic modification of glucose-induced biphasic insulin release in vitro. *J. Clin. Invest.* 53:710–16
304. Shelanski, M. L. 1973. Chemistry of the filaments and tubules of brain. *J. Histochem. Cytochem.* 21:529–39
305. Simpson, R., Benedetti, A., Grodsky, G., Karam, J., Forsham, P. 1968. Early phase of insulin release. *Diabetes* 17: 684–92
306. Sims, E. et al 1968. Experimental obesity in man. *Trans. Assoc. Am. Phys.* 81:153–70
307. Sloboda, R. D., Rudolph, S. A., Rosenbaum, J. L., Greengard, P. 1975. Cyclic AMP-dependent endogenous phosphorylation of microtubule-associated protein. *Proc. Nat. Acad. Sci. USA* 72:177–81
308. Smith, D. S., Järlfors, U., Beranek, R. 1970. The organization of synaptic axoplasm in the lamprey (Petromyzon marinus) central nervous sytem. *J. Cell Biol.* 46:199–219
309. Sodoyez-Goffaux, F., Sodoyez, J. C., Foa, P. P. 1971. Effect of gestational age, birth and feeding on the insulinogenic response to glucose and tolbutamide by fetal newborn rat pancreas. *Diabetes* 20:586–91
310. Somers, G. et al 1974. Dynamics of insulin release and microtubular-microfilamentous system. III. Effect of colchicine upon glucose-induced insulin secretion. *Eur. J. Clin. Invest.* 4:299–305
311. Sorensen, R. L., Steffes, M. W., Lindall, A. W. 1970. Subcellular localization of proinsulin to insulin conversion in isolated rat islets. *Endocrinology* 86:88–96
312. Spellacy, W. N., Buki, W. C., Berk, S. A. 1972. The effect of estrogens on carbohydrate metabolism: Glucose, insulin, and growth hormone studies on one hundred and seventy-one women ingesting premarin, mestranol and ethenyl estradiol for six months. *Am. J. Obstet. Gynecol.* 114:378–92
313. Spellacy, W. N., McLeod, A. G. W., Buki, W. C., Berk, S. A. 1972. The effects of medroxyprogesterone acetate on carbohydrate metabolism: Measurements of glucose, insulin, and growth hormone after twelve months' use. *Fertil. Steril.* 23:239–44

314. Sperling, M. A. et al 1974. Spontaneous and amino acid-stimulated glucagon secretion in the immediate postnatal period: Relation to glucose and insulin. *J. Clin. Invest.* 53:1159–66
315. Spudich, J. A., Lin, S. 1972. Cytochalasin B, its interaction with actin and actomyosin from muscle. *Proc. Nat. Acad. Sci. USA* 69:442–46
315a. Steiner, D. F. 1967. Evidence for a precursor in the biosynthesis of insulin. *Trans. NY Acad. Sci.* 30:60
316. Sussman, K. E., Vaughan, G. D. 1967. Insulin release after ACTH, glucagon and adenosine-3'-5-'phosphate (cyclic AMP) in the perfused isolated rat pancreas. *Diabetes* 16:449–54
317. Täljedal, I. -B. 1975. Problems and issues in insulin secretion. In *Topics in Diabetes Mellitus.* London: Heinemann In press
318. Tanese, T., Lazarus, N. R., Devrim, S., Recant, L. 1970. Synthesis and release of pro-insulin and insulin by isolated rat islets of Langerhans. *J. Clin. Invest.* 49:1394–1404
318a. Thomas, J. E. 1964. Mechanism of action of pancreatic stimuli studied by means of atropine-like drugs. *Am. J. Physiol.* 206:124–29
319. Turner, D. S., McIntyre, N. 1966. Stimulation by glucagon of insulin release from rabbit pancreas in vitro. *Lancet* 1:351–52
320. Turtle, J. R., Kipnis, D. M. 1967. An adrenergic receptor mechanism for the control of cyclic 3'5' adenosine monophosphate synthesis in tissues. *Biochem. Biophys. Res. Commun.* 28:797–802
321. Unger, R. H. 1971. Glucagon and the insulin:glucagon molar ratio in diabetes and other catabolic illnesses. *Diabetes* 20:834–38
322. Unger, R. H. 1974. Alpha- and beta-cell interrelationships in health and disease. *Metabolism* 23:581–93
323. Unger, R. H., Aguilar-Parada, E., Müller, W. A., Eisentraut, A. 1970. Studies of pancreatic alpha cell function in normal and diabetic subjects. *J. Clin. Invest.* 49:837–48
324. Unger, R., Madison, L., Müller, W. 1972. Abnormal alpha cell function in diabetes: Response to insulin. *Diabetes* 21:301–9
325. Unger, R. H., Ohneda, A., Aguilar-Parada, E., Eisentraut, A. M. 1969. The role of aminogenic glucagon secretion in blood glucose homeostasis. *J. Clin. Invest.* 48:810–22

326. Van Lan, V., Yamaguchi, N., Garcia, M. J., Ramey, E. R., Penhos, J. C., 1974. Effect of hypophysectomy and adrenalectomy on glucagon and insulin concentration. *Endocrinology* 94:671–75

327. Vranic, M., Pek, S., Kawamori, R. 1974. Increased glucagon immunoreactivity in plasma of totally depancreatized dogs. *Diabetes* 23:905–12

328. Walter, R. M., Dudl, R. J., Palmer, J. P., Ensinck, J. W. 1974. The effect of adrenergic blockade on the glucagon responses to starvation and hypoglycemia in man. *J. Clin. Invest.* 54:1214–20

329. Watkins, D., Cooperstein, S. J., Lazarow, A. 1971. Stimulation of insulin secretion by pyridine nucleotides. *Endocrinology* 88:1380–84

330. Weir, G., Knowlton, S., Martin, D. 1974. Somatostatin inhibition of epinephrine-induced glucagon secretion. *Endocrinology* 95:1744–46

331. Weir, G. C., Knowlton, S. D., Martin, D. B. 1974. Glucagon secretion from the perfused rat pancreas. Studies with glucose and catecholamines. *J. Clin. Invest.* 54:1403–12

332. Wise, J. K., Hendler, R., Felig, P. 1973. Evaluation of alpha-cell function by infusion of alanine in normal, diabetic and obese subjects. *N. Engl. J. Med.* 288: 487–90

333. Wise, J. K., Hendler, R., Felig, P. 1973. Influence of glucocorticoids on glucagon secretion and plasma amino acid concentrations in man. *J. Clin. Invest.* 52:2774–82

333a. Matschinsky, F. M., Pagliara, A. S., Hover, B. A., Haymond, M. W., Stillings, S. N. 1975. Differential effects of alpha- and beta-D-glucose on insulin and glucagon secretion from the isolated perfused rat pancreas. *Diabetes* 24:369–72

334. Wise, J. K., Lyall, S. S., Hendler, R., Felig, P. 1973. Evidence of stimulation of glucagon secretion by alanine in the human fetus at term. *J. Clin. Endocrinol. Metab.* 37:345–48

335. Woods, S. C. 1972. Conditioned hypoglycemia: Effect of vagotomy and pharmacologic blockade. *Am. J. Physiol.* 223:1424–27

336. Woods, S. C., Alexander, K. R., Porte, D. 1972. Conditioned insulin secretion and hypoglycemia following repeated injections of tolbutamide in rats. *Endocrinology* 90:227–31

337. Woods, S. C., Porte, D. 1974. Neural control of the endocrine pancreas. *Physiol. Rev.* 54:596–619

338. Wollheim, C. B., Blondel, B., Trauheart, P. A., Renold, A. E., Sharp, G. W. G. 1975. Calcium-induced insulin release in monolayer culture of the endocrine pancreas: Studies with ionophore A23187. *J. Biol. Chem.* 250: 1354–60

339. Zawalich, W. S., Karl, R. C., Ferrendelli, J. A., Matschinsky, F. M. 1975. Factors governing glucose-induced elevation of cyclic 3'5'-monophosphate in pancreatic islets. *Diabetologia* In press

340. Zawalich, W. S., Karl, R. C., Ferrendelli, J. A., Matschinsky, F. M. 1975. Effects of alloxan and cyclic-3'5'-AMP (cAMP) levels and insulin release of isolated pancreatic islets. *Diabetes* 24 (Suppl. 2): 405 (Abstr.)

341. Zawalich, W., Ferrendelli, J., Matschinsky, F. M. 1973. Glucose induced elevation of cyclic 3'5' AMP (cAMP) levels in pancreatic islets. *Diabetes* 22 (Suppl. 1):331 (Abstr.)

341a. Leclercq-Meyer, V., Marchand, J., Malaisse, W. J. 1973. The effect of calcium and magnesium on glucagon secretion. *Endocrinology* 93:1360–70

HYPOTHALAMIC HORMONES[1]   ❖1155

Seymour Reichlin, Richard Saperstein[2], Ivor M. D. Jackson,
Aubrey E. Boyd, III[3], and Yogesh Patel[4]

Endocrine Division, New England Medical Center, Department of Medicine,
Tufts University School of Medicine, Boston, Massachusetts 02111

INTRODUCTION

The field of neuroendocrine research is now highly active, as shown by the large
number of new papers published on neuroendocrine topics in both basic and clinical
journals, and by numerous recent monographs. (38, 82, 83, 95, 96, 104, 106, 146,
154–157, 171, 172, 254, 269). Many factors account for this interest, including the
validation of the concept of neurosecretion and of the portal vessel chemotransmitter hypothesis of control of anterior pituitary function; the identification and synthesis of three of the hypothalamic hypophysiotrophic hormones; the widespread
availability of immunoassay, which permits the easy study of neuroendocrine control in animals and man; the delineation of new neuroendocrine disease syndromes;
the application of basic biochemical methods and concepts to pituitary control; the
identification of hormone receptors in brain; and the exuberant growth of neuropharmacology (234). It is no longer possible to encompass advances in all areas of
this broad field. The last review in this publication was that of Blackwell & Guillemin in 1973 (25). In this chapter we cover several areas of particular current interest,
including extrahypothalamic distribution, biosynthesis and degradation, and neurotransmitter control of the hypophysiotrophic hormones. Physiological aspects of a
newly discovered hypophysiotrophic hormone, growth hormone release inhibiting
hormone (GH-RIH), somatostatin, are also discussed.

[1]Work from the authors' laboratory referred to in this review was supported by National
Institutes of Health Grant No. AM 16684 and Endocrinology Training Grant No. AM 05166.
Clinical studies were conducted on the Clinical Study Unit under Grant No. FR 0054.
[2]US PHS Trainee in Endocrinology. Present address: Merck Institute for Therapeutic
Research, Rahway, New Jersey.
[3]US PHS Trainee in Endocrinology.
[4]Recipient of C. J. Martin Traveling Fellowship of the NHMRC, Australia. Present address:
Medical Research Center, Prince Henry's Hospital, Melbourne, Australia.

DISTRIBUTION OF HYPOPHYSIOTROPHIC HORMONES

According to the portal vessel chemotransmitter hypothesis of anterior pituitary regulation, the hypophysiotrophic hormones are believed to be synthesized by neurons in the hypothalamus, transported to nerve endings in the stalk-median eminence region, released into the interstitial space in contiguity with the primary portal capillary plexus, and distributed to the anterior pituitary through the portal vessels (101). On the basis of physiological studies utilizing hypothalamic lesions, surgical cuts, hypothalamic electrical stimulation, and intrahypothalamic pituitary transplants, an anatomical region termed the hypophysiotropic area by Halasz et al (98) has been identified which is apparently the site of cells that synthesize and control the secretion of the releasing hormones. The introduction of sensitive bioassay and immunoassay methods has now made it possible to determine the extent of the hypophysiotrophic area more precisely and, in addition, has revealed that the brain outside the hypothalamus also contains substantial amounts of releasing hormones. So striking is this extrahypothalamic distribution, particularly in lower forms of animals, that it appears reasonable to speculate that these hormones may have an important function in regulation of neural tissues in general. The finding of extrahypothalamic sources of the releasing hormones has also given support to the hypothesis of Knigge and collaborators (152) that the median eminence may regulate anterior pituitary activity through its function in transporting hypothalamic hormones from the third ventricle to the primary portal circulation. In this section, newer findings about hypothalamic releasing factor distribution, blood and urine concentrations, and the transport functions of the median eminence are reviewed.

Thyrotrophin Releasing Hormone (TRH)

HYPOTHALAMUS   The extent of the "thyrotrophic" area of the hypothalamus as defined by physiological studies, including electrical stimulation, has been summarized in several reviews (181, 182, 233, 239). These indicate a rather broad and diffuse region throughout the medial basal hypothalamus extending from the preoptic area to the premammillary area. The isolation and finally the chemical synthesis of TRH (pyro Glu-His-Pro-NH_2) (27, 30, 42–44), made it possible to develop immunoassays for this compound and methods for detecting biosynthesis. Measurement of the content of TRH in whole rat hypothalamus by radioimmunoassay has given values ranging between 3.6 and 15.7 ng in different laboratories (17, 115–117, 213), levels at least 20 times greater than those previously reported by bioassay (181). The discrepancy is probably attributable to the presence in whole extracts of the hypothalamic hormone somatostatin, which inhibits TRH-induced thyroid stimulating hormone (TSH) release (288). The concentration of TRH is quite similar in the hypothalami of pig, hamster, and man (29), and there is a gradient of TRH concentration from the dorsal hypothalamus in the rat (49 pg/mg), through the ventral hypothalamus (64 pg/mg) to the stalk median eminence (3570 pg/mg) (29). A similar gradient was observed by bioassay methods (166). Hypothalamic localization has been studied more precisely using a histological technique for isolating discrete nuclei by microdissection (44). The highest concentration was found in the median eminence (38.38 ng/mg protein) and certain individual nuclei; for example, the nucleus ventromedialis paramedialis and nucleus periventricularis had concentrations as high as 9.02 and 4.25 ng/mg respectively. Significant amounts were found in the preoptic area, in the nuclei of the septum, and outside the hypothalamus (see below). Immunohistochemical methods have been used with difficulty to demonstrate TRH-containing cells. Somatostatin- and luteinizing hormone releasing hormone (LRH) -containing cells, have been more readily demonstrated by such techniques. We interpret this finding to indicate that the TRH may be distributed relatively diffusely and is readily eluted by standard fixation methods rather than bound in granules, as seems to be the case for LRH and somatostatin. The highest concentration of TRH in cells is found in an enriched synaptosomal fraction of hypothalamus (10).

Fragments of hypothalamic tissue have been shown to incorporate amino acid precursors of TRH into peptides with the mobility of TRH in chromatographic separation systems (192, 239). Incorporation was demonstrable in highest concentration in the median eminence, but was also found in dorsal and ventral hypothalamus. Neither mammillary nuclei, preoptic region, cerebral cortex, nor control tissues were active (236). The discrepancy between the localization studies and biosynthesis studies in the preoptic region may be due to differences in dissection techniques.

EXTRAHYPOTHALAMIC BRAIN TRH

Mammals Small but significant concentrations of TRH occur outside the hypothalamus of rat brain (116–118, 213, 214, 301). Although the concentrations are low, the large mass of extrahypothalamic brain tissue as compared to hypothalamus has led to the surprising conclusion that as much as 80% of total brain TRH is found outside the hypothalamus. In an attempt to determine the source of extrahypothalamic TRH, we have studied the effects of classical thyrotrophic area lesions in the rat, which bring about a reduction of hypothalamic TRH concentration by more than two thirds (119). In such animals, cerebral cortical TRH is significantly but only slightly reduced, indicating a possible contribution of the hypothalamus to extrahypothalamic brain TRH, but the relatively well-maintained concentrations suggest that synthesis occurs in situ. In these animals, urinary TRH was unaffected by hypothalamic lesions, thus indicating that urinary (and, therefore, presumably blood TRH) is largely attributable to secretions of the extrahypothalamic brain; however, the significance of urinary TRH measurements has recently been questioned (see below).

TRH is also present in the rat spinal cord (R. Utiger, personal communication, 1975), in ovine, bovine, and porcine pineal glands (299) and in the neurohypophysis of many species (117). Only trace amounts of TRH are found in the rat pineal, and these are unaltered by environmental lighting (122). Low TRH concentrations are also found in the anterior pituitary of the rat (28).

Distribution of TRH in other vertebrates and invertebrates, phylogenetic distribution
The hypothalamus of all classes of vertebrates examined (rat, chicken, snake, frog, tadpole, and salmon) has high concentrations of TRH (118). Amphibia have especially high TRH levels as compared with rat (3620 pg/mg tissue compared with 300 pg/mg tissue). In snake, frog, tadpole, and salmon, TRH is present in surprisingly high concentrations outside the hypothalamus (Table 1). For example, the cerebellum of the frog contains 520 pg/mg of tissue, and salmon olfactory lobe 165 pg/mg. The identity of these substrates with TRH is demonstrated by showing parallel inhibition curves by immunoassay, and TSH-releasing activity by bioassay in the rat. TRH is also found in the whole brain of the larval lamprey, in the head end of amphioxus (118), and in the circumesophageal ganglia of the snail (93). As the lamprey lacks TSH, and the amphioxus and snail lack a pituitary, we suggest that the TSH-regulating functions of TRH may be a late evolutionary development representing an example of an organism acquiring a new function for a preexisting chemical substance or hormone analogous to the evolution of neurohypophysial hormones as shown by Sawyer (249). In a sense, the pituitary has "co-opted" TRH as a regulatory hormone.

In several submammalian forms, as contrasted with mammals, TRH is found in high concentration in circulating blood. Values of 750 ng/ml have been found in the leopard frog, 300 pg/ml in the chicken (120), and significant levels have been reported in the Mexican axolotl (276).

Table 1 Hypothalamic and extrahypothalamic distribution of TRH in vertebrates[a]
TRH (pg/mg tissue)

Species	Brain stem	Cerebellum	Olfactory lobe	Cerebral cortex (forebrain)	Hypothalamus	Pituitary complex
Rat (4)[b]	5[c]	2	6	1	280[e]	(Neurohypophysis)[f]
(*Rattus norvegicus*)						155
	(4–5)[d]	(1–3)	(5–8)	(1–3)	(240–300)	(150–160)
Chicken (3)	9	1	17	2	41	(Neurohypophysis)
(*Gallus domesticus*)						168
	(8–10)	(1–2)	(16–18)	(1–3)	(34–49)	(95–240)
Snake (3)	283	135	757	338	564	865
(*Thamnophis sirtalis*)	(129–359)	(85–186)	(750–764)	(264–381)	(393–731)	(410–1320)
Frog (4)	55	520	326	111	2270	> 5000
(*Rana pipiens*)	(40–85)	(368–724)	(220–444)	(71–150)	(1520–3620)	(> 5000)
Tadpole (3)	303	Not examined	209	477[g]	947	764
(*Rana pipiens*)	(290–310)		(59–461)		(568–1225)	(508–995)
Salmon (3)	13	3	165	37	235	150
(*Salmo sebago*)		(2–3)	(154–181)	(22–52)	(188–264)	(31–366)

[a] Tissues were extracted for TRH with 90% methanol, and the extract was then evaporated to dryness. The residue was dissolved in buffer for subsequent radio immunoassay.
From Jackson & Reichlin (117).
[b] Number of animals examined.
[c] Pg/mg tissue wet weight (mean concentration).
[d] Range of values (in parentheses).
[e] The mean TRH concentrations of other mammalian hypothalami studied were 480 (hamster) and 500 (pig). Human stalk median eminence (SME) contained up to 300 pg/mg tissue wet weight.
[f] Values for rat and chicken pituitary complex refer to neurohypophysis alone (and do not include anterior pituitary tissue).
[g] Only one fragment extracted.

TRH IN BODY FLUIDS   In confirmation of the portal vessel chemotransmitter hypothesis, TRH has been demonstrated in the portal blood of the rat by bioassay (300) and immunoassay (213), and its concentration increased by electrical stimulation of the hypothalamus (300). A number of workers have recently reported measurements of TRH in the peripheral blood of the rat (116, 196, 213) and man (211). Difficulties in measurement are due to the low concentrations of the hormone and to its rapid degradation by proteolytic enzymes; this has led to considerable controversy about the actual concentration in plasma. It has been reported that TRH is undetectable in plasma of hypothyroid rats, around 60 to 70 pg/ml in normal rats and elevated (150 pg/ml) in T_4-treated animals (213). On the other hand, plasma TRH levels have been found in other studies to range in normal animals between 60 and 80 pg/ml, to be unaffected by thyroid status, and to show an acute rise after cold exposure (196). We have determined plasma TRH levels to be around 13 pg/ml by direct assay (117) and Utiger found levels of 7–30 pg/ml (personal communication). However, based on estimates of secretion rate derived from measurement of urinary excretion and metabolic clearance rate (see below), we calculate that plasma TRH levels will prove to be less than 5 pg/ml (121), a value below the level of sensitivity of assays for TRH thus far reported.

Urine TRH   The first report of a TRH-like material in urine (as well as in blood) of mammals was that of Shibusawa et al (262), who introduced the term TRF (thyrotrophin releasing factor). However, other workers failed to confirm this finding (233), and no further studies of urine were carried out until the introduction of immunoassay. TRH appears in urine after the injection of exogenous hormone in man (16, 123, 124), approximately 15% of the administered dose being identified immunologically. Endogenous TRH has also been detected in urine in both humans (123, 124, 211) and rats (115, 117, 197). Values for 24-hr excretion range between 150 and 700 ng and are significantly higher in men than in women (123, 211). Unlike the situation in the rat (121), TRH excretion in humans is not apparently affected by altered thyroid state (hypothyroidism, hyperthyroidism) (123), but is increased by acute cold exposure (immersion in arctic ocean water) (74). Paradoxically, men exposed to this severe cold stress do not show activation of pituitary-thyroid function despite evidence of increased TRH excretion, suggesting that another factor, perhaps somatostatin, may have blocked pituitary response. J. Leppauludto (personal communication) found that urine immunoreactive TRH does not act like TRH in certain biological systems, thus raising a question as to the identity of the urinary material. Vagenakis et al have suggested that urinary TRH is an artifact (307).

Cerebrospinal fluid TRH   TRH has been detected in rat and human (CSF) using bioassay methods. Values of 18.5 ng/ml in rat third ventricular fluid were found in material removed at death (151), and human lumbar CSF is reported by Oliver et al (211) to range between 65 and 290 pg/ml, whereas Shambaugh & Wilber (261) reported levels of 40 pg/ml. The origin of this material (hypothalamus vs extrahypothalamic brain) has not been established.

Function of extrahypothalamic TRH   The finding of relatively large amounts of TRH outside the hypothalamus has led to a number of efforts to identify neural effects of this hormone on behavior or other measures of brain function. Much attention was generated by the observation that TRH administration was of significant benefit in depression (144, 230), but more recent studies have failed to confirm the original claims (50). TRH is reported to increase cerebral norepinephrine turnover (147) and to be a hypothermic agent in rats (190). Extensive studies of the behavioral effects of TRH in experimental animals have been carried out in the mouse pargyline-DOPA model (229). In this preparation, pargyline, a monoamine oxidase inhibitor, when given together with L-DOPA (dihydroxylphenylaline), causes marked changes in behavior including jumping, running, fighting, and irritability. The administration of TRH suppresses the response in normal animals, and in animals either thyroidectomized or hypophysectomized, thus indicating that the effect is independent of stimulation of the pituitary-thyroid axis. A direct effect of TRH on the function of single neurons has also been shown by measurement of electrical activity after local application of the agent by microiontophoresis. Depression of firing rates was observed in populations of cells in the hypothalamus (62, 240) and in the cerebral cortex and cerebellum by one group (240) but not by another (62). These observations are suggestive but do not as yet provide definitive evidence for a neurotransmitter role of TRH. Final proof will require demonstration that these substances are contained in, and released from, nerve terminals, that there are specific receptor binding sites, and that there is a local system for TRH degradation. The latter criterion has already been met.

Luteinizing Hormone Releasing Hormone (LRH)

ANATOMICAL DISTRIBUTION   The first direct evidence for the presence of LRF [a luteinizing hormone releasing hormone (LRH)] in the hypothalamus was reported by McCann and was based on a bioassay method (186). The distribution of LRH activity was subsequently carefully assessed by a number of workers [see Mess for review (189)], and the effects of lesions of the hypothalamus on regional content of LRH determined. On the basis of such experiments, as well as physiological studies, Barraclough (11) proposed dual hypothalamic control of LRH secretion, mediated by two separate "LRH producing areas." It was suggested that the basal secretion of LH is stimulated by the arcuate and ventromedial nuclei (VMN) and the regulation of cyclic LH by the preoptic suprachiasmatic nuclei. Following the isolation and chemical identification of LRH from porcine (250) and ovine (42) hypothalamus, total synthesis of the LRH decapeptide was achieved. This simple linear peptide, with the structural formula pyro Glu-His-Trp-Ser-Tyr-Gly-Leu-Arg-Pro-Gly NH_2 was shown to release FSH as well as LH in a wide variety of mammalian species [see Schally et al (251) for review], leading to the suggestion that LRH is follicle stimulating hormone releasing hormone (FSH-RH) as well, and that the name should be changed to gonadotrophin releasing hormone (GN-RH.). The identity of the decapeptide with the native hormone is shown by studies in which ovulation or the post-castration elevation of LH and FSH is blocked by injection of antibody to LRH (159), but some observations are compatible with a second, distinct FSH-RH (263).

A major development arising out of the preparation of specific antibodies to LRH has been the utilization of immunoassay to measure activity in specific locations, and of immunohistochemical techniques to study the distribution of this neurohormone. By microdissection, the greatest concentration of LRH is shown to be in the median eminence, with lesser amounts in the arcuate nucleus (216). Small amounts are detectable in the anterior region as well, corresponding to earlier reports of LRH in the preoptic area. A number of workers have reported immunohistological localizations of LRH, but there is some dispute as to the extent of distribution in the hypothalamus and the precise nature of structures containing the hormone. All workers agree that the median eminence of rat, mouse, hamster, and guinea pig is particularly rich in LRH (8, 13, 169, 224). A number (3, 201, 257) find that LRH can be detected as far forward as the preoptic area of the rat and mouse, and extends in fine processes towards the median eminence. In the mouse and rat, Alpert et al (1975) demonstrated heavy concentration of LRH in the premammillary area (3), a surprising finding because this region is relatively silent endocrinologically. The cells of origin of the LRH are not clearly established. Barry and colleagues (13, 14) reported that colchicine, a drug which prevents axonal transport, permits the staining of cell bodies in the preoptic and septal hypothalamic areas after castration in guinea pigs, presumably through the piling up of secretory product. Others failed to confirm this finding (257). In part, this discrepancy may be due to differences in specificity of antibodies used (257). The cell bodies of magnocellular neurons in the frog hypothalamus have recently been shown to contain large amounts of material staining with anti-LRH antibody (L. C. Alpert, personal communication).

The most crucial question deals with the identity of cells containing LRH. Is the LRH contained in neural processes and endings, thus conforming to the classical neurotransmitter hypothesis of pituitary control; localized in the ependymal-tanycytes (specialized ependymal cells that reach from the lumenal side to the external zone), thus conforming to the hypothesis of transmedian eminence transport; or contained in both? Evidence is available to support all three suggestions. LRH has been found to be localized to processes corresponding to the tuberohypophysial tract (257). By electron microscopy, granules were believed to be localized to nerve endings (224), but there is uncertainty about the precise identification of the nerve ending. Particulate fractions corresponding to "synaptosomes" prepared from mammalian hypothalamic tissue contain approximately half of the immunoreactive LRH along with all of the dopamine and TRH, and a heavier particulate fraction contains the rest (10). The mode of preparation of these fractions does not permit separation of synaptosomes from end processes of tanycytes. Others found that LRH is associated only with a heavier fraction (271). A strong argument has been made that the distribution of LRH corresponds to the tubero-infundibular tract (257), that the hormone is synthesized in the cell bodies of the arcuate nucleus and probably the preoptic nuclei, and is transported to terminals in the median eminence by axoplasmic flow along neurons distinct from catecholaminergic ner-uons (150). The presence of LRH in tanycytes (162, 201, 306) as well may be caused by absorption from cerebrospinal fluid or by uptake from adjacent neural elements.

Immunoreactive LRH has been detected in methanolic extracts of hypothalamic tissue from human fetuses as early as 4–5 weeks after conception (302). LRH is also detected in the rat fetus as early as the 18th day of gestation (B. Bercu and I. M. D. Jackson, unpublished). These observations lead to the reasonable speculation that hypothalamic hormones may be involved in the differentiation of the pituitary.

EXTRAHYPOTHALAMIC DISTRIBUTION OF LRH   LRH bioactivity has been found in extrahypothalamic areas including the mesencephalon of the dog and rabbit (66) and rat cerebral cortex (226). By immunohistochemical techniques, cells rostral to the anterior commissure and the paraolfactory area stain with anti-LRH antibody. The organum vasculosum of the lamina terminals is (a periventricular organ located in the anterior septum) also contains LRH (3). These anterior locali-zations may have particular significance because of the recent finding that LRH excites sexual activity in both male and female rats in experiments in which gonadal status is maintained at a constant level (184, 199, 200). Like TRH, LRH has been shown to depress the firing rates of single neurons in the hypothalamus, distinct from those affected by TRH (62). Taken together, these observations suggest that LRH serves as a neurotransmitter with effects on sex drive. Recently, White et al (299) reported that ovine, bovine, and porcine pineal glands contained high levels of LRH as determined by radioimmunoassay and bioassay. Concentrations in the pineal were determined to be 20 times higher than the level in respective hypo-thalami. Others find no LRH in the pineal of the rat, sheep, or monkey (5). There is also some dispute as to the concentration of LRH in rat cerebral cortex. White et al (299) reported that immunoreactive LRH appears after acute stress or castra-tion in the rat, but others were unable to identify LRH in extrahypothalamic brain (5), and White recently reported that the earlier findings may be artifactual.

Using a sensitive radioimmunoassay for LRH, Cramer & Barraclough (51) were unable to detect immunoreactive LRH in third ventricle cerebral spinal fluid of the rat under a variety of experimental conditions. These results suggest that the CSF does not serve as a vehicle for transport of LRH to the median eminence under physiological conditions. However, Morris & Knigge (198) reported that adult male rats show a significant rise of immunoreactive LRH in the CSF as well as in blood after ether stress.

LRH IN BODY FLUIDS   Physiological and anatomical studies in experimental ani-mals indicate that LRH may appear in the peripheral blood (cf 57). By bioassay, circulating LRH has been detected in the rat (204). Similar studies have also been carried out in humans. It has been reported that LRH activity appears in short-lived bursts in peripheral plasma (258, 260), that many women at midcycle have bioreac-tive LRH in the blood (175), and that, in men, long-term castration and estrogen administration lead to increases in bioreactive LRH activity (259). These experiments have been interpreted to mean that LRH hypersecretion contributes to the initiation of the midcycle ovulatory surge and that there are both negative and positive elements in feedback control of LRH secretion. One group has also found immunoreactive LRH in the plasma of several patients at midcycle (6). On the other hand, other workers have failed to detect a midcycle surge of LRH by direct plasma immunoassay (149, 205, 206), and one group using methanol extraction detected no LRH at all (133). In the ewe as well, no correlation between plasma LRH and plasma LH levels has been found (206). By bioassay, it is estimated that normal male plasma contains less than 10 pg/ml, and that, during the midcycle surge, transient values as high as 50 to 300 pg/ml are reached (260). Concentrations as high as this are well within the range of available immunoassays for the decapeptide. The reasons for the discrepancy in findings are not clear. It has been proposed that there are different chemical forms of circulating LRH. Immunoreactive LRH has also been found in human urine (28), but chromatographic studies suggest that this material is a metabolite of LRH, possible the 2–10 nonapeptide (127). Little or no bioactive LRH enters the urine. No LRH was detected in the urine of the rat after the injection of crude hypothalamic extracts using a method that would have detected as little as 3% of the injected dose (80). Direct measurements of LRH in rat portal vessel blood show no definite increase at proestrus, but intermittently high values were demonstrated in monkey portal plasma (46) at this time.

PHYLOGENETIC DISTRIBUTION OF LRH   Immunoreactive LRH has been found in chicken (129) and amphibian (54), but not in fish, hypothalamus (54). The decapeptide releases gonadotrophic hormones in the cockerel (73), amphibian (278), and fish (37). It has been reported that chicken FSH-releasing activity is chromatographically different from that of the rat (115).

LRH thus appears to differ from TRH, which, as previously indicated, has a more extensive distribution in vertebrates and is found in nonvertebrates. However, whereas TRH is able to activate thyroidal function only in mammals and birds, LRH can activate gonadal function in amphibians and fish.

Growth Hormone Releasing Factor (GRF)

There is good evidence, based on immunoassay studies, that crude extracts of hypothalamic tissue, in common with certain physiological stimuli, and electrical stimulation of the hypothalamus are capable of releasing immunoassayable GH from the pituitary [see (235) for review]. The chemical structure of GRF is unknown, and assays are far from satisfactory. Only limited studies have been carried out to delineate the extent of the anatomical distribution of areas of the rat hypothalamus containing GRF. These appear to be restricted to the region of the ventromedial nucleus (VMN) of the hypothalamus (164, 165), a localization generally confirmed by electrical stimulation studies which indicate that the ventromedial nucleus and the basal medial hypothalamus are the only hypothalamic structures directly excitable for GH release (179). In the human, a dialyzable factor in acromegalic plasma was reported to increase GH release from pituitaries in vitro (97) and

GH biosynthesis was stimulated by a cerebrospinal fluid factor from patients with acromegaly (9). These observations have been interpreted to indicate that there is a circulating GRF in this disorder, presumably of hypothalamic origin.

Corticotrophin-Releasing Factor (CRF) and Melanocyte Stimulating Hormone (MSH) Inhibitory Factor (MIF)

The status of CRF, still chemically unidentified, has been summarized by Blackwell & Guillemin (25) and Schally et al (251). Circulating CRF activity has been detected in rats and the levels did not change with complete forebrain removal (304). In light of the demonstration of extrahypothalamic TRH and somatostatin (see below), it is likely that there are one or more extrahypothalamic CRFs.

The status of hypothalamic hormones capable of regulating the secretion of melanocyte stimulating hormone (MSH) remains controversial (cf 237). Melanocyte stimulating hormone inhibitory factor (MIF) activity has been found in mammalian hypothalamic tissue (145, 251); extracts of frog and rat extrahypothalamic brain have also been shown to inhibit MSH release (231). One of the peptides proposed to be the physiological MIF is a tripeptide, prolyl-leucyl-glycinamide, derived by enzymatic cleavage from oxytocin (47), but not all workers accept this view (31). At present it appears reasonable not to use the term MIF for this peptide. The chemical nature of extrahypothalamic MIF is even more obscure. In man, prolyl-leucyl-glycinamide is reported to have antidepressant activity (64).

Function of the Median Eminence in the Transport of Releasing Hormones

According to the classical formulation of the portal vessel chemotransmitter hypothesis, secretions of the hypophysiotrophic neurones are liberated at nerve endings in the median eminence and upper pituitary stalk in relationship to the primary portal vessel capillaries. A second or supplemental view of this system has developed from the work of Löfgren and elaborated by Knigge and collaborators (29). These workers proposed that some portion of the releasing hormones reach the primary portal plexus by transmedian eminence transport and postulated that the releasing hormones are secreted into the ventricular system, taken up by the lumenal processes of the tanycytes of the median eminence, and then actively transported for release at the capillary end of the cell.

The median eminence has been shown to have transport functions since certain amino acids (29), TRH (134), and LRH (21), when injected into the lateral or third ventricle, enter the pituitary despite the fact that the lining ependymal cells of the median eminence are joined by "tight junctions." The median eminence maintains an energy-dependent concentration gradient for thyroxine in vitro and autoradiography shows thyroid hormone uptake by the tanycytes (29).

In further support of the transmedian eminence transport hypothesis is the demonstration in some laboratories that cerebrospinal fluid contains TRH (212, 261). LRH has also been shown by some (198) but not other groups (51) to be present in cerebrospinal fluid, and immunoassayable somatostatin has been demonstrated in human CSF (218). Bioassayable CRF has also been demonstrated in CSF (65).

The injection of TRH (81) or LRH (21) into the ventricular system is followed by activation of TSH or LH release respectively. By histochemical study, there is still controversy as to the cellular localization of the releasing hormones (see above). LRH, for which the most complete data are available, is probably found in both nerve endings and tanycytes, thus suggesting dual sources of input (3, 224, 306). On the other hand, somatostatin appears to be distributed mainly in neural elements (3, 111, 225).

At this time, it appears that release from nerve endings is still probably the major route of hypophysiotrophic hormone release; however, the tanycyte may also play a role in maintaining basal function.

HYPOPHYSIOTROPHIC HORMONE BIOSYNTHESIS AND DEGRADATION

Peptide hormones are generally synthesized on ribosomes, usually in the form of a prohormone, which is then broken down by a specific degrading enzyme. Classical examples of this process are insulin (268), parathyroid hormone (148), and vasopressin (245) synthesis. In contrast to vasopressin, the mechanism of the biosynthesis of the hypophysiotrophic hormones has not been established and alternative mechanisms have been proposed [see (237) for review].

TRH Biosynthesis

The isolation and chemical synthesis of TRH made it possible to study the mechanism of biosynthesis of this hormone. Rat hypothalamic fragments, incubated in vitro in the presence of labeled amino acid precursors of TRH, were found to incorporate radioactivity into peptides with chromatographic and electrophoretic behavior similar to that of authentic TRH (192). These experiments were criticized by McKelvy (187) on the basis that proof of identity of the labeled product was not sufficiently rigorous and that only a fraction of the radioactivity moving with TRH on electrophoresis or thin-layer chromatography was authentic TRH. Using guinea pig hypothalamic incubates, this worker showed by exhaustive isolation procedures, including gas chromatography of n-trifluoroacetyl n-butyl ester derivatives, that [^{3}H]proline was incorporated into a compound indistinguishable from TRH. Similar findings were reported by Grimm-Jorgensen (née Grimm) & McKelvy using newt (*Triturus viridescens*) whole brain (92, 92a). In the newt, as in other lower forms, there is an extensive extrahypothalamic distribution of TRH. Mouse hypothalamic fragments were reported to incorporate [^{14}C]histidine into a peptide chromatographically identical with TRH which was co-chromatographed to constant specific activity with authentic [^{3}H-]-TRH (94).

Because TRH formation was observed to continue in the presence of an inhibitor of protein synthesis, it was proposed (193, 236, 239) that the synthesis of TRH might be analogous to those enzymatic processes responsible for biosynthesis of glutathione and ophthalmic acid, both tripeptides (237). This hypothesis was tested by incubating homogenates of porcine and rat tissue with amino acid precursors of TRH together with cofactors recognized to be important to formation of glutathione. These include ATP and Mg^{2+}. Such incubates were reported to incorporate labeled amino acids into a peptide with the chromatographic behavior of TRH in several systems including thin-layer chromatography, electrophoresis, Sephadex, and CM-cellulose chromatography. The activity was found only in the hypothalamus and was detectable in high-speed supernatants presumably devoid of ribosomes. It was proposed on the basis of these findings that TRH was synthesized by a nonribosomal synthetic process mediated by a "TRH synthetase(s)." It was also reported that prior thyroid hormone status influenced the rate of incorporation of [14C] proline into TRH, hypothyroidism decreasing the effect markedly, and thyroid hormone treatment stimulating incorporation. A positive stimulating effect of thyroid hormone on TRH synthesis (and by inference on TRH secretion) was postulated.

Subsequent to these publications, several groups attempted to repeat these experiments and serious criticisms have been raised about the original experiments. Upon incubation, hypothalamic extracts form a number of labeled peptides, and those with the behavior of TRH on charcoal and thin-layer chromatography or electrophoresis were found by elaborate separation procedures to have other properties inconsistent with TRH (18–20). It has also been found that hypothalamic extracts similar to those used for biosynthesis experiments have active enzymatic TRH degrading systems (18–20, 58, 247). An "exchange reaction" in the degrading system may account for the incorporation of amino acids into TRH, as proposed on the basis of studies with pyro-Glu-His-OCH_3 and Glu-His-OCH, TRH analogs (18, 19). This argument is apparently answered by the finding that the concentration of TRH in a hypothalamic incubation system was found to increase after incubation as determined by bioassay (193), thus indicating new hormone synthesis, but we have been unable to confirm our observations using porcine or rat hypothalamic extracts by immunoassay for TRH (R. Saperstein, I. M. D. Jackson, and S. Reichlin, 1975, unpublished). A cell-free extract of newt brain was reported to incorporate [3H] proline into a TRH-like substance, the identify of which was established by rigorous physicochemical methods (92a). The incorporation was not blocked by ribosome synthesis inhibitors, including highly potent purified diphtheria toxin, but was blocked by pancreatic RNase, leading to the novel proposal that TRH synthesis was mediated by a nonribosomal, RNA-dependent enzymic mechanism. In our laboratory, we developed techniques for preventing the breakdown of TRH in hypothalamic incubates (see below) and for specific immunoprecipitation of TRH. Preliminary experiments have thus far failed to demonstrate the incorporation of [3H] proline into immunoprecipitable TRH (S. Reichlin, S. Mothon, R. Saperstein, 1975, unpublished). In the light of these conflicting findings, including those from our own laboratory, we feel that a final judgment as to the mechanism of TRH biosynthesis cannot be made at this time.

TRH Degradation

As mentioned above, TRH is degraded by hypothalamic extracts; the rate of degradation is a function of extract concentration. Extrahypothalamic brain is also active (17). The systems are inactivated by boiling and, to a certain extent, by the addition of benzamidine (247). That plasma inactivates TRH has been known for some time (15, 202, 287); the mechanism of inactivation appears to be both a relatively specific deamidase and a peptidase, since the addition of the dipeptide analog of TRH (pyro-Glu-His-O-methyl ester) prevents the degradation of TRH (287). The products of hypothalamic digestion include deamido-TRH, proline, and prolinamide (18, 19). The addition of certain peptides, both amidated and nonamidated (the latter including deamido-TRH, deamido-LRH, and angiotensin II) will block both the deamidation and the peptidolysis of TRH by hypothalamic extracts (257). On this basis it was concluded that the enzymes responsible for TRH deamidation were similar or identical to those that lysed peptide bonds. The variety of peptides that interfere with TRH degradation suggests that the system is not specific for TRH. Nor is there any evidence that the rate of TRH degradation is a regulatory site in control of TRH secretion, although this may be a theoretical possibility.

LRH Biosynthesis

Relatively little work has been done on the biosynthesis of LRH. Prior to the discovery of the LRH decapeptide, we reported in preliminary studies that particulate-free hypothalamic extracts incubated in the presence of a mixture of 21 amino acids (including all essential amino acids), ATP, and Mg^{2+} formed LRH activity as determined by bioassay (236). We have not attempted to repeat these studies using marker LRH decapeptide or LRH immunoassay, but Johansson et al (130) reported that hypothalamic tissue slices, incubated in vitro, incorporate $[^{14}C]$ glutamic acid into a peptide with the chromatographic characteristics of the decapeptide on polyacrylamide gels and thin-layer chromatography. Similar studies have also been reported by Moguilevsky et al (195), who utilized Sephadex and CM-cellulose–Sephadex column chromatography for separation.

The latter workers also reported that incorporation is increased in castrated rats. In further work, Johansson et al reported that an enriched fraction of hypothalamic tissue (so-called mitochondrial fraction, which undoubtedly contains other particles including synaptosomes) was also capable of incorporating glutamic acid into LRH (131). They postulated that the mechanism of biosynthesis may be akin to the so-called pantetheine-template mechanism.

On the basis of studies thus far reported, it must be concluded that the mechanism of biosynthesis of LRH has not been established with certainty.

LRH Degradation

Hypothalamic extracts of both porcine and rat origin actively degrade the decapeptide LRH, as has been shown by bioassay (88), by chromatography of labeled LRH degradation products (247), by immunoassay (90, 91), and by the isolation of peptide fragments (158). The nature of the product formed was shown by Koch et al to be a 6- and a 4-amino acid fragment (158), corresponding to breakdown of the glycyl-leucyl bond between amino acid residues 6 and 7. That an endopeptidase is responsible for this effect is further shown by the demonstration that a large variety of peptide substrates including oxytocin, deamido-LRH, angiotensin I, angiotensin II, and angiotensin II amide are all capable of interfering with this reaction (247).

It is unlikely that the glycyl-leucyl bond is a unique substrate for the enzyme(s), because a similar grouping is not found in some peptides that can block the reaction.

Griffiths and colleagues (91) have proposed that LRH degrading enzymes may serve a significant functional or physiological role as regulators of LRH secretion. That the rate of breakdown of peptide hormones at both synthesizing and receptor sites, may be important regulators of secretion rate has been proposed as a general mechanism of control (cf 153, 294). The concentration of oxytocin degrading enzymes in the hypothalamus [which appears to be a reflection of the concentration or activity of LRH degrading enzymes (cf 88)] has been shown to be modulated by the sex hormone status of the donor animals (pregnancy, castration, estrus cycle, estrogen administration) (85–87, 112). There is a degree of anatomical specificity of the LRH degrading system (89), but firm opinion as to this view cannot be developed at this time. The degrading systems appear to be relatively nonspecific in their substrate requirements and attack other hormones including TRH, LRH, oxytocin, vasopressin, and angiotensin II (R. Saperstein, S. Mothon, and S. Reichlin, unpublished).

It is also important to recognize that studies of biosynthesis of LRH (like those of TRH biosynthesis) will be affected by simultaneous breakdown of product by the degrading systems.

Biosynthesis of Prolyl-Leucyl-Glycinamide

Very extensive studies have been carried out of the mode of formation of L-prolyl-1-leucyl-glycinamide from its precursor oxytocin (47, 294–296). This substance is believed to be important because it inhibits MSH release in certain bioassay preparations (47), but not all authors agree that this substance is in fact MIF (31). Nevertheless, the formation of "MIF" is of considerable theoretical interest. It has been demonstrated that hypothalami of rabbit and rat contain "a membrane bound" exopeptidase that stepwise degrades radioactively-labeled oxytocin (9-glycinamide-1-^{14}C-oxytocin) to give labeled H-Pro-Leu-Gly-NH$_2$, which is the release-inhibiting hormone of MSH (MIF). Supernatant fractions of rabbit and rat hypothalami contain predominantly an endopeptidase that releases H-leu-gly-NH$_2$ (294). A molecular basis of these reactions and a general discussion of the role of enzymes in hormone formation have been proposed by Walter (294–296).

Biosynthesis of Other Hypothalamic Hormones

Particulate-free extracts of hypothalamic tissue, incubated in the presence of essential amino acids, ATP, and Mg^{2+} were found to show increased bioassayable GRF (238) and (PRF) (194) activity. These studies have not as yet been confirmed in other laboratories and do not clearly differentiate between breakdown of a prohormone to form biological activity and de novo biosynthesis.

NEUROTRANSMITTER CONTROL OF HYPOPHYSIOTROPHIC NEURON FUNCTION

The neurosecretory neurons that synthesize and release hypophysiotrophic hormones serve as the link between the nervous system and the anterior pituitary.

Wurtman has popularized the term *neuroendocrine transducer* to describe cells of this type because they are capable of changing (transducing) a neural message into a hormonal output (303). The hypophysiotrophic neurons are in turn regulated by another set of specialized neurons, which fall into four general classes: dopaminergic, noradrenergic, serotoninergic, and cholinergic. That the hypothalamus is particularly rich in these neurotransmitters was recognized early on the basis of bioassay studies, and for a period of time there was considerable speculation as to whether these substances were in fact direct pituitary regulators. Clear differentiation of these functions did not come, however, until the development of the formaldehyde fluorescent techniques (70, 277), which made it possible to identify amine-containing neurons. These techniques, combined with neuropharmacological manipulations (53) and more sophisticated spectrophotometric methods (283), have delineated separate aminergic tracts in the brain (110). Noradrenergic pathways arise in the mesencephalon and lower brain stem, innervate the hypothalamus, and ascend to the amygdala, hippocampus, and cerebral cortex. Some noradrenergic fibers end in the median eminence as well. Serotoninergic neurons also arise in the midbrain; the cell bodies in this instance are located in the raphe nuclei. Ascending fibers terminate in the hypothalamus and other parts of the limbic system. The dopaminergic system innervating the hypothalamus has a dual origin. One group of dopaminergic neurons arises from the midbrain and, in addition to supplying the hypothalamus, also makes a major contribution to the basal ganglia. Other dopaminergic neurons arise within the hypothalamus itself. The most important of these are in the arcuate nucleus, and are believed to contribute more than 20% of the total neurons in the median eminence. Recently, the techniques of microdissection (215) have been applied to the delineation of the monaminergic pathways and extensive studies carried out on the effects of various endocrine manipulations on the turnover of biogenic amines in the hypothalamus (4) as an index to feedback control of hormone secretion.

In addition to anatomical studies, much work on control of hypophysiotrophic function has utilized neuropharmacologic agents that are neurotransmitter agonists and antagonists [see (72) for review]. In most studies, altered secretion of hypophysiotrophic hormones has been inferred from changes in pituitary function, this approach has an intrinsic drawback in that a putative neurotransmitter may exert an effect directly on the pituitary gland or may affect both inhibitory and stimulatory factors. In this section recent neuropharmacological studies of anterior pituitary regulation are reviewed.

Neurotransmitter Regulation of CRF Secretion

A number of studies in animals support the view that acetylcholine is an excitatory neurotransmitter for CRF release. Implants of the anticholinergic drug atropine into the anterior hypothalamus inhibit the pituitary-adrenal response to stress in the rat (105), whereas implants of a long-acting acetylcholine analog increase basal secretion of corticosteroids (67, 163). Evidence for a monoaminergic control of CRF secretion is less certain and the data are contradictory. Noradrenergic agonists generally appear to be inhibitory of ACTH secretion in the dog (292) and the rat (293). Norepinephrine has no effect on basal CRF levels in rat hypothalami but inhibits the CRF rise in response to acetylcholine (109). Depletion of brain cate-cholamines by reserpine does not affect pituitary-adrenal control (283), and L-DOPA administration (which leads to an increase in central dopamine) has no effect on basal or stimulated cortisol secretion in man (32). On the other hand, ampheta-mines stimulate ACTH secretion, presumably due to α-receptor agonist effects, since the response is blocked by α-adrenergic blocking drugs (22, 232). Adrenergic pathways also mediate ACTH responses to hypoglycemic stress. Phentolamine, an α-receptor blocker, suppresses this response, whereas propranalol, a β-receptor blocker, enhances ACTH secretion (114). Because cyproheptidine, a blocker of serotonin receptors, also blocks hypoglycemia-induced ACTH release (228), it may be postulated that ACTH is influenced by serotoninergic pathways.

Neurotransmitter Regulation of Prolactin Inhibiting Factor (PIF) and Prolactin Releasing Factor (PRF)

Secretion of prolactin is influenced by an inhibitory hypophysiotrophic hormone (PIF) (69, 208) and by two prolactin releasing factors, one of which is TRH (125, 274) and the other, like PIF, is of unknown but presumably peptidic structure (188, 208, 290). Dopamine has both a direct and indirect inhibitory effect on prolactin release, but its role as a direct regulator of prolactin secretion has not been deter-mined because this neurotransmitter has not as yet been unequivocally shown to be present in portal plasma. A number of pharmacologic agents influence prolactin secretion, but the complexity of hypophysiotrophic influences and the lack of direct methods for measuring PIF and PRF secretion have made difficult the analysis of neurotransmitter control of prolactin regulatory hormones.

In man and rat, the administration of drugs that inhibit catecholamine synthesis or storage, such as reserpine, haloperidol, and chlorpromazine, lead to a stimulation of prolactin release (59, 71, 72). The usual interpretation of this finding is that catecholamines regulate the tonic secretion of PIF. In accordance with this view is the finding that L-DOPA, a precursor of dopamine, suppresses prolactin secretion (72, 176) as do the dopamine receptor agonists apomorphine (184) and bromergo-cryptine (55). It was also shown by Kamberi et al that the direct infusion of dopamine into the hypothalamus (but not of norepinephrine) led to inhibition of prolactin secretion (139). Infusion of portal vessels with dopamine was reported by these workers to be ineffective in influencing prolactin secretion, but more recent studies indicate that both dopamine and norepinephrine can inhibit prolactin release in both perfusion studies and organ incubation experiments (174, 272). Dopamine receptor agonists inhibit prolactin secretion in patients with pituitary tumors (184) and also interfere with TRH-stimulated prolactin release (209). For these reasons, both a central and a peripheral action of dopamine have been postulated.

In addition to a PIF regulatory component, presumably under the influence of catecholamines (dopamine ?), there appears to be a stimulatory serotoninergic com-ponent. Tryptophan and 5-hydroxytryptophan, both precursors of serotonin, when administered to the rat (141) and man (173), release prolactin while blockade of 5-hydroxytryptophan synthesis with the agent para-chlorophenylalanine prevents suckling-induced prolactin release in the rat (161). It may be postulated that these stimulatory effects are due to release of PRF (rather than being due to inhibition of PIF). In support of this view is the finding that reserpine administration in the rat raises plasma prolactin levels (presumably by inhibiting PIF secretion) but does not block stress-induced prolactin release (291). On the other hand, stress-induced prolactin release is blocked by methysergide, a serotonin receptor blocker (177). Taken together, one may propose that PIF secretion is regulated by a catecholaminergic pathway and that PRF is regulated by a serotoninergic pathway. The third of the prolactin regulatory hormones, TRH, is not directly involved in reflex prolactin secretion control, since stimuli that affect prolactin release and suppression are not accompanied by alterations in TSH secretion (75). Nevertheless, TRH may well have a modulating influence on prolactin secretion because the parallelism of dose response thresholds of TRH effects on prolactin and TSH release (in man) indicate that amounts of TRH required to maintain pituitary-thyroid function are enough to influence prolactin release (125). In states of hypothyroidism in man, there may be an increase in prolactin secretion in some instances sufficient to stimulate lactation (63). This observation has been variously interpreted to mean that TRH secretion is enhanced, thus leading to hyperprolactinemia, or that the prolactin secretory sensitivity of the pituitary to TRH is enhanced (266) as is the TSH secretory sensitivity.

Neurotransmitter Control of GH Regulatory Hormones

Growth hormone secretion is affected by a releasing factor, named GRF (or somatotrophin releasing factor, SRF), the structure of which has not been elucidated, and by somatostatin, an inhibitory peptide of established structure (see below). Although somatostatin is present in the median eminence, its role as a physiological regulator of GH secretion has not been defined.

Extensive studies of neurotransmitter control of GH secretion indicate that three biogenic amines may be involved and that different kinds of stimuli may alter GH secretion through one or another of these amines. The relationship between a specific amine transmitter and a specific hypophysiotrophic hormone (GRF, somatostatin), as in the case of the prolactin regulatory hormones, has not been established. Noradrenergic pathways play an important role in GH regulation. Direct injection of norepinephrine into the hypothalamus of the baboon is followed by marked rise in plasma GH (280). That the response is due to stimulation of α -receptors is suggested by the finding that phentolamine, an α-receptor blocker, reduces GH response to a number of stimuli, including hypoglycemia (24), vasopressin (107), arginine (41), L-DOPA (143), glucagon (191), amphetamines (232), and theophylline (68). GH secretory responses to these agents are generally enhanced by treatment with propranalol, a β blocker. Although the effects of L-DOPA may be attributable to its product, dopamine, this substance also increases hypothalamic turnover of norepinephrine (244) and displaces serotonin from neurons (207). Thus the increase in GH secretion seen after the use of the drug (33) could be related to changes in secretion of any of these three transmitters. More specific evidence of dopaminergic control is the finding that fusaric acid, an inhibitor of the enzyme dopamine β-hydroxylase, which converts dopamine to norepinephrine, does not block GH release (108). Apomorphine, a relatively specific dopamine receptor stimulator, leads increased GH levels in man (167).

Serotoninergic pathways are apparently involved in sleep-induced GH release. This aspect of GH control is not influenced by α- or β-adrenergic receptor blockers (273), but is blocked by cyproheptidine, a serotonin receptor blocker (203). Serotonin injections into the lateral ventricle of the rat stimulates GH secretion (49) as does 5-hydroxytryptophan, a precursor of serotonin (5-hydroxytryptamine), when administered to man (113) or monkey (126). In the monkey, this agent also induced behavioral sleep and sleep-related changes in the EEG (126).

Neurotransmitter Regulation of TRH Secretion

Relatively little work has been carried out on neurotransmitter control of TRH secretion. In early studies, intrahypothalamic injection of norepinephrine, dopamine, and serotonin were all without effect on thyroid function in the rabbit (102) or the rat (84). However, TSH levels are depressed by administration of reserpine (236). More recently, it has been reported that cold-induced TSH release in warm-adapted rats is decreased by reserpine. Phentolamine and phenoxybenzamine, both α-receptors, and disulfiram, an agent which blocks conversion of dopamine to norepinephrine, also inhibit cold-induced TSH release. These data suggest that TRH secretion is controlled by noradrenergic neurons (281).

Direct studies of TRH secretion utilizing mouse hypothalami, pulse-labeled with the TRH precursor [^{14}C]histidine (94), showed that norepinephrine stimulates TRH release, as does dopamine. The response to dopamine was blocked by disulfiram. In contrast, serotonin inhibited TRH release. Cholinergic agents were without effect. Thus the in vitro and in vivo studies generally support the hypothesis of noradrenergic control of TRH secretion.

Neurotransmitter Regulation of LRH Secretion

The earliest neuroendocrine experiments designed to show neurotransmitter regulation of the anterior pituitary gland were those of Taubenhaus & Soskin (275) who, in 1941, studied the effects of acetylcholine on gonadotrophin function in the rat after direct application of the compound to the exposed pituitary. The vast amount of work in this field has been reviewed by McCann & Moss (185). In early studies, a role of noradrenergic neurotransmitters in regulation of gonadotrophin secretion was demonstrated by the use of dibenzyline, an adrenergic blocking agent (248), and reserpine, a catecholamine depleting agent (12), both of which block ovulation in rat and rabbit. Drugs that decrease the synthesis of catecholamines by inhibiting the rate-limiting tyrosine hydroxylase enzymatic step block the postcastration rise in gonadotrophins (210), the preovulatory gonadotrophin surge (137), and stimulation of gonadotrophin release by estrogen or progesterone in estrogen-primed rats (136, 138). Partial or complete reversal of these effects can be achieved by reinitiating catecholamine synthesis (137, 210). The use of more specific blockers of norepinephrine synthesis indicates that these effects are mediated by noradrenergic neurons.

Additional, though indirect, support for noradrenergic control of gonadotrophin release is the demonstration that hypothalamic norepinephrine turnover is increased at times of increased gonadotrophin secretion, as during proestrus (60) or after castration (4). Catecholamines do not have a direct effect on the pituitary but have been shown to release LRF in vitro from hypothalamic incubates (141). Dopamine and its precursor, L-DOPA, also stimulate LH release, but the effects are blocked with the α-receptor blocker, phentolamine, as well as with haloperidol (141, 252). These effects have been attributed to neuronal uptake of dopamine with subsequent conversion to the active agent norepinephrine (185, 253). More evidence for this view includes the observation that the LH rise that follows electrical stimulation of the hypothalamus is blocked by inhibiting catecholamine synthesis (135).

Other neurotransmitters have been imputed to be involved in control of gonadotrophin secretion. Large doses of atropine block ovulation in the rabbit (178) and, conversely, acetylcholine releases FSH and LH in a hypothalamic-pituitary coincubation system (267). Although inhibition of serotonin biosynthesis does not affect gonadotrophin release (59), direct injection of serotonin or melatonin into the third ventricle is inhibitory (141, 142). Histamine, in high and presumably unphysiological concentrations, has also been shown to release the gonadotrophins following intraventricular injection (170). Prostaglandins have also been implicated in hypothalamic control of gonadotrophins (103), but it is still too early to conclude that this substance has a physiological role in control of LRH secretion.

SOMATOSTATIN (GH RELEASE INHIBITORY FACTOR, SRIF)

One of the major recent achievements in the field of hypothalamic hormones was the elucidation in 1973 by Guillemin and co-workers of the structure of a hypothalamic peptide, which possessed potent growth hormone release inhibitory properties. The first tentative evidence for a GIF was reported by Krulich and collaborators (164) who studied the effects of hypothalamic extracts on GH release by rat pituitary incubates. The inhibitory effect of certain hypothalamic fractions on GH release was rediscovered by Guillemin and collaborators during attempts, still unsuccessful, to isolate GRF (36, 45). The inhibitory compound was isolated from ovine hypothalamic extracts, purified, characterized chemically as a cyclic tetradecapeptide to which the descriptive name *somatostatin* was given. The formula of this compound is H Ala-Gly-Cys-Lys-Asn-Phe-Phe-Trp-Lys-Thr-Phe-Thr-Ser-Cys-OH with a bridge between the two cysteine groups. The synthetic material possesses activities identical to the native compound (36), and antibodies generated against the synthetic form show cross-reactivity to tissue extracts (7, 8, 221) and to tissues studied by immunohistological methods (3, 223, 225). It can be confidently assumed therefore that the synthetic is immunologically identical to the native hormone as found in situ.

In the relatively short time since its discovery, somatostatin has been found to possess a surprising range of biological effects, to have an unexpectedly wide anatomical distribution, and to act in all species of mammals in which it has been tested.

Growth Hormone Secretion

Somatostatin injections have been shown to suppress both basal GH secretion and the GH response to all known stimuli of its secretion in man, dog, baboon, and rat. GH secretion stimulated by exercise (100), sleep (217), insulin-induced hypoglycemia (99), arginine infusion (264), L-DOPA (264), protein-calorie malnutrition (227), and intrahypothalamic injection of norepinephrine (245) are all abolished by treatment with somatostatin. In the rat, somatostatin injections reduce growth rate and block GH secretory response to pentobarbital (79), morphine (183), gentling (79), injections of crude preparations of GRF (270), and electrical stimulation of the ventromedial nucleus of the hypothalamus (180). In patients with GH hypersecretion due to hyperplasia or adenomas of the pituitary, somatostatin also reduces plasma GH levels (23, 99, 217, 227, 305). The rate of decline of GH during somatostatin infusion is rapid; the mean half-time of 24–34 min corresponds closely to that of the biological disappearance of GH, thus suggesting that the hypothalamic hormone has produced almost immediate inhibition of GH release (227, 305). The inhibitory actions of somatostatin on GH release, originally identified by effects on pituitary cell incubates (36), have been repeatedly examined in other in vitro systems (see section on mechanism of somatostatin effect).

Other Pituitary Actions of Somatostatin

Apart from its effects on GH secretion, somatostatin has been found to inhibit the secretion of a number of other pituitary hormones, the most important of which is TSH. TRH-induced TSH secretion in man (99, 265), rat (29, 288), and mouse (288) is completely blocked by prior treatment with somatostatin. The TSH secretion from pituitary incubates stimulated by a variety of secretogogues, including TRH, elevated K^+, and theophyline, is also blocked by this peptide (288).

Both basal and TRH-stimulated prolactin secretion in normal individuals is uninfluenced by somatostatin (99, 264, 265) but in some (305), but not all (99), acromegalics this peptide lowers either normal or elevated basal prolactin levels. The spontaneous release of prolactin by rat pituitary cells in culture is also inhibited by somatostatin but to a much lesser extent than the spontaneous release of GH (288).

The secretion of other pituitary hormones, ACTH (99), LH, and FSH (99, 264, 265) in normal persons is not apparently influenced by somatostatin, but in patients with "Nelson's Syndrome" (ACTH hypersecreting pituitary chromophobe adenoma following adrenalectomy for Cushing's disease), plasma ACTH levels are significantly reduced by somatostatin (282).

Extrapituitary Actions of Somatostatin

One of the most surprising and potentially important aspects of somatostatin action is its effect on certain extrapituitary functions. Plasma glucose was found by Koerker and co-workers (160) to fall during somatostatin administration in baboons fasted overnight. The effect was preceded by a dramatic fall in plasma glucagon and insulin levels. Detailed studies indicate that the effects on glucose levels are secondary to changes in glucagon secretion, thus establishing an important role of tonic glucagon secretion in glucose homeostasis. Somatostatin has no direct effects on either hepatic glucose production or on peripheral glucose utilization (160, 246) and lowers glucose levels even in the absence of the pituitary (77). It does not interfere with hyperglycemic responses to glucagon administration (76).

The effects of somatostatin on glucagon and insulin secretion are readily detected in fasting animals (2, 56, 160) and also in the responses to the usual secretogogues of the islet cells. Thus insulin secretion induced by glucose (1), arginine (78, 79), glucagon (76), and tolbutamide (76) in man, and arginine-stimulated insulin and glucagon release in man and baboons (79, 160), is blocked by the hypothalamic hormone.

Preparations of pancreas from rat (79, 132, 297) and dog (1) perfused in vitro with somatostatin show decreased glucagon and/or insulin responses to arginine, glucose, and theophylline, isoproterenol, and epinephrine. The α cell is apparently more sensitive to somatostatin effects than is the β cell. As shown by Gerich and collaborators (79), glucagon secretion is 20 times more sensitive to somatostatin inhibition than is insulin secretion. Furthermore, because glucagon itself stimulates insulin secretion (52), it is possible that somatostatin decreases the release of insulin from pancreatic β cells in part by inhibiting glucagon release. Glucagon and insulin secreting tumors of the pancreas have also been inhibited by somatostatin.

Limited trials of somatostatin in the management of diabetic patients have given new insight into the role of glucagon in the alterations of glucose metabolism in this disorder. The marked lability of blood glucose regulation in juvenile diabetics ("brittle diabetes") is ameliorated by somatostatin administration (77, 279), and the insulin requirement reduced by 30–50%. In the light of these observations, it is clear that suitable long-acting preparations of somatostatin might be useful adjuncts in the control of diabetes. Moreover, because GH hypersecretion may contribute to the development of microangiopathy, somatostatin, by suppressing GH secretion, may be a useful therapeutic agent in the treatment of the vascular complications of diabetes.

The extrapituitary reactions of somatostatin are not confined to the pancreas. The peptide inhibits gastrin release in normal subjects and in acromegalic patients (26). In a patient with a secreting tumor of the pancreas (Zollinger-Ellison syndrome), the elevated plasma gastrin levels were greatly lowered during somatostatin infusion (26).

Mechanism of Action of Somatostatin, Structure-Activity Relationships

Although the hormone isolated from ovine hypothalamic tissue was in the cyclized (oxidized) form, synthetic linear somatostatin exhibits identical biological activity (36, 242), leaving open the question of the precise form of the substance in tissue or at receptors. In an attempt to elucidate the role of the disulfide bridge, the biological activity of the analog Ala[3,14]somatostatin and SMeCys3,14somatostatin, neither of which can form a covalent cyclic structure, has been tested (243, 256). Both peptides showed low but detectable biological activity in vitro (0.01–1.0% of the cyclic compound). These results may be interpreted to indicate that the disulfide bond is important for receptor interaction, but alternative explanations have been proposed (256). Substitution of the first amino acid alanine with tyrosine (Tyr1-somatostatin), and deletions of the N-terminal dipeptide, Ala1Gly2 (des-Ala-Gly somatostatin or des-Ala-Gly H somatostatin) are compatible with high (33–100%) biological activity (243, 286). Several acyl cyst 3 analogs of somatostatin when administered as a microsuspension have shown prolonged growth hormone secretory inhibitory activity (up to 3 days) (35). Preparations such as these hold eventual promise for the use of somatostatin in therapeutics.

Studies of the biochemical basis of somatostatin action on the pituitary are underway in a number of laboratories. Although it is likely that somatostatin, like TRH and LRH, binds to specific membrane receptors, this has not yet been definitely demonstrated because suitable labeled preparations of native somatostatin are not available. It is not possible to readily iodinate the native compound (due to its lack of either tyrosine or histidine moieties). Nevertheless, it has been shown to suppress GH and TSH release induced by dibutyryl cAMP, theophylline, and PGE$_2$ (29, 285). Theophylline-stimulated glucagon and insulin release by the isolated perfused rat pancreas is also blocked by somatostatin (79). Somatostatin lowers basal levels of adenohypophysial cAMP and blocks the response to either PGE$_2$ or theophylline (29). Although the inhibitory actions are consistent with an effect of the hormone at a step preceding cAMP formation, the evidence that somatostatin inhibits theophylline and dB cAMP-induced GH and TSH release suggests an additional action at a biochemical site distal to AMP formation. The action of somatostatin is not blocked by agents that inhibit protein synthesis (286, 288).

Regulation of Somatostatin Secretion

Little is known of the factors that regulate secretion of somatostatin. The most likely possibility is that hypothalamic somatostatin is controlled by preoptic and anterior hypothalamic pathways that regulate somatostatin-containing neurons in the hypophysiotrophic area. Somatostatin-containing neural processes have been demonstrated in the anterior hypothalamus and median eminence (3, 223). Lesions of the preoptic area or destruction of the prosencephalon in the rat (241) lead to elevation in basal plasma GH levels and prevent the usual inhibition of GH release which follows stressful exposure in this species. Electrical stimulation of the anterior hypothalamus of the rat leads to inhibition of basal GH secretion; stimulation of the median eminence leads to sustained inhibition of GH secretion followed by a marked increase in GH release commencing when hypothalamic stimulation ceases. These observations have been interpreted by Martin and collaborators (179) to indicate that the hypothalamus exerts both excitatory (through GRF) and inhibitory effects on GH release. The final secretion rate depends upon the relative influence of these two factors.

It is important to recognize that cessation of somatostatin secretion is followed by a hypersecretory rebound (180).

Biological Half-Life and Administration of Somatostatin

The time course of the somatostatin effect after intravenous injection is short (approximately 5 min), due for the most part to the very rapid breakdown of the hormone in the blood by peptidolysis (Y. C. Patel, 1975, unpublished). The material is quite ineffective by other routes. Much of the early investigative work in man has utilized a priming dose of 125–500 μg of intravenous followed by a constant infusion of approximately 10 μg/min. Doses as low as 25–100 μg administered over a 75-min period have been found effective in acromegaly (23) and a dose of 4 mg subcutaneous reduces glucagon secretion in diabetics, (77). Concentrations of somatostatin in the range of 0.1–100 ng/ml are effective on the in vitro perfused rat or dog pancreas (1, 79, 297). As little as 1 nM concentrations of somatostatin inhibits GH release from pituitary cell cultures (36). As yet no long-acting preparation has been perfected. Protamine-zinc somatostatin prolongs action in rats (34), but apparently is not effective in man or monkey. Because there is GH hypersecretion after cessation of somatostatin effects, it will be important from the therapeutic point of view to provide a reliable long-acting preparation. At the time that this review was completed (May 1975) no significant toxic effects of somatostatin had been recognized in man (2, 26, 79, 99, 264, 265). However, a series of baboons treated chronically with large doses of somatostatin (ten times higher than doses given to humans) by intravenous infusion have shown pulmonary hemorrhage. Somatostatin has been shown to inhibit platelet aggregation in the rabbit in vivo, but when added in vitro to platelet-rich human or rabbit plasma failed to affect platelet function. These results suggest that the inhibitory effect of (GIF) on platelet aggregations is an indirect one resulting from the in vivo action or metabolism of the hormone (61).

Immunoassay and Extrahypothalamic Distribution of Somatostatin

Because native hormone cannot be iodinated, the preparation of a suitable labeled antigen for immunoassay has required the synthesis of a tyrosine 1-substituted compound (286). Arimura and co-workers (7) and Patel and co-workers (218, 221) have developed immunoassays utilizing this technique. By this method, somatostatin has been found in a surprisingly high concentration in certain areas outside the hypothalamus (see Table 2). These include the extrahypothalamic brain, the pineal gland, the islet cells of the pancreas, stomach, duodenum, and jejunum (8, 220, 221). These localizations correspond surprisingly well to regions known to be responsive to injected somatostatin and confirm earlier reports of bioassayable GIF activity in extrahypothalamic brain (289). The concentrations outside the brain are so high that it appears likely that the substance is formed in situ. The importance of somatostatin in the physiological regulation of these extrahypothalamic structures is unknown.

Table 2   Somatostatin concentration in gastrointestinal and pancreatic tissues

Tissue	(ng/organ)	(pg/μg protein)[a]
Stomach	306 ± 32	2.4 ± 0.22
Pylorus	116 ± 15.7	6.4 ± 0.92
Duodenum	42 ± 9.6	1.96 ± 0.24
Jejunum	50 ± 2.3	1.94 ± 0.20
Pancreatic islets	—	11.5

[a] Mean ± SEM (n = 6).

It may serve as a local "first messenger" in a manner analogous to the effects of prostaglandins. The high concentrations in extrahypothalamic brain further suggest that somatostatin, like TRH, may have neurotransmitter functions. In fact, somatostatin has been reported to have behavioral effects in the rat (39, 48), and to possess an inhibitory action on unit activity of neurons in many parts of the brain (255).

Localization is selective as shown by the fact that liver, kidney, and lung are all lacking in this hormone (8,220).

In recent studies from this laboratory (219), somatostatin has been demonstrated in the spinal fluid of normal individuals, and is elevated in a number of neurological diseases including metabolic and neoplastic disorders. The highest values of somatostatin in CSF were found in a patient with a pinealoma and one with a medulloblastoma, a finding interpreted to suggest that these tumors might secrete the hormone.

It has been proposed that the cell of origin of somatostatin in the gut and pancreatic islets may be derived embryologically from the neural crest and form part of the APUD system (298). The anatomical distribution of somatostatin is very similar to that of substance P found not only in the hypothalamus but throughout the extrahypothalamic brain and within specific endocrine [amine precursor uptake decarboxylase] cells in the gut (168, 222).

Literature Cited

1. Alberti, K. G. M. M. et al 1973. Inhibition of insulin secretion by somatostatin. *Lancet* 2:1299–1301
2. Alford, F. P. et al 1974. Glucagon control of fasting glucose in man. *Lancet* 2:974–76
3. Alpert, L. C., Brawer, J. R., Jackson, I. M. D., Patel, Y. C. 1975. Immunohistochemical evidence for distinct hypothalamic distribution. *Fed. Proc.* 34:239 (Abstr. 114)
4. Anton-Tay, F., Wurtman, R. J. 1968. Norepinephrine: Turnover in rat brains after gonadectomy. *Science* 159:1245
5. Araki, S., Ferin, M., Zimmerman, E. A., Vande Wiele, R. L. 1975. Ovarian modulation of immunoreactive gonadotropins-releasing hormone (Gn-RH) in the rat brain: Evidence for a differential effect on the anterior and mid-hypothalamus. *Endocrinology* 96:1644–50
6. Arimura, A., Kastin, A. J., Schally, A. V. 1974. Immunoreactive LH—releasing hormone in plasma: Midcycle elevation in women. *J. Clin. Endocrinol. Metab.* 38:510–13
7. Arimura, A., Sato, H., Coy, D. H., Schally, A. V. 1975. Radioimmunoassay for GH-release inhibiting hormone. *Proc. Soc. Exp. Biol. Med.* 148:784–89
8. Arimura, A., Sato, H., Dupont, A., Nishi, N., Schally, A. V. 1975. Abundance of immunoreactive GH-release inhibiting hormone in the stomach and the pancreas of rat. *Fed. Proc.* 34:273 (Abstr. 313)
9. Barbato, T., Lawrence, A. M., Kirsteins, L. 1974. Cerebro spinal fluid stimulation of pituitary protein synthesis and growth hormone release in vitro. *Lancet* 1:599–600
10. Barnea, A., Ben-Jonathan, N., Porter, J. C. 1975. Synaptosomal localization of TSH releasing hormone (TRH) and LH releasing hormone (LRH) in the hypothalamus. *Fed. Proc.* 34:239 (Abstr.)
11. Barraclough, C. A. 1967. *Neuroendocrinology* 2:61. New York: Academic
12. Barraclough, C. A., Sawyer, C. H. 1957. Blockade of the release of pituitary ovulating hormones in the rat by chlorpromazine and reserpine: Possible mechanisms of action. *Endocrinology* 61:341–51
13. Barry, J., Dubois, M. P., Carette, B. 1974. Immunofluorescence study of the preoptico-infundibular LRF neurosecretory pathway in the normal, castrated or testosterone treated male guinea pig. *Endocrinology* 95:1416–23
14. Barry, J., Dubois, M. P., Poulain, P., Leonardelli, J. 1973. Caracterisation et topographie des neurones hypothalamiques immunoreactifs avec des an-

ticorps anti-LRF synthesis. *C. R. Acad. Sci. Paris* 276:3191–93

15. Bassiri, R., Utiger, R. D. 1972. Serum inactivation of the immunological and biological activity of thyrotrophin-releasing hormone (TRH). *Endocrinology* 91:657–61

16. Bassiri, R. M., Utiger, R. D. 1973. Metabolism and excretion of exogenous thyrotropin-releasing hormone in humans. *J. Clin. Invest.* 52:1616–19

17. Bassiri, R., Utiger, R. D. 1974. Thyrotropin-releasing hormone in the hypothalamus of the rat. *Endocrinology* 94:188–97

18. Bauer, K. 1974. Degradation of thyrotropin releasing hormone (TRH). Its inhibition by pryo glu-His-OCH₃ and the effect of the inhibitor in attempts to study the biosynthesis of TRH. In *Lipmann Symposium: Energy, Biosynthesis and Regulation in Molecular Biology,* 53–62. Berlin/New York: deGruyter

19. Bauer, K., Kleinkauf, H. 1974. Degradation of thyrotropin-releasing hormone (TRH) by serum and hypothalamic tissue and its inhibition by analogues of TRH. *Z. Physiol. Chem.* 355:1173–76

20. Bauer, K., Sy, J., Lipmann, F. 1973. Degradation of thyrotropin releasing hormone (TRH) by extracts of hypothalamus. *Fed. Proc.* 32 (Abstr. 489)

21. Ben-Jonathan, N., Mical, R. S., Porter, J. C. 1974. Transport of LRF from CSF to hypophysial portal and systemic blood and release of LH. *Endocrinology* 95:18–25

22. Besser, G. M., Butler, P. W. P., Landon, J., Rees, L. 1969. Influence of amphetamines on plasma corticosteroid and growth hormone levels in man. *Br. Med. J.* 4:528–30

23. Besser, G. M. et al 1974. Growth hormone release inhibiting hormone in acromegaly. *Br. Med. J.* 1:352–55

24. Blackard, W. G., Heidingsfelder, S. A. 1968. Adrenergic receptor control mechanisms for growth hormone secretion. *J. Clin. Invest.* 47:1407–14

25. Blackwell, R. E., Guillemin, R. 1973. Hypothalamic control of adenohypophysial secretions. *Ann. Rev. Physiol.* 35:357–90

26. Bloom, S. R. et al 1974. Inhibition of gastrin and gastric acid secretion by growth hormone release inhibiting hormone. *Lancet* 2:1106–9

27. Bøler, J., Enzmann, F., Folkers, K., Bowers, C. Y., Schally, A. V. 1969. The identity of chemical and hormonal properties of the thyrotropin releasing hormone and pyroglutamyl-histidyl-proline-amide. *Biochem. Biophys. Res. Commun.* 37:705–10

28. Bolton, A. E. 1974. Radioimmunoassay of luteinizing hormone releasing hormone-like material in human urine. *J. Endocrinol.* 63:255–56

29. Borgeat, P., Labrie, F., Drouin, J., Belanger, A. 1974. Inhibition of adenosine 3',5'-monophosphate accumulation in anterior pituitary gland in vitro by growth hormone-release inhibiting hormone. *Biochem. Biophys. Res. Commun.* 56:1052–58

30. Bowers, C. Y., Schally, A. V., Enzmann, F., Bøler, J., Folkers, K. 1970. Porcine thyrotrophin releasing factor is (pyro-Glu-His-Pro (NH₂). *Endocrinology* 86:1143–53

31. Bower, A., Hadley, M. E., Hruby V. 1971. Comparative MSH releasing-inhibiting activities of Tocinoic acid (the ring of oxytocin) and L-Pro-L-Leu-Gly-NH₂ (the side chain of oxytocin). *Biochem. Biophys. Res. Commun.* 45: 1185–91

32. Boyd, A. E. III, Lebovitz, H. E., Feldman, J. M. 1971. Endocrine function and glucose metabolism in patients with Parkinson's disease and their alteration by L-Dopa. *J. Clin. Endocrinol.* 33: 829–37

33. Boyd, A. E. III, Lebovitz, H. E., Pfeiffer, J. B. 1970. Stimulation of human growth-hormone secretion by L-dopa. *N. Engl. J. Med.* 283:1425–29

34. Brazeau, P., Rivier, J., Vale, W., Guillemin, R. 1974. Inhibition of growth hormone secretion in the rat by synthetic somatostatin. *Endrocrinology* 94:184–87

35. Brazeau, P., Vale, W., Rivier, J., Guillemin, R. 1974. Acylated Des (Ala¹-Gly²)—somatostatin analogs prolonged inhibition of growth hormone secretion. *Biochem. Biophys. Res. Commun.* 60:1202–7

36. Brazeau, P. et al 1973. Hypothalamic polypeptide that inhibits the secretion of immunoreactive pituitary growth hormone. *Science* 179:77–79

37. Breton, B., Weil, C. 1973. Effects du LH/FSH-RH synthétique et d'extraits hypothalamiques de Carpe sur la sécrétion d'hormone gonadotrope in vivo chez la carpe (cyrinus carpio L). *C.R.Acad. Sci. Paris* 277:2061–64

38. Brown, G. M., Martin, J. B. 1973. Neuroendocrine relationships. *Progr. Neurol. Psychiatry* 28:193–240

39. Brown, M., Vale, W. 1975. Central nervous system effects of hypothalamic peptides. *Endocrinology* 96:1333–36
40. Brownstein, M. J., Palkovits, M., Saavedra, J. M., Bassiri, R. M., Utiger, R. D. 1974. Thyrotropin-releasing hormone in specific nuclei of rat brain. *Science* 185:267–69
41. Buckler, J. M. H., Bold, A. M., Taberner, M., London, D. R. 1969. Modification of hormonal response to arginine by α-adrenergic blockade. *Br. Med. J.* 3:153–54
42. Burgus, R. et al 1972. Primary structure of the ovine hypothalamic luteinizing hormone releasing factor (LRF). *Proc. Nat. Acad. Sci. USA* 69:278–82
43. Burgus, R., Dunn, T., Desiderio, D., Guillemin, R. 1969. Structure moléculaire du facteur hypothalamique hypophysiotrope TRF d'origine ovine: Mise en évidence par spectromètre de masse de la séquence PCA-His-Pro-NH₂. *C. R. Acad Sci. Paris* 269:1870–73
44. Burgus, R. et al 1970. Characterization of ovine hypothalamic hypophysio tropic TSH-releasing factor. *Nature London* 226:321–25
45. Burgus, R., Ling, N., Butcher, M., Guillemin, R. 1973. Primary structure of somatostatin, A hypothalamic peptide that inhibits the secretion of pituitary growth hormone. *Proc. Nat. Acad. Sci. USA* 70:684–88
46. Carmel, P. C., Araki, S., Ferin, M. 1975. Prolonged stalk blood collection in rhesus monkeys: Pulsatile release of gonadotropin-releasing hormone (Gn-RH). Program, 57th Ann. Meet. Endocrine Soc., New York Program, p. 104 (Abstr.)
47. Celis, M. E., Taleisnik, Walter, R. 1971. Regulation of formation and proposed structure of the factor inhibiting the release of melanocyte stimulating hormone. *Proc. Nat. Acad. Sci. USA* 68:1428–33
48. Cohn, M. L., Cohn, M. 1975. "Barrel rotation" induced by intracerebroventricular injections of somatostatin in the nonlesioned rat. *Fed. Proc.* 34:349 (Abstr.)
49. Collu, R., Franchini, F., Visconti, P., Martini, L. 1972. Adrenergic and serotoninergic control of growth hormone secretion in adult male rats. *Endocrinology* 90:1231–37
50. Coppen, A. et al 1974. Thyrotrophin-releasing hormone in the treatment of depression. *Lancet* II:433–35

51. Cramer, O. M., Barraclough, C. A. 1975. Failure to detect luteinizing hormone-releasing hormone in third ventricle cerebral spinal fluid under a variety of experimental conditions. *Endocrinology* 96:913–21
52. Crockford, P. M., Porte, D. Jr., Wood, F. C., Williams, R. H. 1966. Effect of glucagon on serum insulin, plasma glucose and free fatty acids in man. *Metabolism* 15:114–22
53. Dahlström, A., Füxe, K. 1965. Evidence for the existence of monoamine-containing neurons in the central nervous system I. Demonstration of monoamines in the cell bodies on brain stem neurons. *Acta Physiol. Scand.* 62:Suppl. 232, 1–55
54. Deery, D. J. 1974. Determination by radioimmunoassay of the luteinizing hormone releasing hormone (LHRH) content of the hypothalamus of the rat and some lower vertebrates. *Gen. Comp. Endocrinol.* 24:280–85
55. Del Pozo, E. et al 1974. A clinical and hormonal response to bromocriptin (CB-154) in galactorrhea syndromes. *J. Clin. Endocrinol. Metab.* 39:18–26
56. DeVane, G. W., Siler, T. M., Yen, S. S. C. 1974. Acute suppression of insulin and glucose levels by synthetic somatostatin in normal human subjects. *Clin. Endocrinol. Metab.* 38:913–15
57. Dierschke, D. J., Bhattacharya, A. N., Atkinson, L. E., Knobil, E. 1970. Circhoral oscillation of plasma LH levels in the ovariectomized rhesus monkey. *Endocrinology* 87:850–53
58. Dixon, J. E., Acres, S. C. 1975. The inability to demonstrate the nonribosomal biosynthesis of thyrotropin releasing hormone in hypothalamic tissue. *Fed. Proc.* 34:658 (Abstr.)
59. Donoso, A. O., Bishop, W., Fawcett, C. P., Kvalich, L., McCann, S. M. 1971. Effects of drugs that modify brain monoamine concentrations on plasma gonadotropin and prolactin levels in the rat. *Endocrinology* 89:774–44
60. Donoso, A. O., DeGutierrez-Moyano, M. D. 1970. Adrenergic activity in hypothalamus and ovulation. *Proc. Soc. Exp. Biol. Med.* 135:633–41
61. Duckworth, W. C., Chiang, T. M., Beachey, E. H., Kang, A. H. 1975. The inhibitory effect of the in vivo administration of somatostatin on platelet aggregation. Program, 57th Ann. Meet. Endocrine Soc., New York Program, p. 128 (Abstr.)

62. Dyer, R. G., Dyball, R. E. J. 1974. Evidence for a direct effect of LRF and TRF on single unit activity in the rostral hypothalamus. *Nature* 252:486–88
63. Edwards, C. R. W., Forsyth, I. A., Besser, G. M. 1973. Amenorrhea, galactorrhea and primary hypothyroidism with high circulating levels of prolactin. *Br. Med. J.* 3:462–64
64. Ehrensing, R. H., Kastin, A. J. 1974. Melanocyte-stimulating hormone release inhibiting hormone as an antidepressant: A pilot study. *Arch. Gen. Psychiatry* 30:63–65
65. Eik-Nes, K. B., Brown, D. M. B., Brizzee, K. R., Smith, E. L. 1961. Partial purification and properties of a corticotropin influencing factor (CIF) from human spinal fluid: An assay method for CIF in the trained dog. *Endocrinology* 69:411–21
66. Endröczi, E., Hilliard, J. 1965. Luteinizing hormone LRH releasing activity in different parts of rabbit and dog brain. *Endocrinology* 77:667–73
67. Endröczi, E., Schreiberg, G., Lissak, K. 1963. The role of central nervous activating and inhibiting structures in the control of pituitary-adrenal-cortical function. Effects of intracerebral cholinergic and adrenergic stimulation. *Acta Physiol. Acad. Sci. Hung.* 24:211–21
68. Ensinck, J. W. et al 1970. Effect of aminophylline on the secretion of insulin, glucagon, luteinizing hormone and growth hormone in humans. *J. Clin. Endocrinol. Metab.* 31:153–61
69. Everett, J. W. 1954. Luteotrophic function of autographs of the rat hypophysis. *Endocrinology* 54:685–90
70. Falck, B., Hillarp, N.-A. 1959. On the cellular localization of catecholamines in the brain. *Acta Anat.* 38:277–79
71. Friesen, H., Guyda, H., Hwang, P., Tyson, J. E., Barbeau, A. 1972. Functional evaluation of prolactin secretion. A guide to therapy. *J. Clin. Invest.* 51:706–9
72. Frohman, L., Stachura, M. E. 1975. Neuropharmacologic control of neuroendocrine function in man. *Metabolism* 24:211–34
73. Furr, B. J. A., Onuora, G. I., Bonney, R. C., Cunningham, F. J. 1973. The effect of synthetic hypothalamic releasing factors on plasma levels of luteinizing hormone in the cockerel. *J. Endocrinol.* 49:495–502
74. Gale, C. C. et al 1975. Endocrine response to acute cold in man. *Fed. Proc.* 34:301
75. Gautvik, K. M. et al 1974. Thyrotropin-releasing hormone is not the sole physiologic mediator of prolactin release during suckling. *N. Engl. J. Med.* 290: 1162–65
76. Gerich, J. E., Lorenzi, M., Schneider, V., Forsham, P. H. 1974. Effect of somatostatin on plasma glucose and insulin responses to glucagon and tolbutamide in man. *J. Clin. Endocrinol.* 39: 1057–69
77. Gerich, J. E. et al 1974. Effects of somatostatin on plasma glucose and glucagon levels in human diabetes mellitus. *N. Engl. J. Med.* 291:544–47
78. Gerich, J. E. et al 1974. Inhibition of pancreatic glucagon responses to arginine by somatostatin in normal man and in insulin-dependent diabetics. *Diabetes* 23:876–80
79. Gerich, J. E., Lovinger, R., Grodsky, G. M. 1975. Inhibition by somatostatin of glucagon and insulin release from the perfused rat pancreas in response to arginine, isoproterenol and theophylline. Evidence for a preferential effect on glucagon secretion. *Endocrinology* 96: 749–54
80. Gordon, J., Reichlin, S. 1973. Failure to demonstrate urinary excretion of luteinizing hormone releasing factor activity in the rat following intravenous injection of porcine hypothalamic extract. *Endocrinology* 93:259–61
81. Gordon, J., Bollinger, J., Reichlin, S. 1972. Plasma thyrotropin responses to thyrotropin releasing hormone after injection into the third ventricle systemic circulation median eminence and anterior pituitary. *Endocrinology* 91:696–701
82. Greep, R. O., Astwood, E. B., ed. 1974. The pituitary gland and its neuroendocrine control. 1–576 Pt. 1. *Handb. Physiol. Sect. 7: Endrocinology*
83. Greep, R. O., ed. 1974. *Reproductive Physiology* 1–323 London: Med. Tech. Publ.
84. Greer, M. A., Yamada, A. T., Iino, S. 1960. The participation of the nervous system in control of thyroid function. *Ann. NY Acad Sci.* 86:667–75
85. Griffiths, E. C., Hooper, K. C. 1972. The effect of ovariectomy on the activity of certain enzymes in the female rat hypothalamus. *Acta Endocrinol.* 69: 249–56
86. Griffiths, E. C., Hooper, K. C. 1973. The effects of orchidectomy and testosterone propionate injection on peptidase

activity in the male rat hypothalamus. *Acta Endocrinol.* 72:1–8

87. Griffiths, E. C., Hooper, K. C. 1973. Changes in the hypothalamic peptidase activity during the oestrous cycle in the adult female rat. *Acta Endocrinol.* 74: 41–48

88. Griffiths, E. C., Hooper, K. C. 1974. Competitive inhibition between oxytocin and luteinizing hormone-releasing factor (LRF) for the same enzyme system in the rat hypothalamus. *Acta Endocrinol.* 75:435–42

89. Griffiths, E. C., Hopper, K. C. 1974. Peptidase activity in different areas of the rat hypothalamus. *Acta Endocrinol.* 77:10–18

90. Griffiths, E. C., Hopper, K. C., Hopkinson, C. R. N. 1973. Evidence for an enzymic component in the rat hypothalamus capable of inactivating luteinizing hormone releasing factor (LRF). *Acta Endocrinol.* 74:49–55

91. Griffiths, E. C., Hopper, K. C., Jeffcoate, S. L., Holland, D. T. 1974. The presence of peptidases in the rat hypothalamus inactivating luteinizing hormone releasing hormone (LH-RH). *Acta Endocrinol.* 77:435–42

92. Grimm-Jorgensen, Y., McKelvy, J. F. 1974. Biosynthesis of thyrotropin releasing factor by newt (*Triturus viridescens*) brain in vitro. Isolation and characterization of thyrotropin releasing factor. *J. Neurochem.* 23:471–78

92a. Grimm-Jorgensen, Y., McKelvy, J. F. 1974. Control of the in vitro biosynthesis of thyrotropin releasing factor (TRF) in the red spotted newt (*triturus viridescens*). *Program Ann. Meet. Endocrine Soc., Atlanta, 56th,* p A65 (Abstr.)

93. Grimm-Jorgensen, Y., McKelvy, J. F., Jackson, I. M. D. 1975. Immunoreactive thyrotropin releasing factor in gastropod circumerophageal ganglia. *Nature* 254:620–21

94. Grimm, Y., Reichlin, S. 1973. Thyrotropin releasing hormone (TRH): Neurotransmitter regulation of secretion by mouse hypothalamic tissue in vitro. *Endocrinology* 93:626–31

95. Grumbach, M. M., Grave, G. D., Mayer, F. E., eds. 1974. *Control of the Onset of Puberty,* 1–484. New York: Wiley

96. Gual, C. Rosenberg, E., eds. 1973. Hypothalamic hypophysiotropic hormones. Physiological and clinical studies. *Proc. Conf. Acapulco, Mexico, 1972. Excerpta Med. Int. Congr. Ser.* 262:1–428

97. Hagen, T. C., Lawrence, A. M., Kirsteins, L. 1972. In vitro release of monkey pituitary growth hormone by acromegalic plasma. *J. Clin. Endocrinol. Metab.* 33:448–51

98. Halasz, B., Pupp, L., Uhlarik, S. 1962. Hypophysiotrophic area in the hypothalamus. *J. Endocrinol.* 25:147–54

99. Hall, R. et al 1973. Action of growth hormone release inhibitory hormone in healthy men and in acromegaly. *Lancet* 2:581–84

100. Hansen, A. P., Orskov, H., Seyer-Hansen, K., Lundback, K. 1973. Some actions of growth hormone release inhibiting factor. *Br. Med. J.* 2:523–24

101. Harris, G. W. 1955. The function of the pituitary stalk. *Bull. Johns Hopkins Hosp.* 97:358

102. Harrison, T. S. 1961. Some factors influencing thyrotropin release in the rabbit. *J. Endocrinol.* 68:466–78

103. Harms, P. G., Ojeda, S. R., McCann, S. M. 1973. Prostaglandin involvement in hypothalamic control of gonadotropin and prolactin release. *Science* 181:760–61

104. Hatotani, N., ed. 1974. *Psychoneuroendocrinology.* Basel: Karger. 312 pp.

105. Hedge, G. A., Smelik, P. G. 1968. Corticotropin release: Inhibition by intrahypothalamic implantation of atropine. *Science* 159:891–92

106. Hedlund, L. W., Franz, J. M., Kenny, A. D., eds. 1975. Biological rhythms and endocrine function. *Adv. Exp. Med. Biol.* 54:1–194

107. Heidingsfelder, S. A., Blackard, W. G. 1968. Adrenergic control mechanisms for vasopressin induced plasma growth hormone response. *Metabolism* 17:1019–24

108. Hidaka, H., Nagasaka, A., Takeda, A. 1973. Fusaric (5-Butylpicolinic) acid: its effect on plasma growth hormone. *J. Clin. Endocrinol. Metab.* 37:145–47

109. Hillhouse, E. W., Burden, J., Jones, M. T. 1975. The effect of various putative neurotransmitters on the release of corticotrophin releasing hormone from the hypothalamus of the rat in vitro. I. The effect of acetylcholine and noradrenaline. *Neuroendocrinology* 14:1–11

110. Hökfelt, T. 1974. Morphological contributions to monamine pharmacology. *Fed. Proc.* 33(10):2177–86

111. Hökfelt, T., Efendic, S., Johansson, O., Luft, R., Arimura, A. 1974. Immunohistochemical localization of somatostatin (growth hormone releas-

ing factor) in the guinea pig brain. *Brain Res.* 80:165–69

112. Hopper, K. C. 1966. The metabolism of oxytocin during lactation in the rabbit. *Biochem. J.* 100:823–26

113. Imura, H., Nakai, Y., Yoshima, T. 1973. Effect of 5-hydroxytryptophan on growth hormone and ACTH release in man. *J. Clin. Endocrinol.* 36:204

114. Imura, H., Nakai, Y., Kato, Y., Yoshimoto, Y., Moridera, K. 1973. Effect of adrenergic agents on growth hormone and ACTH secretion. *Endocrinology: Proc. 4th Int. Congr. Endocrinol. Wash. DC, June 18–24, 1972.* ed. R. O. Scow, Int. Congr. Ser. No. 273

115. Jackson, G. L. 1972. Partial purification and characterization of chicken and rat follicle stimulating hormone releasing factors. *Endocrinology* 91:1090–94

116. Jackson, I. M. D., Reichlin, S. 1973. TRH radioimmunoassay: Measurements in normal and altered states of thyroid function in the rat. *Proc. Meet. Am. Thyroid Assoc., 49th* T4 (Abstr.)

117. Jackson, I. M. D., Reichlin, S. 1974. Thyrotropin releasing hormone (TRH): Distribution in the brain, blood and urine of the rat. *Life Sci.* 14:2259–66

118. Jackson, I. M. D., Reichlin, S. 1974. Thyrotropin-releasing hormone (TRH): Distribution in hypothalamic and extrahypothalamic brain tissues of mammalian and submammalian chordates. *Endocrinology* 95:854–62

119. Jackson, I. M. D., Reichlin, S. 1975. TRH distribution in brain and urinary excretion following "thyrotrophic area" hypothalamic lesions in the rat. *Program Ann. Meet. Endocrine Soc., 57th, New York,* p. 96 (Abstr.)

120. Jackson, I. M. D., Reichlin, S. 1975. TRH in plasma of several vertebrate classes. In preparation

121. Jackson, I. M. D., Papapetrou, P. D., Reichlin, S. 1974. The metabolism and excretion of TRH in the rat in states of altered thyroid function. *Proc. Am. Thyroid Assoc., 50th,* T-1 (Abstr.)

122. Jackson, I. M. D., Saperstein, R., Reichlin, S. 1974. Thyrotropin releasing hormone (TRH): Distribution in hypothalamic and extra hypothalamic brain tissues of mammalian and submammalian chordates. *Proc. Endocrine Soc., 56th* (Abstr.)

123. Jackson, I. M. D., Gagel, R., Papapetrou, P., Reichlin, S. 1974. Pituitary, hypothalamic and urinary thyrotropin

releasing hormone (TRH) concentration in altered thyroid states of rat and man. *Clin. Res.* 23:342A

124. Jackson, I. M. D., Gagel, R., Papapetrou, P. D., Deprez, D., Reichlin, S. 1975. TRH excretion and metabolism in man. *Clin. Res.* 23:238A

125. Jacobs, L. S., Snyder, P. J., Wilber, J. F., Utiger, R. D., Daughaday, W. H. 1971. Increased serum prolactin after administration of synthetic thyrotropin releasing hormone (TRH) in man. *J. Clin. Endocrinol. Metab.* 33:996–98

126. Jacoby, J. H., Greenstein, M., Sassin, J. F., Weitzman, E. D. 1974. The effect of monoamine precursors on the release of growth hormone in the rhesus monkey. *Neuroendocrinology* 14:95–102

127. Jeffcoate, S. L., Holland, D. T. 1975. Further studies on the nature of the immunoreactive luteinizing hormone-releasing hormone (LH-RH)-like peptide in human urine. *Acta Endocrinol.* 78L 232–38

128. Jeffcoate, S. L., White, N. 1974. Use of benzamide to prevent the destruction of thyrotropin releasing hormone (TRH) by blood. *J. Clin. Endocrinol.* 38:155–57

129. Jeffcoate, S. L., Sharp, P. J., Fraser, H. M., Holland, D. T., Gunn, A. 1974. Immunochemical and chromatographic similarity of rat, rabbit, chicken, and snythetic luteinizing hormone releasing hormones. *J. Endocrinol.* 62:85–91

130. Johansson, K. N. G. et al 1972. Biosynthesis in vitro of the luteinizing releasing hormone by hypothalamic tissue. *Biochem. Biophys. Res. Commun.* 53:502–7

131. Johansson, K. N. G., Currie. B. L., Folkers, K., Bowers, C. Y. 1973. Biosynthesis of the luteinizing hormone releasing hormone in mitochondrial preparations and by a possible pantetheine-template mechanism. *Biochem. Biophys. Res. Commun.* 53:502–7

132. Johnson, D. G., Ensinick, J. W., Koerker, D., Palmer, J., Goodner, C. J. 1975. Inhibition of glucagon and insulin secretion by somatostatin in the rat pancreas perfused in situ. *Endocrinology* 96:370–74

133. Jonas, H. A., Burger, G. G., Cumming, I. A., Fundlay, J. K., DeKretser, D. M. 1975. Radioimmunoassay for luteinizing hormone-releasing hormone (LHRH): its application to the measurement of LHRH in ovine and human plasma. *Endocrinology* 96:384–93

134. Joseph, S. A., Scott, D. E., Vaala, S. S., Knigge, K. M., Krobisch-Dudley, G. 1973. Localization and content of thyrotropin releasing factor (TRF) in median eminence of the hypothalamus. *Acta Endocrinol.* 74:215–25

135. Kalra, S. P., McCann, S. M. 1973. Effects of drugs modifying catecholamine synthesis on LH release induced by preoptic stimulation in the rat. *Endocrinology* 93:356–62

136. Kalra, P. S., McCann, S. M. 1973. Involvement of catecholamines in feedback mechanisms. *Progr. Brain Res.* 39:185–98

137. Kalra, S. P., McCann, S. M. 1974. Effects of drugs modifying catecholamine snythesis on plasma LH and ovulation in the rat. *Neuroendocrinology* 15:79–91

138. Kalra, P. S., Kalra, S. P., Krulich, L., Fawcett, C. P., McCann, S. M. 1972. Involvement of norepinephrine in transmission of the stimulatory influence of progesterone on gonadotropin release. *Endocrinology* 90:1168–76

139. Kamberi, I. A., Mical, R. S. Porter, J. C. 1971. Effect of anterior pituitary perfusion and intraventricular injection of catecholamines on prolactin release. *Endocrinology* 88:1012–20

140. Kamberi, I. A., Mical, R. S., Porter, J. C. 1971. Effects of melatonin and release of FSH and prolactin. *Endocrinology* 88:1288–93

141. Kamberi, I. A., Schneider, H. P. G., McCann, S. M. 1970. Action of dopamine to induce release of FSH-releasing factor (FRF) from hypothalamic tissue *in vitro. Endocrinology* 86:278–84

142. Kamberi, I. A., Mical, R. S., Porter, J. C. 1970. Effect of anterior pituitary perfusion and intraventricular injection of catecholamines and indolamines on LH release. *Endocrinology* 87:1–12

143. Kansal, P. C., Buse, J., Talbert, O. R., Buse, M. 1972. The effect of L-Dopa on plasma growth hormone, insulin, and thyroxine. *J. Clin. Endocrinol. Metab.* 34:99–105

144. Kastin, A. J., Ehrensing, R. H., Schalch, D. S., Anderson, M. S. 1972. Improvement in mental depression with decreased thyrotropin response after administration of thyrotropin-releasing hormone. *Lancet* 2:740–42

145. Kastin, A. J., Viosca, S., Schally, A. V. 1970. Assay of mammalian MSH release regulating factor(s). In *Hypophysiotropic Hormones of the Hypothalamus,* ed. J. Meites, 171–84. Baltimore: Williams & Wilkins

146. Kawakami, M., ed. 1974. *Biological Rhythms in Neuroendocrine Activity.* Tokyo: igaku Shoin. 353 pp.

147. Keller, H. H., Bartholini, G., Pletscher, A. 1974. Enhancement of cerebral noradrenaline turnover by thyrotropin-releasing hormone. *Nature* 248:528–29

148. Kemper, B., Habener, J. F., Potts, J. T. Jr., Rich, A. 1972. Proparathyroid hormone: identification of a biosynthetic precursor to parathyroid hormone. *Proc. Nat. Acad. Sci. USA* 69:643

149. Keye, W. R. Jr., Kelch, R. P., Niswender, G. D., Jaffe, T. B. 1973. Quantitation of endogenous and exogenous gonadotropin releasing hormone by radioimmunoassay. *J. Clin. Endocrinol. Metab.* 36:1263–67

150. Kizer, J. S., Arimura, A., Schally, A. V., Brownstein, M. J. 1975. Absence of luteinizing hormone-releasing hormone (LH-RH) from catecholaminergic neurons. *Endocrinology* 96:523–25

151. Knigge, K. M., Joseph, S. A. 1974. Thyrotropin releasing factor (TRF) in cerebro spinal fluid of the 3rd ventricle of rat. *Acta Endocrinol.* 76:209–13

152. Knigge, K. M., Scott, D. E., Weindl, A., eds. 1972. *Brain-Endocrine Interaction Median Eminence: Structure and Function.* Basel: Karger

153. Knights, E. B., Baylin, S. B., Foster, G. V. 1973. Control of polypeptide hormones by enzymatic degradation. *Lancet* 2:719–23

154. Knobil, E. 1974. On the control of gonadotropin secretion in the rhesus monkey. *Recent Progr. Horm. Res.* 30:1–46

155. Knobil, E., Sawyer, W. H. 1974. The pituitary gland and its neuroendocrine control, Pt. 1. *Handb. Physiol. Sect. 7: Endocrinology,* Vol. 4. 576 pp.

156. Knobil, E., Sawyer, W. H. 1974. See Ref. 155, Pt. 2. 601 pp.

157. Knowles, F. 1974. *Essays on the Nervous System,* ed. R. Bellairs, E. G. Gray, 431–50. Oxford: Clarendon

158. Koch, Y., Baram, T., Chobsieng, P., Fridkin, M. 1974. Enzymic degradation of luteinizing hormone-releasing hormone (LH-RH) by hypothalamic tissue. *Biochem. Biophys. Res. Commun.* 61:95–103

159. Koch, Y. et al 1973. Suppression of gonadotropin secretion and prevention of ovulation in the rat by antiserum to synthetic gonadotropin-releasing hor-

mone. *Biochem. Biophys. Res. Commun.* 55:623–29
160. Koerker, D. J. et al 1974. Somatostatin: Hypothalamic inhibitor of the endocrine pancreas. *Science* 184:482–83
161. Kordon, C., Blake, C. A., Terkel, J., Sawyer, C. H. 1973. Participation of serotonin-containing neurons in the suckling-induced rise in plasma prolactin levels in lactating rats. *Neuroendocrinology* 13:213–23
162. Kozlowski, G. P., Zimmerman, E. A. 1974. Localization of gonadotropin releasing hormone (Gn-RH) in sheep and mouse brain. *Anat. Res.* 178:396
163. Krieger, H. P., Krieger, D. T. 1970. Chemical stimulation of the brain: Effect on adrenal corticoid release. *Am. J. Physiol.* 218:1632–41
164. Krulich, L., Illner, P., Fawcett, C. P., Quijada, M., McCann, S. M. 1972. *Growth and Growth Hormone,* ed. A. Pecile, E. E. Müller, 306–16. Amsterdam: Excerpta Medica
165. Krulich, L., Quijada, M., Illner, P. 1971. Localization of prolactin inhibiting factor (PIF), P-releasing factor (PRF) growth— RF (GRF) and GIF activities in the hypothalamus of the rat. *Proc. Endocrine Soc. 53rd,* No. 83 (Abstr.)
166. Krulich, L., Quijada, M., Hefco, E., Sundberg, D. K. 1974. Localization of thyrotropin-releasing factor (TRF) in the hypothalamus of the rat. *Endocrinology* 95:9–17
167. Lal, S., de la Vega, C. E., Sourkes, T. L., Friesen, H. G. 1973. Effect of apomorphine on growth hormone, prolactin, luteinizing hormone and follicle stimulating hormone in human serum. *J. Clin. Endocrinol. Metab.* 37:719–24
168. Leeman, S. E., Mroz, E. A. 1974. Substance P. *Life Sci.* 15:2033–44
169. Leonardelli, J., Barry, J., DuBois, M. P. 1973. Mise en evidence par immunofluorescence d'un constituant immunologiquement apparenté au LH-RF dans l'hypothalamus et l'éminence médiane chez les mammifères. *C. R. Acad. Sci. Paris* 276:2043–46
170. Libertun, C., McCann, S. M. 1974. Prolactin-releasing effect of histamine injected into the third ventricle. *Proc. Endocrine Soc., 56th,* A-422
171. Lissäk, K. 1973. *Hormones and Brain Function,* 1–608. New York: Plenum
172. Locke, W., Schally, A. V. 1973. *The Hypothalamus and Pituitary in Health and Disease,* 1–608. Springfield, Ill: Thomas
173. MacIndoe, J. H., Turkington, R. W. 1973. Stimulation of human prolactin secretion by intravenous infusions of L-tryptophan. *J. Clin. Invest.* 52: 1972–78
174. MacLeod, R. M., Lehmeyer, J. E. 1974. Studies on the mechanism of the dopamine-mediated inhibition of prolactin secretion. *Endocrinology* 94:1077–85
175. Malacara, J., Seyler, L. E. Jr., Reichlin, S. 1972. Luteinizing hormone releasing factor activity in peripheral blood from women during the midcycle luteinizing hormone ovulatory surge. *J. Clin. Endocrinol. Metab.* 34:271–78
176. Malarkey, W. B., Jacobs, L. S., Daughaday, W. H. 1971. Levodopa suppression of prolactin in nonpuerperal galactorrhea. *N. Engl. J. Med.* 285:1160–63
177. Marchlewska-Koj, A., Krulich, L. 1975. The role of central monoamines in the stress-induced prolactin release in the rat. *Fed. Proc.* 34:252
178. Markee, J. E., Everett, J. W., Sawyer, C. H. 1952. The relationship of the nervous system to the release of gonadotropin and the regulation of the sex cycle. *Rec. Prog. Horm. Res.* 7:139–63
179. Martin, J. B. 1973. Neural regulation of growth hormone secretion. *N. Engl. J. Med.* 288:1384–93
180. Martin, J. B. 1974. Inhibitory effect of somatostatin (SRIF) on the release of growth hormone (GH) induced in the rat by electrical stimulation. *Endocrinology* 94:497–502
181. Martin, J. B., Reichlin, S. 1971. Neural regulation of the pituitary thyroid axis. *Midwest Conf. Thyroid Endocrinol. 6th,* p. 1
182. Martin, J. B., Reichlin, S. 1972. Plasma thyrotropin (TSH) response to hypothalamic electrical stimulation and to injection of synthetic thyrotropin releasing hormone (TRH). *Endocrinology* 90:107–85
183. Martin, J. B., Audet, J., Saunders, A. 1975. Effects of somatostatin and hypothalamic ventromedial lesions on GH release induced by morphine *Endocrinology* 96:839
184. Martin. J. B., Lal, S., Tolis, G., Friesen, H. G. 1974. Inhibition by amorphine of prolactin secretion in patients with elevated serum prolactin. *J. Clin. Endocrinol. Metab.* 39:183–84
185. McCann, S. M., Moss, R. L. 1975. Putative neurotransmitters involved in discharging gonadotropin-releasing neurohormones and the action of LH-

releasing hormone on the CNS. *Life Sci.* 16:883–52

186. McCann, S. M., Taleisnik, S., Friedman, H. M. 1960. LH releasing activity in hypothalamic extracts. *Proc. Soc. Exp. Biol. Med.* 104:432–34

187. McKelvy, J. F. 1974. Biochemical Neuroendocrinology. I. Biosynthesis of thyrotropin releasing hormone (TRH) by organ cultures of mammalian hypothalamus. *Brain Res.* 65:489–502

188. Meites, J., Talwalker, P. K., Nicoll, C. S. 1960. Initiation of lactation in rats with hypothalamic or cerebral tissue. *Proc. Soc. Exp. Biol. Med.* 103:298–300

189. Mess, B. 1969. Progress in endocrinology. *Proc. Int. Congr. Endocrinol., 3rd. Excerpta Int. Congr. Ser.* No. 184, 564–70

190. Metcalf, G. 1974. TRH: A possible mediator of thermoregulation. *Nature* 252:310–11

191. Mitchell, M. L., Suvunrungsi, P. Sawin, C. T. 1971. Effect of propranolol on the response of serum growth hormone to glucagon. *J. Clin. Endocrinol. Metab.* 32:470–75

192. Mitnick, M., Reichlin, S. 1971. Biosynthesis of TRH by rat hypothalamic tissue *in vitro. Science* 172:1241–43

193. Mitnick, M., Reichlin, S. 1972. Enzymatic synthesis of thyrotropin-releasing hormone (TRH) by hypothalamic "TRH Synthetase." *Endocrinology* 91:1145–53

194. Mitnick, M., Valverde, R. C., Reichlin, S. 1973. Enzymatic synthesis of prolactin releasing factor (PRF) by rat hypothalamic incubates and by extracts of rat hypothalamic tissue: Evidence for PRF synthetase. *Proc. Soc. Exp. Biol. Med.* 143:418–21

195. Moguilevsky, J., Enero, M. A., Szwarcfarb, B. 1974. Luteinizing hormone releasing hormone–biosynthesis by rat hypothalamus *in vitro.* Influence by castration. *Proc. Soc. Exp. Biol. Med.* 147:434–37

196. Montoya, E., Wilber, J. F. 1974. Studies of thyrotropin releasing hormone (TRH) physiology by radioimmunoassay: Effects of triiodothyronine (T3) and thyroxine (T4). *Program Ann. Meet. Endocrine Soc., 56th, Atlanta* p. A-65 (Abstr.)

197. Montoya, E., Seibel, M. J., Wilber, J. 1973. Studies of thyrotropin-releasing hormone (TRH) in the rat by means of radioimmunoassay normal values and response to cold exposure. *Program*

Ann. Meet. Endocrine Soc., 55th, Chicago, p. A-138 (Abstr.)

198. Morris, M., Knigge, K. M. 1975. Effect of ether anesthesia on LH-releasing hormone (LH-RH) secretion. *Fed. Proc.* 34:239

199. Moss, R. L., McCann, S. M. 1973. Induction of mating behavior in rats by luteinizing hormone-releasing factor. *Science* 181:177–79

200. Moss, R. L., Dudley, C., Foremen, M. M., McCann, S. M. 1974. Synthetic LHRH: A potential of sexual behavior in the rat. *Hypothalamic Hormones: Chemistry, Physiology, Pharmacology and Clinical Uses, Serono Symp., Milan* (Abstr.)

201. Naik, D. V. 1974. Immunohistochemical and immunofluorescent localization of LH-RF neurons in the hypothalamus of the rat. *Anat. Rec.* 178:424

202. Nair, M. G., Redding, T. W., Schally, A. V. 1971. Inactivation of thyrotropin-releasing hormone by human plasma. *Biochemistry* 10:3621–24

203. Nakai, Y., Imura, H., Sakurai, H., Kurchachi, H., Yoshima, T. 1974. Effect of cyproheptadine on human growth hormone secretion. *J. Clin. Endocrinol. Metab.* 38:446–49

204. Nallar, R., McCann, S. M. 1965. Luteinizing hormone-releasing activity in plasma of hypophysectomized rats. *Endocrinology* 76:272–75

205. Nett, T. M., Akbar, A. M., Niswender, G. D., Hedlund, M. T., White, W. F. 1973. A radioimmunoassay for gonadotropins releasing hormone (Gn-RH) in serum. *J. Clin. Endocrinol. Metab.* 36:880–85

206. Nett, T. M., Akbar, A. M., Niswender, G. D. 1974. Serum levels of luteinizing hormone and gonadotropin releasing hormone in cycling, castrated and anestrous ewes. *Endocrinology* 94:713–18

207. Ng, K. Y., Chase, T. N., Colburn, R. W., Kopin, I. J. 1970. L-Dopa induced release of cerebral monoamines. *Science* 170:76–77

208. Nicoll, C. S., Fiorindo, R. P., McKennee, C. T., Parsons, J. A. 1970. *Hypophysiotropic Hormones in the Hypothalamus.* Baltimore, Md: Williams & Wilkins. 115 pp.

209. Noel, G. L., Suh, H. K., Frantz, A. G. 1973. L-Dopa suppression of TRH stimulated prolactin release in man. *J. Clin. Endocrinol. Metab.* 36:1255–58

210. Ojeda, S. R., McCann, S. M. 1970. Role of catecholamines in stimulating the endocrine release of pituitary ovulating

hormone(s) in rats. *Endocrinology* 86:988–95

211. Oliver, C., Charvet, J. P., Codaccioni, J. L., Vague, J. 1974. Radioimmunoassay of thyrotropin-releasing hormone in human plasma and urine. *J. Clin. Endocrinol. Metab.* 39:406–9

212. Oliver, C., Charvet, J. P., Codaccioni, J. L., Vague, J., Porter, J. C. 1974. TRH in human CSF. *Lancet* 1:873

213. Oliver, C., Eskay, R. L., Mical, R. S., Porter, J. C. 1973. Radioimmunoassay for TRH and its determination in hypophysial and portal and peripheral plasma of rats. *Program Meet. Am. Thyroid Assoc., 49th,* p. T4 (Abstr.)

214. Oliver, C., Eskay, R. L., Ben-Jonathan, N., Porter, J. C. 1974. Distribution and concentration of TRH in the rat brain. *Endocrinology* 95:540–46

215. Palkovits, M. 1973. Isolated removal of hypothalamic or other brain nuclei of the rat. *Brain Res.* 59:449–50

216. Palkovits, M., Arimura, A., Brownstein, M., Schally, A. V., Saavedra, J. M. 1974. Luteinizing hormone releasing hormone (LH-RH) content of the hypothalamic nuclei in the rat. *Endocrinology* 95:554–58

217. Parker, D. C. et al 1974. Inhibition of the sleep-related peak in physiologic human growth hormone release by somatostatin. *J. Clin. Endocrinol. Metab.* 38:496–99

218. Patel, Y. C., Reichlin, S. 1975. Radioimmunoassay of somatostatin. Submitted for publication

219. Patel, Y. C., Rao, K., Reichlin, S. 1975. Immunoreactive somatostatin (SRIF) in human cerebrospinal fluid (SSF). *Clin. Res.* 23:389A

220. Patel, Y. C., Weir, G. C. Reichlin, S. 1975. Immunoreactive somatostatin in gut and pancreatic islets of rat. Submitted for publication

221. Patel, Y. C., Weir, G. C., Reichlin, S. 1975. Anatomic distribution of somatostatin (SRIF) in brain and pancreatic islets as studied by radioimmunoassay. *Program Ann. Meet. Endocrine Soc., 57th, New York,* p. 127 (Abstr. 154)

222. Pearse, A. G. E., Polak, J. M. 1975. Immunocytochemical localization of substance P in mammalian intestine. *Histochemistry* 41:373–75

223. Pelletier, G., Labrie, F., Arimura, A., Schally, A. V. 1974. Electron microscopic immunohistochemical localization of growth hormone release inhibiting hormone (somatostatin) in the rat median eminence. *Am. J. Anat.* 140:445–50

224. Pelletier, G., Labrie, F., Puviani, R., Arimura, A., Schally, A. V. 1974. Immunohistochemical localization of luteinizing hormone releasing hormone in the rat median eminence. *Endocrinology* 95:314–17

225. Pelletier, G. et al 1975. Localization of growth hormone releasing inhibiting hormone (somatostatin) in the rat brain. *Am. J. Anat.* 142:397

226. Piacsek, B. E., Meites, J. 1966. Effects of castration and gonadal hormones on hypothalamic content of luteinizing hormone releasing factor (LRF). *Endocrinology* 79:432–39

227. Pimstone, B. L., Becker, D., Kronheim, S. 1975. Disappearance of plasma growth hormone in acromegaly and protein-caloric malnutrition after somatostatin. *J. Clin. Endocrinol. Metab.* 40:168–71

228. Plunk, J. W., Bivens, C. H., Feldman, J. M. 1974. Inhibition of hypoglycemia induced cortisol secretion by the serotonin antagonist cyproheptadine. *J. Clin. Endocrinol. Metab.* 38:836–40

229. Plotnikoff, N. P., Prange, A. J., Breese, G. R., Anderson, M. S., Wilson, I. C. 1972. Thyrotropin releasing hormone: Enhancement of DOPA activity by a hypothalamic hormone. *Science* 178:417–18

230. Prange, A. J., Wilson, I. C., Lara, P. P., Alltop, L. B., Breese, G. R. 1972. Effects of thyrotropin releasing hormone in depression. *Lancet* 2:999–1002

231. Ralph, C. L., Sampath, S. 1966. Inhibition by extracts of frog and rat brain of MSH release by frog pars intermedia. *Gen. Comp. Endocrinol.* 7:370–74

232. Rees, L., Butler, P. W. P., Gosling, C., Bisser, G. M. 1970. Adrenergic blockade and the corticosteroid and growth hormone responses to methylamphetamine. *Nature* 228:565–66

233. Reichlin, S. 1966. Control of thyrotropic hormone secretion. In *Neuroendocrinology,* 445–536. New York: Academic

234. Reichlin, S. 1972. Hypothalamic pituitary function. *Excerpta Med. Int. Congr. Ser.* 273:1–16

235. Reichlin, S. 1975. Regulation of somatotrophic hormone secretion, Pt. 2. *Handb. Physiol. Sect. 7: Endocrinology* 4:405–47

236. Reichlin, S., Mitnick, M. A. 1973. Biosynthesis of thyrotropin releasing hormone and its control by hormones

central monoamines and external environment. In *Hypothalamic Hypophysiotropic Hormones. Proc. Int. Congr., Acapulco, Mexico, 1972. Excerpta Med. Int. Congr. Ser.* 263:124–35

237. Reichlin, S., Mitnick, M. A. 1973. Biosynthesis of hypothalamic hypophysiotropic hormones. In *Frontiers in Neuroendocrinology*, 61–68. ed. W. F. Ganong, L. Martin; New York: Oxford Univ. Press

238. Reichlin, S., Mitnick, M. A. 1973. Enzymatic synthesis of growth hormone releasing factor (GH-RF) by rat incubates and by extracts of rat and porcine hypothalamic tissue. *Proc. Soc. Exp. Biol Med.* 142:497–501

239. Reichlin, S. et al 1972. The hypothalamus in pituitary thyroid regulation. *Rec. Progr. Horm. Res.* 28:229–77

240. Renaud, L. P., Martin, J. B. 1974. Influence of thyrotropin releasing hormone (TRH) on the activity of single neurons in the CNS. *Clin. Res.* 22:755A

241. Rice, R. W., Critchlow, V. 1975. Extrahypothalamic control of stress induced inhibition of growth hormone secretion in the rat. *Fed. Proc.* 34:273

242. Rivier, J. E. F. 1974. Somatostatin. Total solid phase synthesis. *J. Am. Chem. Soc.* 96:2986–92

243. Rivier, J. E. F., Brazeau, P., Vale, W., Guillemin, R. 1975. Somatostatin analogs. Relative importance of the disulphide bridge and of the Ala-Gly side chain for biological activity. *J. Med. Chem.* 18:123–26

244. Romero, J. A., Lytle, L. D., Ardonez, L. A., Chalmers, J. P., Cottman, K., Wurtman, R. J. 1973. Effects of L-Dopa administration on the concentration of dopa, dopamine and norepinephrine in various tissues. *J. Pharmacol. Exp. Ther.* 184:67–72

245. Sachs, H., Goodman, R., Osinchak, J., McKelvy, J. 1971. Supraoptic neurosecretory neurons of the guinea pig in organ culture. Biosynthesis of vasopressin and neurophysin. *Proc. Nat. Acad. Sci. USA* 68:2782–86

246. Sakurai, H., Unger, R. H. 1974. Effects of somatostatin (SRIF) on Insulin (I) and Glucagon (G) and I/G ratio in normal and diabetic dogs. *Diabetes* 23: Suppl. 1, 356

247. Saperstein, R., Mothon, S., Reichlin, S. 1975. Enzymatic degradation of TRH and LRH by hypothalamic extracts. *Fed. Proc.* 34:239

248. Sawyer, C. H., Marker, J. E., Hollinshead, W. H. 1947. Inhibition of ovulation in the rabbit by the adrenergic blocking agent dibenamine. *Endocrinology* 41:395–402

249. Sawyer, W. H. 1964. Vertebrate neurohypophysial principles. *Endocrinology* 75:981–90

250. Schally, A. V. et al 1971. Isolation and properties of the FSH and LH-releasing hormone. *Biochem. Biophys. Res. Commun.* 43:393–99

251. Schally, A. V., Arimura, A., Kastin, A. J. 1973. Hypothalamic regulatory hormones. *Science* 179:341–50

252. Schneider, H. P. G., McCann, S. M. 1969. Possible role of dopamine as transmitter to promote discharge of LH-releasing factor. *Endocrinology* 85:121–32

253. Schneider, H. P. G., McCann, S. M. 1970. Mono and indolamines and control of LH secretion. *Endocrinology* 86:1127–33

254. Scow, R. O., Ebling, F. J. G., Henderson, I. W. 1973. *Proc. Int. Congr. Endocrinol. 4th, Washington DC, 1972. See Ref. 114*

255. Segal, D. S., Mandell, A. J. 1974. In *The Thyroid Axis, Drugs and Behavior*. New York: Raven. 129 pp.

256. Serantakis, D., McKinley, W. A., Grant, N. H. 1973. The synthesis and biological activity of Ala[3, 14] somatostatin. *Biochem. Biophys. Res. Commun.* 55:538–42

257. Setalo, G., Vigh, S., Schally, A. V., Arimura, A., Flerko, B. 1975. LH-RH containing neural elements in the rat hypothalamus. *Endocrinology* 96: 135–42

258. Seyler, L. E. Jr., Reichlin, S. 1973. Luteinizing hormone releasing factor (LRF) in plasma of post menopausal women. *J. Clin. Endocrinol. Metab.* 37:197–203

259. Seyler, L. E. Jr., Reichlin, S. 1973. Luteinizing hormone releasing factor (LRF) in the blood of men induced by castration or estrogen treatment. *Clin. Res.* 21:502

260. Seyler, L. E. Jr., Reichlin, S. 1974. Episodic secretion of luteinizing hormone releasing factor (LRF) in the human. *J. Clin. Endocrinol. Metab.* 39:471–78

261. Shambaugh, G. E. III, Wilber, J. F. 1974. Thyrotropin releasing hormone: measurements in human spinal fluid by radioimmunoassay. *Clin. Res.* 22:634A

262. Shibusawa, K., Yamamoto, T., Nishi, K., Abe, C., Tomie, S. 1959. Urinary excretion of TRF in various functional

states of the thyroid. *Endocrinol. Jpn.* 6:131–36

263. Shin, S. H., Kraicer, J. 1974. LH-RH radioimmunoassay and its applications: Evidence of antigenically distinct FSH-RH and a diurnal study of LH-RH and gonadotropins. *Life Sci.* 14:281–88

264. Siler, T. M., VandenBerg, G., Yen, S. S. C. 1973. Inhibition of growth hormone release in humans by somatostatin. *J. Clin. Endocrinol. Metab.* 37:632–34

265. Siler, T. M., Yen, S. S. C., Vale, W., Guillemin, R. 1974. Inhibition by somatostatin on the release of TSH induced in man by thyrotropin releasing factor. *J. Clin. Endocrinol. Metab.* 38:742–45

266. Snyder, P. J., Jacobs, L. S., Utiger, R. S., Daughaday, W. H. 1973. Thyroid hormone inhibition of the prolactin response to thyrotropin releasing hormone. *J. Clin. Invest.* 52:2324–29

267. Somonovic, I., Motta, M., Martini, L. 1974. Acetylcholine and the release of the follicle stimulating hormone-releasing factor. *Endocrinology* 95:1373–79

268. Steiner, D. F., Rubenstein, A. H., Peterson, J. D., Kemmler, W., Tager, H. S. Proinsulin and polypeptide hormone biosynthesis. *Excerpta Med. Int. Congr. Ser.* See Ref. 114

269. Swaab, D. F., Schade, J. F. 1974. Integrative hypothalamic activity. *Progr. Brain Res.* 41:1–516

270. Szabo, M., Frohman, L. A. 1975. Effects of porcine stalk median eminence and prostaglandin E2 on rat growth hormone secretion in vivo and their inhibition by somatostatin. *Endocrinology* 96:955

271. Taber, C. A., Karavolas, H. J. 1975. Subcellular localization of LH releasing activity in the rat hypothalamus. *Endocrinology* 96:446–52

272. Takahara, J., Arimura, A., Schally, A. V. 1974. Suppression of prolactin release by a purified porcine PIF preparation and catecholamines infused into a rat hypophysial portal vessel. *Endocrinology* 95:462–65

273. Takahashi, Y., Kipnis, D. M., Daughaday, W. H. 1968. Growth hormone secretion during sleep. *J. Clin. Invest.* 47:2079–90

274. Tashjian, A. H. Jr., Borowsky, N. J., Jensen, D. K. 1971. Thyrotropin releasing hormone: Direct evidence for stimulation of prolactin production by pituitary cells in culture. *Biochem. Biophys. Res. Commun.* 43:516–23

275. Taubenhaus, M., Soskin, S. 1941. Release of luteinizing hormone from anterior hypophysis by an acetylcholine like substance from the hypothalamic region. *Endocrinology* 29:958–64

276. Taurog, A., Oliver, C., Eskay, R. L., Porter, J. C., McKenzie, J. M. 1974. The role of TRH in the neoteny of the Mexican axolotl (*Ambystoma mexicanum*). *Gen. Comp. Endocrinol.* 24:267–79

277. Thieme, G., Torp, A. 1962. Fluorescence of catecholamines and related compounds condensed with formaldehyde. *J. Histochem. Cytochem.* 10:348–54

278. Thornton, V. V. 1974. Hypothalamic control of gonadotropin release in amphibia: Evidence from studies of gonadotropin release in vitro and in vivo. *Gen. Comp. Endocrinol.* 23:294–301

279. Thum, C. H., Meissner, C., Beischer, W., Schroder, K. E., Pfeiffer, E. F. 1975. Juvenile diabetes: somatostatin and insulin requirement. *Acta Endocrinol.* 78:69

280. Toivola, P. T. K., Gale, C. C. 1972. Stimulation of growth hormone release by microinjection of norepinephrine into hypothalamus of baboons. *Endocrinology* 90:895–902

281. Tuomisto, J. et al 1975. Neurotransmitter control of thyrotropin secretion in the rat. *Eur. J. Pharmacol.* 30:221–29

282. Tyrrell, J. B., Lorenzi, M., Forsham, P. H., Gerich, J. E. 1975. Somatostatin inhibits secretion of adrenocorticotrophin in patients with Nelson's syndrome. *Clin. Res.* 23:130A

283. Ulrich, R., Yuwiler, A. 1973. Failure of 6-hydroxydopamine to abolish the circulation rhythm of serum corticosterone. *Endocrinology* 92:611–13

284. Ungerstedt, U. 1971. Stereotoxic mapping of the monoamine pathways in the rat brain. *Acta Physiol. Scand. Suppl.* 367:1–48

285. Vale, W., Brazeau, P., Grant, G., Nussey, A., Burgus, R., Rivier, J., Ling, N., Guillemin, R. 1972. Premières observations sur le mode d'action de la somatostatine, un facteur hypothalamique qui inhibe la sécrétion de l'hormone de croissance. *C. R. Acad. Sci. Paris* 275:2913–16

286. Vale, W., Brazeau, P., Rivier, C., Rivier, J., Guillemin, R. 1973. Biological studies with somatostatin. A symbposim. In *Advances in Human Growth*

Hormone Research, 159–82. Nat. Inst. Health

287. Vale, W. W., Burgus, R., Dunn, T. F., Guillemin, R. 1971. In vitro plasma inactivation of thyrotropin releasing factor (TRF) and related peptides. Its inhibition by various means and by the synthetic decapeptide, PCA-His-OME. *Hormones* 2:193–203

288. Vale, W., Rivier, C., Brazeau, P., Guillemin, R. 1974. Effects of somatostatin on the secretion of thyrotropin and prolactin. *Endocrinology* 95:968–77

289. Vale, W. et al 1974. Ubiquitous brain distribution of inhibitors of adenohypophysial secretion. *Program Ann. Meet. Endocrine Soc., 56th, June Atlanta,* p. A-128 (Abstr.)

290. Valverde, R. C., Chieffo, V., Reichlin, S. 1972. Prolactin releasing factor in porcine and rat hypothalami tissue. *Endocrinology* 91:982–93

291. Valverde, R., Carlos, N. Chieffo, V., Reichlin, S. 1973. Failure of reserpine to block ether induced release of prolactin: Physiological evidence that stress induced prolactin release is not caused by acute inhibition of PIF secretion. *Life Sci.* 12:327–35

292. Vanloon, G. R., Hilger, L., Cohen, R. 1969. Evidence for a hypothalamic adrenergic system that inhibits ACTH secretion in the dog. *Fed. Proc.* 28:438

293. Vanloon, G. R., Scapagnini, U., Cohen, R., Ganong, W. F. 1971. Effect of intraventricular administration of adrenergic drugs on the adrenal venous 17-hydroxy corticosteroid response to surgical stress in the dog. *Neuroendocrinology* 8:257–72

294. Walter, R. 1973. The role of enzymes in the formation and inactivation of peptide hormones. In *Peptides, Proc. Eur. Peptide Symp., 12th,* 363–68. New York: North-Holland

295. Walter, R. 1973. Oxytocin and other peptide hormones as prohormones. *Psychoendocrinol. Workshop, Conf. Int. Soc. Psychoneuroendocrinol.* 285–94. Basel: Mieken

296. Walter, R., Griffiths, E. C., Hooper, K. C. 1973. Production of MSH-release inhibiting hormone by a particulate preparation of hypothalamic: Mechanisms of oxytocin inactivation. *Brain Res.* 60:1449–57

297. Weir, G. C., Knowlton, S. D., Martin, D. B. 1974. Somatostatin inhibition of epinephrine induced glucagon secretion. *Endocrinology* 95:1744–46

298. Welbourn, R. B., Pearse, A. G. E., Polak, J. M., Bloom, S. R., Jaffe, S. N. 1974. The APUD cells of the alimentary tract in health and disease. *Med. Clin. N. Am.* 58:1359–74

299. White, W. F., Hedlund, M. T., Weber, G. F., Rippel, R. H., Johnson, E. S., Wilber, J. F. 1974. The pineal gland: A supplemental source of hypothalamic releasing hormone. *Endocrinology* 94:1422–26

300. Wilber, J. F., Porter, J. C. 1970. Thyrotropin and growth hormone releasing activity in hypophysial portal blood. *Endocrinology* 87:807–11

301. Winokur, A., Utiger, R. D. 1974. Thyrotropin releasing hormone: Regional distribution in rat brain. *Science* 185:265–67

302. Winter, A. J., Eskay, R. L., Porter, J. C. 1974. Concentration and distribution of TRH and LRH in the human fetal brain. *J. Clin. Endocrinol. Metab.* 39:960–63

303. Wurtman, R. J. 1971. Neuroendocrine transducer cells in mammals. In *The Neurosciences: Second Study Program,* 530–38. New York: Rockefeller Univ. Press

304. Yasuda, N., Takebe, K., Greer, M. A. 1975. Demonstration of corticotrophin releasing activity in rat and human blood. *Program Ann. Meet. Endocrine Soc., 57th, New York,* 97 pp. (Abstr.)

305. Yen, S. S. C., Siler, T. M., DeVane, G. W. 1974. Effect of somatostatin in patients with acromegaly: Suppression of growth hormone, prolactin, insulin and glucose levels. *N. Engl. J. Med.* 299:935–38

306. Zimmerman, E. A., Hsu, K. C., Feris, M., Kozlowski, G. P. 1974. Localization of gonadotropin releasing hormone (Gn-RH) in the hypothalamus of the mouse by immunoperoxidase technique. *Endocrinology* 95:1–8

307. Vagenakis, A. G., Roti, E., Mannix, J., Braverman, L. E. 1975. Problems in the measurement of urinary TRH. *J. Clin. Endocrinol. Metab.* 41:801–4

CURRENT MODELS OF   ❖1156
STEROID HORMONE ACTION:
A CRITIQUE

Jack Gorski and Frank Gannon[1, 2]

Departments of Biochemistry and Animal Science, University of Wisconsin, Madison,
Wisconsin 53706

INTRODUCTION

The model of estrogen action shown in Figure 1 was first introduced in the 1960s
(34, 44, 119). That this same model serves to summarize the mechanism of action
of estrogens after close to a decade of extensive research by numerous laboratories
should not, however, be construed as a lack of progress. The model in Figure 1 is
such a general statement that it will become outdated only when one of its five
premises is invalidated. The model is based on the assumptions that (*a*) estrogen
enters cells, (*b*) target tissues contain receptors, (*c*) the receptors, in the absence of
estrogen, are located in the cytoplasm, (*d*) the estrogen-receptor complexes translocate to the nucleus, and (*e*) a consequence of the presence of the estrogen receptors
in the nucleus is an alteration in the pattern of gene expression. Using the technol-
ogy presently available, these premises have been confirmed, not only for estrogens,
but for other steroid hormones (9–12, 24a, 63, 64, 69–71, 75, 84, 93, 95, 118, 128,
138, 141, 146) and 1,25-dihydroxyvitamin D_3 (14, 89, 96, 137) as well. It had been
thought that thyroxine also acts in the same manner, but recent results now suggest
that either the receptors for the thyroid hormones are always present in the nucleus
(97, 114) or are distributed throughout the cell (130a).

  The literature reveals that many of the fine details of the model in Figure 1 have
been examined at length. Yet in all fairness it must be conceded that a definitive
description of any aspect of the mechanism of action of steroid hormones still eludes

  [1]Recent work from our laboratory discussed in this review was supported by the College
of Agricultural and Life Sciences, University of Wisconsin, Madison, and by research grants
HD 08192 from the United States Public Health Service and Ford Foundation Grant No.
6300505A.
  [2]Present address of F. Gannon: Faculté de Médécine, Strasbourg, France.

425

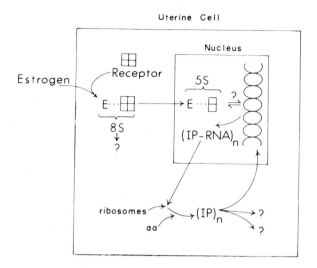

Figure 1 This model of the mechanism of action of estrogen shows the hormone entering the uterine cell, binding to the estrogen receptor in the cytoplasm, and translocating to the nucleus where it induces the synthesis of specific proteins $(IP)_n$ (where n is equal to at least 1 and probably more) (34).

us. Some recent reviews (8, 47, 51, 55, 60, 82, 90, 106, 145), in particular those by Jensen & DeSombre (48) and O'Malley et al (92), have clearly supported the major concepts and basis of this model. In this review, an attempt is made to supplement those reviews with a critical discussion of the more poorly defined aspects of the above model. Attention is focused on the following steps of the model: (*a*) entry of steroid hormone into the cell, (*b*) the nature of the cytoplasmic receptor, (*c*) steroid-induced changes in the cytoplasmic receptor, (*d*) translocation of the receptor from the cytoplasm to the nucleus, (*e*) interaction of steroid receptors with nuclear components, (*f*) dissociation of steroids from receptor sites, and (*g*) tissue responses to steroid hormones and their relationship to receptors. Emphasis is placed on the mechanism of action of estrogen, and we include only a limited discussion of other steroids without attempting to intensively survey the literature. The term *receptor* is used to describe the specific sterioid-binding proteins found in target tissues.

ENTRY OF STEROID HORMONES INTO THE CELL

It has been widely assumed that the cell membrane provides little or no barrier to the diffusion of steroids into cells because of their lipophilic properties. The early experiments of Jensen & Jacobson (50) that showed that estradiol and estrone are taken up rapidly by most tissues of the rat seem to support this theory. Differences in hormone uptake in various tissues were observed, but all tissues with high levels of steroid contained receptors that avidly bind the hormones. Thus it appeared that the greater accumulation of hormone in target tissues resulted from their ability to retain estrogen rather than simply from a difference in uptake of the hormone.

It is difficult, however, to rule out the possibility of a mechanism of facilitated transport of steroids into target cells. The presence of both a large number of undefined low-affinity binding sites and of receptors with very high affinity for the steroid once it has entered the cell could mask the detection of a transport protein at the membrane level. Indeed, most studies designed to detect such a protein have failed to do so (18).

Williams & Gorski showed that at, a temperature of 0°C, steroids do not readily enter cells (142). Unfortunately, while this finding supports the theory of a transport protein, it is also consistent with the diffusion of steroids through the lipid mosaic of the membrane, inasmuch as at temperatures of less than 10°C, the physical state of the lipid bilayer changes from a liquid to a more solid state (41).

Recently, Milgrom et al (76) suggested that estrogen entry into uterine cells is a protein-mediated process. They showed that estradiol entry was saturable in the range of physiological hormone concentrations, inhibited by SH-blocking reagents, and that this inhibition differed from the inhibition observed for estradiol binding to the receptor. Peck et al (100), using similar techniques, did not observe saturation and found no effect on estradiol uptake with N-ethylmaleimide (an SH-blocking reagent not used by Milgrom et al).

Baulieu (7) compared the equilibrium-binding constants of whole tissue uptake of estradiol with cell-free binding. At a temperature of 37°C, a difference of an order of magnitude (5×10^{-9} and 5×10^{-10} M) in the binding constants was observed and interpreted as an indication of a rate-limiting step at the level of steroid entry into the tissue. However, comparison of binding constants between intact tissues and cell-free systems is subject to different interpretations. For example, when binding constants for estrogen of intact tissues are compared with those for free cells prepared by enzyme treatment of the tissue, a similar difference in affinity has been observed (144). Competition with large numbers of nonspecific, extracellular binding sites in the intact tissues could influence uptake, however damage by the proteolytic enzymes to the hypothetical steroid transport system could account for this difference. At present, therefore, there is little evidence either to support or to refute the idea of facilitated transport.

THE NATURE OF THE CYTOPLASMIC RECEPTOR

When estradiol enters the cell, it binds to many proteins. In most cases this binding is nonspecific (as expected for a target tissue receptor); the exception is the binding of the steroid to the receptor. This specific binding is characterized by a high affinity (K_d 2×10^{-10} -1×10^{-9} M) (27, 31, 120, 135), a limited number of receptors per cell ($\sim 10^{-8}$ M or 16,000 receptors) (34, 135), and competition by compounds chemically similar to estradiol. Although these properties distinguish the receptor from nonspecific binding, it proved difficult initially to demonstrate the proteins to be different by physiochemical techniques.

Separation of high-affinity from low-affinity binding components was eventually achieved by using sucrose density gradient centrifugation with low salt ($<$ 0.1 M salt) concentrations in extracting media and sucrose gradients (134). These conditions permitted the estrogen receptor to aggregate to a large ($\sim$ 8S) form. This large form readily sediments on sucrose gradients away from the rat serum albumin ($\sim$4–5S), which appears to be a principal contributor to the low-affinity binding components of the uterus (100).

Since then, sucrose density gradients have been widely used for the characterization of the estrogen receptor. This receptor appears as an 8S molecule (25, 110) in hypotonic (low salt) media and as a 4S molecule (45, 54, 110) in hypertonic (0.4 M KCl) media. In isotonic media the sedimentation velocity of this receptor varies depending on the precise conditions used, but Reti & Erdos (109) and others (17, 111) have observed it as a 6S entity, and Yamamoto & Alberts as a 4S (146a). Mueller et al (82) have shown that in hypotonic media this receptor is a complex aggregate that yields varying S values. A similar observation was made by Stancel et al (125), who further concluded that the native form of the receptor was most apt to be the 4S form. However, the latter study also showed that the concentration of the protein in the sample greatly affected the S value of the receptor; higher protein concentrations yielded larger sedimentation coefficients (125). The inability to duplicate the conditions of the intact cell with regard to salt and protein concentrations, as well as other factors, necessitates a discussion of receptors in terms of these forms found under specific experimental conditions.

The 8S form of the receptor is apparently an aggregate of several proteins that may be formed after homogenization rather than preexisting in the cell (82, 125). However, it may be premature to dismiss the 8S form as an artifact resulting from the presence of unphysiologically low concentrations of salt. It may prove significant that the aggregate does not have dimensions larger than 8S; in other words, the hypotonic salts give rise to a relatively well-defined entity. In addition, it seems certain that the intracellular protein concentration greatly exceeds that used in routine sucrose density gradient centrifugation. The data of Stancel et al (125) imply that more serious consideration should be given to the 8S as the "native" form but, up to the present, there has been no thorough examination of the physical and chemical properties of this form.

Probably the most complete analysis of the cytoplasmic 4S estrogen receptor has been reported by Notides & Nielsen (88). Using both sephadex gel chromatography and sucrose gradient centrifugation, they concluded that the uterine cytoplasmic receptor (4S form) was a protein of 76,000 mol wt. Comparisons of sedimentation and gel chromatographic behavior suggest that the protein is asymmetric, supporting the earlier analysis of Yamamoto & Alberts (146a). Notides & Nielsen also showed that the asymmetry is affected by conformational changes in the protein caused by varying pH's, buffers, etc. The sensitivity of the receptor to the experimental conditions employed serves to underline the difficulty of relating observed physical properties to the form of the receptor when in the cellular milieu.

All studies of steroid hormone receptors have been limited by the fact that the receptor is detected only after the steroid is bound. Therefore the above studies do not deal to any extent with the state of the receptor as it exists in the cell prior to interaction with the steroid. Yet, as discussed in the following sections, we feel that it is important to consider why receptor, in the absence of estradiol, remains in the cytoplasm. Part of the answer to this question resides in the properties of the receptor protein before it is bound to estradiol.

STEROID-INDUCED CHANGES
IN THE CYTOPLASMIC RECEPTOR

As the estrogen-receptor complex is found predominantly in the nucleus, while the free receptor remains in the cytoplasm, it is clear that ligand-induced changes in the cytoplasmic receptor protein provide part of the explanation for the action of the steroid hormone. There is evidence that the steroid-receptor complex has properties that differ from those of the receptor alone. Baulieu (8) and others (56, 101) have shown that free receptor is more thermolabile than the estrogen-receptor complex. Free receptor also appears more sensitive to light than is the estrogen-receptor complex (57). These changes accompany changes in the physical properties of the receptor. Earlier studies (35, 53) had shown that the presence of estrogen was essential to evoke specific changes in the sedimentation behavior of the estrogen receptor at temperatures of 20°C or greater, and Notides & Nielsen (88) confirmed these findings. These studies would also support the widely accepted idea that a conformational change in the receptor occurs when the steroid is bound. This change is frequently described as allosteric, although the precision of this term might be questioned in view of the lack of a site analogous to a catalytic or genome-binding site. From studies of Monod et al (79) and Koshland & Neet (61) it has been suggested that the binding of an allosteric ligand to a protein can result in a net change in the conformation of the protein in at least two ways. In terms of steroid binding, in one case the receptor exists in an equilibrium between two forms, one of which has a high affinity for the steroid. When steroid is introduced into the system and binds to this high-affinity form, the product (estrogen-receptor complex) removes some high-affinity receptor from the preexisting equilibrium causing some of the lower-affinity form of the receptor to transform to the high-affinity state. This equilibrium model is based on the ideas of Monod et al (79). In the alternative model there is only one form of the receptor in the absence of steroid and the binding of the steroid induces a change in the conformation of the receptor. This model is based on the "induced fit" model for regulatory enzymes developed and discussed by Koshland & Neet (61) as well as by Atkinson (6). The net result in both instances is the transformation of receptor into a new form. Samuels & Tomkins (113) used the allosteric equilibrium model to describe glucocorticoid interaction with receptors in hepatic cells; however, the crude nature of receptor studies makes it very difficult to distinguish between the two models. To date, no evidence has been presented for the existence of two forms of the free receptor in the cytoplasm and indeed the very existence of a conformational change remains an assumption based on the lability studies discussed above.

While the occurrence and mechanism of any estrogen-induced conformational change remain matters for theoretical discussion, there is ample evidence for a gross change in the size of the receptor after estrogen binding and exposure to temperatures of 20°C or above. This change is observed on sucrose density gradients; in the presence of 0.4 M KCl, the 4S form of the receptor is converted to a 5S form (49). The 5S form was first described by DeSombre et al (24) and Puca & Bresciani (102) on extraction with 0.4 M KCl of nuclear fractions from uteri labeled with [³H]estradiol. The so-called nuclear 5S receptor accounts for most of the estrogen bound in the nuclear fraction. Jensen and others have also reported that the 4S cytoplasmic receptor was converted to a 5S form upon incubation of uterine cytosol with estrogen at room temperature (∼ 22°C) but not at O°C (35, 53). This appeared particularly significant because the translocation of estrogen-receptor complex into the nucleus in intact cells and in cell-free systems also appears to be a temperature-dependent process (47, 52).

On the basis of these results, Jensen et al proposed a model in which the cytoplasmic 4S receptor binds to estradiol, thereby transforming the estrogen-receptor complex to a 5S form, which then translocates to the nucleus (47). While this model is consistent with most of the observed facts, some data, including the fact that the cytoplasmic receptor may not be 4S, do not support it. Siiteri et al (123) reported finding 4S receptor in carefully washed nuclei. Pulse chase experiments indicated the nuclear 4S receptor decreased as the 5S form increased (123), suggesting that the 4S receptor first binds estrogen and moves into the nucleus where it is then converted to the 5S form. Yamamoto (147) has recently reported that the conversion from 4S to 5S occurs much more rapidly in the presence of DNA. This could be interpreted as supporting a nuclear site of transformation. In addition Jensen et al (46) reported that "cytoplasmic 5S" and "nuclear 5S" sediment a bit differently. Furthermore, when estrogen is bound in both cytoplasm and nucleus at equilibrium, a considerable amount of the 4S form is always found in the cytoplasm in spite of exposure to estrogen and a temperature of 37°C for periods up to several hours (31). This appears to be in contrast to the relatively high percentage of conversion in the cell-free system (35, 53).

It appears wise therefore to treat the Jensen model (47) as a hypothesis that still requires proof. One intriguing piece of evidence upon which the Jensen model is based is the observation that in a cell-free system at 0°C, the estrogen receptor can translocate from cytosol to the nuclei if the cytosol has been preheated to permit the 4S-5S transformation to occur (52). At 0°C the nuclear membrane will be less permeable to proteins than at 37°C (as with the cell membrane discussed in the first section). Cox & Weissbach (20, 21), used purified HeLa nuclei and HeLa cytoplasmic proteins radioactively labeled, and found that very few proteins transferred to the nuclei at 0°C, whereas at 37°C quite a few different proteins did. This result suggests two conclusions: (*a*) in a cell-free system, proteins that normally reside in the cytoplasm can transfer to the nucleus, and (*b*) if heat-transformed receptors truly do translocate to nuclei at 0°C, they have very special properties indeed. Thus while a temperature-sensitive translocation is expected, heat activation of receptors is more difficult to envisage and one must wonder, as with all other studies with cell-free systems, if the translocation observed at 0° is physiological.

While the argument grows as to the locus in the cell where 4S estrogen receptor is transformed into the 5S form, the molecular basis of the changes in sedimentation coefficient have been examined in recent studies. On the basis of density gradient centrifugation and molecular sieve chromatography, Notides & Nielsen (88) concluded that the 5S protein is ∿130,000 mol wt or larger. The 5S cytoplasmic form can be converted to a 4S form in the presence of urea, which is similar to the report of Stancel et al (126) concerning the nuclear 5S form. Notides & Nielsen (88) suggested that the 5S form is composed of a 50,000 mol wt or larger protein subunit bound to the 80,000 mol wt 4S receptor. Yamamoto (147) also concluded that the 5S entity consists of the estrogen receptor and some other protein X. Protein X was found by Yamamoto in nontarget as well as in target tissues (147). Determination of the true nature of X protein may be of importance as this protein, rather than the estrogen receptor, could be the effector in the nucleus.

In summary the estrogen-receptor complex in the cytoplasm may take a variety of forms (4S, 5S, 6S, or 8S) as detected by sucrose density gradient centrifugation. It is not clear which form the receptor is in prior to estrogen binding, when it binds estradiol, or at the point of its entry into the nucleus. Each change in sedimentation coefficient reflects a change in the composition or conformation of the receptor. The molecular basis of these changes is not known, nor is it known if the changes are essential to the action of steroid hormones. They may merely be coincidental and confusing artifacts engendered under in vitro conditions. Most workers consider the changes in the properties of the receptor to be essential in the action of steroid hormones. If this proves to be the case, then the three most important questions arising from our discussion would be: (a) What is the true native form of the receptor before estrogen binding? (b) Where does the 4S-5S transformation occur? (c) Does this transformation introduce a new protein into the overall scheme? These are areas of active research at present and we hope that some clear-cut answers will soon be available. The next section is intended to point out just why these questions are very important.

TRANSLOCATION OF THE RECEPTOR FROM CYTOPLASM TO NUCLEUS

While the translocation of the receptor from the cytoplasm to the nucleus, as a consequence of steroid binding, is perhaps the least controversial step in the model of Figure 1, very little is known about how it actually occurs. It has been observed using either radioautography (44, 49) or cell fractionation procedures (87) that, after in vivo injection or in vitro incubation with [³H]estradiol, the steroid is subsequently found in target cell nuclei. It has been shown that the steroid remains bound to the same protein in both cytoplasmic and nuclear compartments during the translocation process. There is no evidence that the steroid is transferred from one receptor protein to another during translocation. The process is effectively stopped at low temperatures (34, 44); however, various metabolic inhibitors have no effect on translocation, which suggests that an energy utilizing system is not involved (120). The rate of translocation is directly proportional to the concentration of estrogen-receptor complex present in the cytoplasm at the start of the experiment (143). Compounds that interfere with microtubules or microfilaments, such as cytochalasin or vineblastine (33) and RNA and protein synthesis inhibitors (120), have no effect on translocation. Therefore the process of translocation has not been tied to any other cellular function and appears to be a consequence of the inherent properties of the receptor as modulated by the binding of steroid. The basic question then remains: Why or how does translocation of the ($\sim$80,000 mol wt) receptor occur? A frequent assumption in studies of the mechanism of action of steroids has been that translocation is due to the high affinity of the estrogen-receptor complex for nuclear sites to which it binds. Thus, the discussions of translocation and of nuclear action of the steroid-receptor complex are intimately entwined, and we leave this discussion to the next section. At this point, however, it is of interest to present some data on the movement of proteins from the cytoplasm to the nucleus.

Labeled cytoplasmic proteins of protozoa have been observed by Goldstein and colleagues (32, 43) to move into nuclei transplanted from unlabeled cells. Gurdon (36) and Paine & Feldherr (98) injected various materials into oocyte cytoplasm and concluded that the translocation of proteins occurs via the nuclear pores. There appears to be distinct size limitation as to the dimensions of material passing through the pores. Gurdon presented data indicating that proteins larger than serum albumin ($\sim$70,000 mol wt) enter the nuclei only at a very slow rate. Nuclear histones are much smaller than 70,000 Daltons and thus translocate readily. On the other hand, translocation of RNA polymerase [a large, relatively complex nuclear protein that contains subunits, greater than 100,000 in mol wt (140)] is difficult to explain on the basis of this hypothesis. The above concern for the "permeability" of nuclear pores is related to the size of the cytoplasmic receptors. As discussed in a previous section, the cytoplasmic receptor in high salt (0.4 M) media is about 80,000 daltons in its 4S form and 130,000 daltons in its 5S form. Still larger aggregated forms are seen in media of physiological ionic strength. It would be anticipated that the ability to translocate the larger sized proteins from the cytoplasm into the nucleus would be hampered because of their size. In particular, it seems a little difficult to envisage transport into the nucleus being facilitated by the transformation of the receptor from the 4S to the larger 5S form as described by Jensen. Molecular weight alone, however, may not be the main discriminating factor. The axial ratio of the receptor, for instance, might be an important consideration. In addition a uterine cell is not an oocyte and extrapolating from one cell type to another may be hazardous, although many studies suggest that nuclear pores do not appear to differ markedly from cell to cell.

Before discussing the mechanism of translocation of the estrogen-receptor complex, and in the light of the above comments concerning receptor size, it might be of interest to ask why the estrogen receptor, in the absence of estrogen, remains in the cytoplasm. Simple equilibria considerations, or the Horowitz & Moore (40) water exclusion hypothesis (see next section), would lead to the expectation that some free receptors exist in the nucleus. This is not observed and thus suggests three interesting possibilities: (a) perhaps the location of receptor on homogenization is artifactual, the estrogen-receptor complex predominantly partitioning with the nuclear pellet and free receptor predominantly partitioning with the cytoplasm; (b) perhaps free receptor is bound to some cytoplasmic structure and consequently is not subject to the equilibria to which solutes in the cell respond (that the receptor is always observed to be soluble could be due to the disruption of these low-affinity associations on homogenization); or (*c*) the free cytoplasmic receptor may be too large to pass through the nuclear pores. These latter two points relate once more to the question of the "native" form of the receptor and suggest that a full description of the mechanism of action of steroid hormones will require much more than an explanation of the role of the hormone-receptor complex in the nucleus.

INTERACTION OF STEROID RECEPTORS WITH NUCLEAR COMPONENTS

Estrogens

The model of receptor translocation from the cytoplasm to the nucleus developed during the 1960s, a period dominated by studies of the molecular biology of gene expression in prokaryotes. The repressor of the *lac* operon, an allosteric protein whose binding to a specific region of DNA is modulated by small molecular weight regulators, was readily accepted as a model for regulation in eukaryotes. At the same time, the pioneering studies of Mueller and his colleagues on estrogen action on RNA and protein synthesis forged a link between steroid action and gene expression (80, 81). The analogy of a repressor-gene interaction was readily assimilated into the concept of steroid hormone action and the search for the precise nature of this receptor-gene interaction was spurred by the observation of translocation of the steroid-receptor complex to nuclei (34, 44). These observations led to a refinement of studies on nuclear binding, i.e. the search for the specific components or "acceptors" that bind the steroid receptor complex in the nucleus. The development of a cell-free system (13) to observe nuclear binding of the estrogen-receptor complex reinforced the assumption that the driving force for translocation was the concentration gradient of estrogen-receptor complex in the two compartments, which in turn was due to the binding of the receptor to some nuclear component (acceptor). Thus the translocation model evolved to include a nuclear component whose specific interaction with the steroid-receptor could account for both the accumulation of receptor in the nucleus and the nuclear response to the hormone.

In turn, this led to a number of studies all identifying different nuclear components as the specific nuclear binding components. Maurer & Chalkley (72), Teng & Hamilton (131), and King et al (59) had shown earlier that the estrogen receptors associated with crude nuclear chromatin. Several groups found that the estrogen-receptor complex interacts directly with DNA (either from eukaryotes or prokaryotes) (37, 58, 133) and steroid receptors were also reported to bind to specific nuclear proteins that were either basic (104) or acidic (124). In an analogous system, the chick oviduct progesterone receptor was found to consist of two components, one of which could bind the DNA while the other bound to acidic nuclear proteins (see below). Liao and colleagues (65, 67) recently reported that estrogen- and androgen-receptor complexes bind to ribonucleoprotein particles in their respective target tissues. Finally, Jackson & Chalkley (42) presented data implicating receptors bound to nuclear membranes as the ultimate locus of bound estrogen.

Another line of experimentation has implicated an interaction of the estrogen-receptor complex with the enzyme RNA polymerase. This approach was first made by Talwar et al (130), who found that rat uterine cytosol, in the absence of estrogen, inhibited RNA polymerase activity of uterine nuclei, whereas estrogen reversed this inhibition. Subsequently Raynaud-Jammet (107) and Arnaud et al (4) showed that calf uterine cytosol by itself had no effect on nuclear polymerase. However, addition of estrogen to the cytosol increased the activity of RNA polymerase I (nucleolar polymerase). Further, Mohla et al (78) and Arnaud et al (5) demonstrated that only the estrogen- and temperature-activated form of the receptor (5S) activated RNA polymerase and that solubilized RNA polymerase (free of DNA and basic proteins) was also activated in the process. Thus RNA polymerase is another nuclear site of estrogen-receptor action and binding.

The term *acceptor* has been used to designate the nuclear sites that specifically bind steroid-receptor complexes. It is important to recognize that an acceptor is a concept and not a demonstrated fact. The origin of this concept is the binding of repressors with very high affinity to a very limited number of sites on the *lac* operon, thereby modulating gene expression. The evidence to support such a concept in steroid action is remarkably limited even after many years of study and might be summarized as (*a*) the requirement of high concentrations of salt to release nuclear-bound receptors, (*b*) the fact that saturable interactions between receptor-hormone complexes and nuclei or nuclear components have been observed in vitro, and (*c*) the apparent specificity, both with regard to the source of the nuclei and the particular nuclear fraction, to which the estrogen-receptor complex binds.

There are numerous artifacts that could contribute to the difficulty of extracting the receptor so most attention is focused on the other two lines of evidence. Two recent studies have raised questions concerning the use of cell-free systems as a model for translocation from the cytoplasm to the nucleus. In one of these, Chamness et al (16) showed that the saturation of binding observed in vitro is due not only to the increased amount of estrogen receptor added to the cell-free system but also to other cytoplasmic proteins that compete for the putative binding sites in the nucleus. Under controlled conditions, where the total protein content of the system was maintained constant while the estrogen-receptor concentration was increased, no saturation was observed (16). In another study, Higgins et al (39) reported that the presence of steroid receptor in the nucleus, after in vivo receptor translocation, had no influence on subsequent additional translocation in a cell-free system. These data suggest that the so-called saturable binding of the steroid-receptor complex to nuclei in a cell-free system is an artifact and is not comparable to the situation in vivo.

Several groups have shown that nuclei from target tissue bind cytoplasmic receptors to a greater extent than do nuclei from nontarget tissues (35, 85, 127). However, in these studies, comparisons did not usually take into account variations in the protein content of different nuclear preparations. The demonstration of an artifact inherent in the cell-free system and a reexamination of the tissue specificity by Chamness et al (15) led to the inference that cell-free binding does not provide valid evidence for tissue specificity in the binding of estrogen-receptor complex to nuclei.

With regard to the results showing binding to a specific nuclear fraction, it is obvious from the earlier discussion that such binding occurs to a number of different components. This makes it difficult to decide just what an acceptor is, particularly as estrogen receptor has a well-known propensity to bind to other components, biological or inanimate (e.g. it binds to glass). Great caution should therefore be taken in ascribing binding in cell-free systems to that which occurs in a cellular environment. It may prove that there are multiple acceptors, with all of the various constituents mentioned above, at one time or another, bound to the receptor. On the other hand, some or perhaps all of the present conclusions as to possible acceptors may be incorrect.

Recently, there has been a trend to revise thinking on the nature of the binding of the estrogen receptor in the nucleus. The starting point in these changes came from observations (143) that in intact tissue or cells the translocation process for the estrogen receptor behaved like a unimolecular reaction with no evidence for saturation within the range of normal cell concentrations of estrogen receptor ($\sim 10^{-8}$M). This was apparent both in equilibrium and in kinetic studies. The importance of this observation is that the acceptor hypothesis would predict a saturable process and a second-order reaction or an acceptor present in such large numbers that saturation could not be observed. It was concluded from these studies that estrogen-receptor movement from the cytoplasm to the nucleus could not be caused by nuclear binding of estrogen receptor to the limited number of high-affinity acceptors, as was commonly assumed at that time. This, in turn, led to a breakdown of the unified theory that identified translocation and gene activation as the consequences of a single act, i.e. the binding of the estrogen receptor complex to the acceptor.

Another fact to be considered is the presence, at physiological concentrations of estradiol, of approximately 10,000 receptors in the nucleus (18). If the original acceptor idea of a few high-affinity sites is valid, then many (over 90%) of these receptors are redundant. Yet evidence in the literature points to a direct relationship between the nuclear content of the steroid-receptor complex and cell response. When data of Ruh et al (112) are replotted, an in vitro estrogen response can be shown to correlate in a linear fashion with the quantity of estrogen-receptor complex available. In other words, the only rate-limiting factor is the amount of receptor. Clark et al (18) have reported similar conclusions, based on the observation that an early in vivo response correlated with nuclear binding of hormone administered in vivo. Tomkins et al also made similar observations for the glucocorticoid system (132). Therefore, if nuclear acceptors do exist, they do not appear to be rate limiting, at least under the conditions studied to date.

Observing that a fixed percentage of the total number of receptors that bound estradiol translocated to the nucleus at every estrogen concentration, Williams & Gorski (143) concluded that the estrogen receptor responded to an equilibrium, perhaps due to polarity or phase differences between the cytoplasm and nucleus. This suggestion portrayed translocation as absolutely independent of nuclear binding. Support for this concept of intracellular translocation independent of binding came from studies by Horowitz & Moore (40) on the movement of radioactively labeled "inert" macromolecules in frog oocytes. They found, for example, that inulin, injected into the cytoplasm of the oocyte, concentrated in the nuclei and suggested that this was not due to binding in the nucleus but to an equilibrium between available water space in the two compartments. They proposed that the water space in the cytoplasm available to macromolecules is limited by the gel-like nature of cytoplasm. Thus the contents of cytoplasm act like a molecular sieve, excluding marcromolecules of certain sizes. Using such a cytoplasmic exclusion model, one could propose that, prior to ligand interaction, receptors are bound in the cytoplasm or are unable to move through nuclear pores and that the presence of ligand (estrogen) releases the receptor and permits it to equilibrate with the nuclear compartment. Whether the water exclusion model of Horowitz and Moore applies to the movement of the estrogen-receptor complex to the nuclei of rat uterine cells is difficult to test experimentally, but it does provide an interesting model for intracellular movement of macromolecules. Whatever the mechanism involved in the translocation of the estrogen receptor, the kinetic data supports a model of translocation independent of high-affinity binding in the nucleus.

This conclusion has paved the way for a model that includes very large numbers of low-affinity binding sites on the chromatin and just a few crucial genetically responsive sites of higher affinity. The proponents of this model, Yamamoto & Alberts (147, 148) found that the estrogen-receptor complex binds to DNA with a low affinity ($\sim 1 \times 10^{-4}$ M), but they suggested that the number of DNA binding sites available in the cell is in vast excess of the number of estrogen-receptor complexes present such that the net result would be large-scale binding of estrogen receptor to DNA. This binding, in vitro, is not target tissue specific, and Yamamoto & Alberts suggested that it masks the high-affinity binding to DNA sequences involved in regulating tissue response.

The development of the acceptor model was a consequence of theories of the *lac* repressor binding to a very limited number of promoter sites in the *lac* operon. The two-site DNA binding model for receptors is conceptually fathered by another development in the study of the *lac* operon (68, 139). These studies show that, in prokaryotic systems, gene regulatory proteins interact with DNA in a nonspecific manner in addition to having a very high affinity for some specific regions of the DNA. Thus an equilibrium develops between binding to a large number of non-specific low-affinity sites and to the limited number of specific higher-affinity sites. This model, as applied to steroid hormone action, is appealing theoretically because it appears to explain both the binding data and the response data. The estrogen receptor in this model can be thought of as being in an equilibrium between three sites: cytoplasm $\rightleftharpoons$ DNA (low affinity) $\rightleftharpoons$ DNA (high affinity). Depending on the numbers of high- and low-affinity sites as well as their affinity constants, it is possible to produce a model in which the high-affinity sites are not saturated under physiological conditions.

The two-site DNA binding model requires that there be some differences between the estrogen-receptor binding to the two types of loci. In this regard Alberga et al (1) presented evidence that some estradiol remains bound in the nucleus under conditions that remove most of the estrogen-receptor complex. In addition, Anderson et al suggested the necessity of the continuing presence of estrogen to evoke the later responses to estrogen (3). J. H. Clark et al (in preparation) have also concluded that the later responses are functions of a pool of estrogen that shows delayed disappearance from the target tissue. Using an exchange assay, they found a pool of exchangeable estrogen in the nucleus that appears to be maintained for up to 24 hr after estrogen injection and yields a different binding saturation curve from that seen at earlier time periods. These in vivo experiments, at time intervals later than those generally used in binding experiments, may provide a very useful system for the problems of nuclear translocation and nuclear response and may permit the separation of the two sites on DNA proposed by Yamamoto & Alberts.

In summary, then, there is presently increasing strain on the simple idea that the binding of estrogen to a very few high-affinity acceptor sites provides an answer to both the mechanism of translocation of the steroid-receptor complex and the mechanism of gene activation. Instead, the trends lead one to question the very existence of sites with these properties as large numbers of steroid-receptor complexes enter the nucleus and there is a direct relationship between the number of receptors in the nucleus and the nuclear response. This suggests the existence of many gene activation sites rather than few. This suggestion, although unlikely on the basis of present concepts of the control of gene expression, is in keeping with the observations that estrogen receptor binds specifically to each of the possible nuclear candidates (DNA, nuclear proteins, ribonucleoprotein particles, nuclear membranes) by different investigators. To these results should be added the recent data from Tsai et al, who analyzed the induction of ovalbumin biosynthesis by the estrogen receptor in the chick oviduct. They found that estrogen increases the number of new initiation sites for RNA synthesis on oviduct chromatin (supposedly equal to number of transcribed genes) from 8,000 to 25,000 per cell (136), even though it is known that there are only one or two ovalbumin genes in chick DNA (38, 99). It appears that a large part of the genome is influenced by the steroid-receptor complex and that many gene loci, not just a few, are involved.

If one questions the existence of high-affinity sites on the chromatin necessary for gene activation, then nucleoplasmic and other roles for the estrogen-receptor complex become possibilities; e.g. the estrogen-receptor complex could affect the nuclear membrane or have an enzymatic function.

The affinity of the estrogen-receptor complex for DNA as calculated by Yamamoto & Alberts (147, 148) is very low (1×10^{-4} M) and therefore it seems plausible that binding to cytoplasmic constituents occurs with an equivalent affinity. Thus estrogen may cause a change in the receptor's affinity for cytoplasmic constituents permitting the water exclusion model of Horowitz & Moore (40) to come into play. Translocation would be a consequence of changing affinities resulting in shifts in distribution between a series of equilibrating states. Target tissue response would be influenced by the shift in equilibria but would not be a causative factor.

In the whole animal additional equilibria with extracellular and blood proteins must also be considered. This has been elegantly described for aldosterone binding by Funder et al (30a).

Other Steroid Hormones

A receptor protein for progesterone has been shown to be present in the reproductive tracts of chickens, guinea pigs, rabbits, rats, mice, and humans (19, 22, 23, 28–30, 73–75, 77, 105, 108, 118, 141). It has been studied in greatest detail in the chick oviduct, and these studies have been recently reviewed (90–92, 106). Sherman et al found in oviduct cytosol of estradiol-treated chicks (118) a protein that binds progesterone with high affinity ($K_d = 10^{-10}$ M). This receptor has properties very similar to those of the estrogen receptor when analyzed on sucrose density gradients; in high salt (0.4 M KCl) it has a sedimentation constant of 4S, whereas at low ionic strength the sedimentation constant increases to 8S. It was estimated that the molecular weight of the 4S form is 90,000 daltons, whereas that of the 8S is 360,000. The 4S⟶8S transformation is therefore envisaged as a monomer polymerizing to a tetramer, although the basis for this belief resides solely in the molecular weight values that were determined (106).

After binding progesterone, O'Malley et al (94) showed that the hormone-receptor complex moves to the nucleus. The reasons for the movement of hormone-receptor complexes from the cytoplasm to the nucleus, discussed earlier in this review, are no clearer for the progesterone-receptor complex than they are for the estradiol-receptor complex. The problem of the size of the receptor vis-à-vis the size of the nuclear pores once again is pertinent (see above). However, the progesterone receptor is also a very asymmetric molecule; the calculated axial ratios show it to be 14–18 times long as it is wide (118). These calculations have recently been verified by electron micrographs (R. Kuhn, P. M. Conn, W. T. Schrader, B. W. O'Malley, in preparation). A similar asymmetry has been shown for the estrogen receptor by Notides & Nielsen (88), which may provide a general mechanism for facilitating the entry of large hormone-receptor complexes into the nucleus. A new problem would then emerge. Receptors move very quickly into the nucleus; would rapid translocation be possible for molecules that first have to be aligned in the correct plane?

In a series of interesting experiments, Spelsberg et al (124) showed that the progesterone-receptor complex binds to chromatin extracted from the oviduct (the target tissue) to a greater extent than to chromatin from nontarget tissues, after cell-free incubations. Pursuing this observation, using chromatin reconstituted from DNA, histone, and nonhistone proteins, Spelsberg et al concluded that the specificity of the oviduct binding resides in the acidic proteins. Thus if oviduct nonhistone proteins were replaced by nonhistone proteins from a nontarget tissue, binding of the progesterone-receptor complex to reconstituted oviduct chromosomes would not occur, whereas the substitution of oviduct nonhistone proteins for nontarget nonhistone protein in the reconstitution of nontarget chromosomes resulted in the binding of progesterone receptors (124). Fractionation of the acidic proteins demonstrated that one group of nonhistone proteins, designated AP_3, seemed the most effective in conferring the binding ability on the chromatin.

Viewed in isolation, this research constitutes the clearest demonstration of the existence of acceptor sites on the chromatin to which a hormone-receptor complex can bind. Unfortunately, there is much evidence, discussed elsewhere in this review, from the numerous studies on the mechanism of action of estrogens that suggests, contrary to these results, that (*a*) receptors may not distinguish between target and nontarget tissues and (*b*) the postulated acceptors may not be acidic proteins.

The binding of progesterone receptor to the chromatin was of high affinity ($K_d = 1 \times 10^{-8}$ M) and analysis of Scatchard plots suggested the presence of approximately 2000 binding sites per cell (92). These observations were germinal to the idea (previously discussed) that specific acceptors exist and have a high affinity and low capacity for hormone-receptor complexes. Binding analyses also indicated that binding to DNA was possible. Sedimenting progesterone receptor and DNA simultaneously reinforced this idea. The presence of DNA caused the disappearance of the receptor from the 4S position and its sedimentation, with the DNA, to the bottom of the tube. This binding was not restricted to target tissue DNA; calf thymus DNA also caused a similar change in sedimentation.

Subsequently, Schrader & O'Malley (117) partially purified the progesterone receptor. In the course of purification, two progesterone-binding proteins appeared in the cytosol of chick oviduct. These were precipitated by the same concentration of ammonium sulfate, had the same sedimentation coefficient (4S) in sucrose gradients run in the presence of high salts, and were co-eluted from Agarose gel filtration columns. However, they were eluted at quite different positions from DEAE-cellulose columns; one binding component, A, was eluted at 0.15 M KCl and binding component B was eluted at 0.22 M KCl. It was shown that in low salt media the two components sedimented differently on sucrose density gradients; A aggregated to a form greater than 8S, which sedimented to the bottom of the gradient, whereas B did not aggregate and remained 4S. It would thus appear that purification had resolved the cytoplasmic amalgamation of receptors normally seen on homogenizing the tissue into two components of quite different properties. One should be aware, however, that very limited proteolysis of the receptor could produce a form with different properties from the rest of the receptors. Precedent for this suggestion exists in the literature of the case of the estrogen receptor (26, 103).

O'Malley et al then examined the receptors to see if they displayed any specificity in the component of chromatin (i.e. DNA or protein) to which they bind. The B protein bound to chromatin in a manner dependent on the nonhistone proteins present, i.e. the same as observed for the crude cytosol (94). The A protein, however, bound to DNA alone (92). The experiments that suggest this involved the co-sedimentation of DNA and the A protein through either a sucrose density gradient or the cochromatography of the A protein and DNA on a BioRad A-15 M column. The affinity of the interaction was high ($K_d \sim 2 \times 10^{-10}$) and the data correspond to 500 DNA binding sites per nucleus. O'Malley et al concluded that the full binding potential of the nucleus is fulfilled only when both A and B are binding to their respective loci. Recently, Kuhn et al (62a) have shown that receptor purified 4000-fold has the same characteristics as the cruder preparations described above.

Evaluation of these data leads to comparisons between the progesterone receptor and the more extensively studied estrogen receptor. Attempts to purify the estrogen receptor have not led to the isolation of two binding forms such as the A and B proteins for progesterone, nor has the estrogen receptor been characterized by specific binding to a single chromatin component such as the AP_3 acidic protein. Rather, the estrogen receptor binds to a variety of nuclear fractions and the fraction involved (be it DNA, histone, nonhistone, or ribonucleoprotein) seems to depend on the conditions employed (see above).

One interesting assertion by Schrader et al is that the A protein binds specifically to DNA. Receptor-DNA interaction has also been studied for the crude estrogen receptor, most recently by Yamamoto and Alberts. In an appendix to their paper

(148), they pointed out the possible occurrence of receptor aggregations that mimic receptor-DNA binding. Their studies point to the existence, in some DNA preparations, of low levels of natural acidic polysaccharides that can cause extensive aggregation of receptor. If binding to DNA is defined solely by co-sedimentation or co-chromatographing of receptor and DNA, then it is impossible to distinguish between bona fide binding and extensive aggregation of the receptor.

A novel approach to the study of receptor-acceptor interaction has been used recently by Edelman (24a). Using ethidium bromide and actinomycin D, each of which interacts with DNA in a different manner, he showed that aldosterone receptor binding to chromatin was differentially affected by the two inhibitors. These studies were in a cell-free system and are open to questions raised elsewhere in this review, but they do suggest a technique that could be used to good advantage both in vivo and in vitro.

From the data reviewed so far, it is obvious the barriers to progress in understanding the mechanism of action of steroid hormones are technological rather than conceptual. The receptor is detected only when it is bound to steroid; however, the receptor is extremely "sticky," consequently, the observation of binding, even when it appears specific, is never sufficient to overcome the suspicion of an artifact. For that matter, the very fact that tissues must be homogenized to locate the receptor causes great and unavoidable changes in protein concentration, cation concentration, and composition, which again can lead to potential errors in interpreting even the most accurate data.

It is refreshing therefore when a new tool becomes available to researchers, and recently a genetic approach to these problems has become possible. Research by Tomkins and his group culminated in the development of mutant cells in culture, which promises to provide a new dimension to present studies (121). The cells were derived from mouse lymphoma tissue culture cells. Normally, these cells are killed by the addition of glucocorticoid. The mutant cells were resistant to glucocorticoids (122) and their properties, with respect to glucocorticoid receptor and nuclear binding, were presented by Yamamoto et al (150). Initially, they determined the intracellular distribution of the glucocorticoid receptor after incubation with tritiated dexamethasone. The mutant cells fell into three classes: whereas the wild-type cell had 50% of the receptor in the nucleus, one class of mutants had fewer nuclear receptors (8–26%), a second class of mutants had much more receptor in the nucleus (85–93%), and a third class had no receptors. Those mutants with fewer nuclear receptors are called nt^- (nuclear transfer deficient) and those with more nuclear receptors than the wild type are called nt^i (increased nuclear transfer).

On analysis on sucrose density gradients, the glucocorticoid receptor of the wild type sediments with an S value of 5.5 in 50 mM NaCl and 4.0 in 250 nM NaCl. Differences in S value of both nt^- and nt^i were observed: nt^i in high salt had a smaller S value (3.5) than did the wild type. Two nt^- mutants were analyzed, one having a smaller (4.6) and one a larger (6.4) S value than the wild type in low salt gradients.

All the mutants reported to date show an alteration in the properties of the receptor and not the nucleus. It is also reassuring to note that these differences can be detected using sucrose density gradient ultracentrifugation at different salt concentrations.

Yamamoto et al (150) then examined the binding of the receptors from these mutants to DNA on DNA-cellulose columns. They observed that nt^- mutant glucocorticoid receptors had little affinity for the DNA. On the other hand, the nt^i showed approximately the same affinity as did the wild type, as determined by the percentage of added receptor that was bound to the columns, but it had a higher affinity, as suggested by the concentration of NaCl required to release the bound receptor. Yamamoto et al inferred that the crucial interaction of the receptor in the nucleus occurs with DNA. However, in the absence of information on the binding characteristics of the receptors with other nuclear components, it seems premature to accept this hypothesis unequivocally. For instance, one would have to determine the affinity of nt^i mutants for histones, acidic proteins, and other components of the nucleus before determining the "real" site of binding. Moreover, the evidence for increased binding of nt^i to DNA, based on differences in elution by NaCl and the differences in sedimentation properties, suggests a structural change in the receptor protein. Changes in conformation, size, etc could readily explain the differences in translocation of the mutant receptors. There are many plausible explanations as to why such receptors would remain in the cytoplasm. Their failure to bind effectively to DNA cellulose columns could be either coincidental or a property never utilized because the receptors could not translocate from the cytoplasm to the nucleus [if translocation is independent of receptor-chromatin interaction as in the water exclusion hypothesis of Horowitz & Moore (40)].

From our comments, it is clear that we feel the use of mutants can provide very useful information and that the development of such mutants and the analysis of their properties will be an area of very active research in the next few years.

DISSOCIATION OF STEROIDS FROM RECEPTOR SITES

Probably the least understood or least studied aspect of steroid hormone action is the dissociation of the steroid from the receptor site, its exit from the cell, and the question of what subsequently happens to the receptor.

The original studies of Jensen & Jacobson (50) showed that estrogens were lost from target tissues quite slowly when low doses were administered in vivo. Larger doses were lost more rapidly, principally due to larger amounts of nonspecific low-affinity binding at doses of estrogen (1 μg/50g body wt, in rat), which saturate 50% or greater of the tissue binding sites. The specifically bound estradiol has a half-life of approximately 90 min under in vivo conditions. However, when intact uteri are incubated in tissue culture medium for up to 12 hr, bound estrogen does not appear to be released into the medium (F. Gannon and J. Gorski, unpublished observations). That estrogen receptors can lose ligand and then rebind fresh ligand in vitro is shown by the success of the exchange assays developed by Anderson et al (2). On the other hand, earlier work by Jensen et al (54) and Sarff & Gorski (115) indicated that under in vivo conditions receptor sites that lost ligand could not rebind estrogen for some time. Replenishment of cytosol receptors was 100% after

16 hr past the original injection. This appeared to be slower than could be explained by the exponential loss of bound estrogen from the tissue. The replenishment appeared to be dependent upon a protein and RNA synthesis–dependent step. Thus questions remain unanswered in this area. As a starting point, it would seem prudent to reexamine the existing data on the rebinding of estradiol to receptors that had previously released estradiol in the light of the more recent observation that extracellular steroid can complicate binding assays (142). This pool of estradiol was not recognized at the time when the earlier studies were performed. Other questions include: (a) Where does the ultimate dissociation of the estrogen and the receptor occur; in the cytoplasm or in the nucleus? (b) Why can't the receptor rebind estradiol after the estradiol originally bound has dissociated? (c) If the dissociation of the estrogen-receptor complex occurs in the nucleus, does the free receptor move back to the cytoplasm and if so, what is the mechanism for this reverse translocation and what is the molecular form of the surviving receptor?

For steroids other than the estrogens, these steps are even less well studied. Munck & Brinck-Jensen (83) originally detected glucocorticoid binding by differences in rates of dissociation. However, in that case as well as those involving most of the other steroids, the receptors are apt to be even more difficult to work with than the estrogen receptor. This has probably been the reason why so little has been published on this aspect of most steroid receptors.

Answers to the questions raised in this section are very important in order to obtain a complete description of the mechanism of action of steroid hormones. They also lead to a greater emphasis on in vivo studies and on occurrences in target tissues at later time intervals after steroid treatment. Information obtained from looking at these later time points could well prove beneficial to our understanding of earlier events. One would therefore anticipate much greater interest in this aspect of the problem in the years to come.

TISSUE RESPONSES TO STEROID HORMONES AND THEIR RELATIONSHIP TO RECEPTORS

The bulk of data collected over the last decade concerning the action of steroid hormones has focused on the regulation of gene expression in the target cells. This has been eloquently summarized by O'Malley & Means (90, 91) and Jensen et al (51). A more recent review by Katzenellenbogen & Gorski (55) raised some questions concerning the relationships between steroid receptor and the control of gene expression. These data can be summarized by stating that changes in gene expression occur as a result of steroid hormone administration. At the present time, however, the best data still do not reveal how the steroid-receptor complex is involved in this regulation. Response data has been of two sorts: (a) actinomycin D inhibited responses implicating a dependency on RNA synthesis, or (b) measurement of specific mRNAs in steroid responsive systems are reported by Schimke (116) and O'Malley (91). Neither has yet gone beyond correlations between the presence of the hormone in the nucleus and the RNA synthesis response, and many of the correlations appear invalid when closely examined. Certainly future investigation will involve more sophisticated experiments on the effects of steroid hormones.

A number of responses other than transcription have also been studied and provide different perspectives on the question of steroid action. Liang & Liao (66) have recently reported an effect of androgens, within 10 min of administration, on a methionyl-tRNA$_f$ binding protein involved in protein synthesis initiation in prostate tissue. Actinomycin D did not inhibit this response, suggesting a direct cytoplasmic action of the steroid. Follow-up to this important work should be of interest.

Another early response to estrogen (and one of a few that appear to occur in vitro) is an increase in production of cyclic GMP (62, 86). The relationship of this response to RNA and protein synthesis is not yet clear. Recent reports indicate that previously observed cyclic AMP increases in response to estrogen are probably in error (62, 86).

Another interpretation of both tissue response and estrogen-binding data has been proposed by Szego (129). This model is based on the concept that lysosomes serve as a carrier for the steroid and that, in turn, the steroid causes the lysosome to carry certain proteins to the nucleus. Szego reports dramatic increases in the presence of lysosomal enzymes in the nucleus at 2 and 10 min after estradiol injection. Estrogen is also reported to be bound by lysosome-rich cytoplasmic fractions. Szego has recently reviewed her work and theory extensively and readers are referred to this review for further details (129).

It should be apparent to the reader that a wide variety of mechanisms have been suggested to explain steroid hormone action. One of the minority views mentioned here or perhaps not even referred to in this review may hold the key to understanding steroid hormone action. Until more substantial evidence clearly establishes the validity of one model, it is obviously prudent to maintain an open and critical mind when considering new data and their interpretation.

SUMMARY

In this review, we have traced the path of estradiol from its entry into the cell to the time of its release from the receptor. We feel that all of the current models are limited in one respect or another. We have examined most critically those currently most in vogue.

The entry of estradiol into the cell is widely assumed to be simply a matter of diffusion. We have highlighted data that suggest the existence of a protein-mediated transport, but feel that the available data are too limited to make a definite conclusion.

On examining the data, it seems obvious that the native form of the free receptor in the cytoplasm is still unknown and that further investigation of this matter is vital to our understanding of why the receptor remains in the cytosol in the absence of estradiol. We have considered the two-step model of Jensen, which involves a temperature dependent 4S–5S change in the cytoplasmic receptor before entry into the nucleus. Questions have been raised about the apparent increase in size going from 4S to 5S, which should, based on studies from other systems, slow down and perhaps prevent the entry into the nucleus. Also, we have pointed out that translocation of proteins at 0°C across a nuclear membrane is contrary to findings in other systems (irrespective of their prior treatment).

The translocation of the receptor from the cytoplasm to the nucleus is usually considered to be a consequence of the interaction of the hormone-receptor complexes with high-affinity nuclear binding sites. We have discussed data that are very difficult to reconcile with this theory and have presented a mechanism of translocation independent of nuclear binding. We have also found a surfeit of evidence in favor of an acceptor model, in that virtually every component of the nucleus has been reported to show the properties of an acceptor.

The recent model of Yamamoto & Alberts (149), in which numerous low-affinity binding sites mask a few high-affinity binding sites, comes much closer to fitting experimental observations and we have discussed some developments of that theory which might be profitable.

Finally, we have raised questions with regard to the fate of the receptor after it has acted to alter gene expression. This is an area where there are no well-established models and little data, and we feel that consideration of this problem is timely.

The data presented have come almost exclusively from estrogen-receptor studies. Most reviews of steroid hormones support the basic assumption that all steroid hormones work in the same manner. However, the data available suggest that differences do exist between different steroid hormones and we feel that the subtleties of these differences should be considered.

In conclusion we hope that this review will help to make it clear that while much progress has been made in this area, we are still far from understanding the molecular details of the mechanism of action of the steroid hormones.

ACKNOWLEDGMENTS

The authors acknowledge the expert help of Bobbi Maurer, Nancy Wertz, Wendy Radtke, and Christina Haak in the preparation of this manuscript.

Literature Cited

1. Alberga, A., Massol, N., Raynaud, J.-P., Baulieu, E.-E. 1971. Estradiol binding of exceptionally high affinity by a nonhistone chromatin protein fraction. *Biochemistry* 10:3835–43
2. Anderson, J., Clark, J. H., Peck, E. J. Jr. Oestrogen and nuclear binding sites. Determination of specific sites by [³H] oestradiol exchange. *Biochim. J.* 126:561–67
3. Anderson, J. N., Peck, E. J. Jr., Clark, J. H. 1975. Estrogen-induced uterine responses and growth: Relationship to receptor estrogen binding by uterine nuclei. *Endocrinology* 96:160–67
4. Arnaud, M. et al 1971. Les récepteurs de l'oestradiol dans l'uterus de génisse: Stimulation de la biosynthèse de l'ARN in vitro. *Biochim. Biophys. Acta* 232:117–31
5. Arnaud, M., Beziat, Y., Borgna, J. L., Guilleux, J. C., Mousseron-Canet, M. 1971. Le récepteur de l'oestradiol, l'AMP cyclique et la RNA polymerase nucléoaire dans l'uterus de génisse. Stimulation de la biosynthesis de RNA in vitro. *Biochim. Biophys. Acta* 254:241–54
6. Atkinson, D. E. 1966. Regulation of enzyme activity. *Ann. Rev. Biochem.* 35:85–124.
7. Baulieu, E.-E. 1973. Estradiol receptors: A new evaluation. In *Receptors for Reproductive Hormones, Adv. Exp. Med. Biol.* 36:80–84
8. Baulieu, E.-E. et et al 1971. Metabolism and protein binding of sex steroids in target organs: an approach to the mechanism of hormone action. *Rec. Prog. Horm. Res.* 27:351–419
9. Baulieu, E.-E., Jung, I., Blondeau, J.-P., Robel, P. 1971. Androgen receptors in rat ventral prostate. In *Schering Work-*

shop on Steroid Receptors, Adv. Biosci. 7:179–91

10. Baulieu, E.-E., Robel, P. 1970. Testosterone metabolites: Their receptors metabolism and action in the rat ventral prostate. In *Some Aspects of the Aetiology and Biochemistry of Prostatic Cancer,* ed. K. Griffiths, C. G. Pierrespoint, 74–84. Cardiff, Wales: Alpha Omega Alpha

11. Baxter, J. D., Tomkins, G. M. 1971. Specific cytoplasmic glucocorticoid hormone receptors in hepatoma tissue culture cells. *Proc. Nat. Acad. Sci. USA* 68:932–37

12. Beato, M., Brandle, W., Biesewig, D., Scheris, C. E. 1970. On the mechanism of hormone action XVI. Transfer of $(1,2-{}^3H_2)$ cortisol from the cytoplasm to the nucleus of rat liver cells. *Biochim. Biophys. Acta* 208:125–36

13. Brecher, P., Vigersky, R., Wotiz, H. S., Wotiz, H. H. 1967. An in vitro system for the binding of estradiol to rat uterus nuclei. *Steroids* 10:635–51

14. Brumbaugh, P. F., Haussler, M. R. 1974. $1\alpha,25$-dihydroxycholecalciferol receptors in intestine. II. Temperature-dependent transfer of the hormone to chromatin via a specific cytosol receptor. *J. Biol. Chem.* 249:1258–62

15. Chamness, G. C., Jennings, A. W., McGuire, W. L. 1973. Oestrogen receptor binding is not restricted to target nuclei. *Nature* 241:458–60

16. Chamness, G. C., Jennings, A. W., McGuire, W. L. 1974. Estrogen receptor binding to isolated nuclei. A nonsaturable process. *Biochemistry* 13:327–31

17. Chamness, G. C., McGuire, W. L. 1972. Estrogen receptor in the rat uterus. Physiological forms and artifacts. *Biochemistry* 11:2466–72

18. Clark, J. H., Anderson, J. N., Peck, E. J. Jr. 1973. Nuclear receptor estrogen complexes of rat uteri. In *Receptors for Reproductive Hormones, Adv. Exp. Med. Biol.* 36:15–59

19. Corvol, P., Falk, R., Freifeld, M., Bardin, C. W. 1972. In vitro studies of progesterone binding protein in guinea pig uterus. *Endocrinology* 90:1464–69

20. Cox, G. S. 1974. Uptake of cytosol proteins by Hela nuclei. *Meet. Am. Soc. Biol. Chem., 65th, Minneapolis,* p. 151 (Abstr.)

21. Cox, G. S., Weissbach, H. 1975. Stimulation of the uptake of soluble proteins into isolated Hela nuclei by pancreatic

deoxyribonucleases. *J. Biol. Chem.* 250:783–85

22. Davies, I, J., Ryan, K. J. 1972. The uptake of progesterone by the uterus of the pregnant rat in vivo and its relationship to cytoplasmic progesterone-binding protein. *Endocrinology* 90:507–15

23. Davies, I. J., Ryan, K. J. 1973. The modulation of progesterone concentration in the myometrium of the pregnant rat by changes in cytoplasmic "receptor" protein activity. *Endocrinology* 92:394–401

24. DeSombre, E., Hurst, D., Kawashima, T., Jungblut, P. W., Jensen, E. 1967. Sulfhydryl groups and estradiol-receptor interaction. *Fed. Proc.* 26:536 (Abstr.)

24a. Edelman, I. S. 1975. Mechanism of action of steroid hormones. *J. Steroid Biochem.* 6:147–59

25. Erdos, T. 1968. Properties of a uterine oestradiol receptor. *Biochem. Biophys. Res. Commun.* 32:338–43

26. Erdos, T., Fries, J. 1974. The subunit-structure of the uterine "oestradiol-receptor." *Biochem. Biophys. Res. Commun.* 58:932–39

27. Feherty, P., Robertson, D. M., Waynsforth, H. B., Kellie, A. E. 1970. Changes in the concentrations of high-affinity oestradiol receptors in rat uterine supernatant preparations during the oestrous cycle pseudo-pregnancy, maturation and after ovariectomy. *Biochem. J.* 120:837–44

28. Faber, L. E., Sandmann, M. L., Stavely, H. E. 1972. Progesterone-binding proteins of the rat and rabbit uterus. *J. Biol. Chem.* 247:5648–49

29. Faber, L. E., Sandmann, M. L., Stavely, H. E. 1972. Progesterone binding in uterine cytosol of the guinea pig. *J. Biol. Chem.* 247:8000–4

30. Feil, P. D., Glasser, S. R., Toft, D. O., O'Malley, B. W. 1972. Progesterone binding in the mouse and rat uterus. *Endocrinology* 91:738–46

30a. Funder, J. W., Feldman, D., Edelman, I. S. 1973. The roles of plasma binding and receptor specificity in the mineralocorticoid action of aldosterone. *Endocrinology* 92:994–1004

31. Giannopoulos, G., Gorski, J. 1971. Estrogen-binding protein of the rat uterus: Different molecular forms associated with nuclear uptake of estradiol. *J. Biol. Chem.* 246:2530–36

32. Goldstein, L., Prescott, D. M. 1967. Proteins in nucleocytoplasmic interactions. I. The fundamental characteris-

tics of the rapidly migrating proteins and the slow turnover proteins of the *Amoeba proteus* nucleus. *J. Cell Biol.* 33:637–44

33. Gorski, J., Raker, B. 1973. Notes and comments. The effects of cytochalasin B on estrogen binding and 2-deoxy-glucose metabolism in the rat uterus. *Endocrinology* 93:1212–16

34. Gorski, J., Toft, D., Shyamala, G., Smith, D., Notides, A. 1968. Hormone receptors: Studies on the interaction of estrogen with the uterus. *Recent Prog. Horm. Res.* 24:45–80

35. Gschwendt, M., Hamilton, T. H. 1972. The transformation of the cytoplasmic oestradiol-receptor complex into the nuclear complex in a uterine cell-free system. *Biochem. J.* 128:611–16

36. Gurdon, J. B. 1970. Nuclear transplantation and the control of gene activity in animal development. *Proc. R. Soc. London Ser. B* 176:303–14

37. Harris, G. S. 1971. Nature of oestrogen specific binding sites in the nuclei of mouse uteri. *Nature New Biol.* 231:246–48

38. Harris, S. E., Means, A. R., Mitchell, W. M., O'Malley, B. W. 1973. Synthesis of [³H] DNA complementary to ovalbumin messenger RNA: Evidence for limited copies of the ovalbumin gene in chick oviduct. *Proc. Nat. Acad. Sci. USA* 70:3776–80

39. Higgins, S. J., Rousseau, G. G., Baxter, J. D., Tomkins, G. M. 1973. Nuclear binding of steroid receptors: Comparison in intact cells and cell-free systems. *Proc. Nat. Acad. Sci. USA* 70:3415–18

40. Horowitz, S. B., Moore, L. C. 1974. The nuclear permeability, intracellular distribution and diffusion of inulin in the amphibian oocyte. *J. Cell Biol.* 60:405–15

41. Inesi, G., Millman, M., Eletr, S. 1973. Temperature-induced transitions of function and structure in sarcoplasmic reticulum membranes. *J. Mol. Biol.* 81:483–504

42. Jackson, V., Chalkley, G. R. 1974. The binding of estradiol-17B to the bovine endometrial nuclear membrane. *J. Biol. Chem.* 249:1615–27

43. Jelinek, W., Goldstein, L. 1973. Isolation and characterization of some of the proteins that shuttle between cytoplasm and nucleus in *Amoeba proteus. J. Cell Physiol.* 81:181–97

44. Jensen, E. V. et al 1968. A two-step mechanism for the interaction of es-tradiol with rat uterus. *Proc. Nat. Acad. Sci. USA* 59:632–38

45. Jensen, E. V. et al 1969. Estrogen-receptor interaction in target tissues. In *Develop. Biol.* 3 (Suppl.):151–71

46. Jensen, E. V., Brecher, P. I., Numata, M., Mohla, S., DeSombre, E. R. 1973. Transformed estrogen receptor in the regulation of RNA synthesis in uterine nuclei. *Adv. Enzyme Regul.* 11:1–16

47. Jensen, E. V., DeSombre, E. R. 1972. Mechanism of action of the female sex hormones. *Ann. Rev. Biochem.* 41:203–30

48. Jensen, E. V., DeSombre, E. R. 1973. Estrogen-receptor interaction. Estrogenic hormones effect transformation of specific receptor proteins to a biologically functional form. *Science* 182:126–34

49. Jensen, E. V., DeSombre, E. R., Jungblut, P. W., Stumpf, W. E., Roth, L. J. 1969. Biochemical and autoradiographic studies of ³H-estradiol location. In *Autoradiography of Diffusible Substances,* ed. L. J. Roth, W. E. Stumpf, 89–97. New York: Academic

50. Jensen, E. V., Jacobson, H. I. 1960. Fate of steroid estrogens in target tissues. In *Biological Activities of Steroids in Relation to Cancer,* ed. G. Pincus, E. P. Vollmer, 161–78. New York: Academic

51. Jensen, E. V., Mohla, S., Gorell, T. A., DeSombre, E. R. 1974. The role of estrophilin in estrogen action. *Vitam. Horm.* 32:89–127

52. Jensen, E. V., Mohla, S., Gorell, T., Tanaka, S., DeSombre, E. R. 1972. Estrophile to nucleophile in two easy steps. *J. Steroid Biochem.* 3:445–58

53. Jensen, E. V., Numata, M., Brecher, P. I., DeSombre, E. R. 1971. Hormone-receptor interaction as a guide to biochemical mechanism. In *The Biochemistry of Steroid Hormone Action,* ed. R. M. S. Smellie, 133–59. New York: Academic

54. Jensen, E. V., Suzuki, T., Numata, M., Smith, S., DeSombre, E. R. 1969. Estrogen-binding of target tissues. *Steroids* 13:417–27

55. Katzenellenbogen, B. S., Gorski, J. 1975. Estrogen actions on syntheses of macromolecules in target cells. In *Biochemical Action of Hormones,* ed. G. Litwack, Vol. 3:187–243

56. Katzenellenbogen, J., Johnson, H. J. Jr., Carlson, K. E. 1973. Studies of the uterine cytoplasmic estrogen binding protein. Thermal stability and ligand dissociation rate. An assay of empty and

filled sites by exchange. *Biochemistry* 12:4092–9

57. Katzenellenbogen, J. A., Ruh, T. S., Carlson, K. E., Iwamoto, H. S., Gorski, J. 1975. Ultraviolet photosensitivity of the estrogen binding protein from rat uterus: Wave-length and ligand dependence. Photocovalent attachment of estrogens to protein. *Biochemistry.* 4: 2310–16

58. King, R. J. B., Gordon, J. 1972. Involvement of DNA in the acceptor mechanism for uterine oestradiol receptor. *Nature New Biol.* 240:185–86

59. King, R. J. B., Gordon, J., Cowan, D. M., Inman, D. R. 1966. The intranuclear localization of [6,7-^{3}H]-oestradiol-17β in dimethylbenzanthracene induced rat mammary adenocarcinoma and other tissues. *J. Endocrinol.* 36:139–50

60. King, R. J. B., Mainwaring, W. I. P. 1974. *Steroid Cell Interactions.* Chaps. 7, 9. Baltimore: Univ. Park Press

61. Koshland, D. E. Jr., Neet, K. E. 1968. The catalytic and regulatory properties of enzymes. *Ann. Rev. Biochem.* 37: 359–410

62. Kuehl, F. A. et al 1974. Estrogen-related increases in uterine guanosine 3′:5′-cyclic monophosphate levels. *Proc. Nat. Acad. Sci. USA* 71:1866–70

62a. Kuhn, R. W., Schrader, W. T., Smith, R. G., O'Malley, B. W. 1975. Progesterone binding components of chick oviduct. X. Purification by affinity chromatography. *J. Biol. Chem.* 250:422–28

63. Liao, S., Fang, S. 1970. Factors and specificities in the formation of 5α dihydrotestosterone-nuclear-receptor protein complex in rat ventral prostate. See Ref. 10, 105–8

64. Fang, S., Anderson, K. M., Liao, S. 1969. Receptor proteins for androgens. *J. Biol. Chem.* 224:6584–95

65. Liang, T., Liao, S. 1974. Association of the uterine 17β estradiol-receptor complex with ribonucleoprotein in vitro and in vivo. *J. Biol. Chem.* 249:4671–78

66. Liang, T., Liao, S. 1975. A very rapid effect of androgen on initiation of protein synthesis in prostate. *Proc. Nat. Acad. Sci. USA* 72:706–9

67. Liao, S., Liang, T., Tymoczko, J. L. 1973. Ribonucleoprotein binding of steroid-"receptor" complexes. *Nature New Biol.* 241:211–13

68. Lin, S.-Y., Riggs, A. D. 1972. Lac Repressor binding to non-operator DNA: detailed studies and a comparison of equilibrium and rate competition methods. *J. Mol. Biol.* 72:671–90

69. Mainwaring, W. I. P. 1969. A soluble androgen receptor in the cytoplasm of rat prostate. *J. Endocrinol.* 45:531–41

70. Mainwaring, W. I. P. 1970. Androgen receptors. See Ref. 10, 109–17

71. Marver, D., Goodman, D., Edelman, I. S. 1972. Relationships between renal cytoplasmic and nuclear aldosterone-receptors. *Kidney Int.* 1:210–23

72. Maurer, H. R., Chalkley, G. R. 1967. Some properties of a nuclear binding site of estradiol. *J. Mol. Biol.* 27:431–41

73. McGuire, W. L., Barist, C. 1972. Isolation and preliminary characterization of a progesterone specific binding macromolecule from the 273,000 g supernatant of rat and rabbit uterus. *Endocrinology* 90:496–506

74. McGuire, W. L., DeDella, C. 1971. In vitro evidence for a progesterone receptor in the rat and rabbit uterus. *Endocrinology* 88:1099–1103

75. Milgrom, E., Atger, M., Baulieu, E.-E. 1970. Progesterone in uterus and plasma. IV. Progesterone receptor(s) in guinea pig uterus cytosol. *Steroids* 16:741–54

76. Milgrom, E., Atger, M., Baulieu, E.-E., 1973. Studies on estrogen entry into uterine cells and on estradiol-receptor complex attachment to the nucleus—is the entry of estrogen into uterine cells a protein-mediated process? *Biochim. Biophys. Acta* 320:267–83

77. Milgrom, E., Baulieu, E.-E. 1970. Progesterone in uterus and plasma. I. Binding in rat uterus 105,000 g supernatant. *Endocrinology* 87:276–87

78. Mohla, S., DeSombre, E. R., Jensen, E. V. 1972. Tissue-specific stimulation of RNA synthesis by transformed estradiol-receptor complex. *Biochem. Biophys. Res. Commun.* 46:661–67

79. Monod, J., Wyman, J., Changeux, J. P. 1965. On the nature of allosteric transitions: A plausible model. *J. Mol. Biol.* 12:88–118

80. Mueller, G. C. 1959. Biochemical parameters of estrogen action. See Ref. 50, 129–45

81. Mueller, G. C., Herranen, A. M., Jervell, K. F. 1958. Studies on the mechanism of action of estrogens. *Recent Prog. Horm. Res.* 14:95–139

82. Mueller, G. C., Vonderhaar, B., Kim, U. H., LeMahieu, M. 1972. Estrogen action: an inroad to cell biology. *Recent Prog. Horm. Res.* 28:1–49

83. Munck, A., Brinck-Jensen, T. 1968. Specific and nonspecific physiochemical interactions of glucocorticoids and related steroids with rat thymus cells in vitro. *J. Biol. Chem.* 243:5556–65
84. Munck, A. et al 1972. Glucocorticoid-receptor complexes and the earliest steps in the action of glucocorticoids on thymus cells. *J. Steroid Biochem.* 3:567–78
85. Musliner, T. A., Chader, G. V., Villée, C. A. 1970. Studies on estradiol receptors of the rat uterus. Nuclear uptake in vitro. *Biochemistry* 9:4448–57
86. Nicol, S. E., Sanford, C. H., Kuehl, F. A. Jr., Ham, E. A., Goldberg, N. D. 1974. Estrogen-induced elevation of uterine cyclic GMP concentration. *Fed. Proc.* 33:284 (Abstr.)
87. Noteboom, W. D., Gorski, J. 1963. An early estrogen effect on protein synthesis. *Proc. Nat. Acad. Sci. USA* 60:250–55
88. Notides, A. C., Nielsen, S. 1974. The molecular mechanism of the in vitro 4S to 5S transformation of the uterine estrogen receptor. *J. Biol. Chem.* 249:1866–73
89. Norman, A. W. et al 1971. 1,25-dihydroxycholecalciferol: Identification of the proposed active form of Vitamin D_3 in the intestine. *Science* 173:51–54
90. O'Malley, B. W., Means, A. R. 1974. Effects of female steroid hormones on target cell nuclei. In *The Cell Nucleus*, 3:379–416 San Francisco: Academic
91. O'Malley, B. W., Means, A. R. 1974. Female steroid hormones and target cell nuclei. *Science* 183:610–20
92. O'Malley, B. W., Schrader, W. T., Spelsberg, T. C. 1973. Hormone receptor interactions with the genome of eucaryotic target cells. In *Receptors for Reproductive Hormones, Adv. Exp. Med. Biol.* 36:174–96
93. O'Malley, B. W., Sherman, M. R., Toft, D. O. 1970. Progesterone "receptors" in the cytoplasm and nucleus of chick oviduct target tissue. *Proc. Nat. Acad. Sci. USA* 67:501–8
94. O'Malley, B. W., Spelsberg, T. C., Schrader, W. T., Steggles, A. W. 1972. Mechanism of interaction of a hormone-receptor complex with a genome of a eukaryotic target cell. *Nature* 235:141–44
95. O'Malley, B. W., Toft, D. O., Sherman, M. R. 1971. Progesterone-binding components of chick oviduct. II. Nuclear components. *J. Biol. Chem.* 246:1117–22
96. Omdahl, J., Holick, M., Suda, T., Tanaka, Y., DeLuca, H. F. 1971. Biological activity of 1,25-dihydroxycholecalciferol. *Biochemistry* 10:2935–40
97. Oppenheimer, J. H., Koerner, D., Schwartz, H. L., Surks, M. I. 1972. Specific-nuclear triiodothyronine binding sites in rat liver and kidney. *J. Clin. Endocrinol. Metab.* 35:330–33
98. Paine, P. L., Feldherr, C. M. 1972. Nucleocytoplasmic exchange of macromolecules. *Exp. Cell. Res.* 74:81–98
99. Palacios, R., Sullivan, D., Summers, N. M., Kiely, M. L., Schimke, R. T. 1973. Synthesis of a ribonucleic acid sequence complimentary to ovalbumin messenger ribonucleic acid and quantification of ovalbumin genes. *J. Biol. Chem.* 248:7530–39
100. Peck, E. J. Jr., Burgner, J., Clark, J. H. 1973. Estrophilic binding sites of the uterus. Relation to uptake and retention of estradiol in vitro. *Biochemistry* 12:4596–4603
101. Peck, E. J. Jr., DeLibero, J., Richards, R., Clark, J. H. 1973. Instability of the uterine estrogen receptor under in vitro conditions. *Biochemistry* 12:4603–8
102. Puca, G. A., Bresciani, F. 1968. Receptor molecules for oestrogens from rat uterus. *Nature* 218:967–69
103. Puca, G. A., Nola, E., Sica, V., Bresciani, F. 1972. Estrogen-binding proteins of calf uterus. Interrelationship between various forms and identification of a receptor-transforming factor. *Biochemistry* 11:4157–65
104. Puca, G. A., Vincenzo, S., Ernesto, W. 1974. Identification of high-affinity nuclear acceptor site for estrogen receptor of calf uterus. *Proc. Nat. Acad. Sci. USA* 71:979–83
105. Rao, B. R., Wiest, W. G., Allen, W. M. 1973. Progesterone "receptor" in rabbit uterus. I. Characterization and estradiol-17β augmentation. *Endocrinology* 92:1229–40
106. Raspé, G., ed. 1971. *Schering Workshop on Steroid Hormone Receptors, Adv. Biosci.* 7:1–417
107. Raynaud-Jammet, C., Baulieu, E.-E. 1969. Biologie moléculaire—Action de l'oestradiol in vitro: Augmentation de la biosynthèse d'acide ribonucléique dans les noyaux utérins. *C. R. Acad. Sci. Ser. D* 268:3211–14
108. Reel, J. R., Van Dewark, S. C., Shih, Y., Callantine, M. R. 1971. Macromolecular binding and metabolism of progesterone in the decidual and pseudo-preg-

nant rat and rabbit uterus. *Steroids* 18:441–61

109. Reti, I., Erdos, T. 1971. On the "native state" of the uterine estradiol "receptor." *Biochimie* 53:435–37

110. Rochefort, H., Baulieu, E.-E. 1968. Biochimie endocrinienne—Récepteurs hormonaux: Relations entre les "récepteurs" uterins de l'oestradiol, "8S" cytoplasmique et "4S" cytoplasmique et nucléaire. *C. R. Acad. Sci. Ser. D* 267:662–65

111. Rochefort, H., Baulieu, E.-E. 1971. Effect of KCl, $CaCl_2$, temperature and oestradiol on the uterine cytosol receptor of estradiol. *Biochimie* 53:893–907

112. Ruh, T. S., Katzenellenbogen, B. S., Katzenellenbogen, J. A., Gorski, J. 1973. Estrone interaction with the rat uterus: In vitro response and nuclear uptake. *Endocrinology* 92:125–34

113. Samuels, H. H., Tomkins, G. M. 1970. Relation of steroid structure to enzyme induction in hepatoma tissue culture cells. *J. Mol. Biol.* 52:57–74

114. Samuels, H. H., Tsai, J. S. 1973. Thyroid hormone action in cell culture: Demonstration of nuclear receptors in intact cells and isolated nuclei. *Proc. Nat. Acad. Sci. USA* 70:3488–92

115. Sarff, M., Gorski, J. 1971. Control of estrogen binding protein concentration under basal conditions and after estrogen administration. *Biochemistry* 10:2557–63

116. Schimke, R. T., Rhoads, R. E., Palacios, R., Sullivan, D. 1973. Ovalbumin mRNA, complementary DNA and hormone regulation in chick oviduct. In *Karolinska Symp. Res. Methods Reprod. Endocrinol., 6th,* ed. E. Diczfalusy, 357–79

117. Schrader, W. T., O'Malley, B. W. 1972. Progesterone binding components of chick oviduct. IV. characterization of purified subunits. *J. Biol. Chem.* 247:51–59

118. Sherman, M. R., Corvol, P. L., O'Malley, B. W. 1970. Progesterone-binding components of chick oviduct. I. Preliminary characterization of cytoplasmic components. *J. Biol. Chem.* 245:6085–96

119. Shyamala, G., Gorski, J. 1967. Interrelationship of estrogen receptors in the nucleus and cytosol. *J. Cell Biol.* 35:125A (Abstr.)

120. Shyamala, G., Gorski, J. 1969. Estrogen receptors in the rat uterus: Studies on the interaction of cytosol and nuclear binding sites. *J. Biol. Chem.* 244:1097–1103

121. Sibley, C. H., Tomkins, G. M. 1974. Isolation of lymphoma cell variants resistant to killing by glucocorticoids. *Cell* 2:213–20

122. Sibley, C. H., Tomkins, G. M. 1974. Mechanisms of steroid resistance. *Cell* 2:221–27

123. Siiteri, P. K. et al 1973. Estrogen binding in the rat and human. In *Receptors for Reproductive Hormones, Adv. Exp. Med. Biol.* 36:97–112

124. Spelsberg, T. C., Steggles, A. W., O'-Malley, B. W. 1971. Progesterone binding components of chick oviduct. III. Chromatin acceptor sites. *J. Biol. Chem.* 246:4188–97

125. Stancel, G. M., Leung, K. M. T., Gorski, J. 1973. Estrogen receptors in the rat uterus. Multiple forms produced by concentration-dependent aggregation. *Biochemistry* 12:2130–36

126. Stancel, G. M., Leung, K. M. T., Gorski, J. 1973. Estrogen receptors in the rat uterus. Relationship between cytoplasmic and nuclear forms of the estrogen binding protein. *Biochemistry* 12:2137–41

127. Steggles, A. W., Spelsberg, T. C., Glasser, S. R., O'Malley, B. W. 1971. Soluble complexes between steroid hormones and target-tissue receptors bind specifically to target-tissue chromatin. *Proc. Nat. Acad. Sci. USA* 68:1479–82

128. Swaneck, G. E., Chu, L. L. H., Edelman, I. S. 1970. Stereospecific binding of aldosterone to renal chromatin. *J. Biol. Chem.* 245:5382–89

129. Szego, C. M. 1974. The lysosome as a mediator of hormone action. *Recent Prog. Horm. Res.* 30:171–233

130. Talwar, G. P., Segal, S. J., Evans, A., Davidson, O. W. 1964. The binding of estradiol in the uterus: a mechanism for depression of RNA synthesis. *Proc. Nat. Acad. Sci. USA* 52:1059–66

130a. Tata, J. 1975. How specific are nuclear "receptors" for thyroid hormones? *Nature* 257:18–20

131. Teng, C.-S., Hamilton, T. H. 1968. The role of chromatin in estrogen action in the uterus. I. The control of template capacity and chemical composition and the binding of H^3-estradiol-17β. *Proc. Nat. Acad. Sci. USA* 60:1410–17

132. Tomkins, G. M. et al 1970. Regulation of specific protein synthesis in eucaryotic cells. *Cold Spring Harbor Symp. Quant. Biol.* 35:635–40

133. Toft, D. O. 1972. The interaction of uterine estrogen receptors with DNA. *J. Steroid Biochem.* 3:515–22

134. Toft, D., Gorski, J. 1966. A receptor molecule for estrogens: isolation from the rat uterus and preliminary characterizations. *Proc. Nat. Acad. Sci. USA* 55:1574–81

135. Toft, D., Shyamala, G., Gorski, J. 1967. A receptor molecule for estrogens: studies using a cell-free system. *Proc. Nat. Acad. Sci. USA* 57:1740–43

136. Tsai, S. Y. et al 1975. Estrogen effects on gene expression in chick oviduct: Nuclear receptor levels and initiation of transcription. *Proc. Nat. Acad. Sci. USA*. In press

137. Tsai, H. C., Norman, A. W. 1973. Studies on calciferol metabolism. VIII. Evidence for a cytoplasmic receptor for 1,25-dihydroxy-Vitamin D_3 in the intestinal mucosa. *J. Biol. Chem.* 248:5967–75

138. Unhjem, O., Tveter, K. J., Aakvaag, A. 1969. Preliminary characterization of an androgen macromolecular complex from the rat ventral prostate. *Acta Endocrinol.* 62:153–64

139. Von Hippel, P. H., Revzin, A., Gross, C., Wang, A. C. 1974. Non-specific DNA binding of genome regulating proteins as a biological control mechanism: 1. The *lac* operon: Equilibrium aspects. *Proc. Nat. Acad. Sci. USA* 71:4808–12

140. Weaver, R. F., Blatti, S. P., Butler, W. S. 1971. Molecular structure of DNA-dependent RNA polymerase (II) from calf thymus and rat liver. *Proc. Nat. Acad. Sci. USA* 68:2994–99

141. Wiest, W. G., Rao, B. R. 1971. Progesterone binding proteins in rabbit uterus and human endometrium. In *Schering Workshop on Steroid Receptors, Adv. Biosci.* 7:251–66

142. Williams, D., Gorski, J. 1971. A new assessment of subcellular distribution of bound estrogen in the uterus. *Biochem. Biophys. Res. Commun.* 45:258–64

143. Williams, D., Gorski, J. 1972. Kinetic and equilibrium analysis of estradiol in uterus: A model of binding-site distribution in uterine cells. *Proc. Nat. Acad. Sci. USA* 69:3464–68

144. Williams, D., Gorski, J. 1974. Equilibrium binding of estradiol by uterine cell suspensions and whole uteri in vitro. *Biochemistry* 13:5537–42

145. Williams-Ashman, H. G., Reddi, A. H. 1971. Actions of vertebrate sex hormones. *Ann. Rev. Physiol.* 33:31–82

146. Wira, C., Munck, A. 1970. Specific glucocorticoid receptors in thymus cells. *J. Biol. Chem.* 245:3436–38

146a. Yamamoto, K. R., Alberts, B. 1972. In vitro conversion of estradiol-receptor protein to its nuclear form: Dependence on hormones and DNA. *Proc. Nat. Acad. Sci. USA* 69:2105–9

147. Yamamoto, K. R. 1974. Characterization of the 4S to 5S forms of the estradiol receptor protein and their interaction with deoxyribonucleic acid. *J. Biol. Chem.* 249:7068–75

148. Yamamoto, K. R., Alberts, B. 1974. On the specificity of the binding of the estradiol receptor protein to deoxyribonucleic acid. *J. Biol. Chem.* 249:7076–86

149. Yamamoto, K. R., Alberts, B. 1975. The interaction of estradiol-receptor protein with the genome: an argument for the existence of undetected specific sites. *Cell* 4:301–10

150. Yamamoto, K. R., Stampfer, M. R., Tomkins, G. M. 1974. Receptors from glucocorticoid-sensitive lymphoma cell and two classes of insensitive clones: physical and DNA binding properties. *Proc. Nat. Acad. Sci. USA* 71:3901–5

MASS TRANSPORT ACROSS CELL MEMBRANES: The Effects of Antidiuretic Hormone on Water and Solute Flows in Epithelia

Thomas E. Andreoli[1] *and James A. Schafer*[2]

Division of Nephrology, Department of Medicine and the Department of Physiology and Biophysics, University of Alabama in Birmingham, Birmingham, Alabama 35294

INTRODUCTION

The study of mass transport processes across synthetic and biological interfaces has increased in near-exponential fashion in the recent past. Originally, we considered writing a general review of information accumulated in the field during the past three years, but the scope of such a narrative would have permitted, at best, superficial summary of well over 3000 articles. Even a cursory treatment of recent developments in renal tubular physiology, an issue of major interest to workers in this laboratory, would have exceeded by far the space allotted to us in this volume. Consequently, we restricted the scope of this review to an examination of the effects of antidiuretic hormone (ADH) on nonelectrolyte permeation, Na^+ transport, and water flows in hormone-sensitive epithelia. There are other cogent reasons for such a choice.

The effects of ADH on transport processes in epithelia have been and continue to be a widely cited and extensively studied set of physiological events. The elegant dual-barrier hypothesis proposed originally by Andersen & Ussing (2), and subsequently by Leaf & Hays (110, 111, 148), has provided a formidable frame of reference for rationalizing in a unitary fashion the effects of ADH on transport phenomena in amphibian epithelia. It is clear that understanding the physiological effects of ADH on renal tubular epithelia will form the basis for analyzing the

---

[1]Recipient, Research Career Development Award, National Institute of General Medical Sciences.

[2]Established investigator of the American Heart Association.

pathophysiology of clinical disorders of membrane transport processes such as nephrogenic diabetes insipidus. Finally, and most germane to our choice of topic, novel insights into physiological events arise by collating and analyzing data inconsistent with existing hypotheses. In our view, a substantial body of experimental observations now provides ample warrant for a critical reassessment of the dual-barrier hypothesis for ADH action. The present review considers these lines of evidence, including data on seemingly unrelated phenomena such as water and solute permeation in model membrane systems and red blood cells. Several excellent reviews (15, 104, 106, 112, 145) should be consulted for details of ADH physiology and pharmacology not covered in this article.

This review contains two parts. Part 1 summarizes ADH-mediated effects on transport processes in ADH-sensitive epithelia, with particular regard to:

(a) A brief exposition of the dual-barrier hypothesis of Andersen & Ussing (2) and Leaf & Hays (110, 111, 148), which proposes that ADH enlarged pores in the inner barrier of apical surfaces in ADH-sensitive epithelia.

(b) Recent evidence indicating that the effects of ADH on nonelectrolyte permeation, water flows, and Na^+ transport across apical surfaces of ADH-sensitive epithelia are separate and dissociable.

(c) Evidence indicating that the permeation of urea and other small amides across ADH-sensitive epithelia and the effects of ADH on these events may involve transport processes other than independent diffusion streams and/or coupling of solute and solvent flows in aqueous pores.

(d) Experimental observations consistent with the view that ADH affects both active and passive components of Na^+ flux across hormone-responsive epithelia.

(e) An analysis of ADH-mediated water permeation in hormone-sensitive epithelia, coupled to a new hypothesis which proposes that the hormone increases the rate of water diffusion across apical membranes of sensitive cells by altering the solubility and/or fluidity characteristics of such plasma membranes.

Part 2 of this review deals with certain aspects of cellular events involved in ADH-mediated changes in membrane transport processes, including:

(a) A brief summary of the hypothesis that ADH modifies transport processes in epithelia by accelerating the rate of formation of intracellular cyclic 3',5'-adenosine monophosphate (cAMP).

(b) The effect of cAMP on intracellular protein phosphorylation-dephosphorylation reactions.

(c) The relationship between intracellular microtubules, microfilaments, and ADH-mediated effects on epithelial transport processes.

Definition of Terms

Studies of the physiological effects of ADH have utilized various neurohypophyseal extracts, purified and unpurified, as well as synthetic ADH analogs. Pitressin, a widely used commercial neurohypophyseal extract contains predominantly arginine vasopressin, the cyclic octapeptide antidiuretic moiety extracted from most mammalian neurohypophyses (199, 238, 251). Neurohypophyseal extracts from amphibia (7, 114, 175, 251), reptiles (175), and birds (33, 175) contain the octapeptide vasotocin, which has the ring structure of oxytocin and the side chain of arginine vasopressin (133). ADH receptors on the basilar surfaces (146) of amphibian epithelia are much less responsive to arginine vasopressin than to vasotocin (10, 147, 223). Consequently, compared to the mammalian kidney, 10^3-fold greater concentrations of Pitressin are required in amphibian epithelia, to obtain similar hydro-osmotic effects (96, 97, 110, 111, 148, 214, 215). In the present context, the term ADH connotes Pitressin, arginine or lysine vasopressin, vasotocin, oxytocin, and synthetic analogs of different antidiuretic hormones. Specific designations are cited only when they have unique significance for a given set of experimental conditions.

The surfaces of ADH-responsive cells frequently have a different nomenclature depending on the epithelium studied. The epithelial cell interfaces that are continuous with junctional complexes ("tight junctions") and those adjacent either to basement membranes or to lateral intercellular spaces are here termed, respectively, *apical membranes* and *basolateral membranes*. Apical membranes include the luminal surface of the renal tubule, the outer surface of amphibian skin, and the mucosal surface of toad urinary bladder; basolateral membranes face the blood or bath surface of the renal tubule, the inner or blood surface of amphibian skin, and the serosal surface of toad urinary bladder.

PART ONE

The Dual-Barrier Model for ADH Action

ORIGIN OF THE HYPOTHESIS   Capraro & Bernini (23) first showed that ADH dramatically increased the rate of water permeation from apical to basolateral surfaces of frog skin. This ADH-mediated increment in transepithelial water flux, perhaps the most widely documented physiological effect of ADH, requires particular definition.

Two systems for evaluating water permeation are of specific concern. In the first system, net water flow across a membrane is measured in the presence of hydrostatic and/or osmotic driving forces. Under these conditions, J_v (cm³ sec^{-1} cm^{-2}), the net volume flow across the membrane, is given by the familiar Starling expression:

$$J_v = -L_p (\Delta\Pi - \Delta P), \qquad\qquad 1.$$

where L_p is the coefficient of hydraulic conductivity (cm sec^{-1} atm^{-1}), ΔP (atm) is the hydrostatic pressure gradient across the membrane, and $\Delta\Pi$, the osmotic pressure gradient across the membrane, is

$$\Delta\Pi = RT \sum_{i=1}^{n} \sigma_i \Delta C_i, \qquad\qquad 2.$$

where R is the gas constant, T the absolute temperature, σ_i the reflection coefficient (135, 228) of the ith solute, and ΔC_i the transmembrane concentration difference of the ith solute (assuming solutions sufficiently dilute that osmotic coefficients may be taken to be unity). For convenience, L_p may be expressed in terms of P_f, a water permeability coefficient having the dimensions cm sec^{-1}, by using the relationship:

$$P_f = L_p \, RT / \overline{V}_{w'}$$ 3.

where $\overline{V}_w$ is the partial molar volume of water.

A second system for assessing water permeation obtains by measuring isotopic exchange of tagged water (i.e. D_2O or THO). In such experiments, aqueous solutions bathing either side of a membrane are usually identical except for the concentration of tagged water, and net volume flow is zero. Thus the diffusional permeability coefficient for water (P_{D_w}, cm sec^{-1}) or, for that matter, any nonelectrolyte, may be described by Fick's first law:

$$P_{D_w} = - \frac{J_{\bullet}^{1 \rightarrow 2}}{\Delta C_{\bullet}} \, ,$$ 4.

where $J_{\bullet}^{1 \rightarrow 2}$ is the net tracer flux from solution 1 to solution 2 (cpm sec^{-1} cm^{-2}), $\Delta C_{\bullet}$ is the steady-state tracer concentration difference between solutions 2 and 1, and the tracer specific activity (X, cpm $mole^{-1}$) is constant. For convenience, solution 2 ordinarily contains no tracer, in which case $J_{\bullet}^{1 \rightarrow 2}$ becomes a unidirectional tracer flux. It is evident that, in instances where $P_f = P_{D_w}$, water transport across a membrane involes "simple" diffusion, i.e. random frictional interactions between individual water molecules and the membrane matrix. However, in most synthetic or biological membranes, P_f exceeds the apparent value of P_{D_w} and other explanations and/or transport modes have been set forth to account for this discrepancy.

The earliest studies (117) on water permeation involving the use of tracers in untreated frog skin showed that P_f exceeded the apparent P_{D_w}. As indicated above, Capraro & Bernini (23) observed that ADH increased the rate of transepithelial water permeation across frog skin; P_f, measured from apical to basolateral surfaces, exceeded P_{D_w}. Koefoed-Johnsen & Ussing (139) confirmed these findings in toad skin, where ADH increased both P_f and P_{D_w} and the P_f/P_{D_w} ratio rose from 5.3 to 33.5. They reasoned that, since P_{D_w} was inadequate to account for osmosis either in the presence or absence of ADH, net transepithelial water flux involved bulk volume flow through aqueous channels. Because ADH increased the P_f/P_{D_w} ratio, Koefoed-Johnsen & Ussing argued that ADH increased the size of aqueous pores in the rate-limiting membrane to water permeation. By assuming that water diffusion and net volume flow traversed the same areas in the rate-limiting membrane, and that the tracer and/or solute concentrations at the membrane interfaces were identical to those in bulk solution (i.e. that unstirred layer effects were negligible), these workers calculated the effective radii of pores in the rate-limiting membrane to water permeation by combining Fick's first law and Poiseuille's law into an equation of the form (6, 47, 136, 139, 190, 204, 236):

$$\frac{P_f}{P_{D_w}} = 1 + \frac{r^2 \, RT}{8\eta \, V_w D^{\circ}_w},$$ 5.

where η is viscosity (poise), D_w° is the free diffusion coefficient for water (cm^2 sec^{-1}), and r is the effective pore radius. Koefoed-Johnsen & Ussing (139) computed that ADH increased the radii of pores in the rate-limiting site for water permeation from 6 to 20 Å. At approximately the same time, Pappenheimer et al (189, 190) observed P_f/P_{D_w} ratios of approximately 70 in mammalian capillaries and deduced that net volume flux depended on bulk flow through pores whose effective radii were approximately 30 Å.

A number of critical observations on the effects of ADH in amphibian skin were made by Ussing et al. Ussing & Zerahn (247) showed that the hormone appreciably increased open-circuit transepithelial voltage and both short-circuit current and net apical to basolateral Na^+ flux. Andersen & Ussing (2) observed that ADH increased the apparent diffusional permeability coefficients for acetamide (effective hydrodynamic radius ≈ 2.5Å) and thiourea (effective hydrodynamic radius ≈ 2.0 Å), but the ADH-dependent permeability coefficients for these solutes with respect to P_{D_w} were substantially lower than predicted from molecular sieving theory (189, 190, 203) for pores having 20 Å radii. Similarly, computations (132) of reflection coefficients for acetamide and thiourea in toad skin treated with ADH, respectively 0.89 and 0.98, were far greater than expected from the theory of irreversible thermodynamics for diffusion and/or convection of such solutes through 20 Å pores. Andersen & Ussing (2) also showed that the net flux of thiourea and acetamide in ADH-treated frog skin increased in proportion to the rate of osmotic water flow in the same direction. They termed the phenomenon *solvent drag* and attributed it to coupling of solute and solvent flows within aqueous pores. Subsequently, Kedem & Katchalsky (136) and Dainty & Ginzburg (47) developed quantitative expressions describing interactions between solute and solvent flows within aqueous pores in the terminology of irreversible thermodynamics. Finally, MacRobbie & Ussing (163) established clearly that the apical surface of amphibian skin was the rate-limiting site for water and solute permeation. Importantly, these observations did not distinguish whether water permeation involved apical plasma membranes, junctional complexes, or both, i.e. the data provided no information about the fractional area of luminal surfaces involved in water diffusion or net volume flow.

Andersen & Ussing (2) integrated these results into their classical dual-barrier hypothesis for the action of ADH on amphibian epithelia. Apical surfaces were pictured as a series barrier: a dense outer diffusion barrier that admitted water freely, limited solute penetration, and was unresponsive to ADH; and a porous inner barrier sensitive to ADH. Pores in the inner barrier, sufficiently large to permit laminar flow, accounted for the disparity between P_f and P_{D_w} and the apparent solvent drag effect. ADH increased the radii of these pores, resulting in increments in solute permeation rates, P_{D_w}, P_f, and the P_f/P_{D_w} ratio.

Leaf and co-workers subsequently developed convincing arguments in support of the view that a dual-barrier model might account for the effects of ADH on toad urinary bladder (110, 111, 148, 154, 155, 165). Maffly et al (165) observed that the ADH-dependent reflection coefficients of thiourea and Cl^- were virtually unity, and provided direct evidence that apical surfaces contained the ADH-sensitive, rate-limiting sites for urea permeation. These data, like the results of MacRobbie &

Ussing (163) in amphibian skin, provided no information concerning the fractional area (or sites) within apical surfaces involved in water and solute permeation. Hays & Leaf (110) showed that, as in amphibian skin, ADH increased P_f, P_{D_w}, and the P_f/P_{D_w} ratio; from observed P_f/P_{D_w} ratios and equation 5, they calculated that ADH increased the effective pore radii in the inner barrier from 8.4 Å to approximately 40 Å. These workers also noted (111) that the activation energy for THO diffusion fell from 9.8 kcal mol^{-1} without hormone to 4.1 kcal mole^{-1} in the presence of hormone. As the latter value is comparable to the activation energy for water diffusion in free solution, Hays & Leaf (111) argued that, without ADH, small pores in the inner barrier contained structured water; with ADH, enlarged pores contained the equivalent of liquid water. In agreement with the pore enlargement hypothesis, Leaf & Hays reported apparent solvent drag for urea (148). Finally, they observed (148) that ADH-dependent increments in solute permeability coefficients were specific. The hormone increased the apparent permeability coefficients for water, urea, and other low molecular weight amides and, to a lesser degree, alcohols and Na$^+$; the permeability coefficients of other inorganic ions (K$^+$, Cl$^-$, SO$_4^{2-}$), organic ions, and a variety of organic molecules comparable in molecular weight to urea or acetamide, were not affected by the hormone. Leaf & Hays (148) concluded that the outer diffusion barrier of apical surfaces was rate limiting to small solutes whose permeation rates were unaffected by ADH, while the inner porous barrier of apical surfaces limited the transport of water, urea, and other small amides. As with the Andersen-Ussing hypothesis, ADH was considered to increase the radii of pores in the inner barrier. On the basis of subsequent experiments involving the combined use of ADH and amphotericin B, Lichtenstein & Leaf (154, 155) argued that ADH might also enhance urea and Na$^+$ diffusion through the dense outer barrier. Recently, Civan & DiBona (35) have shown that, in toad urinary bladder, the hydro-osmotic effect of ADH involves only granular epithelial cells, rather than all epithelial (or mucosal) cells in that tissue.

A BRIEF SURVEY OF ADH EFFECTS IN MAMMALIAN RENAL TUBULES   The effects of ADH on transport processes in mammalian renal tubules, particularly in the case of water permeation, are quite similar to the effects of the hormone on amphibian skin or toad urinary bladder. A number of micropuncture studies have shown that ADH increases the rate of either diffusional and/or osmotic water flows across mammalian distal tubules and papillary collecting tubules (94, 126, 176, 177, 195, 239).

In the isolated cortical collecting tubule of the rabbit, Grantham et al (96, 97) obtained ADH effects on P_f, P_{D_w}, and the P_f/P_{D_w} ratio similar to those obtained by Hays & Leaf (110, 148) in toad urinary bladder, and have shown clearly that apical surfaces of these tubules are both the rate-limiting site for water permeation and the barrier whose water permeability is increased by ADH; Grantham (95) has also demonstrated that the hydro-osmotic action of ADH in cortical collecting tubules is accompanied by increases in the mechanical compliance of the latter. However, ADH has no effect on the permeability coefficients for urea, thiourea, and acetamide in cortical collecting tubules (20, 96).

Schafer & Andreoli (214, 215) confirmed most of these observations and noted that, with or without ADH: the permeability coefficients of urea and thiourea are less than 0.03×10^{-4} cm sec^{-1}; the reflection coefficients of these solutes are unity; and the apical surfaces of the tubules are rate limiting to the permeation of these solutes, both in cortical and outer medullary collecting tubules (215). The model proposed by us (214, 215, 218, 219) to rationalize the effects of ADH on water permeation in rabbit cortical collecting tubules differs appreciably from the dual-barrier hypothesis of Andersen & Ussing (2) and Leaf & Hays (110, 111, 148) and from modifications of the dual-barrier hypothesis proposed by Hays et al on the basis of recent observations on the effects of ADH on solute (106, 107, 149, 150, 153, 225) and solvent (105, 108, 109) flows in toad urinary bladder.

REQUIREMENTS OF THE DUAL-BARRIER HYPOTHESIS   It is relevant here to reiterate certain cardinal requirements of the dual-barrier hypothesis (2, 110, 111, 148). These include: (a) that apical surfaces are the sole site for ADH-mediated effects on transport processes in ADH-sensitive epithelia; (b) that ADH-dependent increments in Na$^+$, water, and small amide permeation are mediated by a single set of effects on diffusional and/or convective processes in apical surfaces; (c) that the effective areas available for water convection and/or diffusion through apical surfaces are identical; (d) that tracer and/or solute concentrations at membrane interfaces are identical to those in bulk solutions, and (e) that apical plasma membranes and junctional complexes provide a single permeation pathway rather than parallel transport routes.

In the following section, we summarize briefly evidence indicating that the effects of ADH on Na$^+$ transport, urea and other small amide permeation, and water flows are dissociable and may involve effects of the hormone on multiple membrane sites and/or cellular loci.

Dissociation of ADH Effects on Na$^+$, Solute, and H$_2$O Permeation

VARYING EFFECTS OF ADH IN DIFFERENT HORMONE-SENSITIVE EPITHELIA In general, ADH affects so-called tight epithelia (88), i.e. those having relatively high electrical resistances, in the range 200–2000 ohm-cm^2 (cf Table 1). The ADH-dependent increments in water permeation in amphibian skin and toad urinary bladder are accompanied by increases in small amide permeability (2, 148), net Na$^+$ transport (146, 147, 154, 247), and transepithelial electrical conductance (35, 146, 154). Wright & Snart (255) have argued that, in toad bladder, low ADH concentrations increase Na$^+$ permeability of apical membranes by a direct action, while higher concentrations elicit a hydro-osmotic effect by increasing intracellular cAMP. Based on electron microscopic changes in tissue morphology when bathing solution osmolarities were varied, Civan & DiBona (35) have concluded that, in toad bladder, the hydro-osmotic ADH effect is restricted to granular cells on the apical surface.

In isolated segments of rabbit mammalian nephron, the effects of ADH on water, urea, and Na$^+$ permeation are clearly separable. In cortical (96, 97, 214, 215, 218, 219), outer medullary (215), and papillary (206) collecting tubules, ADH increases

Table 1 A comparison of the effects of ADH in amphibian epithelia and isolated mammalian renal tubules

Tissue	ADH	P_f	P_{D_W}	P_f/P_{D_W}	$P_{D_{urea}}$	J_{Na}^{net}	R_m	References
		(cm sec^{-1} × 10^4)			(cm sec^{-1} × 10^6)	(eq sec^{-1} cm^{-2} × 10^{10})	(Ωcm^2)	
Amphibian skin	−	7.9	1.5	5.3	0.26[a]	3.32	3445[b]	2, 139, 247
	+	50	1.5	33.3	3.91[a]	5.96	1955[b]	
Toad urinary bladder: whole tissue	−	4.8	1.0	4.8	2.6	2.21	1000–2500[c]	110, 146–148
	+	185	1.7	109	27.4	3.27	400–1000[c]	
Toad urinary bladder: mucosal cells	−	5.0	—	—	—	—	—	108
	+	228	10.8	21.1	—	—	—	
Isolated rabbit cortical collecting tubules	−	20	4.7	4.3	4.5	4.88	867	87, 96, 97, 115, 214, 215, 218, 219
	+	186	14.2	13.1	5.0	5.87	846	
Isolated rabbit papillary collecting tubules	−	—	4.0	—	21.9	—	—	206
	+	68.4	5.7	12.0	23.6	—	—	

[a] From the data of Andersen & Ussing (2); $P_{D_{thiourea}}$, rather than $P_{D_{urea}}$, was measured.
[b] From the results of Ussing & Zerahn (247). The resistance measurements were computed from open circuit transepithelial voltage and short-circuit current measurements without correction for possible conductance leaks due to edge damage (116).
[c] Computed from the data of Leaf et al (146) for *Bufo marinus* from short-circuit current measurements and open-circuit membrane voltages in the range 20–50 mV. The data have not been corrected for conductance leaks due to edge effects (116).

water permeation in a manner similar to that seen in amphibian skin (139) and toad bladder (110) but has no effect on urea and small amide permeation (20, 96, 107, 206, 215, 219). In cortical collecting tubules, ADH has no effect on transepithelial electrical resistance and produces only minor changes in open-circuit transepithelial voltage or net lumen to bath Na^+ transport (87, 115).

INHIBITION OF UREA BUT NOT WATER PERMEATION IN TOAD URINARY BLADDER Macey & Farmer (159) observed that phloretin, an aglucone of phlorhizin, interferes with urea but not water permeation in red blood cells. Levine et al have shown that phloretin inhibits urea but not water permeation in toad urinary bladder (149) and dogfish kidney (151), both in the presence and absence of ADH, and have obtained comparable results in toad bladder with tanning agents such as chromate or tannic acid (225). However, the permeabilities of relatively lipophilic species, such as ethanol and ethylene glycol, and net Na^+ transport are both unaffected by phloretin, tannic acid, or chromate, either with or without ADH (149, 225). Levine & Hays et al, based on these (107, 149, 150, 225) and subsequent observations (153), argue that urea and small amide permeation in toad urinary bladder involves an ADH-sensitive facilitated diffusion pathway. Their argument is discussed in further detail below.

REDUCED WATER BUT NOT SOLUTE PERMEATION IN AMPHIBIAN EPITHELIA Peterson & Edelman (196) have shown that, in toad bladder, elevated bath Ca^{2+} concentrations antagonize the ADH-dependent increase in P_f, while ADH-dependent increments in urea permeation and net Na^+ transport are reduced slightly or not at all. In the aquatic toad *Xenopus laevis,* ADH stimulates Na^+ transport markedly, but has little or no hydro-osmotic effect (12, 35, 164). Lipson & Sharp (156) have reported that, in toad bladder, prostaglandin E_1 enhances and inhibits, respectively, ADH-dependent stimulation of Na^+ and water transport.

A number of other agents have comparable effects. Chlorpromazine impairs the ADH-dependent increment in P_f, irreversibly increases solute permeation, and stimulates the ADH-dependent increment in net Na^+ transport (166). Quinidine (233) inhibits and stimulates, respectively, ADH-dependent increments in H_2O and net Na^+ transport. Similary, cytochalasin B (53, 234), colchicine (234), vinblastine (234), podophyllotoxin (234), and cortisol (168) inhibit the hydro-osmotic response to ADH but not the stimulatory effects of the hormone on Na^+ or urea transport.

Finally, general anesthetics such as methoxyfluorane and halothane inhibit ADH-dependent increases in water but not urea permeation (152). The latter finding is of particular interest since Pauling (194) has suggested that anesthetic agents may decrease membrane fluidity by forming ice-like clathrates within hydrophobic regions of membranes, and recent NMR observations (193) in lipid bilayer membranes have provided direct experimental evidence in support of this view. As discussed below, we (1, 214, 215, 218, 219) and others (198) have suggested that ADH facilitates water (219) and lipophilic solute permeation (1, 198) by increasing the fluidity and/or solubility characteristics of the apical membranes.

INHIBITION OF Na$^+$ BUT NOT WATER TRANSPORT   A number of agents inhibit Na$^+$ transport but not water permeation in toad urinary bladder. The diuretic amiloride (11) and the antimicrobial agent CM–55 (180) interfere with Na$^+$ but not water entry at apical surfaces, either in the presence or absence of ADH. Verapamil, a coronary vasodilator and anti-arrhythmic drug, blocks the stimulation of Na$^+$ but not water transport produced by adding either ADH or cAMP to basolateral surfaces of toad urinary bladder (13). Lithium reduces basal and ADH or cAMP stimulated short-circuit current and Na$^+$ transport, but does not affect the hydro-osmotic response to ADH (14).

EVIDENCE FOR MULTIPLE SITES OF ADH ACTION ON Na$^+$ TRANSPORT IN AMPHIBIAN EPITHELIA   The dual-barrier hypothesis (2, 110, 111, 148) argues that the effects of ADH on Na$^+$ transport in amphibian epithelia are referable to increases in apical surface Na$^+$ permeability. Evidence has now been adduced that in amphibian skin (174), frog bladder (127, 128), and toad bladder (79, 81), ADH augments both passive Na$^+$ entry at apical surfaces and active Na$^+$ efflux at basolateral surfaces. Indeed, Finn has argued that apical and basolateral membranes "signal" one another and that the effect of ADH on these two surfaces may be related to the signal effect (80). The latter suggestion is reminiscent of the situation in dog red blood cells, where active Na$^+$ efflux varies inversely with cell volume (191, 207).

SUMMARY   It is evident from the preceding discussion that: (a) the effects of ADH vary among different hormone-sensitive tissues, i.e. amphibian epithelia and mammalian renal tubules; and (b) within a given epithelium, such as toad urinary bladder, the effects of either ADH or cAMP on Na$^+$, water, and urea or other small amide permeation may be dissociated. For convenience, certain of these data are summarized in Tables 1 and 2.

Table 1 compares some of the classical observations of Ussing et al (2, 139, 247) in amphibian skin and Leaf et al on toad bladder (110, 146–148) with more recent observations on mucosal cells from toad urinary bladder (108) and isolated mammalian renal tubules (87, 96, 97, 115, 206, 214, 215, 218, 219). Several factors are particularly relevant. First, the data for amphibian epithelia have not been corrected for edge effects (116) on electrical conductance. These considerations do not apply to P_f, P_{D_w} and $P_{D_{urea}}$, which are unaffected by edge damage in amphibian epithelia (116). Likewise, in isolated renal tubules, the experimental arrangement (96, 115, 214) precludes edge effects. However, quite independent of the edge effect, it is clear that ADH augments electrical conductance, net Na$^+$ flux and urea (or other small amide) permeation in amphibian epithelia but not in various segments of isolated mammalian collecting ducts.

Second, in amphibian skin and toad urinary bladder, the P_f/P_{D_w} ratio is appreciably higher than in mucosal cells from toad urinary bladder (i.e. without supporting stromal elements) or in cortical collecting tubules. In comparing intact toad urinary bladder with either isolated mucosal cells from toad bladder or cortical collecting tubules, one finds that, in the latter preparation, P_f/P_{D_w} ratios are appreciably lower because of increases in P_{D_w}. In a subsequent section, we present arguments in

Table 2 The effect of various agents on ADH-stimulated transport processes in toad urinary bladder[a]

Agent	P_f	PD_{urea}	J_{Na}^{net}	References
	(% change in ADH-dependent value)			
10^{-4} M phloretin (apical surface)	none	−80	none	149
10 mM Ca^{2+} (basolateral surface)	−98 / none[b]	−30 / —	none / —	196
0.07–0.1 mM chlorpromazine (basolateral surface)	−21 to −55	—	+33	166
1–20 μg/ml cytochalasin B (basolateral surface)	−50 / −50[b]	— / —	none / —	53, 234
1% methoxyfluorane (both surfaces)	−50 / −100[c]	none / −15[c]	— / —	152
10^{-5} M amiloride (apical)	none / —	— / —	−88 / −72[b]	11
10^{-4} M verapamil (basolateral	−7 / —	— / —	−80 / −75[b]	13
40 mM Li^+ (either surface)	none / —	— / —	−80 / −87[b]	14

[a]Unless otherwise indicated, P_f, PD_{urea}, and J_{Na}^{net} were measured in the presence of ADH with values comparable to those listed in Table 1 for ADH-stimulated values for intact toad bladder.

[b]Transport stimulated by cAMP instead of ADH.

[c]Transport stimulated by theophylline instead of ADH.

support of the view that in mucosal cells of toad urinary bladder or isolated cortical collecting tubules, the remaining discrepancies between P_f and PD_w, either with or without ADH, are referable to cellular constraints to diffusion rather than to bulk flow through aqueous channels.

Table 2 summarizes representative examples indicating that, in toad bladder, the effects of ADH (or, in certain instances, of cAMP or theophylline) may be dissociable. The data are expressed in terms of the percent effect of the indicated agent on the ADH (or cAMP or theophylline)-stimulated value of P_f, PD_{urea}, or J_{Na}^{net}. It is evident from Table 2 and the preceding discussion that ADH-mediated increments in Na^+, urea, and water permeation may be affected separately by a number of agents. Yet the data do not necessarily provide a clear insight into the mechanism by which these agents operate, e.g. by interfering with hormone binding, by perturbing the sequence of metabolic events involving cAMP triggered by ADH, or by a direct action on apical surfaces. To evaluate these and other questions, we now examine separately the effects of ADH on urea and small amide permeation, Na^+ transport, and transepithelial water flows.

The Action of ADH on Nonelectrolyte Permeation

GENERAL CONSIDERATIONS   The effects of ADH on permeation rates for urea, other small amides, and more lipophilic species, both in amphibian epithelia and in mammalian renal collecting tubules, relate in many respects to general questions of nonelectrolyte permeation through synthetic and biological interfaces. It has been recognized since the time of Overton (186) that nonelectrolyte permeation in cells and tissues varies in direct proportion to lipid solubility. In a detailed study of water and nonelectrolyte permeation in algae, Collander and Collander & Bärlund (39, 41) noted a relationship between apparent diffusional permeability coefficients (P_{D_i}, cm sec $^{-1}$) and the term K^n/M^n, where K and M are, respectively, the oil:water partition coefficient and molecular weight of the ith solute, and n is an empirical coefficient. When the partition coefficient involves a solvent other than oil, that solvent is designated by a subscript in the K term. In Nitella, the best relationship with P_{D_i} was noted using $K^{1.3}/M^{1.5}$, i.e. solute permeation varied directly with oil:water partition coefficients and inversely with molecular weights; but urea and methylurea were appreciably more permeable than predicted on the basis of the $K^{1.3}/M^{1.5}$ term. These data, among others, led Höber (119) to postulate that plasma membranes were mosaic structures containing polar and nonpolar permeation routes in parallel. Collander (40) also noted that, in algae, branched chain solutes were less permeant than straight chain homologues having comparable molecular weights and nearly identical high oil:water partition coefficients; he speculated that steric hindrance between branched chain lipophilic molecules and hydrophobic regions of membranes might account for this effect. Subsequently, these permeation patterns, as well as variations of Höber's and Collander's hypotheses, have been reiterated for a wide number of biological interfaces.

Diamond & Wright, in an extensive study of nonelectrolyte permeation in gall bladder [summarized in (56)], confirmed Collander's plant cell observations. These workers noted an excellent empirical relationship between σ and $K/M^{0.5}$ with two exceptions: first, urea and other small amides were more permeant (had lower σ values) than predicted from $K/M^{0.5}$ and the general selectivity pattern; and second, branched chain solutes having relatively high K values, such as isovaleramide and isobutyramide, were significantly less permeant (had higher σ values) than their straight chain homologues. Wright & Diamond (56), like Höber (119) and Collander (40), suggested that anomalously high permeation rates for urea and other small amides might involve preferential interaction of these solutes with membrane polar groups rather than with membrane hydrocarbon tails and that the relative impermeability of branched chain lipophilic solutes, with respect to their straight chain homologues, depended on greater steric restriction encountered by branched chain solutes within hydrocarbon regions of membranes. In a more recent thermodynamic analysis of nonelectrolyte permeation in liposomes, Diamond & Katz (55, 134) have argued that hydrogen-bonding affinities with polar groups of phospholipids might promote urea and small amide permeation, and that hydrophobic regions of liposomes are the rate-limiting site for permeation of such hydrophilic species.

Anomalously high permeation rates for urea and other small amides, with respect to compounds of comparable molecular weight and lipid solubility, exist in a number of cells and tissues. In the erythocyte, Sha'afi et al (224) inferred that hydrophilic solutes traverse an aqueous pathway in which permeation rates are modified by molar volume and hydrogen-bonding ability. And Solomon & Gary-Bobo (227) called attention to the striking similarities between patterns of water and hydrophilic solute permeation in red blood cells and in amphotericin B- or nystatin-treated lipid bilayer membranes, which contain aqueous pores with $\sim$ 4 Å radii (3, 6, 120).

In toad urinary bladders not exposed to vasopressin (148), the apparent permeability coefficients for urea and other small amides are appreciably greater than for solutes of comparable lipid solubility, molecular weight, and molecular volume, even without correction for unstirred layer effects. In a study of seven epithelia, Hingson & Diamond (118) noted that σ values for urea and other amides are lower than for other solutes with comparable $K_{ether}/M^{0.5}$ values in rabbit gall bladder, guinea pig gall bladder, guinea pig intestine, and bullfrog choroid plexus. Wright & Pietras (257) have shown that, in toad urinary bladder, rabbit gall bladder, and frog choroid plexus, permeation rates for urea and acetamide are appreciably greater than predicted on the basis of oil:water partition coefficients and are empirically related, as first suggested by Horowitz & Fenichel (121), to molar volume. Van Os et al (248) have postulated that, in gall bladder, urea permeation involves transport both through 4 Å pores within apical plasma membranes and via an extracellular shunt pathway. In short, a compelling body of experimental evidence indicates that urea and small amide permeation in a wide variety of cells and tissues involves a more complex process than a simple solubility-diffusion pathway.

Nernst (179) first suggested that diffusion-limited liquid layers at phase boundaries might affect reactions involving heterogeneous systems, and a number of early workers (123, 185, 235) called attention to the effects of unstirred layers on biological transport processes. These caveats were largely neglected until Dainty (46) drew attention to unstirred layers as a possible cause for the disparity between P_f and P_{D_w} in biological or synthetic membranes. Since then, a considerable body of evidence has documented clearly the presence of bulk-phase unstirred layers, referable either to inadequate stirring conditions in model membrane systems (6, 26, 93), or to inadequate stirring conditions and/or supporting stromal elements in epithelial tissues (48, 49, 54, 108, 212, 254, 258, 259). The contribution of such unstirred layers to the resistance to solute diffusion may be computed from the equation:

$$\frac{1}{P_{D_i}}\bigg| = \frac{1}{Pm_i} + \frac{\alpha}{D_i},\qquad\qquad 6.$$

where P_{D_i} and Pm_i (cm sec^{-1}) are, respectively, the apparent and true diffusional permeability coefficients for the ith solute across the membrane, and D_i is a diffusion coefficient for the ith solute; for bulk-phase unstirred layers, it is generally assumed that D_i approximates D°_i, the diffusion coefficient in free solution. In that case, the parameter α (cm) expresses the geometric constraints to solute diffusion in the unstirred layer. As bulk solutions are continuous rather than discontinuous phases,

α should not be considered as an actual thickness, but rather as an operational parameter subject to experimental scrutiny (cf 6, 26, 48, 54, 71, 93, 108, 120, 214, 218). In principle, α might include either tortuosity constraints (i.e. a longer path length per unit area), or a reduced area per unit path length [i.e. the fractional area for diffusion in the unstirred layer, with respect to the measured membrane area, is less than unity (218)].

Table 3 summarizes some bulk-phase unstirred layer thicknesses calculated for lipid bilayer membranes and epithelial preparations. Two examples illustrate clearly the relevance of unstirred layer effects to the analysis of water and nonelectrolyte permeability data. First, Cass & Finkelstein (26) demonstrated that, in native lipid bilayer membranes, vigorous aqueous stirring resulted in P_f/P_{D_w} ratios of unity, i.e. that water transport across native bilayer membranes was wholly diffusional in water. A number of laboratories (6, 71, 200) have confirmed these observations by alternate experimental approaches. Second, Hays & Franki (108) showed that, in toad bladder, P_{D_w} values in isolated mucosal cells and the intact tissue were, respectively, 10.8×10^{-4} and 1.7×10^{-4} cm sec^{-1} (cf Table 1). Stated in another way, the bulk of the resistance to water diffusion was referable to both stromal elements and bulk unstirred layers, rather than cells and/or plasma membranes.

More recent evidence indicates that epithelial cells themselves may constrain transepithelial water and nonelectrolyte diffusion. In isolated cortical collecting tubules (214), the reflection coefficients for the highly lipophilic solutes butanol, pyridine, and 5-hydroxyindole are zero, and their permeability coefficients are unaffected by ADH; the diffusion of these solutes is wholly unstirred-layer limited in lipid bilayer membranes (120, 214). Schafer & Andreoli (214) observed that $1/P_{D_i}$ for butanol, 5-hydroxyindole, and pyridine was 10- to 25-fold greater than

Table 3 Bulk-phase unstirred layers associated with lipid bilayer membranes[a] and various epithelial preparations[b]

| Preparation | Unstirred layer thickness | | | References |
	Total	Apical (cm $\times 10^4$)	Basolateral	
Lipid bilayer membrane	100–120	—	—	6, 26
Frog skin	130–290	30–60	100–230	48, 49
Toad bladder	200[c]	—	—	257
	1055[d]	—	236[e]	108
Choroid plexus	900	100	800	258
Gall bladder	900	100–110	800	54, 259
Small intestine	—	180–210	—	212, 254

[a] Due to bulk aqueous phase unstirred layers, i.e. inadequate mixing (26, 93).

[b] Due to inadequate mixing and/or stromal elements.

[c] Data of Wright & Pietras (257) for their stirring conditions.

[d] Calculated from P_{D_w} differences at zero and maximal stirring rates.

[e] Calculated according to equation 6 from P_{D_w} values before and after removal of stromal elements (108).

predicted for a thickness of free solution equivalent to that of the cell layer (6.5 ×
10^{-4} cm). Thus, in isolated cortical collecting tubules, where bulk-phase unstirred
effects are probably negligible (214, 215, 218), the single epithelial cell layer, exclusive of luminal plasma membranes and/or tight junctions, may impede diffusion to
a degree comparable to that expected in a layer of free solution 10- to 25-fold greater
in thickness. Parisi & Piccini (192) have also provided evidence in support of this
view, by showing that THO diffusion is impeded significantly within the mucosal
cell layer of toad bladder.

Taken together, these observations (192, 214) indicate that, at least for cells in
cortical collecting tubules and toad urinary bladder, equation 6 may be rewritten
as:

$$\frac{1}{P_{D_i}} = \frac{1}{Pm_i} + \frac{\alpha}{D_i} + \frac{\beta\Delta x}{D_i^o},$$
7.

where Δx is the measured cell thickness and the dimensionless parameter β expresses the ratio of the diffusion resistance of the epithelial cell layer (exclusive of
luminal plasma membranes and/or junctional complexes) to that of an equivalent
thickness of free solution. As the nature of frictional interactions within cells with
respect to free solution is at present indeterminate, the $\beta\Delta x/D_i^o$ term in equation
7 includes the free diffusion coefficient, which cannot be measured directly, and the
parameter β, which may under appropriate conditions (214) be assessed experimentally. Defined in this manner, β values in excess of unity may be referable either to
frictional interactions within the cell layer which exceed those in free solution, or
to geometric factors such as tortuosity constraints or reductions in the effective
diffusion area per unit path length. In cortical collecting tubules (218), it has been
possible to infer which of these factors is responsible for β values in excess of unity
(cf below).

THE ACTION OF ADH ON AMIDE PERMEATION

Amphibian epithelia   In a variety of tissues, including plant cells (39, 41), red blood
cells (159, 224, 227), and amphibian epithelia (118, 148, 149, 257), urea and other
small amides exhibit "anomalously high" permeation rates with respect to solutes
of comparable water solubility and molecular weight. Until recently the properties
of the putative polar pathway for urea and other small amide permeation remained
obscure. However, the effects of phloretin and comparable agents on red blood cells
and amphibian epithelia now provide strong evidence that some type of facilitated
diffusion mechanism may be responsible for urea and amide permeation in these
cells and tissues.

Macey & Farmer (159) first showed that phloretin inhibited urea but not water
permeation in human red blood cells. Owen & Solomon (187) have confirmed and
extended these observations; at 0.25 mM phloretin, there is a 65% reduction in
$P_{D_{urea}}$, an increment in P_D for the lipophilic solutes 2,3-butanediol, ethylene glycol,
and antipyrine, and a 1.3-fold increment in P_f. They argued that, because phloretin
does not penetrate red cell membranes (9), the agent affects red cells by interaction

with surface proteins; the interaction is presumed to affect urea and lipophilic solute permeation by a common action (187). Owen et al (188) have subsequently noted that phloretin has a bimodal effect on permeation processes in red blood cells. At concentrations less than 10^{-4} M, both hydrophilic and lipophilic solute permeation increase; at higher phloretin concentrations, lipophilic solute permeation increases while hydrophilic solute permeation decreases. Kaplan et al (131) presented evidence that, in red blood cells of amphibia, reptiles, and vertebrates, but not birds and fishes, urea and acetamide permeation exhibit transport characteristics consistent with a facilitated diffusion process inhibitable by 0.6 mM phloretin. Finally, Kaplan, Hays & Blumenfeld (130) noted that the phloretin-sensitive urea permeation route in red blood cells is unaffected by proteolytic enzymes or cross-linking agents such as glutaraldehyde.

With few exceptions, the ADH-dependent and ADH-independent characteristics of urea and small amide permeation in toad urinary bladder resemble those in red cells. Hays et al (149, 150, 225) found that: (a) 10^{-4} M phloretin in apical solutions inhibits urea, acetamide, and propionamide permeation, with and without ADH, but does not affect P_f, Na^+ transport, or ethanol and ethylene glycol permeation; (b) the permeation of both tagged acetamide and tagged urea, with and without ADH, is inhibited by unlabeled acetamide, i.e. the vasopressin-sensitive transport system for urea and acetamide is saturable and exhibits competition between labeled and unlabeled species; (c) tanning agents such as chromate and tannic acid, which cross-link proteins, have effects comparable to those of phloretin on ADH-sensitive urea and amide transport. These observations are consistent with the view (149, 150, 225) that the ADH-sensitive 'polar' urea and amide permeation pathway involves a protein-dependent facilitated diffusion pathway in parallel with the ADH-stimulated water permeation pathway in apical surfaces (35, 162, 163, 165). Eggena's observation (66) that, in toad bladder, thiourea competes with urea but no net water flux, provides additional evidence in support of the hypothesis of Hays et al (149, 150, 225). And Rubin (210) has provided evidence that a surface glycoprotein in toad urinary bladder may be a component of the urea permeation pathway.

Three other conclusions seem warranted. First, given the striking similarities between the effects of phloretin on water and urea permeation in red blood cells (130, 131, 159, 187, 188) and toad urinary bladder (66, 149, 150, 225), it seems reasonable to infer that the ADH-sensitive urea permeation pathway in toad bladder involves apical plasma membranes rather than junctional complexes. Junctional complexes in tight epithelia such as toad urinary bladder have high electrical resistances (cf Table 1) in contrast to "leaky" epithelia such as gall bladder, small intestine, or renal proximal tubule (88); they are sealed, as judged by electron microscopy, to lanthanum and other agents (57, 69); and are relatively impermeant to larger hydrophilic species such as mannitol (17, 83, 167). Under appropriate conditions, however, such as luminal hypertonicity (17, 57, 69, 83, 219, 245) or depolarizing apical surfaces to −100 mV (167), water, electrolyte, and nonelectrolyte permeation through junctional complexes increases appreciably (17, 57, 69, 83, 219, 245) and the complexes widen morphologically (57, 69). Second, the fact that water and urea permeation can be dissociated in toad bladder (83, 149, 150, 225) may indicate that water and urea traverse parallel rather than series pathways in plasma membranes. Thus the effects of phloretin in toad bladder (66, 149, 150, 225) obviate the need for a dual-barrier hypothesis (2, 110, 111, 148) to rationalize the discrepancy between PD_w and PD_{urea} in terms of formulations (2, 110, 111, 136, 139, 148, 190, 204) that assume "simple" diffusion and/or convection processes for water and nonelectrolyte permeation. Similar considerations may apply to calculations of equivalent pore radii (224, 226, 227) in red blood cells.

Finally, Levine et al (153) attempted to distinguish between a fixed channel and a mobile carrier as the system for facilitating ADH-sensitive urea permeation in toad urinary bladder. They observed that the flux of tagged methylurea, urea, or acetamide was accelerated only when the unlabeled compound was added to the *cis* solution. They reasoned that, since cotransport but not countertransport occurred, ADH-sensitive urea permeation involves an amide-selective channel rather than a carrier. However, accelerated counterflow need not occur in a carrier-mediated system if the unloaded carrier moves across the membrane more rapidly than the loaded carrier (125). In fact, given such a carrier, one may observe a decrease in tracer flux when unlabeled solute is added to the *trans* side (124). For example, Schafer & Heinz (216) have shown that carrier-mediated α-aminoisobutyric acid transport does not exhibit accelerative counterflow. Alternatively, Schafer & Jacquez (217) found competitive stimulation (i.e. cotransport) of amino acids, due to the presence of either more than one carrier type or a multiple-site carrier. If the amide transport system in toad bladder involves multiple carriers or a two-site carrier, one could easily rationalize the apparent cotransport effects observed by Levine et al (153) without positing a fixed-site, amide-specific channel. Thus the ADH-sensitive system for facilitated diffusion of urea and other amides in toad bladder remains undefined in terms of carriers versus fixed sites.

Mammalian epithelia   Far less information exists concerning mechanisms for urea and small amide permeation in mammalian renal tubules than in toad urinary bladder, red blood cells, and other epithelia (cf above). Table 1 illustrates that PD_{urea} in cortical [and outer medullary (215)] collecting tubules is at least five times less than PD_{urea} in ADH-treated toad urinary bladder. It is relevant to consider these data in the context of equations 6 and 7. For a β value (equation 7) of 25, i.e. a diffusion resistance 25 times greater for the epithelial cell layer than for a comparable thickness of free solution (214), one obtains a $\beta \Delta x / D^{\,o}_{urea}$ value of approximately 1700 sec cm^{-1}. The ADH-dependent values of $1/PD_{urea}$ (Table 1) for toad urinary bladder and cortical collecting tubules are, respectively, 3.65×10^4 and 2×10^5 sec cm^{-1}, i.e. cellular constraints to urea diffusion are negligible in these preparations. We point out in a subsequent section that an opposite condition probably exists for the case of water permeation in these tissues.

The situation regarding urea permeation is somewhat different in the case of bulk-phase unstirred layers, i.e. the α / D_{urea} term in equations 6 and 7. In cortical collecting tubules, this term is negligible (214). Thus the values of PD_{urea} listed in Table 1 may be taken as realistic estimates for urea transport through apical surfaces (plasma membranes and/or junctional complexes), which are rate limiting to the transport of that solute (215). Given the fact that junctional complexes in cortical collecting tubules are closed to urea unless luminal solutions are made hypertonic (219), the values of PD_{urea} listed in Table 1 for cortical collecting tubules provide a reasonable index to the rate of urea permeation through luminal plasma membranes.

In the case of toad urinary bladder, bulk unstirred layers (the α/D_i^o term in equations 6 and 7) are appreciable in magnitude (Table 3) and may result in erroneously low values for PD_{urea}. For example, taking a total bulk-phase unstirred layer thickness of 1055×10^{-4} cm (Table 3) and the ADH-dependent value of PD_{urea} for toad bladder in Table 1, one obtains from equation 6 a Pm_{urea} value of 35.4×10^{-6} cm sec^{-1}, in close accord with recently reported values for PD_{urea} in toad urinary bladder by Levine et al (149). If one chooses 200×10^{-4} cm (Table 3) as a lower estimate for bulk unstirred layers in toad urinary bladder under optimal stirring conditions (257), the ADH-dependent value of PD_{urea} in Table 1 approximates Pm_{urea} in equation 6.

In either case, the characteristics of urea transport in cortical collecting tubules and amphibian epithelia resemble one another in two respects: (a) luminal surfaces are the rate-limiting site for urea entry into cells (35, 96, 162, 163, 214, 215) and (b) urea permeation involves luminal plasma membranes rather than junctional complexes [(219), cf above]. Urea transport patterns in these tissues differ in four respects: (a) the ADH-dependent value of PD_{urea} is much smaller in cortical collecting tubules than in toad urinary bladder (Table 1), and this difference, as noted above, may be even greater when bulk-phase unstirred layer effects are considered; (b) the ratio PD_{urea}/P_f in the presence of ADH is appreciably smaller in cortical collecting tubules than in toad urinary bladder (Table 1); (c) urea permeation is ADH enhanced in amphibian epithelia but not in cortical collecting tubules (Table 1); and (d) in the absence of phloretin or similar agents, the effects of ADH on water and urea flows are clearly dissociable in cortical collecting tubules (96, 214, 215, 219), but not in amphibian epithelia (2, 110, 139, 148). In short, there is no evidence at present to support the view that luminal plasma membranes of cortical collecting tubules contain the specialized urea permeation pathways present in red cells (130, 131, 159, 187, 188) and various epithelia (66, 149–151, 210, 225).

Indeed, with respect to the ADH-dependent PD_{urea}/P_f ratio, one might say that cortical collecting tubules resemble more closely synthetic lipid bilayer membranes than toad urinary bladder. In lipid bilayers, PD_{urea} is approximately 5×10^{-6} cm sec^{-1} (4, 250) and P_f varies, depending on membrane composition, from 4×10^{-4} to 50×10^{-4} cm sec $^{-1}$ (26, 71, 99, 200). In other words, native lipid bilayers, like ADH-treated cortical collecting tubules, are tight to urea but may be (within a factor of four) as leaky to water as cortical collecting tubules (Table 1). Kokko & Rector (141) recently proposed a model for antidiuresis in mammalian kidney that depends on urea accumulation and concentration in the luminal fluid of urea-impermeant cortical and outer medullary collecting ducts, implying teleological significance to such an arrangement.

In the case of papillary collecting ducts, few data exist concerning mechanisms of urea permeation. Table 1 shows that, in isolated rabbit nephron segments, PD_{urea} is appreciably higher in papillary collecting tubules (206) than in cortical or outer medullary collecting tubules (206, 215) and negligibly responsive to ADH (206). Morgan, Sakai & Berliner (177) showed that, in collecting ducts from the isolated rat papilla, ADH raised PD_{urea} from 2×10^{-4} to 3×10^{-4} cm sec^{-1}. These data, taken together with the results in Table 1, seem to indicate that, in the mammalian nephron, urea permeation and ADH-responsiveness are greater in terminal than more proximal segments of collecting ducts. Such urea transport characteristics for these portions of the mammalian nephron are explicitly those required by the Kokko-Rector countercurrent model (141) for mammalian antidiuresis.

THE ACTION OF ADH ON LIPOPHILIC SOLUTE PERMEATION In their study of solute permeation in toad urinary bladder, Leaf & Hays (148) observed two patterns of response to ADH. ADH increased the apparent permeability coefficients of water, urea, and other amides (except for thiourea), and compounds such as methanol, ethanol, and ethylene glycol, which have K values in the range 10^{-4}–10^{-2} (256). The majority of compounds that did not respond to the hormone, with the exception of thiourea and butanol, were primarily hydrophilic (148). More recent observations with thiourea [$K \approx 10^{-3}$ (256)] indicate that, in toad bladder, $PD_{thiourea}$ is enhanced by ADH (149) and that thiourea is a potent competitor for the urea pathway (66). Recognizing that bulk-phase unstirred layer effects complicated the original measurements of Leaf & Hays (148) [compare, for example, $PD_{thiourea}$ in (148, 149) and PD_{urea} in (148, 149, 198)], one might tentatively conclude from the work by Leaf & Hays (148) that, in addition to enhancing the urea permeation pathway, ADH also increases the permeability coefficients for relatively lipophilic species such as methanol, ethanol, and ethylene glycol.

Such a view is not inconsistent with the hypothesis of Schafer & Andreoli (214, 215, 218, 219), who have proposed that ADH increases the solubility and/or fluidity characteristics of luminal plasma membranes in rabbit cortical collecting tubules. In this regard, five observations are particularly noteworthy. First, Grantham (95) reported that ADH increases the mechanical compliance of apical membranes of rabbit cortical collecting tubules. Second, Pietras & Wright (198) have observed that, in toad bladder, ADH uniformly increased PD_i for seven relatively lipophilic solutes having K values greater than 10^{-3}. Third, Al-Zahid, Schafer & Andreoli (1) noted that, in cortical collecting tubules, ADH increased by two- to threefold PD_i for moderately lipophilic species such as butyramide and isobutyramide, which have K values in the range 10^{-3}–10^{-2} (256). Fourth, in cortical collecting tubules, the ADH-dependent and ADH-independent reflection coefficients for highly lipophilic species such as butanol [$K = 0.53$ (256)] are zero (214); and both in cortical collecting tubules (214) and toad bladder (148), $PD_{butanol}$ is unaffected by ADH. Finally, while phloretin inhibits urea and amide permeation in toad bladder, it does not affect Na$^+$, ethanol, and ethylene glycol transport (149). Similarly, in the red blood cell, phloretin enhances water and lipophilic solute permeation while reducing urea permeation (187). Thus, both in toad urinary bladder and rabbit cortical collecting tubules, ADH-mediated increments in water permeation are accompanied by permeability increases for moderately lipophilic species; in toad bladder, the water permeation pathway is phloretin insensitive. Apical plasma membranes in toad urinary bladder, therefore, may contain at least two ADH-sensitive pathways in parallel, one a facilitated transport system for amides and the other a common permeation route for water and lipophilic species. In rabbit cortical collecting tubules, apical plasma membranes may contain an ADH-sensitive permeation route common to water and lipophilic species.

The Action of ADH on Na^+ Transport

GENERAL CONSIDERATIONS   In recent times, the model devised by Koefoed-Johnsen & Ussing (140) for Na^+ transport in amphibian epithelia has served as the primary frame of reference for evaluating Na^+ transport in most epithelia. In this section we limit ourselves to a cursory review of recent evidence bearing on the mechanism by which ADH increases the rate of Na^+ transport across amphibian skin and toad urinary bladder. As discussed above (cf Table 1), ADH has little or no effect on Na^+ transport in mammalian cortical collecting tubules (87).

In 1938, Krogh (143) demonstrated that frog skin established and maintained enormous transepithelial NaCl chemical gradients. These findings were confirmed by Ussing (242–244) and Ussing & Zerahn (247), who demonstrated that net Na^+ transport was identical to the zero-voltage short-circuit current, occurred against an electrochemical gradient, was responsible for a significant fraction of O_2 consumption (261), and was susceptible to inhibition by agents that poisoned energy-generating metabolic processes. Kirschner (138) postulated, both on theoretical and experimental grounds, the existence of an active Na^+ carrier mechanism, whose location in the skin was not specified. Koefoed-Johnsen & Ussing (140) later showed that transepithelial voltage changes produced by varying Na^+ and/or K^+ concentrations in external solutions could be accounted for quantitatively by treating apical and basolateral surfaces as Na^+-selective and K^+-selective electrodes, respectively. Their model proposed that Na^+ entered cells passively at apical surfaces and was actively transported out of cells at basolateral surfaces via an active Na^+/K^+ exchange pump. Support for this model was provided both by intracellular microelectrode studies, which localized passive Na^+ entry to apical membranes of the outermost cell layer and active Na^+ efflux to basolateral membranes (27, 67), and by histological descriptions of the tissue (72, 73).

Ussing & Zerahn (247) reported that ADH increased the rate of active Na^+ transport across frog skin. These data were later integrated into the dual-barrier hypothesis by supposing that the hormone increased the Na^+ entry step at apical surfaces (2), which was presumed to be the rate-limiting factor in controlling net Na^+ transport. The same general observations were made in the toad bladder by Leaf et al (85, 146–148), who also proposed that ADH increased the Na^+ permeability of the outer (154, 155) or inner (148) barrier of apical surfaces. Thus an ADH-mediated increase in intracellular Na^+ was presumed to increase Na^+ pump rates, both in amphibian skin (2, 45, 140) and in toad bladder (85, 146–148).

Three other observations provided support for this view. First, the apparent total tissue Na^+ pool increased with ADH stimulation (42, 45, 85). Second, net Na^+ transport and the apparent epithelial Na^+ pool both increased as the apical Na^+ concentration increased (42, 45, 85, 86, 138, 140). Finally, microelectrode studies showed that the apical surface had a considerably higher electrical resistance than the basolateral surface, and that ADH decreased the resistance of the apical membrane of epithelial cells with little change in the resistance of the basilar membrane (36, 202).

Clearly, the Koefoed-Johnsen–Ussing model (140) is conceptually formidable, seductive because of its simplicity, and entirely consistent with the dual-barrier hypothesis for the action of ADH on amphibian transport processes (2, 45, 85, 110, 111, 146–148, 154, 155, 165). However, more recent observations indicate that both the basic mechanism of transepithelial Na^+ transport and its modification by ADH may be appreciably more complex. We now consider some reservations concerning the Koefoed-Johnsen–Ussing model, particularly as they relate to the possible mode of action of ADH on Na^+ transport.

THE Na^+ TRANSPORT POOL   One of the major findings supporting an action of ADH on Na^+ permeation across apical surfaces of amphibian epithelia has been the finding of increased tissue Na^+ concentrations after ADH stimulation (36, 42, 45, 85, 86, 202). However, all such experiments are complicated by the possibility that, within intact epithelia, Na^+ may segregate into a number of pools not directly involved in active Na^+ transport, including Na^+ in intercellular spaces, Na^+ in nontransporting cells such as cornified epithelial cells and serosal cells, and Na^+ present in transporting cells but not involved with the functional Na^+ transport pool. Thus, although several investigators found an approximate doubling of tissue Na^+ with ADH stimulation (42, 45, 85), the location of this increased Na^+ pool could not be defined explicitly. Subsequently, Cereijido et al (28) showed that conventional methods of subtracting the 40–80 min inulin volume of distribution as a correction for extracellular Na^+ were not valid, since the inulin space varies widely in the presence and absence of ADH (178). Indeed, it would seem that the small volume of transporting mucosal cells, with respect to the total cell pool in amphibian epithelia, would lead to overwhelming errors in determining the ion content of transporting cells. To be sure, statistically significant increases in total tissue Na^+ may be shown with ADH stimulation. The problem is to clarify whether, in fact, such increases occur within transporting epithelial cells as a consequence of increased apical Na^+ entry.

Several groups of investigators have attempted to answer this question by observing the effect of ADH on the cellular ion content of isolated epithelial cells. In such studies, sheets of epithelial cells are scraped from the mucosal surfaces of toad hemibladders with or without treatment by collagenase (91, 103, 157, 162). In three studies (91, 103, 162), ADH increased mucosal cell Na^+ and water and decreased cell K^+. However, Lipton & Edelman (157) found that the cell water and ion content of scraped epithelial cells were the same whether the scraped cells were exposed to ADH or not. In this regard, Gatzy & Berndt (91) have pointed out that epithelial cells damaged by scraping might accumulate sufficient Na^+ to mask any ADH effect. Such an explanation may not be applicable to the results of Lipton & Edelman (157), as their scraped epithelial cells, which did not respond to ADH, had the same Na^+ content as scraped cells that did accumulate Na^+ in the presence of ADH (91, 103, 162). However, even scraped mucosal cells in toad bladder may not reflect accurately the effect of ADH on Na^+ entry, as all mucosal cells of toad bladder may not be ADH responsive, e.g. DiBona and co-workers (35, 58) provided evidence that, in toad bladder, ADH may stimulate Na^+ transport only in granular rather than all mucosal cells.

Yet another factor complicates analyses of ADH effects on Na^+ transport in amphibian epithelia, i.e. the possibility that total intracellular Na^+ may have little to do with the effective Na^+ transport pool. Two explanations might account for such a view. First, the early studies of Krogh (142, 143) demonstrated net NaCl uptake into intact frogs from solutions containing as little as 10^{-5} M NaCl. The same results have been obtained in isolated frog skin (242–244) and toad bladder (85) using solutions containing as little as 1 mM Na^+. In these cases it might be argued that Na^+ entry across apical surfaces occurs against an electrochemical potential gradient, even though the electrical potential difference across apical surfaces may be negative (cell with respect to apical solution), since intracellular Na^+ concentrations are in the range 20–50 mM (31). However, the possibility seems unlikely; Farquhar & Palade (74) have shown that transport ATPase in amphibian epithelia is localized entirely to basilar and lateral membranes. Thus it is reasonable to infer that there may be multiple Na^+ pools in amphibian epithelian cells (85).

NMR studies indicate that a large fraction of total tissue Na^+ is bound (209), and tracer kinetic studies indicate that only a small fraction of total tissue Na^+ (8–30%) participates in transepithelial transport (29, 30, 79–81). The existence of a small Na^+ transport pool is also supported by the recent experiments of Macknight et al (160, 161) on isolated toad bladder epithelial cells, which indicate that the transport Na^+ pool is only about 20% of total cell Na^+. To make the matter more complex, Cereijido & Rotunno (30) have postulated that the Na^+ transport pool may be either extracellular, or localized to a small intracellular membrane-bound compartment distributed over most of the epithelial cell layer. If their hypothesis is correct, transepithelial Na^+ transport may not involve the Na-K pump, which maintains cell volume (cf also 38, 128).

Regardless of the size of the cellular Na^+ transport pool, net transepithelial Na^+ flux depends on the rate of Na^+ entry across apical surfaces. Both in frog skin and in toad bladder, net Na^+ transport increases in proportion to the Na^+ concentration in apical solutions, reaching a plateau at apical Na^+ concentrations of 30–50 mM (85, 138). The increases in apical solution Na^+ concentrations affect mainly the rate of Na^+ entry into the epithelium, since Kidder et al (137) have shown that the short-circuit current increase that follows an increase in apical solution Na^+ concentrations occurs within 600 msec, i.e. approximately the time required for diffusion from apical solutions to basolateral surfaces. The saturating effect of higher Na^+ concentrations in apical solutions may in principle reflect either a facilitated mechanism for apical entry or pump saturation when the transport pool is sufficiently enlarged. At present, the former conclusion appears warranted, since amiloride, a specific inhibitor of Na^+ entry across apical surfaces, reduces net Na^+ transport (11, 16) and observations on Na^+ uptake on the outer surface of frog skin support the view that apical surfaces contain saturable Na^+ carriers (18).

MICROELECTRODE STUDIES   Another approach to localizing the membrane site of ADH action has been the use of microelectrodes to record separately conductance changes across apical and basilar surfaces of amphibian epithelia. The initial results of Engbaek & Hoshiko (67) in frog skin and of Frazier (84) in toad bladder demonstrated an apparent two-step drop in potential consistent with the Koefoed-Johnsen–Ussing model (140). Cereijido & Curran (27) confirmed that luminal surfaces in frog skin behaved like Na^+ electrodes, but the transepithelial voltage changes in response to variations in serosal K^+ concentrations were only half those expected if basolateral surfaces were equivalent to K^+ electrodes. The results were interpreted to indicate either (a) rapid changes in intracellular ion pools; (b) the presence of several epithelial cell layers; or (c) the presence of an extracellular shunt conductance (246).

In their original work, Ussing & Zerahn (247) demonstrated that ADH lowered transepithelial resistance without affecting apparent pump capacity (i.e. the sodium electromotive force). This result was confirmed in the toad bladder by Civan & Hoffman (37). Similarly, more recent studies with microelectrodes inserted into epithelial cells of intact toad bladder (36) and separated epithelial cell layers of toad skin (202) have shown that almost all of the ADH-dependent decrease in transepithelial resistance observed with ADH is referable to conductance increases across apical membranes with little change in the resistance of basolateral membranes. These data, in combination with the fact that apical membranes are very nearly equivalent to Na^+ electrodes (27, 67, 84, 140), constitute the most direct demonstration that ADH increases the Na^+ permeability of the luminal border of such epithelia.

A DUAL EFFECT OF ADH ON Na^+ TRANSPORT   There are numerous indications that, in amphibian epithelia, ADH not only increases the Na^+ permeability of apical surfaces, but also augments active Na^+ pumping. Morel & Bastide (174) reported that, in untreated frog skin, net Na^+ flux was directed from basolateral to apical surfaces when the apical solutions contained less than 1 mM Na^+; however, the addition of ADH reversed the direction of net Na^+ flux. These workers deduced that such results required a stimulatory effect of ADH on active Na^+ efflux at basolateral surfaces. In another type of experiment, Janáček et al (127, 128) prevented changes in apical Na^+ entry by covering apical surfaces of frog bladders with liquid paraffin while incubating basolateral surfaces in normal amphibian Ringer solutions; ADH resulted in both NaCl and KCl extrusion and a decrease in cell volume. Since Na^+ left the cells against an electrochemical potential gradient, a direct action of ADH on active Na^+ pumping was inferred. Finn (78) noted that, in the presence of amphotericin B, the Na^+ pump in toad bladder saturates at a mucosal Na^+ concentration of 113 mM, and entry across the luminal border is no longer rate limiting; nevertheless, ADH increased net Na^+ transport, presumably by increasing pump action. Similarly, Frazier, Dempsey & Leaf (85) showed that ADH increased net Na^+ transport at apparently saturating mucosal Na^+ concentrations.

Other investigators (45, 78–81) have attempted to evaluate, by compartmental analysis of tracer kinetic data, the possibility that ADH promotes both passive apical Na^+ entry and active basolateral Na^+ efflux. Such models generally include three compartments (apical solution, cell, and basolateral solution) and influx and efflux Na^+ rate constants for, respectively, apical and basolateral surfaces. Curran, Herrera & Flanigan (45), in studying the kinetics of tracer Na^+ uptake in frog skin, found that the primary action of ADH on Na^+ transport was on mucosal entry and not on active serosal efflux. However, as pointed out by Finn & Rockoff (81), it is unlikely that such studies observe more than a single exponential time course for tracer sodium equilibration.

Finn & Rockoff (81), instead of using tracer Na^+ uptake kinetics, have observed the rate of Na^+ washout from tracer-loaded toad bladders using a rapid time resolution method. These experiments have resulted in the identification of three cellular sodium pools, one of which has been taken to be the Na^+ transport pool. The data of these workers (79–81) show that, in untreated bladders, access of Na^+ to the transport pool is ten times more rapid through apical than through basolateral membranes. In the presence of ADH, dual effects are observed (79): first, an increase in the rate constant for apical Na^+ entry, thereby increasing the size of the Na^+ transport pool; and second, an increased rate of active Na^+ pumping across the serosal border. Finn (80) suggested that apical and basolateral membranes "signal" transport changes in the opposite membrane through unidentified pathways, and argued that, if this is the case, both ADH and ouabain might have dual effects on Na^+ transport, i.e. each agent would affect Na^+ transport across apical and basolateral surfaces. Other workers have made similar suggestions. Janáček, Rybová & Slaviková (128), have postulated that, in frog bladder, two Na^+ transport pumps exist: one is a ouabain-inhibitable Na/K exchange pump, which depends on the presence of serosal K^+, and the other a ouabain- and K^+-insensitive pump concerned with cell volume regulation and inhibited by dinitrophenol. Finally, Civan, Kedem & Leaf (38) have also suggested the possibility of parallel and independent Na^+ transport pathways.

In short, the complexities and possibilities of multiple sodium pathways in amphibian epithelia cannot at present be separated into a model with Na^+ pools bounded by discrete anatomical borders whose transport properties are individually described. However, it seems reasonable to infer that, in amphibian epithelia, ADH stimulates both passive Na^+ entry at apical surfaces and active Na^+ efflux at basolateral surfaces. Although there is no explicit information concerning the molecular mechanism by which ADH effects these changes, certain general conclusions concerning Na^+ entry at apical surfaces can be considered.

First, a number of observations (Table 2) indicate that, in toad bladder, the effects of ADH on Na^+, amide, water, and lipophilic solute permeation are dissociable; the most notable of these are (*a*) inhibition of urea, but not Na^+, water, or lipophilic solute transport by phloretin and tanning agents (149, 150, 225); and (*b*) inhibition of Na^+ but not water transport by amiloride (11), verapamil (13), and Li^+ (14). Second, the apparent saturation of Na^+ entry across amphibian apical membranes at apical solution Na^+ concentrations of 30–50 mM (85, 137, 138) is consistent with the possibility that these surfaces contain saturable transport systems (18), or, in currently fashionable terms, Na^+ channels and/or ionophores. Thus it is tempting to speculate that, in toad bladder, where ADH promotes Na^+ but not K^+ transport (148), the hormone might activate, or accelerate the turnover number for, Na^+-specific ionophores and/or channels in apical plasma membranes. Third, regardless of the molecular processes by which ADH promotes passive Na^+ entry at apical surfaces in amphibian epithelia, it is clear that, in mammalian cortical collecting tubules, ADH exerts no consistent effect on Na^+ transport or electrical resistance [Table 1; (87, 115)], but has similar effects on water and lipophilic solute transport in rabbit cortical collecting tubules (Table 1; 1, 96, 97, 219) and in toad urinary bladder (Table 1; 108, 110, 148, 198). Thus we conclude that, in apical plasma membranes of ADH-sensitive epithelial cells, water and certain lipophilic solutes traverse a pathway in parallel with the Na^+ permeation route. In amphibian epithelia, ADH activates both systems; in mammalian cortical collecting tubules, the hormone stimulates the water and lipophilic solute permeation route but not the Na^+ permeation pathway.

The Action of ADH on Water Permeation

Given the fact that apical surfaces of ADH-sensitive epithelia are rate limiting to water permeation (35, 96, 162, 163, 165, 214, 215), the principal reasons for assuming that apical plasma membranes in amphibian skin contain pores enlarged by ADH include P_f/P_{D_W} ratios in excess of unity, which rise in the presence of ADH (96, 110, 139, 214); demonstration of apparent solvent drag for urea and other small amides (2, 148); and arguments based on the apparent effect of ADH on the activation energy for water diffusion (111). In the preceding sections of this review, we summarized evidence consistent with the view that apical plasma membranes contain parallel permeation routes for, respectively, Na^+, urea and other amides, water, and lipophilic solute permeation. In amphibian epithelia, ADH activates each permeation route; in mammalian cortical collecting tubules, ADH activates only the water and lipophilic solute permeation route. In the present section, we consider the possibility that water and lipophilic solute transport in these epithelia, and the action of ADH on these processes, may be rationalized in terms of a solubility-diffusion process through the lipid regions of apical plasma membranes.

THE P_f/P_{D_w} RATIO   Dainty (46) first suggested that bulk-phase unstirred layers might account for the disparity between P_f and P_{D_w} in synthetic and biological membranes. According to this view, P_f is Pm_w, the true diffusional permeability coefficient for water within a membrane. Thus, for a single membrane in series with bulk-phase unstirred layers, e.g. a planar lipid bilayer membrane, equation 6 may be written as:

$$\frac{1}{P_{D_w}} = \frac{1}{P_f} + \frac{\alpha}{D_w^o}. \qquad 8.$$

Cass & Finkelstein (26) first observed that, when bulk aqueous phases were stirred vigorously, the P_f/P_{D_w} ratio in lipid bilayer membranes became unity. Andreoli et al (4) observed that P_f and P_{D_w} in native bilayer membranes made from sheep red cell lipids were, respectively 22.9 $\times$ 10^{-4} and 10.4 $\times$ 10^{-4} cm sec^{-1}, despite reasonable degrees of stirring in the aqueous phases. Thus for $D_w^o = 2.36 \times 10^{-5}$ cm^2 sec^{-1}, a diffusional mode of water permeation across these bilayer membranes would have required an α value of 123 $\times$ 10^{-4} cm, i.e., from equation 8:

$$\alpha = \frac{2.36 \times 10^{-5}}{10.4 \times 10^{-4}} - \frac{2.36 \times 10^{-5}}{22.9 \times 10^{-4}} = 123 \times 10^{-4} \text{ cm}, \qquad 9.$$

which approximates, as an interesting coincidence, the thickness of the plastic apertures on which these bilayer membranes were formed (4).

To assess α for this system, Andreoli & Troutman (6) evaluated P_{D_w} when aqueous phase viscosity was varied with sucrose, a solute having a unity reflection coefficient in native bilayer membranes, i.e. they varied the resistance of bulk aqueous phases but not the membranes to tracer diffusion. From the slope of the relationship between $1/P_{D_w}$ and η, these workers calculated an α value of 114 $\times$ 10^{-4} cm, in close accord with 123 $\times$ 10^{-4} cm (cf above) the required value of α from equation 8. Similarly, there is impressive experimental evidence (71,200) that net osmotic water flow across native bilayer membranes is wholly diffusional in nature.

In the case of isolated cortical collecting tubules, the situation is more complex. Schafer & Andreoli (214) observed that P_{D_w}, with or without ADH, was invariant when the impermeant solute dextran was used to raise the aqueous phase viscosity of both perfusing and bathing solutions from 8.6 $\times$ 10^{-3} to 95 $\times$ 10^{-3} poise, i.e. bulk-phase unstirred layer effects (the α term in equation 8) were negligible. Thus for these conditions, cellular constraints to water diffusion (equation 7) may be expressed as:

$$\frac{1}{P_{D_w}} = \frac{1}{P_f} + \frac{\beta \Delta x}{D_w^o}. \qquad 10.$$

The ADH-dependent values of P_f and P_{D_w} were, respectively, 186 $\times$ 10^{-4} and 14.2 $\times$ 10^{-4} cm sec^{-1}; the ADH-independent values of P_f and P_{D_w} were, respectively, 6 $\times$ 10^{-4} and 4.7 $\times$ 10^{-4} cm sec^{-1} (214). Table 4 summarizes these data and shows that in terms of equation 10, β values of 16–25 are required to rationalize the P_f/P_{D_w} disparity in terms of cellular constraints to diffusion, i.e. by considering osmotic water flow across apical plasma membranes to be wholly diffusional in nature, either with or without hormone.

Table 4 Cellular constraints to diffusion in cortical collecting tubules[a]

ADH	P_f	P_{D_w}	β
	(cm sec^{-1} × 10^4)		
−	6	4.7	16
+	186	14.2	23.6

[a] The values of β required to rationalize the discrepancy between P_f and P_{D_w} according to equation 10 were computed taking ΔX, the thickness of the cell layer in cortical collecting tubules, to be 6.5 × 10^{-4} cm (214) and D_w^o to be 2.36 × 10^{-5} cm^2 sec^{-1}. Adapted from (214).

To test this possibility, Schafer & Andreoli (214) measured the apparent permeability coefficients for the highly lipophilic species butanol, 5-hydroxyindole, and pyridine in cortical collecting tubules. Since these solutes have zero reflection coefficients in cortical collecting tubules (214, 215) and are wholly unstirred layer limited in lipid bilayer membranes (120, 214), it was reasoned that differences between values of P_{D_i} observed for these solutes in cortical collecting tubules and those predicted for free solution would provide an index to the parameter β, i.e. diffusion constraints in cortical collecting tubule cells exclusive of luminal plasma membranes. A comparison of Tables 4 and 5 indicates that the β values computed using these lipophilic solutes were entirely consistent with those required from equation 10 to rationalize the disparity between P_f and P_{D_w} in terms of cellular diffusion constraints. In other words, assuming that the diffusion resistance of the epithelial cell layer (exclusive of luminal plasma membranes) to these lipophilic solutes and to water was comparable, water transport across luminal membranes of cortical collecting tubules, with or without ADH, could be rationalized entirely in terms of a solubility-diffusion process. Several other factors are relevant in this connection.

First, equations 8 and 10 assume that unstirred layers, whether due to bulk phases (the α term in equation 8) or cellular constraints to diffusion (the β term in equation 10), affect P_{D_w} but not P_f. In gall bladder (259), and possibly other electrically leaky epithelia, solute polarization in intercellular spaces and/or bulk unstirred layers may result in substantial underestimates of P_f when the latter is estimated from steady-state osmotic volume flows. Wright et al (259) have provided a dramatic example of this in rabbit gall bladder, by observing that initial rates of osmotic water flow are appreciably greater than steady-state flows.

Schafer, Patlak & Andreoli (218) carried out a theoretical analysis of the "osmotic transient" phenomenon, an experimental study of the process in cortical collecting tubules, and a theoretical and experimental inquiry into the origin of cellular diffusion constraints in cortical collecting tubules. These results may be summarized as follows:

(*a*) In agreement with the deduction of Wright et al (259), unstirred layers may result in drastic understimates of P_f in leaky epithelia. Wright et al (259) calculated P_f values of 30 × 10^{-4} cm sec^{-1} from steady-state osmotic flows, while an evaluation of their osmotic transient data in quantitative terms indicates that P_f for gall bladder may be in the range of 1000×10^{-4} cm sec^{-1} (218). In isolated proximal renal tubules, which have comparable electrical conductances to gall bladder (88) but which are not subject to bulk-phase unstirred layer effects (214), the observed values for P_f during steady-state osmosis are in the range $500-2000 \times 10^{-4}$ cm sec^{-1} (253).

(*b*) In cortical collecting tubules exposed to ADH, no flow transient was detectable, even as early as 20 sec after initiating osmosis (218). Quantitative analysis of these data indicated that cellular constraints to diffusion (even for β values of 25; Tables 4 and 5) resulted in, at a maximum, 10–15% errors in underestimating P_f from steady-state osmotic flows.

(*c*) The origin of β values in the range of 16–25 (Tables 4 and 5) for cortical collecting tubules could be accounted for only in terms of reduction in the area per unit length available for water diffusion in the cell layer, rather than in terms of tortuosity constraints or increased frictional interactions in the cell layer with respect to free solution.

Second, it is instructive to compare ADH-dependent P_f/P_{D_w} ratios in toad bladder and cortical collecting tubules. Hays et al (106, 108) have shown that, by vigorous aqueous phase stirring, the ADH-dependent value of P_{D_w} in intact toad bladder may be raised from 1.7×10^{-4} cm sec^{-1}, the value originally observed in conventional bubble chambers (110), to values in excess of 5×10^{-4} cm sec^{-1} (33, 108); when $1/P_{D_w}$ is plotted against the reciprocal of stirring rate, the zero intercept gives a value of 7.1×10^{-4} cm sec^{-1}, which presumably reflects P_{D_w} for the intact epithelium (106). The bulk-phase unstirred layer thickness required to account for the difference between 1.7×10^{-4} cm sec^{-1} [the ADH-dependent value of P_{D_w} for intact toad bladder observed in conventional bubble chambers (110)], and 7.1×10^{-4} cm sec^{-1} [the ADH-dependent P_{D_w} value for intact toad bladder at infinite stirring rate (106)], is, from equation 6:

$$\alpha = \frac{2.36 \times 10^{-5}}{1.7 \times 10^{-4}} - \frac{2.36 \times 10^{-5}}{7.1 \times 10^{-4}} = 1055 \times 10^{-4} \text{ cm}, \qquad 11.$$

Table 5 Estimation of the parameter β in cortical collecting tubules from the permeability coefficients of highly lipophilic species

Solute	ADH	P_{D_i}[a] (cm sec^{-1} × 10^4)		β
		Observed	Predicted	
Pyridine	−	12.6	146	11.5
	+	13.2	146	11.0
Butanol	−	12.2	154	12.7
	+	12.4	154	12.6
5-hydroxyindole	−	4.03	107.6	26.7
	+	3.94	107.6	28.0

[a] The predicted values for P_{D_i} were computed as $D_i^0/\Delta X$, assuming β (equation 10) to be unity. The parameter β was computed from the ratio of predicted to observed P_{D_i} values. Adapted from (214).

the value listed in Table 3 for total bulk-phase unstirred layer thickness in toad bladder. Note that this value of α does not include the contribution of serosal elements to unstirred layer effects; it does, however, represent the bulk-phase unstirred layer thickness for the experiments in which Hays & Leaf measured apparent solvent drag for urea (148). As shown in Table 6, this value of α is more than adequate to account for the effects of osmotic water flow observed by these workers in the ADH-treated toad bladder, without recourse to coupling of solute and solvent flows within membrane pores.

Even more germane to the present question, the ADH-dependent value of P_{D_w} computed by Hays & Franki (108) for mucosal cells of toad urinary bladder, exclusive of supporting stromal elements, is 10.8×10^{-4} cm sec^{-1} (Table 1). Thus for isolated mucosal cells of toad urinary bladder, the P_f/P_{D_w} ratio [228×10^{-4} cm sec$^{-1}/10.8 \times 10^{-4}$ cm sec^{-1}; (Table 1; 108, 110)] is 21.1, not very different from the ADH-dependent P_f/P_{D_w} ratio or the absolute values for P_f and P_{D_w} in rabbit cortical collecting tubules (Table 1; 96, 97, 214, 218, 219). Since Parisi & Piccini (192) have provided evidence indicating that THO diffusion is impeded significantly in mucosal cells of toad bladder, the ADH-dependent P_f/P_{D_w} ratio of 21.1 in mucosal cells of that tissue (Table 1; 106, 108), as in cortical collecting tubules, may also be referable to cellular constraints to diffusion [i.e. a β value of 16–25 (equation 10, Tables 4 and 5)]. The action of ADH on water permeation in rabbit cortical collecting tubules, toad urinary bladder, and possibly other amphibian epithelia, therefore, may be referable solely to an increase in the rate of water diffusion across apical plasma membranes.

THE SOLVENT DRAG EFFECT   Ussing and co-workers (2, 139) developed the theoretical framework for coupling of solute and solvent flows within aqueous membrane pores and provided an apparent demonstration of the phenomenon for thiourea and acetamide during osmosis in ADH-treated amphibian skin. Subsequently, Leaf & Hays (148) showed apparent solvent drag for urea during osmosis in ADH-treated toad urinary bladder. Both sets of experiments were carried out in conventional chambers, where, judging by the stirring effects obtained by Hays et al (106, 108) on P_{D_w}, the bulk-phase unstirred layer thickness, exclusive of supporting stromal elements (which clearly amplify the problem), was approximately 1055×10^{-4} cm. A number of arguments, both experimental and analytical, now provide strong evidence that the apparent solvent drag effect in ADH-treated amphibian epithelia (2, 148) is referable to bulk-phase unstirred layer effects.

First, Hays (106) compared flux ratios for acetamide in ADH-treated toad bladder using either conventional chambers, in which the apparent ADH-dependent P_{D_w} is 1.7×10^{-4} cm sec^{-1} (110) and apparent solvent drag for urea was first reported (148), or well-stirred chambers in which the apparent ADH-dependent P_{D_w} is in excess of 5×10^{-4} cm sec^{-1} (106, 108). In the conventional chamber, Hays (106) observed apparent solvent drag; at J_v values of 6.95×10^{-5} cm^3 sec^{-1} cm^{-2} (apical to basolateral osmosis with ADH), the flux ratio for acetamide (apical$\longrightarrow$basolateral/basolateral$\longrightarrow$apical) was 1.34, similar to the flux ratio of 1.73 observed for urea (apical$\longrightarrow$basolateral/basolateral$\longrightarrow$apical) in the original studies of Leaf & Hays

(148) at identical J_v values. But when acetamide fluxes were measured in well-stirred chambers, no flux asymmetry for acetamide occurred at comparable rates of net volume flow. Hays concluded that the apparent solvent drag effect may have been referable to unstirred layer effects rather than to coupling of solute and solvent flows within pores (106).

Second, the problem may also be approached analytically, (135, 136). J_i (moles sec^{-1} cm^{-2}), the net flux of the ith solute across a porous membrane separating solutions I and II, is

$$ J_i = Pm_i \, (C_i^{m \, I} - C_i^{m \, II}) + J_v \, (1 - \sigma_i) \, C_i, \qquad 12. $$

where Pm_i is the true diffusional permeability of the ith solute (cf equations 6 and 7), $C_i^{m \, I}$ and $C_i^{m \, II}$ are the concentrations of the ith solute at the membrane-water interfaces with, respectively, solutions I and II, C_i is the mean concentration of the ith solute with membrane pores, and the $J_v \, (1-\sigma_i) \, C_i$ term expresses coupling of solute and solvent flows within pores. In the case of a membrane in series with unstirred layers, it is evident that $C_i^{m \, I}$ and $C_i^{m \, II}$ may not be the same as $C_i^{b \, I}$ and $C_i^{b \, II}$, the bulk phase concentrations in solutions I and II respectively; and, PD_i and Pm_i may not be the same. During osmosis, $C_i^{m \, I}$ and $C_i^{m \, II}$ may change as a result of a "sweeping-away" effect within unstirred layers. Thus the question is to distinguish the true solvent drag phenomenon, i.e. coupling of solute and solvent flows within membrane pores, from changes in the diffusional component of solute flux produced by volume flow-dependent changes in $C_i^{m \, I}$ and $C_i^{m \, II}$.

Andreoli, Schafer & Troutman (5) approached the problem by solving the equation of continuity for a porous membrane in series with unstirred layers. During osmosis, the diffusional component of solute flux (Jd_i) through the membrane is

$$ Jd_i = [C_i^{b \, I} \exp (J_v \alpha^I/D_i^{\circ}) - C_i^{b \, II} \exp (- J_v \alpha^{II}/D_i^{\circ})] \, / $$
$$ \{(1/Pm_i) + (1/J_v)[\exp (J_v \alpha^I/D_i^{\circ}) - \exp (J_v \alpha^{II}/D_i^{\circ})]\}, \qquad 13. $$

and the total solute flux, including diffusion and entrained components, is

$$ J_i = (C_i^{b \, I} \{1 + [J_v(1 - \sigma_i)]/2Pm_i\} \exp (J_v \alpha^I/D_i^{\circ}) - C_i^{b \, II} $$
$$ \{1 - [J_v(1 - \sigma_i)/2Pm_i\} \exp - (J_v \alpha^{II} /D_i^{\circ})) \, / \{(1/Pm_i) + (1 + J_v) $$
$$ [\exp (J_v \alpha^I/D_i^{\circ}) - \exp - (J_v \alpha^{II}/D_i^{\circ})] + [(1 - \sigma_i)/Pm_i] \qquad 14. $$
$$ [\exp (J_v \alpha^I/D_i^{\circ}) + \exp - (J_v \alpha^{II}/D_i^{\circ}) - 2]\}, $$

where α^I and α^{II} are the bulk-phase unstirred layers thicknesses in solutions I and II. In other words, equation 13 describes volume flow-dependent changes in solute flux referable solely to sweeping-away effects in unstirred layers while equation 14 describes the net flux of a solute during osmosis due both to diffusion processes and to coupling of solute and solvent flows within membrane pores.

We now consider the data of Leaf & Hays (148) in terms of equations 13 and 14. During mucosal (solution I) to serosal (solution II) osmosis, they observed a linear relationship between

$$\ln \quad J_{urea}^{I\rightarrow II} / J_{urea}^{II\rightarrow I}$$

and J_v; when J_v was 6.95×10^{-5} cm^3 sec^{-1} cm^{-2}, the flux ratio

$$J_{urea}^{I\rightarrow II} / J_{urea}^{II\rightarrow I}$$

was 1.73. The recent observations of Hays et al on P_{Dw} [(106, 108); cf above] suggest that the bulk-phase unstirred layer thickness (neglecting serosal elements), in the conventional chamber used in the Leaf-Hays experiments (148) was 1055×10^{-4} cm; for convenience, we take α^I and α^{II} each to be 525×10^{-4} cm. The ADH-dependent P_{Durea} value in these experiments was 27.4×10^{-6} cm sec^{-1} (148), which, when corrected according to equation 6 for $\alpha = 1055 \times 10^{-4}$ cm, gives $Pm_{urea} = 35.4 \times 10^{-6}$ cm sec^{-1}; and σ_{urea}, according to Leaf & Hays (148), was 0.79.

Table 6 compares the values for urea flux ratios computed from equations 13 and 14 and the parameters listed above with the flux ratios observed by Leaf & Hays during osmosis in the ADH-treated toad bladder (148). It is evident that the observed flux ratios are in excellent agreement with those predicted from equation 13, and far less than those expected from equation 14, which includes the solvent drag term. In short, those analytical observations, coupled with the recent observations of Hays (106) on the effects of stirring in conventional chambers, provide no evidence for a solvent drag effect in toad bladder, and hence no support for the view that apical plasma membranes of ADH-treated toad bladder contain pores which permit coupling of solvent and solute flows. A similar conclusion may be drawn by carrying out this type of analysis on the apparent solvent drag data of Andersen & Ussing (2). Finally, in lipid bilayer membranes containing 4 Å radii amphotericin B-cholesterol pores (3–6, 120), equations 13 and 14 permit the demonstration of coupling of solute and solvent flows within membrane pores during osmosis, both for glycerol (effective hydrodynamic radius ≈ 3.1 Å) and meso-erythritol (effective

Table 6 An analysis of the apparent solvent drag effect for urea in ADH-treated toad bladder[a]

$J_v^{I\rightarrow II}$	The urea flux ratio $J_{urea}^{I\rightarrow II}/J_{urea}^{II\rightarrow I}$		
	Observed	Predicted	
cm^3 sec^{-1} cm$^{-2} \times 10^5$		Eq. 13 (unstirred layer effect)	Eq. 14 (unstirred layer plus solvent drag)
6.94	1.73	1.78	2.65

[a] The values of J_v and the observed flux ratio for urea are from (148). The predicted flux ratios were computed according to equations 13 and 14 as described in the text.

hydrodynamic radius ≈ 3.6 Å), independent of sweeping-away effects in unstirred layers, i.e. solvent drag may occur in pores having radii of molecular dimensions.

THE ACTIVATION ENERGY FOR WATER DIFFUSION   A major argument in support of the hypothesis that ADH enlarges pores in apical surfaces was the observation of Hays & Leaf (111) that, in intact toad urinary bladder, ADH reduced the activation energy for THO diffusion from 9.8 to 4.1 kcal mole^{-1}, a value comparable to the activation energy for water diffusion in free solution (252). The original interpretation (111) of these experiments was that, without ADH, aqueous pores contained water in a more structured state than in free solution; with ADH, pores enlarged and water assumed the properties of water in free solution. However, the experiments (111), were carried out in conventional chambers, where [as indicated in the above discussion of apparent solvent drag effects (106, 108, 148)] the bulk-phase unstirred layer thickness was 1055×10^{-4} cm (Table 3). Thus, as pointed out by Hays et al (106, 109), the original observations indicating that ADH reduced the activation energy for THO diffusion (111) were probably due to the fact that, with ADH, THO diffusion was rate limited not by epithelial cells and/or interfaces but by bulk-phase unstirred layers.

Hays et al (109) have reevaluated this question by examining the effects of ADH on THO diffusion across toad urinary bladder in chambers designed for varying degrees of aqueous phase stirring. The results that have emerged from these experiments (109) indicate that in intact bladders exposed to vigorous bulk-phase stirring, the activation energies for THO diffusion with and without ADH are, respectively, 10.7 and 9.3 kcal mole^{-1}; when the stirring rate is reduced 14-fold, and ADH-dependent activation energy for THO diffusion in intact toad bladder falls from 9.3 to 6.1 kcal mole^{-1}; finally, in the supporting layer of toad bladder exclusive of epithelial cells, the activation energies for THO diffusion with and without ADH, are respectively, 4.3 and 5.4 kcal mole^{-1}.

Hays et al (109) have drawn two major conclusions from these data. First, they argued that, at low stirring speeds, the activation energies reflect water diffusion in bulk unstirred layers and/or supporting stromal elements. We agree with this view. Second, they suggested that, since the activation energies for water diffusion at high stirring rates are unchanged in the presence and absence of hormone and are appreciably higher than for free solution, ADH does not enlarge pores in apical membranes and proposed that ADH exerts its hydro-osmotic effect by increasing the number of small channels in apical membranes. Because the ADH-dependent activation energy exceeds that for free solution, Hays et al infer that such small channels might contain water in a more organized state than in free solution (109). We do not necessarily agree with this view.

The activation energy for water diffusion across unmodifed lipid bilayer membranes is approximately ≈ 12.7 kcal mole (200), i.e. not very different from the ADH-dependent activation energy for THO diffusion across toad bladders mounted in well-stirred chambers (109), and twice as great as the activation energy for water diffusion in free solution (252). Yet, in unmodified lipid bilayer membranes, there is no component except lipid, and the membranes are virtually impermeable to all molecules except water and lipophilic species (3, 4, 26, 120, 250). The mode of water transport is almost certainly diffusional in nature (3, 4, 6, 26, 71, 99, 120, 200, 250), and, as pointed out later in this review, may easily be explained in terms of a solubility-diffusion process through a hydrocarbon layer equivalent in thickness to a bilayer membrane (26). Thus the high activation energy for water diffusion both in lipid bilayer membranes (200) and in ADH-treated toad bladder might easily be due to factors other than diffusion through aqueous channels containing uniquely organized water.

Price & Thompson (200) pointed out that the activation energy for water diffusion across hydrocarbon interfaces includes the sum of two terms: the enthalpy of water partition into the hydrocarbon region and the energy of activation for water diffusion within the hydrocarbon region. The enthalpy of water partition into various hydrocarbons is approximately 8 kcal mole^{-1} (220, 221), while the activation energy for water diffusion in various hydrocarbons varies from 2.6 to 3.4 kcal mole^{-1} (200, 220, 221). Adding these two terms together, the theoretical activation energy for water transfer through a hydrocarbon interface by a solubility-diffusion mechanism is in the range 10.6–11.4 kcal mole^{-1}, i.e. not very different from the values observed by Price & Thompson (200) in lipid bilayer membranes or by Hays et al (109) in ADH-treated toad bladders mounted in well-stirred chambers. We proposed ADH activates water diffusion through lipid regions of apical plasma membranes, without assuming the presence of small channels containing water more organized than in bulk solution (214, 219). Such a view, in contrast to the small channel hypothesis, is also consistent with the fact that, pari passu with increases in water permeation, ADH also increases the permeability coefficients for relatively lipophilic solutes in apical plasma membranes of toad urinary bladder (198) and rabbit cortical collecting tubles (1).

A Solubility-Diffusion Model for the Hydro-Osmotic Action of ADH

The results described in the preceding section of Part 1 of this review indicate that the effects of ADH on transport processes in ADH-sensitive epithelia are appreciably more complex than originally envisioned by the dual-barrier hypothesis (2, 110, 111, 139, 148).

First, in amphibian epithelia (149, 150, 153, 225) but not in mammalian cortical or outer medullary collecting tubles (20, 96, 97, 215, 218, 219), ADH activates a urea permeation pathway in apical plasma membranes susceptible to inhibition by phloretin, exhibits many of the characteristics of a facilitated transport process, and is dissociable from the effects of the hormone on Na$^+$ transport and water permeation in amphibian epithelia (149, 150, 225; Table 2). Second, in amphibian epithelia (36, 42, 45, 79, 85, 86, 146–148, 154, 155, 247) but not rabbit cortical collecting tubules (87, 115), the hormone increases Na$^+$ permeation through apical plasma membranes by an as yet undefined manner. Based on the apparent saturation effect for Na$^+$ entry into cells of amphibian epithelia (18, 85, 137, 138), we speculate that ADH activates Na$^+$-specific ionophores or channels in apical membranes, whose kinetic properties govern the rate of Na$^+$ entry into cells. However, regardless of the manner in which ADH facilitates Na$^+$ entry into amphibian cells, the data in

Table 2 indicate clearly that the effects of the hormone on apical Na^+ transport in toad urinary bladder are dissociable from those on urea and water permeation. Third, in amphibian epithelia, ADH may also stimulate active Na^+ efflux from basolateral surfaces (38, 80, 128). Fourth, both in amphibian epithelia (2, 110, 139) and in mammalian cortical and outer medullary collecting tubules (96, 97, 214, 215, 218, 219), ADH increases water permeation and, concomitantly, the permeability coefficients for relatively lipophilic species (1, 198) across apical plasma membranes.

These observations are consistent with the view that, in amphibian epithelia, a single apical barrier with parallel transport sites for urea, Na^+, water, and lipophilic solute permeation accounts for the effects of ADH, without recourse to a dual-barrier series model. In mammalian cortical and outer medullary collecting tubules, only the pathway for water and relatively lipophilic solute permeation is enhanced by ADH. Handler & Orloff (103) recently provided evidence that, in toad bladder, cAMP stimulates the phosphorylation of different proteins which specifically activate Na^+ entry, urea transport, and water permeation across apical plasma membranes.

In the case of water permeation, we argued previously (214, 215, 218, 219) that the hydro-osmotic effect of ADH in cortical collecting tubules, and possibly amphibian epithelia, depends on increasing the rate of water diffusion through the lipid region of apical plasma membranes, rather than by enlarging (2, 110, 111, 148) and/or increasing (106, 109) the number of aqueous pores in these interfaces. The evidence for this argument, cited in detail above, includes the following:

(a) In rabbit cortical collecting tubules, the P_f/P_{D_w} discrepancy (214, 215; Table 1) may be rationalized quantitatively in terms of cellular diffusion constraints, i.e. the parameter β in Tables 4 and 5. In mucosal cells from toad bladder (108), the P_f/P_{D_w} ratio and values for P_f and P_{D_w} are nearly identical to those in cortical collecting tubules (Table 1). And mucosal cells of toad bladder significantly hinder THO diffusion in that tissue (192).

(b) In toad urinary bladder, the apparent solvent drag effect (148) is absent when aqueous phases are well stirred (106); the apparent solvent drag effect for toad bladder in conventional unstirred bubble chambers (148) can be accounted for quantitatively by "sweeping-away" effects of volume flow in unstirred layers (Table 6).

(c) The activation energy for water diffusion in toad bladders mounted in well-stirred chambers is approximately 10 kcal mole^{-1} and unaffected by ADH (109). This value is not very different from 12.7 kcal mole^{-1} (200), the activation energy for water transport across native lipid bilayer membranes during osmotic volume flow, and there is strong evidence that water permeation in such bilayer membranes is entirely by a solubility-diffusion process (3, 4, 6, 26, 71, 120, 200, 250).

(d) Finally, both in toad bladder (198) and mammalian cortical collecting tubules (1), ADH-dependent increases in P_f and P_{D_w} are accompanied by increments in P_{D_i} for relatively lipophilic solutes.

In the remaining part of this section, we consider the manner in which ADH might promote increases in the rate of water diffusion in cortical collecting tubules and, presumably, in amphibian epithelia.

If one assumes that P_f in cortical collecting tubules and in amphibian epithelia is equal to Pm_w, the true diffusional permeability coefficient for water in apical plasma membranes, we have:

$$P_f = Pm_w = \frac{K_m D_w^m}{X}, \qquad\qquad 15.$$

where K_m is the partition coefficient for water between aqueous and membrane phases, D_w^m is the diffusion coefficient of water within the membrane phase, and X is the membrane thickness. It is instructive to compare the ADH-dependent and ADH-independent values of P_f in cortical collecting tubules, respectively, 186×10^{-4} and 20×10^{-4} cm sec^{-1} (Table 1), with those predicted for water diffusion through a layer of hydrocarbon solution. For bulk hexadecane, K_m and D_w are, respectively, 0.6×10^{-4} and 4.1×10^{-5} cm^2 sec^{-1} (220, 221), i.e. the diffusion coefficient for water in hexadecane is greater than in more viscous liquid water. Thus for a 60 Å thick layer of bulk hexadecane, i.e. the approximate thickness of a bilayer membrane, equation 15 yields:

$$P_f = [(0.6 \times 10^{-4}) (4.1 \times 10^{-5})]/60 \times 10^{-8} = 41 \times 10^{-4} \text{ cm sec}^{-1}. \qquad 16.$$

Cass & Finkelstein (26) and Price & Thompson (200) have pointed out the close similarity between this P_f value and P_f values observed in synthetic lipid bilayer membranes (3, 6, 26, 71, 99, 120, 200). As previously noted (219), the P_f value computed for bulk hexadecane differs by less than a factor of five from the ADH-dependent and ADH-independent values of P_f in toad urinary bladders or cortical collecting tubules (Table 1), i.e. ADH might be expected to increase water diffusion in apical membranes by modifying hydrophobic regions of these membranes. One presumes that these modifications may also be responsible for the hormone-dependent increases in PD_i for relatively lipophilic species (1,198).

How might ADH exert such an effect? The answer at present is unknown. Yet some speculative notions might be considered. Even in a liquid crystal state, lipid bilayers and/or biomembranes are evidently more organized than bulk hexadecane; thus it is unreasonable to assume that D_w^m (equation 15) in such organized interfaces would exceed that for bulk hexadecane. Moreover, there is, to our knowledge, no evidence that apical plasma membranes could shrink enough to increase P_f from 40×10^{-4} cm sec^{-1} (that predicted for a 60 Å thick layer of hexadecane) to 186×10^{-4} cm sec^{-1} (the ADH-dependent value of P_f in cortical collecting tubules). It is also recognized that, in lipid bilayer membranes, changes in lipid composition— specifically, increased unsaturation of fatty acid chains, reduced fatty acid chain lengths, or reductions in membrane cholesterol (99)—have dramatic effects on P_f. Yet even in lipid bilayers containing short chain unsaturated fatty acid moieties and no cholesterol, the maximum values observed for P_f have been (99) in the range of 60×10^{-4} cm sec^{-1}, i.e. substantially less than 186×10^{-4} cm sec^{-1}. Finally, the hydro-osmotic effects of ADH in rabbit cortical collecting tubules occur within 5 min

(96, 214), and we find it intuitively difficult to envision, for a mammalian membrane, turnover of membrane lipid components or synthesis of new proteins within that time span. Thus we concluded (219) that, in cortical collecting tubules and possibly amphibian epithelia, ADH increases water diffusion through apical membranes by an effect on the K_m term in equation 15. It is not unreasonable to suppose that the ADH-dependent increases in lipophilic solute permeation (1,198) and the deformability of apical membranes in cortial collecting tubules (95) might also be referable to increase in K_m.

Two final possibilities should be considered. First, there is now abundant evidence that both synthetic bilayers and living biomembranes undergo phase transitions from condensed crystalline arrays to the liquid crystal state (68, 70, 122, 158, 208, 211, 229, 249). In the transition from crystalline to liquid crystal state, membranes become more fluid and less well ordered, and membrane phospholipids acquire greater degrees of rotational and translational mobility (68, 158, 211). Träuble (237) has provided a quantitative account of these effects, describing in picturesque terms the formation of increasing numbers of "kinks," or molecular cavities, within less ordered liquid crystal phases. ADH may increase apical membrane fluidity and K_m by promoting a redistribution of proteins and/or lipids, particularly sterols, which have a condensing effect on membrane structure (50, 92, 99, 171) and reduce water permeation in bilayer membranes (77, 99). Second, as cited in Part 2 of this review, Masur et al (170) observed that, in toad bladder, ADH or dibutyryl cAMP increase the numbers of secretory granules in continuity with apical plasma membranes. Such a phenomenon might, in effect, increase the effective surface area and/or fluidity of apical membranes, and hence K_m. Clearly, these possibilities deserve further consideration.

PART 2

The Role of Intracellular cAMP in ADH Action

It is widely accepted that the effects of ADH on transport processes in hormone-sensitive epithelia are mediated in accord with the second messenger hypothesis (231): ADH binds to receptors on basolateral surfaces of responsive epithelial cells and results in an adenyl cyclase-mediated acceleration of cAMP synthesis from ATP. The evidence for this chain of events has been reviewed extensively, both in regard to ADH-receptor interactions (15, 43) and control of cellular cAMP levels in amphibian epithelia and mammalian renal tubules (15, 75, 104, 112, 205). In this section, we mention briefly the major aspects of this theory as a prelude to an analysis of recent investigations which bear on the ways in which cAMP may change membrane transport processes in ADH-responsive cells. These mechanisms may involve at least two sets of processes: the kinetics of membrane-bound protein phosphorylation-dephosphorylation reactions; and microtubule and microfilament structures within these cells.

The hypothesis that the physiological effects of ADH on hormone-sensitive epithelia are dependent on cAMP was proposed originally by Orloff & Handler (182,

183), who observed that application of cAMP or theophylline [an inhibitor of cyclic nucleotide phosphodiesterase (21)] to toad bladder brought about changes in Na^+ and water transport (101, 172, 182, 183, 241) identical to those observed with ADH. This finding has been documented by subsequent work in a number of intact tissues, including isolated mammalian cortical collecting tubules (96, 97) and the in vivo rabbit (8).

The hypothesis has been supported further by the finding that ADH increases cAMP levels in whole toad bladder (101, 184, 230). Similarly, the hormone raises adenyl cyclase activity in tissue slices, cell homogenates, and membrane fractions of mammalian renal medulla (22, 32, 59, 63, 65, 184), but not in comparable preprations from mammalian renal cortex (32). The receptor-ADH interaction has been shown to be both tissue and hormone specific (19, 62), and localized to basolateral but not apical membranes (222). Cellular adenyl cyclase activity is also proportional to the degree of hormone binding on receptor sites (19, 201).

Orloff & Handler (104, 184) have pointed out that modulation of ADH effects may occur at one or any combination of four steps: (a) hormone-receptor interactions; (b) adenyl cyclase activity, (c) cAMP dephosphorylation mediated by cyclic nucleotide phosphodiesterase; and (d) the coupling of cAMP to cellular mechanisms responsible for changes in membrane transport processes. To this list should be added the actual cell concentration of cAMP, which depends, among other factors, upon cell volume and the rate at which cAMP exits from the cell (240). Clearly, these factors all have importance in understanding the ways in which physiological, pathological, and pharmacological vectors may alter an organism's response to ADH.

Although the mediation of ADH action by cAMP is both well supported and widely accepted, there are also reports showing direct effects of antidiuretic hormone on membrane permeability that are independent of cAMP. Graziani & Livne (98, 100) have reported that, in lecithin bilayer membranes, 5–50 μU ml^{-1} pitressin or lysine-vasopressin raise P_f from 25×10^{-4} to approximately 46×10^{-4} cm sec^{-1}. These doses are well within the range effective in the isolated cortical collecting tubule (97, 214) and far lower than those required for amphibian epithelia (2, 110, 111, 148). In the same bilayer system (98, 100), cAMP, oxytocin, or a mixture of the amino acids present in vasopressin do not affect P_f, but Ca^{2+} and prostaglandin E_1 inhibit the hydro-osmotic action of ADH in an apparently competitive manner. ADH does not alter the electrical conductance of these bilayers in NaCl solutions (98, 100). Graziani & Livne (98, 100) have attributed these effects to the formation of ADH-lipid complexes in bilayer membranes which mediate hydro-osmotic but not electrical conductance effects. Fettiplace, Haydon & Knowles (76) reported that 5–10 units/ml lysine-8-vasopressin produce 10–100-fold increases in the electrical conductance of bilayer membranes formed from lecithin-hexadecane or lecithin-decane solutions. With the lecithin-decane system, a significant effect occurs only at pH values below 3.0; with lecithin-hexadecane membranes, the effect is seen at pH 5.6. Fettiplace et al (76) have also observed that comparable ADH concentrations increase P_f in lipid bilayers from 45×10^{-4} to 95×10^{-4} cm sec^{-1}. Finally, both oxytocin and vasotocin bind to various lipid monolayers (213). The relevance of these observations to the effects of ADH on biomembranes is at present indeterminate.

Under appropriate conditions, the application of ADH to apical surfaces may also affect electrolyte and water transport in biological systems. Pietras & Wright (197) observed that, with La^{3+} in apical solutions, ADH increases short-circuit current and P_f in toad urinary bladder by, respectively, 180% and 125%. Presumably, La^{3+} screens membrane-bound ionic groups and allows ADH interaction with apical membranes (197). These effects seem to be far removed from the actions of the hormone under physiological conditions and offer, in our view, no significant exception to the hypothesis that ADH operates in vivo exclusively by binding to basolateral surfaces.

The Link Between cAMP and Membrane Permeability Changes

PROTEIN PHOSPHORYLATION-DEPHOSPHORYLATION REACTIONS   In the last five years, a provocative body of evidence has accumulated which may eventually clarify the link between cAMP and the changes in membrane transport processes observed in the presence of ADH. In their early studies, Handler & Orloff (102) observed that ADH activated a phosphorylase in toad urinary bladder, an effect reminiscent of the action of epinephrine in liver and muscle, which increases cAMP-mediated phosphorylation (232). Cunningham (44) later suggested that cAMP accelerated phosphorylation of an endoplasmic reticulum fraction isolated for dog renal medulla. More recently, Handler & Orloff (103) proposed that a protein kinase is both activated by cAMP and coupled to specific and separate protein components involved in the water, urea, and Na^+ permeability response to ADH. Inhibitors of both RNA and protein synthesis decreased the hydro-osmotic and Na^+ transport response of toad bladder to ADH, due presumably to diminished availability of these specific proteins.

The presence of such a protein kinase activated by cAMP has now been demonstrated in frog bladder (129) and numerous other tissues (144). Forte et al (82) have shown that cAMP enhances phosphorylation of plasma membranes isolated from hog renal cortex, an effect presumably involved in the cAMP-mediated action of parathyroid hormone on renal proximal tubule (173). Similarly, Dousa et al (64), using homogenates of bovine renal medulla, demonstrated the presence of a cAMP-activated protein kinase; a membrane protein fraction that could serve as a phosphate acceptor; and a protein phosphatase whose activity was not altered by changes in cAMP. Thus one might envision that cAMP exerts its effects on the transport properties of apical membranes of ADH-sensitive cells by accelerating the rate of phosphorylation but not dephosphorylation of specific proteins. The latter, in turn, exert separate, direct effects on the parallel permeation routes for, respectively, urea and small amides, Na^+, water, and lipophilic solutes in apical plasma membranes (cf Part 1).

By utilizing free-flow electrophoresis to separate apical and basolateral fractions of bovine collecting duct epithelial cell membranes (113), Schwartz et al (222) have recently demonstrated that, while adenyl cyclase activity was associated exclusively with basolateral membranes, the apical membrane fraction contained a cAMP-sensitive membrane-bound protein kinase, as well as the protein which was phosphorylated by the kinase system. These results support the possibility that protein phosphorylation is enhanced by cAMP, and that the phosphorylated proteins are bound to apical membranes, i.e. those membranes whose permeability properties are altered by basolateral addition of ADH.

In contrast, DeLorenzo et al (51, 52) noted that the phosphorylation of a specific protein fraction (protein D) was decreased by ADH and cAMP, apparently as a consequence of activating the protein phosphorylase described by Dousa et al (64). DeLorenzo et al (52) also have shown that the decreased phosphorylation of protein D in the presence of ADH or cAMP precedes the increases in electrical potential difference produced by these agents across the toad bladder. As yet, the relevance of these results, which seem to conflict with data favoring cAMP-mediated protein phosphorylation (64, 82, 103, 129, 144, 222), is unresolved.

MICROTUBULES AND MICROFILAMENTS AND THE RESPONSE TO ADH   The second line of evidence regarding the cellular mechanism of cAMP action concerns effects on cell microtubule and microfilament systems [for an excellent recent review of the former, see (181)]. Microtubules are involved in at least five diverse cellular functions: chromosome movement in mitosis and meiosis; intracellular transport of organelles, vesicles, and various granules; cell shape; cell motility; and cellular sensory transduction (181). The role of microtubules and microfilaments in the action of ADH has been investigated almost exclusively with the use of the vinca alkaloids, vinblastine and vincristine, and of colchicine. These agents inhibit microtubule aggregation and are noted for their ability to arrest mitosis in metaphase by disrupting microtubular aggregation. Another agent of interest in such studies is cytochalasin B, a compound isolated from numerous molds. While cytochalasin B does not prevent nuclear cleavage, it arrests mitosis by interfering with cytoplasmic cleavage (cytokinesis); the compound also inhibits cell mobility (25).

Recently, Taylor et al (234) found that colchicine, vinblastine, podophyllotoxin (a similar agent), or cytochalasin B inhibit the hydro-osmotic response of toad urinary bladder to ADH. These authors (234) also observed numerous microtubules and microfilaments within all four types of toad bladder epithelial cells, and suggested that the inhibitory effects of these agents relate to their disruption of these elements. Similar effects of cytochalasin B on the hydro-osmotic response were reported at the same time for frog urinary bladder by Carasso et al (24), who reported additional morphological alterations. Specifically, cytochalasin B elongated microvilli on apical surfaces while shortening and swelling intercellular spaces between adjacent cells (24). The agent altered the distribution of microfilaments associated with lateral membranes. However, these morphological changes were not observed with colchicine, which also inhibits the hydro-osmotic response of this tissue to ADH (24).

Dousa & Barnes (60, 61), using the in vivo rat, extended these observations by showing that colchicine and vinblastine inhibit the antidiuretic response to ADH during water diuresis, with no change in total solute excretion. These effects occur in spite of the fact that neither colchicine nor vinblastine affects renal medullary levels of adenyl cyclase, phosphodiesterase, cAMP-dependent protein kinase or protein phosphatase (60, 61). Thus, the inhibition induced by these agents appears to be subsequent to cAMP production and protein phosphorylation reactions. In contrast to results in toad and frog bladder, Dousa & Barnes find no effect of cytochalasin B on antidiuresis in the rat (60).

ADH-responsive membrane transport processes are certainly not the only transport system altered by these agents. For example, Fyfe & Goldman (90) have shown a reduction in energy-dependent α-aminoisobutyric acid transport into Ehrlich mouse ascites tumor cells by vincristine, vinblastine, and colchicine, which cannot be accounted for by a reduction in the electrochemical potential gradient for Na^+. These workers (89) previously reported that vincristine and vinblastine reduce the energy-dependent efflux of methotrexate from these same cells.

The question is, how might microtubules and/or microfilaments alter the permeability properties of apical membranes of ADH-responsive cells? Wunderlich et al (260) inferred from freeze-fracture data that colchicine impairs the temperature-dependent translational and vertical mobility of membrane-associated particles in the alveolar membrane which lies beneath the plasma membrane of *Tetrahymena pyriformis*. Chevalier et al (34) reported that apical faces of freeze-fractured toad bladders have a decreased number of membrane-associated particles compared to lateral membranes and exposure to ADH resulted in the reversible accumulation of numerous particle aggregates on the cleaved apical membrane. Masur et al (169) noted that, in toad bladder, ADH increased uptake of horseradish peroxidase from apical solutions by endocytosis and also increased rates of exocytosis (170). They postulated that the latter phenomenon might result in addition of secretion granules to apical membranes, since the frequency of membrane continuities between secretion granules and apical plasma membranes is greatly increased by ADH or by dibutyryl cAMP (170).

Although these data are intriguing, their role as the link between cAMP and changes in membrane transport processes in ADH-sensitive epithlia remains uncertain. As pointed out by Dousa & Barnes (61), any or all of the phenomena described above may play a role in ADH action either because microtubules and/or microfilaments are an integral part of the mechanism by which cAMP changes membrane permeability, or because these elements serve a passive or permissive role in ADH action. The resolution of this issue is a fascinating challenge to further research.

Literature Cited

1. Al-Zahid, G., Schafer, J. A., Andreoli, T. E. 1975. The effect of ADH on branched and straight chain lipophilic solute permeation in cortical collecting tubules. *The Physiologist* (Abstr.) 18:120

2. Andersen, B., Ussing, H. H. 1957. Solvent drag on non-electrolytes during osmotic flow through isolated toad skin and its response to antidiuretic hormone. *Acta Physiol. Scand.* 39:228–39

3. Andreoli, T. E. 1973. On the anatomy of amphotericin B-cholesterol pores in lipid bilayer membranes. *Kidney Int.* 4:337–45

4. Andreoli, T. E., Dennis, V. W., Weigl, A. M. 1969. The effect of amphotericin B on the water and nonelectrolyte permeability of thin lipid membranes. *J. Gen. Physiol.* 53:133–56

5. Andreoli, T. E., Schafer, J. A., Troutman, S. L. 1971. Coupling of solute and solvent flows in porous lipid bilayer membranes. *J. Gen. Physiol.* 57:479–93

6. Andreoli, T. E., Troutman, S. L. 1971. An analysis of unstirred layers in series with "tight" and "porous" lipid bilayer membranes. *J. Gen. Physiol.* 57:464–78

7. Archer, A. A., Morel, F., Maetz, J. 1960. Présence d'une vasotocine dans la neurohypophyse de la grenouille (*Rana esculenta*). *Biochim. Biophys. Acta* 42:379–80

8. Barraclough, M. A., Jones, N. F. 1970. Effects of adenosine 3',5'-monophosphate on renal function in the rabbit. *Br. J. Pharmacol.* 40:334–41

9. Benes, I., Kolinská, J., Kotyk, A. 1972. Effect of phloretin on monosaccharide transport in erythrocyte ghosts. *J. Membr. Biol.* 8:303–9

10. Bentley, P. J. 1966. The physiology of the urinary bladder of amphibia. *Biol. Rev.* 41:275–316

11. Bentley, P. J. 1968. Amiloride: a potent inhibitor of sodium transport across the toad bladder. *J. Physiol. London* 195:317–30

12. Bentley, P. J. 1969. Neurohypophyseal hormones in amphibia: a comparison of their actions and storage. *Gen. Comp. Endocrinol.* 13:39–44

13. Bentley, P. J. 1974. Effects of verapamil on the short-circuit current of an epithelial membrane: the toad urinary bladder. *J. Pharmacol. Exp. Ther.* 189:563–69

14. Bentley, P. J., Wasserman, A. 1972. The effects of lithium on the permeability of an epithelial membrane, the toad urinary bladder. *Biochim. Biophys. Acta* 266:285–92

15. Berde, B., ed. 1968. Neurohypophyseal hormones and similar polypeptides. *Handbuch der Pharmakologie*, Vol. 23. New York: Springer-Verlag. 967 pp.

16. Biber, T. U. L. 1971. Effects of changes in transepithelial transport on the uptake of sodium across the outer surface of the frog skin. *J. Gen. Physiol.* 58:131–44

17. Biber, T. U. L., Curran, P. F. 1968. Coupled solute fluxes in toad skin. *J. Gen. Physiol.* 51:606–20

18. Biber, T. U. L., Sanders, M. L. 1973. Influence of transepithelial potential difference on the sodium uptake at the outer surface of the isolated frog skin. *J. Gen. Physiol.* 61:529–51

19. Bockaert, J., Roy, C., Rajerison, R., Jard, S. 1973. Specific binding of (^{3}H) lysine-vasopressin to pig kidney plasma membranes. Relationship of receptor occupancy to adenylate cyclase activation. *J. Biol. Chem.* 248:5922–31

20. Burg, M., Helman, S. I., Grantham, J., Orloff, J. 1970. Effect of vasopressin on the permeability of isolated rabbit cortical collecting tubules to urea, acetamide, and thiourea. In *Urea and the Kidney*, ed. B. Schmidt-Nielsen, D. W. S. Kerr, 193–99. Amsterdam: Excerpta Medica. 495 pp.

21. Butcher, R. W., Sutherland, E. W. 1962. Adenosine 3',5'-phosphate in biological materials. I. Purification and properties of cyclic 3',5'-nucleotide phosphodiesterase and use of this enzyme to characterize adenosine 3',5'-phosphate in human urine. *J. Biol. Chem.* 237:1244–50

22. Campbell, B. J., Woodward, G., Borberg, V. 1972. Calcium-mediated interactions between antidiuretic hormone and renal plasma membranes. *J. Biol. Chem.* 247:6167–75

23. Capraro, V., Bernini, G. 1952. Mechanism of action of extracts of the posthypophysis on water transport through the skin of the frog (*Rana esculenta*). *Nature* 169:454

24. Carasso, N., Favard, P., Bourguet, J. 1973. Action de la cytochalasine B sur la réponse hydrosmotique et l'ultrastructure de la vessie urinaire de la grenouille. *J. Microsc. Paris* 18:383–400

25. Carter, S. B. 1972. The cytochalasins as

research tools in cytology. *Endeavour* 31:77–82

26. Cass, A., Finkelstein, A. 1967. Water permeability of thin lipid membranes. *J. Gen. Physiol.* 50:1765–84

27. Cereijido, M., Curran, P. F. 1965. Intracellular potentials in frog skin. *J. Gen. Physiol.* 48:543–57

28. Cereijido, M., Reisin, I., Rotunno, C. A. 1968. The effect of sodium concentration on the content and distribution of sodium in the frog skin. *J. Physiol. London* 196:237–53

29. Cereijido, M., Rotunno, C. A. 1967. Transport and distribution of sodium across frog skin. *J. Physiol. London* 190:481–97

30. Cereijido, M., Rotunno, C. A. 1968. Fluxes and distribution of sodium in frog skin: a new model. *J. Gen. Physiol.* 51:280s–89s

31. Cereijido, M., Rotunno, C. A. 1970. *Introduction to the Study of Biological Membranes,* 163–81. New York: Gordon & Breach. 261 pp.

32. Chase, L. R., Aurbach, G. D. 1968. Renal adenyl cyclase: anatomically separate sites for parathyroid hormone and vasopressin. *Science* 159:545–47

33. Chauvet, J., Lenci, M. T., Archer, R. 1960. Présence de deux vasopressins dans la neurohypophyse du poulet. *Biochim. Biophys. Acta* 38:571–73

34. Chevalier, J., Bourguet, J., Hugon, J. S. 1974. Membrane associated particles: distribution in frog urinary bladder epithelium at rest and after oxytocin treatment. *Cell Tissue Res.* 152:129–40

35. Civan, M. M., DiBona, D. R. 1974. Pathways for movement of ions and water across toad urinary bladder. II. Site and mode of action of vasopressin. *J. Membr. Biol.* 19:195–220

36. Civan, M. M., Frazier, H. S. 1968. The site of the stimulatory action of vasopressin on sodium transport in toad bladder. *J. Gen. Physiol.* 51:589–605

37. Civan, M. M., Hoffman, R. E. 1971. Effect of aldosterone on electrical resistance of toad bladder. *Am. J. Physiol.* 220:324–28

38. Civan, M. M., Kedem, O., Leaf, A. 1966. Effect of vasopressin on toad bladder under conditions of zero net sodium transport. *Am. J. Physiol.* 211:569–75

39. Collander, R. 1954. The permeability of Nitella cells to non-electrolytes. *Physiol. Plant.* 7:420–45

40. Collander, R. 1959. Das Permeationsvermögen des Pentaerythrits verglichen mit dem des Erythrits. *Physiol. Plant.* 12:139–44

41. Collander, R., Bärlund, H. 1933. Permeabilitätsstudienen an Chara cerotophylla. II. Die Permeabilität für Nichtelectrolyte. *Acta Bot. Fenn.* 11:1–114

42. Crabbé, J., DeWeer, P. 1965. Action of aldosterone and vasopressin on the active transport of sodium by the isolated toad bladder. *J. Physiol. London* 180:560–68

43. Cuatrecasas, P. 1974. Membrane receptors. *Ann. Rev. Biochem.* 43:169–214

44. Cunningham, E. B. 1968. The enhancement of phosphoryl transfer by adenosine 3',5'-monophosphate in the presence of a membranous fraction from canine kidney. *Biochim. Biophys. Acta* 165:574–77

45. Curran, P. F., Herrera, F. C., Flanigan, W. J. 1963. The effect of Ca and antidiuretic hormone on Na transport across frog skin. II. Sites and mechanisms of action. *J. Gen. Physiol.* 46:1011–27

46. Dainty, J. 1963. Water relations of plant cells. *Adv. Bot. Res.* 1:279–326

47. Dainty, J., Ginzburg, B. Z. 1963. Irreversible thermodynamics and frictional models of membrane processes, with particular reference to the cell membrane. *J. Theor. Biol.* 5:256–65

48. Dainty, J., House, C. R. 1966. "Unstirred layers" in frog skin. *J. Physiol. London* 182:66–78

49. Dainty, J., House, C. R. 1966. An examination of the evidence for membrane pores in frog skin. *J. Physiol. London* 185:172–84

50. de Kruyff, B., de Greef, W. J., van Eyk, R. V. W., Demel, R. A., van Deenen, L. L. M. 1973. The effect of different fatty acids and sterol composition on the erythritol flux through the cell membrane of *Acholeplasma laidlawii. Biochim. Biophys. Acta* 298:479–99

51. DeLorenzo, R. J., Greengard, P. 1973. Activation by adenosine 3',5'-monophosphate of a membrane-bound phosphoprotein phosphatase from toad bladder. *Proc. Nat. Acad. Sci. USA* 70:1831–35

52. DeLorenzo, R. J., Walton, K. G., Curran, P. F., Greengard, P. 1973. Regulation of phosphorylation of a specific protein in toad-bladder membrane by antidiuretic hormone and cyclic AMP, and its possible relationship to membrane permeability changes. *Proc. Nat. Acad. Sci. USA* 70:880–84

53. DeSousa, R. C., Gorsso, A., Rufener, C. 1974. Blockade of the hydrosmotic

effect of vasopressin by cytochalasin B. *Experientia* 15:175–77

54. Diamond, J. M. 1966. A rapid method for determining voltage-concentration relations across membranes. *J. Physiol. London* 183:83–100

55. Diamond, J. M., Katz, Y. 1974. Interpretation of nonelectrolyte partition coefficients between dimyristoyl lecithin and water. *J. Membr. Biol.* 17:121–54

56. Diamond, J. M., Wright, E. M. 1969. Biological membranes: the physical basis of ion and non-electrolyte selectivity. *Ann. Rev. Physiol.* 31:581–646

57. DiBona, D. R., Civan, M. M. 1973. Pathways for movement of ions and water across toad urinary bladder. I. Anatomic site of transepithelial shunt pathways. *J. Membr. Biol.* 12:101–28

58. DiBona, D. R., Civan, M. M., Leaf, A. 1969. The cellular specificity of the effect of vasopressin on toad urinary bladder. *J. Membr. Biol.* 1:79–91

59. Dousa, T. P. 1972. Effect of renal medullary solutes on vasopressin-sensitive adenyl cyclase. *Am. J. Physiol.* 222:657–62

60. Dousa, T. P., Barnes, L. D. 1974a. Effects of colchicine (CLC), vinblastine (VBL) and cytochalasin B (CB) on the renal response to vasopressin. *Fed. Proc.* 33:388 (Abstr.)

61. Dousa, T. P., Barnes, L. D. 1974b. Effects of colchicine and vinblastine on the cellular action of vasopressin in mammalian kidney. *J. Clin. Invest.* 54:252–62

62. Dousa, T., Hechter, O., Walter, R., Schwartz, I. L. 1970. [8-arginine]–vasopressionic acid: an inhibitor of rabbit kidney adenyl cyclase. *Science* 167:1134–35

63. Dousa, T., Hechter, O., Walter, R., Schwartz, I. L. 1971. Cyclic 3',5'-AMP dependent phosphorylation of renal medullary plasma membranes. *Fed. Proc.* 30:200 (Abstr.)

64. Dousa, T. P., Sands, H., Hechter, O. 1972. Cyclic AMP-dependent reversible phosphorylation of renal medullary plasma membrane protein. *Endocrinology* 91:757–63

65. Dousa, T. P., Walter, R., Schwartz, I. L., Sands, H., Hechter, O. 1972. Role of cyclic AMP in the action of neurohypophyseal hormones on kidney. *Adv. Cyclic Nucleotide Res.* 1:121–35

66. Eggena, P. 1973. Inhibition of vasopressin-stimulated urea transport across the toad bladder by thiourea. *J. Clin. Invest.* 52:2963–70

67. Engbaek, L., Hoshiko, T. 1957. Electrical potential gradients through frog skin. *Acta Physiol. Scand.* 39:348–55

68. Engelman, D. M. 1970. X-ray diffraction studies of phase transitions in the membrane of *Mycoplasma laidlawii. J. Mol. Biol.* 47:115–17

69. Erlij, D., Martinez-Palomo, A. 1972. Opening of tight junctions in frog skin by hypertonic urea solutions. *J. Membr. Biol.* 9:229–40

70. Esfahani, M., Limbrick, A. R., Knutton, S., Oka, T., Wakil, S. J. 1971. The molecular organization of lipids in the membrane of *Escherichia coli:* Phase transition. *Proc. Nat. Acad. Sci. USA* 68:3180–84

71. Everitt, C. T., Redwood, W. R., Haydon, D. A. 1969. Problem of boundary layers in the exchange diffusion of water across bimolecular lipid membranes. *J. Theor. Biol.* 22:20–32

72. Farquhar, M. G., Palade, G. E. 1963. Junctional complexes in various epithelia. *J. Cell Biol.* 17:375–412

73. Farquhar, M. G., Palade, G. E. 1965. Cell junctions in amphibian skin. *J. Cell Biol.* 26:263–91

74. Farquhar, M. G., Palade, G. E. 1966. Adenosine triphosphotase in amphibian epidermis. *J. Cell Biol.* 30:359–88

75. Ferguson, D. R., Price, R. H. 1972. The actions of cyclic nucleotides on the toad bladder. *Adv. Cyclic Nucleotide Res.* 1:113–19

76. Fettiplace, R., Haydon, D. A., Knowles, C. D. 1971. The action of lysine vasopressin on artificial lipid bilayers. *Proc. Physiol. Soc.* 221:18P-20P

77. Finkelstein, A., Cass, A. 1967. Effect of cholesterol on the water permeability of thin lipid membranes. *Nature* 216:717–18

78. Finn, A. L. 1968. Separate effects of sodium and vasopressin on the sodium pump in toad bladder. *Am. J. Physiol.* 215:849–56

79. Finn, A. L. 1971. The kinetics of sodium transport in the toad bladder. II. Dual effects of vasopressin. *J. Gen. Physiol.* 57:349–62

80. Finn, A. L. 1975. Action of ouabain on sodium transport in toad urinary bladder. Evidence for two pathways for sodium entry. *J. Gen. Physiol.* 65:503–14

81. Finn, A. L., Rockoff, M. L. 1971. The kinetics of sodium transport in the toad bladder. I. Determination of the transport pool. *J. Gen. Physiol.* 57:326–48

82. Forte, L. R., Chao, W. T. H., Walkenbach, R. J., Byington, K. H. 1972. Kidney membrane cyclic AMP receptor and cyclic AMP-dependent protein kinase activities: comparison of plasma membrane and cytoplasmic fractions. *Biochem. Biophys. Res. Commun.* 49: 1510–17

83. Franz, T. J., van Bruggen, J. T. 1967. Hyperosmolality and the net transport of nonelectrolytes in frog skin. *J. Gen. Physiol.* 50:933–45

84. Frazier, H. S. 1962. The electrical potential profile of the isolated toad bladder. *J. Gen. Physiol.* 45:515–28

85. Frazier, H. S., Dempsey, E. F., Leaf, A. 1962. Movement of sodium across the mucosal surface of the isolated toad bladder and its modification by vasopressin. *J. Gen. Physiol.* 45:529–43

86. Frazier, H. S., Leaf, A. 1964. Cellular mechanisms in the control of body fluids. *Medicine* 43:281–89

87. Frindt, G., Burg, M. B. 1972. Effect of vasopressin on sodium transport in renal cortical collecting tubules. *Kidney Int.* 1:224–31

88. Frömter, E., Diamond, J. 1972. Route of passive ion permeation in epithelia. *Nature New Biol.* 235:9–13

89. Fyfe, M. J., Goldman, I. D. 1973. Characteristics of the vincristine-induced augmentation of methotrexate uptake in Ehrlich ascites tumor cells. *J. Biol. Chem.* 248:5067–73

90. Fyfe, M. J., Goldman, I. D. 1975. The relationship between inhibition of uphill α-aminoisobutyric acid transport by vincristine and transmembrane gradients of Na$^+$ and K$^+$ in Ehrlich ascites tumor cells. *Fed. Proc.* 34:250 (Abstr.)

91. Gatzy, J. T., Berndt, W. O. 1968. Isolated epithelial cells of the toad bladder. Their preparation, oxygen consumption and electrolyte content. *J. Gen. Physiol.* 51:770–84

92. Ghosh, D., Williams, M. A., Tinoco, J. 1973. The influence of lecithin structure on their monolayer behavior and interaction with cholesterol. *Biochim. Biophys. Acta* 291:351–62

93. Ginzberg, B. Z., Katchalsky, A. 1963. The frictional coefficients of the flows of nonelectrolytes through artificial membranes. *J. Gen. Physiol.* 47:403–8

94. Gottschalk, C. W., Mylle, M. 1959. Micropuncture study of the mammalian urinary concentrating mechanism: evidence for the countercurrent hypothesis. *Am. J. Physiol.* 196:927–36

95. Grantham, J. J. 1970. Vasopressin: Effect on deformability of urinary surface of collecting duct cells. *Science* 168:1093–95

96. Grantham, J. J., Burg, M. B. 1966. Effect of vasopressin and cyclic AMP on permeability of isolated collecting tubules. *Am. J. Physiol.* 211:255–59

97. Grantham, J. J., Orloff, J. 1968. Effect of prostaglandin E$_1$ on the permeability response of the isolated collecting tubule to vasopressin, adenosine 3',5'-monophosphate, and theophylline. *J. Clin. Invest.* 47:1154–61

98. Graziani, Y., Livne, A. 1971. Vasopressin and water permeability of artificial lipid membranes. *Biochem. Biophys. Res. Commun.* 45:321–26

99. Graziani, V., Livne, A. 1972. Water permeability of lipid bilayer membranes: sterol-lipid interactions. *J. Membr. Biol.* 7:275–84

100. Graziani, Y., Livne, A. 1973. Bilayer lipid membrane as a model for vasopressin, prostaglandin and Ca^{2+} effects on water permeability. *Biochim. Biophys. Acta* 291:612–20

101. Handler, J. S., Butcher, R. W., Sutherland, E. W., Orloff, J. 1965. The effect of vasopressin and of theophylline on the concentration of adenosine-3',5'-phosphate in the urinary bladder of the toad. *J. Biol. Chem.* 240:4524–26

102. Handler, J. S., Orloff, J. 1963. Activation of phosphorylase in toad bladder and mammalian kidney by antidiuretic hormone. *Am. J. Physiol.* 205:298–302

103. Handler, J. S., Orloff, J. 1971. Factors involved in the action of cyclic AMP on the permeability of mammalian kidney and toad urinary bladder. *Ann. NY Acad. Sci.* 185:345–50

104. Handler, J. S., Orloff, J. 1973. The mechanism of action of antidiuretic hormone. In *Handb. Physiol. Sect.* 8, 791–814

105. Hays, R. M. 1968. A new proposal for the action of vasopressin based on studies of a complex synthetic membrane. *J. Gen. Physiol.* 51:385–98

106. Hays, R. M. 1972. The movement of water across vasopressin-sensitive epithelial. In *Current Topics in Membranes and Transport*, ed. F. Bronner, A. Kleinzeller. 3:339–66. New York: Academic. 436 pp.

107. Hays, R. M. 1972b. Independent pathways for water and solute movement across the cell membrane. *J. Membr. Biol.* 10:367–71

108. Hays, R. M., Franki, N. 1970. The role of water diffusion in the action of vasopressin. *J. Membr. Biol.* 2:263–76

109. Hays, R. M., Franki, N., Soberman, R. 1971. Activation energy for water diffusion across the toad bladder: evidence against the pore enlargement hypothesis. *J. Clin. Invest.* 50:1016–18

110. Hays, R. M., Leaf, A. 1962. Studies on the movement of water through the isolated toad bladder and its modification by vasopressin. *J. Gen. Physiol.* 45:905–19

111. Hays, R. M., Leaf, A. 1962. The state of water in the isolated toad bladder in the presence and absence of vasopressin. *J. Gen. Physiol.* 45:933–48

112. Hays, R. M., Levine, S. D. 1974. Vasopressin. *Kidney Int.* 6:307–22

113. Heidrich, H. G., Kinne, R., Kinne-Saffran, E., Hannig, K. 1972. The polarity of the proximal tubule cell in rat kidney. Different surface charges for the brush-border microvilli and plasma membranes from the basal infoldings. *J. Cell Biol.* 54:232–45

114. Heller, H. 1941. Differentiation of an (amphibian) water balance principle of the posterior pituitary gland. *J. Physiol. London* 100:125–41

115. Helman, S. I., Grantham, J. J., Burg, M. B. 1971. Effect of vasopressin on electrical resistance of renal cortical collecting tubules. *Am. J. Physiol.* 220:1825–32

116. Helman, S. I., Miller, D. A. 1974. Edge damage effect on measurements of urea and sodium flux in frog skin. *Am. J. Physiol.* 226:1198–1203

117. Hevesy, G., Hofer, E., Krogh, A. 1935. The permeability of the skin of frogs to water as determined by D_2O and H_2O. *Skand. Arch. Physiol.* 72:199–214

118. Hingson, D. J., Diamond, J. M. 1972. Comparison of nonelectrolyte permeability patterns in several epithelia. *J. Membr. Biol.* 10:93–135

119. Höber, R. 1945. *The Physical Chemistry of Cells and Tissues,* 229–42. Philadelphia: Blakiston. 676 pp.

120. Holz, R., Finkelstein, A. 1970. The water and nonelectrolyte permeability induced in thin lipid membranes by the polyene antibiotics nystatin and amphotericin B. *J. Gen. Physiol.* 56:125–45

121. Horowitz, S. B. Fenichel, I. R. 1964. Solute diffusional specificity in hydrogen bonding systems. *J. Phys. Chem.* 68:3378–85

122. Hubbell, W. L., McConnell, H. M. 1971. Molecular motion in spin-labeled phospholipids and membranes. *J. Am. Chem. Soc.* 93:314–26

123. Jacobs, M. H. 1935. Diffusion processes. *Ergeb. Biol.* 12:1–160

124. Jacquez, J. A. 1963. Carrier-amino acid stoichiometry in amino acid transport in Ehrlich ascites cells. *Biochim. Biophys. Acta* 71:15–33

125. Jacquez, J. A. 1964. The kinetics of carrier-mediated transport: stationary-state approximations. *Biochim. Biophys. Acta* 79:318–28

126. Jaenike, J. R. 1961. The influence of vasopressin on the permeability of the mammalian collecting duct to urea. *J. Clin. Invest.* 30:144–51

127. Janáček, K., Rybová, R. 1970. Nonpolarized frog bladder preparation. The effects of oxytocin. *Pfluegers Arch.* 318:294–304

128. Janáček, K., Kybová, R., Slaviková, M. 1972. Sodium-potassium pump and cell volume regulation in frog bladder. *Biochim. Biophys. Acta* 288:221–24

129. Jard, S., Bastide, F. 1970. A cyclic AMP-dependent protein kinase from frog bladder epithelial cells. *Biochem. Biophys. Res. Commun.* 39:559–66

130. Kaplan, M. A., Hays, R. M., Blumenfeld, O. O. 1975. Membrane proteins and urea and acetamide transport in the human erythrocyte. *J. Membr. Biol.* 20:181–90

131. Kaplan, M. A., Hays, L., Hays, R. M. 1974. Evolution of facilitated diffusion pathway for amides in the erythrocyte. *Am. J. Physiol.* 226:1327–32

132. Katchalsky, A., Curran, P. F. 1967. *Nonequilibrium Thermodynamics in Biophysics,* 123. Cambridge, Mass: Harvard Univ. Press. 248 pp.

133. Katsoyannis, P. G., DuVigneaud, V. 1958. Arginine-vasotocin: a synthetic analogue of the posterior pituitary hormones containing the ring of oxytocin and the side chain of vasopressin. *J. Biol. Chem.* 233:1352–54

134. Katz, Y., Diamond, J. M. 1974. Thermodynamic constants for nonelectrolyte partition between dimyristoyl lecithin and water. *J. Membr. Biol.* 17:101–20

135. Kedem, O., Katchalsky, A. 1958. Thermodynamic analysis of the permeability of biological membranes to non-electrolytes. *Biochim. Biophys. Acta* 27:229–46

136. Kedem, O., Katchalsky, A. 1961. A physical interpretation of the phenomenological coefficients of membrane

permeability. *J. Gen. Physiol.* 45: 143–79

137. Kidder, G. W., Cereijido, M., Curran, P. F. 1964. Transient changes in electrical potentials across frog skin. *Am. J. Physiol.* 207:935–40

138. Kirschner, L. B. 1955. On the mechanism of active sodium transport across the frog skin. *J. Cell Comp. Physiol.* 45:61–87

139. Koefoed-Johnsen, V., Ussing, H. H. 1953. The contributions of diffusion and flow to the passage of D_2O through living membranes. *Acta Physiol. Scand.* 28:60–76

140. Koefoed-Johnsen, V., Ussing, H. H. 1958. The nature of the frog skin potential. *Acta Physiol. Scand.* 42:298–308

141. Kokko, J. P., Rector, F. C. 1972. Countercurrent multiplication system without active transport in inner medulla. *Kidney Int.* 2:214–23

142. Krogh, A. 1937. Osmotic regulation in the frog (*R. esculenta*) by active absorption of chloride ions. *Skand. Arch. Physiol.* 76:60–74

143. Krogh, A. 1938. The active absorption of ions in some fresh water animals. *Z. Vergl. Physiol.* 25:335–50

144. Kuo, J. F., Greengard, P. 1969. Cyclic nucleotide-dependent protein kinases. IV. Widespread occurrence of adenosine 3',5'-monophosphate-dependent protein kinase in various tissues and phylla of the animal kingdom. *Proc. Nat. Acad. Sci. USA* 64:1349–55

145. Leaf, A. 1965. Transepithelial transport and its hormonal control in toad bladder. *Ergeb. Physiol.* 56:216–63

146. Leaf, A., Anderson, J., Page, L. B. 1958. Active sodium transport by the isolated toad bladder. *J. Gen. Physiol.* 41:657–68

147. Leaf, A., Dempsey, E. 1960. Some effects of mammalian neurohypophyseal hormones on metabolism and active transport of sodium by the isolated toad bladder. *J. Biol. Chem.* 235:2160–63

148. Leaf, A., Hays, R. M. 1962. Permeability of the isolated toad bladder to solutes and its modification by vasopressin. *J. Gen. Physiol.* 45:921–32

149. Levine, S., Franki, N., Hays, R. M. 1973a. Effect of phloretin on water and solute movement in the toad bladder. *J. Clin. Invest.* 52:1435–42

150. Levine, S., Franki, N., Hays, R. M. 1973b. A saturable, vasopressin-sensitive carrier for urea and acetamide in the toad bladder epithelial cell. *J. Clin. Invest.* 52:2083–86

151. Levine, S. D., Kaplan, M. D., Franki, N., Myers, J. D., Hays, R. M. 1973. The effect of phloretin on renal urea and sodium transport in Squalus acanthias. *Bull. Mt. Desert Isl. Biol. Lab.* 13:70–71

152. Levine, S. D., Levine, R. D., Worthington, R. E., Hays, R. M. 1975. Selective inhibition of osmotic water flow by methoxyfluorane and halothane. *Clin. Res.* 23:432A (Abstr.)

153. Levine, S. D., Worthington, R. E., Hays, R. M. 1975. Amide transport channels in toad urinary bladder. *Clin. Res.* 23:368A (Abstr.)

154. Lichtenstein, N. S., Leaf, A. 1965. Effect of amphotericin B on the permeability of the toad bladder. *J. Clin. Invest.* 44:1328–42

155. Lichtenstein, N. S., Leaf, A. 1966. Evidence for a double series permeability barrier at the mucosal surface of the toad bladder. *Ann. NY Acad. Sci.* 137:556–65

156. Lipson, L. C., Sharp, G. W. G. 1971. Effect of prostagland in E_1 on sodium transport and osmotic water flow in the toad bladder. *Am. J. Physiol.* 220: 1046–52

157. Lipton, P., Edelman, I. S. 1971. Effects of aldosterone and vasopressin on electrolytes to toad bladder epithelial cells. *Am. J. Physiol.* 221:733–41

158. Luzzati, V. 1968. X-ray diffraction studies of lipid-water systems. In *Biological Membranes: Physical Fact and Function,* ed. D. Chapman, p. 71. London & New York: Academic. 438 pp.

159. Macey, R. I., Farmer, R. E. C. 1970. Inhibition of water and solute permeability in human red cells. *Biochim. Biophys. Acta* 211:104–6

160. Macknight, A. D. C., Civan, M. M., Leaf, A. 1975a. The sodium transport pool in toad urinary bladder epithelial cells. *J. Membr. Biol.* 20:365–86

161. Macknight, A. D. C., Civan, M. M., Leaf, A. 1975b. Some effects of ouabain on cellular ions and water in epithelial cells of toad urinary bladder. *J. Membr. Biol.* 20:387–401

162. Macknight, A. D. C., Leaf, A., Civan, M. M. 1970. Vasopressin: evidence for the cellular site of the induced permeability change. *Biochim. Biophys. Acta* 222:560–63

163. MacRobbie, E. A. C., Ussing, H. H. 1961. Osmotic behaviour of epithelial cells of frog skin. *Acta Physiol. Scand.* 53:348–65

164. Maetz, J. 1963. Physiological aspects of neurohypophyisal (sic) function in fishes with some reference to the Amphibia. *Symp. Zool. Soc. London* 9: 107–40

165. Maffly, R. H., Hays, R. M., Lamdin, E., Leaf, A. 1960. The effect of neurohypophyseal hormones on the permeability of the toad bladder to urea. *J. Clin. Invest.* 39:630–41

166. Mamelak, M., Weissbluth, M., Maffly, R. H. 1970. Effect of chlorpromazine on permeability of toad bladder. *Biochem. Pharmacol.* 19:2303–15

167. Mandel, L. J., Curran, P. F. 1972. Response of the frog skin to steady-state voltage clamping. 1. The shunt pathway. *J. Gen. Physiol.* 59:503–18

168. Marumo, F. 1968. The effect of glucocorticoid on the water permeability of the toad bladder. *Pfluegers Arch.* 299:149–57

169. Masur, S. K., Holtzman, E., Schwartz, I. L., Walter, R. 1971. Correlation between pinocytosis and hydroosmosis induced by neurophypophyseal hormones and mediated by adenosine 3',5'-cyclic monophosphate. *J. Cell Biol.* 49:582–89

170. Masur, S. K., Holtzman, E., Walter, R. 1972. Hormone-stimulated exocytosis in the toad urinary bladder. Some possible implications for turnover of surface membranes. *J. Cell Biol.* 52:211–19

171. McElhaney, R. N., deGier, J., van der Neuf-Kak, E. C. M. 1973. The effect of alterations in fatty acid composition and cholesterol content on the non-electrolyte permeability of *Acholeplasma laidlawii* B cells and derived liposomes. *Biochim. Biophys. Acta* 298:500–12

172. Mendoza, S. A., Handler, J. S., Orloff, J. 1970. Effect of inhibitors of sodium transport on response of toad bladder to ADH and cyclic AMP. *Am. J. Physiol.* 219:1440–45

173. Michelakis, A. M. 1970. Hormonal effects on cyclic AMP in a renal-cell suspension system. *Proc. Soc. Exp. Biol. Med.* 135:13–16

174. Morel, F., Bastide, F. 1965. Action de l'ocytocine sur la composante active der transport de sodium par la peau de grenouille. *Biochim. Biophys. Acta* 94: 609–11

175. Morel, F., Jard, S. 1968. Actions and functions of the neurophyophyseal hormones and related peptides in lower vertebrates. In *Hanbuch der Experimentellen Pharmocologie,* ed. B. Berde. 23:655–716. New York: Springer-Verlag. 967 pp.

176. Morgan, T., Berliner, R. W. 1968. Permeability of the loop of Henle, vasa recta, and collecting duct to water, urea and sodium. *Am. J. Physiol.* 215:108–15

177. Morgan, T., Sakai, F., Berliner, R. W. 1968. In vitro permeability of medullary collecting ducts to water and urea. *Am. J. Physiol.* 214:574–81

178. Natochin, J. V., Janáček, K., Rybová, R. 1965. The swelling of frog bladder cells produced by oxytocin. *J. Endocrinol.* 33:171–77

179. Nernst, W. 1904. Theorie der Reactionsgeschwindigkeit in heterogenen Systemen. *Z. Phys. Chem.* 47:52–55

180. Ohno, T., Goodman, D. B. P., Rasmussen, H., Omura, S. 1974. A new type of sodium transport inhibitor in the toad bladder. *J. Membr. Biol.* 18:295–304

181. Olmsted, J. B., Borisy, G. G. 1973. Microtubules. *Ann. Rev. Biochem.* 42: 507–40

182. Orloff, J., Handler, J. S. 1961. Vasopressin-like effects of adenosine 3'5'-phosphate (cyclic 3',5'-AMP) and theophylline in the toad bladder. *Biochem. Biophys. Res. Commun.* 5:63–66

183. Orloff, J., Handler, J. S. 1962. The similarity of effects of vasopressin adenosine-3',5'-monophosphate (cyclic AMP) and theophylline on the toad bladder. *J. Clin. Invest.* 41:702–9

184. Orloff, J., Handler, J. S. 1967. The role of adenosine 3',5'-phosphate in the action of antidiuretic hormone. *Am. J. Med.* 42:757–68

185. Osterhout, W. J. V. 1933. Permeability in large plant cells and in models. *Ergeb. Physiol.* 35:967–1021

186. Overton, E. 1902. Beitrage zur allgemeinen Muskel und Nerven physiologie. *Pfluegers Arch.* 92:115–280

187. Owen, J. D., Solomon, A. K. 1972. Control of nonelectrolyte permeability in red cells. *Biochim. Biophys. Acta* 290:414–18

188. Owen, J. D., Steggall, M., Eyring, E. M. 1974. The effect of phloretin on red cell nonelectrolyte permeability. *J. Membr. Biol.* 19:79–92

189. Pappenheimer, J. R. 1953. Passage of molecules through capillary walls. *Physiol. Rev.* 33:387–423

190. Pappenheimer, J. R., Renkin, E. M., Borrero, L. M. 1951. Filtration, diffusion and molecular sieving through peripheral capillary membranes. *Am. J. Physiol.* 167:13–46

191. Parker, J. C., Hoffman, J. F. 1965. Interdependence of cation permeability,

cell volume, and metabolism in dog red cells. *Fed. Proc.* 24:589 (Abstr.)

192. Parisi, M., Piccini, Z. F. 1973. The penetration of water into the epithelium of toad urinary bladder and its modification by oxytocin. *J. Membr. Biol.* 12:227–46

193. Parrish, R. G., Kurland, R. J. 1975. Effect of some general anesthetics on water near lipid bilayer surfaces. *Biophys. Soc. Abstr.* 15:303a (Abstr.)

194. Pauling, L. 1961. A molecular theory of general anesthesia. *Science* 134:15–21

195. Persson, E. 1970. Water permeability in rat distal tubules. *Acta Physiol. Scand.* 78:364–75

196. Peterson, M. J., Edelman, I. S. 1964. Calcium inhibition of vasopressin on the urinary bladder of the toad. *J. Clin. Invest.* 43:583–94

197. Pietras, R. J., Wright, E. M. 1974. Effects of mucosal ADH on toad urinary bladder. *Fed. Proc.* 33:216 (Abstr.)

198. Pietras, R. J., Wright, E. M. 1974. Nonelectrolyte probes of membrane structure in ADH-treated toad urinary bladder. *Nature London* 247:222–24

199. Popenoe, E. A., Lawler, H. C., DuVigneaud, V. 1952. Partial purification and amino acid content of vasopressin from hog posterior pituitary glands. *J. Am. Chem. Soc.* 74:3713

200. Price, H. D., Thompson, T. E. 1969. Properties of lipid bilayer membranes separating two aqueous phases: temperature dependence of water permeability. *J. Mol. Biol.* 41:443–57

201. Rajerison, R., Marchetti, J., Roy, C., Bockaert, J., Jard, S. 1974. The vasopressin-sensitive adenylate cyclase of the rat kidney. *J. Biol. Chem.* 249:6390–6400

202. Rawlins, F., Mateu, L., Fragachan, F., Whittenbury, G. 1970. Isolated toad skin epithelium: Transport characteristics. *Pfluegers Arch.* 316:64–80

203. Renkin, E. M. 1955. Filtration, diffusion, and molecular sieving through porous cellulose membranes. *J. Gen. Physiol.* 38:225–43

204. Robbins, E., Mauro, A. 1960. Experimental study of the independence of diffusion and hydrodynamic permeability coefficients in collodion membranes. *J. Gen. Physiol.* 43:523–32

205. Robison, G. A., Nahas, G. G., Triner, L., eds. 1971. Cyclic AMP and cell function. *Ann. NY Acad. Sci.* 185:1–551

206. Rocha, A. S., Kokko, J. P. 1974. Permeability of medullary nephron segments to urea and water: effect of vasopressin. *Kidney Int.* 6:379–87

207. Romualdez, A., Sha'afi, R. I., Lange, Y., Solomon, A. K. 1972. Cation transport in dog red cells. *J. Gen. Physiol.* 60:46–57

208. Rothman, J. E. 1973. The molecular basis of mesomorphic phase transitions in phospholipid systems. *J. Theor. Biol.* 38:1–16

209. Rotunno, C. A., Kowalewski, V., Cereijido, M. 1967. Nuclear spin resonance evidence for complexing of sodium in frog skin. *Biochim. Biophys. Acta* 135:170–73

210. Rubin, M. S. 1975. Chemical modification of vasopressin (ADH)-induced urea transport across toad bladder. *Fed. Proc.* 34:327 (Abstr.)

211. Sackman, E., Träuble, H. 1972. Studies of the crystalline-liquid crystalline phase transition of lipid model membranes. I. Use of spin labels and optical probes as indicators of the phase transition. *J. Am. Chem. Soc.* 94:4482–91

212. Sallee, V. L., Dietschy, J. M. 1973. Determinants of intestinal mucosal uptake of short- and medium-chain fatty acids and alcohols. *J. Lipid Res.* 14:475–84

213. Sanyal, N. N., Snart, R. S. 1967. Absorption of octapeptide hormones onto lipid monolayers. *Nature* 213:798–99

214. Schafer, J. A., Andreoli, T. E. 1972. Cellular constraints to diffusion. The effect of antidiuretic hormone on water flows in isolated mammalian collecting tubules. *J. Clin. Invest.* 51:1264–78

215. Schafer, J. A., Andreoli, T. E. 1972. The effect of antidiuretic hormone on solute flows in isolated mamalian collecting tubules. *J. Clin. Invest.* 51:1279–86

216. Schafer, J. A., Heinz, E. 1971. The effect of reversal of Na^+ and K^+ electrochemical potential gradients on the active transport of amino acids in Ehrlich ascites tumor cells. *Biochim. Biophys. Acta* 249:15–33

217. Schafer, J. A., Jacquez, J. A. 1967. Transport of amino acids in Ehrlich ascites cells: competitive stimulation. *Biochim. Biophys. Acta* 135:741–50

218. Schafer, J. A., Patlak, C. S., Andreoli, T. E. 1974. Osmosis in cortical collecting tubules. A theoretical and experimental analysis of the osmotic transient phenomenon. *J. Gen. Physiol.* 64:201–27

219. Schafer, J. A., Troutman, S. L., Andreoli, T. E. 1974. Osmosis in cortical collecting tubules. ADH-independent

osmotic flow rectification. *J. Gen. Physiol.* 64:228–40

220. Schatzberg, P. 1963. Solubilities of water in several normal alkanes from C_7 to C_{16}. *J. Phys. Chem.* 67:776–79

221. Schatzberg, P. 1965. Diffusion of water through hydrocarbon liquids. *J. Polym. Sci. P. C* 10:87–92

222. Schwartz, I. L., Shlatz, L. J., Kinne-Saffran, E., Kinne, R. 1974. Target cell polarity and membrane phosphorylation in relation to the mechanism of action of antidiuretic hormone. *Proc. Nat. Acad. Sci. USA* 71:2595–99

223. Schwartz, I. L., Walter, R. 1967. Factors influencing the reactivity of the toad bladder to the hydro-osmotic action of vasopressin. *Am. J. Med.* 42:769–76

224. Sha'afi, R. I., Gary-Bobo, C. M., Solomon, A. K. 1971. Permeability of red cell membranes to small hydrophilic and lipophilic solutes. *J. Gen. Physiol.* 58:238–58

225. Shuchter, S. H., Franki, N., Hays, R. M. 1973. The effect of tanning agents on the permeability of the toad bladder to water and solutes. *J. Membr. Biol.* 14:177–91

226. Solomon, A. K. 1968. Characterization of biological membranes by equivalent pores. *J. Gen. Physiol.* 51:335s–64s

227. Solomon, A. K., Gary-Bobo, C. M. 1972. Aqueous pores in lipid bilayers and red cell membranes. *Biochim. Biophys. Acta* 255:1019–21

228. Staverman, A. J. 1951. The theory of measurement of osmotic pressure. *Rec. Trav. Chim. Pays–Bas* 70:344–52

229. Steim, J. M., Tourtellotte, M. E., Reinert, J. C., McElhaney, R. N., Radar, R. L. 1969. Calorimetric evidence for the liquid-crystalline state of lipids in a biomembrane. *Biochemistry* 63:104–9

230. Stoff, J. S., Handler, J. S., Orloff, J. 1972. The effect of aldosterone on the accumulation of adenosine 3',5'-cyclic monophosphate in toad bladder epithelial cells in response to vasopressin and theophylline. *Proc. Nat. Acad. Sci. USA* 69:805–8

231. Sutherland, E. W. 1961–62. The biological role of adenosine-3',5'-phosphate. *Harvey Lect.* 57:17–33

232. Sutherland, E. W., Robison, G. A. 1969. The role of cyclic AMP in the control of carbohydrate metabolism. *Diabetes* 18:797–819

233. Taylor, A. 1975. Effect of quinidine on the action of vasopressin. *Fed. Proc.* 34:285 (Abstr.)

234. Taylor, A., Mamelak, M., Reaven, E., Maffly, R. 1973. Vasopressin: possible role of microtubules and microfilaments in its action. *Science* 181:347–50

235. Teorell, T. 1936. A method of studying conditions within diffusion layers. *J. Biol. Chem.* 113:735–48

236. Thau, G., Block, R., Kedem, O. 1966. Water transport in porous and nonporous membranes. *Desalination* 1:129–38

237. Träuble, H. 1971. The movement of molecules across lipid membranes: A molecular theory. *J. Membr. Biol.* 4:193–208

238. Turner, R. A., Pierce, S. G., DuVigneaud, V. 1951. The purification and the amino acid content of vasopressin preparations. *J. Biol. Chem.* 191:21–28

239. Ullrich, K. J., Rumrich, G., Fuchs, G. 1964. Wasserpermeabilität und transtubulärer Wasserfluss corticales Nephronabschnitte bei verschiedenen Diuresezuständen. *Pfluegers Arch.* 280:99–119

240. Urakabe, S., Handler, J. S., Orloff, J. 1975. Release of cyclic AMP by toad urinary bladder. *Am J. Physiol.* 228:954–58

241. Urakabe, S., Shirai, D. 1970. Effect of vasopressin, cyclic 3',5'-AMP, and chlorpropamide on water permeability of toad urinary bladder. *Med. J. Osaka Univ.* 21:151–59

242. Ussing, H. H. 1948. The use of tracers in the study of active ion transport across animal membranes. *Cold Spring Harbor Symp. Quant. Biol.* 13:193–200

243. Ussing, H. H. 1949a. The active transport through the isolated frog skin in the light of tracer studies. *Acta Physiol. Scand.* 17:1–37

244. Ussing, H. H. 1949b. The distinction by means of tracers between active transport and diffusion. *Acta Physiol. Scand.* 19:43–56

245. Ussing, H. H. 1966. Anomalous transport of electrolytes and sucrose through the isolated frog skin induced by hypertonicity of the outside bathing solution. *Ann. NY Acad. Sci.* 137:543–55

246. Ussing, H. H., Windhager, E. E. 1964. Nature of the shunt pathway through frog skin epithelium. *Acta Physiol. Scand.* 61:484–504

247. Ussing, H. H., Zerahn, K. 1951. Active transport of sodium as the source of electric current in the short-circuited isolated frog skin. *Acta Physiol. Scand.* 23:110–27

248. van Os, C. H., deJong, M. D., Slegers, J. F. G. 1974. Dimensions of polar path-

ways through rabbit gallbladder epithelium. The effect of phloretin on nonelectrolyte permeability. *J. Membr. Biol.* 15:363–82

249. Veksli, Z., Salsbury, N. J., Chapman, D. 1969. Physical studies of phospholipids: XII. Nuclear magnetic resonance studies of molecular motion in some pure lecithin-water systems. *Biochim. Biophys. Acta* 183:434–46

250. Vreeman, H. J. 1966. Permeability of thin phospholipid films. 1. *Koninkl. Nederl. Akademie van Wetenschappen Amsterdam Ser. B* 69:542–77

251. Walter, R., Rudinger, J., Schwartz, I. L. 1967. Chemistry and structure activity relations of the antidiuretic hormones. *Am. J. Med.* 42:653–77

252. Wang, J. H., Robinson, C. V., Edelman, I. S. 1953. Self-diffusion and structure of liquid water. III. Measurement of the self-diffusion of liquid water with H^2, H^3 and O^{18} as tracers. *J. Am. Chem. Soc.* 75:466–70

253. Welling, L. W., Grantham, J. J. 1972. Physical properties of isolated perfused renal tubules and tubular basement membranes. *J. Clin. Invest.* 51:1063–75

254. Wilson, F., Dietschy, J. M. 1972. Characterization of bile acid absorption across the unstirred water layer and brush border of the rat jejunum. *J. Clin. Invest.* 51:3015–25

255. Wright, D. W., Snart, R. S. 1971. Simultaneous measurement of the effect of vasopressin on sodium and water transport across toad bladder. *Life Sci.* 10:301–8

256. Wright, E. M., Diamond, J. M. 1969. Patterns of non-electrolyte permeability. *Proc. R. Soc. Ser. B* 172:227–71

257. Wright, E. M., Pietras, R. J. 1974. Routes of nonelectrolyte permeation across epithelial membranes. *J. Membr. Biol.* 17:293–312

258. Wright, E. M., Prather, J. W. 1970. The permeability of the frog choroid plexus to nonelectrolytes. *J. Memb. Biol.* 2:127–49

259. Wright, E. M., Smulders, A. P., Tormey, J. M. 1972. The role of the lateral intercellular spaces and solute polarization effects on the passive flow of water across the rabbit gallbladder. *J. Membr. Biol.* 7:198–219

260. Wunderlich, F., Müller, R., Speth, V. 1973. Direct evidence for a colchicine-induced impairment in the mobility of membrane components. *Science* 182:1136–38

261. Zerahn, K. 1956. Oxygen consumption and active sodium transport in the isolated and short-circuited frog skin. *Acta Physiol. Scand.* 36:300–18

THE PLATELET: MEMBRANE AND SURFACE REACTIONS

❖1158

H. A. Cooper,[1] *R. G. Mason, and K. M. Brinkhous*[2]
Thrombosis Center and Department of Pathology, University of North Carolina,
Chapel Hill, North Carolina 27514

INTRODUCTION

The platelet plays an essential role in hemostasis and in the preservation of the organism. Without platelets, catastrophic hemorrhage ensues. With full platelet activation, catastrophic thrombosis may occur. Physiologically the platelet helps maintain the integrity of the vascular system by interacting with the vessel wall and other elements of the blood, particularly the procoagulant plasma proteins of the fibrin clotting mechanism. The platelet also participates in the defense mechanism of the body, including the inflammatory and immunologic responses as well as the clearing function of the blood in removal of particulate material such as bacteria. It likewise serves as a vehicle of transport of many materials. Pathologically, the platelet plays a central role in hemorrhage and thrombosis, in the pathogenesis of altered permeability states, and in atherosclerosis.

Only a few years ago, the study of the platelet changed from a quiescent field to one in which rapid strides are being made. As in other fields, recent advances have come about from studies utilizing improved methodology. Most important have been (*a*) ultrastructural investigations with scanning and freeze-fracture electron microscopy, (*b*) studies of the cell membrane and the phenomenon of storage and release of many compounds such as nucleotides and serotonin, and (*c*) new developments in protein chemistry and enzymology, including recognition of the role of contractile protein in platelet function and new approaches to the study of the antihemophilic factor-the von Willebrand factor macromolecular complex of plasma-and its interaction with platelets. From these and other studies, a more comprehensive concept of the role of the platelet in hemostasis has developed.

The circulating platelet is the smallest of the blood cells, anuclear and disc-shaped, with a complex metabolism common to most cells. It is sparse in mitochondria and almost devoid of rough endoplasmic reticulum, but is rich in lysosomal-like organelles or granules. It possesses a complex canalicular network,

[1]Recipient of a Research Career Development Award (HL-D008).
[2]Aided in part by NIH grant H1-14228.

501

the surface connecting system, which provides the basis of many secretory events and for phagocytosis. The plasma membrane and glycocalyx of the platelet apparently contain several functionally specific proteins, including glycoprotein receptors, which, on reacting with enzymes, other proteins, cations, and nucleotides in the environment, contribute to a dramatic alteration of the platelet, so-called activation. The activated platelet may undergo contraction and secretion—the release reaction —and its surface then becomes "sticky." This surface change promotes adherence to nonplatelet surfaces (adhesion) and to other platelets (aggregation, or, in the older literature, agglutination), and the platelet is transformed from a discrete circulating cell to a fixed, albeit unstable, cell as in a developing hemostatic or other thrombus. Products of many different biochemical pathways may trigger activation of platelets and their self-assembly into the platelet thrombus. While the earliest phases of the platelet response may be reversible, drastic morphologic alterations develop in later stages with eventual self-destruction of the platelet. This whole process of adhesion and aggregation, once the altered environment starts the transformation from the poised circulating platelet to the activated platelet, can occur very rapidly—in a matter of seconds—depending upon the type and intensity of the activating stimuli.

A voluminous literature on the platelet has appeared since 1960. A two-volume survey of the field in 1969 by Maupin (149) contained over 7500 entries. A computer printout from the National Library of Medicine for 1972–1974, the period covered by this review, contained over 1300 entries. Nearly half of the articles in four periodical publications, *Thrombosis et Diathesis Haemorrhagica, Thrombosis Research, Progress in Hemostasis and Thrombosis,* and *Haemostasis,* deal with platelets. A number of monographs and reviews on various aspects of the platelet have been published recently. Several monographs, all published conference proceedings, provide an overview of the platelet field (35, 37, 112, 186, 240). Others deal with more limited topics, including thrombopoiesis (6), platelet metabolism and mathematical models (177), mechanisms of platelet aggregation (41, 230) and the release reaction (94), platelet electrophoresis (82), histogenesis of the platelet thrombus (36), pathophysiology and platelet transfusions (6, 173), clinical methods of studying platelet function (138), platelet disorders (198), physiological pharmacology and drug-induced antiplatelet antibodies (194), platelet anti-aggregating agents and drugs (43, 67, 135, 145, 209), and platelet reactions to biomaterials (19, 199).

This review summarizes some of the recently developed concepts and data relating to the reaction of the platelet with its microenvironment. Four interrelated topics are considered: (*a*) the structural basis for platelet reactions; (*b*) the nature of the platelet plasma membrane; (*c*) the reaction of the platelet with certain platelet-active plasma proteins; and (*d*) factors contributing to the interfacial or adhesion reactions of platelets. Even with this limited scope, the recent literature can only be partially considered because of space limitations.

ULTRASTRUCTURE OF PLATELETS

The older data on platelet ultrastructure and its relation to platelet function were obtained with transmission and scanning electron microscopy. The relatively new techniques of freeze-etch and freeze-fracture have been applied to platelets only recently (90, 189, 254). Use of these methods has permitted a three-dimensional visualization of platelet granules, mitochondria, glycogen, canalicular systems, microtubules, and microfilaments. Much of the information obtained by earlier morphologic studies of platelets prepared by standard fixation methods has been confirmed and expanded (6, 20, 193, 240). In addition, platelets have been shown to possess membrane-associated particles similar to those found in other cell types (189). The marked decrease in membrane-associated particles reported in thrombasthenic platelets is of interest, but this work must be confirmed (189). Indeed, many of the reported findings with these new methods require confirmation, since both techniques are artifact-prone and the resulting images may be difficult to interpret. The advent of higher-resolution scanning electron microscopy, however, may soon supplant some of the usefulness of freeze-etch techniques. A recent study utilized transmission electron microscopy in the examination of the nucleated thrombocytes of six species of domestic birds. Like platelets, their mitochondria were small and sparse and there was no rough endoplasmic reticulum (150).

Platelet Plasma Membranes

Transmission electron microscopy has been used to characterize isolated platelet plasma membranes prepared by various procedures (84, 116) and to determine the degree of contamination by non-membrane constituents. A comparison of five separate methods by platelet lysis with and without the use of hardening or stabilizing agents failed to show a single procedure that was entirely satisfactory in terms of yielding the platelet membrane as a single, continous envelope (10). The ultrastructural studies showed that the largest membrane fragments were obtained by glycerol lysis of untreated platelets. An understanding of the form in which plasma membrane fragments occur in isolated preparations and of the degree of contamination is extremely important in assessing biochemical studies of the platelet membrane discussed later in this review. Transmission electron microscopy has also been used in autoradiographic studies to demonstrate that protein structures enzymatically labeled with ^{125}I are externally situated on the platelet membrane (168) and to show the binding of ^{125}I-thrombin to platelets (224). In a similar study with ferritin-labeled antibody technique, a platelet-specific antibody has been shown to react with the outer surface of the platelet plasma membrane (216). Such antibodies may be useful in localizing platelet antigens in the walls of blood vessels as in atherosclerosis and in extravascular sites.

Both scanning and transmission electron microscopy have been used extensively in studies of the reactions of plasma membranes of intact platelets. A recent study of decompression sickness in rats illustrates the reactivity of blood platelets to the plasma protein layer formed on the surface of intravascular air bubbles (236). In addition, the air emboli were reported to damage endothelial cells and to produce platelet aggregation and fibrin formation. Platelets obtained 22 hr after intravenously administered lipid emulsions into ten volunteer individuals were studied by both scanning electron microscopy and transmission electron microscopy with negative staining technique (96). Lipid particles coated the surface and were phagocytosed. No evidence of platelet aggregation was demonstrated and the platelet shape and internal structure were strikingly well preserved. On the other hand, platelets from rats fed high fat diets of different proportions of saturated and unsaturated fats showed no accumulated lipid on the platelets, but did show aggregation of platelets with fusion of the plasma membrane (169). A study of the reactivity of blood platelets with latex particles revealed that, unlike the engulfment of lipid particles, platelets do not phagocytize latex particles in the usual sense (251). Instead, the latex particles are found to be lodged within channels of the surface-connected canalicular system. Channels that contained latex did not pinch off to form sealed phagocytic vacuoles but remained open. Bacteria, on the other hand, react with platelets predominantly by an extracellular phenomenon (49). Bacteria adhered to the surfaces of platelets in a reaction that required divalent cations. This adhesion of bacteria to platelets produced localized platelet aggregation, but the bacteria remained between the platelets within the aggregates. The bacteria-platelet reaction did not trigger a generalized platelet aggregation in areas devoid of bacteria.

Ultrastructural studies of platelet aggregation by the newer aggregation agents, arachidonic acid and ristocetin, have also been reported. Aggregation induced by arachidonic acid was similar to that reported with conventional aggregating agents such as collagen and ADP (205). On the other hand, the aggregation of platelets induced by the addition of ristocetin to platelet-rich plasma differed morphologically from that induced by ADP or collagen (226). Platelets aggregated by ristocetin had tortuous boundaries with electron-dense lines between adjacent platelet plasma membranes. Other aspects of ristocetin aggregation are covered in detail below.

A scanning and transmission electron microscopic study of platelets and tissue culture endothelial cells exposed to thrombin was interpreted to show that both platelets (24) and endothelial cells extruded cytogel (188). The extruded cytogels interacted to form attachments between platelets and endothelial cells. Such findings are surprising in that transmission electron microscopic studies have heretofore not revealed extrusion of platelet cytogel under similar conditions.

Ferritin-conjugated antifibrin/fibrinogen antibodies were used to demonstrate the occurrence of fibrin or fibrinogen within platelet aggregates (210). These findings indicate that fibrinogen released from within platelets contributed to the structural bonds between platelets in aggregates. A dense layer of fibrin was present on the outer surfaces of platelet aggregates formed in response to thrombin.

Release Reaction of Platelets

Ultrastructural aspects of the platelet release reaction have been reviewed recently (132, 252). Electron microscopy has also been important in developing the concept of the two canalicular systems of platelets and ascertaining their role in the platelet release reaction. The surface-connected canalicular system or open canalicular system has been implicated as the channel through which released substances leave the platelet (248). A counterpart of this system has been found in mast cells (119). The dense canalicular or closed system (32) has been described as the calcium sequestering organelle in platelets, similar to the sarcoplasmic reticulum of muscle (248). The apparent openings on the platelet surface of the surface-connecting system have been observed by scanning electron microscopy (203).

Phorbol myristate acetate produces irreversible platelet aggregation (64, 256). Interestingly, the release reaction of platelets brought about by this agent is limited and late and occurs without loss of the discoid shape of the platelet. Phorbol myristate acetate is thought to alter the permeability barrier separating storage granules from the surface-connected canalicular system, thus leading to swelling of the storage organelles.

A calcium ionophore A23187 has been used by several investigators to study platelet aggregation and release (66, 76, 258). The ionophore transports calcium across plasma membranes as well as other membranes within cells. It is thought to release calcium from its stored site, permitting the contraction of thrombasthenin, the supposed trigger of platelet aggregation. Similar findings have been reported for the ionophore X537A (66). These findings are cited as further proof that the release reaction is a manifestation of platelet contractile activity. Release, however, can occur without loss of the discoid shape, since cytochalasin B, an agent that stabilizes the discoid shape, does not inhibit release (255).

Platelets exposed to cationic polypeptides such as polybrene or polylysine under appropriate conditions take up and deposit these polymers in the storage granules (249, 250). Following aggregation of platelets by polylysine, the storage granules appeared in the surface-connected canalicular system in an intact state. These results were interpreted to indicate that cationic polypeptides are stored in certain cytoplasmic granules and stabilize these structures so that, in response to appropriate stimuli, the storage granules are extruded intact through the channels of the surface-connected canalicular system. Further support for the concept that this system furnishes the conduits for release from platelets has been gained by the demonstration of electron-dense material similar to fibrin within the surface-connected channels of platelets that have been treated with thrombin (61).

Release of materials, especially storage pool ADP, from the platelet requires more than the presence of an inducing agent and a patent surface-connected canalicular system. Two groups of patients with an "aspirin-like" defect or impairment of collagen-induced adhesion, release, and aggregation have been studied (241). The first group had normal platelet ultrastructure prior to collagen exposure but lacked ultrastructural evidence of the early phases of the release reaction, such as centripetal rearrangements of granules, after collagen contact. These patients had normal levels of storage pool ADP and, as in individuals with normal platelets treated with aspirin, they are paralyzed in their ability to respond to release-inducers. On the other hand, a second group showed ultrastructural evidence, albeit transient, of the early release phase after collagen. Their inability to complete the release reaction is thought to result from a marked deficit in their storage pool ADP, demonstrated ultrastructurally by the reduced number of dense granules in these defective platelets. The dense granules have been shown to contain serotonin and adenine nucleotides (2) as well as calcium (139). The α granules that contain sulfomucopolysaccharides (2) were present in normal number. The low storage pool ADP defect was shown to be corrected through an unknown mechanism by mixing with a small number of normal platelets treated with aspirin (259).

An alternative morphologic route for the platelet release reaction has been proposed recently (237, 238). Instead of release via a surface-connected canalicular system, the separation of vesicles from the tips of pseudopods formed by platelets interacting with subendothelial structures has been suggested as the mechanism whereby stored intracellular components may be released to the outside. Histochemical support of this hypothesis is lacking.

Platelet Shape Change

Platelets undergo a complicated shape change, in both the adhesion and the aggregation reactions, which has been well described. An analysis of the functional meaning of these structural alterations has been made (253). Platelets adhering to glass appear to flatten out in contact with the substrate plasma proteins absorbed on the glass (201), if the specimen is air-dried and studied by scanning electron microscopy. A comparison has been made of air-dried and lyophilized platelets (166). The lyophilized platelets, unlike the air-dried, showed many free floating projections. Artifacts may be responsible for these differences, as transmission electron micrographs showed close contact of adherent platelets with the substrate (201). Scanning and transmission electron microscopy were used to examine the influence of cytochalasin B on the shape change and pseudopod formation that develop when discoid blood platelets are exposed to low temperatures (257). Cytochalasin B was found to stabilize the platelet disc shape in a dose-dependent fashion when platelets were chilled. Further, cytochalasin B preserved the microtubules of chilled platelets, indicating that preservation of the discoid shape is the result of stabilizing its cytoskeletal support system.

Platelet morphology was studied by both phase contrast and electron microscopy after freeze preservation in 6% dimethylsulfoxide (52). About 60% of the platelets retained the discoid shape characteristic of fresh platelets. The remainder changed to irregular or regular spheres. The shape change occurred on freezing and thawing rather than with the addition or removal of the cryoprotective agent. The shape change was associated with extensive intracellular ultrastructural changes, while the platelets that retained the disc shape had a well-preserved ultrastructure. Freeze-dried platelets, even if prepared with cryoprotective agents, showed vacuolization and loss of microtubules and structural detail (54).

Reactions with Subendothelium

The scanning electron microscope has added new dimensions to our understanding of the reactivity of platelets with subendothelial components. These studies have depicted clearly the appearance of endothelial cells and the reaction of platelets with collagen and other subendothelial structures (85, 217, 221). The effect of blood flow on platelet adhesion to subendothelium has received attention recently (11, 13, 213). High blood flow velocities in the arteries produce platelet mural thrombi, while fibrin deposition on subendothelial structures occurs predominantly in stagnant blood or with slowly flowing venous blood. While it was previously suggested that platelet sequestration in the splenic sinusoids might be due to reaction with "exposed" subendothelium, a recent transmission electron microscopic study of spleens of dogs, rats, and mice indicates that the platelets are present in aggregates in the lumen, possibly representing trapping of activated platelets (69).

Ultrastructural Evaluation of Isolated Platelets

Suspensions of isolated platelets, largely devoid of other elements of the blood, are a valuable reagent in the study of platelet physiology. A number of methods of isolating platelets have evolved over the years, but only recently has ultrastructure become a standard part of evaluation of procedures for preparation of isolated platelet concentrates. The chief methods of isolating platelets are those using differential centrifugation (methods of K. M. Brinkhous, of J. F. Mustard, and of E. C. Rossi), gel filtration, or albumin density gradient centrifugation (144). The ultrastructure of platelets varied according to the method of preparation; the albumin density procedures yielded the most altered platelets (266). Gel filtrated platelets showed increased number of pseudopodia (220) but were functionally somewhat better than those prepared by other methods (144). A combination of albumin density and gel filtration methods yielded better preserved platelets judged both morphologically and functionally than either method alone (105). Platelet suspensions kept in acidified ACD maintained a more normal morphology than those kept in EDTA, although the latter were more reactive to thrombin (55).

BIOCHEMISTRY OF THE PLATELET MEMBRANE

The role of the platelet in hemostasis and thrombosis involves a variety of interactions of the platelet membrane surface with other platelet membranes, with other solid surfaces, and with a large number of soluble agents introduced into the platelet's environment. Thus it has become imperative to develop knowledge of the structure, biochemical composition, and orientation of the components of the platelet membrane in order to understand the physiological and biochemical role of this cell.

Evidence that platelet function relies on the position and orientation of these membrane components is accumulating, and it appears that various regions or sites on the membrane have a particular molecular specificity, leading to the postulation of specific receptors on the platelet surface. The number and specificity of these sites on the platelet membrane would then determine the response to a number of varied stimuli; the structural arrangement of the various components of the membrane would play a role in facilitating the response to receptor-mediated events. Data available are compatible with the model of the platelet membrane as a fluid matrix.

Protein Composition

The protein composition of the platelet membrane has been shown to consist of some 20 polypeptides ranging in molecular weight from 10,000 to 200,000 (8, 167, 181); in these studies 5% polyacrylamide gel electrophoresis was used in the presence of sodium dodecyl sulfate (SDS). This marked heterogeneity of protein components was not a reflection of secondary proteolysis by cellular proteases (167). Further characterization of the membrane polypeptides by staining of the gels for carbohydrate revealed the presence of three major glycoproteins in the molecular weight range of 70,000 to 150,000 (167, 181).

Lactoperoxidase Iodination

Lactoperoxidase is an enzyme that catalyzes the iodination of exposed tyrosine groups on proteins. Its use as a technique for probing the membrane surface is related, under controlled conditions, to its unique property of only labeling those proteins externally oriented in the membrane (104, 183). Of the heterogenous group of platelet membrane polypeptides, at least seven are on the exposed surface of the platelet (181). The labeled polypeptides include the three major glycoproteins and four additional polypeptides that do not appear to be glycoproteins, since they do not stain with fuchsin sulfate. Lactoperoxidase iodination with ^{125}I intensely labels a glycoprotein of molecular weight 93,000–100,000 (168, 181). The other peaks are labeled less intensely and are variable in their appearance.

Enzymatic Hydrolysis

In an effort to relate structure to function, lactoperoxidase iodination followed by polyacrylamide gel electrophoresis was performed after treatment with proteolytic agents known to affect platelets. Trypsin hydrolyzed only the three glycoproteins while the other four surface-exposed polypeptides were unaffected, suggesting that the primary target on the membrane for proteolytic enzymes is glycoprotein (181). After hydrolysis, the iodinated tryosine residues of the major glycoproteins remained on the membrane. Trypsin also caused a conformational change in membrane components primarily affecting the major glycoproteins. Previous information that three glycopeptide fragments arise from hydrolysis of platelet membranes (8, 109) can be extrapolated to assume that each of the peptides arises from one of the glycoproteins (181).

Thrombin, on the other hand, was found to cause no alteration in the steric relationship of the membrane components when intact cells were exposed to this enzyme (168). However, a recent study (182), using a two-label technique and combining lactoperoxidase iodination and polyacrylamide gel electrophoresis, indicated that in isolated membranes the three major glycoproteins and a high molecular weight polypeptide serve as substrates for thrombin. In the intact platelet, only one of the three major glycoproteins, with a molecular weight of 118,000, is affected by thrombin. The amount of this glycoprotein removed by thrombin from intact cells varies from 10–50%. Thus it was speculated that after partial hydrolysis of this glycoprotein, a conformational change in the membrane occurred, rendering the residual glycoprotein inaccessible to thrombin. A similar finding has been reported confirming the partial hydrolysis of a major glycoprotein of 100,000 molecular weight after thrombin treatment (214). Thrombin also binds to the platelet membrane at a site different from its proteolytic site (58, 74, 224). Whether the functional response of the platelet to thrombin is the partial hydrolysis of a specific membrane glycoprotein with subsequent conformational change of the membrane surface, or the binding of thrombin to a specific receptor, or both, remains to be clarified.

Complement is also capable of altering intact platelets in a manner comparable to thrombin by deletion of polypeptides of high molecular weight (264). Platelets had to be intact at the time of complement activation for the polypeptide deletions to occur, suggesting that complement per se may not be directly involved.

Isolation and Characterization of Membrane Components

A surface glycoprotein has been isolated from 30 units of platelets in 2–3 mg amounts when isolated cell membranes were extracted with lithium diiodosalicylate and the extract subjected to affinity chromatography with bound concanavalin A (168). SDS acrylamide gel analysis of the material demonstrated a major protein band in the molecular weight range of 100,000, with strong periodic acid Schiff staining properties. The isolated glycoprotein reacted with an antibody prepared to the material and also precipitated with concanavalin A. The antibody to this isolated membrane glycoprotein agglutinated platelets in both platelet-rich plasma and washed platelet suspension. Addition of 5% α-methyl-D-mannoside to the washed system blocked the concanavalin A agglutination but not the agglutination by the antibody to the membrane glycoprotein.

A similar membrane glycoprotein has been purified with the use of a precipitation technique for isolation of soluble glycoproteins (131). Acrylamide gel analysis of this material showed a single protein band both in the presence and absence of SDS. The molecular weight was 148,000 in the SDS gel. The principal amino acids present in the glycoprotein were threonine and serine; neither cysteine nor methionine were detected. Carbohydrate composed nearly two thirds of the glycoprotein on a molar basis. Galactose was the principal monosaccharide, sialic acid was present in about half that amount, and glucosamine and galactosamine were present in equimolar quantities.

Lectins and Platelet Membranes

The use of various plant lectins and their specificity for certain glycopeptide structures have been widely exploited as tools for (a) probing membrane structure and organization of membrane components, (b) investigating a wide variety of phenomena at cell surfaces, and (c) studying many properties of the surface plasma membranes themselves (40, 130). While most of this work relates to other cell types, including malignant transformation of cells, the techniques are now being employed to look at the platelet surface.

Two phytohemagglutinins from *Phaseolus vulgaris*, erythroagglutinating phytohemagglutinin (E-PHA) and leukoagglutinating phytohemagglutinin (L-PHA), bind to the platelet surface. The binding can be reversed by using appropriate oligosaccharide haptene inhibitors (137). The binding of these lectins by the platelet was shown to result in aggregation, inhibition of adenylate cyclase, and release of a large protein from the particulate fraction of the cell. This response is analogous to the effects seen when platelets are incubated with thrombin (38). Subsequent studies demonstrated that E-PHA could release [^{14}C]serotonin in addition to the thrombin-sensitive protein but at a much slower rate than that seen with thrombin (225). Binding of the lectin was a prerequisite for release, since the glycoprotein fetuin reduced the binding of E-PHA by 91% and prevented [^{14}C]serotonin release.

The lectin prepared from *Lens culinaris* (lentil-PHA) binds tightly to platelets but does not cause any of the previously described secondary responses (137). Lentil-PHA does not block the reaction of platelets to either L-PHA or thrombin. Prior incubation with either L-PHA or thrombin increased the number of binding sites for lentil-PHA, suggesting that thrombin and L-PHA cause a conformational change in the platelet surface.

Lectins of known specificity have been used to study aggregation of both intact platelets and platelet membranes. The use of such agents to cause the platelet release reaction and to inhibit the initiation of aggregation by collagen, ADP, and thrombin have recently been described (79). In general, lectins with specificities directed towards α-D-mannopyranose or α-D-glucopyranose moieties (*Lens culinaris, Pisum savitum,* and *Lathyrus savitus*) as well as N-acetylgalactosamine (soybean lectin) were without detectable effect on aggregation of the platelet. Lectins with a galactose-directed specificity, such as those of *Ricinus communis* and *Agaricus bisporus,* interact with platelets to varying degrees. Wheat germ agglutinin that is specific for N-acetylglucosamine interacts strongly with platelets, as does the lectin of *Phaseolus coccineus* whose specificity is not yet known. Concanavalin A, the lectin from jack bean meal, although previously reported to aggregate platelets (168), was found in more recent studies to be unable to aggregate intact platelets but able to aggregate isolated platelet membranes (79). The lectins that caused aggregation of intact platelets also caused release of both ADP and serotonin, as did concanavalin A that only aggregated platelet membranes. Lectins specific for D-glucose and D-mannose that did not aggregate platelets or release ADP could release serotonin, suggesting that release of ADP and of serotonin from the platelet occur independently of each other.

The three glycopeptides associated with the platelet membrane after proteolytic digestion (8) described above were studied for their effect in inhibiting lectin aggregation of platelets. Glycopeptide I specifically inhibited aggregation of platelet membranes by wheat germ agglutinin, while glycopeptide II specifically inhibited aggregation induced by *P. coccineus.* Glycopeptide III had no inhibiting effect with any of the lectins tested. This suggests that these glycopeptides or their glycoprotein precursors on the membrane surface may be the receptors to which the lectins bind. Thus the use of lectins brings a great deal of experimental evidence to bear on the developing concept of specific receptor sites on the platelet surface, the binding of which initiates a series of events leading to platelet activation.

PLATELET-ACTIVE MACROMOLECULES

Studies concerning the aggregation of platelets with or without the concomitant release reaction have documented the role played by a number of macromolecules. One such instance, not covered in this review, is the special requirement of fibrinogen for the aggregation of platelets by ADP. Other macromolecules such as aggregated immunoglobulin G (IgG), antigen-antibody complexes, certain cationic polypeptides such as polylysine, the platelet-aggregating factor (PAF) of bovine and porcine plasma, and human von Willebrand factor (vWF) are covered in some detail.

Gamma Globulins, Immune Complexes, and the Role of Complement

Heterologous platelet antibodies directed against the platelet membrane, in the presence of complement, cause cytolysis with loss of all cytoplasmic constituents.

In the absence of complement, the same antibody causes an energy-dependent release primarily of vasoactive amines. Similarly, complement-fixing isoantibodies result in release and aggregation, whereas non-complement-fixing antiplatelet isoantibodies cause release and increase platelet metabolism but do not aggregate platelets (211).

Human platelets can also be aggregated by IgG, which is unrelated to platelet antigen. Platelet reactivity is not complement dependent and requires interaction of the immunoglobulin with antigen to form an immune complex or aggregation of the IgG or its Fc fragment by heat or chemical treatment (180). All the aggregated subclasses of IgG (IgG1, IgG2, IgG3, and IgG4) aggregate platelets and cause release of serotonin. On the other hand, IgA, IgA2, IgD, IgE, and IgM are completely inactive even in their aggregated forms (88, 179). The aggregated IgG myleoma proteins and their Fc fragments, even when mildly reduced and alkylated, retain 50% of their activity, whereas aggregated F(ab')2 fragments are completely inactive.

The mechanism of platelet aggregation with IgG could be due to either of two possibilities. (*a*) Fc fragments and not F(ab')2 fragments participate in aggregation, suggesting the presence on the platelet of an Fc receptor that would allow direct fixation of the Fc portion of IgG to the platelet surface. Evidence has been reported for the existence of such a receptor (106). This receptor does not bind native 7S antibody, suggesting that the binding site of the Fc portion of the antibody is formed or exposed upon aggregation of antibody, through mediation of antigen (immune complexes), by physicochemical means (heat or bisdiazobenzidine), or by papain digestion (Fc fragment). Further evidence for such a receptor is that preincubation of the platelets with Fc, but not with F(ab), prevents aggregation by immune complexes or aggregated IgG. (*b*) IgG could react with complement or at least some of its components present on the platelet membrane. C1 is the complement component that preferentially binds to active complexes. Investigators studying the aggregation of platelets by aggregated IgG of different subclasses speculated that this mechanism was possible because both serum (88) and C1q (179) inhibit the release of serotonin, but they were unable to demonstrate complement on the platelet surface (239). As the Fc fragment carries the site for attachment to C1, the finding of this component on the platelet surface may also explain the studies suggesting an Fc receptor unrelated to complement.

Several bits of information suggest that a simple explanation regarding the role of complement is not possible. Although in most instances, modification of aggregated IgG or its subclasses results in the loss of both complement fixing and platelet stimulatory activity, the degree of loss is not strictly parallel. IgG4 does not bind complement, yet it can aggregate platelets. IgG3 has good complement-binding capability but is only a fair-to-poor platelet aggregator. Periodate oxidation of the IgG carbohydrate, a part of the molecule that appears to play no role in complement fixation, completely destroys platelet stimulatory activity. Also, immune stimuli can elicit the release reaction independent of Ca^{2+}, even though chelating agents inhibit aggregation (161). These data make it difficult to implicate participation of the first components of complement in the reaction, since Ca^{2+} is an essential requirement for the integrity and activity of the C1 complex. Thus the finding of C1 on the platelet could represent merely C1 adsorbed on the membrane like so many other plasma constituents. Further studies are necessary to delineate the exact mechanism by which immune stimuli cause platelet aggregation and release.

Polylysine

Cationic polypeptides such as polylysine are another category of macromolecules that cause aggregation of human platelets. The use of these materials has produced a wide variety of conflicting data, but most investigators seem to agree that polylysine, like other cationic polymers, adheres to the negatively charged platelet membrane and causes aggregation in the absence of cations by neutralization of the negative surface charge, by forming bridges between adjacent platelets, or both (111).

Polylysine was first reported to be unable to cause the release of serotonin, ATP, or ADP from platelets (111). Other investigators then reported that polylysine could elicit the release reaction, provided calcium ions, a small amount of ADP, and a plasmatic cofactor were present (147). However, these same investigators (148), after using a variety of polylysine preparations ranging in molecular weight from 2000 to 400,000, were able to show that all types, under certain conditions, could cause the release reaction in a suspension of washed platelets during aggregation. No protein cofactor is necessary if optimum concentrations are used. Fibrinogen and ADP, earlier thought to be requirements, were shown to potentiate each other in the extension or widening of the effective concentration range. The potentiating effect of fibrinogen may be that it is a cationic protein possessing a relatively high positive-charge density. Thus fibrinogen is capable of participating in the reduction of the net negative charge on the membrane and facilitating the decrease in electrostatic repulsion between individual platelets. This concept is further substantiated by studies showing that acetylated cationic proteins such as acetylated γ-globulin become potent inhibitors of platelet aggregation. Acetylated γ-globulin completely abolishes collagen-, ADP-, and thrombin-induced aggregation (7). The marked differences in the release-inducing capacities of different commercial polylysine preparations are not the result of molecular weight or peculiarities in the secondary structure, since the D- and D,L-forms are as effective as the L-form (148). Recent studies, however, suggest that structure may play a significant role both in terms of direct aggregating ability and reliance on other plasma cofactors (153). Circular dichroism was used to show that conformational variations of various polylysines were directly related to the ability of polylysine to interact with washed platelets. Polylysine with a significant percentage of random coil conformation requires a plasma protein cofactor in order to cause aggregation. Samples with little or no random coil and nearly 100% β configuration possess marked aggregating capabilities independent of any plasma cofactor.

Platelet-Aggregating Factor and Human von Willebrand Factor

Two other macromolecules and their relationship to platelets have been the basis of a tremendous amount of current research: the human von Willebrand factor (vWF) and its counterpart in certain animal plasmas, the human platelet-aggregating factor (PAF). Although much of the research concerning these two factors has been intimately associated, they are discussed separately for ease of presentation.

PLATELET-ACTIVE VON WILLEBRAND FACTOR OF ANIMAL PLASMA   PAF of animal plasmas was emphasized when antihemophilic factor (factor VIII) concentrates prepared from animal plasma were used for the treatment of human hemophilia. The prompt thrombocytopenia that developed was first thought to be the result of a heterologous antibody (133) or animal fibrinogen (70). However, subsequent investigations demonstrated that when various commercial animal fibrinogens were subjected to agarose gel chromatography, the factor VIII activity and PAF eluted in the void volume, while the fractions containing clottable protein eluted later (60, 71). Further evidence that PAF was intimately associated with factor VIII activity was the demonstration of PAF in highly purified factor VIII preparations (60, 72, 80) and inhibition of its aggregating activity by incubation with a heterologous antibody to porcine factor VIII but not to a rabbit antiporcine fibrinogen (72).

The mechanism of platelet aggregation by PAF is not dependent upon the platelet release reaction. Both aged platelets and fragmented platelets aggregate promptly upon incubation with PAF (80), and PAF results in aggregation of human platelets in the presence of EDTA and known inhibitors of the platelet release reaction (60, 80). Thus PAF interacts directly with the platelet surface to cause aggregation, and the platelet receptor is relatively stable except following freeze-thaw of intact cells (80).

Although PAF and factor VIII activities are difficult to separate under ordinary conditions, some evidence suggests that the activities reside on different molecules. When agarose gel void volumes containing PAF and factor VIII activity are chromatographed in 0.25 M Ca^{2+}, the activities separate (80). The PAF remains in the void volume and the factor VIII elutes later in fractions denoting small molecular size. The fractions containing the small active factor VIII fragment have no detectable platelet-aggregating activity. In addition, factor VIII activity free of PAF was obtained using ion exchange chromatography (39, 80). Separation of the two activities was also possible by repeated adsorption of bovine plasma with human platelets, a procedure that selectively removed PAF, leaving factor VIII activity in the supernatant (80). In vivo evidence that PAF is the platelet-active von Willebrand factor was demonstrated in studies with bleeder swine that had a hemophilia-like disease indistinguishable in most respects from human von Willebrand's disease (vWD) (81). A recently developed assay for PAF based on macroscopic aggregation of human platelets was used in these studies (80). Swine, homozygous for the defect, had no detectable PAF, while known heterozygotes had levels of 26–55% relative to normal porcine plasma. In vivo transfusion studies using bleeder swine recipients again demonstrated a type of separation of the activities in that 24 hr after transfusion, when factor VIII activity was at its height, the PAF level had fallen to an undetectable level.

Chemical modification of PAF–factor VIII preparations by progressive desialization results in loss of PAF activity with no loss of factor VIII activity (126). PAF is rapidly lost in a concentration-dependent process during periodate oxidation, whereas factor VIII activity is lost at a rate paralleling the degree of oxidation (152). Exposure of bovine factor VIII to galactose oxidase completely abolishes PAF activity (231). These experiments point to a specific role for carbohydrate and the interaction of galactose containing side chains in PAF with the human platelet membrane.

HUMAN VON WILLEBRAND FACTOR AND RELATIONSHIP TO FACTOR VIII
A large body of information has accumulated that characterizes a glycoprotein in human plasma of very high molecular weight that is closely associated with factor VIII. This plasma constituent appears to be vWF. Considerable data have accumulated characterizing this macromolecule and defining its relationship to plasma factor VIII and its possible role in hemostasis and thrombosis.

Immunoprecipitation and glass bead retention   A heterologous antisera was raised in rabbits to a partially purified factor VIII preparation that apparently also possessed vWF activity. Apparent monospecificity of the antisera was achieved after appropriate adsorption. Using this adsorbed antisera, an antigen could be detected by immunoprecipitation in the plasma of normal and hemophilia A subjects that was reduced or absent in patients with classic vWD (101, 157, 263, 265). The blood of vWD patients also demonstrated reduced retention of platelets by glass bead columns (29, 165). Studies showed that the factor necessary for correction of glass bead retention was present in normal and hemophilia A plasma but missing in the plasma of vWD patients. This missing factor was shown to be related to factor VIII preparations (27, 245, 246) and specifically identified by the heterologous antisera above (26, 27). The rabbit antisera not only measured the level of antigen quantitatively but also inhibited glass bead retention of platelets in normal plasma (27, 151, 156). Gel chromatography demonstrated that the antigen and the factor responsible for correction of glass bead retention chromatographed in the void volume with the factor VIII activity when cryoprecipitate was eluted from 6% agarose gels (27, 246). Thus a highly purified human plasma fraction, containing proteins in excess of 1×10^6 molecular weight, contained the antigen detected by immunoprecipitation techniques, the factor VIII procoagulant activity, and a factor that interacted with platelets to correct the abnormal retention of platelets to glass beads in vWD.

The most simplistic concept at this point would be that factor VIII is a trace glycoprotein of greater than 1×10^6 molecular weight, with multiple functions—procoagulant activity, glass bead retention, and antigenicity—that participates in both the cellular and fluid phase of hemostasis. Additional information in favor of this concept is the parallel rise of both factor VIII activity and antigen in a variety of physiological and nonphysiological situations (16, 17, 57, 185). The problem with such a concept is that these activities could reside on different molecules or both activities could be on different components of a molecular complex. The problems of specificity of the immunologic probes and the insensitivity of the glass bead retention test may explain the difficulty in separating these activities of high molecular weight, should they be on separate molecules, as subsequent data suggest.

Evidence for macromolecular complex   Factor VIII dissociates under conditions that disrupt noncovalent bonds, e.g. high ionic strength, into a large carrier protein and a small fragment that contains the procoagulant active site (176, 190, 234, 244). Under appropriate conditions, reassociation of these two parts of the factor VIII complex is possible and results in a high molecular weight protein indistinguishable from untreated plasma factor VIII (50). Using the recombination technique to study hemophilic and vWD plasmas, it was shown that human hemophilic plasma contains a normally functioning carrier protein that can bind the small active fragment from normal plasma, while the plasma from severe vWD lacks such a protein (51). This technique allows a functional assessment of the antigen in hemophilic plasma detected by immunoprecipitation and shows that it is a normal functioning carrier protein, instead of an abnormal factor VIII without procoagulant activity, as had been suggested. These data, together with the information that, under dissociating conditions of high ionic strength, factor VIII activity can be separated from the antigen detected by the heterologous rabbit antibody (242), permit an extension of the concept of a single macromolecule with multiple functions to a macromolecular complex. This complex would be composed of a large carrier protein and a noncovalently bound smaller molecule that contains the procoagulant active site. The carrier molecule possesses the antigenic site to the heterologous rabbit antibody and is capable of interacting with platelets to cause their retention in glass bead columns. Even though this concept embodies most of the data available to this point, it does not fit all the information. For example, the in vivo studies in humans (15, 22, 118, 163) and bleeder swine (81) suggest that factor VIII can exist in the circulation without the presence of detectable vWF activity. Using the latter concept one would suppose that the increased factor VIII activity post-transfusion of vWD subjects, since it has no detectable vWF, would be of small molecular weight. In one study (22), such a small molecular weight activity has been reported, although other data suggest that the factor VIII activity in question is actually large (118, 163). Further studies are needed to answer this question regarding the molecular size of post-transfusion factor VIII. Nevertheless, the post-transfusion factor VIII activity does appear to have some properties different from native factor VIII in regard to stability (65) and effectiveness in stimulating further production of factor VIII when auto-transfused into a patient with vWD (28).

Another line of evidence suggesting the possibility of more than one molecular entity comes from the use of solid-phase immunochemical studies (262). This technique employs covalent bonding of the γ-globulin fraction of heterologous anti–factor VIII rabbit antisera to agarose beads and studying the activities removed from plasma with increasing concentrations of the antibody beads. If both activities, vWF and factor VIII, are on one molecule, then the activities should decrease in parallel. Instead, there is a discordant fall of the two activities, suggesting that the activities reside on separate molecular entities.

Still another line of reasoning concerns the studies showing that normal endothelial cells contain the factor VIII antigen or vWF (23, 102). Furthermore, biopsy specimens of superficial veins from five vWD patients were studied for the presence of factor VIII antigen in the vascular endothelium by an immunofluorescent technique (91). No evidence of fluorescence was noted in three patients with severe vWD but fluorescence was present in one patient with moderate vWD (6% antigen) and one with an atypical form of the disease (72% antigen). Through the use of cell culture it was demonstrated that human endothelial cells actually produce vWF (107). Interestingly, however, endothelial cells do not produce a material with procoagulant factor VIII activity. Studies of endothelial cell cultures from human vWD patients have not been reported.

With techniques using quantitative immunoelectrophoresis (99) and immunofluorescence (206), the factor VIII antigen was also found to be intimately associated with the platelet itself. The antigen was not removed from the platelet even with repeated washings. When the washed platelets were lysed, generally higher values of factor VIII–like antigen were found, but when the lysate was fractionated into membrane and cytoplasmic components, the antigen was found almost entirely in the membrane fraction (99). Although antigen in amounts 5–15% of that found in normal platelet-rich plasma was associated with the normal platelet fraction, no antigen was found associated with the platelets of a patient with severe vWD whose plasma also lacked measurable antigen. These vWD platelets would not adsorb antigen even after incubation for 2 hr at 37°C with normal plasma, factor VIII concentrates, or the patient's own plasma with added factor VIII concentrate (99).

Individual patients with severe vWD vary, however, because a patient with undetectable vWF in her plasma was found by immunofluorescence to have normal amounts of antigen associated with her platelets (206). In addition, patients with Bernard-Soulier syndrome (see below) were found to have increased amounts of antigen in or on their platelets. While the plasma of a single patient with thrombasthenia had normal antigen, the platelets had reduced antigen (99).

Ristocetin–von Willebrand factor platelet aggregation   In 1958 the antibiotic ristocetin was removed from the market because of complications of thrombocytopenia in patients taking the drug. Investigations concerning the mechanism showed that rabbits receiving therapeutic levels of ristocetin developed thrombocytopenia and hypofibrinogenemia. When the drug was added to human platelet-rich plasma in vitro, macroscopic aggregation of the platelets occurred (73). These reports were essentially unnoticed for the next ten years until investigators in Australia confirmed that ristocetin aggregates human platelets in plasma with subsequent initiation of the platelet release reaction (97). Initial aggregation was shown to precede the release of ADP, and inhibitors of the release reaction did not abolish aggregation. The antibiotic was noted to precipitate fibrinogen from plasma, but this was not associated with its ability to cause platelet aggregation, since platelets in afibrinogenemic plasma aggregated normally with ristocetin. In addition, ristocetin would aggregate platelets low in platelet fibrinogen from patients with thrombasthenia. The fortuitous extension of these studies to include platelet-rich plasma from three vWD patients led to a discovery that has had enormous impact on the study of this disease. The platelets of two of the three patients did not aggregate with ristocetin. A subsequent report (100) demonstrated that platelets in vWD plasma that failed to aggregate with ristocetin alone would promptly aggregate with addi-tion of normal or hemophilic platelet-poor plasma. In addition, vWD platelets, when suspended in normal platelet-poor plasma, would also aggregate normally with ristocetin, whereas normal washed platelets suspended in vWD platelet-poor plasma failed to aggregate. Thus it became clear that a fourth technique was able to demonstrate a plasma factor missing in vWD plasma but present in normal and hemophilia A plasma. It was also noted that the vWD patients who had marked abnormalities of platelet retention to glass beads were the same ones whose platelets did not aggregate with ristocetin.

Applying the same techniques used to characterize the factor responsible for platelet retention, it was shown that the plasma factor that participated with ristoce-tin to aggregate normal platelets was also a macromolecule that eluted in the void volume of agarose gels in fractions that also contained factor VIII procoagulant activity (175, 247). In addition, gel chromatography of hemophilic cryoprecipitate resulted in the elution of the vWD-correcting factor in the void volume fractions. The heterologous rabbit antisera to factor VIII completely abolished the ability of ristocetin to aggregate normal platelet-rich plasma (155, 247). Evidence that the ristocetin-aggregating activity is associated with the large molecular weight vWF was again demonstrated by both in vivo transfusion studies (28, 163) and in vitro dissociation techniques (80, 81, 242).

Two naturally occurring inhibitors in hemophilia A and vWD respectively have been tested for their neutralizing effect on the ristocetin plasma cofactor. A human inhibitor to factor VIII from a patient with hemophilia A had no effect on the ability of ristocetin to aggregate normal platelet-rich plasma (200, 247), although others have not been able to confirm this observation (222). A specific inhibitor was found in the plasma of a multitransfused patient homozygous for vWD that completely inhibited platelet aggregation with ristocetin and normal plasma (200). The inhibi-tor plasma also inhibited the PAF activity of bovine plasma but had no neutralizing effect on the procoagulant activity of either human or bovine factor VIII. The vWD inhibitor plasma showed no ability to alter aggregation with ADP or other conven-tional aggregating agents (200).

A double-antibody technique, using the IgG fraction of a hemophilic patient with an inhibitor to factor VIII activity, demonstrated that the procoagulant activity was selectively removed from cryoprecipitate, leaving the vWF measured by ristocetin aggregation in solution. The same technique using the rabbit antisera to factor VIII resulted in selective removal of both the factor VIII antigen and the ristocetin-aggregating activity with little change in the factor VIII procoagulant activity over that present in the control (95). Bovine factor VIII, which aggregates human plate-lets, was also noted to aggregate bovine platelets in the presence of ristocetin. By use of QAE Sephadex A-25 ion exchange chromatography, the ristocetin-aggregat-ing activity of a bovine factor VIII preparation was separated from the procoagulant factor VIII (39).

The concept for factor VIII and vWF that emerges out of all these data strongly implicates a macromolecular complex of at least two molecules. One is a large molecular weight protein that has, at this point, four activities: (a) it possesses the antigenic determinants for the heterologous rabbit antibody; (b) it participates with the antibiotic ristocetin in the aggregation of human platelets or, in the case of animal vWF, aggregates human platelets directly; (c) it is responsible for platelet retention in glass bead columns; and (d) it binds noncovalently the second molecule that is smaller in molecular size and contains the procoagulant-active site. Some of the immunologic, platelet adsorption, and dissociation data still make this model tenuous. Some of the data can also be used to make a strong case for two macromolecules. One could be the factor VIII-like antigen or vWF, which has as its biologic function the participation in cellular hemostasis through interaction with the platelet. The other could be a large polymer with factor VIII activity, held together by noncovalent bonds, whose biological function is to participate in the fluid phase of hemostasis leading to the formation of a fibrin clot.

Although a definitive answer is not available at this time, the present state of knowledge has allowed further characterization of the platelet-active vWF, has produced two methods of quantitating the presence of vWF in normal and pathologic plasmas, and has begun to divide vWD patients into a number of variants.

Assay methods for von Willebrand factor   Two methods for the quantitative determination of vWF in the presence of ristocetin have been described. The simpler of the two assays uses the macroscopic aggregation of platelets as the endpoint, the other uses aggregometry tracings.

The macroscopic test for vWF is based on the observations that the aggregation time of platelets can be determined as accurately as the clotting time of fibrinogen and that a linear relationship on a semilog plot exists between aggregation time and concentration of vWF within certain limits (80, 200). Initially, fresh washed platelets or washed gel-filtered platelets were used in the assay, either for PAF or vWF. Modification of this assay has recently been reported (1). Based on the information that viable platelets are not a requirement for aggregation with PAF and vWF and that bovine plasma will aggregate human platelet membrane fragments (80), a method was devised for preparing a stable platelet reagent. Human washed or washed gel-filtered platelets fixed in buffered 4% paraformaldehyde retain their ability to aggregate with PAF or vWF in the presence of ristocetin (1). Agents that aggregate metabolically functioning platelets such as ADP or release reaction inducers such as collagen or thrombin had no effect on the fixed washed platelets. Thus the use of fixed washed platelets eliminates adventitious platelet reactions unrelated to primary vWF function and permits the evaluation of vWF or PAF aggregation without the added effects of secondary release. This type of platelet eliminated a problem in standardization produced by the variability inherent in making fresh platelets each time the assay is performed. Fixed platelets were stable when stored at 4°C for periods of 4–6 wk.

Using fixed washed platelets in the macroscopic test system, vWF was assayed in normal subjects and in vWD patients and hemophilia (34). The mean vWF level for 20 normal subjects was 95% with a range of 61–144%. Repeated determinations on the same sample fell within the range of ±10%. The vWF levels of the subjects were consistently reduced from < 5 to 28%. Severe hemophilia A subjects had vWF levels in the normal range. In one mild hemophiliac and two obligate carriers, the vWF level was also in the normal range, although the factor VIII activity was less than the comparable vWF levels (34).

The assay for the vWF using the aggregometer system is based on the observation that a log-log relationship exists between the amount of ristocetin-induced aggregation of fresh washed normal platelets (243) or washed gel-filtered platelets (174) and the concentration of normal plasma present. The index of platelet aggregation is the percentage of change in optical density of the platelet suspension in the aggregometer. This assay for vWF was used to study the plasma of patients with vWD and normal subjects. A high correlation was found between vWF values and levels of both factor VIII-related antigen and the procoagulant factor VIII activity (243). A range of 99–185% vWF with a mean of 135% for 19 normal subjects was obtained. The precision of the test on repeated assay of the same sample was 5–10%. vWF activity in plasma stored at –20°C was noted to be stable for at least two months. Variation in the potency of various lots of ristocetin was observed. Washed gel-filtered platelets as well as fresh washed platelets became reactive with ristocetin without added vWF over time unless glucose was omitted from the buffer (174).

The fixed washed platelets have also been used in the aggregometry assay for vWF (1). Two phases were identified in the aggregometer during ristocetin-induced aggregation of fixed washed platelets. The first phase was indicated by a decrease of light transmission observed when ristocetin was stirred with fixed washed platelets. The degree of decrease in light transmission was dependent on ristocetin concentration but independent of pH and plasma proteins. This effect may be related to a precipitation of fibrinogen on the surface of the platelet membrane (226). Ristocetin with plasma also causes multiple interruptions in the outer membrane and, at times, completely through the membrane (33). The latter suggests that ristocetin modifies the receptor to make it reactive to vWF. The second phase is due to the aggregation of the fixed washed platelets themselves, which is pH dependent.

Chemical modification of von Willebrand factor   Human vWF alone has no platelet-aggregating activity. However, preincubation of vWF with neuraminidase renders it capable of causing human platelet aggregation. When galactose oxidase is added to vWF preparations simultaneously with neuraminidase, no aggregating activity develops (229, 231). This suggests that human vWF, like PAF, interacts with platelets when galactose-containing side chains not terminated by sialic acid are exposed. Enzymatic treatment with thrombin results in no detectable change in vWF activity (242). This is in contrast to the ability of thrombin to increase the procoagulant activity of factor VIII. Plasmin, on the other hand, destroys both vWF and factor VIII activity. The disappearance of vWF activity after plasmin treatment occurs at a much slower rate than the disappearance of factor VIII activity measured in the same incubation mixture (60). After extensive degradation with plasmin, the products of vWF possess an inhibitory effect on platelet aggregation by undegraded vWF, ADP, collagen, and Thrombofax (53). However, the degradation products do not affect the thrombin time or partial thromboplastin time of normal plasma. In studies reporting inhibition of platelet aggregation by plasmin digests of fibrinogen, the preparations used also contained vWF. Inhibition of platelet aggregation by some plasmin digests may be due primarily to plasmin degradation products of vWF rather than fibrinogen (53). These findings suggest that the relationship of the inhibition of platelet aggregation by plasmin digests of human fibrinogen should be reexamined.

Treatment of normal human platelet-rich plasma with the sulfhydryl reactive agent P-chloromercuribenzoic acid (PCMB) inhibited platelet aggregation upon the addition of ristocetin. The inhibitory effect of PCMB was shown to be on the platelets and vWF activity was unaffected (114). vWF, previously shown to be unaffected by high salt concentrations, is dissociated under mild conditions with the sulfhydryl reducing agent dithiothreitol (DTT) (4, 5). The subunits produced by DTT are detectable by using both immunologic techniques and their functional ability to support ristocetin aggregation of washed human platelets.

It has recently been shown that ristocetin preparations contain a proteolytic contaminant that can cleave peptide bonds in fibrinogen and that can be inactivated by diisopropylphosphofluoridate (DFP). The proteolytic contaminant can be separated from ristocetin by Sephadex G-25 chromatography. DFP-treated ristocetin is still capable of aggregating normal human platelet-rich plasma (160) but the implications are clear that no activity of ristocetin preparations should be attributed to ristocetin itself until contaminating proteolytic activities have been eliminated.

Bernard-Soulier platelets and von Willebrand factor   Recent studies of platelets from subjects with the Bernard-Soulier syndrome (hereditary giant platelet syndrome) suggest that there may be a specific platelet membrane receptor for vWF. Unlike the platelets from vWD, the platelets from subjects with this syndrome do not aggregate with either PAF or with ristocetin and vWF (21, 42, 98), indicating a specific defect in the platelets, not in the plasma as in vWD. Bernard-Soulier platelet-poor plasma will correct ristocetin aggregation of vWD platelet-rich plasma, but Bernard-Soulier platelets suspended in normal platelet-poor plasma do not aggregate when ristocetin is added. It would appear that in these giant platelet syndromes the platelet surface apparently contains an abnormality that interferes with the ability of vWF in the presence of ristocetin to cause platelet aggregation. Bernard-Soulier platelets have normal to increased levels of factor VIII–related antigen associated with the membrane fraction of their lysed platelets (99). This suggests that, rather than a defect or absence of a specific receptor, the abnormality could be a blockage of all the vWF receptor sites.

von Willebrand factor variants   The vWF is not always reduced or absent in patients with vWD. Studying large numbers of patients with this disorder has shown that they are a heterogeneous group that can be divided into several more or less distinct types (68, 92, 93, 117, 120, 178, 223, 228). As with the various abnormal hemoglobinopathies, the classification of vWD may be approaching the molecular level. Evidence for the presence of vWF with abnormal physiochemical properties and aberrant function are being reported. Various possibilities for expression of the defect can be postulated. Among them are (*a*) failure to synthesize vWF or an essential precursor, (b) synthesis of an abnormal vWF that maintains some of the functional properties of normal vWF but not all, and (c) synthesis of vWF but abnormal retention or release from site of synthesis or storage.

Considerable progress has been made in studying vWF of animal and human plasma. Continued effort, however, is necessary to place in perspective the biological role of this factor and its relationship to factor VIII in hemostasis. Ultimately the progress should lead to further insight into the genetic and molecular abnormality of a heterogenous group of patients presently classified as having vWD.

PLATELET REACTIONS AT INTERFACES

The initial participation of platelets in hemostasis is their adhesion to exposed basement membrane and to altered vascular endothelium. The adhesion of platelets at interfaces is also observed on foreign surfaces, such as glass, various biomaterials used in vascular protheses, membrane oxygenators, vascular catheters, and at the air-liquid interface as in air embolism. The adhesion reaction at interfaces may involve the same basic mechanisms causing platelet-platelet cohesion in the formation of platelet aggregates, but certain aspects of the adhesion reaction appear unique. Although the basic mechanisms concerned with platelet adhesion are incompletely understood, the central roles of collagen, polymerizing fibrin, and plasma proteins adsorbed at interfaces are well established.

Collagen

The sequence of events of the platelet-collagen reaction appears to be first adhesion to the collagen fibril or microfibril, followed by activation of the platelet with the usual reactions of contraction, shape change, release, and aggregation. The tertiary structure of collagen (monomer) appears sufficient for its recognition by platelets— simple adhesion—but the quaternary structure (polymer) with a fibrillar arrangement appears essential for platelet activation (31). The highly ordered microfibrils of molecular weight of 10^6–10^9, like the particulate macrofibrils, bring about the platelet adhesion/aggregation reaction (108, 187). The soluble microfibrils may be the component responsible for platelet adhesion to subendothelial amorphous material (12). Platelets can not adhere to this material after it has been treated with collagenase.

Shape change and the contractile process may not be intrinsic parts of the adhesion reaction, separate from release and aggregation, since the inhibitors cytochalasin B, which preserves the discoid shape, and colchicine, which does not, both inhibited adhesion to collagen-coated surfaces (44, 45). Although ADP released from the platelet after contact with collagen undoubtedly contributes to the overall reaction (62, 164), ADP participation appears to be a secondary event, as the shape change associated with the collagen adhesion reaction appears independent of ADP-induced shape changes (44). Also, platelets refractory to ADP can still be aggregated with collagen (172). In addition, α- and β- receptor blocking agents that interfere with the ADP-induced release reaction do not inhibit the release induced by collagen (121). A number of materials have been reported to inhibit platelet adhesion to collagen (44, 134, 159), including an agent of endothelial cell origin that inhibits platelet response to collagen and other aggregation agents (196, 197). The adhesion of platelets to collagen does not require divalent cations and hence adhesion can be studied as a phenomenon distinct from aggregation in test systems deficient in cations.

A number of discrepancies regarding the nature of the collagen-platelet reaction are encountered in the recent literature. Unfortunately distinction is often not made of results obtained with methods that measure only adhesion and those that measure release and aggregation. Species variables of both blood reactivity and collagen may account for some of the discrepancies. Species differences in platelet reactivity may be considerable (141). It has been suggested that, in the rat, for example, platelet adhesion may not be the first event in hemostasis (221). Human, rat, and chick collagen may react differently (47, 113, 187). Tissue sources of collagen, such as skin, bone, tendon, and renal glomerulus, may also be significant variables (103, 187), since they may represent different types of collagen. Platelets react with vitreous collagen (219). Microcrystalline collagen, which has hemostatic properties, exerts its effect by inducing the platelet adhesion/aggregation reaction (142).

The biochemical basis of the collagen-platelet reaction is uncertain. Multiple types of reactions may occur. The substructure of collagen required for the reaction with platelets is important. One proposed mechanism for the adhesion of platelets to collagen is by the formation of an enzyme-acceptor complex. First proposed by Barber & Jamieson (9), the concept is that glucosyl transferases on the platelet surface attach to incomplete galactosyl hydroxylysine groups in collagen. The enzyme is contained both in the platelet membrane and cytoplasm and has been purified considerably (212). The theory has stimulated a tremendous amount of research regarding the critical role of carbohydrate side chains in platelet interactions (47, 113, 108, 187). Denatured chick skin collagen and specifically the α_1 chains have been shown to possess platelet aggregating activity (113, 115), while those of rats and cows are inactive (187). Only one of the cyanogen bromide peptides of chick skin α_1 chain can induce platelet aggregation and periodate treatment of the active glycopeptide demonstrated the need for carbohydrate. Chick and rat skin tropocollagen, however, both possess platelet aggregation activity that is resistant to periodate treatment and thus presumably independent of carbohydrate groups (113, 187).

Other reactions appear important for the collagen effect on platelets. It was shown years ago that SH-groups are important in platelet aggregation and that SH-inhibitors block the reaction (192). These groups may likewise be important in the collagen-platelet reaction; N-ethylmaleimide blocked adhesion to a collagen-coated surface (44). The possible role of plasma vWF in adhesion of platelets to collagen has been suggested in both in vitro (200) and in vivo (227) testing. The aspirin-induced prolonged bleeding time and platelet aggregation is associated with impaired collagen-platelet adhesion (78, 89) and has led to the suggestion that aspirin competes for the same platelet membrane sites as does collagen (78). On the other hand, in a standardized collagen test system, aspirin did not inhibit adhesion, only aggregation (134). Collagen in Ehlers-Danlos syndrome, previously shown to be abnormal in terms of its reactivity with platelets, may actually vary from one pedigree to another [a recent report (56) demonstrated normal reactivity]. The adhesion reaction of platelets with bacteria appears similar to the collagen adhesion/aggregation reaction (149). In addition, collagen, by its activation of factor XI on the platelet surface (235), may help activate the intrinsic clotting mechanism and thus participate in recruitment of fibrin clotting for hemostasis.

Fibrin

The platelet adhesion/aggregation phenomenon and fibrin clotting appear inextricably intermeshed at many points. The close structural relationship of fibrin and platelets in the hemostatic plug appears related to the platelet's interaction with partially polymerized fibrin (83, 162, 170). Fully formed fibrin appears inert. The reaction requires cation but, unlike fibrinogen, the polymerizing fibrin appears not to have an ADP cofactor effect (170), although divergent data on this point have been published. Platelet adherence to exposed vascular basement membrane thus may be to polymerizing fibrin as well as to exposed collagen.

Adsorbed Plasma Proteins

The interfacial adhesion reaction between the platelet and the plasma proteins adsorbed onto foreign surfaces exposed to blood has been studied both morphologically and biochemically (75, 110, 123, 146, 201). The strong attraction of the platelet to the adsorbed protein layer has given rise to the term *thrombogenic membrane.* This membrane varies both in morphology and composition according to the conditions of exposure to the blood or protein solution. Rheological factors (261) and the nature of the foreign surface, whether glass, silicone-treated surfaces, or relatively nonthrombogenic biomaterials, influence the dynamics and composition of the protein layer. This membrane forms not only at blood-solid interfaces but also at blood-air interfaces (236). Ultrastructural studies of the thrombogenic membrane reveal a delicate electron-dense structure, sometimes known as the Mason-Scarborough line (201), to which platelets adhere. Momentarily the platelets undergo no shape change. Then they flatten out to give the "cocked-hat" or "rising-sun" appearance, with progression to platelet aggregate-fibrin formation. This adhesion/aggregation reaction may remove a sufficient number of platelets from the circulation to cause thrombocytopenia, as has been observed in human subjects decompressed in a hyperbaric chamber (184).

The protein layer consists of the various plasma proteins; of these, fibrinogen, γ-globulin, albumin, and certain procoagulant fractions such as crude prothrombin concentrates are the most studied. Isotherm curves obtained with internal reflection infrared spectroscopy are consistent with Langmuir-type adsorption kinetics (30, 123). The adsorbed proteins of the thrombogenic membrane equilibrate with the dissolved proteins in their fluid environment. Thus adsorption and desorption may be responsible for the changing composition of the membrane with time. In the evolution of the membrane's composition, macromolecules, including fibrinogen, are somewhat selectively adsorbed initially, but albumin eventually becomes the major constituent (122, 123, 127, 128, 244). The qualitative changes responsible for the adsorbed proteins to attract platelets are not understood. While change in surface charge may have a role in platelet adhesion, it does not appear to be the essential reaction, since both the platelet and the protein layer have a net negative charge (232). Conformational changes in the adsorbed proteins have been considered but are also not believed responsible for platelet "chemotaxis" by the thrombogenic membrane (123). One suggestion is, as in collagen-platelet adhesion, that a complex enzyme-substrate bridge forms between the glycoproteins of the Mason-Scarborough membrane and the platelet glycosyltransferase (124). Fibrinogen and γ-globulins are the proposed glycoprotein acceptors for the transferase. Fibrinogen appears needed for the adhesion reaction (146), although only in trace amounts, as was demonstrated in studies with a patient with afibrinogenemia (143). In addition, fibrinogen coating of surfaces promotes cation-dependent platelet adhesion (110, 158). The simpler forms of glycoproteins appear the more reactive, suggesting that the more incomplete the glycosylation, the greater the attraction for the platelet. These findings are substantiated by the enzymatic modification of the carbohydrate moieties of the adsorbed proteins. Removal of sialic acid or galactose from proteins render them more reactive (124). Neuraminidase treatment given in vivo causes progressive platelet damage (48); in vitro, it reduces the electrophoretic mobility of platelets (25). Albumin with no carbohydrate residues is nonreactive. The higher the albumin content of the adsorbed layer, the less is the thrombogenicity of the surface. For example, precirculation of albumin solutions through membrane oxygenators and hemodialysis membranes reduces their capacity to trap platelets (63, 267). The highly charged polysaccharide, heparin, whether in the blood (18) or coated on the biomaterial surface (125), does not inhibit the adhesion reaction. Covalent bonding of Evan's Blue to the surface appears inhibitory to platelet adhesion, possibly by increasing the density of the negative charges (171).

A number of in vitro and in vivo model systems have been developed to assess the platelet adhesion reaction under different circumstances. In vitro test systems include those designed to judge the intrinsic adhesivity of the platelets (75, 140, 158) and those to determine the thrombogenicity of various biomaterials (129). A number of model systems to study the platelet adhesion reaction in the early stages of microthrombus formation have also been devised, including the adherence of platelets to glomerular basement membrane (103), exposed basement membrane of the abdominal aorta or heart valves of various experimental animals (132, 207, 208, 218), and after laser-induced injury of the microvasculature (3).

Platelet adhesion appears to be responsible in good part for trapping platelets observed with membrane oxygenators (63, 215), hemodialysis membranes (267), the cardiopulmonary bypass procedure (14, 191, 195), and isolated organ perfusion (59, 260). Also, hemoperfusion through thrombogenic materials such as activated charcoal (46) and ultrafilters (77) causes platelet trapping. The three-dimensional ultrastructure of platelets and leucocytes adherent to fibers of blood filters as well as of trapped microemboli has been well demonstrated (204). If venous catheters are used in the collection of blood for platelet studies, e.g. indwelling catheters, it should be recognized that platelets adhere to their surfaces (202). Retention of platelets in glass bead columns described by Hellem and co-workers several years ago (87) was attributed to simple platelet adhesion to glass, but it has now been well established that platelet aggregation with the release reaction is also responsible (86, 136, 154).

Literature Cited

1. Allain, J. P., Cooper, H. A., Wagner, R. H., Brinkhous, K. M. 1975. Platelets fixed with paraformaldehyde: a new reagent for assay of von Willebrand factor and platelet aggregating factor. *J. Lab. Clin. Med.* 85:318–28

2. Anderson, P., Slorach, S. A., Uvnäs, B. 1974. 5–HT storage in rat and rabbit blood platelets: The separation of ATP-containing and sulphomucopolysaccharide-containing granules. *Acta Physiol. Scand.* 90:522–32

3. Arfors, K. E., Bergqvist, D., Bygde-man, S., McKenzie, F. N., Svensjö, E. 1972. The effect of inhibition of the platelet release reaction on platelet behaviour in vitro and in vivo. *Scand. J. Haematol.* 9:322–32

4. Austen, D. E. G. 1974. Factor VIII of small molecular weight and its aggregation. *Br. J. Haematol.* 27:89–100

5. Austen, D. E. G., Carey, M., Howard, M. A. 1975. Dissociation of factor VIII-related antigen into subunits. *Nature* 253:55–56

6. Baldini, M. G., Ebbe, S., eds. 1974. *Platelets: Production, Function, Transfusion, and Storage.* New York: Grune & Stratton. 418 pp.

7. Bang, N. U., Heidenreich, R. O., Tryg-stad, C. W. 1972. Plasma protein requirements for human platelet aggregation. *Ann. NY Acad. Sci.* 201:280–99

8. Barber, A. J., Jamieson, G. A. 1971. Isolation of glycopeptides from high and low density platelet plasma membranes. *Biochemistry* 10:4711–17

9. Barber, A. J., Jamieson, G. A. 1971. Platelet collagen adhesion: characterization of collagen glucosyltransferase of plasma membranes of human blood platelets. *Biochim. Biophys. Acta* 252:533–45

10. Barber, A. J., Pepper, D. S., Jamieson, G. A. 1971. A comparison of methods for platelet lysis and the isolation of platelet membranes. *Thromb. Diath. Haemorrh.* 26:38–57

11. Baumgartner, H. R. 1973. The role of blood flow in platelet adhesion, fibrin deposition, and formation of mural thrombi. *Microvasc. Res.* 5:167–79

12. Baumgartner, H. R., Haudenschild, C. 1972. Adhesion of platelets to subendothelium. *Ann. NY Acad. Sci.* 201:22–36

13. Baumgartner, H. R., Grimm, L., Zbinden, G. 1973. Effect of generation of mural platelet thrombi on circulating blood in rabbit aorta. *Experientia* 29:442–45

14. Becker, R. M., Smith, M. R., Dobell, A. R. C. 1974. Effect of platelet inhibition on platelet phenomena in cardiopulmonary bypass in pigs. *Ann. Surg.* 179:52–57

15. Bennett, B., Ratnoff, O. D., Levin, J. 1972. Immunologic studies in von Willebrand's disease. Evidence that the antihemophilic factor (AHF) produced after transfusions lacks an antigen associated with normal AHF and the inactive material produced by patients with classic hemophilia. *J. Clin. Invest.* 51:2597–2601

16. Bennett, B., Oxnard, S. C., Douglas, A. S., Ratnoff, O. D. 1974. Studies on antihemophilic factor (AHF, factor VIII) during labor in normal women, in patients with premature separation of the placenta, and in a patient with von Willebrand's disease. *J. Lab. Clin. Med.* 84:851–60

17. Bennett, B., Ratnoff, O. D. 1972. Changes in antihemophilic factor (AHF, factor VIII) procoagulant activity and AHF-like antigen in normal pregnancy, and following exercise and pneumoencephalography. *J. Lab. Clin. Med.* 80:256–63

18. Bern, M. M., Tullis, J. L. 1974. Platelet adhesion from nonanticoagulated rat arterial blood. *Thromb. Diath. Haemorrh.* 31:493–504

19. Berger, S., Salzman, E. W. 1974. Thromboembolic complications of prosthetic devices. *Progr. Hemostasis Thromb.* 2:273–309

20. Bessis, M. 1973. *Living Blood Cells and Their Ultrastructure,* Chap. 4, 367–411, transl. R. I. Weed. New York, Heidelberg, Berlin: Springer-Verlag. 767 pp.

21. Bithell, T. C., Parekh, S. J., Strong, R. R. 1972. Platelet function studies in the Bernard-Soulier syndrome. *Ann. NY Acad. Sci.* 201:145–60

22. Bloom, A. L., Peake, I. R., Giddings, J. C. 1973. The presence and reactions of high and lower-molecular-weight procoagulant factor VIII in the plasma of patients with von Willebrand's disease after treatment: significance for a structural hypothesis for factor VIII. *Thromb. Res.* 3:389–404

23. Bloom, A. L., Giddings, J. C., Wilks, C. J. 1973. Factor VIII on the vascular intima: Possible importance in haemos-

tasis and thrombosis. *Nature New Biol.* 241:217–19

24. Booyse, F. M., Hoveke, T. P., Kisieleski, D., Rafelson, M. E. 1972. Mechanism and control of platelet-platelet interaction. I. Effects of inducers and inhibitors of aggregation. *Microvasc. Res.* 4:179–98

25. Bosmann, H. B. 1972. Platelet adhesiveness and aggregation. II. Surface sialic acid, glycoprotein: N-acetylneuraminic acid transferase, and neuraminidase of human blood platelets. *Biochim. Biophys. Acta* 279:456–74

26. Bouma, B. N. et al 1973. Factor-VIII antigen and platelet retention in a glass bead column. *Br. J. Haematol.* 25: 645–56

27. Bouma, B. N., Wiegerinck, Y., Sixma, J. J., van Mourik, J. A., Mochtar, I. A. 1972. Immunological characterization of purified anti-haemophilic factor A (factor VIII) which corrects abnormal platelet retention in von Willebrand's disease. *Nature New Biol.* 236:104–6

28. Bowie, E. J. W., Fass, D. N., Olson, J. D., Owen, C. A. 1974. Transfusion and autotransfusion of plasma in von Willebrand's disease. *Thromb. Res.* 5:479–94

29. Bowie, E. J. W., Owen, C. A. 1972. Abnormalities in platelet function associated with other congenital defects. Platelet abnormalities in von Willebrand's disease. *Ann. NY Acad. Sci.* 201:400–20

30. Brash, J. L., Uniyal, S., Samak, Q. 1974. Exchange of albumin adsorbed on polymer surfaces. *Trans. Am. Soc. Artif. Intern. Organs.* 20:69–76

31. Brass, L., Bensusan, H. 1975. The platelet: collagen interaction. *Fed. Proc.* 34:241

32. Breton-Gorius, J., Guichard, J. 1972. Ultrastructural localization of peroxidase activity in human platelets and megakaryocytes. *Am. J. Pathol.* 66:277–86

33. Brinkhous, K. M. 1975. Hemophilia and von Willebrand's disease—some biological determinants. *Am. J. Clin. Pathol.* 63:609–17

34. Brinkhous, K. M., Graham, J. E., Cooper, H. A., Allain, J. P., Wagner, R. H. 1975. Assay of von Willebrand factor in von Willebrand's disease and hemophilia: use of a macroscopic platelet aggregation test. *Thromb. Res.* 6:267–72

35. Brinkhous, K. M., Hinnom, S., eds. 1973. Thrombosis: Mechanisms and

Control. *Thromb. Diath. Haemorrh. Suppl.* 54:239–70, 345–57

36. Brinkhous, K. M., Johnson, J. H. 1972. *Thrombus. A Syllabus for Medical Students.* Kalamazoo, Mich: Upjohn Co. 32 pp.

37. Brinkhous, K. M., Shermer, R. W., Mostofi, F. K., eds. 1971. *The Platelet.* Baltimore, Md: Williams & Wilkins. 420 pp.

38. Brodie, G. N., Baenziger, N. L., Chase, L. R., Majerus, P. W. 1972. The effects of thrombin on adenyl cyclase activity and a membrane protein from human platelets. *J. Clin. Invest.* 51:81–88

39. Brown, J. E., Baugh, R. F., Sargeant, R. B., Hougie, C. 1974. Separation of bovine factor VIII-related antigen (platelet aggregating factor) from bovine antihemophilic factor. *Proc. Soc. Exp. Biol. Med.* 147:608–11

40. Burger, M. W. 1973. Surface changes in transformed cells detected by lectins. *Fed. Proc.* 32:91–101

41. Caen, J., ed. 1971. *Platelet Aggregation.* Paris: Masson. 228 pp.

42. Caen, J. P., Levy-Toledano, S. 1973. Interaction between platelets and von Willebrand factor provides a new scheme for primary haemostasis. *Nature New Biol.* 244:159–60

43. Caprino, L., Rossi, E. C., eds. 1974. *Platelet Aggregation and Drugs.* London: Academic. 298 pp.

44. Cazenave, J. P., Packham, M. A., Guccione, M. A., Mustard, J. F. 1974. Inhibition of platelet adherence to a collagen-coated surface by agents that inhibit platelet shape change and clot retraction. *J. Lab. Clin. Med.* 84:483–90

45. Cazenave, J. P., Packham, M. A., Mustard, J. F. 1973. Adherence of platelets to a collagen-coated surface: Development of a quantitative method. *J. Lab. Clin. Med.* 82:978–90

46. Chang, T. M. S. 1974. Platelet-surface interaction: Effect of albumin coating or heparin complexing on thrombogenic surfaces. *Can. J. Physiol. Pharmacol.* 52:275–85

47. Chesney, C. M., Harper, E., Colman, R. W. 1972. Critical role of the carbohydrate side chains of collagen in platelet aggregation. *J. Clin. Invest.* 51:2693–2701

48. Choi, S. I., Simone, J. V., Journey, L. J. 1972. Neuraminidase-induced thrombocytopenia in rats. *Br. J. Haematol.* 22:93–101

49. Clawson, C. C. 1973. Platelet interac-

tion with bacteria. III. Ultrastructure. *Am. J. Pathol.* 70:449–72

50. Cooper, H. A., Griggs, T. R., Wagner, R. H. 1973. Factor VIII recombination after dissociation by CaCl₂. *Proc. Nat. Acad. Sci. USA* 70:2326–29

51. Cooper, H. A., Wagner, R. H. 1974. The defect in hemophilic and von Willebrand's disease plasmas studied by a recombination technique. *J. Clin. Invest.* 54:1093–99

52. Crowley, J. P., Rene, A., Valeri, C. R. 1974. Changes in platelet shape and structure after freeze preservation. *Blood* 44:599–603

53. Culasso, D. E., Donati, M. B., de Gaetano, G., Vermylen, J., Verstraete, M. 1974. Inhibition of human platelet aggregation by plasmin digests of human and bovine fibrinogen preparations: role of contaminating factor VIII-related material. *Blood* 44:169–75

54. Davis, R. B. 1972. Ultrastructural characteristics of freeze-dried human blood platelets. *Am. J. Pathol.* 68:303–16

55. Dechavanne, M., Bryon, P. A., Thouverez, J. P., Viala, J. J. 1973. Étude comparative de l'ultrastructure et de l'excrétion induite par la thrombine d'une suspension de plaquettes lavées préparée à partir de sang prélevé sur EDTA et ACD "acidifié." *Pathol. Biol.* 21:1063–72

56. Deliyannis, A. A., Kontopoulou-Griva, I., Tsevrenis, H. V. 1974. Normal platelet aggregating properties of Ehlers-Danlos syndrome "collagen." *Thromb. Diath. Haemorrh.* 32:203–6

57. Denson, K. W. E. 1973. The detection of factor-VIII-like antigen in haemophilic carriers and in patients with raised levels of biologically active factor VIII. *Br. J. Haematol.* 24:451–61

58. Detwiler, T. C., Feinman, R. D. 1973. Kinetics of the thrombin-induced release of calcium (II) by platelets. *Biochemistry* 12:282–89

59. Dodds, W. J., Raymond, S. L., Pert, J. H. 1973. Isolated kidney perfusion: a model for testing platelet function. *Proc. Soc. Exp. Biol. Med.* 144:189–94

60. Donati, M. B., de Gaetano, G., Vermylen, J. 1973. Evidence that bovine factor VIII, not bovine fibrinogen, aggregates human platelets. *Thromb. Res.* 2:97–104

61. Droller, M. J. 1973. Ultrastructure of the platelet release reaction in response to various aggregating agents and their inhibitors. *Lab. Invest.* 29:595–606

62. Drummond, A. H., Gordon, J. L. 1974. Kinetics of the platelet release reaction induced by collagen. *Br. J. Pharmacol.* 52:130P–31P

63. Dutton, R. C., Edmunds, L. H. 1974. Formation of platelet aggregate emboli in a prototype hollow fiber membrane oxygenator. *J. Biomed. Mater. Res.* 8:163–83

64. Estensen, R. D., White, J. G. 1974. Ultrastructural features of the platelet response to phorbol myristate acetate. *Am. J. Pathol.* 74:441–52

65. Fass, D. N., Bowie, E. J. W., Owen, C. A., Mann, K. G. 1975. Stability of porcine factor VIII. *Thromb. Res.* 6:109–18

66. Feinman, R. D., Detwiler, T. C. 1974. Platelet secretion induced by divalent cation ionophores. *Nature* 249:172–73

67. Fields, W. S., Hass, W. K., eds. 1971. *Aspirin, Platelets and Stroke. Background for a Clinical Trial.* St. Louis, Mo: Green. 163 pp.

68. Firkin, B., Firkin, F., Stott, L. 1973. Von Willebrand's disease type B: a newly defined bleeding diathesis. *Aust. NZ J. Med.* 3:225–29

69. Elgjo, R., Følling, R. F., Hovig, T. 1972. Ultrastructural studies of platelet "activation" and aggregation in normal spleen from different species. *Scand. J. Haematol.* 9:587–602

70. Forbes, C. D., Barr, R. D., McNicol, G. P., Douglas, A. S. 1972. Aggregation of human platelets by commercial preparations of bovine and porcine antihaemophilic globulin. *J. Clin. Pathol.* 25:210–17

71. Forbes, C. D., Prentice, C. R. M. 1972/73. Aggregation of human platelets by commercial porcine and bovine fibrinogen preparations. *Haemostasis* 1:156–60

72. Forbes, C. D., Prentice, C. R. M. 1973. Aggregation of human platelets by purified porcine and bovine antihaemophilic factor. *Nature New Biol.* 241:149–50

73. Gangarosa, E. J., Johnson, T. R., Ramos, H. S. 1960. Ristocetin-induced thrombocytopenia: Site and mechanism of action. *Arch. Intern. Med.* 105:83–89

74. Ganguly, P. 1974. Binding of thrombin to human platelets. *Nature* 247:306–7

75. George, J. N. 1972. Direct assessment of platelet adhesion to glass: A study of the forces of interaction and the effects of plasma and serum factors, platelet function, and modifications of the glass surface. *Blood* 40:862–73

76. Gerrard, J. M., White, J. G., Rao, G. H. R. 1974. Effects of the ionophore A23187 on blood platelets. II. Influence on ultrastructure. *Am. J. Pathol.* 77:151–66
77. Gervin, A. S., Mason, K., Limbird, T., Silver, D. 1974. Ultrapore filter-induced thrombocytopenia. *Surgery* 75:566–72
78. Green, D., Dunne, B., Schmid, F. R., Rossi, E. C., Louis, G. 1973. A study of the variable response of human platelets to collagen: Relation to aspirin-induced inhibition of aggregation. *Am. J. Clin. Pathol.* 60:920–26
79. Greenberg, J. H., Jamieson, G. A. 1974. The effects of various lectins on platelet aggregation and release. *Biochim. Biophys. Acta* 345:231–42
80. Griggs, T. R., Cooper, H. A., Webster, W. P., Wagner, R. H., Brinkhous, K. M. 1973. Plasma aggregating factor (bovine) for human platelets: A marker for study of antihemophilic and von Willebrand factors. *Proc. Nat. Acad. Sci. USA* 70:2814–18
81. Griggs, T. R., Webster, W. P., Cooper, H. A., Wagner, R. H., Brinkhous, K. M. 1974. Von Willebrand factor: gene dosage relationships and transfusion response in bleeder swine—a new bioassay. *Proc. Nat. Acad. Sci. USA* 71:2087–90
82. Hampton, J. R., Mitchell, J. R. A. 1974. Platelet electrophoresis: the present position. *Thromb. Diath. Haemorrh.* 31:204–44
83. Han, P., Ardlie, N. G. 1974. The influence of pH, temperature, and calcium on platelet aggregation: Maintenance of environmental pH and platelet function for in vitro studies in plasma stored at 37°C. *Br. J. Haematol.* 26:373–89
84. Harris, G. L., Crawford, N. 1973. Isolation of pig platelet membranes and granules. Distribution and validity of marker enzymes. *Biochim. Biophys. Acta* 291:701–19
85. Hattori, A., Jinbo, C., Iizumi, T., Ito, S., Matsuoka, M. 1975. A scanning electron microscope study on hemostatic reaction. Early hemostatic plug formation and the effect of aspirin. *Arch. Histol. Jpn.* 37:343–64
86. Hattori, A., Tsukada, T., Ito, S., Koike, K., Matsuoka, M. 1974. Scanning electron microscope study of platelet "adhesiveness" to glass beads (Hellem II method). Normal subjects, the effect of aspirin and patients with von Willebrand's disease. *Thromb. Diath. Haemorrh. Suppl.* 60:447–57

87. Hellem, A. J. 1960. The adhesiveness of human blood platelets in vitro. *Scand. J. Clin. Lab. Invest.* 12(*Suppl.* 51):1–117
88. Henson, P. M., Spiegelberg, H. L. 1973. Release of serotonin from human platelets induced by aggregated immunoglobulins of different classes and subclasses. *J. Clin. Invest.* 52:1282–88
89. Hirsh, J., Street, D., Cade, J. F., Amy, H. 1973. Relation between bleeding time and platelet connective tissue reaction after aspirin. *Blood* 41:369–77
90. Hoak, J. C. 1972. Freeze-etching studies of human platelets. *Blood* 40:514–22
91. Holmberg, L., Mannucci, P. M., Turesson, I., Ruggeri, Z. M., Nilsson, I. M. 1974. Factor VIII antigen in the vessel walls in von Willebrand's disease and hemophilia A. *Scand. J. Haematol.* 13:33–38
92. Holmberg, L., Nilsson, I. M. 1972. Genetic variants of von Willebrand's disease. *Br. Med. J.* 3:317–20
93. Holmberg, L., Nilsson, I. M. 1973. Two genetic variants of von Willebrand's disease. *N. Engl. J. Med.* 288:595–98
94. Holmsen, H., Day, H. J., Stormorken, H. 1969. The blood platelet release reaction. *Scand. J. Haematol. Suppl.* 8:3–26
95. Hougie, C., Sargeant, R. B., Brown, J. E., Baugh, R. F. 1974. Evidence that factor VIII and the ristocetin aggregating factor (VIII$_{Rist}$) are separate molecular entities. *Proc. Soc. Exp. Biol. Med.* 147:58–61
96. Hovig, T., Grøttum, K. A. 1973. Lipid infusions in man. Ultrastructural studies on blood platelet uptake of fat particles. *Thromb. Diath. Haemorrh.* 29:450–60
97. Howard, M. A., Firkin, B. G. 1971. Ristocetin—a new tool in the investigation of platelet aggregation. *Thromb. Diath. Haemorrh.* 26:362–69
98. Howard, M. A., Hutton, R. A., Hardisty, R. M. 1973. Hereditary giant platelet syndrome: a disorder of a new aspect of platelet function. *Br. Med. J.* 2:586–88
99. Howard, M. A., Montgomery, D. C., Hardisty, R. M. 1974. Factor-VIII-related antigen in platelets. *Thromb. Res.* 4:617–24
100. Howard, M. A., Sawers, R. J., Firkin, B. G. 1973. Ristocetin: A means of differentiating von Willebrand's disease into two groups. *Blood* 41:687–90
101. Hoyer, L. W. 1973. Immunologic properties of antihemophilic factor. *Progr. Hematol.* 8:191–221

102. Hoyer, L. W., de los Santos, R. P., Hoyer, J. R. 1973. Antihemophilic factor antigen. Localization in endothelial cells by immunofluorescent microscopy. *J. Clin. Invest.* 52:2737–44
103. Huang, T. W., Lagunoff, D., Benditt, E. P. 1974. Nonaggregative adherence of platelets to basal lamina in vitro. *Lab. Invest.* 31:156–60
104. Hubbard, A. L., Cohn, Z. A. 1972. The enzymatic iodination of the red cell membrane. *J. Cell Biol.* 55:390–405
105. Hutton, R. A., Howard, M. A., Deykin, D., Hardisty, R. M. 1974. Methods for the separation of platelets from plasma. A comparison of functional and morphological integrity. *Thromb. Diath. Haemorrh.* 31:119–32
106. Israels, E. D., Nisli, G., Paraskevas, F., Israels, L. G. 1973. Platelet Fc receptor as a mechanism for Ag-Ab complex-induced platelet injury. *Thromb. Diath. Haemorrh.* 29:434–44
107. Jaffe, E. A., Hoyer, L. W., Nachman, R. L. 1973. Synthesis of antihemophilic factor antigen by cultured human endothelial cells. *J. Clin. Invest.* 52:2757–64
108. Jaffe, R., Deykin, D. 1974. Evidence for a structural requirement for the aggregation of platelets by collagen. *J. Clin. Invest.* 53:875–83
109. Jamieson, G. A., Fuller, N. A., Barber, A. J., Lombart, C. 1971. Membrane glycoproteins of human platelets. *Ser. Haematol.* 4(1):125–34
110. Jenkins, C. S. P., Packham, M. A., Guccione, M. A., Mustard, J. F. 1973. Modification of platelet adherence to protein-coated surfaces. *J. Lab. Clin. Med.* 81:280–90
111. Jenkins, C. S. P., Packham, M. A., Kinlough-Rathbone, R. L., Mustard, J. F. 1971. Interactions of polylysine with platelets. *Blood* 37:395–412
112. Johnson, S. A., ed. 1971. *The Circulating Platelet.* New York: Academic. 601 pp.
113. Kang, A. H., Beachey, E. H., Katzman, R. L. 1974. Interaction of an active glycopeptide from chick skin collagen (α1-CB5) with human platelets. *J. Biol. Chem.* 249:1054–59
114. Kattlove, H. E., Gomez, M. H. 1975. Studies on the mechanism of ristocetin-induced platelet aggregation. *Blood* 45:91–96
115. Katzman, R. L., Kang, A. H., Beachey, E. H. 1973. Collagen-induced platelet aggregation: involvement of an active glycopeptide fragment (α1-CB5). *Science* 181:670–71
116. Kaulen, H. D., Gross, R. 1973. Metabolic properties of human platelet membranes. I. Characterization of platelet membranes prepared by sucrose and Ficoll density gradients. *Thromb. Diath. Haemorrh.* 30:199–214
117. Kernoff, P. B. A., Gruson, R., Rizza, C. R. 1974. A variant of factor VIII related antigen. *Br. J. Haematol.* 26:435–40
118. Kernoff, P. B. A., Rizza, C. R., Kaelin, A. C. 1974. Transfusion and gel filtration studies in von Willebrand's disease. *Br. J. Haematol.* 28:357–70
119. Kessler, S., Kuhn, C. 1975. Scanning electron microscopy of mast cell degranulation. *Lab. Invest.* 32:71–77
120. Koutts, J., Stott, L., Sawers, R. J., Firkin, B. G. 1974. Variant patterns in von Willebrand's disease. *Thromb. Res.* 5:557–64
121. Kubisz, P., Suranova, J. 1972. The effect of alpha- and beta-receptor blocking agents on collagen-induced platelet release reaction (a comparison with ADP-induced release). *Thromb. Diath. Haemorrh.* 27:278–91
122. Lee, R. G., Adamson, C., Kim, S. W. 1974. Competitive adsorption of plasma proteins onto polymer surfaces. *Thromb. Res.* 4:485–90
123. Lee, R. G., Kim, S. W. 1974. Adsorption of proteins onto hydrophobic polymer surfaces: Adsorption isotherms and kinetics. *J. Biomed. Mater. Res.* 8:251–59
124. Lee, R. G., Kim, S. W. 1974. The role of carbohydrate in platelet adhesion to foreign surfaces. *J. Biomed. Mater. Res.* 8:393–98
125. Leininger, R. I., Crowley, J. P., Falb, R. D., Grode, G. A. 1972. Three years' experience in vivo and in vitro with surfaces and devices treated by the heparin complex method. *Trans. Am. Soc. Artif. Intern. Organs* 18:312–15
126. Levy-Toledano, S., Caen, J. P., Halmos, T., Mester, L. 1973. Dissociation between human platelet agglomerating activity and factor VIII procoagulant activity of bovine plasma preparations by chemical treatment. I. Effect of neuraminidase. *Pathol. Biol. Suppl.* 21:60–62
127. Limber, G. K., Glenn, C. H., Mason, R. G. 1974. Studies of the proteins elutable from certain artificial surfaces exposed to human plasma. *Thromb. Res.* 5:735–46
128. Limber, G. K., Mason, R. G. 1975. Studies of proteins elutable from cupro-

phane exposed to human plasma. *Thromb. Res.* 6:421–30

129. Lindsay, R. M., Prentice, C. R. M., Ferguson, D., Muir, W. M., McNicol, G. P. 1973. A method for the measurement of platelet adhesiveness by use of dialysis membranes in a test-cell. *Br. J. Haematol.* 24:377–89

130. Lis, H., Sharon, N. 1973. The biochemistry of plant lectins (phytohemagglutinins). *Ann. Rev. Biochem.* 42:541–74

131. Lombart, C., Okumura, T., Jamieson, G. A. 1974. Isolation of a surface glycoprotein of human platelets. *FEBS Lett.* 41:30–34

132. Maca, R. D., Hoak, J. C. 1974. Endothelial injury and platelet aggregation associated with acute lipid mobilization. *Lab. Invest.* 30:589–95

133. Macfarlane, R. G., Biggs, R., Bidwell, E. 1954. Bovine antihaemophilic globulin in the treatment of haemophilia. *Lancet* 1:1316–19

134. MacKenzie, R. D., Thompson, R. J., Gleason, E. M. 1974. Evaluation of a quantitative platelet-collagen adhesiveness test system. *Thromb. Res.* 5:99–109

135. McNicol, G. P., Mitchell, J. R. A., Reuter, H., van de Loo, J. 1974. Platelets in thrombosis. Their clinical significance and the evaluation of potential drugs. *Thromb. Diath. Haemorrh.* 31:379–94

136. McPherson, V. J., Zucker, M. B., Friedberg, N. M., Rifkin, P. L. 1974. Platelet retention in glass bead columns: Further evidence for the importance of ADP. *Blood* 44:411–25

137. Majerus, P. W., Brodie, G. N. 1972. The binding of phytohemagglutinins to human platelet plasma membranes. *J. Biol. Chem.* 247:4253–57

138. Mannucci, P. M., Gorini, S., eds. 1972. *Platelet Function and Thrombosis. A Review of Methods.* New York: Plenum. 358 pp.

139. Martin, J. H., Carson, F. L., Race, G. J. 1974. Calcium-containing platelet granules. *J. Cell Biol.* 60:775–77

140. Mason, R. G., Gilkey, J. M. 1971. A simple test for quantitation of platelet adhesion to glass. Studies in bleeder and nonbleeder subjects. *Thromb. Diath. Haemorrh.* 25:21–29

141. Mason, R. G., Read, M. S. 1967. Platelet response to six agglutinating agents: Species similarities and differences. *Exp. Mol. Pathol.* 6:370–81

142. Mason, R. G., Read, M. S. 1974. Some effects of a microcrystalline collagen

preparation on blood. *Haemostasis* 3:31–45

143. Mason, R. G., Read, M. S., Brinkhous, K. M. 1971. Effect of fibrinogen concentration on platelet adhesion to glass. *Proc. Soc. Exp. Biol. Med.* 137:680–82

144. Mason, R. G., Read, M. S., Shermer, R. W. 1974. Comparison of certain functions of human platelets separated from blood by various means. *Am. J. Pathol.* 76:323–32

145. Mason, R. G., Sarji, K., Brinkhous, K. M. 1974. Antithrombotic agents: their effects on platelets and methods for their evaluation. *Principles and Techniques of Human Research and Therapeutics: Vol 5, Cardiovascular Drugs,* ed. F. G. McMahon, E. D. Frohlich, F. H. Gross, R. F. Palmer, A. J. Seaman. 183–99. Mount Kisco, NY: Futura. 269 pp.

146. Mason, R. G., Shermer, R. W., Zucker, W. H. 1973. Effects of certain purified plasma proteins on the compatibility of glass with blood. *Am. J. Pathol.* 73:183–200

147. Massini, P., Lüscher, E. F. 1972. On the mechanism by which cell contact induces the release reaction of blood platelets; the effect of cationic polymers. *Thromb. Diath. Haemorrh.* 27:121–33

148. Massini, P., Metcalf, L. C., Näf, U., Lüscher, E. F. 1974. Induction of aggregation and of the release reaction in human platelets by polylysine. *Haemostasis* 3:8–19

149. Maupin, B. 1969. *Blood Platelets in Man and Animals.* Oxford: Pergamon. 2 vols. 541 pp., 487 pp.

150. Maxwell, M. H. 1974. An ultrastructural comparison of the mononuclear leucocytes and thrombocytes in six species of domestic bird. *J. Anat.* 117:69–80

151. Mazurier, C., Parquet-Gernez, A., Goudemand, M. 1973. Action des anticorps anti-facteur VIII sur la rétention des plaquettes aux billes de verre. *Pathol. Biol. Suppl.* 21:72–75

152. Mello Périssé, A. C., Soria, J., Soria, C., Mester, L. 1973. Dissociation between human platelet agglomerating activity and factor VIII procoagulant activity of bovine plasma preparations by chemical treatment. II. Effect of periodate oxidation. *Pathol. Biol. Suppl.* 2:63–65

153. Metcalf, L. C., Lyman, D. J. 1974. The effect of conformational changes on the blood platelet reactivity of polylysine. *Thromb. Res.* 5:709–17

154. Meyer, D. 1972. In vitro platelet adhesiveness. Methods of study and clinical significance. *Adv. Exp. Med. Biol.* 34: 123–47

155. Meyer, D., Dreyfus, M. D., Larrieu, M. J. 1973. Willebrand factor: immunological and biological study. *Pathol. Biol.* 21, Suppl: 66–71

156. Meyer, D., Jenkins, C. S. P., Dreyfus, M., Larrieu, M. J. 1973. An experimental model for von Willebrand's disease. *Nature* 243:293–94

157. Meyer, D., Lavergne, J.-M., Larrieu, M.-J., Josso, F. 1972. Cross-reacting material in congenital factor VIII deficiencies (haemophilia A and von Willebrand's disease). *Thromb. Res.* 1: 183–96

158. Mohammad, S. F. et al 1975. Adhesion of human blood platelets to glass and polymer surfaces. I. Studies with platelets in plasma. *Haemostasis* 3:257–70

159. Mohammad, S. F., Mason, R. G. 1974. Inhibition of human platelet-collagen adhesion reaction by amitriptyline and imipramine. *Proc. Soc. Exp. Biol. Med.* 145:1106–13

160. Morgan, F. J., Goh, A., Firkin, B. G. 1974. Proteolytic activity in platelet preparations. *Thromb. Res.* 5:565–69

161. Mueller-Eckhardt, C., Lüscher, E. F. 1968. Immune reactions of human blood platelets. I. A comparative study on the effects on platelets of heterologous antiplatelet antiserum, antigen-antibody complexes, aggregated gammaglobulin and thrombin. *Thromb. Diath. Haemorrh.* 20:155–67

162. Müller-Berghaus, G., Heinrich, D. 1972. Fibrin monomer and platelet aggregation in vitro and in vivo. *Br. J. Haematol.* 23:177–88

163. Muntz, R. H., Ekert, H., Helliger, H. 1974. Properties of post-infusion factor VIII in von Willebrand's disease. *Thromb. Res.* 5:111–23

164. Murakami, M., Yoshino, K., Takase, M., Odake, K. 1972. Adenine nucleotide metabolism of human platelets during collagen-induced aggregation. *Thromb. Diath. Haemorrh.* 27:416–24

165. Murphy, E. A., Salzman, E. W. 1972. Platelet adhesiveness in von Willebrand's disease: A cooperative study. *Thromb. Diath. Haemorrh. Suppl.* 51:341–76

166. Murphy, M. J. 1972. The shape of blood platelets. An application of lyophilisation and scanning electron microscopy. *Thromb. Diath. Haemorrh.* 28:237–43

167. Nachman, R. L., Ferris, B. 1972. Studies on the proteins of human platelet membranes. *J. Biol. Chem.* 247: 4468–75

168. Nachman, R. L., Hubbard, A., Ferris, B. 1973. Iodination of the human platelet membrane. Studies of the major surface glycoprotein. *J. Biol. Chem.* 248: 2928–36

169. Nathaniel, E. J. H., Nathaniel, D. R., Nordöy, A. F., Chandler, A. B. 1972. Electron microscopic observations of platelets in rats fed on different fat diets. *J. Ultrastruct. Res.* 38:360–70

170. Niewiarowski, S., Regoeczi, E., Stewart, G. J., Senyi, A. F., Mustard, J. F. 1972. Platelet interaction with polymerizing fibrin. *J. Clin. Invest.* 51:685–700

171. Nishizawa, E. E., Wynalda, D. J., Lednicer, D. 1973. Non-thrombogenic surface inhibiting platelet adherence. *Trans. Am. Soc. Artif. Intern. Organs* 19:13–18

172. Nunn, B. 1972. The role of adenosine diphosphate (ADP) in collagen-induced platelet aggregation. *Br. J. Pharmacol.* 46:579P–80P

173. O'Brien, J. H., ed. 1972. *Clinics in Haematology, Vol. I: Platelet Disorders,* 231–444. London: Saunders

174. Olson, J. D., Brockway, W. J., Fass, D. N., Magnuson, M. A., Bowie, E. J. W. 1975. Evaluation of ristocetin-Willebrand factor assay and ristocetin-induced platelet aggregation. *Am. J. Clin. Pathol.* 63:210–18

175. Olson, J. D., Fass, D. N., Bowie, E. J. W., Mann, K. G. 1973. Ristocetin-induced aggregation of gel filtered platelets. A study of von Willebrand's disease and the effect of aspirin. *Thromb. Res.* 3:501–14

176. Owen, W. G., Wagner, R. H. 1972. Antihemophilic factor: separation of an active fragment following dissociation by salts or detergents. *Thromb. Diath. Haemorrh.* 27:502–15

177. Paulus, J. M. 1971. *Platelet Kinetics. Radioisotopic, Cytological, Mathematical and Clinical Aspects.* Amsterdam: North-Holland. 360 pp.

178. Peake, I. R., Bloom, A. L., Giddings, J. C. 1974. Inherited variants of factor-VIII-related protein in von Willebrand's disease. *N. Engl. J. Med.* 291:113–17

179. Pfueller, S. L., Lüscher, E. F. 1972. The effects of aggregated immunoglobulins on human blood platelets in relation to their complement-fixing abilities. I.

Studies of immunoglobulins of different types. *J. Immunol.* 109:517–25

180. Pfueller, S. L., Lüscher, E. F. 1972. The effects of immune complexes on blood platelets and their relationship to complement activation. *Immunochemistry* 9:1151–65

181. Phillips, D. R. 1972. Effect of trypsin on the exposed polypeptides and glycoproteins in the human platelet membrane. *Biochemistry* 11:4582–88

182. Phillips, D. R., Agin, P. P. 1974. Thrombin substrates and proteolytic site of thrombin action on human-platelet plasma membranes. *Biochim. Biophys. Acta* 352:218–27

183. Phillips, D. R., Morrison, M. 1971. Exposed protein on the intact human erythrocyte. *Biochemistry* 10:1766–71

184. Philp, R. B., Inwood, M. J., Ackles, K. N., Radomski, M. W. 1974. Effects of decompression on platelets and hemostasis in men and the influence of antiplatelet drugs (RA233 and VK744). *Aerospace Med.* 45:231–40

185. Prentice, C. R. M., Forbes, C. D., Smith, S. M. 1972. Rise of factor VIII after exercise and adrenaline infusion, measured by immunological and biological techniques. *Thromb. Res.* 1:493–506

186. Pudlak, P., Libansky, F., Hermansky, F., eds. 1972. *The Role of Platelets in Haemostasis and Thrombosis. Acta Univ. Carol. Med. Monogr.,* 53–54. 471 pp.

187. Puett, D., Wasserman, B. K., Ford, J. D., Cunningham, L. W. 1973. Collagen-mediated platelet aggregation. Effects of collagen modification involving the platelet and carbohydrate moieties. *J. Clin. Invest.* 52:2495–2506

188. Rafelson, M. E., Hoveke, T. P., Booyse, F. M. 1973. The molecular biology of platelet-platelet and platelet-endothelial interactions. *Ser. Haematol.* 6:367–81

189. Reddick, R. L., Mason, R. G. 1973. Freeze-etch observations on the plasma membrane and other structures of normal and abnormal platelets. *Am. J. Pathol.* 70:473–88

190. Rick, M. E., Hoyer, L. W. 1973. Immunologic studies of antihemophilic factor (AHF, factor VIII). V. Immunologic properties of AHF subunits produced by salt dissociation. *Blood* 42:737–47

191. Rittenhouse, E. A., Hessel, E. A., Ito, C. S., Merendino, K. A. 1972. Effect of dipyridamole on microaggregate forma-tion in the pump oxygenator. *Ann. Surg.* 175:1–9

192. Robinson, C. W., Mason, R. G., Wagner, R. H. 1963. Effect of sulfhydryl inhibitors on platelet agglutinability. *Proc. Soc. Exp. Biol. Med.* 113:857–61

193. Rodman, N. F. 1973. Thrombosis. *The Inflammatory Process,* ed. B. W. Zweifach, L. Grant, R. T. McCluskey, 2:363–92. New York: Academic. 2nd ed. 418 pp.

194. Root, W. S., Berlin, N. I., eds. 1974. *Physiological Pharmacology, Vol. 5: Blood,* 99–133, 177–249. New York: Academic. 588 pp.

195. Ross, J. N. et al 1974. Role of platelet aggregation in prolonged extracorporeal respiratory support. *Circulation* 50, Suppl. II:219–35

196. Saba, S. R., Mason, R. G. 1974. Studies of an activity from endothelial cells that inhibits platelet aggregation, serotonin release, and clot retraction. *Thromb. Res.* 5:747–57

197. Saba, S. R., Zucker, W. H., Mason, R. G. 1973. Some properties of endothelial cells isolated from human umbilical cord vein. *Ser. Haematol.* 6: 46–68

198. Sahud, M. A. 1972. Platelet disorders. A review of disturbances in adhesion, aggregation, and release reaction. *Calif. Med.* 116:21–31

199. Salzman, E. W. 1972. Surface effects in hemostasis and thrombosis. *The Chemistry of Biosurfaces,* ed. M. L. Hair, 2:489–522. New York: Dekker

200. Sarji, K. E., Stratton, R. D., Wagner, R. H., Brinkhous, K. M. 1974. Nature of von Willebrand factor: a new assay and a specific inhibitor. *Proc. Nat. Acad. Sci. USA* 71:2937–41

201. Scarborough, D. E., Mason, R. G., Dalldorf, F. G., Brinkhous, K. M. 1969. Morphologic manifestations of blood-solid interfacial reactions. A scanning and transmission electron microscopic study. *Lab. Invest.* 20:164–69

202. Schlossman, D. 1973. Thrombogenic properties of vascular catheter materials in vivo. A device and objective method of comparing thrombus formation on vascular catheter materials. *Acta Radiol. Diagn.* 14:97–105

203. Schneider, M. D. 1972. Preparative technique for platelet preservation for SEM. *Scanning Electron Microsc.* Pt. 2:343–49 Chicago: IIT Res. Inst.

204. Schneider, M. D. 1974. Particulate emboli retained by bypass blood filters. *Scand. J. Haematol.* 12:185–203

205. Sedar, A. W., Silver, M. J., Smith, J. B., Ingerman, C. M., Kocsis, J. J. 1974. Ultrastructural changes in human platelets during arachidonic acid-induced aggregation. *Blood* 44:177–87

206. Shearn, S. A. M., Giddings, J. C., Peake, I. R., Bloom, A. L. 1974. A comparison of five different rabbit antisera to factor VIII and the demonstration of a factor VIII related antigen in normal and von Willebrand's disease platelets. *Thromb. Res.* 5:585–99

207. Sheppard, B. L. 1972. Platelet adhesion in the rabbit abdominal aorta following removal of endothelium with EDTA. *Proc. R. Soc. London Ser. B* 182:103–8

208. Sheppard. B. L. 1972. The effect of acetylsalicyclic acid on platelet adhesion in the injured abdominal aorta. *Q. J. Exp. Physiol.* 57:319–23

209. Sherry, S., Scriabine, A., eds. 1974. *Platelets and Thrombosis.* Baltimore, Md: Univ. Park Press. 332 pp.

210. Shirasawa, K., Barton, B. P., Chandler, A. B. 1972. Localization of ferritin-conjugated anti-fibrin/fibrinogen in platelet aggregates produced in vitro. *Am. J. Pathol.* 66:379–406

211. Shulman, N. R., Lange, R. F., Tomasulo, P. A., Coleman, C. N. 1973. Antibodies and platelet membranes. *Thromb. Diath. Haemorrh. Suppl.* 54:261–70

212. Smith, D. F., Kosow, D. P., Jamieson, G. A. 1975. Mechanism of collagen: glycosyltransferase and relation to platelet:collagen adhesion. *Fed. Proc.* 34:241

213. Stemerman, M. B. 1974. Platelet interaction with intimal connective tissue. *Platelets: Production, Function, Transfusion, and Storage,* 157–70, ed. M. G. Baldini and S. Ebbe. New York: Grune & Stratton. 418 pp.

214. Steiner, M. 1973. Effect of thrombin on the platelet membrane. *Biochim. Biophys. Acta* 323:653–58

215. Stibbe, J. et al 1973/74. Influence of prostaglandin E_1 on platelet decrease in the heart-lung machine. *Haemostasis* 2:294–303

216. Stoltzner, G., Dzoga, K., Wissler, R. W. 1972. Electron microscopy of ferritin-labeled platelet-specific antibody. *Lab. Invest.* 27:357–65

217. Stoner, G. E., Chisolm, G. M., Srinivasan, S., Lucas, T. R., Sawyer, P. N. 1974. Vascular injury and thrombosis: a scanning electron microscopic study. *Thromb. Res.* 4:699–706

218. Suresh, A. D., Stemerman, M. B., Spaet, T. H. 1973. Rabbit heart valve basement membrane: Low platelet reactivity. *Blood* 41:359–67

219. Swann, D. A. et al 1974. The role of vitreous collagen in platelet aggregation in vitro and in vivo. *J. Lab. Clin. Med.* 84:264–74

220. Tangen, O., McKinnon, E. L., Berman, H. J. 1973. On the fine structure and aggregation requirements of gel filtered platelets (GFP). *Scand. J. Haematol.* 10:96–105

221. Thilo, D., Böhm, E. 1973. A 3.5-second phenomenon in haemostasis. A scanning electron microscopic study. *Thromb. Diath. Haemorrh.* 30:363–70

222. Thompson, C., Forbes, C. D., Prentice, C. R. M. 1973. Relationship of factor VIII to ristocetin-induced platelet aggregation; effect of heterologous and acquired factor VIII antibodies. *Thromb. Res.* 3:363–72

223. Thompson, C., Forbes, C. D., Prentice, C. R. M. 1974. Evidence for a qualitative defect in factor-VIII-related antigen in von Willebrand's disease. *Lancet* 1:594–97

224. Tollefsen, D. M., Feagler, J. R., Majerus, P. W. 1974. The binding of thrombin to the surface of human platelets. *J. Biol. Chem.* 249:2646–51

225. Tollefsen, D. M., Feagler, J. R., Majerus, P. W. 1974. Induction of the platelet release reaction by phytohemagglutinin. *J. Clin. Invest.* 53:211–18

226. Ts'ao, C. H., Green, D., Rossi, E. C. 1973. Ultrastructure of ristocetin aggregated normal human platelets: Tortuous boundaries and swollen granules. *Scand. J. Haematol.* 11:287–97

227. Tschopp, T. B., Weiss, H. J., Baumgartner, H. R. 1974. Decreased adhesion of platelets to subendothelium in von Willebrand's disease. *J. Lab. Clin. Med.* 83:296–300

228. Veltkamp, J. J., van Tilberg, N. H. 1974. Autosomal haemophilia: a variant of von Willebrand's disease. *Br. J. Haematol.* 26:141–52

229. Vermylen, J., de Gaetano, G., Donati, M. B., Verstraete, M. 1974. Platelet aggregating activity in neuraminidase-treated human cryoprecipitates: Its correlation with factor-VIII-related antigen. *Br. J. Haematol.* 26:645–50

230. Vermylen, J., de Gaetano, G., Verstraete, M., eds. 1971. Round-the-table conference on normal and modified platelet aggregation. *Acta Med. Scand. Suppl.* 525:3–289

231. Vermylen, J., Donati, M. B., de Gaetano, G., Verstraete, M. 1973. Aggregation of human platelets by bovine or human factor VIII: Role of carbohydrate side chains. *Nature* 244:167–68

232. Vroman, L. 1974. Surface charge, protein adsorption, and thrombosis. *Science* 184:585–86

233. Vroman, L., Adams, A. L. 1969. Identification of rapid changes at plasma-solid interfaces. *J. Biomed. Mater. Res.* 3:43–67

234. Wagner, R. H., Cooper, H. A., Owen, W. G. 1973. Dissociation of antihemophilic factor and separation of a small active fragment. *Thromb. Diath. Haemorrh. Suppl.* 44:185–90

235. Walsh, P. N. 1972. The effect of collagen and kaolin on the intrinsic coagulant activity of platelets. Evidence for an alternative pathway in intrinsic coagulation not requiring factor XII. *Br. J. Haematol.* 22:393–405

236. Warren, B. A., Philp, R. B., Inwood, M. J. 1973. The ultrastructural morphology of air embolism: Platelet adhesion to the interface and endothelial damage. *Br. J. Exp. Pathol.* 54:163–72

237. Warren, B. A., Vales, O. 1972. The adhesive dendritic pseudopodium of the platelet and the release reaction. *Microvasc. Res.* 4:159–78

238. Warren, B. A., Vales, O. 1972. The release of vesicles from platelets following adhesion to vessel walls in vitro. *Br. J. Exp. Pathol.* 53:206–15

239. Wautier, J. L., Tobelem, G. M., Peltier, A. P., Caen, J. P. 1973–1974. Evidence for C1 on human platelets. *Haemostasis* 2:281–86

240. Weiss, H. J., ed. 1972. Platelets and their role in hemostasis. *Ann. NY Acad. Sci.* 201:3–450

241. Weiss, H. J., Ames, R. P. 1973. Ultrastructural findings in storage pool disease and aspirin-like defects of platelets. *Am. J. Pathol.* 71:447–66

242. Weiss, H. J., Hoyer, L. W. 1973. von Willebrand factor: dissociation from antihemophilic factor procoagulant activity. *Science* 182:1149–51

243. Weiss, H. J., Hoyer, L. W., Rickles, F. R., Varma, A., Rogers, J. 1973. Quantitative assay of a plasma factor deficient in von Willebrand's disease that is necessary for platelet aggregation. *J. Clin. Invest.* 52:2708–16

244. Weiss, H. J., Phillips, L. L., Rosner, W. 1972. Separation of subunits of antihemophilic factor (AHF) by agarose

gel chromatography. *Thromb. Diath. Haemorrh.* 27:212–19

245. Weiss, H. J., Rogers, J. 1972. Correction of the platelet abnormality in von Willebrand's disease by cryoprecipitate. *Am. J. Med.* 53:734–38

246. Weiss, H. J., Rogers, J., Brand, H. 1973. Properties of the platelet retention (von Willebrand) factor and its similarity to the antihemophilic factor (AHF). *Blood* 41:809–15

247. Weiss, H. J., Rogers, J., Brand, H. 1973. Defective ristocetin-induced platelet aggregation in von Willebrand's disease and its correction by factor VIII. *J. Clin. Invest.* 52:2697–2707

248. White, J. G. 1972. Interaction of membrane systems in blood platelets. *Am. J. Pathol.* 66:295–312

249. White, J. G. 1972. Effects of cationic polypeptides on thrombasthenic and afibrinogenemic blood platelets. *Am. J. Pathol.* 68:447–60

250. White, J. G. 1972. Exocytosis of secretory organelles from blood platelets incubated with cationic polypeptides. *Am. J. Pathol.* 69:41–54

251. White, J. G. 1972. Uptake of latex particles by blood platelets. Phagocytosis or sequestration? *Am. J. Pathol.* 69: 439–58

252. White, J. G. 1973. Identification of platelet secretion in the electron microscope. *Ser. Haematol.* 6:429–59

253. White, J. G. 1974. Shape change. *Thromb. Diath. Haemorrh. Suppl.* 60:159–71

254. White, J. G., Conard, W. J. 1973. The fine structure of freeze-fractured blood platelets. *Am. J. Pathol.* 70:45–56

255. White, J. G., Estensen, R. D. 1972. Degranulation of discoid platelets. *Am. J. Pathol.* 68:289–96

256. White, J. G., Estensen, R. D. 1974. Cytochemical electron microscopic studies of the action of phorbol myristate acetate on platelets. *Am. J. Pathol.* 74:453–66

257. White, J. G., Krumwiede, M. 1973. Influence of cytochalasin B on the shape change induced in platelets by cold. *Blood* 41:823–32

258. White, J. G., Rao, G. H. R., Gerrard, J. M. 1974. Effects of the ionophore A23187 on blood platelets. I. Influence on aggregation and secretion. *Am. J. Pathol.* 77:135–50

259. White, J. G., Witkop, C. J. 1972. Effects of normal and aspirin platelets on defective secondary aggregation in the Hermansky-Pudlak syndrome. A test for

storage pool deficient platelets. *Am. J. Pathol.* 68:57–66

260. White, M. K., Shepro, D., Hechtman, H. B. 1973. Pulmonary function and platelet-lung interaction. *J. Appl. Physiol.* 34:697–703

261. Yu, S. K., Goldsmith, H. L. 1973. Behavior of model particles and blood cells at spherical obstructions in tube flow. *Microvasc. Res.* 6:5–31

262. Zimmerman, T. S., Edgington, T. S. 1973. Factor VIII coagulant activity and factor VIII-like antigen: Independent molecular entities. *J. Exp. Med.* 138:1015–20

263. Zimmerman, T. S., Edgington, T. S. 1974. Molecular immunology of factor VIII. *Ann. Rev. Med.* 25:303–14

264. Zimmerman, T. S., Müller-Eberhard, H. J. 1973. Complement-induced platelet protein alterations. *Science* 180: 1183–85

265. Zimmerman, T. S., Ratnoff, O. D., Powell, A. E. 1971. Immunologic differentiation of classic hemophilia (factor VIII deficiency) and von Willebrand's disease. *J. Clin. Invest.* 50: 244–54

266. Zucker, W. H., Shermer, R. W., Mason, R. G. 1974. Ultrastructural comparison of human platelets separated from blood by various means. *Am. J. Pathol.* 77:255–68

267. Zucker, W. H., Shinoda, B. A., Mason, R. G. 1974. Experimental interactions of components of hemodialysis units with human blood. *Am. J. Pathol.* 75:139–60

OVERALL CARDIOVASCULAR REGULATION[1]

♦1159

Bengt Öberg

Department of Physiology, Veterinärhögskolan, Uppsala 7, Sweden

INTRODUCTION

The enormous amount of literature presented annually in the field of cardiovascular control cannot possibly be adequately reviewed within a reasonably limited space. A selection must obviously be made. The important local control mechanisms, such as those operating to secure a blood flow and blood flow distribution over the capillary network in correspondence with the actual metabolic requirements of the organ, are thus not dealt with here. The review is limited to basic concepts on the superimposed remote control systems, neuronal and hormonal. As the last review in this series (195) was, to a large extent, devoted to an excellent and comprehensive description of cardiovascular control mechanisms emanating from higher brain structures, the present description limits itself to the most important cardiovascular homeostatic reflex mechanisms. This topic has been treated in some recently published reviews (15, 79, 122, 167, 168, 172), but mainly with regard to functional characteristics of the endings and the afferent pathways. In the following, more emphasis is placed on the efferent arm of the various reflex mechanisms. The cardiac receptors, which have enjoyed an escalating interest among cardiovascular physiologists in the last few years, are also more extensively treated. The literature cited has been published essentially during 1973–1974; many important and relevant papers published within this period must have escaped the reviewer's attention and therefore, unfortunately, have been omitted from this review.

AFFERENT MECHANISMS

Arterial Baroreceptors

The arterial baroreceptors do not constitute a homogeneous group of endings. They differ not only morphologically but also with regard to type of afferent fiber, medullated or nonmedullated (2, 53). These dissimilarities may also imply differences in

[1]Studies from this laboratory and cited in the text were supported by grants from the Swedish Medical Research Council (14X-644-11).

function. Only medullated baroreceptors however, have been analyzed so far with regard to firing characteristics and reflex effects. This is an unsatisfactory circumstance, considering that the nonmedullated afferents apparently have marked influences on the cardiovascular system, to judge from the pronounced depressor responses obtained when the sinus nerve is electrically stimulated and the stimulus intensity increased to activate the nonmedullated fiber group (2, 43, 99). The presence of nonmedullated baroreceptor afferents in the aortic nerves has been questioned, however (168). Moreover, after selective anodal blockade of the medullated afferents in the aortic nerve, leaving impulse propagation in nonmedullated fibers undisturbed, there was no evidence of remaining baroreceptor activity (2). The nonmedullated endings may therefore be normally silent and become activated first at higher blood pressure levels.

The function of baroreceptors also seems to vary according to whether they are located in the carotid sinus or aortic region, possibly because of different functional characteristics of the vessel walls. The aortic receptors are thus known to induce far less powerful reflex effects than the carotid sinus baroreceptors (45); this has been claimed to be the case only when the receptors are exposed to nonpulsatile pressures (7). The gain of the carotid baroreceptor reflex is consequently greater than that of the aortic receptors, whereas the threshold and saturation pressures, as well as the pressure level for maximal reflex sensitivity, are higher for aortic receptors (45). The aortic receptors seem, in fact, to be relatively silent at normal blood pressure levels (45), and they seem to be organized mainly to combat hypertensive episodes and not, for example, the hypotension following hemorrhage (45). Moreover, aortic arch baroreceptors do not seem to increase their activity when a nonpulsating pressure is substituted for a pulsating pressure, when the latter is suprathreshold throughout the cycle (4). In fact, if the diastolic pressure is subthreshold, net activity per cycle time will decrease. The increased total nerve activity observed when switching from nonpulsating to pulsating pressure is evidently mainly due to recruitment of formerly silent fibers. Despite such recruitment and in contrast to the carotid baroreceptors, the aortic baroreceptor reflex effects are reported to be essentially uninfluenced whether the receptors are exposed to pulsatile or nonpulsatile pressures (7). Increasing the pulsation frequency while other variables remain constant leads to reduction of the number of impulses per cycle, but the activity per unit time is rather constant; in fact, there may be a certain recruitment of new fibers at higher pulse frequencies and $\Delta P/\Delta t$, leading to a net increase of total baroreceptor activity (4) and augmented reflex depressor responses (7). This tendency toward increased baroreceptor activity when the pulse rate increases in physiological situations, as in hemorrhage, seems to be effectively cancelled by the concomitant reduction in pulsation amplitude; the combined effect of these two oppositely directed influences is a net reduction of baroreceptor activity (97).

During baroreceptor stimulation a slow potential with the characteristics of a generator potential has been recorded from the baroreceptor fiber terminals in the common carotid artery (141). Upon baroreceptor stimulation there is an initial transient depolarization of high amplitude followed by a smaller sustained potential, evidently corresponding to the dynamic and static components of receptor activation respectively (141).

Stimulation of the sinus nerve is reported to induce more marked heart rate (85) and blood pressure (103) responses when the stimuli are presented as bursts of impulses rather than as continuous stimulation. Simultaneous activation of chemoreceptor afferents, which may influence the responses, must always be considered in this kind of study. Also of importance is whether stimulation intensities that also activate nonmedullated afferents are employed. These fibers have low discharge frequencies and often produce maximal reflex effects at stimulation rates below 10 Hz. If these nonmedullated afferents are activated by considerably higher stimulation frequencies, it probably does not matter how these stimuli are presented—as constant stimulation or as impulse trains—as maximal effects will be obtained in either case. Even if temporal summation of baroreceptor afferent impulses occurs to a certain extent in central synapses it appears as if the number of impulses reaching the medullary vasomotor neurons per unit time is more important than the time of their arrival (7, 85).

Arterial Chemoreceptors

In addition to the carotid and aortic bodies, microglomeruli, located along the carotid artery, also have a chemosensory function (142). The receptors respond to reductions of arterial and hence glomerular tissue, Po_2 (3, 16, 17, 183). Even if the sensitivity of individual chemoreceptors seems to differ so that there is a spectrum of Pao_2-receptor response curves (17, 183), most receptors show an escalated firing when Pao_2 is reduced below $\sim$ 100 mm Hg; this results in hyperbolic Po_2-receptor response curves (16, 182). This marked alteration of receptor activity within a physiological Pao_2 range is not compatible with the well-known fact that chemoreceptor stimulation of respiration and circulation (169) in anoxia occurs first at considerably lower Pao_2 levels. This apparent discrepancy has been ascribed to an artificially high recorded chemoreceptor activity (16, 17), which is in turn due to interruption of efferent chemoreceptor-inhibitory activity in the sinus nerve (79, 153, 154). The idea that chemoreceptors respond briskly to a reduced glomus blood flow following a blood pressure fall is not supported by the observations that steady-state receptor activity is unchanged when carotid body perfusion pressure and flow are varied between 60–160 mm Hg and 10–60 μl min^{-1}, respectively. Large variations in carotid body flow, measured by hydrogen clearance technique, were found to have no influence on local Po_2 or chemoreceptor activity (3). Pressures below 60 mm Hg were, however, accompanied by increased chemoreceptor activity, indicating that the receptors do respond to stagnant anoxia, although with a much reduced sensitivity (16). Howe & Neil (79) suggested that chemoreceptor activity will increase during systemic hypotension because of the reflex increase of efferent sympathetic activity to the carotid body vessels, which will further reduce blood flow to critical levels. In the above-mentioned studies a strictly local hypotension was produced with probably no reflex alterations of carotid body circulation. Alterations of $Paco_2$ between 25–65 mm Hg produced linear increases of chemoreceptor activity (17), whereas clear-cut circulatory responses were obtained first when Pco_2 increased above 39 mm Hg (169).

Stimulation of chemoreceptors with nicotine, cyanide, and similar substances may also imply a simultaneous stimulation of other predominantly nonmedullated endings (166) such as baroreceptors. Recent studies, however, seem to justify the usage of drugs to achieve a selective activation of chemoreceptors (82, 145). The reflex bradycardia in response to nicotine and cyanide thus remained after denervation of the baroreceptors, but was eliminated by denervation of the carotid body (82). The nicotinic drug suberyldicholin activates chemoreceptors but not baroreceptors, to judge from recordings of the impulse activity in the sinus nerve (145). However, as recordings of baroreceptor activity evidently were made from medullated afferents, a possible increase of activity in nonmedullated baroreceptor fibers cannot be excluded in this study.

Atrial Receptors

Besides the classical, complex unencapsulated endings with medullated vagal afferents, located mainly in the veno-atrial junctions, other types of atrial receptors have also been described, with both sympathetic (134, 215) and nonmedullated vagal afferents (212). Although the function of the medullated receptors has been studied quite extensively (167, 168), the two latter groups of endings are little analyzed with regard to discharge rates, natural stimuli, and reflex effects. Both the vagal and sympathetic endings seem to respond to mechanical stimuli (212, 215) and to a distension of the atria. The vagal receptors exhibit a low frequency, nonrhythmic discharge, which is significantly increased and becomes bursting with peak activity synchronous with the V-wave when atrial pressure is elevated above 3–12 mm Hg (33, 212). The endings are thus distension receptors, responding to stimuli similar to those that excite the medullated receptors. Analyses of the medullated unencapsulated endings suggest no principal differences between receptors with A- and B-type firing, and only a modest dynamic component in the receptor function (9). The number of afferent impulses generated per unit time was thus not different when the stretch frequency increased; the impulses per cycle decreased in proportion to the increased frequency. Similarly, a rapid pacing of the atria in dogs with complete atrioventricular block did not increase B-receptor discharge (63), and maximal B-receptor discharge occurred at the peak of the V-wave, where the $\Delta P/\Delta t$ was zero (62). Negative inotropic influences led to increased atrial receptor activity as a consequence of the increased atrial pressure (62). There was little or no tendency for adaptation of the atrial receptors (62, 63).

Ventricular Receptors with Vagal Afferents

Besides the ventricular baroreceptors, originally described and recently reviewed by Paintal (167, 168), there is an abundance of endings with nonmedullated vagal afferents, particularly in the left ventricle (150, 160). The endings, which can be described as epi-myocardial receptors, have been studied in dogs (150, 151) and cats (160), and may exist also in birds (50) and humans (139). The resting discharge is irregular and occurs at a low rate. Many receptors are normally silent, at least in animals with open-chests. Their activity increases in response to various procedures, including transfusions, occlusion of the ascending aorta (8, 160), and elevation of coronary venous pressure, leading to a diastolic distention of the ventricle. with no noticeable impairment of coronary flow or ventricular performance (88, 150, 151).

Like nonmedullated endings in general (166) they are excited by various drugs, such as nicotine, veratridin, digitalis alkaloids (150, 160, 193), and probably bradykinin (178). There seems to be a close correlation between the end-diastolic ventricular pressure (volume) and ventricular receptor activity. Increased activity was seen at threshold end-diastolic pressures between 5–12 mm Hg (213). There is, on the other hand, no good correlation between intraventricular systolic pressure and receptor activity (213). Other reports suggested, however, that the increased intraventricular pressure is the exciting factor (29).

When receptor activity increases, it assumes a cardiac-modulated rhythmicity, which makes possible a correlation of receptor activation with a certain event in the cardiac cycle. It was proposed from such calculations, based on an assumed intra-cardial conduction time, that receptor activation took place in diastole (160), which seemed reasonable considering the relationship between diastolic volume and recep-tor activity. Recent studies by P. Thorén (personal communication), in which the intracardiac conduction time has been actually measured, indicate that this time is considerably longer than was originally assumed and that the main part of the receptor firing in fact occurs in systole. It may seem somewhat puzzling, but not completely inconceivable, that the receptor discharge in systole is quantitatively determined by the extent of myocardial distension in the preceding diastolic period. An ischemic distension or systolic bulging of the ventricle as a result of anoxia or coronary artery obstruction also activates the receptors (210); this is in all likelihood due to mechanical deformation of the receptors and not to accumulation of "chemi-cal" factors (137).

Ventricular Receptors with Sympathetic Afferents

Cardiac receptors with afferents coursing with the sympathetics have attracted much interest recently and have been extensively studied. As with endings asso-ciated with vagal afferents, the sympathetic receptors are not a homogeneous group, but differ with regard to their location, functional characteristics, and type of afferent connection. While, as mentioned, some endings are located in the atria, most are concentrated in the ventricles (134). Some sympathetic receptors are attached to thin, medullated fibers (190, 216–218), while others have nonmedullated afferents (216, 218). Some receptors are tonically active and some, particularly those with medullated afferents, exhibit a cardiac rhythmicity (134, 135, 216). Other endings again respond only to different kinds of provocations, and individual endings then seem to respond to different types of stimuli (23). The sympathetic receptors have been proposed to signal noxious events in the heart (see below); it then seems reasonable that this modality is served by the normally silent group of receptors, while the normally tonically active receptors signal physiological cardiac events. Many endings both with medullated and with nonmedullated afferents are mechano-sensitive, responding to touch and probing of the ventricular wall (23, 77, 216, 219) and to increased pressure or distention of the ventricles (77, 132, 134), for example, in response to transfusions and increased outflow resistance. The receptor activity then increases with the peak ventricular pressure in the range 30–180 mm Hg (77). Ischemic distension of the myocardium, caused by coronary obstruction (134, 218) as well as increased coronary artery pressure (23, 216, 134), excites the endings. The endings however, are not necessarily placed in the coronary vessel wall but rather in close proximity to the vessels. Finally, drugs such as veratrum (133, 134, 190) are also effective in exciting the sympathetic endings.

EFFERENT CONTROL OF RECEPTOR FUNCTION

Arterial Baroreceptors

The possibilities of a central control of cardiovascular receptor function via efferent nervous pathways have been explored quite extensively. Sympathetic efferent fibers reach the carotid sinus regions (11) and are also present in the aortic nerve (13). Stimulation of the sympathetic supply to the sinuses in dogs has been found to reduce vessel diameter and elastic modulus, which would tend to stimulate the baroreceptors in the media-adventitia border (11). In cats, stimulation of the cervical sympathetic fibers reduced the pressor response to carotid occlusion considerably, but the stimulation itself produced no discernible effects on blood pressure (226). A reduction of activity in brachiocephalic baroreceptors was observed in dogs on stimulation of the ansae subclaviae with physiological frequencies (102). The effect was abolished by α-adrenergic blockers. Administration of norepinephrine was found to increase aortic baroreceptor activity in the rabbit at a given aortic diameter (1). Since, however, the diameter usually decreased upon norepinephrine infusion, the net effect was often a reduced receptor activity. The efferent sympathetic influence on baroreceptor function is thus most likely an indirect effect caused by neurogenic adjustments of vascular smooth muscle tone at the receptor sites with consequent changes in vessel distensibility. A direct effect of the adrenergic transmitter on the receptors has, however, also been proposed (113). Regardless of the precise mechanism behind the generally increased baroreceptor activity when sympathetic activity is increased, the phenomenon implies a negative feedback that tends to reduce baroreceptor activity when this activity is high and augment receptor activity when it is low. The quantitative importance of this feedback control mechanism under normal physiological conditions is not known. Of importance, however, is the relative reduction of baroreceptor activity known to occur in hypertension (5) which contributes to the "resetting" of the baroreceptor reflex mechanism in this condition. The baroreceptors of hypertensive animals show higher thresholds, less sensitivity, maximal sensitivity in a higher pressure range, higher saturation pressures, and lower maximal discharge rates than normal animals (5). Similar alterations of baroreceptor function are seen in rabbits with experimental atherosclerosis (6) and are most likely due to the altered distensibility characteristics of the vessel wall (5).

Arterial Chemoreceptors

Stimulation of the sympathetic efferent fibers to the carotid and aortic bodies (3, 17, 176), which run from both cervical and thoracic sympathetic ganglia to the chemoreceptor regions and along the sinus (3) and aortic (13) nerves, produces an increased chemoreceptor discharge and a decreased O_2 consumption (176). These effects are, in all likelihood, due to vasoconstriction and stagnant anoxia in the chemoreceptor regions. The effects of sympathetic stimulation on chemoreceptor discharge are blocked with α-adrenergic blockers (3). Withdrawal of the sympathetic activity to the carotid bodies results in an increased O_2 consumption and increased flow (17), indicating a certain neurogenically induced tone of the carotid body vessels. Alteration of blood flow otherwise produced, as by lowering the perfusion pressure, does not alter the O_2 consumption; this response to sympathetic stimulation thus seems to be a direct effect (176). The sympathetic excitation of the chemoreceptors apparently constitutes a positive feedback, leading to intensified chemoreceptor pressor responses in situations of a general increase of sympathetic activity, also affecting the carotid and aortic body vessels. When the sinus nerve is stimulated in a peripheral direction, an inhibition of chemoreceptor activity and an increased carotid body blood flow were observed (153). These effects were ascribed to a direct inhibition of the type I glomus cells, rather than to an effect secondary to the vasodilator response, since inhibition also occurred in an ischemic carotid body and was not abolished by atropine, which eliminated the vasodilator response. The inhibitory fibers were activated by ipsilateral chemoreceptor stimulation (154); the reflex inhibition of receptor activity that followed thus constituted a negative feedback mechanism. De-efferentation of the endings by cutting the sinus nerve leads to an increased receptor sensitivity, which may explain why chemoreceptor activity in such cases increases at high Po_2 levels (17, 183).

Divergent opinions concerning this efferent system exist. The receptor inhibition by efferent stimulation has thus been argued to be at least partly due to an "antidromic" depression of the chemosensitive fibers, at least at high stimulation frequencies (12, 64), rather than a physiological, efferent inhibition. Furthermore, it has been proposed that receptor inhibition is a secondary effect to the vasodilatation (64), as atropine was found to diminish receptor inhibition in parallel with the reduced vascular effects. Arguments in favor of a direct inhibitory effect on the chemosensitive cells were provided in a recent study on an ischemic carotid body preparation (164); the efferent fibers in the carotid body were activated physiologically, which seems to exclude antidromic excitation. Intravenous epinephrine and hypoxic hypoxia thus depressed chemoreceptor activity. A clear-cut depression was seen only in some tests, however, and the depression may therefore also be due to circulatory phenomena in addition to a direct effect on the receptors (3, 164).

CENTRAL MECHANISMS

The Medullary Vasomotor Area

The afferent fibers from the main cardiovascular proprioreceptors project primarily to the vasomotor areas in the medulla oblongata, which traditionally and conveniently has been called the medullary vasomotor or cardiovascular center. This designation has been considered a misnomer (78); according to this concept it would be more appropriate to consider the medullary structures merely as one of several equally important, diffusely organized vasomotor areas placed longitudinally along the neuroaxis. However, this diffusely organized medullary structure is particularly important in that the main cardiovascular feedback reflex mechanisms have their primary projections in this area, and that the tonic, spontaneous sympathetic vasomotor fiber activity is normally generated in these medullary structures.

The organization of the synaptic contacts between the cardiovascular receptor afferents and the efferent autonomic motor fibers has been explored in several recent studies, utilizing different approaches. Electrophysiological recordings of unit activity in medullary structures in response to stimulation of the afferent fiber systems (18, 58, 147, 148) or recordings of antidromically propagated potentials in the afferents following stimulation in the medulla have confirmed that the first synapse is located in or near the nucleus tractus solitarius. Electrical stimulation of this structure produces hypotension and bradycardia, whereas electrolytic lesions are followed by opposite effects, i.e. a marked hypertension due to an increased flow resistance and increased adrenal medullary secretion (44). Such lesions also abolish, or greatly attenuate, the reflex effects of baroreceptor stimulation (120).

The destination of the second neuron in the reflex pathway seems to be the medially placed "depressor area" (26, 120), which comprises the parahypoglossal area, the paramedian reticular nucleus, and medial parts of nucleus reticularis ventralis and nucleus olivae (196). Stimulation in this area is known to produce decrease in blood pressure, bradycardia, and inhibition of spontaneous sympathetic vasomotor fiber activity (196). Some primary baroreceptor afferents may also reach this structure, mainly the paramedian reticular nucleus (148), but recorded unit activity in this area following baroreceptor activation indicates mainly polysynaptic connections (198). Baroreceptor afferents are said to project to the ventral parts of the medial depressor area (120), as is also known to be the case with inhibitory afferents from somatic muscle afferents, whereas effects mediated by vagal inhibitory afferents are uninfluenced by destruction of these ventral parts of the depressor area (120). Short-latency unit responses within a restricted area in the anterior hypothalamus in response to baroreceptor stimulation have been reported (197), showing that baroreceptor afferents reach structures outside the medulla. Also, structures not involved in cardiovascular control, such as the cuneate nucleus (59), are reached by baroreceptor afferents. Chemoreceptor afferents have also been found to project to the nucleus tractus solitarius (42, 43, 148) and further to the parahypoglossal area and the paramedian reticular nucleus (148). Ablation of this latter area gives rise to accentuated chemoreceptor pressor responses, indicating elimination of buffering impulses. Moreover, the failure to abolish pressor responses to chemoreceptor stimulation by destruction of the paramedian reticular nucleus indicates other connections for the chemoreceptor afferents within the medulla (148).

The vagal motor neurons to the heart seem to arise from the nucleus ambiguus. Stimulation in this structure produces bradycardia (208), whereas stimulation of nucleus dorsalis vagus does not; destruction of the latter structure does not influence the bradycardia response to brain ischemia, for example (20). Furthermore, antidromic stimulation of cardiac efferent vagal fibers causes short-latency potentials in the nucleus ambiguus with high following frequency, whereas similar activity in nucleus dorsalis vagus was found only when nonmedullated noncardiac fibers in the vagal stem were stimulated (144).

The structures in the medulla responsible for the generation of the tonic vasomotor fiber activity, and which constitute the so-called pressor area, seem to be diffusely distributed in the mediolateral parts of the medulla, comprising the periventricular gray and the nucleus reticularis parvocellularis, nucleus gigantocellularis, and nucleus ventralis (60). Stimulation of these structures leads to increase in blood pressure and increased activity in sympathetic vasomotor fibers (60). According to recent studies by Gebber and associates (60, 196, 205) there exist two different vasopressor fiber systems, activated at separate locations in the medulla and supramedullary structures, which impinge on the same preganglionic spinal sympathetic vasomotor neurons. One system, with faster conducting pathways, is not receptive to baroreceptor inhibition, while the other system, with slower conducting pathways, can be inhibited by baroreceptor stimulation. It remains to be elucidated whether the system that is uninfluenced by a baroreceptor activation is involved in the regulation of cardiovascular homeostasis or rather in other control systems, such as thermoregulation, and therefore influences the sympathetic outflow to quite specialized parts of the circulation. It has been suggested that cutaneous vasomotor fibers (157, 222), above all those to the arteriovenous anastomoses (104), are not influenced by the arterial baroreceptors. However, recordings from peripheral vasomotor fibers (156, 206) indicate that strong baroreceptor stimulation is capable of inducing a complete inhibition in vasomotor fiber activity. From morphological studies and exploration of splanchnic efferent activity in response to stimulations of various places in the medulla oblongata, it has been suggested (152) that one of the last, if not the last, of the relay stations for excitatory impulses passing from the bulb down the spinal cord is the nucleus reticularis ventralis. Lesions in rostral parts of the medulla cause degeneration of fibers in this structure.

Spinal Vasomotor Areas

Activity in the spinal preganglionic sympathetic neurons in the intermediolateral cell column is normally determined to a large extent by influences from supraspinal structures via descending excitatory vasomotor pathways, which run chiefly in the dorsolateral funiculi (54, 60, 80), and via inhibitory pathways in the ventrolateral (60) or dorsolateral funiculi (35). However, once withdrawn from such supraspinal influences, the spinal vasomotor neurons seem capable of performing rather independently and inducing relatively complex circulatory adjustments. Spontaneous activity thus occurs in vasomotor neurons even in a completely isolated cord (136) and the rhythmic modulations of sympathetic nerve activity, responsible for the Mayer waves, for example, may be induced on a spinal as well as on a medullary level (90). Electrical stimulations of somatic efferents, or applications of natural stimuli such as blood pressure elevations, are known to be capable of both exciting (132) and depressing (132, 227) sympathetic afferent activity. Afferent signals in somatic sensory fibers are known to affect vasomotor fiber activity and may exert their reflex influence either on a spinal level or via supraspinal structures. The neurophysiological mechanisms behind the spinal and supraspinal components of these somatosympathetic reflexes have been much studied and were recently reviewed (112, 186). The spinal component thus seems to be elicited mainly by impulses in thin afferents from muscle and skin, although larger fibers may also contribute. The supraspinal component of the somatosympathetic reflex, which is relayed in the medulla or in still more rostrally placed structures, seems to be induced by larger fibers belonging to Groups II and A, respectively; reflexes induced by Group IV afferent stimulation also seem to pass via the medulla oblongata (184).

Whereas the supraspinal component has a generalized influence, affecting sympathetic activity at all spinal levels, the purely spinal component has been said to have a clear local sign, affecting sympathetic outflow only at the same level at which somatic afferent input occurs. However, quite widespread cardiovascular adjustments such as tachycardia and increased forearm resistance have been described in patients with spinal transection, following pain stimuli, etc (36).

The question of whether the baroreceptor inhibition of sympathetic vasoconstrictor fiber activity occurs in the medulla oblongata or at a spinal level via descending inhibitory pathways from the medullary depression region has been subjected to several analyses. The fact that a certain depression of activity in the medullary pressor area is obtained by stimulation of the arterial baroreceptors suggests a medullary inhibition (18). A bilateral destruction of the descending excitatory fiber systems in the dorsolateral part of the cord leads to a fall in blood pressure and abolition of reflex pressor responses. No further blood pressure effects were observed on a subsequent spinalization, suggesting that no tonic descending depressor system was operating (54).

On the other hand, increased activity in sympathetic fibers, resulting from stimulation of descending tracts in the cord, could be inhibited by baroreceptor reflexes in 50% of the cases (60), indicating that there may be both a medullary and spinal inhibition. Comparisons of the latencies for evoking inhibition and excitation of efferent splanchnic activity from stimulations of medullary depressor and pressor areas, respectively, showed that the latency for inducing inhibition was significantly shorter than the latency for the excitatory responses (65). Moreover, direct stimulation of descending tracts in the ventral funiculus of the cord (80) leads to sympathetic inhibition. These findings strongly support the idea of two separate descending systems mediating excitation and rapid inhibition respectively. Further support for this concept is provided by recent studies by Coote & Macleod (35). Baroreceptor inhibition of a spinal sympathetic reflex was abolished by destruction of a localized region of the lateral funiculus, which evidently contains the descending inhibitory pathways; stimulation in this spinal area inhibited tonic and reflex-augmented vasomotor discharge, indicating descending inhibitory systems. The latency for baroreceptor reflex inhibition of activity in thoracic and lumbar sympathetic fibers was found to be longer than the latency for the inhibitory effects produced by depressor area stimulation. The conclusion was that at least a part of the baroreceptor inhibition occurs at a spinal level, via descending pathways that are probably monoaminergic (35).

"Spontaneous" Vasomotor Activity

The average discharge rate in pre-or postganglionic vasomotor fibers during "resting" conditions varies between 0.5 and 2 imp sec^{-1} (impulses per second) in different studies (114, 185, 191, 205), probably depending on variations in the prevailing baroreceptor restraint, depth of anesthesia etc. In individual fibers the resting activity varied between 0 and $>$3 imp sec^{-1}; the majority of the active fibers fired at 1–2 imp sec^{-1} (114). A considerable portion of the vasomotor fibers seem to be normally silent. Thus the percentage of active fibers in a population of sympathetic vasomotor neurons has been reported to be from around 50–60% (205) up to 90% (114).

The cause of spontaneous activity in vasomotor neurons is not known. The marked reduction of spontaneous firing, from 2.1 to 0.7 imp sec,$^{-1}$, and in the number of active vasomotor neurons after spinalization, along with the fact that the activity is in many cases unaffected by intercollicular decerebration (136), suggests that it is normally generated in the medullary vasomotor area. However, excitatory influences from rostral areas may contribute to a certain extent. Lesions of certain hypothalamic structures (130) and intercollicular decerebration (107) produce a fall in blood pressure evidently due to elimination of excitatory influences from suprabulbar structures. In other studies essentially no effect on vasomotor fiber activity was observed after midcollicular decerebration (120). The fact that activity remains in the vasomotor neurons in the isolated bulb or spinal cord suggests endogenous mechanisms, perhaps based on a nonstable cell membrane potential, which intermittently arrives at a firing level, a phenomenon observed in autonomic motor fibers in lower species (143). At any rate, the spontaneous excitation of vasomotor neurons seems to be influenced by fluctuations in the chemical composition of the body fluids with regard to Po_2, Pco_2, and pH. Concerning the medulla oblongata, such chemical influences may affect the autonomic motor neurons directly or via specific chemosensitive areas that are especially sensitive to chemical disturbances and that affect respiratory and cardiovascular neuronal activity. Such areas are known to be located on the ventral surface of the medulla (128). Electrical stimulation of this area causes a marked rise of blood pressure (128), while bilateral destruction of, or application of, for example, pentobarbital bilaterally on this area leads to marked decreases in blood pressure (70), indicating that a tonic, excitatory influence on vasomotor neurons is exerted from this structure. Furthermore, in the area postrema, where the blood-brain barrier is lacking, a rapid exchange of substances with the surrounding fluids (plasma and the cerebrospinal fluid) can occur (203), indicating a possible chemosensitive function. Neurons, evidently monoaminergic (204), connect this structure with cardiovascular and respiratory neurons in the medulla oblongata, allowing for appropriate adjustments of circulation and respiration to correct for disturbances in the chemical composition of plasma and the cerebrospinal fluid.

The above-mentioned figures for the recorded resting discharge rate in individual vasomotor fibers clearly demonstrate the nonuniformity of this activity among individual fibers in the whole vasomotor neuron population. Such differences in resting tonic discharge rate may be related to functional differences among the vasomotor fibers. Thus, for example, the discharge rates in vasomotor fibers to the kidneys (104) and to the veins (125) seem to be considerably lower than the rates in vasomotor fibers to the muscles when the vasomotor system operates without opposing inhibitory effects from the arterial baroreceptors. These differences in activity levels between separate vasomotor neurons pools have been ascribed to variations in excitation threshold to neuronal or chemical stimuli (104); the normally silent fibers constitute a high threshold group, which is less excitable via spinal and supraspinal pathways (136). This nonuniform tonic activity has also been regarded as the main cause of the differentiated reflex engagement of various cardiovascular target organs (95). For example, hypercapnia increases the activity in renal high threshold vasomotor neurons significantly more than in low threshold skeletal muscle vasomotor fibers (165) and causes a "reset" of the baroreceptor reflex mechanism (105). When baroreceptor restraint was removed by cold block of the aortic nerves with all other baroreceptor afferents eliminated flow resistances in muscle and kidney increased 49% and 28% respectively; when the same maneuver was repeated during hypercapnia, the corresponding figures were 56% and 69% (165), indicating a considerable increase of renal sympathetic tone in the latter situation.

EFFERENT MECHANISMS

Nervous Pathways

The traditionally held opinion that the sympathetic adrenergic vasoconstrictor fibers constitute the sole efferent nervous pathway in cardiovascular homeostatic reflex mechanisms and that reflex vasodilatations are due to inhibition of tonic vasoconstrictor activity has been challanged in recent studies, and alternative vasodilator mechanisms have been proposed. A reflex activation of β-adrenergic dilator fibers after intravenous administration of veratridine or epinephrine has been reported (214). Reflex activation of the cholinergic sympathetic fibers from arterial baroreceptors (202) has been reported but has not been confirmed in other studies (124, 162). So far, conclusive proof for a reflex activation of the cholinergic sympathetic fibers is still lacking. The presence of histaminergic vasodilator fibers has been confirmed in experiments on dogs (66). Efferent stimulation of ventral roots in the lower lumbar region was thus found to cause a vasodilatation that persisted after atropine and β-receptor blockade, was abolished by antihistamines and ganglionic blockers, and was associated with a release of [^{14}C]histamine into the blood (66, 123). Whether such a release occurs from nerve terminals or perhaps from mast cells supplied with collaterals from sympathetic vasomotor fibers is not known (181), nor is the function of such an histaminergic mechanism. The possibility that purinergic fibers contribute to the innervation of the cardiovascular system (25) cannot be disregarded, although direct experimental support for this has not yet been presented.

The idea of active reflex vasodilatation is not supported by studies in which a neurophysiological approach was utilized (223). Recordings of activity in efferent sympathetic pathways in the cord that mediated reflex vasodilator responses showed that this vasodilatation was always accompanied by a decrease in nerve activity and never by an augmented discharge, which would have been the case if the dilatation were active.

Humoral Pathway

RENIN-ANGIOTENSIN SYSTEM   Activation of the regional sympathetic fibers to the kidneys by direct stimulation (34, 127) or via central nervous structures (72, 179, 221) causes an increase in renin release. Inhibition of renal vasomotor fiber activity induced reflexly by hypothalamic stimulation was accompanied by suppression of renin activity (228). The adrenergic influence on renin release seems to be mediated via a β-adrenergic mechanism (179). α-receptor blockade has also been shown to inhibit renin release (72), probably as a result of the blockade of the circulatory responses to sympathetic stimulation.

Angiotensin appears to contribute to cardiovascular control in several ways. Besides its direct vasoconstrictor effects, angiotensin also augments the sympathetic vasoconstrictor activity by a central, stimulatory action on vasomotor neurons (52). Infusions of angiotensin, in amounts that produce no circulatory effects when given intravenously, cause hypertension and tachycardia when administered into the vertebral arteries. These effects are proposed to be mediated via the earlier-mentioned myelencephalic structure, the area postrema (86), where the polypeptide may penetrate the brain barrier and reach structures involved in vasomotor control (203, 204). Intravertebral infusions of angiotensin, in amounts that did not increase the blood pressure markedly, reduced the reflex blood pressure and heart rate responses to sinus nerve stimulation (56). This effect is due either to a central blockade of the baroreceptor effects by angiotensin or to a mere competition between inhibitory and excitatory influences on the medullary autonomic motor neurons. Finally, angiotensin also seems capable of mobilizing another pressor system, namely the antidiuretic hormone (30, 31). This mechanism is, however, by no means essential for the increased ADH release in, for example, nonhypotensive hemorrhage; the vasopressin concentration in plasma increased in response to a nonhypotensive hemorrhage to the same extent whether or not renin concentration in plasma was prevented from increasing (30). ADH in turn seems to inhibit the secretion of renin in dogs (201), which may explain the biphasic renin response to hemorrhage; the fall of renin concentration after the initial peak might be due to the inhibition from a steadily increasing ADH titer in plasma.

It has been postulated that the renin-angiotensin system, instead of being mobilized only in critical situations calling for prompt compensatory adjustments of the circulation (as after a blood loss), also plays a role in the normal tonic control of blood pressure (38). Small, stepwise reductions of renal perfusion pressure in the range between 100–65 mm Hg were found to release renin in such amounts that a 65% compensation of the fall of renal pressure was accomplished. This effect was reached within 20 min. In fact, increased renin activity in renal venous blood following a reduction of renal artery pressure can be detected within minutes (71). The system thus has enough gain and operates with enough speed to be of importance in the moment-to-moment control of blood pressure. Elimination of the tonic angiotensin influence through administration of an angiotensin II antagonist caused a fall in blood pressure in unanesthetized dogs with caval constriction and ascites, and therefore probably with stimulated renin release (121) and high angiotensin titers in the blood, but not when given to normal, anesthetized dogs (83). Even if the renin-angiotensin system is mobilized in various pressor response patterns, it does not necessarily follow that angiotensin produces, or even contributes to, the hypertensive response. For instance, electrical stimulation in the brain stem was in one study (72) found to produce marked blood pressure responses and a fourfold increase in renin release. However, identical pressor responses were obtained in animals with such high anti-renin titers in the blood that no pressor response whatsoever was obtained with intravenous administration of renin, which suggests that the renin-angiotensin system was not necessary for inducing hypertension.

VASOPRESSIN   That vasopressin is released during a moderate hemorrhage in such amounts that significant cardiovascular effects are produced has been confirmed in some recent studies. Blood losses, reducing systemic diastolic pressure 5 and 22 mm Hg, respectively, were accompanied by increases of plasma ADH concentration by 35 and 138 μU ml^{-1}, respectively (37), and in dogs bled to 40 mm Hg the peak plasma concentration of ADH reached 800 μU ml^{-1} (49). Intravenous administration of ADH in amounts that elevate plasma concentrations by only 25 μU ml^{-1} (199), produces marked circulatory effects (200) particularly after baroreceptor denervation and decapitation of the animals (40). The circulatory responses were characterized by increases of arterial and central venous pressures and total plasma volume, while heart rate, cardiac output, and central blood volume decreased. The latter effect must, in view of the increased central venous pressure, imply an active tightening of the low pressure system. The concentration of ADH in the blood starts to rise within the first minute after a blood loss and reaches a peak value after 2 min (37). Since the half-life of the hormone also seems to be very short, around 5 min (49, 199), the vasopressin system seems capable of contributing rapidly and efficiently to the compensatory cardiovascular adjustments in hypovolemia. This compensation seems, however, to be a disadvantage to the organism in certain situations, since animals with experimental diabetes incipidus have longer survival times in hemorrhagic shock than do control animals, a difference abolished after administration of ADH to the diabetic animals (37).

REFLEX PATTERNS

The vasomotor system seems capable of inducing quite differentiated response patterns, implying that separate cardiovascular target organs are influenced to different extents in a particular reflex mechanism, and that a given effector may be engaged to different extents in two separate reflexes. Two different approaches have been used primarily when quantitative analyses of the reflex engagement of various cardiovascular effectors have been made: first, recording reflex alterations in visceromotor fiber activity to various effectors and, second, recording the reflex hemodynamic responses in terms of changes in blood pressure, heart rate, flow resistance, etc. Both methods have their advantages and drawbacks. The neurophysiological approach requires recordings from single or few fiber preparations, and to allow for comparisons several such recordings from different efferent nerves must be performed simultaneously. Aside from the obvious technical difficulties involved in this approach, one cannot be sure whether the recordings of activity are made from vasomotor fibers or from sympathetic efferents innervating other structures. Even if recordings are definitely made from vasomotor fibers, one does not know which vascular bed or which vascular section is supplied. For instance, the skin and muscle vascular beds differ considerably with regard to their function and therefore most likely, with regard to their engagement in various reflex patterns (157, 222). Similarly, the pre- and postcapillary sections are functionally different: the precapillary vessels regulate flow resistance; the postcapillary vessels influence the holding capacity of the circulation. Even if the destination of the fibers can be defined, one does not know whether the fiber is a constrictor or a dilator fiber. Furthermore, the discharge frequency/effector response relation is nonlinear and often very steep in the lower range of physiological discharge rates, particularly with regard to heart and veins. Therefore even small, perhaps hardly noticeable, changes of impulse frequency may sometimes imply significant hemodynamic effects. Measurement of these hemodynamic effects is then of advantage, because small shifts in fiber activity are amplified, and also because the reflex response is then functionally characterized. However, because neuro-effector sensibility, etc differ among different target organs, comparisons again become difficult and must ultimately be made by "translating" the effector response to alterations in vasomotor fiber activity by, for example, comparing the reflex responses to those obtained by direct electrical stimulation of the regional fibers with known frequencies (104). Such regional stimulation then implies a simultaneous, stereotyped activation of all efferent fibers and it is indeed doubtful whether all these fibers can actually be reflexly activated from supraspinal structures. Many studies indicate rather that spinal and supraspinal reflex mechanisms engage somewhat different sets of efferent fibers (112, 186). If identical vascular responses are obtained with direct electrical stimulation and reflexly, this does not necessarily mean identical mean discharge rates in the efferent fibers in the two situations. Even if there is a considerable divergence with regard to vasomotor fiber innervation of the effectors, there may still be a certain underestimation of the reflexly governed impulse frequencies, since the reflex responses are produced via a smaller number of efferent fibers. As the situation is probably much the same in all different effectors, a relative comparison may, however, still be possible to perform. It seems as if a combination of both approaches would provide the best solution to the problems of quantifying the reflex engagement of various effectors in different reflex patterns.

Baroreceptor Reflexes

Baroreceptor stimulation induces, besides an inhibition of sympathetic cardio-acceleration and vasoconstrictor fiber (206) activity, an activation of vagal efferent fibers to the heart (47). In cats no efferent parasympathetic activity to the heart is observed at blood pressures below 140–150 mm Hg; at higher pressures there is a heart-synchronous rhythmic vagal activity (117). The net cardiac effect of baroreceptor stimulation is thus a decreased heart rate and reduced myocardial contractility (74), while opposite effects are obtained when the receptors are unloaded, e.g. by carotid occlusion. In this latter situation, the induced heart-rate responses contribute, but are not essential, to the rise in blood pressure (69). When the heart rate was kept constant, the blood pressure response to carotid occlusion was the same as when heart rate was allowed to increase, but the response developed slower, the cardiac output remained unchanged, and the total flow resistance increased considerably more. The relative contribution by cardiac output changes, on the one hand, and shifts in total flow resistance, on the other, to the blood pressure responses in baroreceptor reflexes were analyzed in another study (187). Stepwise increases of sinus pressure in the pressure range 50–200 mm Hg produced stepwise reductions of blood pressure and cardiac output in the range 75–175 mm Hg, while total flow resistance changed within a more narrow range of 110–150 mm Hg.

Contrary to the traditional concept, there seems to be a significant reflex inhibition of vascular activity in the cerebral circulation when the baroreceptors are stimulated (175). A reflex activation of vagal efferent cholinergic fibers to the coronary vessels has also been suggested (73). Of the remaining parallel-coupled circuits, the renal vessels seem to be less engaged in baroreceptor reflexes than, for example, muscle vessels, and the arteriovenous anastomoses do not seem to be affected at all, whereas "nutritional" skin vessels and intestinal resistance vessels appear to be influenced to the same extent as muscle vessels in baroreceptor reflexes (104). If curves relating effector response (in percentage of maximum) to the change in sinus pressure (so-called characteristic curves) are determined for different target organs, it is found that the muscle vessel and renal vessel curves coincide and have an identical course with blood pressure response curves (105). In other words, alterations of sinus pressure produce identical relative changes in vasomotor fiber discharge to muscle and kidney, although, as mentioned above, the absolute discharge rate is higher in the muscle vasoconstrictor fibers. The corresponding curves for heart rate and, evidently, the veins (75) are displaced to give less relative response for a given sinus pressure, in all probability because of the very steep sympathetic discharge frequency/effector response curves for the sinus node and the capacitance vessels, implying maximum tachycardia and venoconstriction respectively at relatively low discharge sympathetic rates, i.e. at relatively high sinus pressures. Concerning the functionally different, series-coupled vascular sections, the baroreceptors seem to engage the venous side less than the precapillary vessels (192) although active venomotor responses are known to occur (46, 68, 75, 192). Activation of nonmedullated baroreceptor afferents apparently induces a more pronounced slowing of the heart (99, 103) and less marked vascular effects than activation of the medullated ones. Similarly, there is indirect evidence in support of the idea that aortic baroreceptors influence heart rate more and the vascular beds less than do the carotid baroreceptors (47).

The nonuniform engagement of different cardiovascular target organs in baroreceptor reflexes, as described above, is also evident from experiments where the reflex changes in efferent sympathetic activity have been followed. Baroreceptor stimulation has thus been reported to cause an almost complete inhibition of activity in renal vasomotor fibers, but a rather modest inhibition in cutaneous vasomotor nerves (157), particularly when the skin was cooled. Similarly, when renal nerve activity was brought down to noise level by baroreceptor stimulation, the activity in sympathetic nerves to the intestine often showed an increased discharge or a biphasic decrease-increase of activity (81); on the other hand, in another study there was, at least transiently, a complete inhibition of efferent sympathetic activity in both the kidney and the intestine, as well as in the skeletal muscle when the carotid sinus baroreceptors were stimulated (206). With continued baroreceptor stimulation, activity recovered, particularly in the kidney, but also in the other circuits. Simultaneous recordings of cardiac, renal, and splenic sympathetic activity when baroreceptor activity was altered have shown that the relation sinus pressure/nerve activity differed for the three effectors (158). A complete inhibition of activity was obtained in the splenic nerve at the lowest sinus pressure; the renal nerves required the highest pressure to become silenced. During bleeding the activity increased relatively more in cardiac than in renal (158) and vertebral (115) sympathetic nerves. Comparisons of gastric and renal sympathetic activity showed that the baroreceptors were capable of completely inhibiting renal nerve activity, while gastric sympathetic activity was to a certain extent uninfluenced by the baroreceptors (159). The fibers not influenced by the baroreceptors may be involved in other autonomic functions, such as the control of gastric motility.

By utilizing an elegant microneurographic technique for recording action potentials in peripheral nerve fibers in conscious humans, Hagbarth and co-workers have managed to analyze the responses of muscle and skin postganglionic sympathetic fibers in various situations; the results of these studies were summarized recently (222). In muscle sympathetic fibers there were burst of activity, synchronous with pulse and blood pressure oscillations; these bursts disappeared when blood pressure increased above 120–150 mm Hg systolic and 70–90 mm Hg diastolic. Elevations of blood pressure, due to excitement or stress, caused a baroreceptor-induced inhibition of activity in muscle fibers. The cutaneous sympathetic activity was, in contrast, respiratory modulated, and increased activity was accompanied, in some cases, by decreased skin electrical resistance, and in others, by vasomotor effects, suggesting the presence of both sudomotor and vasomotor fibers in cutaneous sympathetic nerves. In contrast to the muscle sympathetic fibers, the skin fibers were much less influenced by baroreceptors, but responded more promptly to emotional stress, excitement, etc. In hypertensive patients, higher blood pressures were required to completely stop muscle sympathetic activity, suggesting a reset of the baroreceptor mechanism in these patients.

The baroreceptors also seem to engage various hormonal efferent systems. There is thus an increased ADH release following elimination of baroreceptor restraint, but only in vagotomized animals (19). The earlier reported increase of renin release when baroreceptor activity is reduced was not confirmed in a recent study (21). However, in these experiments, no significant reflex increase of efferent renal sympathetic activity occurred, to judge from the unchanged renal flow resistance. Considering that the renal vasomotor fiber engagement in baroreceptor reflexes is rather moderate (104), and in many experimental situations is completely absent, it does not seem likely that the baroreceptor control of renin release is very powerful. Stimulation of the carotid baroreceptors in nonanesthetized rats has been shown to produce a natriuretic response reaching maximum after 1–3 hr, which was not related to changes in renal circulation or glomerular filtration rate (101). A hormonal mechanism was implicated in this response.

Elimination of baroreceptor activity leads to an acute hypertension, which, however, is not maintained; after a certain time, the mean blood pressure is no different in normal and in baroreceptor-denervated animals (39). The blood pressure variations during the day were, however, more pronounced in the baroreceptor-denervated animals than in normal animals, which suggests that the baroreceptors are mainly involved in short-term, acute adjustments of blood pressure (39).

Chemoreceptor Reflexes

Stimulation of carotid body chemoreceptors by perfusion of the carotid bifurcation with venous blood in artifically ventilated cats with cut vagal and aortic nerves and controlled carotid sinus pressure produced marked increases of blood pressure, mainly due to vasoconstriction in muscle, skin, renal, and intestinal vascular beds, while heart rate was only moderately increased (125). In a similar perfusion setup in anesthetized, vagotomized, and artifically ventilated dogs, with blood perfused at controlled Po_2, Pco_2, and pH, marked blood pressure rises and increases in hindlimb resistance occurred when Po_2 decreased below 70 mm Hg and Pco_2 increased above 33 mm Hg (169). Essentially similar responses were also obtained with nicotine and cyanide stimulation of the receptors (27); however, a reflex nonadrenergic and noncholinergic skin vasodilatation, whose mechanism is unclear, was observed. A chemoreceptor reflex inhibition of sympathetic activity in cutaneous vessels, ordinarily engaged in temperature regulation, is reported (171). This chemoreceptor response seems to be mediated via supramedullary structures (116). Activation of the carotid body chemoreceptors has been found to cause an increase of cerebral blood flow in anesthetized baboons (175). Chemoreceptor activation with nicotine and cyanide produced a dilatation of the coronary vessels (73), which was abolished by bilateral vagotomy or atropinization, suggesting a reflex activation of vagal cholinergic dilator fibers to the coronary vessels from arterial chemoreceptors. Electrophysiological studies have shown a reflex increase of vagal afferent activity to the heart during chemoreceptor stimulation (117) and increased firing in thoracic and lumbar sympathetic fibers (43) following stimulation of medullated afferents in the sinus nerve, which seem to arise mainly from chemoreceptors (53).

Quantitative comparisons of effector responses to chemoreceptor excitation, using the skeletal muscle resistance vessel responses as a reference to describe the extent of overall vasomotor fiber excitation, revealed that, although the renal resistance and muscle capacitance vessels responded somewhat more to excitation from chemoreceptors than to withdrawal of baroreceptor inhibition, these stimulation responses were still much less pronounced than the reflex effects in muscle resistance vessels (125), just as was the case when baroreceptor restraint was removed (104).

Reflexes from Atrial Receptors

There are controversial opinions concerning the role of atrial receptors in cardiovascular control. Linden and co-workers reported that balloon distension of those parts of the atria where the unencapsulated complex endings are situated, i.e. at the venoatrial junctions of both the left (57) and the right (93) atrium and in the appendages (92, 94) causes a reflex tachycardia. This reflex is mediated through vagal afferents and sympathetic efferents; curiously enough, no concomitant inotropic influence was found (57, 96). The reflex vascular effects of atrial receptor stimulation are small: inconsistent decreases in flow resistance in the extremity (28) and essentially unchanged efferent sympathetic activity in lumbar sympathetic fibers, but a slight inhibition of renal vasomotor fiber activity (100), particularly when the initial tone is high (89). Obstruction of the mitral orifice or distension of the left veno-atrial junction (140) produced tachycardia, renal vasodilatation, and muscle vasoconstriction; after vagotomy there was a reflex constriction in both beds, suggesting that atrial vagal receptors were responsible for the renal vasodilatation. In contrast to these findings, a reflex slowing of the heart was observed by Edis, Donald & Shepherd (48) in dogs when the initial heart rate was above 140–150 beats min^{-1}; otherwise tachycardia was seen as well as a marked decrease of blood pressure and limb flow resistance. The vascular effects were mediated via sympathetic fibers, the heart rate effects via both vagal and sympathetic fibers. A vagal component in the reflex heart rate response has also been suggested in other studies (24) in which a clear-cut reflex of heart rate was observed in response to left atrial distension even after spinalization of the animals. These responses were abolished by vagotomy, an observation that eliminates sympathetic cardio-cardiac spinal reflexes as the cause of tachycardia. Electrical stimulation of afferent pathways from the heart, with such low intensities that only medullated afferents were excited, produced pressor responses, tachycardia, and constriction of renal and skeletal muscle vessels (161). These effects were probably due to activation of atrial afferents, which seem to constitute the major part of the medullated fiber group in cardiac afferent nerves. A possible explanation for the discrepant findings reported above may be that other atrial receptors located outside the veno-atrial junctions, e.g. the endings with non-medullated vagal fibers (33, 212), may also become activated to a varying extent in the different studies. Such nonmedullated endings in the heart have been found to induce marked depressor responses when activated (161). However, this explanation does not seem compatible with the findings that distension of several atrial balloons (so that receptors outside the veno-atrial junctions were also probably stimulated) caused rather augmented tachycardic responses (91).

The circulatory effects elicited from atrial receptors are, quantitatively, not very impressive; the most important function of the atrial receptors may be to regulate extracellular fluid volume by adjusting renal function. Several recent studies confirm that distension of the left and right atria (22, 61, 95, 118) and of the atrial appendages (94) causes diuresis. The efferent mechanisms mediating this response seem less clear. The diuresis is known to remain after denervation of the kidneys, which suggests that nervous mechanisms are not essential for the response but may contribute and that humoral factors undoubtedly are of importance. Inhibition of ADH release from balloon distension of the left atrium is reported, although the response is hardly statistically significant (22). Elimination of water diuresis by endogenous vasopressin administration in adequate amounts supports the concept that ADH is involved in the renal response (119). The findings that balloon distension of the left atrium elicits altered activity in hypothalamic cells sensitive to osmotic stimuli demonstrates that the necessary neuronal connections between atrial receptors and the ADH-releasing structures in the hypothalamus do exist (146). Because distension of the right atrium, for example, induces both diuresis and natriuresis (95) the latter effect possibly via inhibition of renin (22) or adrenocortical hormone (41) release, the atrial receptors have been considered to have a dual effect, influencing tubular reabsorption of both water and sodium (61). The idea of control of ADH release through atrial receptors has, however, been seriously questioned recently (97). The diuretic and natriuretic responses to left atrial distension were not correlated with changes in plasma concentrations of ADH, which in fact increased in many cases with diuresis. Ablation of the pituitary gland did not abolish the diuretic response (98), which was suggested to be mediated by a diuretic factor rather than via inhibition of ADH release. Uncontrolled stimulations of other groups of atrial receptors such as nonmedullated vagal endings (212) might partly explain the above-mentioned divergent results. It is then of interest to note that stimulation of afferent fibers from the heart was effective in inhibiting ADH release only when such high stimulation intensities were used that the nonmedullated fibers became activated (76).

Reflexes from Ventricular Receptors with Nonmedullated Vagal Afferents

Stimulation of the epi-myocardial nonmedullated endings leads to pronounced depressor responses of the Bezold-Jarisch type (29, 126, 138, 149, 162); the dominating feature is the vagally mediated bradycardia. There is also a more or less generalized inhibition of sympathetic tone leading to vasodilatation that contributes to the hypotensive response (162). Comparisons of the two inhibitory reflexes from arterial baroreceptors and cardiac ventricular receptors indicate that considerable quantitative differences exist; when the magnitude of reflex muscle vessel response was taken as the reference variable to describe the extent of receptor activation in the individual experiments, for a given muscle vessel response the renal vessels dilated more and the heart rate decreased more when the cardiac receptors were stimulated than when the baroreceptors were activated (162). This discrepancy appears to be due to a relatively weak response of the reference effector, i.e. the muscle vessels in ventricular receptor reflexes (125a). However, the reflex bradycardia response was, by any standard, more pronounced during ventricular receptor stimulation, above all because of a particularly marked reflex increase of the vagal outflow but also because of a relatively powerful inhibition of activity in cardiac sympathetic fibers (125a).

Because the ventricles during diastole constitute a part of the low pressure system, the ventricular epi-myocardial distension receptors must be well suited to serve as volume receptors, contributing to the regulation of body fluid volume. Moderate changes in blood volume are known to alter ventricular receptor activity significantly (160) and then produce especially marked reflex adjustments of the renal vascular bed (162) with consequences for renal excretory function and body fluid homeostasis (see below). Certain observations may be taken to indicate such a volume-regulating function of the ventricular receptors. Cardiac autotransplantation, leaving the atrial receptors with intact afferent connections, but eliminating the ventricular receptor influence, is thus associated with disturbances in fluid volume regulation resulting in an increased blood volume and in clearly reduced renin responses in hemorrhage, etc (207). This idea may seem inconsistent with the well-known fact that fluid retention and increased sympathetic discharge to, for example, the kidneys (110) occur in cases with cardiac failure, where the cardiac dilatation ought to be associated with an augmented ventricular receptor activity. However, the absence of reflex renal vasodilation and adequate adjustments of fluid volume in these cases may be due to a reset of the ventricular receptor function, comparable to that occurring in atrial receptors in cases with tricuspid insufficiency (67) and arterial baroreceptors in hypertension (see above), and which have been ascribed to structural changes of the walls to which the receptors are anchored. The ventricular receptors may, however, become stimulated in decompensated hearts by stimuli that are normally subthreshold. Patients with aortic stenosis thus show abnormal vascular reflex adjustments in exercise; instead of the normal vasoconstriction in nonexercising muscles there is now a clear cut vasodilatation (139), which has been ascribed to ventricular receptor activation when even trifling elevations of blood pressure increase outflow resistance to critical levels in these patients.

An abrupt increase of ventricular rate in dogs with atrioventricular block leads to a reflex slowing of atrial rate (180). This response may at least partly result from an increased number of afferent inhibitory impulses from the ventricular receptors.

Reflexes from "Low Pressure" Receptors

Because of the difficulties involved in isolating cardiac receptor sites and, particularly, the ventricular endings while at the same time maintaining circulation intact and the afferent influence from other receptor areas unchanged, relatively few studies contain a detailed analysis of the circulatory responses to controlled, separate stimulations of these endings. There is, however, an abundance of experiments in which the intrathoracic, low pressure vascular receptors, taken as a group, their location not defined, have been studied with respect to their role in cardiovascular and body fluid control. The effects of interruption of the afferent impulse traffic from intrathoracic receptors, and of alterations in intrathoracic blood volume following negative pressure breathing, bleedings, transfusions, peripheral pooling of blood, etc, have been observed.

The results of such studies confirm, in many respects, those obtained in experiments where a circumscribed stimulation of a relatively well-defined receptor group was performed, for instance, that intrathoracic receptors have a particularly strong influence on renal vasomotor fiber activity. Interruption of the afferent influence from intrathoracic receptors by cervical vagal cooling has thus been found to induce a marked renal vasoconstriction (32, 163), especially when vasomotor activity was raised by carotid occlusion (163) or hypercapnia (165). Bleedings and transfusions, altering the total blood volume by ± 10% in rabbits with cut sinus and aortic nerves, produced 30–40% increase and decrease, respectively, in renal vasomotor fiber activity; cutting of the cervical vagus markedly attenuated this response (170). Reduction of intrathoracic blood volume by constriction of the inferior vena cava produced increased renal vasoconstrictor fiber activity (89), while the reverse occurred upon infusions of saline (87). Reduction of intrathoracic blood volume, as by constriction of the caval veins (121), peripheral venous pooling (51), negative pressure breathing (229), or hypovolemia (121, 224) produced significant increases in plasma renin activity. Considering the importance of neurogenic factors for renin release, these data are also compatible with a strong reflex influence on renal sympathetic fibers from intrathoracic receptors. Such changes in renal vasoconstrictor fiber activity imply not only adjustments of renal flow resistance, with consequences for overall cardiovascular function, but also neuronal reflex control of renal excretory function. In other words, the low pressure volume receptors seem to utilize both hormonal and neuronal efferent pathways to influence renal function and control fluid and salt homeostasis. The normal natriuretic response to saline loading, abolished by a constriction of the caval veins, is thus partly restored by acute surgical denervation of the kidneys (10), indicating that the reflex increase of renal sympathetic activity that follows a diminished low pressure receptor activity is of importance for this antinatriuretic response. In other reports the antinatriuretic effects of caval constriction remained after renal denervation, suggesting that humoral mechanisms are also involved (188). The reflex antinatriuretic response is not due to alterations of glomerular filtration rate (10), but rather to an increased tubular reabsorption of sodium.

Several mechanisms by which an augmented adrenergic activity in the kidneys may influence sodium reabsorption have been proposed. A redistribution of renal blood flow from cortical salt-losing to deep salt-preserving nephrons has been discussed; such a redistribution appears to occur when the low pressure receptors are unloaded following hemorrhage (129) or constriction of the inferior caval vein (109, 155). An increased outer cortex flow is noted following expansion of body fluid volume (111), in which case an activation of low pressure receptors, inhibition of the sympathetic influence to the kidneys, and a denervation diuresis is to be expected (14). The advantage of such redistributions of flow from salt-losing cortical nephrons to salt-preserving juxtaglomerular nephrons in situations of fluid and salt deficiency and vice versa is obvious. Besides the influence on total blood flow and flow distribution, variations in renal sympathetic activity may also affect sodium reabsorption by altering the peritubular capillary pressure as a consequence of the neurogenic adjustments of precapillary vessel tone. Such shifts of peritubular capillary hydrostatic pressure and transcapillary fluid transport have been proposed to affect the tubular sodium reabsorption (189). Finally, an enhancement of sodium reabsorption via a direct sympathetic nervous effect on the tubular cells has been proposed (194).

Moderate reductions of intrathoracic blood volume in humans by means of applications of lower body negative pressure lead to decreased central venous pressure and a clear-cut constriction of forearm and splanchnic (84) vessels while heart rate and arterial blood pressure are not significantly changed (84). This has been taken to indicate that an unloading of intrathoracic receptors was responsible for the reflex forearm vessel constriction. Atrial receptors were suggested, but apparently ventricular receptors may also contribute (160). Stimulation of low pressure receptors in humans by lower body immersion leads to a dilatation of the veins (46a). Moderate alterations of blood volume, which cause significant changes of central venous pressure but not of arterial blood pressure, lead to inverse changes in plasma ADH concentrations (30, 31, 37, 199).

Reflexes from Cardiac Receptors with Sympathetic Afferents

Reflex responses, elicited from sympathetic cardiac receptors, both medullated and nonmedullated, are mainly excitatory in nature. There is a general increase of the sympathetic outflow, producing increased heart rate and contractility and peripheral vasoconstriction; the net effect is increased blood pressure (23, 131, 133, 190). These responses were obtained also in spinalized, vagotomized animals, indicating that the reflexes can be mediated entirely via spinal pathways (133). Normally, however, supraspinal structures also seem to be involved; receptor stimulation thus inhibits vagal activity (190), which contributes to the tachycardic response. An inhibition of sympathetic efferent activity when cardiac sympathetic endings were stimulated has been reported (132), but denied in other studies (23). Little is known about the functional role of the tonically, rhythmically active cardiac sympathetic receptors. They apparently respond to similar types of stimuli as do the nonmedullated vagal receptors (160), but the reflex effects of the two system are quite opposite; the vagal receptors induce powerful depressor reactions, the sympathetic receptors induce essentially excitatory pressor effects. If, and at what level along the neuroaxis, these two systems are integrated to produce optimal cardiovascular responses has not been explored. It seems, however, as if the vagal and sympathetic afferents converge to the same efferent vagal and sympathetic cardiac neurons (190) so that interference between the two systems is indeed possible. When a simultaneous activation of the two systems occurs, as during coronary obstruction, the effects from vagal receptors appear to dominate with respect to the cardiovascular adjustments, as the net effect is often a depressor response with regard to blood pressure and efferent sympathetic activity to the kidneys (220).

The Role of Cardiac Receptors in Circulatory Adjustments to Coronary Obstruction

Because both sympathetic (23, 134, 217, 218) and vagal (210, 211, 230) atrial and ventricular receptors show an increased activity in response to coronary artery obstruction or embolization, they must to a varying extent, contribute to the circulatory adjustments in this situation (220). The sympathetic fibers have long been associated with the pain of myocardial ischemia (217, 218) and their receptors respond, for example, to administration of lactic acid, bradykinin, and potassium ions (178, 215, 219); the latter is known to leak into the interstitium from damaged cells. Whether receptors signaling in vagal afferents contribute to the mediation of pain is not known. However, nicotine, which is known to activate these fibers, does not seem to cause any discomfort when administered intrapericardially to nonanesthetized dogs (193). Both medullated sympathetic (215, 217, 218) and medullated (230) and nonmedullated vagal fibers (210) become activated upon the occurrence of signs of cardiac failure [rising atrial and end-diastolic ventricular pressures and systemic hypotension (210, 230)] and fire with rhythmic bursts in phase with the movements of the bulging ventricular wall. The sympathetic C-fibers have an irregular activity, which lasts for a considerable time after release of the occlusion (218), suggesting that the endings respond to chemical factors that accumulate in the tissue when blood supply becomes insufficient.

Both excitatory and inhibitory influences that manifest themselves as reflex tachycardia (55, 173, 174) and as bradycardia, hypotension, and decreased sympathetic efferent activity (108, 211, 220), respectively, have been reported in response to coronary occlusion. The excitatory influences emanate in part from cardiac afferents but also partly from systemic baro- and chemoreceptors when arterial pressure falls along with a progressive failure of the pump (174, 220). The inhibitory influences from vagal endings during coronary artery obstruction are often difficult to demonstrate because of the opposing excitatory effects; they often manifest themselves as an unchanged flow resistance instead of the expected, baroreceptor-induced vasoconstriction, which is obtained at equal reductions of blood pressure produced by other means (211). Deafferentation of vagal cardiac receptors causes enhanced vasoconstriction and augmented vasomotor fiber activity during coronary obstruction, demonstrating a background inhibitory activity, possibly from ventricular endings, in this situation (211, 220). Similarly, if opposing influences from the baroreceptors are minimized, an exaggerated fall in blood pressure and a clear vasodilatation occur during coronary obstruction (211). Because baroreceptor reflex influence is marked in skeletal muscle, while cardiac receptors affect this bed to a minor extent (125a), the net effect of a simultaneous engagement of the two reflex mechanisms is likely to be a vasoconstriction (173); as soon as the baroreceptor influences are removed, a reflex vasodilatation in the muscles becomes apparent (173, 211). On the other hand, baroreceptor reflex effects on renal circulation are relatively moderate (104), while the cardiac receptor influence is more dominant in this circuit (162), and the simultaneous activation of the two reflexes will then cause a reflex vasodilator response (173). Other reports suggest that inhibitory reflexes presumably from the heart and mainly affecting renal circulation are important during hypotension caused by coronary obstruction. Thus although the renal flow resistance is markedly elevated in hemorrhagic hypotension, a similar hypotension resulting from cardiogenic shock produced little reflex constriction within the kidney (65a).

INTEGRATED REFLEX RESPONSES

In most disturbances of circulatory homeostasis that call for appropriate adjustments of the cardiovascular performance, as in hemorrhage, anoxia, etc, there is simultaneous engagement of several different reflex mechanisms, which work in concert to produce the response. The contribution of various afferent inputs to the circulatory adjustment in different states has been analyzed in some recent studies and has been discussed at length in a recent review (116). Such explorations are important also in that they may provide essential information concerning the extent of convergent occlusion, facilitation etc, between various afferent systems. The interaction between centrally induced circulatory responses and baroreceptor reflexes was recently reviewed in this series (195) and only limited space is therefore devoted to this topic.

Activation of hypothalamic structures seems to block, more or less completely, the vagal component of the reflex bradycardia normally obtained when inhibitory afferent systems from baroreceptors and cardiac receptors (225) or the nucleus tractus solitarius (209) are stimulated, while the baroreceptors apparently are then still capable of producing inhibition of the efferent sympathetic discharge to the vascular beds. The interference between baroreceptor and hypothalamic influences on the sympathetic vasomotor neurons therefore seems to be a mere competition, or a simple additive phenomenon, between excitatory and inhibitory influences that impinge on the same neuron pools, while the blockade of the vagal bradycardia seems to imply more complex interneuronal interaction. The vagal bradycardia following stimulation of the final common path, i.e. the motor neurons in the nucleus ambiguus, is, as expected, not blocked by hypothalamic stimulation (209). Maximal depressor responses (225) and a more or less complete cessation of vasomotor fiber activity are obtained, at least transiently (156, 206), when only one or two of the main four baroreceptor areas are strongly excited. If further inhibitory influences via, for example, ventricular receptor afferents are then presented, there are no additional depressor responses (225). These findings indicate a considerable convergent occlusion of baroreceptor afferents and of other inhibitory afferents onto the vasomotor neuron pools in the medulla oblongata. In contrast, an intense activation of the ventricular receptor afferents is apparently not capable of completely inhibiting the vasomotor activity in the skeletal muscles but evidently is capable of doing so in the kidney (125a). A certain population of muscle vasomotor neurons is evidently not accessible for inhibition via cardiac receptor afferents.

Baroreceptor stimulation occurring during a period of increased chemoreceptor discharge, a situation likely to occur during hypoxia or asphyxia, is capable of effectively reducing blood pressure, but the pressure is higher for a given sinus pressure when the chemoreceptors are simultaneously stimulated (76a, 225). This reset of the baroreceptor reflex seems to be most pronounced at low sinus pressures, where little or no baroreceptor inhibitory activity is present; an intense baroreceptor stimulation could completely overwhelm the chemoreceptor excitation and bring the blood pressure down to the same level as when no chemoreceptor activity is at hand (225). These observations seem to indicate that chemoreceptor and baroreceptor afferents project to the same neuron pools in the medulla and that the interference between the two afferent systems is a matter of a simple competition between their respective inhibitory and excitatory influences.

Literature Cited

1. Aars, H. 1971. Effects of noradrenaline on activity in single aortic baroreceptor fibres. *Acta Physiol. Scand.* 83:335–43
2. Aars, H., Myhre, L. 1974. Cardiovascular reflexes mediated through non-medullated afferents in the aortic nerve. *J. Physiol. London* 242:78–79P
3. Acker, H., Keller, H. -P., Lubbers, D. W. 1973. The relationship between neuronal activity of chemoreceptor fibers and tissue Po_2 of the carotid body of the cat during changes in arterial Po_2 and blood pressure. *Pfluegers Arch.* 343:287–96
4. Angell-James, J. E. 1971. The effects of altering mean pressure, pulse pressure and pulse frequency on the impulse activity in baroreceptor fibres from the aortic arch and right subclavian artery in the rabbit. *J. Physiol. London* 214:65–88
5. Angell-James, J. E. 1973. Characteristics of single aortic and right subclavian baroreceptor fibre activity in rabbits with chronic renal hypertension. *Circ. Res.* 32:149–61
6. Angell-James, J. E. 1974. Arterial baroreceptor activity in rabbits with experimental atherosclerosis. *Circ. Res.* 34:27–39
7. Angell-James, J. E., Daly, M. deBurgh 1970. Comparison of the reflex vasomotor responses to separate and combined stimulation of the carotid sinus and aortic arch baroreceptors by pulsatile and non-pulsatile pressures in the dog. *J. Physiol. London* 209:257–73
8. Armour, J. A. 1973. Physiological behavior of thoracic cardiovascular receptors. *Am. J. Physiol.* 225:177–85
9. Arndt, J. O., Brambring, P., Hindorf, K., Röhnelt, M. 1974. The afferent discharge pattern of atrial mechanoreceptors in the cat during sinusoidal stretch of atrial strips *in situ*. *J. Physiol. London* 240:33–52
10. Azer, M., Gannon, R., Kaloyanides, G. J. 1972. Effect of renal denervation on the antinatriuresis of caval constriction. *Am. J. Physiol.* 222:611–16
11. Bagshaw, R. J., Peterson, L. H. 1972. Sympathetic control of the mechanical properties of the canine carotid sinus. *Am. J. Physiol.* 222:1462–68
12. Belmonte, C., Eyzaguirre, C. 1974. Efferent influences on carotid body chemoreceptors. *J. Neurophysiol.* 37:1131–43

13. Belmonte, C., Simon, J., Gallego, R., Baron, M. 1972. Sympathetic fibers in the aortic nerve of the cat. *Brain Res.* 43:25–35
14. Bencsáth, P., Takács, L. 1971. Intrarenal distribution of blood flow and cortico-medullary sodium gradient after unilateral splachnicotomy in the dog. *J. Physiol. London* 212:629–40
15. Biscoe, T. J. 1971. Carotid body: Structure and function. *Physiol. Rev.* 51:437–95
16. Biscoe, T. J., Bradley, G. W., Purves, M. J. 1970. The relation between carotid body chemoreceptor discharge, carotid sinus pressure and carotid body venous blood. *J. Physiol. London* 208:99–120
17. Biscoe, T. J., Purves, M. J., Sampson, S. R. 1970. The frequency of nerve impulses in single carotid body chemoreceptor afferent fibres recorded in vivo with intact circulation. *J. Physiol. London* 208:121–31
18. Biscoe, T. J., Sampson, S. R. 1970. Field potentials evoked in the brain stem of the cat by stimulation of the carotid sinus, glossopharyngeal, aortic and superior laryngeal nerves. *J. Physiol. London* 209:341–58
19. Bond, G. C., Trank, J. W. 1972. Plasma antidiuretic hormone concentration after bilateral aortic nerve section. *Am. J. Physiol.* 222:595–98
20. Borison, H. L., Domjan, D. 1970. Persistence of the cardio-inhibitory response to brain stem ischaemia after destruction of the area postrema and dorsal vagal nucleus. *J. Physiol. London* 211:263–77
21. Brennan, L. A., Henninger, A. L., Jochim, K. E., Malvin, R. L. 1974. Relationship between carotid sinus pressure and plasma renin level. *Am. J. Physiol.* 227:295–99
22. Brennan, L. A., Malvin, R. L., Jochim, K. E., Roberts, D. E. 1971. Influence of right and left atrial receptors on plasma concentrations of ADH and renin. *Am. J. Physiol.* 221:273–78
23. Brown, A. M., Malliani, A. 1971. Spinal sympathetic reflexes initiated by coronary receptors. *J. Physiol. London* 212:685–705
24. Burkhart, S. M., Ledsome, J. R. 1974. The response to distension of the pulmonary vein-left atrial junctions in dogs with spinal section. *J. Physiol. London* 237:685–700

25. Burnstock, G. 1972. Purinergic nerves. *Pharmacol. Rev.* 24:509–81
26. Calaresu, F. R., Thomas, M. R. 1971. The function of the paramedian reticular nucleus in the control of heart rate in the cat. *J. Physiol. London* 216:143–58
27. Calvelo, M. G., Abboud, F. M., Ballard, D. R., Abdel-Sayed, W. 1970. Reflex vascular responses to stimulation of chemoreceptors with nicotine and cyanide. Activation of adrenergic constriction in muscle and noncholinergic dilatation in dog's paw. *Circ. Res.* 27:259–76
28. Carswell, F., Hainsworth, R., Ledsome, J. R. 1970. The effect of distension of the pulmonary vein-atrial junctions upon peripheral vascular resistance. *J. Physiol. London* 207:1–14
29. Chevalier, P. A., Weber, K. C., Lyons, G. W., Nicoloff, D. M., Fox, I. J. 1974. Hemodynamic changes from stimulation of left ventricular baroreceptors. *Am. J. Physiol.* 227:719–28
30. Claybaugh, J. R., Share, L. 1972. Role of the renin-angiotensin system in the vasopressin response to hemorrhage. *Endocrinology* 90:453–60
31. Claybaugh, J. R., Share, L. 1973. Vasopressin, renin and cardiovascular responses to continuous slow hemorrhage. *Am. J. Physiol.* 224:519–23
32. Clement, D. L., Pelletier, C. L., Shepherd, J. T. 1972. Role of vagal afferents in the control of renal sympathetic nerve activity in the rabbit. *Circ. Res.* 31:824–30
33. Coleridge, H. M. et al 1973. Impulses in slowly conducting vagal fibers from afferent endings in the veins, atria and arteries of dogs and cats. *Circ. Res.* 33:87–97
34. Coote, J. H., Johns, E. J., Macleod, V. H., Singer, B. 1972. Effect of renal nerve stimulation, renal blood flow and adrenergic blockade on plasma renin activity in the cat. *J. Physiol. London* 226:15–36
35. Coote, J. H., Macleod, V. H. 1974. Evidence for the involvement in the baroreceptor reflex of a descending inhibitory pathway. *J. Physiol. London* 241:477–96
36. Corbett, J. L., Frankel, H. L., Harris, P. J. 1971. Cardiovascular reflex responses to cutaneous and visceral stimuli in spinal man. *J. Physiol. London* 215:395–409
37. Cousineau, D., Gagnon, D. J., Sirois, P. 1973. Changes in plasma levels of vasopressin and renin in response to hamorrhage in dogs. *Br. J. Pharmacol.* 47:315–24
38. Cowley, A. W. Jr., Guyton, A. C. 1972. Quantification of intermediate steps in the renin-angiotensin-vasoconstrictor feedback loop in the dog. *Circ. Res.* 30:557–66
39. Cowley, A. W. Jr., Liard, J. F., Guyton, A. C. 1973. Role of the baroreceptor reflex in daily control of arterial blood pressure and other variables in dogs. *Circ. Res.* 32:564–76 ·
40. Cowley, A. W. Jr., Monos, E., Guyton, A. C. 1974. Interaction of vasopressin and the baroreceptor reflex system in the regulation of arterial blood pressure in the dog. *Circ. Res.* 34:505–14
41. Cryer, G. L., Gann, D. S. 1973. Location of vagal receptors controlling adrenal corticosteroid secretion. *Am. J. Physiol.* 225:1346–50
42. Davies, R. O., Edwards, M. W. Jr. 1973. Distribution of carotid body chemoreceptor afferents in the medulla of the cat. *Brain Res.* 64:451–54
43. De Groat, W. C., Lalley, P. M. 1974. Reflex sympathetic firing in response to electrical stimulation of the carotid sinus nerve in the cat. *Brain Res.* 80:17–40
44. Doba, N., Reis, D. J. 1974. Role of central and peripheral adrenergic mechanisms in neurogenic hypertension produced by brainstem lesions in rat. *Circ. Res.* 34:293–301
45. Donald, D. E., Edis, A. J. 1971. Comparison of aortic and carotid baroreflexes in the dog. *J. Physiol. London* 215:521–38
46. Drees, J. A., Rothe, C. F. 1974. Reflex venoconstriction and capacity vessel pressure-volume relationships in dogs. *Circ. Res.* 34:360–73
46a. Echt, M. Lange, L. Gauer, O. H. 1974. Changes of peripheral venous tone and central transmural venous pressure during immersion in a thermo-neutral bath. *Pfluegers Arch.* 352:211–17
47. Eckberg, D. L., Fletcher, G. F., Braunwald, E. 1972. Mechanism of prolongation of the R-R interval with electrical stimulation of the carotid sinus nerves in man. *Circ. Res.* 30:131–38
48. Edis, A. J., Donald, D. E., Shepherd, J. T. 1970. Cardiovascular reflexes from stretch of pulmonary vein-atrial junctions in the dog. *Circ. Res.* 27:1091–1100
49. Errington, M. L., Rocha e Silva, M. 1972. Vasopressin clearance and secre-

tion during haemorrhage in normal dogs and in dogs with experimental diabetes insipidus. *J. Physiol. London* 227:395–418

50. Estavillo, J., Burger, R. E. 1973. Cardiac afferent activity in depressor nerve of the chicken. *Am. J. Physiol.* 225:1063–66

51. Fasola, A. F., Martz, B. L. 1972. Peripheral venous renin activity during 70° tilt and lower body negative pressure. *Aerosp. Med.* 43:713–15

52. Ferrario, C. M., Gildenberg, P. L., McCubbin, J. W. 1972. Cardiovascular effects of angiotensin mediated by the central nervous system. *Circ. Res.* 30:257–62

53. Fidone, S. J., Sato, A. 1969. A study of chemoreceptor and baroreceptor A- and C-fibres in the cat carotid nerve. *J. Physiol. London* 205:527–48

54. Foreman, R. D., Wurster, R. D. 1973. Localization and functional characteristics of descending sympathetic spinal pathways. *Am. J. Physiol.* 225:212–17

55. Fowlis, R. A. F., Sang, C. T. M., Lundy, P. M., Ahuja, S. P., Colhoun, E. H. 1974. Experimental coronary artery ligation in conscious dogs six months after bilateral cardiac sympathectomy. *Am. Heart J.* 88:748–57

56. Fukiyama, K., Omae, T. 1973. Change in baroreceptor sensitivity by angiotensin. *Jpn. Circ. J.* 37:1247–49

57. Furnival, C. M., Linden, R. J., Snow, H. M. 1971. Reflex effects on the heart of stimulating left atrial receptors. *J. Physiol. London* 218:447–63

58. Gabriel, M., Seller, H. 1970. Interaction of baroreceptor afferents from carotid sinus and aorta at the nucleus tractus solitarii. *Pfluegers Arch.* 318:7–20

59. Gahery, Y., Vigier, D. 1974. Inhibitory effects in the cuneate nucleus produced by vago-aortic afferent fibers. *Brain Res.* 75:241–46

60. Gebber, G. L., Taylor, D. G., Weaver, L. C. 1973. Electrophysiological studies on organization of central vasopressor pathways. *Am. J. Physiol.* 224:470–81

61. Gillespie, D. J., Sandberg, R. L., Koike, T. I. 1973. Dual effect of left atrial receptors on excretion of sodium and water in the dog. *Am. J. Physiol.* 225:706–10

62. Gilmore, J. P., Zucker, I. H. 1974. Discharge of type B atrial receptors during changes in vascular volume and depression of atrial contractility. *J. Physiol. London* 239:207–33

63. Goetz, K. L., Bond, G. C. 1973. Reflex diuresis during tachycardia in the dog. *Circ. Res.* 32:434–41

64. Goodman, N. W. 1973. Efferent control of arterial chemoreceptors mediated by glossopharyngeal fibres and artifacts introduced by stimulation techniques. *J. Physiol. London* 230:295–311

65. Gootman, P. M., Cohen, M. I. 1971. Evoked splanchnic potentials produced by electrical stimulation of medullary vasomotor regions. *Exp. Brain Res.* 13:1–14

65a. Gorfinkel, H. J., Szidon, J. P., Hirsch, L. J., Fishman, H. P. 1972. Renal performance in experimental cardiogenic shock. *Am. J. Physiol.* 222:1260–68

66. Graham, B. H., Lioy, F. 1973. Histaminergic vasodilatation in the hindlimb of the dog. *Pfluegers Arch.* 342:307–18

67. Greenberg, T. et al 1973. Impaired atrial receptor responses in dogs with heart failure due to tricuspid insufficiency and pulmonary artery stenosis. *Circ. Res.* 32:424–33

68. Greenway, C. V., Lister, G. E. 1974. Capacitance effects and blood reservoir function in the splanchnic vascular bed during nonhypotensive haemorrhage and blood volume expansion in anaesthetized cats. *J. Physiol. London* 237:279–94

69. Gross, R., Kirchheim, H. 1972. Der Einfluss einer konstanten Herzfrequenz auf den Carotis-sinus Reflex am wachen Hund. *Pfluegers Arch.* 337:59–70

70. Guertzenstein, P. G., Silver, A. 1974. Fall in blood pressure produced from discrete regions of the ventral surface of the medulla by glycine and lesions. *J. Physiol. London* 242:489–503

71. Gutmann, F. D., Tagawa, H., Haber, E., Barger, A. C. 1973. Renal arterial pressure, renin secretion and blood pressure control in trained dogs. *Am. J. Physiol.* 224:66–72

72. Haas, E., Goldblatt, H., Rowland, V., Vrtunski, P. 1974. Neurogenic pressor response due to mesencephalic electrical stimulation. Effect of blockade of renin-angiotensin system. *Am. J. Physiol.* 226:771–75

73. Hackett, J. G., Abboud, F. M., Mark, A., Schmid, P. G., Heistad, D. D. 1972. Coronary vascular responses to stimulation of chemoreceptors and baroreceptors. Evidence for reflex activation of vagal cholinergic innervation. *Circ. Res.* 31:8–17

74. Hainsworth, R., Karim, F. 1972. Inotropic responses of the left ventricle to changes in aortic arch pressure in anes-

thetized dogs. *J. Physiol. London* 223:213–28

75. Hainsworth, R., Karim, F. 1975. Carotid baroreceptors and abdominal vascular capacitance. *J. Physiol. London* 244:81P–82P

76. Harris, M. C., Spyer, K. M. 1973. Inhibition of ADH release by stimulation of afferent cardiac branches of the right vagus in cats. *J. Physiol. London* 231:15P–16P

76a. Heistad, D. D., Abboud, F. M., Mark, A. L., Schmid, P. G. 1974. Interaction between baroreceptor and chemoreceptor reflexes. Modulation of chemoreceptor reflex by changes in baroreceptor activity. *J. Clin. Invest.* 53:1226–36

77. Hess, G. L., Zuperku, E. J., Coon, R. L., Kampine, J. P. 1974. Sympathetic afferent nerve activity of left ventricular origin. *Am. J. Physiol.* 227:543–46

78. Hilton, S. M. 1970. A critique of current ideas of the nervous system control of circulation. In *Cardiovascular Regulation in Health and Disease,* ed. C. Barlorelli, A. Zanchetti, 57–62. Milan: Milan

79. Howe, A., Neil, E. 1973. Arterial chemoreceptors. In *Handbook of Sensory Physiology,* ed. E. Neil, 3:47–80. Berlin: Springer

80. Illert, M., Gabriel, M. 1972. Descending pathways in the cervical cord of cats affecting blood pressure and sympathetic activity. *Pfluegers Arch.* 335:109–24

81. Irisawa, H., Ninomiya, I., Woolley, G. 1973. Efferent activity in renal and intestinal nerves during circulatory reflexes. *Jpn. J. Physiol.* 23:657–66

82. Jacobs, L., Sampson, S. R., Comroe, J. H. Jr. 1971 Carotid sinus versus carotid body origin of nicotine and cyanide bradycardia in the dog. *Am. J. Physiol.* 220:472–76

83. Johnson, J. A., Davis, J. O. 1973. Angiotensin II. Important role in the maintenance of arterial blood pressure. *Science* 179:906–7

84. Johnson, J. M., Rowell, L. B., Niederberger, M., Eisman, M. M. 1974. Human splanchnic and forearm vasoconstrictor responses to reductions of right atrial and aortic pressures. *Circ. Res.* 34:515–24

85. Jonzon, A., Öberg, P. Å., Sedin, G., Sjöstrand, U. 1972. Studies on blood-pressure regulation. IV. The effects of impulse train stimulation of the carotid-sinus nerves. *Acta Physiol. Scand.* 85:323–42

86. Joy, M. D., Lowe, R. D. 1970. Evidence for a medullary site of action in the cardiovascular response to angiotensin II. *J. Physiol. London* 206:41P–42P

87. Judy, W. V., Thompson, J. R., Wilson, M. F. 1971. Effects of isotonic saline loading on renal nerve activity. *The Physiologist* 14:169

88. Juhász-Nagy, A., Szentiványi, M. 1973. Effect of venous coronary reflexes on cardiovascular dynamics. *Acta. Physiol. Acad. Sci. Hung.* 43:287–99

89. Kahl, F. R., Flint, J. F., Szidon, J. P. 1974. Influence of left atrial distention on renal vasomotor tone. *Am. J. Physiol.* 226:240–46

90. Kaminski, R. J., Meyer, G. A., Winter, D. L. 1970. Sympathetic unit activity associated with Mayer waves in the spinal dog. *Am. J. Physiol.* 219:1768–71

91. Kappagoda, C. T., Linden, R. J., Mary, D. A. S. 1975. Reflex increase in heart rate from stimulation of left atrial receptors. *J. Physiol. London* 244:78P–79P

92. Kappagoda, C. T., Linden, R. J., Saunders, D. A. 1972. The effect on heart rate of distending the atrial appendages in the dog. *J. Physiol. London* 225:705–19

93. Kappagoda, C. T., Linden, R. J., Snow, H. M. 1972. A reflex increase in heart rate from distension of the junction between the superior vena cava and the right atrium. *J. Physiol. London* 220:177–97

94. Kappagoda, C. T., Linden, R. J., Snow, H. M. 1972. The effect of distending the atrial appendages on urine flow in the dog. *J. Physiol. London* 227:233–42

95. Kappagoda, C. T., Linden, R. J., Snow, H. M. 1973. Effect of stimulating right atrial receptors on urine flow in the dog. *J. Physiol. London* 235:493–502

96. Kappagoda, C. T., Linden, R. J., Scott, E. M., Snow, H. M. 1974. The efferent pathway of the reflex increase in heart rate produced by stimulation of left atrial receptors. *J. Physiol. London* 242:79P–80P

97. Kappagoda, C. T., Linden, R. J., Snow, H. M., Whitaker, E. M. 1974. Left atrial receptors and the antidiuretic hormone. *J. Physiol. London* 237:663–83

98. Kappagoda, C. T., Linden, R. J., Snow, H. M. Whitaker, E. M. 1974. Effect of ablation of the pituitary gland on the diuresis from atrial receptors. *J. Physiol. London* 238:11P–12P

99. Kardon, M. B., Peterson, D. F., Bishop, V. S. 1973. Reflex bradycardia due to

aortic nerve stimulation in the rabbit. *Am. J. Physiol.* 225:7–11

100. Karim, F., Kidd, C., Malpus, C. M., Penna, P. E. 1972. The effects of stimulation of the left atrial receptors on sympathetic efferent nerve activity. *J. Physiol. London* 227:243–60

101. Keeler, R. 1974. Natriuresis after unilateral stimulation of carotid receptors in unanesthetized rats. *Am. J. Physiol.* 226:507–11

102. Keith, I. C., Kidd, C., Malpus, C. M., Penna, P. E. 1974. Reduction of baroreceptor impulse activity by sympathetic nerve stimulation. *J. Physiol. London* 238:61P–62P

103. Kendrick, J. E., Matson, G. L., Öberg, B., Wennergren, G. 1973. The effect of stimulus pattern on the pressure response to electrical stimulation of the carotid sinus nerve of cats. *Proc. Soc. Exp. Biol. Med.* 144:412–16

104. Kendrick, E., Öberg, B., Wennergren, G. 1972. Vasoconstrictor fibre discharge to skeletal muscle, kidney, intestine and skin at varying levels of arterial baroreceptor activity in the cat. *Acta Physiol. Scand.* 85:464–76

105. Kendrick, E., Öberg, B., Wennergren, G. 1972. Extent of engagement of various cardiovascular effectors to alterations of carotid sinus pressure. *Acta Physiol. Scand.* 86:410–18

106. Kendrick, J. E., Öberg, B., Wennergren, G. 1972. The effect of simultaneous but opposite alterations in pulse amplitude and frequency on arterial baroreceptor activity. *Acta Physiol. Scand.* 84:51A

107. Kent, B. B., Drane, J. W., Manning, J. W. 1971. Suprapontine contribution to the carotid sinus reflex in the cat. *Circ. Res.* 29:534–41

108. Kezdi, P., Kordenat, R. K., Misra, S. N. 1974. Reflex inhibitory effects of vagal afferents in experimental myocardial infarction. *Am. J. Cardiol.* 33:853–60

109. Kilcoyne, M. M., Cannon, P. J. 1971. Neural and humoral influences on intrarenal blood flow distribution during thoracic caval occlusion. *Am. J. Physiol.* 220:1231–37

110. Kilcoyne, M. M., Schmidt, D. H., Cannon, P. J. 1973. Intrarenal blood flow in congestive heart failure. *Circulation* 47:786–97

111. Kinney, M. J., DiScala, V. A. 1974. Volume expansion and intrarenal blood flow of normal and salt-deprived rats. *Am. J. Physiol.* 227:652–56

112. Koizumi, K., Brooks, C.Mc.C. 1972. The integration of autonomic system reactions; a discussion of autonomic reflexes, their control and their association with somatic reactions. *Ergeb. Physiol. Biol. Chem. Exp. Pharmakol.* 67:1–68

113. Koizumi, K., Sato, A. 1969. Influence of sympathetic innervation on carotid sinus baroreceptor activity. *Am. J. Physiol.* 216:321–29

114. Koizumi, K., Sato, A. 1972. Reflex activity of single sympathetic fibres to skeletal muscle produced by electrical stimulation of somatic and vago-depressor afferent nerves in the cat. *Pfluegers Arch.* 332:283–301

115. Kollai, M., Fedina, L., Kovách, A. G. B. 1973. Effect of bleeding, cooling and asphyxia on the activity of vertebral and cardiac sympathetic nerves. *Acta Physiol. Acad. Sci. Hung.* 44:145–55

116. Korner, P. I. 1971. Integrative neural cardiovascular control. *Physiol. Rev.* 51:312–67

117. Kunze, D. L. 1972. Reflex discharge patterns of cardiac vagal efferent fibres. *J. Physiol. London* 222:1–15

118. Lawrence, M., Ledsome, J. R., Mason, J. M. 1973. The time course of the diuretic response to left atrial distension. *Q. J. Exp. Physiol.* 58:219–27

119. Ledsome, J. R., Mason, J. M. 1972. The effects of vasopressin on the diuretic response to left atrial distension. *J. Physiol. London* 221:427–40

120. Lee, T. M., Kuo, J. S., Chai, C. Y. 1972. Central integrating mechanism of the Bezold-Jarisch and baroreceptor reflexes. *Am. J. Physiol.* 222:713–20

121. Leenen, F. H., Stricker, E. M. 1974. Plasma renin activity and thirst following hypovolemia or caval ligation in rats. *Am. J. Physiol.* 226:1238–42

122. Linden, R. J. 1973. Function of cardiac receptors. *Circulation* 48:463–80

123. Lioy, F., White, K. P. 1973. ^{14}C-histamine release during vasodilatation induced by lumbar ventral root stimulation. *Pfluegers Arch.* 342:319–24

124. Lisander, B., Martner, J. 1971. Cerebellar suppression of the autonomic components of the defence reaction. *Acta Physiol. Scand.* 81:84–95

125. Little, R., Öberg, B. 1975. Circulatory responses to stimulation of the carotid body chemoreceptors in the cat. *Acta Physiol. Scand.* 93:34–51

125a. Little, R., Wennergren, G., Öberg, B. 1975. Aspects of the central integration of arterial baroreceptor and cardiac ventricular receptor reflexes in the cat. *Acta Physiol. Scand.* 93:85–96

126. Lloyd, T. C. 1972. Control of systemic vascular resistance by pulmonary and left heart baroreflexes. *Am. J. Physiol.* 222:1511–17

127. Loefler, J. R., Stockigt, J. R., Ganong, W. F. 1972. Effect of alpha- and beta-adrenergic blocking agents on the increase in renin secretion produced by stimulation of the renal nerves. *Neuroendocrinology* 10:129–38

128. Loeschcke, H. H., Lattre, J. de, Schläfke, M. E., Trouth, C. O. 1970. Effects on respiration and circulation of electrically stimulating the ventral surface of the medulla oblongata. *Respir. Physiol.* 10:184–97

129. Logan, A., Jose, P., Eisner, G., Lilienfield, L., Slotkoff, L. 1971. Intracortical distribution of renal blood flow in hemorrhagic shock in dogs. *Circ. Res.* 29:257–66

130. Lopes, O. U., Neto, J. C. 1973. The effect of hypothalamic lesions on the carotid occlusion reflex. *J. Physiol. London* 232:37P–38P

131. Malliani, A., Parks, M., Tuckett, R. P., Brown, A. M. 1973. Reflex increases in heart rate elicited by stimulation of afferent cardiac sympathetic nerve fibers in the cat. *Circ. Res.* 32:9–14

132. Malliani, A., Pagani, M., Recordati, G., Schwartz, P. J. 1971. Spinal sympathetic reflexes elicited by increases in arterial blood pressure. *Am. J. Physiol.* 220:128–34

133. Malliani, A., Peterson, D. F., Bishop, V. S., Brown, A. M. 1972. Spinal sympathetic cardiocardiac reflexes. *Circ. Res.* 30:158–66

134. Malliani, A., Recordati, G., Schwartz, P. J. 1973. Nervous activity of afferent cardiac sympathetic fibres with atrial and ventricular endings. *J. Physiol. London.* 229:457–69

135. Malliani, A., Recordati, G., Schwartz, P. J., Pagani, M. 1972. Tonic afferent sympathetic activity from the heart. *Experientia* 28:269–70

136. Mannard, A., Polosa, C. 1973. Analysis of background firing of single sympathetic preganglionic neurons of cat cervical nerve. *J. Neurophysiol.* 36:398–408

137. Mark, A. L., Abboud, F. M., Heistad, D. D., Schmid, P. G., Johannsen, U. J. 1974. Evidence against the presence of ventricular chemoreceptors activated by hypoxia and hypercapnia. *Am. J. Physiol.* 227:178–82

138. Mark, A. L., Abboud, F. M., Schmid, P. G., Heistad, D. D. 1973. Reflex vascular responses to left ventricular outflow obstruction and activation of ventricular baroreceptors in dogs. *J. Clin. Invest.* 52:1147–53

139. Mark, A. L., Kioschos, J. M., Abboud, F. M., Heistad, D. D., Schmid, P. G. 1973. Abnormal vascular response to exercise in patients with aortic stenosis. *J. Clin. Invest.* 52:1138–46

140. Mason, J. M., Ledsome, J. R. 1974. Effects of obstruction of the mitral orifice or distension of the pulmonary vein-atrial junctions on renal and hindlimb vascular resistance in the dog. *Circ. Res.* 35:24–32

141. Matsuura, S. 1973. Depolarisation of sensory nerve endings and impulse initiation in common carotid baroreceptors. *J. Physiol. London* 235:31–56

142. Matsuura, S. 1973. Chemoreceptor properties of glomous tissue found in the carotid region of the cat. *J. Physiol.* 235:57–73

143. Mayeri, E., Koester, J., Kupferman, I., Liebeswar, G., Kandel, E. R. 1974. Neural control of circulation in *Aplysia*. I. Motoneurons. *J. Neurophysiol.* 37:458–75

144. McAllen, R. M., Spyer, K. M. 1975. The origin of cardiac vagal efferent neurones in the medulla of the cat. *J. Physiol. London* 244:82P–83P

145. McQueen, D. S. 1974. Effects of suberyldicholine on carotid baroreceptors and chemoreceptors. *Neuropharmacology* 13:829–35

146. Menninger, R. P., Frazier, D. T. 1972. Effects of blood volume and atrial stretch on hypothalamic single-unit activity. *Am. J. Physiol.* 223:288–93

147. Middleton, S., Woolsey, C. N., Burton, H., Rose, J. E. 1973. Neural activity with cardiac periodicity in medulla oblongata of cat. *Brain Res.* 50:297–314

148. Miura, M., Reis, D. J. 1972. The role of the solitary and paramedian reticular nuclei in mediating cardiovascular reflex responses from carotid baro- and chemoreceptors. *J. Physiol. London* 223:525–48

149. Muers, M. F., Sleight, P. 1972. The reflex cardiovascular depression, caused by occlusion of the coronary sinus in the dog. *J. Physiol. London* 221:259–82

150. Muers, M. F., Sleight, P. 1972. Action potentials from ventricular mechanoreceptors stimulated by occlusion of the coronary sinus in the dog. *J. Physiol. London* 221:283–309

151. Muers, M. F., Shight, P. 1972. The cardiovascular effects of coronary sinus distension in the anaesthetised dog. *Q. J. Exp. Physiol.* 57:359–70

152. Nathan, M. A. 1972. Pathways in medulla oblongata of monkeys mediating splanchnic nerve activity. Electrophysiological and anatomical evidence. *Brain Res.* 45:115–26

153. Neil, E., O'Regan, R. G. 1971. The effects of electrical stimulation of the distal end of the cut sinus and aortic nerves on peripheral arterial chemoreceptor activity in the cat. *J. Physiol. London* 215:15–32

154. Neil, E., O'Regan, R. G. 1971. Efferent and afferent impulse activity recorded from few-fibre preparations of otherwise intact sinus and aortic nerves. *J. Physiol. London* 215:33–47

155. Newsome, H. H., Kafka, M. S., Bartter, F. C. 1971. Intrarenal blood flow in dogs with constriction of the inferior thoracic vena cava. *Am. J. Physiol.* 221:48–52

156. Ninomiya, I., Irisawa, H. 1969. Summation of baroreceptor reflex effects on sympathetic nerve activities. *Am. J. Physiol.* 216:1330–36

157. Ninomiya, I., Irisawa, A., Nisimaru, N. 1973. Nonuniformity of sympathetic nerve activity to the skin and kidney. *Am. J. Physiol.* 224:256–64

158. Ninomiya, I., Nisimaru, N., Irisawa, H. 1971. Sympathetic nerve activity to the spleen, kidney and heart in response to baroreceptor input. *Am. J. Physiol.* 221:1346–51

159. Nisimaru, N. 1971. Comparison of gastric and renal nerve activity. *Am. J. Physiol.* 220:1303–8

160. Öberg, B., Thorén, P. 1972. Studies on left ventricular receptors signalling in non-medullated vagal afferents. *Acta Physiol. Scand.* 85:145–63

161. Öberg, B., Thorén, P. 1973. Circulatory responses to stimulation of medullated and non-medullated afferents in the cardiac nerve in the cat. *Acta Physiol. Scand.* 87:121–32

162. Öberg, B., Thorén, P. 1973. Circulatory responses to stimulation of left ventricular receptors in the cat. *Acta Physiol. Scand.* 88:8–22

163. Öberg, B., White, S. 1970. Circulatory effects of interruption and stimulation of cardiac vagal afferents. *Acta Physiol. Scand.* 80:383–94

164. O'Regan, R. G. 1974. Efferent inhibition of the chemoreceptor activity of the ischaemic carotid body. *J. Physiol. London* 239:95P–96P

165. Ott, N. T., Shepherd, J. T. 1973. Modifications of the aortic and vagal depressor reflexes by hypercapnia in the rabbit. *Circ. Res.* 33:160–65

166. Paintal, A. S. 1971. Action of drugs on sensory nerve endings. *Ann. Rev. Pharmacol.* 11:231–40

167. Paintal, A. S. 1973. Vagal sensory receptors and their reflex effects. *Physiol. Rev.* 53:159–227

168. Paintal, A. S. 1973. Cardiovascular receptors. See Ref. 79, 1–45

169. Pelletier, C. L. 1972. Circulatory responses to graded stimulation of the carotid chemoreceptors in the dog. *Circ. Res.* 31:431–43

170. Pelletier, C. L., Edis, A. J., Shepherd, J. T. 1971. Circulatory reflex from vagal afferents in response to hemorrhage in the dog. *Circ. Res.* 29:626–34

171. Pelletier, C. L., Shepherd, J. T. 1972. Venous responses to stimulation of carotid chemoreceptors by hypoxia and hypercapnia. *Am. J. Physiol.* 223:97–103

172. Pelletier, C. L., Shepherd, J. T. 1973. Circulatory reflexes from mechanoreceptors in the cardio-aortic area. *Circ. Res.* 33:131–38

173. Peterson, D. F., Bishop, V. S. 1974. Reflex blood pressure control during acute myocardial ischemia in the conscious dog. *Circ. Res.* 34:226–32

174. Peterson, D. F., Kaspar, R. L., Bishop, V. S. 1973. Reflex tachycardia due to temporary coronary occlusions in the conscious dog. *Circ. Res.* 32:652–59

175. Ponte, J., Purves, M. J. 1974. The role of the carotid body chemoreceptors and carotid sinus baroreceptors in the control of cerebral blood vessels. *J. Physiol. London* 237:315–40

176. Purves, M. J. 1970. The role of the cervical sympathetic nerve in the regulation of oxygen consumption of the carotid body of the cat. *J. Physiol. London* 209:417–31

177. Recordati, G., Schwartz, P. J., Pagani, M., Malliani, A., Brown, A. M. 1971. Activation of cardiac vagal receptors during myocardial ischemia. *Experientia* 27:1423–24

178. Riccioppo, N. F., Brasil, J. C. F., Antonio, A. 1974. Bradykinin-induced coronary chemoreflex in the dog. *Naunyn-Schmiedeberg's Arch. Pharmacol.* 283:135–42

179. Richardson, D., Stella, A., Leonetti, G., Bertorelli, A., Zanchetti, A. 1974.

Mechanisms of renal release of renin by electrical stimulation of the brainstem in the cat. *Circ. Res.* 34:425–34

180. Robinson, J. L., Farr, W. C., Grupp, G. 1973. Atrial rate response to ventricular pacing in the unanesthetized A-V blocked dog. *Am. J. Physiol.* 224:40–45

181. Ryan, M. J., Brody, M. J. 1972. Neurogenic and vascular stores of histamine in the dog. *J. Pharmacol. Exp. Ther.* 181:83–91

182. Sampson, S. R. 1972. Mechanism of efferent inhibition of carotid body chemoreceptors in the cat. *Brain Res.* 45:266–70

183. Sampson, S. R., Hainsworth, R. 1972. Responses of aortic body chemoreceptors of the cat to physiological stimuli. *Am. J. Physiol.* 222:953–58

184. Sato, A. 1972. Somato-sympathetic reflex discharges evoked through supramedullary pathways. *Pfluegers Arch.* 332:117–26

185. Sato, A. 1972. The relative involvement of different reflex pathways in somatosympathetic reflexes, analyzed in spontaneously active single preganglionic sympathetic units. *Pfluegers Arch.* 333:70–81

186. Sato, A., Schmidt, R. F. 1973. Somatosympathetic reflexes: afferent fibers, central pathways, discharge characteristics. *Physiol. Rev.* 53:916–47

187. Schmidt, R. M., Kumada, M., Sagawa, K. 1971. Cardiac output and total peripheral resistance in carotid sinus reflex. *Am. J. Physiol.* 221:480–87

188. Schrier, R. W., Humphreys, M. H. 1971. Factors involved in the antinatriuretic effects of acute constriction of the thoracic and abdominal inferior vena cava. *Circ. Res.* 29:479–89

189. Schrier, R. W., de Wardener, M. E. 1971. Tubular reabsorption of sodium ions: Influence of factors other than aldosterone and glomerular filtration rate. *New Engl. J. Med.* 285:1231–43, 1292–1303

190. Schwartz, P. J., Pagani, M., Lombardi, F., Malliani, A., Brown, A. M. 1973. A cardiocardiac sympathovagal reflex in the cat. *Circ. Res.* 32:215–20

191. Seller, H. 1973. The discharge pattern of single units in thoracic and lumbar white rami in relation to cardiovascular events. *Pfluegers Arch.* 343:317–30

192. Shoukas, A. A., Sagawa, K. 1973. Control of total systemic vascular capacity by the carotid sinus baroreceptor reflex. *Circ. Res.* 33:22–33

193. Sleight, P. 1964. A cardiovascular depressor reflex from the epicardium of the left ventricle in the dog. *J. Physiol. London* 173:321–43

194. Slick, G. L., DiBona, G. F., Kaloyanides, G. J. 1974. Renal sympathetic nerve activity in sodium retention of acute caval constriction. *Am. J. Physiol.* 226:925–32

195. Smith, O. A. 1974. Reflex and central mechanisms involved in the control of the heart and circulation. *Ann. Rev. Physiol.* 36:93–123

196. Snyder, D. W., Gebber, G. L. 1973. Relationships between medullary depressor region and central vasopressor pathways. *Am. J. Physiol.* 225:1129–37

197. Spyer, K. M. 1972. Baroreceptor sensitive neurons in the anterior hypothalamus of the cat. *J. Physiol. London* 224:245–57

198. Spyer, K. M., Wolstencroft, J. H. 1971. Problems of the afferent input to the paramedian reticular nucleus, and the central connections of the sinus nerve. *Brain Res.* 26:411–14

199. Szczepánska-Sadowska, E. 1972. The activity of the hypothalamo-hypophyseal antidiuretic system in conscious dogs. I. The influence of isoosmotic blood volume changes. *Pfluegers Arch.* 335:139–46

200. Szczepánska-Sadowska, E. 1973. Hemodynamic effects of a moderate increase of the plasma vasopressin level in conscious dogs. *Pfluegers Arch.* 338:313–22

201. Tagawa, H., Vander, A. J., Bonjour, J.-P., Malvin, R. L. 1971. Inhibition of renin secretion by vasopressin in unanesthetized sodium-deprived dogs. *Am. J. Physiol.* 220:949–51

202. Takeuchi, T., Manning, J. W. 1971. Muscle cholinergic dilators in the sinus baroreceptor response in cats. *Circ. Res.* 29:350–57

203. Torack, R. M., Finke, E. H. 1971. Evidence for a sequestration of function within the area postrema based on scanning electron microscopy and the penetration of horseradish peroxidase. *Z. Zellforsch.* 118:85–96

204. Torack, R. M., Stranahan, P., Hartman, B. K. 1973. The role of norepinephrine in the function of the area postrema. I. Immunflourescent localization of dopamine-beta-hydroxylase and electron microscopy. *Brain Res.* 61:235–52

205. Taylor, D. G., Gebber, G. L. 1973. Sympathetic unit responses to stimula-

tion of cat medulla. *Am. J. Physiol.* 225:1138–46

206. Tedeschi, R. E., Sherman, S., De Sanctis, N., Davidheiser, S., Scheinbaum, J. 1971. Effect of carotid sinus baroreceptor stimulation on blood pressure and sympathetic outflow. *Am. J. Physiol.* 221:405–12

207. Thames, M. D., U1-Hassan, Z., Brackett, N. C., Lower, R. R., Kontos, H. A. 1971. Plasma renin responses to hemorrhage after cardiac auto-transplantation. *Am. J. Physiol.* 221:1115–19

208. Thomas, M. R., Calaresu, F. R. 1974. Localization and function of medullary sites mediating vagal bradycardia in the cat. *Am. J. Physiol.* 226:1344–49

209. Thomas, M. R., Calaresu, F. R. 1974. Medullary sites involved in hypothalamic inhibition of reflex vagal bradycardia in the cat. *Brain Res.* 80:1–16

210. Thorén, P. 1972. Left ventricular receptors activated by severe asphyxia and by coronary artery occlusion. *Acta Physiol. Scand.* 85:455–63

211. Thorén, P. 1973. Evidence for a depressor reflex elicited from left ventricular receptors during occlusion of one coronary artery in the cat. *Acta Physiol. Scand.* 88:23–34

212. Thorén, P. 1974. Characteristics of atrial receptors with non-medullated vagal afferents. *The Physiologist* 17:344

213. Thorén, P. 1974. Characteristics of left ventricular receptors with non-medullated vagal afferents. *Circulation* 50: Suppl. 3, 154

214. Tuttle, R. S., Moe, G. K. 1973. Reflex beta-adrenergic vasodilatation in the cat. *Am. J. Physiol.* 225:402–7

215. Uchida, Y., Murao, S. 1974. Afferent sympathetic nerve fibers originating in the left atrial wall. *Am. J. Physiol.* 227:753–58

216. Uchida, Y., Kamisaka, K., Murao, S., Ueda, H. 1974. Mechanosensitivity of afferent cardiac sympathetic nerve fibers. *Am. J. Physiol.* 226:1088–93

217. Uchida, Y., Kamisaka, K., Ueda, H. 1971. Experimental studies on anginal pain: mode of excitation of afferent cardiac sympathetic nerve fibers. *Jpn. Circ. J.* 35:147–61

218. Uchida, Y., Murao, S. 1974. Excitation of afferent cardiac sympathetic nerve fibers during coronary occlusion. *Am. J. Physiol.* 226:1094–99

219. Uchida, Y., Murao, S. 1974. Potassium-induced excitation of afferent cardiac sympathetic nerve fibers. *Am. J. Physiol.* 226:603–7

220. Uchida, Y., Sakamoto, A. 1974. Role of autonomic nerves in the pathogenesis of hypotension produced by coronary embolization. *Jpn. Circ. J.* 38:491–98

221. Ueda, H., Sakamoto, A., Ebihara, A., Uchida, Y. 1974. Renin release and renal sympathetic nerve activity following vertebral artery embolism. *Jpn. Heart J.* 15:271–79

222. Wallin, G., Delius, W., Hagbarth, K. -E. 1973. Comparison of sympathetic nerve activity in normotensive and hypertensive subjects. *Circ. Res.* 33:9–21

223. Weaver, L. C., Gebber, G. L. 1974. Electrophysiological analysis of neural events accompanying active dilatation. *Am. J. Physiol.* 226:84–89

224. Weber, M. A., Thornell, I. R., Stokes, G. S. 1973. Effect of hemorrhage with and without fluid replacement on plasma renin activity. *Am. J. Physiol.* 225:1161–64

225. Wennergren, G. Little, R., Öberg, B. 1976. Studies on the central integration of excitatory chemoreceptor influences and inhibitory baroreceptor and cardiac receptor influences. *Acta Physiol. Scand.* accepted for publication

226. Wurster, R. D., Trobiani, S. 1973. Effects of cervical sympathetic stimulation on carotid occlusion reflexes in cats. *Am. J. Physiol.* 225:978–81

227. Wyszogrodsky, I., Polosa, C. 1973. The inhibition of sympathetic preganglionic neurons by somatic afferents. *Can. J. Physiol. Pharmacol.* 51:29–38

228. Zehr, J. E., Feigl, E. O. 1973. Suppression of renin activity by hypothalamic stimulation. *Circ. Res.* 32: Suppl. 1, 17–27

229. Ziegler, M. et al 1974. Effects of positive and negative pressure breathing on plasma renin concentration in the dog. *Pfluegers Arch.* 348:185–96

230. Zucker, I. H., Gilmore, J. P. 1974. Atrial receptor discharge during acute coronary occlusion in the dog. *Am. J. Physiol.* 227:360–63

CEREBRAL BLOOD FLOW AND BRAIN FUNCTION DURING HYPOTENSION AND SHOCK[1]

❖1160

Arisztid G. B. Kovách and Péter Sándor

Experimental Research Department, Semmelweis Medical University,[2] Budapest, Hungary

INTRODUCTION

Apart from a few early suggestions to the contrary, it has been generally assumed that the brain's vital functions are protected during hypotension in hypovolemic and other types of shock. Research in this field accelerated during the last two decades, after it was established that the central nervous system is in fact vulnerable during hypotension and shock (106–126). Because many interesting investigations on changes in cerebral blood flow and brain function, especially from physiological laboratories, have recently been published we have chosen to limit this review to this area. Although the omission of metabolic changes may seem arbitrary, thorough coverage of the subject reviewed here requires that metabolic factors be treated elsewhere.

The brain plays a decisive role in the regulation of vital processes. No other organ is as involved in the rapid control responses associated with the body's homeostasis during moment-to-moment changes in the external and internal environments. Afferent neural and humoral impulses can induce complex neural and neurohumoral processes in the CNS in order to control and coordinate the function of the different organs subjected to changing conditions (e.g. injuries).

The homeostasis of the central regulatory coordinating organ itself is strongly protected by various autoregulatory mechanisms similar to those of the heart. However, in the state of sustained, serious injury, cerebral metabolic rates increase as a consequence of increased afferent activity and information exchange at the cellular level and of increased blood catecholamine content. At the same time, the oxygen transport to the nervous tissue decreases with diminished nutritional blood flow. Sustained oxygen demand, conversion to anaerobic metabolism, and the accu-

---

[1]The survey of literature for this review was concluded in April 1975.
[2]1082 Budapest, Üllöi út 78/a.

mulation of metabolic end products eventually lead to the inhibition of the defense mechanisms of the brain. Metabolic changes in brain cells cause general deterioration in different physiological functions, with early tissue damage to the heart (25), lung (159), and kidneys (62, 63, 69, 124) as a consequence of brain hypoxia.

Defects in nervous functions are presented even in the first description of shock by Ambroise Paré (172) in 1575. In 1899 Crile (28) suggested on the basis of his experimental results that the CNS, especially the medulla, played an important role in the development of shock. Finnerty et al (58) in 1934 described the changes in cerebral hemodynamics during ischemia induced by acute hypotension. Slome & O'Shaughnessy (206) in 1938 discussed the role of nociceptive afferent impulses in the development of irreversible shock. Blalock (12) in 1944 observed an increased arteriovenous oxygen difference in the head during shock. In 1944, Phemister et al (178) published a study on afferent depressor nerve impulses as a cause of shock. In 1950, Jourdan et al (94), using a window technique, found no changes in the caliber of the cerebrocortical vessels during traumatic shock. The first detailed review of the role of the CNS in shock was published by Wiggers in 1950 (235).

The currently increasing amount of data on the role of the central nervous system in shock shows not only the importance of this problem, but also that many questions still await answers in this field.

While there may be quite different pathological mechanisms causing or contributing to the shock state, more and more findings show the importance of one common factor: the impairment of the central integrative role of the CNS during the development of irreversibility (106, 107, 109, 111, 112, 115). This factor has been emphasized by studies on the role of the nervous system in hemorrhagic (23, 46, 106, 109, 115, 159, 176, 177, 203), hemolytic (149, 197, 226), septic (84, 204), tourniquet (125, 221), traumatic (137, 201), and cardiogenic (38) forms of shock.

The term *shock* here refers exclusively to the above-mentioned forms of shock— no data on anaphylaxis, insulin-induced shock, direct head injury, or electroshock are discussed. The data have been collected primarily from original articles appearing in journals, periodicals, or symposium abstracts. In general, data from monographs on cerebral blood flow (CBF) or on shock have not been included.

A review such as this one can never be complete. Our apologies are offered to authors who do not find their work among the literature cited; however, the significance of really valuable studies never depends on the skill or errors of reviewers.

CEREBRAL HEMODYNAMIC CHANGES DURING SHOCK

All of the main factors determining the velocity and volume of cerebral blood flow (i.e. perfusion pressure and volume, cerebrovascular resistance, chemical composition, and the physicochemical properties of the blood) are subject to marked changes during shock.

Decreased perfusion pressure and cardiac output are widely recognized as major symptoms in different forms of shock. However, there are exceptions, such as elevated blood pressure during the early phase of cardiogenic shock and increased cardiac output during septic shock.

Effect of Cerebral Blood Perfusion on Susceptibility to Shock

An experimental preparation was described by Golden & Jane (67) in which adequate perfusion pressure in the heart, lung, and brain was maintained during hypovolemic shock. Significant increases in survival rates occurred in comparison to control animals not so perfused. Further studies (68) on the importance of these three organs during shock showed that cerebral ischemia after dogs were bled until arterial pressure was at 30 mm Hg for 4 hr caused death even when the heart was adequately perfused. Finnerty et al (58) arrived at the same conclusion from experiments on man. These studies strongly support the earlier findings of Kovách et al (123, 189) which showed that perfusion of the brain with normal blood at normal perfusion pressure during hemorrhagic shock doubled the survival time in such animals. Their results were confirmed by Lillehei et al (133).

Redistribution of Cardiac Output to the Brain in Shock

Previously published data on the redistribution of cardiac output (CO) and on changes in the brain fraction during hemorrhage have shown that good self-regulation exists for this parameter. During ischemic shock, the percentage decrease in blood flow perfusing the head was less than the percentage fall in cardiac output. The amount of blood perfusing the head did not diminish to a value low enough to produce hypoxia of the brain (Kovách 106). Slater et al (205) repeatedly measured cardiac output distribution in successive stages of hemorrhagic shock using microspheres labeled with five different isotopes in unanesthetized dogs. The brain fraction increased in the early hypotension phase, then gradually decreased but remained higher than the control value during the whole 10 hr bleeding period. By the end of the hypotension period, fractions to the heart, liver, and lung increased, while those to the brain, adrenal gland, and kidney decreased. Similar increases in the brain fraction during hemorrhage have been reported in rats, rabbits, dogs, monkeys, and man (54, 73, 162, 187, †98, 214, 230).

From the data available one can conclude that 1. the brain fraction of the total CO shows a two-phase reaction (initial increase, then gradual decrease) during hemorrhage, 2. it seems very unlikely that the circulatory and functional disturbances occurring in the brain during shock are consequences of the decreased brain fraction of the total CO.

Cerebral Blood Flow in Shock

The number of reports on cerebral blood flow (CBF) changes during shock is relatively small compared to the increasing amount of data appearing on CBF changes in hypotension or in hypoxia. It should be emphasized at this point that shock, due to its complex pathological mechanism, is not comparable to hypoxia, anoxia, hypotension, or rapid exsanguination. The data obtained from these situations need special interpretation when applied to changes observed during shock.

TOTAL CEREBRAL BLOOD FLOW   The average decrease in total CBF in the late phase of hemorrhagic shock is approximately 26% in anesthetized baboons (186) and varies between 25–44% in anesthetized dogs (42, 71, 131). Fazekas et al (51, 58) reported decreased total CBF in man with shock of various etiologies, although they did not specify the state of the cerebral circulation prior to observation. According to the data of Kovách et al (113, 188), mean blood flow through the head decreased 20–25% during tourniquet shock. Mchedlishvili et al (1949) also reported decreased CBF in hemolytic shock.

[133]Xe clearance measurements, carried out on baboons anesthetized with sernylan and artificially ventilated, showed significant decreases in total CBF during a two-step standardized hemorrhagic shock. CBF was 70–85% of control flow at a mean arterial pressure (MAP) of 55 mm Hg for 90 min and 50–65% during the second bleeding period lasting 90 min at 35 mm Hg. After reinfusion at 90 mm Hg MAP, CBF was 200% of control (112, 165, 186). Phenoxybenzamine pretreatment (5 mg kg[-1]) prevented any decrease in CBF during hemorrhagic hypotension (117).

Autoregulation was impaired after hemorrhagic shock developed and reduction of blood flow through the brain was present at MAP of 80–90 mm Hg. Application of phenoxybenzamine broadened the pressure flow plateau. In hemorrhagic shock, phenoxybenzamine pretreatment prevented pressure-dependent decreases in blood flow at MAP levels of 35 mm Hg.

REGIONAL CEREBRAL BLOOD FLOW   Several studies on regional cerebral blood flow (rCBF) changes in the dog have been reported (108, 110, 121, 180 187, 192, 207, 208, 213, 236). Substantial regional blood volume differences were identified by the benzidine method both in hemorrhagic and in tourniquet shock(106, 107). The most significant changes were ischemia of the cerebral cortex, breaking up of the normal capillary pattern, appearance of empty capillaries, and intravascular sludge formation. Using ^{32}P-labeled erythrocytes Erdélyi et al (47) demonstrated that a portion of the blood in the brain did not take part in the active circulation. The results of [^{14}C]antipyrine studies showed an uneven reduction in rCBF during hypovolemia. In addition to a substantial reduction of CBF, patchy and circumscribed ischemic areas developed in different cerebrocortical regions and in other deeper brain structures. Areas deprived of circulation showed persistant ischemia after reinfusion even in the neighborhood of hyperperfused brain regions (112, 165), confirming earlier results obtained by the benzidine staining method (106). Phenoxybenzamine pretreatment significantly influenced rCBF changes during shock. It also had a protective effect against the reduction in rCBF measured with [^{14}C]antipyrine and against the development of focal cortical patchy ischemic areas. Subcortical nuclei, the brain stem, and cerebellum also failed to show flow reduction (117).

Regional blood flow measured by a heat conductivity technique and by the H_2-gas clearance method, decreased to 70% in the parietal cortex, to 40% in the ventromedial hypothalamus, and to 55% in the hypophysis during the late phase of hemorrhage in anesthetized dogs (108, 109, 120, 166, 195, 196). Blood flow decreased to about 40% in the hypothalamus, to 60% in the VPL nucleus of the thalamus, and to 70% in the white matter (20, 166, 197), while vasodilatation of the pial vessels and decreased cortical blood flow were observed during hemolytic shock brought about by transfusion of incompatible blood (149). Blood flow to the deep nuclei of the brain remained at a significantly decreased level even 3 hr after the onset of the transfusion in spite of the mean arterial blood pressure returning to normal (197). In rats, experimental traumatic shock caused a brief spasm of the arteries of the median eminence, an increase in the number and diameter of the venovenous anastomoses in the anterior lobe of the hypophysis, an increase in the number of functioning sinuses, and a compensatory reduction in the circulation rate in the veins, draining the area of the median eminence into the systemic circulation. A retrograde blood flow in the vessels of the anterior lobe of the hypophysis was noted in some of these experiments (146). Marked and progressive reduction in blood flow in the grey and white matter of the spinal cord occurred following mechanical injury (74).

Interesting reports have appeared on the reaction of different parts of cerebrovascular bed during shock. The great arteries of dog and rabbit brains showed a gradual increase in resistance during hemorrhagic hypotension, while arteries of the pia mater showed a regular dilatation and the pressure in the venous sinuses of the brain fell (3). Phasic changes in circulation in the pial vessels were reported in traumatic shock in rats. At the beginning of the torpid phase of shock there was a spasm of small arteries and arterioles and reduced flow velocity. These phenomena terminated after 5 min, and the blood flow approached normal. During the preterminal and terminal phases of shock, an aggregation of the formed elements and a secondary flow reduction occurred (98). Baeckström et al (6) found evidence that plugging of the microcirculation occurs following acute hemorrhage in cats, and can be prevented by adrenalectomy. Another author (127) described dilatation of the cerebral vessels during the torpid phase of traumatic shock. Constriction of the major arteries of the brain was reported as a consequence of incompatible blood transfusion (140). These changes in the brain vessels were similar to those observed during asphyxia in dogs, using hemodynamically isolated arteries and photomicrography, in which the internal carotid artery underwent vasoconstriction, pial arteries dilated regularly, smaller cortical arteries and arterioles showed constriction, and the diameter of the capillaries showed no change (151). Regarding the functional role of these diamater changes, Koo & Cheng (103) described an interesting method for measuring cerebral microvascular volume flow in hemorrhagic hypotension. Their results may help to explain the fact that diameter changes do not always directly reflect changes in volume flow, so that increased flow velocity may induce increased volume flow even in constricted vessels.

Neural and Neurohumoral Influences on the Cerebrovascular Bed in Shock

The influence of neural impulses on the cerebrovascular bed during shock must be considered, as our knowledge in this respect has increased considerably in the last few years. A large series of reports, only a few of which are mentioned here, have strongly suggested sympathetic, parasympathetic, and somatic afferent control of the cerebral circulation. Hartman, Zide & Udenfriend (81) and Raichle et al (183) described the presence of central noradrenergic fibers originating in the brain stem associated with the regulation of cerebrovascular smooth muscle tone in addition to the sympathetic innervation coming from the superior cervical ganglion. Rosendorff & Mitchell (191) reported dual innervation of the hypothalamic resistance vessels (adrenergic constrictor and dilator fibers). Edvinsson & Owman (45) described three types of cholinergic receptor mechanisms in brain vessels. As Stoner (221) pointed out, catecholaminergic fibers innervating the hypothalamus and other parts of the brain concerned with homeostasis play a beneficial role in defense against injury (limb ischemia).

AUTONOMIC NERVOUS HYPERACTIVITY AND CBF   Although it is still not clear whether or not the autonomic innervation plays a functional role in cerebrovascular tone in normal situations (170), it would be difficult to say that it has no role in conditions where the discharge of the sympathetic nerves increases drastically, such as in hemorrhagic (52, 53, 102, 114), tourniquet (118), cardiogenic (38), and traumatic (199) forms of shock. According to Hinshaw's data (84), no evidence has been obtained to support assigning a detrimental role to the sympathoadrenal system in dog, cat, or monkey during endotoxin shock, although effects of the endotoxin on the central nervous system may well have contributed to the evolution of this form of shock (204).

The effect of sympathetic hyperactivity on the CBF during shock can only be estimated indirectly. Ponessa et al (180) studied the effect of cervical sympathectomy on regional brain blood flow during hemorrhagic shock. Sympathetic α-blockade by phenoxybenzamine prevented changes in total CBF changes (117, 208) as well as the microcirculatory impairment in the parietal cortex (112) of cats, but did not favor local blood flow in the hypothalamus during hemorrhagic shock (109).

Although it has been clearly demonstrated that parasympathetic nerve stimulation affects the diameter of the pial vessels (150) and that the parasympathetic system is involved in the development of shock (33, 47, 106), no data have been found on the role of this system in CBF during shock.

Painful somatic afferent nerve stimulation can decrease local blood flow and tissue P_{O_2} in the thalamus, hypothalamus, and white matter (32, 194) in anesthetized dogs with stabilized mean arterial pressure and blood gases, and can change the regional distribution of lactate and catecholamines in the brain (144). Painful cutaneous electrical stimulation can increase the mean CBF and the flow in the premotor and frontal regions in man (88). The role of these impulses in regulation of CBF during shock has not yet been studied.

Because the effect of increased sympathetic activity on CBF seems to be significant and can be blocked by adrenergic receptor blocking agents (29, 30, 92, 93, 111, 117, 154, 161), one might predict the same effect for the circulating catecholamines and other biogenic amines. However, the effect of these substances seems to be quite different in both man and other animals and depends on the levels of the arterial blood gases, dosage, and site of the injection (intracarotid, intravenous, intraparenchymal microinjection, etc); moreover the effective dose was usually higher than the local concentrations obtained by physiological release. As Rapela & Martin (185) pointed out, intra- and extraparenchymal cerebral arteries may respond differentially to humoral stimuli. A blood-brain barrier for epinephrine (209), norepi-nephrine (167–234), and serotonin (167) has been proven, but whether it is located in the endothelium or in the adventitia of the cerebral vessels is not yet clear (78, 222), although the former seems very likely. A detailed review on the effect of vasoactive substances on CBF was published by Olesen (168).

CIRCULATORY RESPONSE TO CATECHOLAMINES   Epinephrine caused no CBF changes when injected into the carotid artery of man (72), but large intravenous doses increased CBF significantly (99). Constriction of the pial arteries could be observed after direct application of epinephrine with a micropipette technique (233).

In the course of the development of hemorrhagic and tourniquet shock, circula-tory responses to epinephrine underwent gradual diminution, which seems to be a consequence of the decreased plasma volume (125). Dunker et al (43) studied in vitro the reactivity of the common carotid and basilar arteries during hemorrhagic shock. They found a relative insensitivity of α-adrenergic receptors to epinephrine in arteries obtained from animals subjected to shock. According to Corday & Williams (26), the use of vasopressor drugs in shock increased circulation to the brain, and pressor drugs may be lifesaving because of this effect. On the contrary, studies on the efferent neural pathways in tourniquet shock showed that epinephrine administration significantly diminished survival time (48), while experimental pro-duction of increased epinephrine tolerance resulted in improved survival (38), and administration of sympathetic receptor blocking agents caused increased cerebral blood flow (58, 112) and better survival rates (106, 109, 111, (117–119), 154, 164).

Norepinephrine injected either intravenously or into the carotid artery caused no change in CBF in human studies (70, 168). Microinjection into the hypothalamus of the rabbit caused increased flow at low concentrations and decreased flow at higher concentrations (190). Harper et al (80) observed marked CBF reduction after norepinephrine injection in hypercapnia. Maklári et al (138–140) found increased cerebral tissue CO_2 content in hemorrhagic shock. Especially high levels were detected in the hypothalamus and frontal cortex. Correction of the acidosis did not restore elevated cerebral tissue CO_2 content (141, 142). Phenoxybenzamine pretreat-ment protected against the development of a high level of cerebral tissue CO_2 (138, 139). These results are also interesting because cerebral blood flow does not increase in the baboon in hemorrhagic shock upon administration of 6% CO_2 (186). Kovách et al (105) reported that, in cross-circulation experiments in which the brain of the recipient dog was hemodynamically isolated from the trunk and perfused by a donor dog, intravenous epinephrine or norepinephrine injection into the recipient's trunk caused reflexly a significant increase in its total cerebral blood flow. Intracarotid injection of both catecholamines produced a significant fall in cerebral blood flow (105).

Increased CBF could be measured during intravenous infusion of norepinephrine in hemorrhagic shock, while the cerebrovascular resistance showed no change, according to Frank et al (64). On the contrary, increased CBF accompanied by increased cerebrovascular resistance followed norepinephrine administration during tourniquet shock (224).

CATECHOLAMINE CONTENT OF THE HYPOTHALAMUS DURING SHOCK
Stoner et al (220, 221) showed that during tourniquet shock the concentration of norepinephrine in the hypothalamus decreased about 30% and remained depressed after fatal periods of ischemia. Hypothalamic norepinephrine is nearly entirely in the terminals of axons arising from nerve cells in the pons and medulla. The concentration of norepinephrine in these cell bodies was unaltered but its turnover was increased during limb ischemia. Stoner & Elson (219) reported that a significant change in serotonin content and turnover occurred after both mild and severe injuries in the hypothalamic and other areas of the brain.

EFFECT OF ANGIOTENSIN, SEROTONIN, AND ACETYLCHOLINE ON CBF   Angiotensin had no effect on the CBF after either intravenous or intracarotid administration, according to Agnoli (1), Olesen (168), and Greenfield & Tindall (72). Changes in arterial pressure after angiotensin injection into the vertebral artery have been reported (55). There was an interesting difference between the complete lack of effect of angiotensin in the hemispheres and its effect on specific areas of the brain stem according to Olesen (169).

Several reports have dealt with the effect of angiotensin in experimental and clinical shock (31, 34, 35, 57, 212, 226). Szabó & Magyar (225) reported a favorable influence of angiotensin on the flow distribution during tourniquet shock; coronary and carotid flow increased in response to arterial pressure increases, while cardiac and cerebral vascular resistance increased only slightly or not at all after intravenous angiotensin infusion.

Serotonin caused increased carotid artery flow in dogs (223) and a marked reduction in monkeys (75). Cerebral tissue blood flow did not change after serotonin infusion in monkeys or in man (36, 170). Local application to the pial vessels caused arterial and arteriolar constriction (10), and cerebral vasospasm occurred after intracisternal serotonin injection (24). Interestingly, hypothalamic injection of serotonin caused a significant increase in the local blood flow to this region (190).

Acetylcholine had no effect on total CBF after intravenous or intra-arterial administration (37, 70), but local cerebral blood flow, measured by either pial diameter changes or heat conductivity, increased (209). The total acetylcholine content of the brain increased significantly during traumatic shock, and it seems very likely that this was the consequence of an impaired resynthesis of choline-containing lipids, as has been reported by Kovách et al (106).

The Lower Limit of the Circulatory, Metabolic, and Functional Homeostasis of the Central Nervous System

The threshold for CBF autoregulation during arterial blood pressure decrease has been extensively studied. It is widely accepted that the autoregulation of CBF is abolished below a mean arterial pressure (MAP) of 50 mm Hg (11, 21, 79, 82, 87, 130, 156, 184, 237). How has this figure been reached? According to Hoyer et al (87), reduction of MAP to 41 mm Hg induced decreases in cerebral blood flow, oxygen uptake, carbon dioxide production, and glucose utilization, and an increase in cerebral lactate production during normocapnia and normoxia. This finding supports the assumption that when MAP falls below approximately 40 mm Hg the oxidative metabolism of the brain becomes insufficient. Farrar (50) suggested that cerebral arterial resistance is the flow-limiting factor that determines the lower limit of autoregulation. Fitch et al (59) showed that the lower limit of autoregulation in hemorrhagic hypotension could be extended to lower pressures if arterial smooth muscle tone were reduced by α-adrenergic blockade. The data of Golden & Jane (68) suggested that, while at MAP of 35 mm Hg the functional role of the heart seems to be crucial in irreversible hemorrhagic shock, at MAP of 30 mm Hg the failure of neural mechanisms accounts for the irreversibility. According to the data of Branston et al (13), neuronal function in the cortex failed when local blood flow fell below 16 ml $(100 \text{ g})^{-1} \text{ min}^{-1}$, and the rate of depression increased with the degree of ischemia. The studies of Sanderson et al (193) suggested that not only the perfusion pressure to the brain but also the presence or absence of pulsation influenced the impairment of the CNS during hypotension. They found diffuse ischemic nerve cell changes after 2 and 3 hr nonpulsatile perfusion, but not after pulsatile perfusion of the same duration. In conditions with decreased pulse pressure, as in shock, this difference can be an important factor.

Foreman (60) studied the redistribution of residual blood volume in hemorrhagic shock and its relation to lethal bleeding volume. As Williams (236) pointed out, symptoms from the CNS are closely related to the degree of blood volume decrease. A decrease of 20–25% in the blood volume produced anxiety; 30–35%, restlessness; 35–40%, depression. Profound shock following a 40–50% decrease produced semicoma.

Several studies have dealt with the effect of hypoxia on cerebral autoregulation. According to Siesjö (202) the reduction of the arterial Po_2 below 45–50 mm Hg led to lactacidosis and vasodilatation. Kogura et al (101) found that autoregulation was not lost until arterial Po_2 was maintained below 25 mm Hg for 4–6 min. Autoregulation was maintained even after hypoxia produced increased CBF and decreased cortical pH, indicating that loss of autoregulation in hypoxia is not due to parenchymal acidosis or to maximal vasodilatation.

HYPOXIC VASODILATATION   When does hypoxia cause vasodilatation? According to Korner's data (104), vasodilatation of the cerebral vessels became obvious only after cerebrovenous Po_2 fell to about 28 mm Hg. Opitz & Schneider (171) have pointed out that impaired cerebral activity occurred when the venous Po_2 fell below 19 mm Hg, and irreversible damage may result below 12–10 mm Hg. According to the data of Siesjö (202), because hypoxemia was associated with loss of the usual longitudinal O_2 diffusion gradient, the critical venous Po_2 was somewhat higher (19 mm Hg) in hypoxia than in ischemia (17 mm Hg). Ponte & Purves (181) have suggested that the hyperemia of hypoxia is reflexly elicited by the carotid body.

It was believed for a long time that a local tissue Po_2 of 6–10 mm Hg was necessary to maintain adequate function of mitochondrial phosphorylation. Recent in vivo and in vitro studies have demonstrated that a Po_2 of 1–2 mm Hg or lower is sufficient to allow maximal phosphorylation in brain mitochondria (22, 112, 135, 136).

SECONDARY EFFECTS OF BRAIN HYPOXIA IN THE LUNG AND MYOCARDIUM
Some interesting data have been obtained in connection with the circulatory and functional changes in the lung and myocardium as a consequence of brain hypoxia or brain damage. Moss et al (159) concluded that the entire pathophysiological sequence of the so-called shock-lung can be explained by autonomically mediated pulmonary venular spasm, initiated by hypothalamic hypoxia during shock. However, Kusajima et al (128) found no pulmonary pressure or gradient changes in animals with cerebral hypotension. Connor (25) described myocardial tissue damage secondary to brain lesions.

In discussing the changes in the CNS during shock one must remember that the pathophysiological changes induced by hypoxia and those by ischemia of the brain are different. As Siesjö pointed out (202), capillary flow and tissue oxygenation differ markedly in ischemic and hypoxic conditions. He suggested a unified hypothesis to explain the relation between microcirculatory and metabolic changes in hypoxemia, ischemia, and hypercapnia.

The results of Ledingham (131) with hyperbaric oxygen treatment in shock also demonstrate differences between hypoxia and ischemia. Administration of oxygen at 2 atm during hemorrhagic shock in dogs did not increase CBF and the progressive metabolic acidosis was also unaffected; however, cerebral cortical O_2 consumption returned to the preshock level. Although there was no direct evidence to suggest that improvement in cerebral O_2 uptake indicates improvement in cerebral function, it seems not unreasonable that administration of hyperbaric O_2 in shock can be beneficial to the brain.

Morphologic Changes in the CNS During Brain Ischemia

Extensive attempts to describe the morphologic changes in the nervous system during ischemia began after Spielmeyer (211) introduced the term "ischemic cell change" in 1922. Brierley & Excell (14–16) showed in the rhesus monkey that profound arterial hypotension could result in discrete lesions in the cortex at the boundary zones between the territories supplied by their major arteries. In more severely affected animals, ischemic neuronal alterations were found diffusely throughout the cerebral and cerebellar hemispheres. Selective vulnerability could be detected in different brain regions (14, 15, 17, 18, 199). The most vulnerable parts were layers 3, 5, and 6 of the cerebral cortex, hippocampus, amygdaloid nucleus, cerebellar Purkinje and basket cells, and brain stem. The spinal cord seemed to be the most resistant, while involvement of the thalamus, striatum, pallidum, and subthalamic nucleus was variable. Ames et al suggested (4) that a "no-reflow phenomenon," failure of brain reperfusion, was responsible for the irreversible brain damage observed after circulatory arrest.

Cowley et al (27) who studied 300 cases, comprising all of the major classes of shock, described small focal areas of acute necrosis in the brain. Hardaway (77) introduced the term and theory of "disseminated intravascular coagulation" to explain the morphologic basis of the irreversible circulatory damage in different forms of shock. Tamura et al (228) and Simeone & Witoszka (203) presented a detailed analysis of brain morphology during experimental hemorrhagic shock.

Kardasjan (95) described morphologic changes in different hypothalamic nuclei during traumatic shock. Drommer (41) reported ultrastructural alterations in the cerebral vessels of pigs after endotoxin shock. Several reports have dealt with the morphology of the nervous system (hypothalamus, hypophysis) in extensive burn cases (91, 96, 160). Mayer (147) described the distribution pattern of cerebral cortex damage following cardiogenic shock. An interesting study by Ashford et al (5) reported disordered myofilaments in the arterial and venous walls (femoral, cephalic, portal vessels) in traumatic shock, which suggests that a structural analog to the functional disorders may exist in vascular smooth muscle.

CEREBRAL FUNCTIONAL CHANGES IN SHOCK

Bioelectrical Activity in Shock

Of all mammalian tissues, nervous tissue is the least capable of withstanding an oxygen deficit (46). It has a high oxygen consumption, but contains only a small amount of dissolved oxygen (97) and small reserves of energy (134, 152). The brain is more sensitive than the peripheral nerve to ischemia (76). Hypoxia is known to change the electrical activity of the nervous system (232). Kovách et al (112) have established significant correlations between the redox state, electrical activity, and blood flow in the brain cortex during hemorrhagic shock.

ELECTROENCEPHALOGRAPHIC CHANGES IN SHOCK Kovách et al (106, 109, 114, 115) found in unanesthetized dogs and cats in both standardized hemorrhagic and tourniquet shock that impairment of electrocorticographic (ECoG) activity occurred at 50–60 mm Hg MAP; after a period of 20–30 min at 30–40 mm Hg MAP, activity ceased almost entirely and restoration of the MAP with additional blood failed to reverse these changes. Before the isoelectric "flat" ECoG developed, decreases in frequency and amplitude were characteristic, and in some cases monophasic spindle activity was recorded. Phenoxybenzamine pretreatment (5 mg kg^{-1} intravenously or 0.5 mg kg^{-1} injected into the carotid artery) prevented the development of "flat" ECoG at the same (35 mm Hg) MAP level (108–111). The spontaneous bioelectric activity in the hypothalamus behaved the same way as in the cortex (108–110).

Opinion as to the usefulness of recording spontaneous electric activity of the brain during shock is not unanimous. The disagreement over the relationship between spontaneous electric activity, brain blood flow, and function is a product of the different and not always standardized shock models that have been used by various investigators. Yashon et al (238) reported that, although profound oligemic hypotension caused an 80–90% reduction in both mean arterial pressure and common carotid blood flow, very little change was observed in the electrocorticogram of anaesthetized dogs. Similarly, Bushart & Rittmeyer (19) found that considerable electroencephalographic (EEG) changes were observed only in the severe tourniquet shock states and that subsequent transfusion of blood could cause deterioration of the EEG. Meldrum & Brierley (153) and Brierley et al (14) concluded that the EEG has smaller predictive value than the changes of the somatosensory evoked potentials with respect to brain damage severity in profound arterial hypotension. The way hypotension was produced was unique, however, to these experiments.

Cantu & Ames (20) and Hossman et al (86) reported a recovery of the electrophysiological signs of brain function even after serious ischemia. Fink et al (56) found the EEG to be a highly effective guide to the speed and quantity of treatment necessary to ensure survival. They used unanesthetized, unheparinized sheep and found that the irreversibility of hemorrhagic shock was directly correlated with the EEG changes. Pashkovsky & Lasta (173) described early EEG changes in patients with traumatic shock and considered EEG to be a good criterion for estimating the severity of the shock state. Pokrovsky et al (179) reported that the characteristics of the EEG are specific for patients in different phases of traumatic and hemorrhagic shock. Pásztor et al (174) found an early deterioration of the central neural mechanisms during hemorrhagic shock and an unfavorable effect of catecholamine administration. Hill (83) suggested the use of the digital computer in the management of shock to watch for significant increases in EEG amplitude and in the proportion of slow wave activity indicating the onset of incipient cerebral hypoxia. In experiments performed on anesthetized baboons, good correlation was found between irreversibility and EEG changes in hemorrhagic shock (112, 117, 165).

Freeman & Ingvar (65) showed that systemic hypoxia can disrupt the normal high correlation between cortical blood flow and EEG frequency. Masopust et al (143) published a detailed study on the effect of the severity of hypoxia on the ECoG of monkeys. A detailed study on the effect of asphyxia on activity changes of spinal neurons was published by Speckmann et al (210). A direct dependence was shown between EEG dynamics and spirometabologram deviations during traumatic shock by Zhilis et al (179). Leonov & Vornovsky (132) showed that under hyperbaric oxygenation the persistence of the bioelectric activity of the cortex during experimental hemorrhagic shock was significantly longer than in untreated control animals.

Hinzen et al (85) reported that while after 60 min of complete ischemia no spontaneous activity could be detected, strychnine solution applied topically to the cortex restored electrical potentials. The results showed a discrepancy between cerebral cortical energy metabolism and ECoG, and the authors concluded that the long-lasting depression of ECoG after prolonged ischemia cannot be interpreted as a lack of energy reserves or an absence of excitability of the cerebral cortex. Isakin (90) found an interhemispheric assymetry of electric activity, with phasic intensification and reduction alternately reversing in the two hemispheres during tourniquet shock.

EVOKED POTENTIALS IN SHOCK   Some interesting data have appeared on the changes of the evoked potentials and cardiovascular responses to different kinds of stimuli during shock. Peterson et al (175) presented results of a neurophysiologic investigation of spontaneous and evoked patterns of response at the level of the spinal cord and the brain stem reticular formation in hemorrhagic shock. A transient state of hyperexcitability reflected an "alerting" type of response to the early challenge of blood loss. If the reduction in blood flow were sustained, a progressive and inexorable deterioration in all parameters of nervous system function ensued. A functional breakdown of the nervous system was apparent before severe hemorrhagic hypotension could be detected.

Kovách et al (109, 114) have found that the character of the electrical responses in the hypothalamus (n. ventromedialis anterior) evoked by stimulation of the fornix was altered in standardized hemorrhagic shock. When arterial pressure was held below 55 mm Hg for 60 min, evoked response was reduced and further bleeding to 30 mm Hg led to the complete disappearance of the evoked response within 30 min, although reduction in ECoG persisted. These results were confirmed by Dóra et al (39, 40) and Pásztor et al (174). The interesting studies of Meldrum & Brierley (153) and Brierley et al (14) indicated that the nature of the time course of changes in the amplitude of the primary surface-positive wave of the evoked somatosensory response during hypotension permits the differentiation of animals that will recover with no brain damage, those that will develop discrete cortical lesions, and those that will develop diffuse cortical lesions.

McCutcheon et al (148), studying hemorrhagic shock, reported a decrease in the amplitude of the cortical and cuneate evoked responses, which preceded or was concomitant with the period of spontaneous reuptake of blood. Changes in the amplitude and frequency of the EEG paralleled these changes but were more variable. There was no correlation between changes in systemic blood-gas levels and the disappearance of the electrical responses. The responsiveness of the cortex and visual pathway during hemorrhagic hypotension was studied by Nicholson et al (163). Depression of both the electroretinogram and optic tract discharges was observed consistently only when the decrease in arterial pressure exceeded 55% of the control value. During severe reductions in arterial pressure, a prolonged depression of the ECoG was observed.

SYNAPTIC TRANSMISSION IN SHOCK   Within the CNS itself, there are large variations in the vulnerability of different parts of the brain to ischemia. According to an interesting paper by Grossman & Williams (76) synaptic transmission is the most sensitive link in intracortical electrophysiologic processes affected by ischemia. Although failure of postsynaptic membrane activity occurred comparatively early in ischemia, the membrane potential of the larger cortical neurons appeared to recover more quickly than did synaptic transmission when cerebral circulation was restored. This failure of restoration of synaptic transmission left viable neurons nonfunctional or not connected in meaningful circuits. The same observations were made by Sheveleva (200), who studied the arrest of transmission of impulses in sympathetic ganglia and the subsequent lack of regulatory influence by the central nervous system on the tissue metabolism as a possible cause of shock.

Hypothalamic Function in Shock

ELECTRICAL STIMULATION EXPERIMENTS   Studies during the last decade (106, 107, 114, 115, 120, 216, 217, 221, 231) called attention to the role of hypothalamic functions during shock. As previously discussed, hypothalamic blood flow is seriously affected in shock conditions (108, 109, 120, 121, 166, 197, 198). The importance of this region in the coordination of cardiovascular responses has been confirmed by many studies, such as those of Forsyth (61) and Kovách et al (122); who found profound changes in blood flow distribution during hypothalamic stimulation.

Kovách and co-workers (108, 109, 114) found that in anesthetized dogs the effects of stimulation of the hypothalamus and reticular formulation in regions which caused marked cardiovascular alterations in the control state were completely abolished in the irreversible phase of hemorrhagic shock. In some cases reinfusion produced transient recovery, but this later disappeared. To ascertain that peripheral disturbances were not responsible for these results, Kovách and co-workers stimulated the medulla directly and obtained blood pressure responses.

Trzebski (231) studied the excitability of the cardiovascular centers of the hypothalamus and brain stem during hemorrhagic shock in cats. He found that the excitability of the pressor area of the bulbar reticular system was preserved in irreversible shock, while reduction of the pressor effects upon stimulation of the hypothalamus and brain stem centers ran a course parallel to that of the reduction of the pressor effects due to norepinephrine and epinephrine.

Laborit et al (129) found that irreversible hemorrhagic shock suppressed cortical desynchronization evoked by stimulation of the posterior hypothalamic reticular formation. It suppressed the afterdischarges that ordinarily follow the stimulation of the dorsal hippocampus. It also suppressed the hypertensive peak that appears upon stimulation of the posterior hypothalamus in the normal animal. Tyrosine and chlorpromazine restored the normal reactions.

THERMOREGULATORY FUNCTION OF THE HYPOTHALAMUS IN SHOCK   An extensive investigation was made by Stoner et al (215–218) into the problem of the thermoregulatory function of the CNS after severe injury. Their findings have special importance, as the time of survival after severe injury is dependent on the environmental temperature. If the temperature is below the thermoneutral zone, body temperature declines after injury. The decrease in body temperature is due to an inability to produce heat in the required amounts and, because it occurs in the absence of any obvious failure of oxygen transport to the heat-producing organs, thermoregulation itself is probably affected by trauma. Contrary to the authors' earlier views, it is now thought that these changes do not represent a lowered value for the constant temperature that the body is able to maintain, but rather a progressive inhibition of the thermoregulatory mechanism. The possibility that the release of the inhibitory transmitter norepinephrine in the hypothalamus in response to injury may play a role in the mechanism of thermoregulatory changes is under investigation.

OTHER ASPECTS OF HYPOTHALAMIC FUNCTION   Irányi et al (89) and Kovách et al (106) studied the effect of lesions in eight different hypothalamic areas on susceptibility to shock in rats. All animals with hypothalamic lesions died sooner than controls following tourniquet and traumatic shock, except those with lesions in the medial tubular and medial infundibular areas. Previous work in the same laboratory demonstrated that hypothalamic lesions depressed the adrenal response to trauma or epinephrine injection.

Eremina (49) studied the mechanism of the hypothalamus-hypophysis-adrenal reaction in anaphylactic, hemolytic, and traumatic shock. Denisenko & Dolgushina (33) reported on the effect on the course of traumatic shock of cholinotropic agents introduced into the hypothalamus, and concluded that the cholinergic systems of the hypothalamus participate in transmitting pain impulses and in regulating MAP during traumatic conditions. The involvement of pain in the mechanisms triggering shock was discussed by Sherman & Yakovlev (199). It has been proposed that nonpainful afferent impulses from the injured area are of crucial importance in the mechanism of shock. Dyskin & Mazurkevich (44) showed in experiments on dogs that, in traumatic shock lasting for as long as 3–5 hr, no exhaustion of the adenohypophyseal or adrenocortical functions takes place, and Mazurkevich (145) reported that the ACTH activity of the hypophysis increased only during the later stages of traumatic shock.

Reflex Mechanisms in Shock

One of the earliest signs of the functional disintegration of the CNS during shock is the marked change in various reflex mechanisms. Only a few papers on this subject have appeared. Porter (182) reported that the threshold for stimuli eliciting the ipsilateral flexion reflex was elevated by bleeding in cats with spinal transection. Kissel & Domino (100) studied the effect of graded hypotension on the cat's spinal reflexes. Kovách & Fonyó (116) observed that during traumatic shock in rats, placing and hopping reflexes disappear long before cerebral metabolic changes are detectable. Mori et al (158) investigated the ipsilateral femoral quadriceps stretch reflex and the crossed-extension reflex functions during hemorrhagic shock in intact and decerebrated dogs and cats. They concluded that the functional integrity of the multisynaptic reflex, represented by the cross-extension reflex, was readily impaired almost irreversibly by hemorrhagic shock, while that of the monosynaptic stretch reflex was rather refractory to hemorrhagic shock and easily restored. In another study (157), these authors showed that the spino-bulbo-spinal multisynaptic reflex in decerebrated cats and rabbits was more vulnerable and far less capable of recovering from the effects of hemorrhagic shock than was the comparatively paucisynaptic reflex, represented by the spinal segmental polysynaptic reflex.

Peterson & Haugen (176) observed the brain stem reticular formation inhibitory and facilitatory systems during graded hemorrhagic shock and found more vulnerable neural circuitry in the facilitatory system than in the descending inhibitory influences from the brain stem. According to their data, the brain stem reticular formation showed greater durability under conditions of hemorrhage than did the brain cortex. According to these authors, the carotid sinus reflex mechanism seemed to be a shock-resistant, high-gain servomechanism. It was not possible to demonstrate abrogation of this negative control system at a MAP well below 50 mm Hg. This observation supports the earlier findings of Kovách & Takács (125, 126, 227) who described the reappearance of the carotid sinus reflex in hemorrhagic and in tourniquet shock after restoration of the lost blood and of normal hemoglobin concentration.

Changes in higher nervous activity during experimental sublethal tourniquet shock were studied by Biró et al (7–9) in rats. Immediately after the inception of shock, positive conditioned reflexes for both sound and light stimuli were inhibited. The initial, almost complete, inhibition gradually subsided until, 24 hr after ischemia, it was demonstrable in only 16% of the cases. After ischemia, the animals differentiated negative conditioned reflexes more effectively than positive ones. Mietkiewski et al (155) published results of nervous system function tests in rats performed with the aid of conditioned reflexes during traumatic shock.

Some attempts have been made to correlate the mental status of the patient in shock with changes in hemodynamic parameters. Mori et al (158) found that mortality was high in those patients who were stuporous or unconscious in the stage of deep hemorrhagic shock, although some of them responded to massive blood transfusion, regained consciousness, and survived shock without any trace of brain damage. This suggested that a reversible depression of central nervous function occurs before the process of shock becomes irreversible. Akimov et al (2) and Gladish et al (66) described different types of neurological disorders in traumatic, hemorrhagic, myocardial, and septic shock. In the latter paper, data on the relationship between blood loss, blood lactic acid level, and mental status were presented. Williams (236) presented important results on the relationship between bleeding volume and mental status and discussed hemorrhagic shock as a source of unconsciousness.

CONCLUSION

In conclusion, the reviewed results clearly suggest that vital functions of the brain —in spite of the well-developed autoregulatory mechanisms—are impaired during long-lasting hypovolemic and other shock conditions. The insufficiency of the cerebrocortical and hypothalamic regulatory mechanisms can contribute to the development of the irreversible shock. In other words, failure of the body suffering from shock to restore the homeostatic equilibrium can be attributed to the inadequacy of the central nervous servocontrol system.

According to the available results, the regional cerebral microcirculatory defect develops through sludge formation. The unevenly distributed local brain damage could be the background of the functional impairment. The focal appearance suggests that, in addition to generalized (blood borne) changes, local factors play an important role in the production of patchy ischemic areas in the brain.

The protective effect of phenoxybenzamine on cerebral microcirculatory and functional impairment in shock suggests the involvement of the sympathetic nervous system and/or catecholamine metabolism in brain damage during hemorrhagic shock. Baeckström et al (6) have demonstrated that the formation of sludge in skeletal muscle after hemorrhage was prevented by adrenalectomy.

Afferent neural input to the brain seems to be elevated during shock. It may be presumed that this leads to increased tissue metabolism and the accumulation of metabolites. The low flow combined with elevated cellular metabolism produces an imbalance between oxygen delivery and oxygen utilization. The local nature of afferent activation can explain the regional impairment in the brain tissue.

The reviewed literature shows that many meaningful contributions were made recently in the field of involvement of the central nervous system in shock. We can also conclude that much basic scientific work needs to be done to understand the nature of shock and to develop successful methods of preventing and treating shock. This review and comments on the central nervous system involvement should in no way imply the lack of importance of other organ impairments in the pathophysiology of the complex progressive shock syndrome.

Literature Cited

1. Agnoli, A., Battistini, N., Bozzao, L., Fieschi, C. 1965. Drug action on regional cerebral blood flow in cases of acute cerebro-vascular involvement. *Acta Neurol. Scand.* 41: Suppl. 14, pp. 142–44
2. Akimov, G. A. et al 1973. Neurological disorders in severe mechanical trauma. *Voenno Med. Zh.* 2:33–37
3. Amashukeli, G. V. 1969. Analysis of circulatory changes in the brain in hemorrhage and hemotransfusion. *Patol. Fiziol. Eksp. Ter.* 13:29–32
4. Ames, A. et al 1968. Cerebral ischemia: II. The no-reflow phenomenon. *Am. J. Pathol.* 52:437–53
5. Ashford, T., Palmerio, C., Fine, J. 1966. Structural analogue in vascular muscle to the functional disorder in refractory traumatic shock and reversal by corticosteroid:electron microscopic evaluation. *Ann. Surg.* 164:575–86
6. Baeckström, P., Folkow, B., Kovách, A. G. B., Löfving, B., Öberg, B. 1971. Evidence of plugging of the microcirculation following acute haemorrhage. In *6th European Conference on Microcirculation.* ed. J. Ditzel, D. H. Lewis, 16–22. Basel:Karger
7. Biró, J. B., Büki, B., Dénes, I., Kovách, A. G. B. 1958. Higher nervous activity of adrenalectomized animals after ischemia of the limbs. *Acta Physiol. Acad. Sci. Hung.* 14:45–56
8. Biró, J., Büki, B., Kovách, A. G. B. 1956. Veränderungen der höheren Nerventätigkeit im ischämischen Schock. *Acta Physiol. Acad. Sci. Hung.* 9:Suppl., pp. 46–47
9. Biró, J., Büki, B., Kovách, A. G. B. 1956. Changes of the higher nervous activity following ischemic shock in the rat. *Acta Physiol. Acad. Sci. Hung.* 10:277–89
10. Bell, W. H. III, Sundt, T. M. Jr., Nofzinger, J. D. 1967. The response of cortical vessels to serotonin in experimental cerebral infarction. *J. Neurosurg.* 26:203–12
11. Bernsmeier, A. 1963. Durchblutung des Gehirns. In *Physiologie und Pathophysiologie des vegetativen Nervensystems,* Bd. 3. p. 607
12. Blalock, A. 1944. Utilization of oxygen by the brain in traumatic shock. *Arch. Surg.* 49:167–69
13. Branston, N. M., Symon, L., Crockard, H. A., Juhász, J. 1975. Dependence of the cortical evoked response on the local tissue blood flow in baboons and its sensitivity to arterial pO_2. *Cerebral Blood Flow and Metabolism. Symp. Aviemore,* p. 149. (Abstr.)
14. Brierley, J. B., Brown, A. W., Excell, B. J., Meldrum, B. S. 1969. Brain damage in the rhesus monkey resulting from profound arterial hypotension. I. Its nature, distribution and general physiological correlates. *Brain Res.* 13:68–100
15. Brierley, J. B., Brown, A. W., Meldrum, B. S. 1970. The nature and time course of the neuronal alterations resulting from oligaemia and hypoglycaemia in the brain of macaca mulatta. *Brain Res.* 25:483–99
16. Brierley, J. B., Excell, B. J. 1966. The effects of profound systemic hypotension upon the brain of *M. rhesus.* Physiological and pathological observations. *Brain* 89:269–98

17. Brierley, J. B., Meldrum, B. S., Brown, A. W. 1973. The threshold and neuropathology of cerebral "anoxic-ischemic" cell change. *Arch. Neurol.* 29:367–74
18. Brown, A. W., Brierley, J. B. 1971. The nature and time course of anoxic-ischaemic cell change in the rat brain. An optical and electron microscope study. In *Brain Hypoxia.* ed. J. B. Brierley, B. S. Meldrum, 49–60. London: Heinemann
19. Bushart, W., Rittmeyer, P. 1966. EEG Untersuchungen im Schock: klinische und experimentelle Ergebnisse. *Muenchen Med. Wochenschr.* 108:1296–99
20. Cantu, R. C., Ames, A. III. 1969. Experimental prevention of cerebral vasculature obstruction produced by ischemia. *J. Neurosurg.* 30:50–54
21. Carlyle, A., Grayson, J. 1955. Blood pressure and the regulation of brain blood flow. *J. Physiol. London* 127: 15–16
22. Chance, B., Cohen, P., Jöbsis, F., Schoener, B. 1962. Intracellular oxidationreduction. States in vivo. The microfluorometry of pyridine nucleotide gives a continuous measurement of the oxidation state. *Science* 137:499–508
23. Chien, S. 1964. Role of sympathetic nervous system in surviving acute hemorrhage. *Am. J. Physiol.* 206:21–24
24. Chow, R. W., Newton, T. H., Smith, M. C., Adams, J. E. 1968. Cerebral vasospasm induced by subarachnoid blood and serotonin. An angiographic study. *Invest. Radiol.* 3:402–7
25. Connor, R. C. R. 1969. Myocardial damage secondary to brain lesions. *Am. Heart J.* 78:145–48
26. Corday, E., Williams, J. H. Jr. 1960. Effect of shock and of vasopressor drugs on the regional circulation of the brain, heart, kidney and liver. *Am. J. Med.* 29:228–41
27. Cowley, R. A. et al 1969. Some significant biochemical parameters found in 300 shock patients. *J. Trauma* 9: 926–38
28. Crile, G. W. 1899. *An Experimental Research into Surgical Shock.* Philadelphia: Lippincott. 160 pp.
29. D'Alecy, L. G. 1973. Sympathetic cerebral vasoconstriction blocked by adrenergic alpha receptor antagonists. *Stroke* 4:30–37
30. D'Alecy, L. G., Feigl, E. O. 1972. Sympathetic control of cerebral blood flow in dogs. *Circ. Res.* 31:267–83
31. Del Greco, F., Johnson, D. C. 1961. Clinical experience with angiotensin II in the treatment of shock. *J. Am. Med. Assoc.* 178:994–99
32. Demchenko, I. T. Sándor, P., Moskalenko, Y. E., Kovách, A. G. B. 1975. Cerebral blood flow and oxygen tension changes during somatic afferent stimulation. *Sechenov Physiol. J. USSR* 8:1153–59
33. Denisenko, P. P., Dolgushina, A. T. 1972. Effect of cholinotropic agents introduced into the hypothalamus on the control of traumatic shock. *Farmakol. Toksikol. Moscow* 35:657–60
34. Derrick, J. R., Anderson, J. R., Roland, B. J. 1962. Adjunctive use of a biologic pressor agent, angiotensin, in management of shock. *Circulation* 25:263–67
35. Derrick, J. R. 1962. Blood pressure control during surgical procedures. New possibilities with administration of angiotensin. *Arch. Surg. Chicago* 85: 725–29
36. Desmukh, V. D., Harper, A. M. 1971. Effect of serotonin on cerebral blood flow and external carotid artery flow in the baboon. In *Brain and Blood Flow,* ed. R. W. Ross Russell, 136–37. London: Pitman
37. Desmukh, V. D., Meyer, J. S., Aoyagi, M., Matsuda, M., Tagashira, Y., 1975. Evidence for cholinergic influences on cerebral blood flow and metabolism. *Cerebral Blood Flow and Metabolism. Symp. Aviemore,* p. 33. (Abstr.)
38. Dietzmann, R. H., Romero, L. H., Beckman, C. B., Shatney, C. H., Lillehei, R. C. 1973. The influence of the sympathetic nervous system during cardiogenic shock. *Surg. Gynecol. Obstet.* 137:773–89
39. Dóra, E., Kovách, A. G. B., Nyáry, I. 1973. Hypothalamic and cortical evoked potential in hemorrhagic shock. In *Neurohumoral and Metabolic Aspects of Injury.* ed. A. G. B. Kovách, H. B. Stoner, J. J. Spitzer, 481–87. New York & London:Plenum
40. Dóra, E., Nyáry, I., Kollai, M., Kovách, A. G. B. 1971. Hypothalamic evoked potentials in hemorrhagic shock. *25th Int. Congr. Physiol. Sci. Munich,* p. 148. (Abstr.)
41. Drommer, W. 1972. Feinstrukturelle Alterationen an den Capillaren und Venulen im zentralen Nervensystem des Schweines nach experimentellem Colitoxinschock. *Acta Neuropathol. Berlin.* 22:13–28

42. Drost, R., Pilchmayr, I., Soga, D. 1971. Tierexperimentelle Untersuchungen über die-Gehirndurchblutung im protrahierten hämorrhagischen Schock. *Anaesthesist* 20:146–48

43. Dunker, R. O. Jr. et al 1970. In vitro common carotid and basilar artery reactivity in hemorrhagic shock. *Surg. Forum.* 21:432–33

44. Dyskin, A. A., Mazurkevich, G. S. 1965. The function of the adenohypophysis and the adrenal cortex in experimental traumatic shock. *Bjull. Eksp. Biol. Med.* 60:19–21

45. Edvinsson, L., Owman, C. 1975. Three types of cholinergic receptor mechanisms in brain vessels. *Cerebral Blood Flow and Metabolism. Symp. Aviemore,* p. 32. (Abstr.)

46. Eklöf, B. 1974. The brain in shock. In *Symposium on Shock.* ed. H. Skjoldborg, 57–63. Aarhus:Merck, Sharp & Dohme

47. Erdélyi, A. et al 1957. Die Verteilung der kreisenden Blutmenge nach Organen bei normalen und im Schockzustand befindlichen Ratten. *Acta Physiol. Acad. Sci. Hung.* 12:Suppl. 5

48. Erdélyi, A., Menyhárt, J., Mitsányi, A. 1962. The role of afferent and efferent neural mechanisms in experimental shock. *Int. Congr. Physiol. Sci. 22nd, Leiden. Abstr. Free Communications,* p. 686

49. Eremina, S. A. 1969. On the mechanism of hypothalamus-hypophysis-adrenal reaction to stress. *Bjull. Eksp. Biol. Med.* 67:40–43

50. Farrar, J. K. 1975. Cerebral arterial resistance at the lower limit of autoregulation. *Cerebral Blood Flow and Metabolism. Symp. Aviemore,* p. 53. (Abstr.)

51. Fazekas, J. F., Kleh, J., Parrish, A. E. 1955. The influence of shock on cerebral hemodynamics and metabolism. *Am. J. Med. Sci.* 229:41–45

52. Fedina, L., Kollai, M., Kovách, A. G. B. 1973. Sympathetic nervous activity after hemorrhage. In *Neurohumoral and Metabolic Aspects of Injury.* ed. A. G. B. Kovách, H. B. Stoner, J. J. Spitzer, 473–80. New York & London: Plenum

53. Fedina, L., Kovách, A. G. B., Vanik, M. 1965. Sympathetic activity in haemorrhagic shock. *Acta Physiol. Acad. Sci. Hung.* Suppl. 26:35

54. Fell, C. 1966. Changes in distribution of blood flow in irreversible hemorrhagic shock. *Am. J. Physiol.* 210:863–68

55. Ferrario, C. M., Gildenberg, P. L., McCubbin, J. W. 1972. Cardiovascular effects of angiotensin mediated by the central nervous system. *Circ. Res.* 30:257–62

56. Fink, R. A., Burham, W. A., Owen, T. L., Dixon, A. C., Goldstein, J. D. 1970. Hemorrhagic shock: the role of the central nervous system in fatality or survival. *Neurology* 20:408

57. Finnerty, F. A. 1962. Hemodynamics of angiotensin in man. *Circulation* 25: 255–58

58. Finnerty, F. A. Jr., Witkin, L., Fazekas, J. F. 1954. Cerebral Hemodynamics during cerebral ischemia induced by acute hypotension. *J. Clin. Invest.* 33:1227–32

59. Fitch, W., Mackenzie, E. T., Harper, A. M. 1975. Effect of sympathectomy on the autoregulation of cerebral blood flow. *Cerebral Blood Flow and Metabolism., Symp. Aviemore,* p. 13

60. Foreman, R. C. 1947. Redistribution of residual blood volume in hemorrhagic shock: relation to lethal bleeding volume. *Proc. Soc. Exp. Biol. NY* 65:29–33

61. Forsyth, R. P. 1970. Hypothalamic control of the distribution of cardiac output in the unanesthetized rhesus monkey. *Circ. Res.* 26:783–94

62. Földi, M., Kovách, A. G. B. 1955. Effect of isolated cerebral hypoxia and hypercapnia on sodium excretion. *Nature* 176:74

63. Földi, M., Kovách, A. G. B., Koltay, E. 1954. Wirkung von isolierter Kopfhypoxämie auf die Na-Ausscheidung. *Acta Physiol. Acad. Sci. Hung.* Suppl. 5:66

64. Frank, E. D. et al 1956. Effect of norepinephrine on circulation of the dog in hemorrhagic shock. *Am. J. Physiol.* 186:74–79

65. Freeman, J., Ingvar, D. H. 1968. Elimination by hypoxia of cerebral blood flow autoregulation and EEG relationship. *Exp. Brain Res.* 5:61–71

66. Gladish, J. T., Winnie, H. P., Collins, V. J. 1967. Shock: Recognition and modern treatment. *Postgrad. Med. J.* 43:41–51

67. Golden, P. F., Jane, J. A. 1969. Survival following profound hypovolaemia: Role of heart, lung and brain. *J. Trauma* 9:784–89

68. Golden, P. F., Jane, J. A. 1973. Experimental study of irreversible shock and the brain. *J. Neurosurg.* 39:434–41

69. Gömöri, P., Kovách, A. G. B., Földi, M., Szabó, Gy., Nagy, Z. 1953. Die

Folgen isolierter Hirnhypoxämie auf die Nierendurchblutung. *Acta Physiol. Acad. Sci. Hung.* Suppl. 4:42

70. Gotoh, F., Ebihara, S. I., Toyoda, M., Shinohara, Y. 1972. Role of autonomic nervous system in autoregulation of human cerebral circulation. *Europ. Neurol.* 6:203–7

71. Green, H. D., Rapela, C. E. 1968. Cerebral vascular responses to localized and systemic hypotension induced by hemorrhage and shock. In *Microcirculation as Related to Shock.* ed. D. Shepro and G. P. Fulton, 93–119. New York: Academic

72. Greenfield, J. C. Jr., Tindall, G. T. 1968. Effect of norepinephrine, epinephrine and angiotensin on blood flow in the internal carotid artery of man. *J. Clin. Invest.* 47:1672–84

73. Gregg, D., Arcidiancono, F., Sapirstein, L. A. 1967. Distribution of the cardiac output in the unanesthetized hemorrhaged rat. *Fed. Proc.* 26:268

74. Griffiths, I. R. 1975. Spinal cord blood flow following acute injury. *Cerebral Blood Flow and Metabolism. Symp. Aviemore,* p. 41. (Abstr.)

75. Grimson, B. S., Robinson, S. C., Danford, E. T., Tindall, G. T., Greenfield, J. C. Jr. 1969. Effect of serotonin on internal and external carotid artery blood flow in the baboon. *Am. J. Physiol.* 216:50–55

76. Grossman, G. R., Williams, V. F. 1971. Electrical activity and ultrastructure of cortical neurons and synapses in ischemia. In *Brain Hypoxia.* ed. J. B. Brierley, B. S. Meldrum, 61–75. London: Heinemann

77. Hardaway, R. M. 1966. *Syndromes of Disseminated Intravascular Coagulation. With Special Reference to Shock and Hemorrhage.* Springfield: Thomas. 466 pp.

78. Hardebo, J. E., Edvinsson, L., Falck, B., Owman, C., Rosengren, E. 1975. The blood-brain barrier for amines and their precursor aminoacids. *Cerebral Blood Flow and Metabolism. Symp. Aviemore,* p. 24. (Abstr.)

79. Harper, A. M. 1965. The inter-relationship between apCO$_2$ and blood pressure in the regulation of blood flow through the cerebral cortex. *Acta Neurol. Scand.* Suppl. 14:94–103

80. Harper, A. M., Desmukh, V. D., Rowan, J. O., Jennett, W. B. 1972. The influence of sympathetic nervous activity of cerebral blood flow. *Arch. Neurol. Chicago* 27:1–6

81. Hartman, B. K., Zide, D., Udenfriend, S. 1972. The use of dopamine beta-hydroxylase as a marker for the central noradrenergic nervous system in rat brain. *Proc. Nat. Acad. Sci.* 69:2722–26

82. Häggendal, E. 1965. Blood flow autoregulation of the cerebral grey matter with comments on its mechanism. *Acta Neurol. Scand.* Suppl. 14. p. 104–10

83. Hill, D. W. 1969. Computers in the management of shock. *Int. Anesth. Clin.* 194:1035–56

84. Hinshaw, L. B. et al 1964. Participation of sympathoadrenal system in endotoxin shock. *Am. J. Physiol.* 207:925–30

85. Hinzen, D. J. et al 1972. Metabolism and function of dog's brain recovering from longtime ischemia. *Am. J. Physiol.* 223:1158–64

86. Hossmann, K. A., Olsson, V. 1970. Suppression and recovery of neuronal function in transient cerebral ischemia. *Brain. Res.* 22:313–25

87. Hoyer, S., Hamer, J., Alberti, E., Stoeckel, H., Weinhardt, F. 1974. The effect of stepwise arterial hypotension on blood flow and oxidative metabolism of the brain. *Pfluegers Arch.* 351:161–72

88. Ingvar, D. H., Rosen, I., Elmquist, D. 1975. Effects of sensory stimulation upon rCBF. *Cerebral Blood Flow and Metabolism Symp. Aviemore,* p. 151 (Abstr.)

89. Irányi, M., Kovách, A. G. B., Antal, J. 1954. Die Wirkung verschiedener Hypothalamusläsionen auf das Hypophysen-Nebennierenrinden System und auf die Empfindlichkeit gegenüber traumatischen Schock. *Acta Physiol. Acad. Sci. Hung.* 6:Suppl. 23

90. Isakin, A. F. 1966. Coupled activity of the cerebral hemispheres in shock caused by prolonged soft tissue compression. *Patol. Fiziol. Eksp. Ter.* 10:35–38

91. Itkin, S. I. 1964. Examination of the morphology of the nervous system of the internal organs in extensive burns under experimental conditions during life. *Eksp. Khir. Aneszt.* 9:59–63

92. James, I. M., Millar, R. A., Purves, M. J. 1968. Neural pathways involved in the control of cerebral blood flow in the baboon. *J. Physiol. London* 196:37

93. James, I. M., Millar, R. A., Purves, M. J. 1969. Observations on the extrinsic neural control of cerebral blood flow in the baboon. *Circ. Res.* 25:77–93

94. Jourdan, F., Collet, A., Masbernard, A. 1950. Les réactions artérielles céré-

brales du cours du choc traumatique. *C R Soc. Biol. Paris* 144:1507–9
95. Kardasjan, G. H. 1972. Morphologic changes in different nuclei of the hypothalamus following turniquet shock. In *Traumatic Shock.* ed. G. D. Shushkova, S. A. Seleznieva, L. I. Garvina, p. 47. Leningrad:LISP
96. Kerkhoven, P. 1965. Necrosis of the anterior lobe of the pituitary following shock caused by burns. *Schweiz. Med. Woschnschr.* 95:1066–71
97. Kety, S. S. 1957. Determinants of tissue oxygen tension. *Fed. Proc.* 16:666–70
98. Khrabrova, O. P. 1969. Character of microcirculation in the brain in traumatic shock. *Patol. Fiziol. Eksp. Ter.* 13:58–61
99. King, B. D., Sokoloff, L., Wechster, L. 1952. The effects of l-epinephrine and l-norepinephrine upon cerebral circulation and metabolism in man. *J. Clin. Invest.* 31:273–79
100. Kissel, J. W. Domino, E. F. 1959. Effects of controlled progressive hypotension on some spinal reflexes in the cat. *Am. J. Physiol.* 196:59
101. Kogure, K., Scheinberg, P., Fujishima, M., Busto, R., Reinmuth, O. M. 1970. Effects of hypoxia on cerebral autoregulation. *Am. J. Physiol.* 219:1393–95
102. Kollai, M., Fedina, L., Kovách, A. G. B. 1973. Effect of bleeding, cooling and asphyxia on the activity of vertebral and cardiac sympathetic nerves. *Acta Physiol. Acad. Sci. Hung.* 44:145–55
103. Koo, A., Cheng, K. K. 1974. Cerebral microvascular volume flow: Its measurement and responses to hemorrhagic hypotension in the rat. *Microvasc. Res.* 8:151–55
104. Korner, P. I. 1959. Circulatory adaptations in hypoxia. *Physiol. Rev.* 39:687–730
105. Kovách, A. G. B. 1955. W aprawie dzialania adrenaliny nakrazenie krwi w mozgu. *Acta Physiol. Polon.* 6:241–43
106. Kovách, A. G. B. 1961. Importance of nervous and metabolic changes in the development of irreversibility in experimental shock. *Fed. Proc.* 20: Part 3, 122–37
107. Kovách, A. G. B. 1966. Az idegrendszer shockban. *Orvosképzés* 41:321–32
108. Kovách, A. G. B. 1968. Circulatory adjustment and its comparative physiological aspects after changing blood volume. *Int. Congr. IUPS 24. Wash. DC* 6:35–36 (Abstr.)
109. Kovách, A. G. B. 1970. The function of the central nervous system after hemorrhage. *J. Clin. Pathol.* 23: Suppl. (R. Coll. Pathol.) 4.202–12
110. Kovách, A. G. B. 1972. Blood flow and metabolism in brain and in adipose tissue during hemorrhagic shock. In *Shock in Low- and High-Flow States.* Proc. Sym. Brook Lodge, 1971. Ed. B. K. Forscher, R. C. Lillehei, S. S. Stubbs. Amsterdam: Excerpta Med. Int. Congr. Ser. 247:65–76
111. Kovách, A. G. B. 1973. Tissue blood flow and metabolism in control and phenoxybenzamine-pretreated animals in experimental shock. In *Traumatic Shock.* Symp. Hung. Traumatol. Soc. ed. Gy. Szantó, V. Hönig, O. Székley, 163–85. Budapest: Akadémiai Kiadó.
112. Kovách, A. G. B., Eke, A., Dóra, E., Gyulai, L. 1975. Correlation between the redox state, electrical activity and blood flow in cat brain cortex during hemorrhagic shock. In *Proc. 2nd Int. Symp. on Oxygen Transport to Tissue, Mainz.* New York: Plenum. In press
113. Kovách, A. G. B. et al 1959. Circulation and metabolism in the head of the dog in ischemic shock. *Acta Physiol. Acad. Sci. Hung.* 15:217–29
114. Kovách, A. G. B., Fedina, L., Mitsányi, A., Naszlady, A., Biro, Z . 1962. Neurophysiological and circulatory changes in hemorrhagic shock. *Int. Congr. Physiol. Sci. 22. Leiden.* Excerpta Med. Int. Congr. Ser. 48:678
115. Kovách, A. G. B., Fonyó, A. 1960. Metabolic responses to injury in cerebral tissue. In *The Biochemical Response to Injury.* ed. H. B. Stoner, C. I. Threlfall. Oxford: Blackwell 129–60
116. Kovách, A. G. B., Fonyó, A., Kovách, E. 1959. Cerebral phosphate metabolism in traumatic shock. *Acta Physiol. Acad. Sci. Hung.* 16:157–64
117. Kovách, A. G. B., Hamar, J., Nyáry, I., Sándor, P., Reivich, M. 1975. Cerebral blood flow and metabolism in hemorrhagic shock in the baboon. *Cerebral Blood Flow and Metabolism. Symp. Aviemore,* p. 14. (Abstr.)
118. Kovách, A. G. B., Menyhárt, J., Erdélyi, A., Molnár, G., Kiss, S. 1961. The role of the sympatho-adrenal system in ischemic shock. *Acta Physiol. Acad. Sci. Hung.* 19:199–208
119. Kovách, A. G. B., Menyhárt, J., Kiss, S., Erdélyi, A., Kovách, E. 1954. Untersuchungen über die Ausbildung des irreversiblen Schockes. *Acta Physiol. Acad. Sci. Hung.* 5:Suppl. 33–34

120. Kovách, A. G. B., Mitsányi, A., Monos, E., Nyáry, I., Sulyok, A. 1973. Control of organ blood flow following hemorrhage. *Adv. Exp. Med. Biol.* 33:1–17

121. Kovách, A. G. B., Mitsányi, A., Stekiel, W. 1965. Local blood flow and oxygen tension of brain tissue in haemorrhagic shock. *Acta Physiol. Acad. Sci. Hung.* 26:Suppl. 35–36

122. Kovách, A. G. B., Monos, E., Koltay, E., Desrius, A. 1970. Effect of hypothalamic stimulation on adrenal blood flow and glycocorticoid release prior to and after acute hypophysectomy. *Acta Physiol. Acad. Sci. Hung.* 38:205–16

123. Kovách, A. G. B., Roheim, P. S., Irányi, M., Kiss, S., Antal, J. 1958. Effect of the isolated perfusion of the head on the development of ischaemic and hemorrhagic shock. *Acta Physiol. Acad. Sci. Hung.* 14:231–38

124. Kovách, A. G. B., Roheim, P. S., Irányi, M., Kovách, E. 1958. Renal function in hemorrhagic shock, with the head perfused with normal blood. *Acta Physiol. Acad. Sci. Hung.* 14:247–54

125. Kovách, A. G. B., Takács, L. 1952. Responsiveness of the vegetative nervous system in shock. *Acta Physiol. Acad. Sci. Hung.* 3:91–101

126. Kovách, A. G. B., Takács, L. 1953. Response of the vascular system to sympathetic stimuli during shock. *Nature* 171:433

127. Kulagin, V. G. 1963. The significance of cerebral circulation changes in the development of the nervous activity disturbances in traumatic shock. *Patol. Fiziol. Eksp. Ter.* 7:26–30

128. Kusajima, K., Wax. S. D., Webb, W. R. 1974. Cerebral hypotension and shock lung syndrome. *J. Thorac. Cardiovasc. Surg.* 67:969–75

129. Laborit, H., Baron, C., Weber, B. 1969. Treatment of experimental hemorrhagic shock designated irreversible. Role of SH group and restoration of intraparticular reserves of catecholamines. 3. Stereotaxic study of cerebral stimulations. *Agressologie* 10:205–15

130. Lassen, N. A. 1959. Cerebral blood flow and oxygen consumption in man. *Physiol. Rev.* 39:183–238

131. Ledingham, I. M. 1969. Hyperbaric oxygen in shock. *Int. Anesth. Clin.* 194:819–39

132. Leonov, A. N., Vornovsky, V. A. 1971. The effect of hyperbaric oxygenation on bioelectrical activity of the cerebral cortex in acute hemorrhagic collapse. *Patol. Fiziol. Eksp. Ter.*

133. Lillehei, R. C., Longerbeam, J. K., Block, J. H., Manax, W. G. 1964. The nature of irreversible shock: Experimental and clinical observations. *Ann. Surg.* 160:682–710

134. Lowry, O. H., Passonneau, J. V., Hasselberger, F. X., Shultz, D. W. 1964. Effects of ischemia on known substrates and cofactors of the glycolytic pathway in brain. *J. Biol. Chem.* 239:18–30

135. Lübbers, D. W. 1968. The oxygen pressure field of the brain and its significance for the normal and critical oxygen supply of the Brain. In *Oxygen Transport in Blood and Tissue.* ed. D. W. Lübbers, U. Luft, G. Thews, E. Witzleb, 124–139. Stuttgart: Thieme

136. Lübbers, D. W., Kessler, M. 1968. Oxygen supply and rate of tissue respiration. In *Oxygen Transport in Blood and Tissue.* ed. D. W. Lübbers, U. Luft, G. Thews, E. Witzleb, 90–99. Stuttgart: Thieme

137. Lushchitzkii, M. A., Borshchagouskii, M. L. 1961. Traumatitseskij sok i tserepnomozgovüe povrezdenija. *Voenno Med. Zh.* 7:31–34

138. Maklári, E., Kovách, A. G. B. 1966. Carbon dioxide content of brain tissue in controla and phenoxybenzamine-pretreated experimental haemorrhagic shock. *Acta Physiol. Acad. Sci. Hung.* 29:414

139. Maklári, E., Kovách, A. G. B. 1968. Carbon dioxide content of brain tissue and acid base balance in haemorrhagic shock after pretreatment with dibenzyline. *Acta Med. Acad. Sci. Hung.* 25:13–22

140. Maklári, E., Kovách, A. G. B. 1968. Acid-base balance in haemorrhagic shock. *34th Annual Conf. Hung. Physiol. Soc. Debrecen 1970 Abstr.* ed. K. Lissák, p. 170 Budapest: Akadémiai Kiadó

141. Maklári, E., Kovách, A. G. B., Nyáry, I. 1973. Acid-base balance and regional CO_2 content of the brain in hypovolaemic shock. *Acta Physiol. Acad. Sci. Hung.* 44:157–69

142. Maklári, E., Kovách, A. G. B., Nyáry, I. 1973. Effect on central nervous tissue CO_2 content of the correction of acidosis due to hemorrhage. *Acta Physiol. Acad. Sci. Hung.* 44:171–81

143. Massopust, L. C. Jr., Wolin, L. R., Kadoya, S., White, R. J. 1969. The effect of hypoxia on electrocortical activity in the rhesus monkey. *Exp. Neurol.* 25:116–28

144. Matrosov, V. D. 1975. The effect of sustained nociceptive stimulation on the adrenaline and noradrenaline contents in different brain areas and in adrenal glands of rats prior to and after removal of the upper cervical sympathetic ganglia. *Sechenov Physiol. J. USSR* 61:385

145. Mazurkevich, G. S. 1964. Modification of adrenocorticotropic function of the anterior lope of the hypophysis in traumatic shock. *Patol. Fiziol. Eksp. Ter.* 8:18–21

146. Mazurkevich, G. S. 1973. Blood flow in the portal system of vessels of the hypophysis in rats under normal conditions and in shock. *Probl. Endokrinol. Gormonoter.* 19:68–73

147. Mayer, E. T. 1967. Distribution pattern of cerebral cortex damages following heart arrest and circulatory collapse. *Verh. Dtsch. Ges. Pathol.* 51:371–76

148. McCutcheon, E. P., Frazier, D. T., Boyarsky, L. L. 1971. Changes in the somatosensory cortical evoked potential produced by hypovolemic shock. *Proc. Soc. Exp. Biol. Med.* 136:1063–67

149. Mchedlishvili, G. I., Garfunkel, M. L., Ormotsadze, L. G. 1972. Cerebral circulation under conditions of heterotransfusion shock. *Pat. Fiziol. Eksp. Ter.* 16:25–31

150. Mchedlishvili, G. I., Nikolaishvili, L. S. 1970. Evidence of a cholinergic nervous mechanism mediating the autoregulatory dilation of the cerebral blood vessels. *Arch. Ges. Physiol.* 315:27

151. Mchedlishvili, G. I., Ormotsadze, L. G., Nikolaishvili, L. S., Baramidze, D. G. 1967. Reaction of different parts of the cerebral vascular system in asphyxia. *Exp. Neurol.* 18:239–52

152. McIlwain, H. 1959. *Biochemistry and the Nervous System.* London: Churchill 288 pp.

153. Meldrum, B. S., Brierley, J. B. 1969. Brain damage in the rhesus monkey resulting from profound arterial hypotension. II. Changes in the spontaneous and evoked electrical activity of the neocortex. *Brain Res.* 13:101–18

154. Menyhárt, J., Kovách, A. G. B., Kiss, S., Erdélyi, A., Kovách, E. 1954. Die Wirkung von Dibenamin in ischaemischen Schock. *Acta Physiol. Acad. Sci. Hung.* 5:Suppl. 32–33

155. Mietkiewski, E. et al 1960. Nervous system function tests in rats performed with the aid of conditioned reflexes in traumatic shock. *Acta Physiol. Pol.* 11:826–28

156. Miller, J. D., Stanek, A., Langfitt, T. W. 1972. Concepts of cerebral perfusion pressure and vascular compression during intracranial hypertension. *Prog. Brain Res.* 35:411–32

157. Mori, S. et al 1970. Hemorrhagic shock and central nervous functions: Spinal and spino-bulbo-spinal reflexes. *Surgery* 68:870–77

158. Mori, S., Simeone, F. A. 1970. Effects of hemorrhagic hypotension and shock on the central nervous functions. *J. Surg. Res.* 10:299–314

159. Moss, G., Staunton, C., Stein, A. A. 1972. Cerebral etiology of the "shock lung syndrome." *J. Trauma* 12:885–90

160. Muzykant, L. I. 1969. Morphological peculiarities of the hypothalamus, hypophysis and adrenal glands in burn shock. *Arh. Pat.* 31:23–33

161. Nelson, E., Rennels, M. 1970. Innervation of intracranial arteries. *Brain* 93:475–90

162. Neutze, J. M., Wyler, F., Rudolph, A. M. 1968. Changes in distribution of cardiac output after hemorrhage in rabbits. *Am. J. Physiol.* 215:857–64

163. Nicholson, A. N., Macnamara, W. D., Borland, R. G. 1972. Responsiveness of the cortex and visual pathway during transient hypotension. *Electroencephalogr. Clin. Neurophysiol.* 25:330–37

164. Nickerson, M. 1963. Sympathetic blockade in the therapy of shock. *Am. J. Cardiol.* 12:619–23

165. Nyáry, I., Dóra, E., Sándor, P., Kovách, A. G. B., Reivich, M. 1974. Cerebral blood flow and metabolism in hemorrhagic shock in the baboon. *Third Tbilisi Symp. on Brain Blood Supply.* Symp. Tbilisi, p. 51. (Abstr.)

166. Nyáry, I., Maklári, E., Kovách, A. G. B. 1975. Hypothalamic blood flow in hemorrhagic shock after administration of buffer solutions. *Acta Physiol. Acad. Sci. Hung.* In press

167. Oldendorf, W. H. 1971. Brain uptake of radiolabelled amino acids, amines, and hexoses after arterial injection. *Am. J. Physiol.* 221:1629–39

168. Olesen, J. 1972. The effect of intracarotid epinephrine, norepinephrine and angiotensin on the regional cerebral blood flow in man. *Neurology* 22:978–87

169. Olesen, J. 1974. *Cerebral Blood Flow. Methods for Measurement, Regulation, Effects of Drugs and Changes in Disease* p. 50 Kobenhavn: Fadls Forlag.

170. Olesen, J., Skinhøj, E. 1971. The influence of certain vasoactive amines on the regional cerebral blood flow in man.

Proc. Int. Headache Symp. Elsinore. Basel: Sandoz. 145–52

171. Opitz, E., Schneider, M. 1950. Über die Sauerstoffversorgung des Gehirns und den Mechanismus von Mangelwirkungen. *Ergeb. Physiol.* 6:126

172. Paré, A. 1575. Quoted by Kovách, A. G. B. 1970. The function of the central nervous system after hemorrhage. *J. Clin. Pathol.* 23. Suppl. 4:202–12

173. Pashkovsky, E. V., Lasta, F. P. 1966. Early electroencephalographic changes in patients with grave mechanic injuries. *Vestn. Khir.* 96:69–73

174. Pásztor, A., Sarkadi, A., Tomka, I., Ortutay, K. 1972. EEG and evoked potentials in hemorrhagic shock. *Acta Physiol. Acad. Sci. Hung.* 42:411–18

175. Peterson, C. G. et al 1965. Hemorrhagic shock and the nervous system. I. Spinal cord reflex activity and brain stem reticular formation. *Ann. Surg.* 161:485–96

176. Peterson, C. G., Haugen, F. P. 1963. Hemorrhagic shock and the nervous system. *Am. J. Surg.* 106:233–42

177. Petrov, I. R. 1967. Concerning the degree of inhibition of the central nervous system functioning in blood losses and shock, and the use of craniocerebral hypothermia. *Vesztn. Hir.* 99:13–17

178. Phemister, D. B., Laestar, C. H., Eichelberger, L., Schachter, R. J. 1944. Afferent depressor nerve impulses as a cause of shock. *Ann. Surg.* 119:26

179. Pokrovsky, G. A., Lapshin, V. P., Boev, M. Yu. 1966. Electroencephalography in traumatic and hemorrhagic shock. *Khirurgiia Moscow* 42:98–101

180. Ponessa, J. T., Sándor, P., Kovách, A. G. B., Angelakos, E. T. 1974. The effect of cervical sympathectomy on regional brain blood flow during hemorrhagic shock. *Physiologist* 17:309

181. Ponte, J., Purves, M. 1974. The role of the carotid body chemoreceptors and carotid sinus baroreceptors in the control of cerebral blood vessels. *J. Physiol.* 237:315–40

182. Porter, E. L. 1912–13. Variations in irritability of the reflex arc. I. Variations under asphyxial conditions, with blood-gas determinations. *Am. J. Physiol.* 31:223

183. Raichle, M., Hartman, B., Eichling, J., Sharpe, L. 1975. Central noradrenergic regulation of brain microcirculation. *Cerebral Blood Flow and Metabolism. Symp. Aviemore,* p. 1 (Abstr.)

184. Rapela, C. E., Green, H. D. 1964. Autoregulation of canine cerebral blood flow. *Circ. Res.* 15: Suppl. 1, 205–11

185. Rapela, C. E., Martin, J. 1975. Reactivity of cerebral extra and intraparenchymal vasculature to serotonin and vasodilator drugs. *Cerebral Blood Flow and Metabolism. Symp. Aviemore,* p. 34 (Abstr.)

186. Reivich, M., Kovách, A. G. B., Spitzer, J. J., Sándor, P. 1973. Cerebral blood flow and metabolism in hemorrhagic shock in baboons. In *Neurohumoral and Metabolic Aspects of Injury.* ed. A. G. B. Kovách, H. B. Stoner, J. J. Spitzer, 19–26. New York & London: Plenum

187. Rittmann, W. W., Smith, L. L. 1966. Cerebral blood flow following severe hemorrhage. *Surg. Gynol. Obstet.* 123:67–72

188. Roheim, P. et al 1954. Der Kreislauf und Stoffwechsel des Kopfes im Schock. *Acta Physiol. Acad. Sci. Hung.* 6: Suppl. 26

189. Roheim, P., Kovách, A. G. B., Irányi, M., Kiss, S., Antal, J. 1954. Die Wirkung der isolierten Durchströmung des Kopfes auf das Zustandekommen von ischämischem Schock. *Acta Physiol. Acad. Sci. Hung.* 5: Suppl., 31–32

190. Rosendorff, C. & Cranston, W. I. 1971. Effects of intrahypothalamic and intraventricular norepinephrine and 5-hydroxtryptamine on hypothalamic blood flow in the conscious rabbit. *Circ. Res.* 28:492–502

191. Rosendorff, C., Mitchell, G. 1975. Functional studies on a possible dual innervation of hypothalamic resistance vessels. *Cerebral Blood Flow and Metabolism. Symp. Aviemore,* p. 25 (Abstr.)

192. Rutherford, R. B. et al 1968. Regional blood flow in hemorrhagic shock by the distribution of labelled microspheres. *Surg. Forum.* 19:14–15

193. Sanderson, J. M., Wright, G., Sims, F. W. 1972. Brain damage in dogs immediately following pulsate and nonpulsate blood flows in extracorporeal circulation. *Thorax* 27:275

194. Sándor, P., Demchenko, I. T., Kovách, A. G. B. 1974. Hypothalamic and thalamic blood flow and pO_2 changes evoked by somatic afferent stimulation. *Int. Congr. Physiol. Sci. 26. Abstr. New Delhi.* 2:390

195. Sándor, P. et al 1970. Modifications locales de la circulation cérébrale dans diverses régions du cerveau pendant l'é-

morragie. *Regional Congr. Int. Union Phys. Sci. Brasow. Abstr. Pap.* p. 568
196. Sándor, P. et al 1971. Cortical, hypothalamic and hypophyseal blood flow during hemorrhagic shock. *25th Int. Congr. Physiol. Sci. Munich,* p. 49. (Abstr.)
197. Sándor, P., Tomka, N., Kovách, A. G. B. 1975. Regional cerebral blood flow during incompatible blood transfusion. *41st Ann. Conf. Hung. Physiol. Soc. Szeged. Abstr. Acta Physiol. Acad. Sci. Hung.* In press
198. Sapirstein, L. A., Sapirstein, E. H., Bredemeyer, A. 1960. Effect of hemorrhage on the cardiac output and its distribution in the rat. *Circ. Res.* 8:135–48
199. Sherman, D. M., Yakovlev, D. S. 1974. On some controversial tenets in neurogenic theory of shock. *Eksp. Khir. Aneszt.* 4:76–81
200. Sheveleva, V. S. 1959. Electrophysiological analysis of functional conditions of various segments of the nervous system in shock. *Bjull. Eksp. Biol. Med.* 48:43–50
201. Shushkova, G. D., Seleznieva, S. A., Garvina, L. I. 1972. *Traumatic Shock. A Bibliography 1961–70.* (Travmatitseskij sok. Bibliografija otetsestvennoj i zarubeznoj literaturü 1961–70) Leningrad:LISP. 268 pp.
202. Siesjö, B. K. 1971/1972. Metabolism and flow in the hypoxic brain. *Europ. Neurol.* 6:43–48
203. Simeone, F. A., Witoszka, M. 1970. The central nervous system in experimental hemorrhagic shock. *Am. J. Surg.* 119:427–32
204. Simmons, R. L., Ducker, T. B., Martin, A. M. Jr., Anderson, R. W., Noyes, H. E. 1968. The role of the central nervous system in septic shock: I. Pathologic changes following intraventricular and intracisternal endotoxin in the dog. *Ann. Surg.* 167:145–57
205. Slater, G. I., Vladeck, B. C., Bassin, R., Kark, A. E., Shoemaker, W. C. 1973. Sequential changes in distribution of cardiac output in hemorrhagic shock. *Surgery* 73:714–22
206. Slome, D., O'Shaughnessy, L. 1938. The nervous factor in traumatic shock. *Bri. J. Surg.* 25:900–9
207. Smith, L. L., Reeves, C. D., Hinshaw, D. B. 1965. Hemodynamic alterations and regional blood flow in hemorrhagic shock. *Shock and Hypotension.* eds. L. C. Mills, J. H. Moyer, New York: Grune & Stratton. 373–84

208. Smith, L. L. Rittmann, W. W. 1967. Cerebral blood flow changes following severe hemorrhage and treatment. *Surg. Gynecol. Obstet.* 124:1047–56
209. Sokoloff, L. 1959. The action of drugs on the cerebral circulation. Pharmacol. Rev. 11:1–85
210. Speckmann, E. J., Caspers, H., Sokolov, W. 1970. Aktivitätsänderungen spinaler Neurone während und nach einer Asphyxie. *Pfluegers Arch.* 319:122–38
211. Spielmeyer, W. 1922. *Histopathologie des Nervensystems,* Berlin: Springer 74–79
212. Spink, W. W., Vick, J. 1962. Canine endotoxin shock: reversal with aldosterone and angiotensin II. *Proc. Soc. Exp. Biol. Med.* 109:521–22
213. Stone, H. H. et al 1965. The effect of acute hemorrhagic shock on cerebral circulation and metabolism of man. See Ref. 207, 257–64
214. Stone, H. H., MacKrell, T. N., Brandstater, G. L., Hardak, B. J., Nemir, P. 1954. The effect of induced hemorrhagic shock on the cerebral circulation and metabolism of man. *Surg. Forum.* 5:789–803
215. Stoner, H. B. 1969. Studies on the mechanism of shock. The impairment of thermoregulation by trauma. *Br. J. Exp. Pathol.* 50:125–38
216. Stoner, H. B. 1972. Effect of injury on the responses to thermal stimulation of the hypothalamus. *J. Appl. Physiol.* 33:665–72
217. Stoner, H. B. 1973. Thermoregulation after injury. In *Neurohumoral and Metabolic Aspects of Injury.* ed. A. G. B. Kovách, H. B. Stoner, J. J. Spitzer, 495–99. New York London: Plenum
219. Stoner, H. B., Elson, P. M. 1971. The effect of injury on monoamine concentrations in the rat hypothalamus. *J. Neurochem.* 18:1837
220. Stoner, H. B., Elson, P. M., Koltay, E. 1973. The effect of limb ischaemia on the turnover of noradrenaline in the hypothalamus and brain stem of the rat. *J. Neurochem.* 21:223
221. Stoner, H. B., Marshall, H. W. 1975. Studies on the mechanism of shock. The importance of central catecholaminergic neurons in the response to injury. *Br. J. Exp. Pathol.* 56:157–66
222. Stulc, J., Masek, K., Friedrich, R. 1969. Brain uptake of ^3H noradrenaline in normal and shigella dysenterial exotoxin treated mice. *Experientia* 25:278–79

223. Swank, R. L., Hissen, W. 1964. Influence of serotonin on cerebral circulation. *Arch. Neurol. Chicago* 10:468–72

224. Szabó, G. 1963. The effect of norepinephrine on cerebral circulation and cerebral metabolism in ischaemic shock. *Magy. Sebesz* 16:253–58

225. Szabó, G., Magyar, Z. 1964. The effect of angiotensin on circulation and cerebral metabolism in experimental shock. *Acta Med. Sci. Hung.* 20:145–51

226. Szabó, I., Kovács, P., Hadnagy, C. 1961. Der hämolytische Schock. III. Die Rolle des Nervensystems in hämolytischen Schock. *Immunitätsforsch. Exp. Therap.* 161:95–104

227. Takács, L., Kovách, A. G. B. 1952. Die Empfindlichkeit des Blutgefäss-System gegen sympathische Reize im Schock. *Acta Physiol. Acad. Sci. Hung.* 3:Suppl. 31–32

228. Tamura, H., Witoszka, M. M., Hopkins, R. W., Simeone, F. A. 1972. The nervous system in experimental hemorrhagic shock: morphology of the brain. *J. Trauma* 12:869–75

229. Thämer, V., Weidinger, H., Kirchner, F. 1969. Sympathische Aktionspotentiale im hämorrhagischen Schock. *Z. Kreislaufforsch.* 58:472–84

230. Tindall, G. T., Greenfield, J. C., Dillon, M. L., Odom, G. I. 1964. Effect of hemorrhage of blood flow in the carotid arteries: Studies on ten rhesus monkeys. *J. Neurosurg.* 21:763–68

231. Trzebski, A. 1960. Studies on the excitability of the cardiovascular centers in the hypothalamus and brain stem during hypovolemic hemorrhagic shock in cats. *Acta Physiol. Pol* 11:503–17

232. Van Liere, E. J., Stickney, J. C. 1963. Effect of hypoxia on the nervous system. In *Hypoxia.* 276–349. Chicago: Univ. Press

233. Wahl, M. et al 1972. Adrenergic control of cerebral vascular resistance. A micropuncture study. *Eur. Neurol.* 6:185–90

234. Weil-Malherbe, H., Whitby, L. G., Axelrod, J. 1961. The uptake of circulating (^{3}H) norepinephrine by the pituitary gland and various areas of the brain. *J. Neurochem.* 8:55–64

235. Wiggers, C. J. 1950. *Physiology of Shock.* New York. Commonwealth Fund. 459 pp

236. Williams, L. F. Jr. 1968. Hemorrhagic shock as a source of unconsciousness. *Surg. Clin. N. Am.* 48:263–72

237. Wüllenweber, R., Gött, U., Szántó, J. 1967. Beobachtungen zur Regulation der Hirndurchblutung. *Acta Neurochir.* 16:137–53

238. Yashon, D. et al 1971. Cerebral function during profound oligemic hypotension in the dog. *J. Neurosurg.* 34:494–99

AUTHOR INDEX

A

Aakvaag, A., 425
Aars, H., 537, 538, 542
Abboud, F. M., 540, 541,
552, 554, 556, 557, 561
Abdel-Sayed, W., 554
Abe, C., 393
Abood, L. G., 188
Abraira, C., 361
Abramczuk, J., 96, 97
Abramow, M., 21, 28
Abu Haydar, N., 339
Acker, H., 539, 542, 543
Ackles, K. N., 523
Acres, S. C., 400
Adam, W., 57, 58, 61
Adams, J. E., 578
Adams, P. W., 355
Adamson, C., 523
Adaro, F., 72, 73, 76, 82
Adelman, W., 143
Adey, W. R., 123, 226,
234
Adler, S., 59
Adrian, R. H., 294-96, 298-
300, 306, 308
Afifi, A. K., 339
Afzelius, B., 339
Aganon, M. A., 53
Aghajanian, G. K., 155, 164,
165, 169
Agin, P. P., 508
Agnoli, A., 578
Aguilar, C. E., 192
Aguilar-Parada, E., 355,
358, 364, 374
Agulian, S. K., 22, 28, 30,
32
Ahlabo, I., 332, 335
Ahlborg, B., 281
Ahuja, S. P., 560
Aitken, J. T., 191
Aitkin, L. M., 222
Akbar, A. M., 397
Akera, T., 262, 263
Aketa, K., 106
Akimov, G. A., 586
Albe-Fessard, D., 123, 124
Alberga, A., 436
Albers, R. W., 192, 193
Alberti, E., 578
Alberti, K. G. M. M., 358,
409, 411
Albertini, D. F., 98, 111
Alberts, B., 428, 436, 437,
440, 444
Alberts, E., 219
Albisser, A. M., 368
Albuquerque, E. X., 178,

180, 181, 187, 189-91, 196,
198-200, 203
Aldinger, E. E., 285
Alexander, J. C., 49
Alexander, K. R., 361
Alford, F. P., 361, 409,
411
Allain, J. P., 518, 519
Allen, D. O., 370
Allen, J. C., 259, 260, 262,
263
Allen, W. M., 437
Alleyne, G. A. O., 59, 61
Alltop, L. B., 394
Almaraz-Ugalde, A., 361
Almendares, J. A., 53
Almers, W., 298-300, 306,
308
Aloisi, M., 180, 188
Alpert, L. C., 395, 396, 399,
407, 410
Alvarez, J., 199
Alving, A. S., 46
Al-Zahid, G., 459, 469, 475,
483-86
Amashukeli, G. V., 575
Ames, A. III, 574, 580,
582
Ames, R. P., 505
Amy, H., 522
Anagnostopoulos, T., 25, 31
Andersen, B., 451, 452, 455,
457, 458, 460, 467, 468,
470, 471, 475, 479, 481,
484, 487
Anderson, D. K., 257
Anderson, E., 98, 100, 105,
111
Anderson, J., 46, 453, 457,
458, 460, 470, 471, 483
Anderson, J. N., 427, 435,
436, 441
Anderson, J. R., 578
Anderson, J. W., 53
Anderson, K. M., 425
Anderson, L. E., 198
Anderson, M. S., 394
Anderson, P., 505
Anderson, R. W., 572, 576,
577
Anderson, S. L., 373
Andersson, A., 354
Andersson, K., 88
Andrade, L. L., 362, 363
ANDREOLI, T. E., 451-500;
21, 23, 26, 453, 454, 457-
60, 463-69, 475-81, 483-87
Andrew, G. M., 75
Andrews, S. S., 358, 361,
362

Angelakos, E. T., 574, 576,
577
Angeletti, P. U., 184
Angeletti, R. H., 184
Angell-James, J. E., 538,
539, 542
Angyan, L., 222, 223, 227,
233
Antal, J., 571, 573, 577,
584
Antonio, A., 541, 559
Anton-Tay, F., 403, 407
Aoki, T. T., 355, 357, 364
Aoki, V. S., 78
Aoyagi, M., 578
Appeltauer, G. S. L., 199
Aprison, M. H., 153, 160,
162
Araki, H., 320
Araki, S., 396, 397
Arana, L. C., 184
Aras, E., 126
Arborelius, M., 78
Archer, A. A., 453
Archer, R., 453, 478
Arcidiancono, F., 573
Ardill, J., 355, 362, 363
Ardlie, N. G., 523
Arendshorst, W. J., 10
Arey, L. B., 95
Arfors, K. E., 524
Ariano, M. A., 332
Ariens, E. J., 155, 162,
163
Arimura, A., 361, 394-99,
401, 404, 410-12
Armour, J. A., 540
Armstrong, C. M., 139, 141,
144-47, 250, 251, 298, 299
Armstrong, M. E., 224
Armstrong, R. B., 273, 275,
283, 285, 332
Arnaud, M., 434
Arndt, J. O., 540
Arregui, A., 161
Arrhenius, E., 322, 324
Asanuma, H., 122, 128,
226
Ashby, S. M., 220
Ashcroft, S. J. H., 356, 368,
370
Ashford, T., 581
Ashley, C. C., 301
Ashmore, C. R., 179
Ashmore, J., 359, 360
Askanas, V., 179
Askew, E. W., 275, 277
Assan, R., 364
Asterita, M. F., 25, 26,
31

597

Guillemin, R., 361, 389,
390, 398, 401, 407-11
Guilleux, J. C., 434
Guleria, J. S., 77
Gump, F. E., 338
Gun, D. R., 275, 277,
283
Gunn, A., 397
Gunther, S. J., 42
Gurdon, J. B., 96, 185, 432
Gurtner, G. H., 74, 83
Gustafsson, R., 322, 324,
336
Guth, L., 177-79, 182, 187,
189-93, 196-98, 202, 203
Guthrow, C. E. Jr., 373
GUTMANN, E., 177-216;
177-83, 186-98, 201-3, 284
Gutmann, F. B., 549
Guttmann, L., 191
Guyatt, A. R., 82, 83
Guyda, H., 404
Guyton, A. C., 549, 550,
554
Guyton, J. R., 368
Gwatkin, R. B. L., 98, 102,
107
Gyntelberg, F., 355, 357
Györy, A. Z., 47, 48
Gysin, R., 183
Gyulai, L., 571, 572, 574,
576, 577, 579, 581, 582

H

Haab, P., 72, 81
Haas, E., 549, 550
Haas, H., 165
Haastert, H. P., 253
Haaxma, R., 130, 227
Habener, J. F., 399
Haber, E., 549
Hackenbrock, C. R., 340
Hackett, J. G., 552, 554
Hadden, E. M., 324
Hadden, J. W., 324
Haddy, F. J., 257
Hadley, M. E., 398, 402
Hadnagy, C., 572, 577,
578
Hafez, E. S. E., 95, 105,
110
Haffner, M., 235
Hagbarth, K.-E., 545, 551,
553
Hagen, T. C., 397
Hager, D. L., 362, 363,
373
Häggendal, E., 279, 281,
578
Hagiwara, S., 307
Hagura, R., 355, 358, 366
Hahn, W. E., 98, 99, 102,
104
Haigler, H. J., 155, 164,
165
Hainaut, K., 302, 306

Hainsworth, R., 539, 543,
552, 555
Haist, R. E., 356
Hajek, I., 189
Hajjar, J. J., 22, 30
Hakanson, R., 361
Hakerem, G., 220
Halasz, B., 390
Hales, C. N., 371
Halicka, D. H., 279
Hall, R., 408, 411
Halliday, R. P., 306
Halmos, T., 513
Ham, E. A., 443
Hamada, Y., 103
Hamar, J., 571, 574, 576-
78, 582
Hamburger, V., 185
Hamilton, C. R., 230
Hamilton, T. H., 429, 430,
433, 434
Hamilton, W. J., 95, 97
Hammel, H. T., 327
Hammerstad, J. P., 161
Hammond, R. P., 334
Hamolsky, M. W., 334
Hampton, J. R., 502
Han, P., 523
Han, P. W., 360
Handa, H., 320
Handler, J. S., 49, 452, 471,
472, 484, 486-89
Hane, S., 355, 358
Hanes, G. E., 325, 336
Hanley, H. G., 265
Hannig, K., 55, 488
Hansen, A. P., 408
Hansen, L., 28, 31
Hansen, O., 278, 281
Hanson, R. W., 61
Hanzlikova, V., 179-82, 186,
187, 189, 191-93, 196, 202,
203
Hardak, B. J., 573, 577
Hardaway, R. M., 580
Hardebo, J. E., 577
Hardisty, R. M., 507, 516,
520
Harmon, P. M., 278, 281
Harms, P. G., 407
Harper, A. M., 577-79
Harper, E., 522
Harrigan, P., 355
Harris, A. J., 177, 178, 181,
183, 184, 187, 189, 191,
192, 196, 199-203
Harris, C. A., 9
Harris, G. L., 503
Harris, G. S., 433
Harris, G. W., 390
Harris, J. B., 189, 198
Harris, M. C., 556
Harris, P. J., 546
Harris, S. E., 437
Harrison, T. S., 406
Hart, J. S., 337
Hartje, W., 229

Hartley, C. J., 265
Hartman, B. K., 547, 549,
575, 577
Hartog, M., 362, 363
Hartzell, H. C., 179, 185,
188, 199, 200
Harvey, A. L., 188, 189,
200
Harvey, R., 362, 363
Haslam, J. M., 61
Hass, W. K., 502
Hasselbach, W., 304
Hasselberger, F. X., 581
Hastings, R. A., 98, 111
Hatotani, N., 389
Hattori, A., 506, 524
Haudenschild, C., 521
Haugen, F. P., 572, 577,
582, 585
Hauser, D., 167
Haussler, M. R., 425
Havel, R. J., 277
Hawkins, R. A., 358
Haydar, N. A., 339
Haydon, D. A., 464, 468,
483-85, 487
Hayes, J., 355, 362, 363
Haylett, D. G., 331, 332
Haymond, M. W., 353, 354,
357, 374
Hays, L., 466, 468
Hays, R. M., 451-53, 455-
61, 463-71, 475, 478-84,
487
Hayslett, J. P., 22, 24, 49,
50
Hayward, J. S., 330, 331,
340
Hazlett, D. R., 76
Hazlewood, C. F., 321
Hbous, A., 335, 336
Hebb, C. O., 182
Hechter, O., 487-89
Hechtman, H. B., 524
Hedeskov, C. J., 356
Hedge, G. A., 403
Heding, L. G., 355, 357
Hedlund, L. W., 389
Hedlund, M. T., 391, 396,
397
Hedman, R., 322, 324
Hee, D., 179
Hefco, E., 390
Heffley, E., 220
Hegel, U., 20, 22, 25, 28
Hegsted, D. M., 328
Heidenreich, R. O., 512
Heidingsfelder, S. A., 405
Heidrich, H. G., 55, 488
Hein, A., 225
Heinemann, H. O., 41
Heinemann, S., 178, 181,
184, 186, 188, 196, 200
Heinrich, D., 523
Heinz, E., 467
Heistad, D. D., 540, 541,
552, 554, 556, 557, 561

AUTHOR INDEX 611

SUBJECT INDEX

active transport in, 111, 112
amino acid transport, 109-10
fluid accumulation in, 112
ions and blastocyst formation, 110-12
transtrophoblasts potential difference and, 111
tubal journey of, 95
End organs, sensory development of
neurotrophic effects on, 186
Endothelium
cytogel extrusion by, 504
Epinephrine
effects in shock, 577
see also Catecholamines
Estradiol
cell binding of, 427
Estrogens
cyclic GMP and, 443
dissociation of receptors of, 441, 442
model for action of, 425, 426
nuclear pool for, 437
receptors for, 428
chromatin interaction with, 437
cytoplasmic form of, 431
cytoplasm to nucleus motion, 431-33
interaction with DNA, 433, 433, 436, 437
interaction with nuclear components, 433-37
interaction with RNA, 433, 437
nature before estrogen binding, 429-31
nuclear origin of, 429, 430
types of, 428-32
Ethacrynic acid
mechanism of diuretic action of, 41-43
Ethacrynic-cysteine
mechanism of diuretic action of, 42
Ethanol
metabolism of, 328
alcoholics and, 328, 329
Etorphine
low dosage effects of, 156
Evoked potentials
attention and, 219, 220
see also Brain, evoked potentials
Excitation-contraction coupling, 293-309
Ca release from the SR, 301-4
Ca-induced Ca release, 302
electrically induced, 302,

303
muscle relaxation and, 304
osmotically induced, 303
problems regarding, 303, 304
pharmacology of, 305-8
sarcoplasmic reticulum and, 300-4
electrical phenomena with, 301
optical changes indicating electrical, 300, 301
T system, 294-96
depolarization charge movement, 298-300
"detubulation," 295, 296
excitability of, 295
glycerol treatment of fibers and, 295, 296
lateral T system, 294
morphogical aspects, 294, 295
opening of, 294
propagated contraction of skinned fibers, 296
spiral arrangement of, 294, 295
T system-sarcoplasmic reticulum, 296-300
inactivation of, 297, 298
morphological considerations, 296
Exercise
lung diffusion during, 71, 75, 83
Exercise, endurance
biochemical changes in muscle, 273-86
actomyosin ATPase and, 284
adenine nucleotide cycle enzymes in, 283
aerobic metabolism, 278-82
background information on, 273, 274
blood flow-oxygen extraction, 279
different muscle types and, 284-86
glycogen synthesis in, 283
glycolysis enzymes, 282, 283
maximum O_2 uptake, 281, 282
mitochondrial adaptations, 274-77
myoglobin concentration, 278
pyruvate removal and, 276
reduced contractibility and mitochondria, 277
submaximal exercise, 278-81

triglyceride metabolism and, 277, 278
types of, 273

F

Factor VIII
chemistry of, 514, 515
endothelial cell content of, 515, 516
Fasting
insulin and glucagon in, 364
Fatty acids
insulin secretion and, 358
Fibrin
platelet adhesion to, 523
Fibrinogen
adhesion reaction and, 524
Food
specific dynamic action of, 327
ATP for incorporation of food, 327
Formaldehyde
excitation-contraction coupling and, 308
Furosemide
kidney transepithelial potentials, 26
mechanism of diuretic action of, 41, 43
thick ascending limb of Henle transepithelial potential of, 27
Fusaric acid
dopamine β-hydroxylase and, 406

G

GABA
see λ-Aminobutyric acid
Gastrointestinal hormones
insulin and glucagon secretion and, 362, 363
Geniculate nucleus, lateral
control of visual input by, 218
excitability of
attention and, 218
transmission through, 218
Glucagon
binding to islet receptor, 369
growth hormone response to, 405
kinetics of release of, 365-68
secretion of
A-like cells of intestines and, 354
amino acids and, 357
glucose and, 354-57
growth hormone and, 361
hormonal influences on, 361-64

CUMULATIVE INDEXES

CONTRIBUTING AUTHORS VOLUMES 34-38

CHAPTER TITLES VOLUMES 34-38